Armstrong Oil Directories

(800) 375-1838   WWW.ARMSTRONGOIL.COM

This is our 37th annual edition since we started in 1979. We want to thank you for your business. We hope that this coming year will be a very good year for both you and your company.

If you ever have any questions about our directories, please do not hesitate to give us a call. If you want more information about our products, please take a look at our website:
www.armstrongoil.com

Again, thanks for the business. It is deeply appreciated.
- May God Bless you and yours -
Alan Armstrong, Publisher

Please be sure and check out the back portion of the directory for our cross reference section. I think you will find it very useful.

To Order Call (800) 375-1838 or www.armstrongoil.com

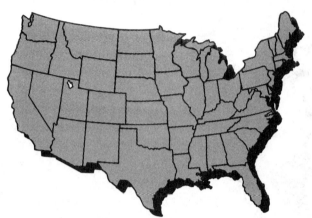

Nationwide Office Directory
Full 8 1/2" x 11" book size
Entire Nation
over 16,000 companies listed

$ 225 (no discount available)

Nationwide Mini Directory (Briefcase)
Small Size 5 1/4" x 8 1/4"
Same complete nationwide information
over 16,000 companies listed

$ 140 w / discount*

Texas Directory
Includes
Texas and S.E. New Mexico

$ 80 w / discount*

Louisana / Gulf Coast Directory
Includes the following states:
Gulf coast of Texas, Louisana
Arkansas, Mississippi,
Alabama, Georgia, Florida
N.E. states

$80 w / discount*

Rocky Mountain / Central U.S. Directory
Includes the following states:
West Texas and Panhandle of Texas
Oklahoma, New Mexico
Colorado, Alaska and all
Western U.S. states

$80 w / discount*

* discount applies when invoice is paid within 30 days after receipt of order.

GULF COAST
2016 EDITION
COPYRIGHT ALAN ARMSTRONG 2015
ARMSTRONG OIL DIRECTORIES
P O BOX 52106
AMARILLO, TX 79159
PH 806 457-9300

A & E EXPLORATION
2007 LEXINGTON AVE
OWENSBORO,KY 42301-4688 PH 270 684-4002
AVERY E SMITH,MBR/GEOL
EDWARD W SMITH,MBR/LDMN
BARBARA J SMITH,MBR

A & F PRODUCTION CO
PO BOX 489
OIL CITY,LA 71061 PH 318 995-7910
A C FRIZZELL,OWNER

A G OIL
7387 ROMINE RD NE
FRAZEYSBURG,OH 43822-9518 PH 740 828-3534
DARRELL L ROMINE,OWNER,OPER

A N R PIPELINE SEE
TENNESSEE GAS PIPELINE

A P LAND SERVICES,INC
PO BOX 644
KATY,TX 77492-0644
PH 281 391-4100 FAX 281 391-3999
BOB ASHWANDER,PRES
BASHWANDER@APLANDSERVICESINC.COM
WWW.APLANDSERVICESINC.COM

A.D. VENTURES,INC
2200 PAKENHAN DR
CHALMETTE,LA 70043 PH 504 276-5858
FAX 504 277-0502
HAROLD J ANDERSON,PRES
PAUL E DUBROC,VP

A.E. ACQUISITION CORP SEE
AMERICAN EXPLORATION COMPANY

A.J. BLAIR COMPANY LLC
PO BOX 53036,725 COOLIDGE ST
LAFAYETTE,LA 70505-3036
PH 337 232-7559 FAX 337 232-9811
ROBERT B HARGROVE,MNGNG MEMBER
TONNI MAW,OFC MGR

A-N-A OPERATING COMPANY,INC
PO BOX 1229
PEARLAND,TX 77588-1229 PH 281 993-1424
FAX 281 993-1424
ARCH W HELTON,PRES

A-1 HOMES
OILFIELD HOUSING/OFFICE UNITS
LOCATIONS IN TX & NM
700 N GRANT STE 600
ODESSA,TX 79761 PH 432 334-8881
MIKE SELF MSELF@NWOL.NET

AARCO OIL & GAS COMPANY
9901 IH-10 STE 500
SAN ANTONIO,TX 78230 PH 210 828-4312
BARBARA MOSS,PRES

ABACO OPERATING LLC
1020 NE LOOP 410 STE 660
SAN ANTONIO,TX 78209-1223
PH 210 828-4567
ERIK G HANSON,MGR

ABBENGTON OILFIELD BROKERS-TRADERS
PO BOX 70919
HOUSTON,TX 77270-0919 PH 713 222-6676
FAX 713 868-1240
ROD CAMMACK,PRES
I CONTELLO,VP

ABBINGTON PETROLEUM
PO BOX 70919
HOUSTON,TX 77270-0919 PH 713 222-6676
FAX 713 868-1240
ROD CAMMACK,OWNER
I CONTELLO,SECY

ABC NITROGEN SERVICE CORP
PO BOX 2114
MONT BELVIEU,TX 77580-2114
PH 281 385-2645 FAX 281 385-5495
WWW.ABCNITROGEN.COM
BAYTOWN,TX OFFICE - 11425 I-10 E 77523
RICHARD SMITH,GEN MGR
RICHARD@ABCNITROGEN.COM
DONNA ELLIFF,HSE COORD
DONNA@ABCNITROGEN.COM
JOE DOBSON,SLS MGR
JOE DOBSON,SLS

ABCO OIL & GAS INC
PO BOX 5370
VIENNA,WV 26105-5370 PH 304 295-3333
DRILLER@WIREFIRE.COM
W H ALLEN,PRES,GEN MGR
MIKE ROBERTS,FIELD SUPT

ABEL LELAND L & ASSOCIATES
6167 W DUNBAR RD
MONROE,MI 48161-9011 PH 734 269-6094
FAX 734 269-6094
LELAND L ABEL,CPL,LDMN
KATHERINE L ABEL,LDMN

ABEL WILLIAM C & ASSOCIATES,INC
P O BOX 910409
LEXINGTON,KY 40591-0409
PH 859 278-8088 WWW.WCABEL.COM
W C ABEL JR,PRES WABELJR@MSN.COM
NEW PHILADELPHIA,OH OFFICE - 243 MONROE
AVE 44663 PH 800 948-0343

ABER OIL & GAS CO
100 E FERGUSON ST STE 404
TYLER,TX 75702-5758
PH 903 526-1100 FAX 903 592-3231
CHRIS PHILLIPS
FRED J HABERLE

ABRAXAS PETROLEUM CORPORATION
OIL PRODUCTION & EXPL
18803 MEISNER DR
SAN ANTONIO,TX 78258 PH 210 490-4788
FAX 210 490-8816 WWW.ABRAXASPETROLEUM.COM
ROBERT L G WATSON,PRES,CEO
GEOFF KING,CFO
WILLIAM H WALLACE,VP,OPERS
STEPHEN T WENDEL,VP,LAND & MKTG
LEE T BILLINGSLEY,VP,EXPL
PETE BOMMER,VP ENG
SINTON,TX OFFICE - PO BOX 220, 78387
PH 361 364-1000 FAX 361 364-5657
IRA,TX OFFICE - PO BOX 158, 79527
PH 325 573-6010 FAX 325 573-3660
PYOTE,TX OFFICE - PO BOX 433, 79777
PH 432 389-5545 FAX 432 389-5546

LUSK,WY OFFICE - PO BOX 1169, 82225
PH 307 334-9919 FAX 307 334-9988

AC EXPLORATION LLC
952 ECHO LANE STE 390
HOUSTON,TX 77024
PH 713 881-9030 FAX 713 881-9078
KEN FLOYD,PARTNER
MICHAEL A ODEGARD,PARTNER
MAODEGARD@ACEXPLORATION.COM
CINDI NETTLES,LAND DEPT
TEENA TRON,ACCT
DAN BREAUX,GEOL

ACADIAN LAND SERVICES,LLC
101 W FARREL BLDG 1
LAFAYETTE,LA 70508
PH 337 237-0069 FAX 337 233-3020
ROBERT TODD FONTENOT,CPL
NICHOLAS OGE',CPL
BILL LACHAUSSEE,CPL

ACADIAN LOG LIBRARY INC
117 HEYMANN BLVD STE 100
LAFAYETTE,LA 70503-2397 PH 337 233-1430
FAX 337 232-1707
CATHY DOHON,MGR

ACADIAN OIL & GAS,INC
6125 HURST ST
NEW ORLEANS,LA 70118 PH 504 528-1074
SEYMOUR SMITH,PRES
DAVID SMITH,VP
DOUGLAS W BLACK,SECY/TREAS

ACADIANA ENERGY,INC
7419 DEARBORN ST
HOUSTON,TX 77055 PH 713 682-8575
STEPHEN HOLSTEAD,PRES

ACADIANA OIL & ENVIRONMENTAL CORPORATION
PO BOX 9088
NEW IBERIA,LA 70562-9088
PH 337 560-5573 FAX 337 560-5575
MIKE LEBLANC,PRES
RUSS ROMERO,VP

ACADIANA SHELL & LIMESTONE,INC
PO BOX 280
ABBEVILLE,LA 70511-0280 PH 337 893-1111
FAX 337 893-3985 WWW.ACADIANASHELL.COM
EDDIE YOUNG,PRES, GEN MGR
YOUNG@ACADIANASHELL.COM
SONNY GROS,OPERS MGR
CLAY YOUNG,SALESPERSON
GUSSIE BROUSSARD,SALESPERSON
LAFAYETTE,LA OFFICE - 627 E BROUSSARD RD
70508 PH 337 981-9891
KIM YOUNG,SECY/TREAS
DOUGLAS KOONCE,OFC MGR
KROTZ SPRING,LA OFFICE - 117 PHIBRO RD
70750 PH 337 566-2101
DUKE LANDRY,OFC MGR
NEW IBERIA,LA OFFICE - 4616 MARINA RD
70560 PH 337 369-3300
RONALD STELLY,OFC MGR

ACCESS EXPLORATION CORP
PO BOX 20607
HOUSTON,TX 77225
PH 713 621-2777 FAX 713 621-2779
WWW.ACCESSEXPLORATION.COM
T J MORROW,PRES/FOUNDER

ACCESS LAND & TITLE SERVICES,INC
3500 N CAUSEWAY BLVD STE 160
METAIRIE,LA 70002-3592
PH 504 833-0003 FAX 504 833-0332
WWW.ACCESS-LAND.COM
LONI D MOUTON,CPL
LONIMOUTON@ACCESS-LAND.COM

ACCRETION ENTERPRISES,INC
PO BOX 2269
NATCHEZ,MS 39121-2269
PH 601 446-5828 FAX 601 442-0054
JAMES C MCGEHEE,PRES,LDMN
JAMESCMCGEHEE@BELLSOUTH.NET

ACE ENERGY SUPPLY
16475 DALLAS PKWY STE 780
ADDISON,TX 75001 PH 972 381-9009
FAX 972 381-9330
WWW.ACEENERGYSUPPLY.COM
SONY ROETHEMEYER,PRES
MARK WATERS,VP

ACE PETROLEUM COMPANY
402 COACHMAN LN
HOUSTON,TX 77024-6401 PH 713 467-5653
ANDY CLIFFORD

ACE RENTAL TOOLS SEE
SUPERIOR ENERGY SERVICES

ACE SPECIALTIES,INC
PIPELINE,PLT,IND SUPPLIES,EQUIP RENTAL
PO BOX 1189
ODESSA,TX 79760-1189
PH 432 332-0691 FAX 432 333-4561
JIM VOLK,PRES
JON THOMAS,VP

ACE TRICONE BITS
SUPPLY ROTORY TRICONE DRILL BIT'S FOR
OIL,WATER & GAS DRLG INDUSTRY/CUSTOM
BUILT HOLE-OPENERS/HAMMER'S & HAMMER BITS
22537 STATE HIGHWAY 34
THOMPSONVILLE,IL 62890 PH 618 439-7275
PH 800 333-1816 FAX 618 435-4347
INFO@ACETRICONEBITS.COM
MICHAEL VICK

ACID & CEMENTING SERVICE,INC
PO BOX 1258
PALESTINE,TX 75802-1258
PH 903 729-2500 FAX 903 729-4184
CHARLES D WALKER,PRES

ACID ENGINEERING,INC SEE
NOWSCO WELL SERVICE INC

ACME OILFIELD SERVICES,COMPLETE PUMPING
UNIT REPAIR,OILFIELD CONSTRUCTION,PU
EQUIPMENT SALES
5624 AMERICAN LEGION RD
TYLER,TX 75708-6115
PH 903 877-3917 WWW.ACMEOILSERVICE.COM
BILL BAILEY,OPERS MGR
DANA TAYLOR,ADMIN ASST
ADMINASST@ACMEOILSERVICE.COM

ACME TOOL SEE
HOMCO INTERNATIONAL,INC

ACOCK/ANAQUA OPERATING CO LP
520 STARR ST
CORPUS CHRISTI,TX 78401-2345
PH 361 888-8288 FAX 361 888-4617
WWW.AAOPERATING.COM
RANDY ACOCK,PARTNER,COO

PAUL KNOWLES,PARTNER,CEO
DARRELL ATKINS,VP OPERS

ACTION OIL SERVICES INC
PO BOX 2428
BEAUMONT,TX 77704-2428 PH 409 832-2663
FAX 409 769-9594 ACTIONOILSVC@YAHOO.COM
WWW.ACTIONOILSERVICES.COM
GENE TANNEHILL,PRES
LANDON TANNEHILL,VP

ADA OIL EXPLORATION CORPORATION SEE
ADAMS RESOURCES EXPLORATION CORP

ADAIR & ASSOC
SEE ADAIR LAND AND LEASING

ADAIR DUANE & ASSOC SEE
ADAIR OIL AND GAS PROPERTIES

ADAIR DUANE OIL & GAS PROP SEE
ADAIR OIL AND GAS PROPERTIES

ADAIR LAND AND LEASING SEE
ENERGY LAND CONSULTANTS

ADAIR T W JR,PETR ENGR
4640 FM 61
NEWCASTLE,TX 76372-3310 PH 512 440-7735

ADAMS AND REESE
4500 ONE SHELL SQ
NEW ORLEANS,LA 70139 PH 504 581-3234
FAX 504 566-0210
WWW.ARLAW.COM INFO@ARLAW.COM
CHARLES P ADAMS JR,MNGNG PRTNR
ROBERT M SHOFSTAHL,CAO
F LEE BUTLER,CHRMN,EXEC COMMITTEE
THOMAS G O'BRIEN,MGR,ENERGY PRACTICE LEAD

ADAMS ENERGY COMPANY OF TEXAS
PO BOX 21470,1437 S BOULDER AVE STE 930
TULSA,OK 74121-1470 PH 918 582-7713
FAX 918 592-3232

ADAMS FRANK B/MARIE ADAMS
615 LEOPARD ST STE 720
CORPUS CHRISTI,TX 78401 PH 361 884-9004

ADAMS JOE B,CONSULTANT
21010 VERMONT ST
LIVINGSTON,LA 70754 PH 225 929-6097
FAX 225 929-6098

ADAMS RESOURCES EXPLORATION CORPORATION
PO BOX 844
HOUSTON,TX 77001-0844 PH 713 881-3601
FAX 713 881-3644
K S ADAMS JR,CHRMN
JAMES BROCK MOORE III,PRES
RICHARD B ABSHIRE,VP,FIN
W R RUSTY HOWARD,VP,LAND
JOHN RINEY,CONTROLLER
STEVE ALLEN,SR EXPL GEOL

ADAMS ROGER,CPL
PO BOX 416
SHREVEPORT,LA 71162-0416 PH 318 747-4347
FAX 318 747-3307 RACPL@BELLSOUTH.NET
BOSSIER CITY,LA OFFICE - 207 RAMPART
71112

ADAMS WELL SERVICE,LLC
7248 KOSSUTH RD
BOLIVAR,NY 14715-9503
PH 585 928-1655 FAX 585 928-1132
EDDIE D ADAMS SR,PRES

ADAMSON & KENNEDY
PO BOX 111
KILGORE,TX 75663-0111 PH 214 984-3094

JOHN N ADAMSON,PRTNR

ADCOR DRILLING INC SEE
NABORS DRILLING USA,LP

ADDINGTON ENTERPRISES,OPR & PROD
8626 TESORO DR STE 801
SAN ANTONIO,TX 78217-6217 PH 210 828-4373
CRANDELL ADDINGTON,OWNER
WILLIAM R LOCKLEAR,SR ENGR

ADDINGTON OIL PROPERTIES
8626 TESORO DR STE 801
SAN ANTONIO,TX 78217-6217 PH 210 828-4373
CRANDELL ADDINGTON,OWNER
WILLIAM R LOCKLEAR,SR PETR ENGR

ADIT PETROLEUM,INC SEE
SCOTT ROYCE ARNOLD

ADKINS W GREGG
1309 BUTTONWOOD DR
FRIENDSWOOD,TX 77546-5270
PH 281 992-3270

ADLER ENERGY,LC
PO BOX 1857
TRAVERSE CITY,MI 49685-1857
PH 231 668-6868 FAX 231 674-0098
JORDAN MILLER,PRES
JORDAN.MILLER@ADLERLC.COM

ADVANCED LANDMAN INC
3 WISTERIA
ANGLETON,TX 77515 PH 979 549-8877
MARK DUMOIT
MARK@ADVANCEDLANDMAN.COM

ADVANCED MICROMAGNETICS,INC
5773 WOODWAY DR #305
HOUSTON,TX 77057
PH 713 439-7927 713 443-3884
CARL MCCUTCHEON,PRES

ADVENT OIL AND GAS COMPANY
PO BOX 741
MORRISON,CO 80465 PH 303 829-7306
DENVERADVENT@GMAIL.COM
DANA VEITCH,PRES

AED GROUP,LLC
6301 GASTON AVE STE 240
DALLAS,TX 75214-3922 PH 214 306-7800
FAX 214 203-0400 WWW.AEDGRP.COM
MATTHEW ANDERSON,PRIN
BEDFORD,TX OFFICE - 2350 AIRPORT FWY,
STE 130,76022
BOWIE,TX OFFICE - 301 SANDERS ST,76230
MIDLAND,TX OFFICE - 410 W OHIO STE 204,
79701
PLEASANTON,TX OFFICE - 1501 BENSDALE
STE C,78064 PH 830 569-3452

AEI-K DRILLING VENTURES
7317 W ROADWAY ST
NEW ORLEANS,LA 70124-1649 PH 504 524-4918
FAX 504 586-8372
TED ALCUS,MGR

AFTON CHEMICAL CORPORATION
501 MONSANTO AVE
SAUGET,IL 62201-1138 PH 618 583-1000
FAX 618 583-1391 WWW.AFTONCHEMICAL.COM

AFTON PUMPS,INC
7335 AVENUE N
HOUSTON,TX 77011 PH 713 923-9731
PH 713 923-3902
MICHAEL L DERR,PRES

DAVID A DERR,EXEC VP

AGATE PETROLEUM,INC SEE
  ST MARY LAND & EXPLORATION COMPANY

AGEMO,INC
  107 CHARLES READ AVE
  LAFAYETTE,LA 70503-3311 PH 337 234-5116
  JIM STRINGFIELD

AGERON ENERGY,LLC
  8610 N NEW BRAUNFELS STE 405
  SAN ANTONIO,TX 78217-6358
  PH 210 829-4888 FAX 210 824-3950
    WWW.AGERONLLC.COM
    BRUCE C GATES,PRES BCGATES@AGERONLLC.COM

AGHORN OIL & GAS,INC, SEE
  AGHORN ENERGY,INC

AIKMAN BROTHERS LLC SEE
  AIKMAN COMPANIES

AIKMAN OIL AND GAS COMPANY SEE
  AIKMAN COMPANIES

AIR DRILLING SERVICES,INC SEE WEATHERFORD

AIR LIQUIDE AMERICA SPECIALTY GASES LLC
  PO BOX 310,6141 EASTON ROAD
  PLUMSTEADVILLE,PA 18949
  PH 215 766-8860 FAX 215 766-2476
    WWW.ALSPECIALTYGASES.COM
    ALASG.INFO@AIRLIQUIDE.COM
    STEVE DZIAK,PRES
    ROBERT JEFFERYS,DIR/MKTG COMMUNICATIONS

AIR LOGISTICS,LLC SEE BRISTOW U.S.,LLC

AJAX OIL CORP
  810 RUE BOURBON
  METAIRIE,LA 70005-3421 PH 504 833-1461
  FAX 504 832-7975
    M H WEST,PRES
    A W STRAIN,VP
    SALLY W JANKE,VP,TREAS

AKIN ENERGY CORP
  1727 PRAIRIE GROVE DR
  HOUSTON,TX 77077-5019 PH 281 558-2003
    RALPH AKIN,PRES

AKRON/OIL CORP
  PO BOX 129
  HACKENSACK,NJ 07602-0129 PH 201 342-2900
  FAX 201 342-7134
    ANTHONY J CANCRO,PRES

ALABAMA STATE OIL AND GAS BOARD
  PO BOX 869999
  TUSCALOOSA,AL 35486-6999
      PH 205 349-2852 FAX 205 349-2861
    JAMES H GRIGGS,CHRMN
    CHARLES E PEARSON,VICE CHRMN
    M BARNETT LAWLEY,BOARD MEMBER
    DR BERRY H TEW JR,STATE GEOL,OIL/GAS SUPR
    KIRK MCQUILLAN,DEPUTY DIR
    S MARVIN ROGERS,COUNSEL
    IRENE BURGESS,EXEC SECY
    MARVIN ROGERS,HEARINGS
    KIRK MCQUILLAN,TECH OPERS
    BUTCH GREGORY,GROUNDWATER PROTECTION
    GANIU ALABI,RECORDS MGMT
  MOBILE,AL OFFICE - 250 N WATER ST
  36602 PH 334 438-4848
    RALPH HELLMICH,COMPLIANCE OPERS/SO AL

ALAMEDA ENERGY,INC
  727 N WACO ST STE 400
  WICHITA,KS 67203-3900 PH 316 263-3201

R TODD SLAWSON,PRES (DENVER OFC)

ALAMO ENERGY
  PO BOX 6779
  SAN ANTONIO,TX 78209 PH 210 828-4300
  FAX 210 828-5490
    WWW.ALAMOENERGY.COM
    STEPHEN R WEST,CO-OWNER
    THOMAS G MCDONALD,CO-OWNER
    SYLVIA A PLAYER,OFC MGR

ALAMO RESOURCES,LLC
  820 GESSNER STE 1650
  HOUSTON,TX 77024
  PH 713 224-2500 FAX 713 224-6096
    A F (TONY) PELLETIER,PRES
    TONY@ALAMORESOURCES.COM
    CARL D CAMPBELL,EXEC VP
    CARL@ALAMORESOURCES.COM

ALAN C PRIGGE & ASSOCIATES,INC
  1919 HIGHWAY 35N # 451
  ROCKPORT,TX 78382-3344 PH 281 850-7826
    ALAN C PRIGGE,PRES
    APRIGGE60@GMAIL.COM

ALBRECHT & ASSOCIATES,INC
  1401 WYNKOOP S STE 350
  DENVER,CO 80202 PH 303 839-0067
  PH 303 830-0331 FAX 303 302-1357
    CHARLES RUDOLPH,ASSOC
    NORM BROWN,ASSOC
    DON MCDONALD PH 303 839-0067
    DON@ALBRECHTAI.COM
  HOUSTON,TX OFFICE - 711 LOUISIANA
  STE 1600,77002 PH 713 951-9586
  FAX 713 658-0654
    KIRK THOLEN PH 713 546-5703
    BOB ALBRECHT
    HARRISON WILLIAMS

ALCORN EXPLORATION,INC
  1800 BERING DR STE 510
  HOUSTON,TX 77057-3158
  PH 713 622-3800 FAX 713 622-8015
    GEORGE A ALCORN
    NORMAN PULLMAN,GEOL
    RICHARD B BEARD,LAND

ALDRIDGE COURTNEY G,PETR GEOL
    OIL EXPLORATION & PRODUCTION
  PO BOX 629
  NATCHEZ,MS 39121
  PH 601 446-5585 FAX 601 446-5798
    COURTNEY G ALDRIDGE,OWNER

ALDRIDGE OPERATING CO,LLC
    OIL PRODUCTION & OPERATIONS
  PO BOX 629,151 PROVIDENCE RD
  NATCHEZ,MS 39121
  PH 601 446-5585 FAX 601 446-5798
    ALDRIDGEOPERATING@LIVE.COM
    COURTNEY G ALDRIDGE,MNGNG PRTNR
    KEN TILGHMAN,ENGR
    BYRON D ALDRIDGE IV,LAND DEPT
    JESSICA KNAPP,SECY

ALEGRE ENERGY,INC
  12451 STARCREST DR STE 104
  SAN ANTONIO,TX 78216-2988
  PH 210 496-6918 FAX 210 402-0620
    BEN A CULPEPPER,PRES
    SHAWN TELLANDER,PROD ADMIN
    LYNNE GRIBBEN,CONTROLLER

ALEX OIL COMPANY
  PO BOX 964
  NATCHEZ,MS 39121-0964
  PH 601 445-5727 FAX 601 304-0733
    THOMAS W MIDDLETON,PRES

ALEXANDER & ASSOCIATES
  PO BOX 1638
  NATCHEZ,MS 39121 PH 601 446-8438
  FAX 601 442-2980 DAVEBAITY@CABLEONE.NET

ALEXANDER BOYD D & ASSOCIATES
  PO BOX 1638,104 N TEMPLE RD
  NATCHEZ,MS 39121-1638 PH 601 446-8438
    BOYD D ALEXANDER,CPL,OWNER
    BDALEXANDER@CABLEONE.NET
    MARJORIE W ALEXANDER,ASSOC
    DAVID C BAITY,ASSOC
    SHARON A BAITY,ASSOC
    MELINDA J KRICK,SECY

ALEXANDER ENERGY CORPORATION SEE
  NATIONAL ENERGY GROUP,INC

ALEXANDER PRODUCTION COMPANY
  700 N SAINT MARYS ST STE 1200
  SAN ANTONIO,TX 78205-3510 PH 210 271-9000
    JOHN D ALEXANDER JR,PRES
    JOHN SCHIEFFER,CONTROLLER

ALEXANDER UTILITY ENGINEERING,INC
  CONSULTANT POWER,COMMUNICATIONS
  975 W BITTERS RD
  SAN ANTONIO,TX 78216 PH 210 496-3200
  FAX 210 494-9987
    WWW.ALEXUTIL.COM
    R D ALEXANDER,PE,PRES
    DAN BANKS,VP,COMMUNICATIONS DIV
    LEONARD HILL,PE,VP ELECTRIC POWER
    BRYAN HILL,MGR OF PLANNING AND MAPPING

ALGONQUIN GAS TRANSMISSION SEE
  DUKE ENERGY GAS TRANSMISSION

ALI-BRON LTD SEE
  BOYD THOMAS & ASSOC

ALICE SIDNEY OIL COMPANY
  440 N JEFFERSON AVE
  EL DORADO,AR 71730-5692
  PH 870 863-4177 FAX 870 863-0254
    DAVID M YOCUM IV,MNGNG MEMBER
    JAMES T INGRAM,GEOL,PROD SUPVSR
    JEFFREY E DWIGHT,CFO
    SANDRA MATTHEWS,ROYALTY/DIV ORDER ANALYST
    LARRY B TUCKER,ACCT

ALL SEASONS FOAM COATINGS & SERVICES
    TRENCH BREAKERS,LINERS,PILLOWS
    SECONDARY & TEMPORARY CONTAINMENTS
  PO BOX 501
  SANGER,TX 76266 PH 940 458-9078
    VANESSA MEYER,OFC MGR
    VANESSA@ALLSEASONSFOAM.COM
    RACHEL CORBIN,SALES
    RACHEL@ALLSEASONSFOAM.COM
    CLINT CORBIN,SALES
    CLINT@ALLSEASONSFOAM.COM

ALL STATE PIPE TESTERS INC SEE
  ALLSTAR PIPE SERVICES,INC

ALLEN & KIRMSE,LTD
  PO BOX 52187,209 5TH ST
  LAFAYETTE,LA 70505-2187
  PH 337 232-2024 FAX 337 237-0883
    DURELLE L ALLEN JR,CPL,PRES

DURELLEA@AKLAF.COM
C DAVID ALLEN
JENNIFER MOLBERT
MELISSA POWELL
PAUL HEBERT
CENTENNIAL,CO OFFICE - 6304 S MONACO CT
80111 PH 303 771-1208
RANDALL KIRMSE,VP

ALLEN B R RANDY ,ATTORNEY
PO BOX 2366
BOERNE,TX 78006
PH 830 443-4900 FAX 830 443-4901
B R (RANDY) ALLEN,OWNER
BRA@BRALLENLAW.COM

ALLEN OPERATING COMPANY,LLC
PO BOX 1364
NATCHEZ,MS 39121 PH 601 442-3562
FAX 601 442-1646

ALLEN PERRY COMPANY
WILLIAMS CHEMICAL PUMPS
PO BOX 652,212 MARKET ST
WINNSBORO,TX 75494-0652 PH 903 342-3074
PH 800 256-6868 FAX 903 342-5774
ANN BRADSHAW,PRES
CLARENCE BRADSHAW,MGR

ALLEN PETROLEUM SERVICES,INC
PO BOX 1364,521 MAIN ST STE M-1
NATCHEZ,MS 39121-1364
PH 601 442-3562 FAX 601 442-1646
WOODY@ALLENPETROLEUM.COM
W W (WOODY) ALLEN JR,IND PETR LDMN

ALLEN THOMAS TIM D
PO BOX 16268
JACKSON,MS 39236-6268 PH 601 362-3170

ALLEN W W,JR,CPL,IND PETR LDMN
PO BOX 1364,521 MAIN ST STE M-1
NATCHEZ,MS 39121-1364 PH 601 442-3562
FAX 601 442-1646 WOODY@ALLENPETROLEUM.COM

ALLEN-HOFFMAN EXPLORATION COMPANY
1 GREENWAY PLAZA STE 440
HOUSTON,TX 77046 PH 713 871-2350
PAUL HOFFMAN PHOFFMAN@ALLEN-
HOFFMAN.COM

ALLIANCE BUSINESS INVESTMENT CO SEE
ENERGY MINERALS,LLC

ALLIANCE DRILLING CONSULTANTS,LLC
PO BOX 2990,1120 E OAK ST
JENA,LA 71342-2990
PH 318 992-9600 FAX 318 992-7201
ALLIANCE@CENTURYTEL.NET
WAYNE PRITCHARD,PRES

ALLIANCE OIL AND GAS COMPANY,LLC
2204 TIMBERLOCH PL STE 140
THE WOODLANDS,TX 77380-1170
PH 281 466-1078 FAX 281 466-1079
R T (TOM) FETTERS,CHRMN
PERRY L DRAGON,CEO
WYNNESELLERS@ALLIANCEOIL.COM
C WYNNE SELLERS,VP,LAND
LON MCCARLEY,VP,EXPL

ALLIANCE PETROLEUM CORPORATION
4150 BELDEN VILLAGE ST NW STE 410
CANTON,OH 44718-2553 PH 330 493-0440
FAX 330 493-3409
JOHN W MILLER,PRES
MARIETTA,OH SOUTHERN BRANCH OFFICE

214 WARNER ST
MARIETTA,OH 45750-3457 PH 740 373-8771

ALLIANCE PETROLEUM RESOURCES
PO BOX 16428
SUGAR LAND,TX 77496-6428 PH 281 208-3593
FAX 281 208-0824
PERRY L DRAGON
C WYNNE SELLERS

ALLIANCE PROPERTIES,INC
304 LA RUE FRANCE STE 202
LAFAYETTE,LA 70508-3136
PH 337 235-6964 FAX 337 235-6961
GOALLIANCE@AOL.COM
J W (JACK) RAINE IV,PRES
JRAINE@AOL.COM
MARY M RAINE,SECY/TREAS

ALLIED SORBENT
926 GULF DR
GRETNA,LA 70053-6212 PH 504 362-9654
FAX 504 364-1498
MARION HESS,PRES
KIM HUGHES,OFC MGR
JAMES BERGGREN,SLS MGR

ALLIN PHILIP R,PETR CONS
3302 WATER LOCUST DR
SUGAR LAND,TX 77479-2808 PH 337 232-6236

ALLIS-CHALMERS ENERGY INC
-CORP HEADQUARTERS/PROD SVCS/RENTAL
SVCS-
10613 W SAM HOUSTON PKWY N STE 600
HOUSTON,TX 77064-4663 PH 713 856-4222
FAX 713 856-4246 WWW.ALCHENERGY.COM
STEVE COLLINS,PRES PROD SVCS
MARK PATTERSON,PRES RENTAL SVCS/SR VP
HOUSTON,TX DIRECTIONAL DRLG SCVS OFFICE -
911 REGIONAL PARK DR 77060
PH 713 934-9600 FAX 713 934-9067
DAVID BRYAN,PRES
HOUSTON,TX TUBULAR SVCS OFFICE -
911 REGIONAL PARK DR 77060
PH 281 951-2481 FAX 713 934-9067
GREG PRICE,PRES
HOUSTON,TX UNDERBALANCED SVCS OFFICE -
911 REGIONAL PARK DR 77060
PH 281 951-4040
TERRY KEANE,PRES UNBALANCED SVCS/SR VP
OILFIELD SVCS
BUENOS AIRES,ARGENTINA DRLG & COMPLETION
OFFICE - SARMIENTO 663-P4,C1041AAM
PH 54.11.51229.2900
CARLOS ETCHEVERRY,PRES-DLS DRILLING,
LOGISTICS & SERVICE CORP
RIO DE JANEIRO,RJ BRAZIL OFFICE -
AV RIO BRANCO,01-80,ANDAR-SALA 804
20090-003 PH 21.3213.8350
LUIZ AZEVEDO,PRES-BCH LTD

ALLRED PAUL,CPL
108 WASHINGTON BLVD
FOLEY,AL 36535-3056 PH 601 765-6681

ALLRED WILLIAM WALLACE
PO BOX 550,604 MAIN ST
COLLINS,MS 39428-0550 PH 601 765-8285
PH 765-8286 FAX 601 765-4829
KAREN SPEED,SECY

ALLSTAR PIPE SERVICES,INC
PO BOX 60722

LAFAYETTE,LA 70596-0722
PH 337 234-8071
THOMAS WRIGHT,PRES

ALLSTATE PERMIT SERVICES
PROFESSIONAL PERMIT ACQUISITION
PO BOX 1
LEWISTON,UT 84230 PH 303 903-5873
ALLSTATEPERMIT@ALLSTATEPERMIT.COM
BRAD JONES,VP BUS DEV PH 713 805-1512

ALLTEX EXPLORATION INC
2121 SAGE ST STE 220
HOUSTON,TX 77056
PH 713 627-8787 FAX 713 961-4519
ALLTEXEXPLORATION@HOTMAIL.COM
ELLWOOD T BARRETT II,OWNER/PRES
PATRICK H MACBRIDE,ENGR
KARINA WILLIAMS,ADMIN

ALOG,LLC
PO BOX 649,315 BELLEVILLE AVE
BREWTON,AL 36427-0649 PH 251 867-5413
FAX 251 867-5427
THOMAS E MCMILLAN JR,PRES/GEN PRTNR
TMCMILLAN@LONGLEAFENERGY.COM
RAY ROBERTSON JR,LDMN
ROGER M CHAPMAN,GEOL

ALPHA GEO INC
PO BOX 440274
HOUSTON,TX 77244-0274 PH 832 816-1886

ALPINE EXPLORATION
15581 WILKINSON DR
TYLER,TX 75707 PH 903 566-1969
FAX 903 595-2190
MICHAEL S WILLEY,PRES

ALPINE RESOURCES,LTD
12600 HILL COUNTRY BLVD
AUSTIN,TX 78738-6723 PH 713 655-1221
FAX 713 951-0079
DENNIS FERSTLER,PRES
DAN KELLOGG,VP

ALPINE WELL SERVICE,INC
PO BOX 2217,144 PROVIDENCE RD
NATCHEZ,MS 39121-2217 PH 601 442-0021
FAX 601 442-0421
DEBORAH PARKS,PRES,SECY,TREAS

ALRAM INC,MFG OF OILFIELD PUMPING UNITS
SEE WEATHERFORD

ALTA MESA HOLDINGS LP
15021 KATY FWY STE 400
HOUSTON,TX 77094-1900
PH 281 530-0991 FAX 281 530-5278
HARLAN H CHAPPELLE,PRES
MIKE E ELLIS,CHRMN
MICHAEL MCCABE,CFO
DAVID SMITH,VP EXPL
F DAVID MURRELL,VP LAND
DMURRELL@ALTAMESA.NET

ALTEX ENERGY CORPORATION SEE
EQUAL ENERGY US INC.

ALTUDA ENERGY CORPORATION
401 AUSTIN HWY STE 209
SAN ANTONIO,TX 78209-4670 PH 210 829-8080
FAX 210 829-8008
WWW.ALTUDA.COM
ANDREW R SCOTT,PRES
PH 512 970-7041 ANDREW@ALTUDA.COM

ALVARO FRED
INVESTMENT ADVISOR/OIL & GAS
833 WESTWIND WAY
THE VILLAGES,FL 32162 PH 352 391-1842

ALVORD HORACE H (BUBBA) IV,IND OPR
PO BOX 5597
SHREVEPORT,LA 71135-5597 PH 318 868-1435

ALVORD J MARK,IND LDMN
PO BOX 5597
SHREVEPORT,LA 71135-5597 PH 318 347-9251
FAX 318 869-2638
MARKALVORD@AOL.COM

AMARADO OIL COMPANY,LTD
3001 RR 620 SOUTH STE 323
AUSTIN,TX 78738
PH 512 346-9241 FAX 512 346-9249
DAVID DACHNER,LDMN/PRES
DDACHNER@AMARADO.NET

AMAZON ROYALTIES,LTD
PO BOX 703
FULSHEAR,TX 77441-0703 PH 281 346-2866
JOHN W BAHR,PRES

AMBAR LONE STAR TECHNOLOGY CENTER SEE
NATIONAL OILWELL VARCO TECHNOLOGY CENTER

AMBOY OIL CO,LLC
3610 WEST ST
LANSING,MI 48917-8547
PH 517 331-8126 FAX 517 322-2895
RUSSELL S SHINEVAR,MEMBER/MGR
MILANDMAN@COMCAST.NET

AMBRA OIL & GAS COMPANY
SUBSIDIARY OF AMAZON RESOURCES
2700 W SKYLINE DR
LORAIN,OH 44053-2246
PH 440 244-6300 FAX 440 244-6331
DR HENRY MAZOROW,PRES
KERRY MILLER,ADMIN

AMBRAW SUPPLY COMPANY,INC
PO BOX 672,800 W HIGH ST
OLNEY,IL 62450-0672 PH 618 392-0800
FAX 618 392-0808 SALES@AMBRAWPIPE.COM
HAROLD MURBARGER,PRES
GEORGE LAMBIRD,SECY/TREAS
MICHAEL MURBARGER,SLS
JAMES GOSNELL,SLS

AMBROSE PROPERTIES,INC
FORMERLY INTERSTATE GAS CORPORATION
PO BOX 472149
FORT WORTH,TX 76147 PH 817 312-1149
J D AMBROSE III,PRES

AMBROSE RESOURCES,LLC
7700 SAN FELIPE STE 480
HOUSTON,TX 77063 PH 832 327-2246
ALEX 'SANDY' HUNTER,COO
LASSE WAGENE,CFO

AMCOG ACQUISITION CORP SEE
AMERICAN EXPLORATION CO

AMEGY BANK
PO BOX 27767
HOUSTON,TX 77227-7767
PH 713 232-1796 FAX 713 561-0249
MARK C EDWARDS,SR VP/MGR TRUST REAL
ESTATE AND OIL & GAS
MARK.EDWARDS@AMEGYBANK.COM
JACK QUINN,R/E TRUST ADMIN,III
PH 713 232-1118 FAX 713 571-5449

JACK.QUINN@AMEGYBANK.COM

AMER INDUSTRIAL TECHNOLOGIES,INC
CUSTOM DESIGNING,ENGRG & MFG NUCLEAR
PROD
PO BOX 293
YORKLYN,DE 19736-0293
PH 302 765-3900 WWW.AMERINDUSTRIAL.COM
INFO@AMERINDUSTRIAL.COM
RALPH E LECKY,VP

AMERAC ENERGY CORP SEE
PETROCORP INCORPORATED

AMERADA HESS CORPORATION SEE
HESS CORPORATION

AMEREX RESOURCES CORPORATION
330 RAYFORD RD #124
SPRING,TX 77386 PH 281 419-9277
FAX 281 419-9270 WWW.AMEREXOIL.COM
R J ABERCROMBIE,PRES RJ@ARCOUSA.COM
KARA SCHULTZ,OPERS MGR
TULSA,OK OFFICE - 5103 S SHERIDAN STE 542
74145 PH 918 894-9373 PH 281 685-9993

AMERICAN ASSN OF PROFESSIONAL LANDMEN
800 FOURNIER ST
FORT WORTH,TX 76102
PH 817 847-7700 FAX 817 847-7704
WWW.LANDMAN.ORG AAPL@LANDMAN.ORG
MARTY SCHARAT,EXEC VP

AMERICAN ASSOCIATION OF PETROLEUM GEOLS
PO BOX 979,125 W 15TH ST
TULSA,OK 74101-0979 PH 918 584-2555
PH 800 364-2274 FAX 918 560-2665
WWW.AAPG.ORG POSTMATER@AAPG.ORG
DAVID CURTISS,EXEC DIR
PH 918 560-2639 DCURTISS@AAPG.ORG
DAVID LANGE,CFO
PH 918 560-2659 DLANGE@AAPG.ORG
LARRY NATION,COMMUNICATIONS DIR
PH 918 560-2648 LNATION@AAPG.ORG
(ROSE & ASSOCIATES,LLP) 3405 GLENVIEW AVE

AMERICAN AUGERS
135 US ROUTE 42
WEST SALEM,OH 44287 PH 419 869-7107
KELLY FOOS SALES@AMERICANAUGERS.COM

AMERICAN COASTAL ENERGY,INC
PO BOX 20265
HOUSTON,TX 77225-0265 PH 713 796-2623
FAX 713 796-2665
A PRENTISS FATHERREE,CHRMN
SAM ALBARAL,VP,FIN

AMERICAN DATA CORPORATION
315 S COLLEGE RD STE 163
LAFAYETTE,LA 70503-3213 PH 318 234-1125
FAX 318 237-2607
TIMOTHY H SUPPLE,OWNER,PRES
RICHARD HINES,VP
RICHARD@AMERLAND.COM

AMERICAN DISPOSAL SERVICES,LTD
330 MAIN ST STE 3
SEALY,TX 77474-2300 PH 979 885-7431
FAX 979 885-6976
J D IVEY,PRES

AMERICAN ENERGY ASSOCIATES INC
FORMERLY B T I ENERGY,INC
PO BOX 471
CORTLAND,OH 44410-0471 PH 440 862-4041
AMENERGY@EARTHLINK.NET

ROBERT G BARNETT,PRES

AMERICAN ENERGY DISTRIBUTORS,INC
PO BOX 462
PHARR,TX 78577-0462 PH 512 787-3571
TOM EARL AYCOCK,PRES
TOM ERNEST AYCOCK,VP
HOUSTON,TX OFFICE - 6511 SPRINGER
77251 PH 713 649-6413
NORMAN OLIVER,SLS MGR

AMERICAN ENERGY INVESTMENT GROUP
1700 POST OAK BLVD STE 600,2 BLVD PLACE
HOUSTON,TX 77056 PH 713 334-4464
ROBERT E DOYLE,PRES

AMERICAN ENERGY LLC
PO BOX 129
LAKE ZURICH,IL 60047-0129 PH 847 550-1111
BILL HOIDAS,MNGNG PRTNR
ENERGYBILL@AOL.COM

AMERICAN ENERGY SERVICES SEE
KEY ENERGY PRESSURE PUMPING SERVICES

AMERICAN ENERGY SERVICES,INC
1105 SCHROCK RD STE 602
COLUMBUS,OH 43229-1174 PH 614 885-1901
FAX 614 885-3006
GERALD S JACOBS,PRES

AMERICAN ENERGY SOURCES,INC
NATURAL RESOURCE INVESTMENT & MGMNT
PO BOX 90961
HOUSTON,TX 77290-0961 PH 281 355-1137
FAX 281 355-1137 AESI@VIPINBOX.COM
R A OXENREITER,PRES
CHARLES M BERRY,VP,OPERS
J F OXENREITER,SECY/TREAS

AMERICAN ENVIRONMENTAL RESEARCH,INC
PO BOX 52928
LAFAYETTE,LA 70505 PH 337 989-7238
FAX 337 989-7279 WWW.MERLINGAS.COM

AMERICAN EXPLORATION ACQUISITION CO SEE
AMERICAN EXPLORATION CO

AMERICAN EXPLORATION ACQUISITION-VI CORP
SEE AMERICAN EXPLORATION CO

AMERICAN EXPLORATION COMPANY SEE
LOUIS DREYFUS NATURAL GAS CORP

AMERICAN EXPLORATION GAS SYSTEMS CORP SEE
AMERICAN EXPLORATION CO

AMERICAN EXPLORER,INC SEE
PETROQUEST ENERGY,LLC

AMERICAN GAS ASSOCIATION
WWW.AGA.ORG

AMERICAN NATURAL ENERGY CORPORATION
6100 S YALE AVE STE 2010 ONE WARREN PL
TULSA,OK 74136
PH 918 481-1440 FAX 918 481-1473
MICHAEL PAULK,PRES
RICHARD MULFORD,VP,OPERS
ROBERT SNEAD,VP,EXPL
THE WOODLANDS,TX OFFICE - PO BOX 132137
77318
STEVEN ENSZ,CFO

AMERICAN PETROLEUM INSTITUTE
1220 L ST NW
WASHINGTON,DC 20005-4018
PH 202 682-8000 WWW.API.ORG

AMERICAN PRODUCING PROPERTIES CO SEE
AMERICAN EXPLORATION CO

AMERICAN PRODUCTION PARTNERSHIPS SEE
AMERICAN EXPLORATION CO

AMERICAN RESERVE CORP SEE
AMERICAN EXPLORATION CO

AMERICAN SHORELINE INC
802 N CARANCAHUA STE 1250
CORPUS CHRISTI,TX 78401-0019
PH 361 888-4496 FAX 361 888-4588
WWW.AMSHORE.COM
PAUL M STRUNK,CEO
DENNIS TAYLOR,PRES
JENA NELSON,VP FIN/ADMIN
DEBRA ROWE,PROD ANALYST
JEFF NEVES,WIND PROJ DEV

AMERICAN SULPHUR & OIL CO
PO BOX 1866,823 MOSS ST 70601
LAKE CHARLES,LA 70602-1866
PH 337 430-0033 FAX 337 494-0149
ROBERT NOLAND,PRES
DOUG COOK,VP

AMERICAN TRADING & PRODUCTION CORP
SEE TEMA OIL AND GAS COMPANY

AMERICAN WARRIOR INC
GAS COMPRESSOR,DESIGN,FABRICATION,SALES,
SERVICE,LEASING
1347 EVANGELINE THRUWAY
BROUSSARD,LA 70518-8018 PH 337 364-1263
FAX 337 364-9785
WWW.AMERICANWARRIOR.COM
ARNOLD MURY,REG SALES REP
COLUMBIA,MS OFFICE - PO BOX 1316
HWY 35 NORTH,39429 PH 601 736-1246
FAX 601 736-1250
COLUMBUS,MS OFFICE - PO BOX 2010
HWY 69 SOUTH,39704 PH 662 329-2400
FAX 662 328-1645
DON GREEN,MGR
DICK DAUGHERTY,RENTAL FLEET MGR
GRETNA,LA/NEW ORLEANS,LA SALES OFFICE -
PO BOX 1850,70054 PH 504 374-9520
FAX 504 368-9768
JOHN FARRELL,EXEC VP,FIN
JIM STEPHENS,REG SLS REP
JOE BELLON,GEN MGR
KEITH MARCOTTE,REG ACCOUNT MGR

AMERICAN WEST
PO BOX 301
BURKETT,TX 76828-0301 PH 325 624-5201
CODY W GOLSON,OWNER

AMERICO ENERGY RESOURCES,LLC
7575 SAN FELIPE STE 200
HOUSTON,TX 77063 PH 713 984-9700
FAX 713 984-9933
EDDIE TAJ,PRES
EDDIE.TAJ@AMERICOENERGY.COM
MOSSI ALAVI,CFO
MOSSI.ALAVI@AMERICOENERGY.COM
ASGHAR NOSRATI,VP,OPER
OSCAR.NOSRATI@AMERICOENERGY.COM

AMERIDRIVES INTERNATIONAL
COUPLING PRODUCTS
1802 PITTSBURGH AVE
ERIE,PA 16512
PH 814 480-5000 FAX 814 453-5891

AMERIPLOR CORP SEE
AMERICAN EXPLORATION CO

AMERITAS LIFE INSURANCE CORP
PO BOX 40888,1876 WAYCROSS RD
CINCINNATI,OH 45240-0888
PH 513 595-2371 FAX 513 595-5418
DIANE T THOMAS,MINERAL MGR
DTHOMAS@AMERITAS.COM

AMERITEX MINERALS & EXPLORATION,LTD SEE
AMERITEX MINERALS,INC

AMEROX ACQUISITION CORP SEE
AMERICAN EXPLORATION CO

AMES EUGENE L,JR
711 NAVARRO ST STE 535
SAN ANTONIO,TX 78205 PH 210 824-8253
PH 210 414-4030 FAX 210 824-6423
GAMESJR33@GMAIL.COM

AMES FINANCIAL,INC
416 TRAVIS ST STE 1106
SHREVEPORT,LA 71101-5504 PH 318 227-8944
FAX 318 221-6401

AMES JOHN Y,OIL & GAS PRODUCER
711 NAVARRO ST STE 535
SAN ANTONIO,TX 78205 PH 210 824-8882
FAX 210 824-6423 JYAMES1@SBCGLOBAL.NET

AMES OIL & GAS CORPORATION
340 FAIRWAY DR
NEW ORLEANS,LA 70124-1021 PH 504 488-2234
WILLIAM M GRAY,TRUSTEE

AMEX OIL CO SEE
AMERICAN EXPLORATION CO

AMEXCO,LLC
711 NAVARRO ST STE 535
SAN ANTONIO,TX 78205-0174
PH 210 824-8882 FAX 210 824-6423
JYAMES1@SBCGLOBAL.NET

AMKAM ACQUISITION CORP SEE
AMERICAN EXPLORATION CO

AMM OPERATING LLC
5773 WOODWAY DR #305
HOUSTON,TX 77057
PH 713 439-7927 713 443-3884
CARL MCCUTCHEON,PRES

AMOCO CORPORATION SEE
BP AMOCO CORPORATION

AMOCO GAS COMPANY
5200 GENOA RED BLUFF RD
PASADENA,TX 77505-5709 PH 281 366-3637
S D BOJACK,PRES
TEXAS CITY,TX OFFICE - PO BOX 2609,77592
PH 409 938-5901
R E OGDEN,V P,OPERS

AMOCO PRODUCTION CO SEE
AMOCO CORPORATION

AMORUSO JOHN J,GEOL
1001 MCKINNEY ST STE 1225
HOUSTON,TX 77002 PH 713 652-4031

AMORUSO PETROLEUM CO,EXPLOR
1001 MCKINNEY ST STE 1225
HOUSTON,TX 77002-6450 PH 713 652-4031

AMRON PETROLEUM INC
3301 SAINT JAMES CT
TYLER,TX 75701 PH 903 597-0933
GEORGE E WALTER JR,PRES

AMS-PAR
14950 HEATHROW FOREST PKWY STE 330
HOUSTON,TX 77032 PH 281 866-8256
DAVID JOHNSON,PRTNR-HOUSTON

ROBERT MOORE,PRTNR-HOUSTON
CAROLYN SCZEPANSKI,MGR-DALLAS
PH 972 966-0009
CAROLYN.SCZEPANSKI@AMS-PAR.COM

ANACONDA OPERATING COMPANY
6814 BLUEJACKET ST
SHAWNEE MISSION,KS 66203-3828
PH 913 268-7300
GUS BOGINA JR,PRES
ANGIE BOGINA,VP,OPERS

ANADARKO GATHERING COMPANY SEE
ANADARKO PETROLEUM CORPORATION

ANADARKO PETROLEUM CORPORATION
PO BOX 1330
HOUSTON,TX 77251-1330 PH 832 636-1000
FAX 832 636-8051 WWW.ANADARKO.COM
THE WOODLANDS,TX OFFICE-1201 LAKE ROBBINS
DR 77380-1046
ROBERT J ALLISON JR,CHRMN EMERITUS
H PAULETT EBERHART,DIR
JOHN R GORDON,DIR
PETER J FLOUR,DIR
KEVIN P CHILTON,DIR
RICHARD L GEORGE,DIR
ERIC D MULLINS,DIR
CHARLES W GOODYEAR,DIR
JOSEPH W GORDER,DIR
ANTHONY R CHASE,DIR
DON SINCLAIR,SVP
MARIO M COLL,SVP,CIO
JAMES J KLECKNER,EVP INTL & DEEPWATER
EXPLORATION
ROBERT P DANIELS,EVP INTL & DEEPWATER
EXPLORATION
CHARLES A MELOY,EVP US ONSHORE EXPL &
PRODUCTION
GREGORY M PENSABENE,VP GOV RELS & PUBLIC
AFFAIRS WASHINGTON,DC PH 202 861-8064
ROBERT K REEVES,EVP GEN COUNSEL & CAO
ROBERT G GWIN,EVP,FIN,CFO
ALBERT L RICHEY,SVP,FIN,TREASURER
ROBERT A WALKER,CHRMN,PRES,CEO
LARRY J ABSTON,VP CORP AUDIT
ROBERT D ABENDSCHEIN,VP E&P SVCS &
MINERALS
DANNY E BROWN,VP OP
DAVID D ANDERSON,INTL COMMERCIAL DEV MGR
ROBERT L BECK,SR COMMERCIAL DEV ADVISOR
C BRUCE BOWERSOCK,COMMERCIAL DEV REG MGR
M CATHY DOUGLAS,SVP,CAO
DARRELL E HOLLEK,SVP,OPERS DEEPWATER
AMERICAS
STEVEN J BOSWORTH,VP WORLDWIDE DRILLING
JOHN A BROMAN,VP OPERS AFRICA/ASIA
IAN J COOLING,VP BD INTL
JACQUI DIMPEL,VP MIDSTREAM
BENJAMIN M FINK,VP FIN
JOSEPH A FLAKE,VP CORP PLANNING
GREG JEWELL,VP EXPL WEST AFRICA
ROBERT J LUNN,VP INTL NEW VENTURES
DON VARDEMAN,VP WORLDWIDE PROJ MGMT
ROBERT F TALLEY,VP GEOSCIENCE TECH &
RISK CONSISTENCY TEAM
LARRY SANDERS,VP OPERS ALGERIA
JOHN RIPPLE,MARKETING DIR NGLS
SCOTT MARSHALL,MARKETING DIR GAS

JOHN A BRETZ,GEN MGR DOMESTIC CRUDE OIL & NGL
MICHAEL R CIESLAK,ASST CONTROLLER, EXPENDITURE,INTL RISK
DONALD H MACLIVER,VP INTL OPERS
FRANK J PATTERSON,SVP EXPL INTL
MICHAEL C PEARL,VP FIN
RON C CLEMENTS,MGR CONTRACT ADMIN
JOHN M COLGLAZIR,SVP IR & COMMUNICATIONS
JOHN CHRISTIANSEN,PUBLIC AFFAIRS DIR
ERNEST A LEYENDECKER,SVP EXPL (GOM)
RONALD W HICKS,DIR SECURITY
R ALAN HIGGINS,MGR SPEC PROJ & CONTRACT ADMIN
JEFFREY A KITTRELL,GEN MGR INTL CRUDE OIL & COMMERCIAL RISK
SARIKA AGARWALA,MKTNG REG MGR
WANDA M MARCELL,SR COMMERCIAL MKTG ADVSR
KATHY J MATUS,MGR GAS MKTG OPERS
LORI A MORAN,SR COMMERCIAL MKTG ADVSR
HARRY E NAGEL,MGR MINERALS ENGRG
KELLY A FONTENOT,SR COMM MKTG ADVSR
JULIA STRUBLE,VP HUMAN RESOURCES
LANCE RILEY,COMMERCIAL DEV REG MGR
RANDALL W TONNESEN,ASST TREAS
JOE TOUPS,ASST CONTROLLER
STEVE A WILBURN,SR COMMERCIAL MKTG ADVSR
BOB COOPER,CORP CREDIT SVCS MGR
JERRY L WINDLINGER JR,VP CORP DEV
PHILIP H PEACOCK,ASSOCIATE GEN COUNSEL
DEBRA BROUSSARD,ASSOC GEN COUNSEL LITIGATION
AMANDA MCMILLIAN,VP DEPUTY GEN COUNSEL & CHEIF COMP OFFICER
JOE F CARROLL,VP NEGOTIATIONS & TRANS
Y J BOURGEOIS,COMMERCIAL DEV REG MGR
BRENT BEITER,COMMERCIAL DEV REG MGR
CRIS BARNETT,COMMERCIAL MKTG ADVSR
JIM FUCHS,SR STAFF RESERVOIR ENGINEER
DAVE PENDER,DIR SUPPLY CHAIN MGMNT
JAMES B RANEY,DIR ENGRG TECH
EDWARD L WOOD,VP LAND (US ONSHORE)
DOUGLAS P HAZLETT,VP EXPL
JEFF STAHLEY,DIR OPERS
DAVID MCBRIDE,VP HSE
CHARLES D JOHNSON,COMMERCIAL DEV REG MGR
C TOM HEINZLER,GEN MGR
MARIO REYES,GEN MGR
FRANK DAVIS,DIR REG AFFAIRS
STEVE J FOSTER,ASST TREASURER
STEVEN HOYLE,DIR LNG MKTNG
BRADLEY J HOLLY,VP OPERS (ROCKIES)
TAMMY L CAMPBELL,MGR MKTNG ACCTNG
JOANN P DUVAL,DIR REVENUE ACCTNG
DENVER,CO OFFICE - 1099 18TH ST STE 1200 80202-1964 PH 720 929-6000
A SCOTT MOORE,VP WORLDWIDE MKTG
CHRIS C BRIGGS,GEN MGR GAS MKTG
MICHAEL D FRIEND,SR STAFF COMMERCIAL MKTG
BRETT R MARKOWSKI,SR COMM MKTG ADVSR
TROY A MARSH,MKTG REG MGR
MIKE ROSS,GEN MGR
GARY E PFEIFER,GAS MKTG OPERS MGR
DOUG NATH,DIR BUS DEV
CHIRS L WILSON,COMMERCIAL DEV REG MGR
JIM A PASCHKE,COMMERCIAL DEV REG MGR

KEVIN A KELLY,DIR MARKET FUNDAMENTALS
GARY SILVEY,MKTG DIR NGLS (DENVER)

ANADRILL/SCHLUMBERGER LOGGING SVC SEE
SCHLUMBERGER

ANALOG SERVICES INC
WELL LOGGING/WIRELINE SERVICES
1169 HAYNESVILLE RD
REYNOLDS STATION,KY 42368 PH 270 276-5671
PH 270 775-2020WWW.LOGWELL.COM
SYD H LEVINE

ANALYTICAL SERVICES INC,NATURAL GAS & OIL
MEASUREMENTS & LABORATORY ANALYSIS
PO BOX 1001
OCEAN SPRINGS,MS 39564-1001
PH 228 875-6972
JOHN H YOUNG,PRES & OWNER

ANATESCO,INC
DIGITAL DYNAMOMETERS,SONIC FLUID LEVELS
PUMP-OFF CONTROLLERS,TRANSIENT TESTING
PO BOX 8225
TYLER,TX 75711-8225 PH 903 839-7888
PH 800 256-6567 FAX 903 839-7889
RICK B TAYLOR,PRES

ANAYA WELDING & LEASE
1701 W OWASSA RD
EDINBURG,TX 78539 PH 956 781-5745
WWW.ANAYAWELDING.COM
HERBERT ANAYA
HERIBERTO@ANAYAWELDING.COM

ANCHOR OGM,LLC
3499 OAKS WAY #203
POMPANO BEACH,FL 33069 PH 330 280-0856
ANCHORLWC@GMAIL.COM
LARRY W CATSONIS

ANCON PARTNERSHIP,LTD SEE
AMERICAN EXPLORATION CO

ANDERSON & ASSOCIATES
MINERAL & ENERGY LAND SERVICES
PO BOX 701,92 CHERRY DR
MOUNT VERNON,IL 62864-8488
PH 618 242-7155 FAX 618 242-1486
ADAROT@CHARTER.NET
A DALE ANDERSON,CPL/ESA DIR OF DEV

ANDERSON ENGINEERING CO
919 MILAM ST STE 1965
HOUSTON,TX 77002 PH 713 659-4463
ROBERT W ANDERSON,GEN MGR

ANDERSON ENVIRONMENTAL SERVICES INC
2200 PAKENHAM DR
CHALMETTE,LA 70043 PH 504 276-5858
FAX 504 277-0502
HAROLD J ANDERSON,PRES

ANDERSON EXPLORATION CO,INC
PO BOX 1411,1632 HODGES ST
LAKE CHARLES,LA 70602-1411
PH 337 480-6877 FAX 337 480-6877
CHARLES ANDERSON,PRES

ANDERSON FEAZEL MANAGEMENT,INC
333 TEXAS ST STE 2020
SHREVEPORT,LA 71101-5357
PH 318 227-2000 FAX 318 425-5935
DALE EARWOOD,CEO
WILLIAM G ANDERSON,PRES
H F ANDERSON,VP
DAVID GARRETT,GEN COUNSEL,LAND MGR
MIKE KOVALSKY,CPA,CFO

JAY CROOKS JR,EXPLOITATION MGR
WILLIAM R MEANEY,EXPL MGR
T COLE ANDERSON,MGR OIL & GAS OPERS
G MURPHY ANDERSON,MGR/ANDERSON LAND
MALLORY CRANDALL,GEOL ENGR
FRANK FLOWES,ENGR
DANIEL SEVIER,GEOL
LANCE LAVERDIERE,CPA ACCT
DANIELLE CUTRERA,CPA ACCT
PENNY SHEPHARD,CPL
ELIZABETH AUCHARD,SECY
MICHELLE BERGERET,SECY
JANET GOULD,SECY
DEBBYE KILPATRICK,SECY
LISA WALKER,SECY
SHEILA MORRIS,SECY

ANDERSON HAROLD J,INC
381 HWY 21 STE 205
MADISONVILLE,LA 70447
PH 504 276-5858 FAX 504 277-0502
HAROLD J ANDERSON,PRES
CHALMETTE LA OFFICE - 2200 PAKENHAM DR 70043

ANDERSON JAMES K INC
PO BOX 1188
NORMAN,OK 73070-1188 PH 405 329-2992
FAX 405 447-6445
JOHN S SIMS,PRES

ANDERSON JOHN F,GEOPHY
14618 KELLYWOOD LN
HOUSTON,TX 77079-6425 PH 409 242-3453

ANDERSON OIL & GAS INC SEE
ANDERSON FEAZEL MANAGEMENT,INC

ANDERSON OIL CO INC SEE
ANDERSON OPERATING,LLC

ANDERSON OIL LTD
5005 WOODWAY DR STE 300
HOUSTON,TX 77056-1784
PH 713 652-5746 FAX 713 652-9002
JACQUELINE ANDERSON,PRES
NEAL B ANDERSON,VP,GEN COUNSEL
SCOTT ANDERSON,VP,PETR ENGR
CRAIG F ANDERSON,VP
MARY ELLEN WILT,VP,TREAS
CORPUS CHRISTI,TX OFFICE - 615 N UPPER BROADWAY ST STE 1020,78401
PH 361 881-8600 FAX 361 881-8660
KEVIN ANDERSON,VP
LEXINGTON,KY OFFICE - 836 EUCLID AVE STE 305,40502 PH 859 268-7747
FAX 859 268-9141
MICHAEL SANDERS,EXPL MGR

ANDERSON OPERATING LLC
PO BOX 1000
WASHINGTON,MS 39190 PH 601 442-2960
FAX 601 442-0189
ANDERSONOPERATING@CABLEONE.NET
JACK COX,PRES
NATCHEZ,MS OFFICE - 679 HWY 61 NORTH

ANDERSON PRODUCING,INC
1411 BRIARMEAD DR
HOUSTON,TX 77057-4944 PH 713 782-5647
REECE B ANDERSON,OWNER,PRES

ANDERSON REECE B & ASSOCIATES,INC
1411 BRIARMEAD DR
HOUSTON,TX 77057-4944 PH 713 782-5647

REECE B ANDERSON,PRES

ANDERSON ROBERT W
919 MILAM ST STE 1965
HOUSTON,TX 77002 PH 713 659-4463

ANDERSON WELL REPORTS
WWW.WELLREPORTS.COM

ANDEX RESOURCES,LLC
700 LOUISIANA STE 1100
HOUSTON,TX 77002-2731 PH 713 650-3330
FAX 713 650-3331
TOM L DODDS,PRES

ANDRESS OIL & GAS CO SEE
BREITBURN ENERGY COMPANY LLC

ANDREWS & ASSOCIATES,INC
OIL & GAS EXPLORATION & PRODUCTION
PO BOX 295
VINCENNES,IN 47591 PH 812 882-8191
JONATHAN C ANDREWS,PRES

ANDREWS EXPLORATION CO
8007 ROOS RD
HOUSTON,TX 77036-6441 PH 713 774-1572
CHARLES H ANDREWS,PRES

ANDREWS OIL PROPERTIES
PO BOX 295
VINCENNES,IN 47591 PH 812 882-3363
JONATHAN C ANDREWS,OWNER
PERRY C ANDREWS JR,CONSLT

ANDRIKOPOULOS OIL AND GAS SEE
A.G. ANDRIKOPOULOS RESOURCES INC

ANGELLE & DONOHUE,OIL GAS PROPERTIES,INC
PO BOX 52901
LAFAYETTE,LA 70505-2901 PH 337 264-1151
FAX 337 264-1152
PATRICK L DONOHOE,PRTNR,CPL
PLDCPL@AOL.COM
ROBERT MCFAUL,PRTNR
RJMCFAUL@BELLSOUTH.NET

ANGELLE J BURTON,IND
PO BOX 52901,1116 COOLIDGE
LAFAYETTE,LA 70505-2901 PH 318 232-0781

ANGERS JUDY A,OIL & GAS PROPERTIES
107 GEORGETOWN LOOP
LAFAYETTE,LA 70506 PH 318 984-4940

ANGLER'S CHOICE GUIDES
PO BOX 954
DEWEYVILLE,TX 77614-0954 PH 409 746-9228
ARTIE LONGRON,PRES

ANGLO EXPLORATION CORPORATION
3009 POST OAK BLVD STE 1212
HOUSTON,TX 77056-6599
PH 713 658-1142 PH 713 658-0739
ROBERT W KENT,VP LAND/ACQS

ANIXTER WIRE & CABLE,INC
184 RIVERBEND DR
SAINT ROSE,LA 70087 PH 504 465-5930
PH 800 662-7700 FAX 504 465-5923
24 HR EMERGENCY SVC 800 323-8166
CHAD ESCHETE,LOCATION MGR

ANKOR ENERGY LLC
1615 POYDRAS ST STE 1100
NEW ORLEANS,LA 70112 PH 504 596-3700
FAX 504 596-3762 DCOCRAN@ANKORENERGY.COM
W DENTON COPELAND,PRES
FRANK D BARBER III,VP LAND,CONTRACTS
& NEGOTIATIONS
ROBERT GERDES,VP EXPL

ANTHONY M LAROCCA,TREAS
WARREN P MIGUEZ,MGR,LAND & ACQS
P CASEY GEOHEGAN,FACILITIES ENGNG MGR
JAMES A MCCARTY,GEOPHY MGR
TROY MICHEL,SAFETY MGR
PAUL D DUPONT,SAFETY CONTROL SYSTEMS/
COMPLIANCE MGR
DIANNA WADDEL,REGULATORY SPEC
CALVIN F LEFEVE JR,PURCHASING MGR
STEVE GOFF,OPERS MGR
BRUCE WILLIAMS,SR PROD SUPT
EDDIE ST MARTIN,SR PROD SUPT
KEN ALPAUGH,DRILLING MGR
BRANDT PRAT,STAFF LDMN

ANM SERVICES CORP SEE
AMERICAN EXPLORATION CO

ANNANDALE PRODUCTION CO INC
119 DOGWOOD CT
MADISON,MS 39110
PH 601 856-1028 FAX 601 898-0979
PAUL DAY,PRES/GEOL

ANR PIPELINE COMPANY SEE
EL PASO PIPELINE GROUP

ANSARCO LLC
SEE YOAKAM COLER A JR,PETR GEOL

ANSCHUTZ EXPLORATION CORPORATION
555 17TH ST STE 2400
DENVER,CO 80202-3941
PH 303 298-1000 FAX 303 299-1518
P F ANSCHUTZ,CHRMN
CHRIS HUNT,CHRMN/CEO
W J MILLER,PRES
MARGOT K TIMBEL,SR VP
GALEN BRENIZE,VP OPERS/ENGRG
PAM KALSTROM,VP LAND

ANSYTHE EXPLORATION CO,INC
3705 CLEVELAND PL
METAIRIE,LA 70003 PH 504 887-3432
DONALD I ANDREWS,PRES
JANET M GIROIR,SECY/TREAS

ANTELOPE OIL TOOL & MANUFACTURING CO
912 HOOD ST
MINERAL WELLS,TX 76067-9202
PH 940 325-8989 FAX 940 325-8999
J M YOUNG,PRES,COO
KEITH MOSING,CHRMN,CEO
JEAN BUYTAERT,VP INTL BUS DEV
LANIE HARRISON,OFC MGR

ANTHONY OIL & GAS COMPANY
PO BOX 5684
SHREVEPORT,LA 71135
PH 318 797-8554
W HENRY ANTHONY,MNGNG PRTNR
LISA A VERCHER,OFC MGR

ANVIL OIL & GAS COMPANY
PO BOX 1230
FAIRMONT,WV 26555-1230 PH 304 363-1362
FAX 304 363-1363
JUSTIN L HENDERSON,ESQ,PRES
GENE DILLON,VP
BELINDA BIAFORE,LAND DEPT,OFC MGR

APACHE CORPORATION
2000 POST OAK BLVD STE 100
HOUSTON,TX 77056-4400
PH 800 272-2434 PH 713 296-6000
-EXECUTIVE OFFICERS-

JOHN J CHRISTMANN IV,CEO & PRES
THOMAS E VOYTOVICH,EXEC VP & COO-INTL
MICHAEL S BAHORICH,EXEC VP & CTO
RODNEY J EICHLER,EXEC VP & ADVISOR TO CEO
ANTHONY LANNIE,EXEC VP & GEN COUNSEL
MARGERY M HARRIS,EXEC VP-HUMAN RESOURCES
STEPHEN J RINEY,EXEC VP & CFO
KREGG OLSON,EXEC VP-CORP RESERVOIR ENGRG
MATTHEW W DUNDREA,SR VP-TREASURY & ADMIN
REBECCA HOYT,SR VP/CAO & CONTROLLER
JANINE J MCARDLE,SR VP-GAS MONETIZATION
JON SAUER,SR VP-TAX
SARAH TESLIK,SR VP-COMMUNICATIONS/PUBLIC
AFFAIRS/GOVERNANCE
GARY T CLARK,VP-INVESTOR RELS
JON A GRAHAM,VP-HEALTH/SFTY/SECURITY/
ENVIRO
RODNEY GRYDER,VP-AUDIT
AARON MERRICK,VP-INF TECH
OBIE F O'BRIEN,VP-GOVT AFFAIRS
CHERI L PEPER,CORP SECY
- REGIONAL OFFICERS -
GRADY ABLES,VP-CENTRAL REG
BRETT DARLEY,VP-AUSTRALIA REG
JAMES HOUSE,VP-UK REG & MNGNG DIR
APACHE NORTH SEA
STEVEN J KEENAN,VP-UNCONVENTIONAL RESO
CORY LOEGERING,VP-GULF OF MEXICO REG
THOMAS MAHER,VP-EGYPT REG & GEN MGR-
APACHE EGYPT
TIMOTHY SULLIVAN,VP-CANADA REG & PRES-
APACHE CANADA
FARON THIBODEAUX,VP-PERMIAN REG
TIMOTHY WALL,PRES-KITIMAT UPSTREAM OPERS
- STAFF OFFICERS -
MARK BRIGHT,VP-N AMERICA OIL & GAS MKTG
TIMOTHY CUSTER,VP-LAND
DAVE GILBRONSON,VP-INTL OIL & GAS MKTG
DOMINIC RICOTTA,VP & ASSOC GEN COUNSEL
THOMAS YELICH,VP-BUS DEV
ANCHORAGE,AK OFFICE - 510 L ST STE 310
99501 PH 907 272-2722
LISA PARKER,MGR-GOV RELS
MIDLAND,TX OFFICE - 303 VETERANS AIRPARK
LN STE 3000,79705 PH 432 818-1000
FAX 432 818-1190
TULSA,OK CENTRAL REG OFFICE - 6120 S YALE
STE 1500 74136-4224 PH 918 491-4900
FAX 918 491-4854
CALGARY ALBERTA CANADA OFFICE - 421 7TH
AVE SW STE 2800 T2P 4K9 PH 800 422-9771
PH 403 261-1200 FAX 403 466-5987

APACHE OIL CO,INC
PO BOX 177,5136 SPENCER HWY
PASADENA,TX 77501 PH 281 487-5400
FAX 281 487-5091

APEX GEOPHYSICAL SERVICES,INC
3337 N HULLEN ST STE 201
METAIRIE,LA 70002-3455
PH 504 779-5006 WWW.APEXGEOPHYSICAL.COM
RICHARD D PROVENSAL,CEO/GEOPHY
DAN TODD,GEOPHY
ANGELA D HOLLOWAY,TREAS
JACQUELYN SCOBEY,GEOTECH

APEX LAND CORP SEE
ANCHOR OGM,LLC

APPALACHIA OIL CO
169 W WHITEHALL RD
COOKEVILLE,TN 38501 PH 931 526-2493
JIM BROWN,PRES
JIM.BROWN@CHARTER.NET

APPALACHIAN ENERGY TECHNOLOGY,INC
380 N BAYSHORE BLVD #207
CLEARWATER,FL 33759 PH 740 630-5974
TODD HEFTER,CEO

APPALACHIAN OIL PURCHASERS
CRUDE OIL PUCHASER/TRANSPORTER-WV,PA,OH
BRINE HAULING/DISPOSAL
PO BOX 430
FRAZEYSBURG,OH 43822
PH 800 846-6642 FAX 740 828-3660
BOB GERST,WV STATE MGR
IDA LEWIS,DIV ORDERS

APPALACHIAN WELL SERVICE,INC
PO BOX 636
INDIANA,PA 15701-0636 PH 724 354-4400
FAX 724 354-4749
WWW.APPALACHIANWELLSERVICES.COM
AWS@APPALCHIANWELLSERVICES.COM
JACK L ALBERT,PRES
DOUGLAS L HENSON,VP

APPALOOSA ENERGY LLC
PO BOX 7280
THE WOODLANDS,TX 77387 PH 832 418-0889
BRAD POSEY,MNGNG DIR
BPOSEY@APPALOOSAENERGY.COM
MARTIN SHIELDS,MNGNG DIR
MSHIELDS@APPALOOSAENERGY.COM

APPLACHIAN LAND & ENERGY LLC
22 DUNCAN AVE
PITTSBURGH,PA 15205 PH 412 480-2158
JEFF WHITAKER

APPLIED DRILLING TECHNOLOGY INC
1311 BROADFIELD BLVD STE 600
HOUSTON,TX 77084
PH 281 925-7100 FAX 281 925-7167
STEPHEN E MORRISON

APPLIED GEOPHYSICS,INC
AEROMAGNETIC SURVEYING & CONSULTING
661 S 400 E
SALT LAKE CITY,UT 84111-3926
PH 801 328-8541 FAX 801-363-6243
WWW.APPLIEDGEOPHYSICS.COM
BENAGI@AOL.COM
S PARKER GAY,PRES, CHF GEOPHY
BEN OPFERMANN,VP,OPERS

APPLIED MECHANICS CORPORATION
PO BOX 4609
BRIDGEPORT,WV 26330-4609
PH 304 622-9599
CHARLES STOUT,PRES
CSTOUT@CITYNET.NET

APPLIED RADON TECHNOLOGY SEE
COMPUTER PLACE

APPLING FLOYD E
PO BOX 311,102 1/2 N WASHINGTON
EL CAMPO,TX 77437-0311 PH 409 543-4422
FAX 409 543-8151

AQUA CONTROL SUPPLY
2257 N LOOP 336 W STE 140
CONROE,TX 77304 PH 281 371-9282
FAX 281 754-4374

WWW.ACSCOI.COM ACSCOI@ACSCOI.COM
OWEN F JENSEN III,PRES

AQUA TECH WATER AND DISPOSAL,LLC
100 HIGHLAND PARK VILLAGE STE 200
DALLAS,TX 75205 PH 214 295-3284

ARBOL RESOURCES,INC
10777 WESTHEIMER RD STE 1125
HOUSTON,TX 77042-3460 PH 713 784-1675
FAX 713 782-2626
ALLEN LAZENBY,JR,PRES
VALERIE NOWAK,SECY

ARCADIA OPERATING,LLC
3811 TURTLE CREEK BLVD STE 1900
DALLAS,TX 75219
PH 214 521-4900 FAX 214 521-4989
INFO@BURNETTPETRO.COM WWW.ARCA-
DIAOP.COM
KYLE R BURNETT,CEO
SVETLANA FAMORCA,VP FIN
ROBERT SHANNON,CONTROLLER
R J CREE,VP LEGAL & LAND
SHARON CHAMPAGNE,LAND MGR
RUS RICHARDS,OPERS MGR
VAN,TX OFFICE - PO BOX 590,75790
JOHN P NASH,OPERS SUPT

ARCADIS G&M,INC
1004 N BIG SPRING STE 300
MIDLAND,TX 79701-3872
PH 432 687-5400 FAX 432 687-5401
WWW.ARCADIS-US.COM
SHARON HALL,ASSOC VP,LOCATION LEADER
SHARON.HALL@ARCADIS-US.COM
AUSTIN,TX OFFICE - 1717 W 6TH ST STE 210
78703,PH 512 451-1188
PHIL MARTIN
PHIL.MARTIN@ARCADIS-US.COM
CORPUS CHRISTI,TX OFFICE - 711 N
CARANCHUA STE 1080,78475-1801
PH 361 883-1353
KEN BRANDNER,LOCATION LEADER
KEN.BRANDNER@ARCADIS-US.COM
HOUSTON,TX OFFICE - 2929 BRIARPARK DR
STE 300,77042 PH 713 953-4732
PAUL BARNES,LOCATION LEADER
PAUL.BARNES@ARCADIS-US.COM

ARCH PETROLEUM INC SEE POGO PRODUCING CO

ARCHER J M & ASSOCIATES,ATTORNEY (RPL)
17431 BOROUGH LN
SPRING,TX 77379-6247 PH 281 257-1909

ARCHON RESOURCES LLC
9301 SOUTHWEST FWY STE 100
HOUSTON,TX 77074-1500 PH 713 988-3300
BOB MARIN,PRES BOB@ARCHONRESOURCES.COM
DAVID MCDUFFIE,VP/TREAS
LARRY BREWER,VP ENGRG & OPERS
JEFF MARIN,GEOSCIENTIST
JERRY EDRINGTON,BUS DEV

ARCIS RESOURCES CORP
6586 HYPOLUXO RD # 225
LAKE WORTH,FL 33467 PH 205 453-9650
BUTCH FLATT BUTCH@FUELITGREEN.COM

ARCO ALASKA,INC
A SUBSIDIARY OF ATLANTIC RICHFIELD CO
PO BOX 100360
ANCHORAGE,AK 99510-0360 PH 907 276-1215
H L BILHARTZ,ARCO ALASKA,INC

J D WEEKS,SR VP,PRUDHOE,LISBURNE
H P FOSTER,SR VP,KUPARUK,COOK INLET
J P MCCOY,VP,FIN,PLNG & CONTROL
R IDEN,VP,EXTERNAL AFFAIRS
J M DAVIS,SR VP,EXPL
N T THOMPSON,VP,HUMAN RESOURCES

ARDAGA RESOURCES,PETR LDMN SERVICES
14407 DARK STAR ST
SAN ANTONIO,TX 78248-1115 PH 210 492-4122
FAX 210 492-2260
ARTHUR D GALVAN

ARDIS & COMPANY
PO BOX 75
SHREVEPORT,LA 71161-0075
PH 318 868-7751 PH 318 861-8668
GEORGE HARDWICK MILLS,MNGNG PRTNR

ARDO PRODUCTION CO,SEE
ARLEDGE TERRY & CO

ARENDALE OIL & GAS COMPANY
770 S POST OAK LN STE 630
HOUSTON,TX 77056-1913 PH 713 961-9395

ARETE ACQUISITIONS,LLC
1143 NORTHERN BLVD STE 131
CLARKS SUMMIT,PA 18411
PH 570 877-0795 FAX 570 521-5706
WWW.ARETEACQUISITIONS.COM
EMAIL@ARETEACQUISITIONS.COM
JUSTIN BURGESS,PRTNR
ADAM JOHNSON,PRTNR
TYLER DAFFINEE,PRTNR

ARGOS MINERALS,INC
2802 TIMMONS LN UNIT 56265
HOUSTON,TX 77256-0115
PH 713 961-9401 FAX 713 961-9402
A HEYWOOD COOPER,PRES
HCOOPER@ARGOSMINERALS.COM

ARIES MARINE CORPORATION
PO BOX 51789
LAFAYETTE,LA 70505-1789
PH 337 232-8147 FAX 337 232-8818
WWW.ARIESMARINE.COM
EMAIL@ARIESMARINE.COM
D S RAMSAY,CFO DSRAMSAY@ARIESMARINE.COM
C B RAMSAY,PRES CBRAMSAY@ARIESMARINE.COM
J L HOLDEN,CONTROLLER
JHOLDEN@ARIESMARINE.COM
CLYDE MUNSON,MKTG CMUNSON@ARIESMA-
RINE.COM
PETER FINSTAD,MKTG
PFINSTAD@ARIESMARINE.COM
LYNN GUIDRY,ADMIN LYNN@ARIESMARINE.COM
BRENDA MARTIN,ACCT
BMARTIN@ARIESMARINE.COM
YOUNGSVILLE,LA LIFTBOAT OPERS OFFICE -
PH 337 232-0335 FAX 337 856-7380
RICHARD JOHNSON,COO
FRJOHNSON@ARIESMARINE.COM
BUTCH BAZER,OPERS MGR
WDBAZER@ARIESMARINE.COM
VIRGINIA JOHNSON,OFC MGR
VJOHNSON@ARIESMARINE.COM
WIKOFF MCMILLAN,SAFETY DIR
WMCMILLAN@ARIESMARINE.COM
YOUNGSVILLE,LA SUPPLY BOAT OPERS OFFICE -
PH 337 232-0335 PH 337 856-9015
FAX 337 856-7380

PETER ROMERO,OPERS MGR
PROMERO@ARIESMARINE.COM
TOMMY BROWN TBROWN@ARIESMARINE.COM

ARIES OPERATING,LP
1301 MCKINNEY ST STE 3350
HOUSTON,TX 77010-3120 PH 713 759-1981
FAX 713 759-0360
WWW.ARIESOPERATING.COM
REUVEN HOLLO,PRES
RHOLLO@ARIES-OPERATING.COM

ARK-LA-TEX ENERGY LLC
415 TEXAS ST STE 201
SHREVEPORT,LA 71101
PH 318 676-2018 FAX 318 222-7222
MICHAEL H BOUDREAUX,PRES MIKEB@SHREVE.NET
RICKY RUTHERFORD,LAND MGR
KAREN TIEMANN,ACCT
STEVE GREBER,GEOL

ARKANSAS LA GAS CO,SEE ARKLA INC

ARKANSAS MINERALS INC,PUR OIL & GAS
ROYALTIES & MINERALS
314 E OAK ST
EL DORADO,AR 71730-5834 PH 870 863-7047
FAX 870 863-5308
W L COOK,II,SECY/TREAS

ARKANSAS OKLAHOMA GAS CORPORATION
PO BOX 2415
FORT SMITH,AR 72902 PH 479 783-3181
FAX 479 784-2006 WWW.AOGC.COM
FORT SMITH,AR OFFICE- 115 N 12TH
72902 PH 479 783-3181
MIKE CALLAN,PRES
FRED KIRKWOOD,SR VP/CUST SVC
KIM LINAM,VP/FIN & ACCT

ARKLA ENERGY MARKETING CO
PO BOX 21734
SHREVEPORT,LA 71151 PH 318 429-3407
FAX 318 429-3957
RICHARD CARRUTH,SR VP
BILL DEWARE,DIR
BILLY MAXWELL,MGR
JACK LABORDE,MGR,OFF-SYS SUPPLY
SID BROWN,MGR,ON-SYS SUPPLY
SCOTT GENTRY,SR GAS SUPPLY REP
RANDY TIMMS,SUPPLY REP
GREG DORRIS,SUPPLY REP

ARLINGTON EXPLORATION CO
535 BOYLSTON ST
BOSTON,MA 02116-3720 PH 617 447-2251
DAVID A T DONOHUE,PRES
TIMOTHY D A DONOHUE,VP

ARMADA OIL,INC
5220 SPRING VALLEY RD STE 615
DALLAS,TX 75254 PH 972 490-9595
FAX 972 490-9161 WWW.ARMADAOIL.US
RANDY M GRIFFIN,CEO
RACHEL DILLARD,CFO
J CLINT UNRUH,COO
RAY UNRUH,EXEC VP

ARMADA OPERATING,LLC
5220 SPRING VALLEY RD STE 615
DALLAS,TX 75254 PH 972 490-9595
FAX 972 490-9161 WWW.ARMADAOIL.US
RANDY M GRIFFIN,CEO
RAY UNRUH,PRES
J CLINT UNRUH,VP

ARMADILLO PIPELINE CO
3300 S BROADWAY AVE STE 103
TYLER,TX 75701-7849 PH 903 592-3311
FAX 903 592-1339
BRUCE FAULKNER,PRES
W R GUFFEY,VP

ARMBRECHT JACKSON LLP
PO BOX 290
MOBILE,AL 36601-0290
PH 251 405-1300 FAX 251 432-6843
WWW.AJLAW.COM
CONRAD P ARMBRECHT
DUANE A GRAHAM

ARMSTRONG OIL AND LAND CORPORATION
PO BOX 2299
NATCHEZ,MS 39121-2299 PH 601 442-0122
THOMAS K ARMSTRONG,PRES
JOHN H JAMES,VP

ARMSTRONG THOMAS K
PO BOX 2299
NATCHEZ,MS 39120-2299 PH 601 422-0122

ARNAUDVILLE COMPANY INC
3304 NOTTINGHAM ST
HOUSTON,TX 77005-2216
PH 318 439-2094
W R FARLEY,PRES

ARNOLD OIL COMPANY
PO BOX 7889
CORPUS CHRISTI,TX 78467-7889
PH 361 884-6621
JAMES B ARNOLD,PRES & MGR

ARNOLD RICHARD J,PETR ENGR
506 OPELOUSAS AVE
NEW ORLEANS,LA 70114-4342 PH 504 366-1526

ARO CORP
209 N MAIN ST
BRYAN,OH 43506-1319 PH 419 636-4242
L D BLACK,PRES

ARRINGTON BROTHERS SEE
ARRINGTON PRODUCTION CO

ARROW DRILLING COMPANY,INC
PO BOX 529
BENAVIDES,TX 78341
PH 361 256-3354 FAX 361 643-4441
ARROWDRILLING@CABLEONE.NET
NESTOR GARZA JR,CEO
LUIS R GARZA,PRES

ARROW PETROLEUM CO
900 NE LOOP 410 STE A123
SAN ANTONIO,TX 78209-1402 PH 210 824-2331

ARROWHEAD ENERGY EXPLORATION,LLC
3233 S SHERWOOD FOREST BLVD STE 100
BATON ROUGE,LA 70816-2250 PH 225 293-6530
FAX 225 293-6585
DONALD W SOLANAS JR,PRTNR
PAUL R RADLE JR,PRTNR

ARTERO ENERGY CO
2607 VALLEY FIELD DR
SUGAR LAND,TX 77479-1551 PH 281 980-6455
ALAN H MORGAN,PRES,CPL

ARTEX OIL COMPANY
2337 STATE ROUTE 821
MARIETTA,OH 45750-5318 PH 740 373-3313
FAX 740 373-2750 AOC@ARTEXOIL.COM
JERRY JAMES,PRES
EUGENE L HUCK,VP

MATT LUPARDUS,EXPL
JOE SYNDER,DRLG ENGR
DON HUCK,EXPL MGR

ARTHUR BURNETT,INC
CONTRACT PERMITTING
217 MAGNOLIA HILL RD
WAYNESBORO,MS 39367
PH 601 818-2684 FAX 601 735-2319
ARTHUR BURNETT,OWNER,PERMIT AGENT
ARTHURBURNETTINC@GMAIL.COM

ARTHUR PATRICK W PRODUCTION COMPANY SEE
PENDRAGON PRODUCTION COMPANY

ASHBY FRANK A,JR,OIL OPR,EXPL & DEV
228 SAINT CHARLES AVE STE 1300
NEW ORLEANS,LA 70130-2605 PH 504 522-8388
FAX 504 522-8380
LELONG@BELLSOUTH.NET

ASHFORD OIL & GAS COMPANY,LLC
1210 TRACE DR
HOUSTON,TX 77077 PH 832 512-0495
ROBERT PLEDGER RPLEDGER@HOTMAIL.COM

ASSOCIATED ENERGY CONSULTANTS,LLC SEE
BAUGH RONALD

ASSOCIATED NATURAL GAS CORPORATION SEE
PANENERGY NATURAL GAS CORPORATION

ASSOCIATED NATURAL GAS,INC SEE
PANENERGY FIELD SERVICES,INC

ASSOCIATED PERMIT AGENTS
4938 FM 765
SAN ANGELO,TX 76905
PH 325 226-5158 WWW.PERMITAGENTS.COM
TOM WILDE,GEN MGR
BRAD WILDE,PRES/DATABASE ADMIN
CORY WILDE,VP/PERMIT AGENT

ASSOCIATED RESOURCES INC
OIL & GAS CONSULTANTS
15 E 5TH ST STE 200
TULSA,OK 74103-3842
PH 918 584-2111 FAX 918 584-3111
WWW.ARITULSA.COM WWW.LANDMEN.COM
TOM HAVENSTRITE,PRES
BRENDON WORD,VP

ASSOCIATION OF AMERICAN RAILROADS
WWW.AAR.ORG

ASSOCIATION OF ENERGY SERVICE COMPANIES
14531 FM 529 STE 250
HOUSTON,TX 77095 PH 713 781-0758
FAX 713 781-7542 WWW.AESC.NET
KENNY JORDAN,EXEC DIR
PATTY JORDAN,PRES WELL SERVICING MAGAZINE
RONI ASHLEY,DIR OF ACCT SVCS
NIKKI JAMES,DIR ASSOC PROG/MTG PLANNER
KRISTEN KOHUT,ADMIN ASST

ASSOCIATION OF OIL PIPE LINES
1808 EYE ST NW
WASHINGTON,DC 20006 PH 202 408-7970
WWW.AOPL.ORG AOPL@AOPL.ORG
ANDY BLACK,PRES,CEO
STEVE CRAMER,GEN COUNSEL
BRYDEN ROSS,DIR,GOV RELS

ASTRO DRILLING CO INC,OIL WELL DRLG
4503 FERN AVE
SHREVEPORT,LA 71105-3115 PH 318 861-6337
JOHN W THOMAS,PRES

ATASCA RESOURCES,INC SEE
TRIBO PRODUCTION COMPANY,LTD

ATC ASSOCIATES INC
200 WELLINGTON MANOR ST STE 100
ALABASTER,AL 35007-4164 PH 205 733-8775
 SCOTT R VINSANT,PG,BRANCH MGR
 BRAD JINKINS,PG,ENV MGR
 LESLIE GREENWOOD,DIR OF BUS DEV

ATCHISON CHARLES D S
11808 PARKSIDE
MONTGOMERY,TX 77356-4802 PH 281 759 9293

ATCO PRODUCING CO,OIL PROD
PO BOX 859
SOUR LAKE,TX 77659-0859 PH 409 287-3661

ATEC INC
12600 EXECUTIVE DR
STAFFORD,TX 77477-3604 PH 281 276-2700
FAX 281 240-6514
 HOWARD LEDERER,CEO
 PAUL R FENLEY,VP
 KEN E NEEF,VP
 DAN L CARLEY,VP
 MIKE RIGDON,VP

ATHANOR TEXAS INC SEE
APPROACH RESOURCES INC

ATKINS JOHN E
333 TEXAS ST STE 2300
SHREVEPORT,LA 71101 PH 318 222-2161

ATLANTA EXPLORATION COMPANY
 LAND BROKERAGE SERVICES IN S ARK & N LA
PO BOX 9,627 E MAIN ST
MAGNOLIA,AR 71754-0009
PH 870 234-2526 FAX 870 234-8490
 ALAN RIBBLE,PRES
  ALAN@ATLANTAEXPLORATION.COM
 RODNEY MAY,VP LAND

ATLANTIC ENERGY HOLDINGS,LLC SEE
CENTENNIAL RESOURCE PRODUCTION LLC

ATLANTIC EXPLORATION,LLC SEE
CENTENNIAL RESOURCE PRODUCTION LLC

ATLANTIC GEOPHYSICAL COMPANY
1867 GARTH RD
PHILADELPHIA,PA 19116-3827
PH 215 676-6257
 KALMAN N ISAACS,GEOPHY,GEOL

ATLANTIC RICHFIELD COMPANY,SEE
BP AMERICA,INC

ATLANTIS OIL CO,INC
727 S CHILTON
TYLER,TX 75701-1554 PH 903 597-7277
 MICHAEL N ROMINES,PRES
  MICHAEL@SOUTHWESTOPERATING.COM

ATLAS ACQS,LAND,TITLE,CORROSION SERVICES
8820 MARYLAND CT
DENTON,TX 76207
PH 817 915-9993 FAX 800 610-9875
 L D DODGEN,CEO
 DR ROBERT C BESS,PHD,MNGNG DIR
 RCBESS44@GMAIL.COM

ATLAS ENERGY,LP
3500 MASSILLON RD STE 100
UNIONTOWN,OH 44685-9575
PH 330 896-8510 FAX 330 896-8518
 WWW.ATLASENERGY.COM
 JEFFREY C SIMMONS,EXEC VP-OPERS
 JSIMMONS@ATLASENERGY.COM

ATLAS PETROLEUM EXPLORATION
 WORLDWIDE, LTD (APE)

16600 PARK ROW
HOUSTON,TX 77084
PH 281 994-5400 FAX 281 994-5410
 DOUGLAS W GAITHER,PRES,COO
 DWG@APXWW.COM
 O DUANE GAITHER II,DIR
 PATRICK GORDON,VP EXPL

ATLAS WIRELINE SERVICES SEE
WESTERN ATLAS LOGGING SERVICES

ATMIC,INC
2450 FONDREN RD STE 112
HOUSTON,TX 77063-2314
PH 713 266-0322 FAX 713 266-0324
 STEPHEN T CARROLL,VP EXPL
 STEPHENTCARROLL@ATT.NET
DENVER,CO OFFICE - 1825 LAWRENCE
STE 300,80202 PH 303 295-0050
FAX 303 296-0375
 GORDON SMALE,PRES
 JUDY BUNCH,COMPTROLLER

ATMOS ENERGY GATHERING,LLC
2929 W SAM HOUSTON PKWY N #200
HOUSTON,TX 77043-1613
PH 713 316-6607 FAX 713 688-5124
 MARK WALSH

ATP OIL & GAS CORPORATION
4600 POST OAK PL STE 200
HOUSTON,TX 77027-9726 PH 713 622-3311
FAX 713 622-5101
 WWW.ATPOG.COM ATPINFO@ATPOG.COM
 T PAUL BULMAHN,CHRMN,CEO
 LELAND E TATE,PRES
 GEORGE R MORRIS,CHF OPERS OFCR
 JOHN E TSCHIRHART,SR VP,INTL GEN COUNCIL
 G ROSS FRAZER,VP,ENGRG
 KEITH R GODWIN,CAO
 AL REESE JR,CFO
 ROBERT M SHIVERS,VP,PROJ
 ISABEL M PLUME,CORP SECY,CHF COM OFCR
 KEVIN L MCCARTY,MGR,GEOSCIENCES
 JERRY R KENNEDY,MGR,RESERVOIR ENGR

ATTLEBORO & PLAINVILLE OIL COMPANY
PO BOX 2400
PLAINVILLE,MA 02762-0299
PH 800 398-3835 FAX 508 643-9811
 SANTORO4541@AOL.COM
 JOSEPH A SANTORO,PRES

ATWATER CONSULTANTS LTD,GEOL & PETR ENGRS
3525 HESSMER AVE STE 304
METAIRIE,LA 70002-6407 PH 504 581-6527
FAX 504 883-9079 WWW.ATWATER.COM
 T A JOHNSTON,PRES,TJOHNSTO@ATWATER.COM
 K G HAYS,VP

ATWOOD H KIRBY SEE GULF CAPITAL RESOURCES

ATWOOD OCEANICS INC
PO BOX 218350,15835 PARK TEN PLACE DR
HOUSTON,TX 77218-8350 PH 281 749-7800 OR
PH 800 231-5924 FAX 281 492-0345
 WWW.ATWD.COM
 ROBERT J SALTIEL,PRES/CEO
 MARK L MEY,SR VP,CFO
 ARTHUR M POLHAMUS,VP,OPERS
 WALTER A BAKER,VP,GEN COUNSEL,CORP SECY
 BARRY M SMITH,VP,TECH SVCS
 LUIS A JIMENEZ,VP,HR
 GEOFFREY C WAGNER,VP,MKTNG & BUS DEV

 MARK W SMITH,VP CORP SVCS
 MICHAEL A CAMPBELL,VP CONTROLLER
 EVELYN A NORDIN,TREAS

ATWOOD PROFESSIONAL SEARCH,INC
PO BOX 58411
HOUSTON,TX 77258-8411 PH 281 333-1061
FAX 281 333-1063

AU LAND SERVICES,LLC
1910 ESE LOOP 323 STE 164
TYLER,TX 75701 PH 903 570-3838
 DON PARKINS PARKINS12@GMAIL.COM

AUBAINE CORPORATION, THE
14302 CINDYWOOD DR
HOUSTON,TX 77079-6615 PH 281 531-4585
 CHARLES R HORNE,PRES & CHIEF GEOL

AUDITORS - OIL & GAS
12651 BRIAR FOREST DR STE 165
HOUSTON,TX 77077-2376 PH 281 531-1500
FAX 281 531-7415
 ROBERT P MALONE,CFE

AULTMAN H D
128 POUNCEY RD
SUMRALL,MS 39482-8513 PH 601 264-7717

AUSTERITY EXPLORATION INC
5806 RUTHERGLENN DR
HOUSTON,TX 77096-4808 PH 713 723-8484
 DONNFRANSCH@COMCAST.NET
 DONALD R SCHERER,PRES
 FRANCES H SCHERER,SECY/TREAS

AUSTIN EXPLORATION INC
10333 WESTOFFICE DR
HOUSTON,TX 77042-5386 PH 713 780-7141
FAX 713 780-3118

AUSTIN RIDGE ENERGY CORPORATION
PO BOX 19447
HOUSTON,TX 77224-9447 PH 713 461-0852
 MACKEY BARNES,PRES

AUSTRAL OIL CO,INC
2701 MAPLEWOOD DR
SULPHUR,LA 70663-6165 PH 337 625-5452
FAX 337 625-9887

AUSTRAL OIL COMPANY INC SEE
AMERICAN EXPLORATION CO

AUSTRALIAN-CANADIAN OIL ROYALTIES,LTD
PO BOX 1629,1301 AVE M
CISCO,TX 76437-1629 PH 254 442-2638
FAX 254 442-3843 WWW.AUSSIEOIL.COM
 ANDRE SAKHAI,PRES
 HOWARD SIEGEL,SECY

AUTOMATIC POWER,INC
198 TECHNOLOGY LN
GRAY,LA 70359 PH 985 223-8700
FAX 985 223-8710 WWW.AUTOMATICPOWER.COM
 WWW.AUTOMATICPOWER.COM
 RENE LEBLANC,LA DIV MGR
 MIKE HYMEL,LA OFC MGR

AVALON INTERESTS LLC
PO BOX 985,6801 CEDAR RUN
MONTROSE,AL 36559-0985
PH 251 990-8732 AVALON@JELLENC.BIZ

AVERILL & SWOPE
PO BOX 1727
VICTORIA,TX 77902-1727 PH 361 573-6471

AWP OPERATING COMPANY
6104 BROADWAY STE C-1
SAN ANTONIO,TX 78209

PH 210 820-3868 FAX 210 820-3869
    BARNEY DISHRON,PRES
        BDISHRON@AWP-OPERATING.COM

AWS-TECHNOLOGY SEE
    WESTERN ATLAS LOGGING SERVICES

AX ACQUISITION CORP SEE
    AMERICAN EXPLORATION CO

AXCON CORP SEE
    AMERICAN EXPLORATION CO

AXELSON INC SEE
    DRESSER OIL TOOLS

AYCO ENERGY,LLC
    2909 HILLCROFT AVE STE 103
    HOUSTON,TX 77057 PH 281 398-4501
    FAX 281 398-7576
        JOHN B ASHMUN,PRES
            JBASHMUN@AYCOENERGY.COM
        W M YATES,SECY RYATES@AYCOENERGY.COM
        JONATHAN MARCANTEL,GEOL
            JMARCANTEL@AYCOENERGY.COM

AYRES GEORGE C
    4141 S BRAESWOOD BLVD APT 610
    HOUSTON,TX 77025-3339 PH 713 652-3140
    FAX 713 658-0401

AZTEC FR (FIRE RETARDANT) APPAREL INC
    2144 CIENEGAS RD
    DEL RIO,TX 78840 PH 915 309-2685
        MARK FOGLE MFOGLE@AZTECFRAPPAREL.COM

AZTEC MFG CO
    400 N TARRANT
    CROWLEY,TX 76036 PH 817 297-4361
    FAX 817 297-4621
        BOBBY MARTIN,SALES MGR
        RIP MARTIN,GEN MGR

AZTEC PIPE,INC
    PO BOX 217
    BROUSSARD,LA 70518-0217 PH 337 839-4990
    FAX 337 839-0097 APIPEINC@BELLSOUTH.NET
        I.LEE LANGE,PRES

A2D TECHNOLOGIES SEE
    TGS WELL DATA DIVISION

B & B OIL & GAS PRODUCTION COMPANY
    370 PIPELINE RD
    DAYTON,PA 16222 PH 814 257-8760
    FAX 814 257-8604 BBOILGAS@WINDSTREAM.NET
        PATRICIA A HETRICK,OWNER
        VENTON L HETRICK,OPERS MGR
        KYLE L HETRICK,PROD COORDINATOR

B & B OIL TOOLS INC
    PO BOX 21,101 WHITEHEAD DR
    MAGNOLIA,AR 71753-0021 PH 870 234-7222
    PH 888 771-5007 FAX 870 234-7272
        BOBBY B.D. ALLEN,PRES/OWNER
            PH 870 904-5522
        ROBBY ALLEN,TOOL HAND 870 904-4753
        MICHEAL ALLEN,SHOP HAND
        PEGGY MANESS,SECY
        KIM BEASON,SECY
        JERRY ZEPNERICK,TUBING TESTER
        TIM HERION,VACUUM TRK
        BOBBY FLOW,TUBING TESTER
        RICKY SIMMONS,VACUUM TRK
        NICKY HOLLIS,VACUUM TRK
        JAY MILLER,TUBING TESTER
        DALE COCKRELL,TOOL HAND

B & B PRODUCTION CO
    5868 WESTHEIMER RD STE 535
    HOUSTON,TX 77057-5641 PH 832 203-8858
        SAM SKIPPER,CEO
        LORETTA HIGGINS,CFO
        JOHN HIGGINBOTHAM,VP OPERS

B & B RESOURCES,INC
    149 CREEK TER STE 1
    SOMERSET,KY 42503-1704 PH 606 679-1509
        RON ABSHER,PRES,OWNER

B & D SLEDGE DRILLING CO
    PO BOX 2427
    MOUNT VERNON,IL 62864-2427
    PH 618 244-4210
        BOBBY G SLEDGE,PRES
        DAVID L SLEDGE,SECY/TREAS

B & J DRILLING CO INC
    13911 MILLERSBURG RD
    DANVILLE,OH 43014 PH 740 599-6700
        BILL SAMPLES

B & S SERVICES,INC
        CEMENTING,ACIDIZING/HIGH PRESSURE PUMP-
        ING
    11928 FM 1301 RD
    BOLING,TX 77420-9354
    PH 979 657-3580 FAX 979 657-3039
        KEVIN BANNERT,PRES,OWNER

B B L LTD,SEE
    BRECK OPERATING CORP

B D PRODUCTION COMPANY INC
    615 N UPPER BROADWAY ST STE 1900
    CORPUS CHRISTI,TX 78477-0042
    PH 361 888-4741 FAX 361 888-4744
        BDPRODUCTION@BDPRODUCTION.NET
    LEE A DURST JR,PRES

B H & M OIL CO LEASES & ROYALTIES
    101 W MAIN ST STE 313
    EL DORADO,AR 71730-5639 PH 870 863-6813

B J INC
    PO BOX 461,HWY 127 NORTH
    CROSSVILLE,TN 38557-0461 PH 931 484-8969
        JAMES D BURGIN,PRES

B S E PRODUCTION CO
    PO BOX 4260,805 E MOCKINGBIRD STE B
    VICTORIA,TX 77903-4260
    PH 361 578-9021 FAX 361 578-4280
        WILLIAM SPRADLIN,PRES
        MARY ANN GRANTHAM,OFC MGR

B S F I WESTERN E & P INC
    6513 PERKINS RD
    BATON ROUGE,LA 70808-4259
    PH 225 769-9555 FAX 225 769-9222
        JOSEPH P BRANTLEY,PRES,CEO
            JPBRANTLEY@GMAIL.COM
        RUSSELL FRANQUES,CFO,VP LAND

B SERVICES
    1606 SHADY LN
    ERATH,LA 70533-5876 PH 337 685-3155
        BILL BADEAUX,OWNER BNBADEAUX@COX.NET

B T OPERATING CO SEE B & B PRODUCTION CO

B.B.I.
    7237 FLINT RD
    DELLROY,OH 44620 PH 330 735-2267
        MICHELE SWINEY,SECY

B.R. ALLEN & ASSOCIATES, LLP
    PO BOX 2366

BOERNE,TX 78006 PH 830 433-4900
FAX 830 433-4901
    RANDY ALLEN,PRINCIPLE

B.W.R INVESTMENT,INC SEE
    BUCK WHEAT RESOURCES INC

BABCOCK EAGLETON,INC
    2900 NORTH LOOP W STE 1000
    HOUSTON,TX 77092 PH 713 871-8787
    FAX 713 871-1914 WWW.EAGLETONINC.COM
        C D CAGLE,PRES
        CHARLIE CROWELL,VP,PROJ
        J L WALKER,VP,PROJ
        R D BOATES III,VP,DRAFTING/SURVEY
        M F MEIS,CFO

BABECO
    1101 CARLOS PARKER BLVD NW
    TAYLOR,TX 76574 PH 512 352-5355
        TROY WADE,TROY W@BABECOINC.COM

BABIN LOGAN H INC,IND DEV
    PO BOX 269, 400 LAFAYETTE ST
    HOUMA,LA 70361-0269 PH 985 872-4597
    FAX 985 872-2402 WWW.LOGANBABIN.COM
        LOGAN H BABIN JR,CRE,FRICS,PRES
        APPRAISER & REALTOR

BADER LEO JR, PETR GEOL
    PO BOX 51515,201 HEYMAN BLVD OFC 5
    LAFAYETTE,LA 70505 PH 337 237-0274

BADGER OIL CORP
    PO BOX 52745
    3861 AMBASSADOR CAFFREY BLVD STE 400
    LAFAYETTE,LA 70505-2745 PH 337 233-9200
    FAX 337 237-5158
        C PAUL HILLIARD,PRES
            P.HILLIARD@BADGEROIL.COM
        ARTHUR J PRICE,VP,FIN
            A.PRICE@BADGEROIL.COM
        DAVID ETIENNE,VP,EXPL
            D.ETIENNE@BADGEROIL.COM
        RUSTY PEYTON,LAND MGR
            R.PEYTON@BADGEROIL.COM
        STEVE MALEY,OPERS MGR
            S.MALEY@BADGEROIL.COM

BAGBY ENERGY LLC
    3811 TURTLE CREEK BLVD STE 1900
    DALLAS,TX 75219-4545 PH 214 446-0891
    FAX 214 522-4913
        BOND W BEAMS,VP LAND
        HOWARD BAGBY,PRES

BAGLEY ROY
    14603 WILDWOOD TRACE
    MAGNOLIA,TX 77354-1867 PH 281 356-4357
    FAX 281 356-4357
        ROY BAGLEY,OWNER,OPERATOR
            R.BAGLEYJR@WORLDNET.ATT.NET

BAGNALL & BARBER,INC,PETR CONS
    PO BOX 3483,608 E CRESTWOOD DR
    VICTORIA,TX 77903-3483 PH 361 575-7486
        GARY BAGNALL,PRES,ENGR
        DAVID BAGNALL,PETR ENGR

BAHAN MICHAEL W
    PO BOX 17215
    SAN ANTONIO,TX 78217-0215 PH 210 828-4006
    FAX 210 824-8405 MWB215@AOL.COM

BAHR OIL & GAS
    127 GARDNER DR
    SHALIMAR,FL 32579

PH 903 235-7999

DON BAHR,PRINCIPAL DJBAHR@AOL.COM

BAILEY L J

627 N MAIN ST

PLEASANTON,TX 78064-3027 PH 830 569-2946

BAIRD GEOPHYSICAL COMPANY SEE

BAIRD PETROPHYSICAL INTERNATIONAL,INC

BAIRD PETROPHYSICAL INTERNATIONAL,INC

1784 W SAM HOUSTON PKWY N

HOUSTON,TX 77043-2723

PH 713 461-1784 WWW.BAIRDPETRO.COM

R W BAIRD,PRES RALPH@BAIRDUSA.COM

BAJON RIC & ASSOCIATES,PETROLEUM LANDMEN

19461 ARCADIAN SHORES AVE

BATON ROUGE,LA 70809-6711 PH 225 756-5600

FAX 225 756-2056

BAKER ATLAS NORTH AMERICA SEE

BAKER HUGHES

BAKER ATLAS SEE BAKER HUGHES

BAKER HUGHES

BAKER DEAN W,DRLG CONSULTANT

INTERNATIONAL,STATESIDE ON/OFFSHORE

5222 S LAKESHORE DR

SHREVEPORT,LA 71109-1810

PH 318 631-0817 FAX 318 631-0817

DEANWBAKER@GMAIL.COM

BAKER HAROLD D RIP ,PETR GEOL

125 S CONGRESS ST STE 1230

JACKSON,MS 39201-3399 PH 601 354-3383

RES 601 366-8758 FAX 601 354-1331

HDRIPBAKER2230@ATT.NET

BAKER HUGHES

2929 ALLEN PKWY STE 2100

HOUSTON,TX 79019-2118 PH 713 439-8600

- UNITED STATES -

- REGION HEADQUARTERS -

HOUSTON,TX OFFICE-17015 ALDINE WESTFIELD

77073 PH 713 625-6654 FAX 713 625-6655

- CENTRAL US -

QUITMAN,AR OFFICE - 6290 HEBER SPRINGS

RD W 72131 PH 501 589-3330

FAX 401 589-2995

LIBERAL,KS OFFICE - 2007 W THIRD ST,67901

PH 620 655-8892 FAX 620 624-5390

BROKEN ARROW,OK OFFICE - 3000 N HEMLOCK

CIR 74012 PH 918 455-3000

FAX 918 259-2046

MCALESTER,OK OFFICE - 202 S SWALLOW DR

74501 PH 918 426-6585 FAX 918 426-6596

OKLAHOMA CITY,OK OFFICE - 3030 NW EXPY

STE 300, 73112 PH 405 917-6700

FAX 405 917-6740

OKLAHOMA CITY,OK OFFICE - 1124 E RENO

73117 PH 405 290-7162 FAX 405 278-7336

WEATHERFORD,OK OFFICE - 219 S 8TH ST

73096 PH 580 772-2310 FAX 580 772-3718

FORT WORTH,TX OFFICE - 500 W 7TH STE 1729

UNIT 42,76102 PH 817 348-8105

FAX 817 348-8192

WOODWARD,OK OFFICE - 1421 34TH ST,73801

PH 580 256-3872 FAX 580 254-5200

GRANBURY,TX OFFICE - 2525 WAN PERKINS CIR

76049 PH 817 579-6014 FAX 817 579-6865

SAGINAW,TX OFFICE - 940 S BLUE MOUND RD

76131 PH 817 232-7018 FAX 817 232-3154

PAMPA,TX OFFICE - 126 S HOUSTON,79065

PH 806 665-5022 FAX 806 665-5026

- EASTERN US -

SHREVEPORT,LA OFFICE - 1461 HAWN AVE

71107 PH 318 222-9553 FAX 318 221-8558

LAUREL,MS OFFICE - 2410 MOOSE DR,39440

PH 601 649-7400 FAX 601 649-1005

CARTHAGE,TX OFFICE - 1409 S ADAMS,75633

PH 903 694-2611 FAX 903 694-2992

PALESTINE,TX OFFICE - 7584 HWY 79 SOUTH

75801 PH 903 538-2095 FAX 903 538-2566

FLINT,TX OFFICE - 4556 FM2813,75762

PH 903 871-2900 FAX 903 839-2174

BEAUMONT,TX OFFICE - 4080 WASHINGTON BLVD

STE 4 PH 409 840-9475 FAX 409 840-9662

MT PLEASANT,MI OFFICE - 5580 VENTURE WAY

44858 PH 989 775-6608 FAX 989 775-6909

CANTON,OH OFFICE - 1807 ALLEN AVE SE

44707 PH 330 455-2140 FAX 330 445-2151

CROSSVILLE,IL OFFICE - 315 S STATE ST

62827 PH 304 993-3125 FAX 724 695-2266

DUBOIS,PA OFFICE - 14 INDUSTRIAL DR STE 1

15801 PH 814 375-9209 FAX 814 375-9203

IMPERIAL,PA OFFICE - PO BOX 134

400 IMPERIAL INDUSTRIAL PK BLDG 400,15126

PH 724 695-2266 FAX 724 695-2295

MOUNTAIN TOP,PA OFFICE - 1150 CRESTWOOD

RD 18707 PH 570 403-5600 FAX 570 403-5610

ELKVIEW,WV OFFICE - 4998B ELK RIVER RD S

25071 PH 304 965-5800 FAX 304 965-3715

- GULF COAST -

HOUMA,LA OFFICE - 136 EQUITY BLVD 70360

PH 985 223-7600 FAX 985 718-4442

LAFAYETTE,LA OFFICE - 118 SOUTH PARK

70508 PH 337 837-1414 FAX 337 837-1022

NEW ORLEANS,LA OFFICE -

1515 POYDRAS STE 2400,70112

PH 504 561-8826 FAX 504 561-8829

HOUSTON,TX OFFICE- 17015 ALDINE WESTFIELD

77073 PH 713 625-6654 FAX 713 625-6655

- SOUTHERN US -

BRENHAM,TX OFFICE - 401 S PARK ST,77833

PH 979 421-9775 FAX 979 421-9776

CORPUS CHRISTI,TX OFFICE - 800 N

SHORELINE BLVD STE 700,N TOWER,78401

PH 361 880-4063 FAX 361 880-4071

CORPUS CHRISTI,TX OFFICE -

430 NAVIGATION BLVD,78408

PH 361 883-0241 FAX 361 887-0487

LAREDO,TX OFFICE - 129 RANCH RD/6086 B

HWY 359 EAST,78043

PH 956 723-5434 FAX 956 723-5962

PHARR,TX OFFICE - 5510 N CAGE,BLDG M,

78577 PH 956 702-9912 FAX 956 283-7408

SAN ANTONIO,TX OFFICE - 12950 COUNTRY

PKWY STE 120,78216-2004 PH 210 491-9058

FAX 210 491-9624

STAFFORD,TX OFFICE - 13003 MURPHY RD

STE M-13,77477

PH 281 498-4442 FAX 281 498-2318

VICTORIA,TX OFFICE - 2604-A E RIO GRANDE

77901 PH 361 575-0594 FAX 361 578-6498

- WEST TEXAS/NEW MEXICO -

HOBBS,NM OFFICE - 3237 INDUSTRIAL DR

88240 PH 505 392-1284 FAX 505 392-1474

FT STOCKTON,TX OFFICE - 409 N NELSON ST

79735 PH 432 336-0255 FAX 432 336-0265

MIDLAND,TX OFFICE - 2105 MARKET ST 79703

PH 432 681-7800 FAX 432 495-7200

MIDLAND,TX OFFICE - 3300 N A ST 79705

PH 432 570-1050 FAX 432 683-7209

SAN ANGELO,TX OFFICE - 27 SOUTHRIDGE

76904 PH 325 650-4557 FAX 325 949-4759

SAN ANGELO,TX OFFICE - 5005 TABOSA

76904 PH 325 944-4999 FAX 325 944-7199

- WESTERN US -

ANCHORAGE,AK OFFICE - 7260 HOMER DR

99518 PH 907 267-6600 FAX 907 267-6623

PRUDHOE BAY,AK - POUCH 340004, 99734

PJ 907 659 2362 FAX 907 659 2464

BAKERSFIELD,CA OFFICE - 5010 LISA MARIE

CT,93313 PH 661 837-9711 FAX 661 837-9601

WOODLAND,CA OFFICE - 430 DOUGLAS LN

95776 PH 530 666-2119 FAX 530 666-4726

DENVER,CO OFFICE - 1675 BROADWAY STE 1500

80202 PH 303 573-8606 FAX 303 825-5706

FAX 303 825-5707

FT COLLINS,CO OFFICE - 449 INDUSTRIAL DR

80524 PH 970 493-3018 FAX 970 493-3037

GRAND JUNCTION,CO OFFICE - 554 25 RD

UNIT 6,81505 PH 970 241-7934

FAX 970 241-7956

CARSON CITY,NV OFFICE - 2150 DEANN DR

89701 PH 775 882-7983 FAX 775 882-8387

DICKINSON,ND OFFICE - 125 48TH AVE SW

58601 PH 701 483-6512 FAX 701 483-6513

WILLISTON,ND OFFICE - 2916 1ST AVE WEST

58801 PH 701 774-0375 FAX 701 572-8669

VERNAL,UT OFFICE - 1700 EAST 1586 SOUTH

84078 PH 435 789-3413 FAX 435 789-2815

FARMINGTON,NM OFFICE - 5773 US HWY 64

87401 PH 505 632-1452 FAX 505 632-0438

EVANSVILLE,WY OFFICE - 5151 RESERVE DR

82636 PH 307 472-0001 FAX 307 472-0161

ROCK SPRINGS,WY OFFICE - 2721 KILLPECKER

DR,82901 PH 307 362-6844 FAX 307 362-6735

- INTERNATIONAL OFFICES -

- ABU DHABI -

ABU DHABI OFFICE - ARAB TOWER,2ND FLOOR

PH 9712 677 3200 FAX 9712 676 3498

- ALGERIA -

ALGERIA OFFICE - BP 527 RT D'EL BORMA

HASSI-MESSAOUD 30500 WILAYA DE OUARGLA

PH 213 29 739134 FAX 213 29 739130

- ANGOLA -

CABINDA,ANGOLA OFFICE - MOLONGO TERMINAL

392 646, PH 44 171 487 8100 X2391

FAX 44 171 487 8100 X2701

REPUBLICA DE ANGOLA OFFICE - SONILS BASE

488 PORTO DE LUANDA

PH 244 2 311 747 FAX 244 2 311 762

- ARGENTINA -

BUENOS AIRES,ARGENTINA OFFICE -

PH 54 11 4378 6400 FAX 44 11 4378 6460

CHUBUT,ARGENTINA OFFICE - 9000 COMODORO

RIVADAVIA, RUTA3,N 3396

PH 54 297 448 4666 FAX 54 297 448 3555

NEUQUEN,ARGENTINA OFFICE - RUTA 7,KM 3.5

PH 54 299 441 3378 FAX 54 299 441 3384

SALTA ARGENTINA OFFICE - RUTA 34,KM 1427

A4560CJA GRAL MOSCONI

PH 54 3875 481958 FAX 54 3875 481964

- AUSTRALIA -
QUEENSLAND,AUSTRALIA OFFICE - LYTTON,
  BRISBANE,4178 PH 61 7 3362 7995
  FAX 61 7 3362 7972
QUEENSLAND,AUSTRALIA OFFICE - TINGIRA ST
  PINKENBA BRISBANE,4008
  PH 61 (0) 7 3243 7622
  FAX 61 (0) 7 3243 7698
VICTORIA,AUSTRALIA OFFICE - LVL 23 HWT
  TOWER,40 CITY RD,SOUTHBANK MELBOURNE
  3006 PH 61 39674 7140 FAX 61 39674 7240
VICTORIA,AUSTRALIA OFFICE - OFFICE 2741,
  LEVEL 27,RIALTO S TOWER,525 COLLINS ST
  MELBOURNE 3000 PH 61 (0) 3 9935 2805
  FAX 61 (0) 3 9935 2750
AUSTRALIA OFFICE - 256 ST GEORGES
  TERRACE PERTH,6000
  PH 61 8 9217 7100 FAX 61 8 9217 7101
- AZERBAIJAN -
BAKU,AZERBAIJAN OFFICE - ISR PLAZA
  69 NIZAMIST,6TH FL PH 994 12 4973026
  FAX 994 12 4973004
- BOLIVIA -
SANTA CRUZ,BOLIVIA OFFICE - KM 7 1/2
  CARRETERA ANTIGUA A COCHABAMBA
  PH 591 3 355 3910 FAX 591 3 355 3912
- BRAZIL -
BRAZIL OFFICE - ESTRADA DE IMBOASSICA,
  S/N-GRANJA DAS GARCAS MACAE-RJ-27920-340
  PH 55 24 2773 6514 FAX 55 24 2773 6559
RIO DE JANEIRO,BRAZIL OFFICE - RUA
  DEZENOVE DO FEVEREIRO,30 CEP 22280-030
  BOTAFOGO PH 55 21 2266 8400
  FAX 55 21 2266 8496
- BRUNEI -
NEGARA BRUNEI DARUSSALAM OFFICE -
  TAPAK PERINDUSTRIAN PEKAN JALAN SETIA
  DI-RAJA,KUALA BELAIT,KA3131
  PH 673 3222 042 FAX 673 3222 184
- CANADA -
CALGARY,ALBERTA,CANADA OFFICE -
  1000,401 - 9TH AVE SW,T2P 3C5
  PH 403 537 3400 FAX 403 537-3905
CALGARY,ALBERTA,CANADA OFFICE -
  27,4948 - 126TH AVE SE PH 403 250-2111
  PH 403 250-1221
DARTMOUTH,NOVA SCOTIA,CANADA OFFICE -
  141B JOSEPH ZATZMAN DR B3B 1M7
  PH 902 481-0808 FAX 902 481-0810
EDMONTON,ALBERTA,CANADA OFFICE -
  5119 - 67TH AVE T6B 2R8 PH 780 434-8800
  FAX 780 437-5706
EDSON,ALBERTA,CANADA OFFICE -
  5525 - 3RD AVE T7E 1L8 PH 780 723-5622
  FAX 780 723-6332
ESTEVAN,SK,CANADA OFFICE - 83 DEVONIAN ST
  S4A 2L7 PH 306 636-1656 FAX 306 636-1650
FORT ST.JOHN BC,CANADA OFFICE -
  10415 - 89TH AVE V1J 5P8 PH 250 785-3309
  FAX 250 785-3600
GRANDE PRAIRIE,ALBERTA,CANADA OFFICE -
  9509 - 110TH ST T8V 4Z2 PH 780 532-2942
  FAX 780 539-3529
RED DEER,ALBERTA,CANADA OFFICE -
  2,6761 - 67TH AVE T4P 1K3 PH 403 346-4765
  FAX 403 341-6330

VERMILION,AB,CANADA OFFICE - BOX 3654
  T9X 2B6 PH 780 581-8522 FAX 780 853-7367
ST JOHN'S,NL,CANADA OFFICE - 215 WATER ST
  A1C 6C9 PH 709 748-4900 FAX 709 738-8624
- CHINA -
DONGCHENG DIST,BEIJING,CHINA OFFICE -
  5TH SQ NO 7 TOWER C 6TH FL,CHAOYANGMEN
  AVE 100010 PH 86 10 8400 7888
  FAX 84 10 8400 7922
PEOPLE'S REPUBLIC OF CHINA OFFICE -
  CHIWAN BLDG SHEKOU 518068,SHENZHEN GD
  PH 86 755 2681 5577 FAX 86 755 2669 3852
- COLUMBIA -
BOGATA D.C. COLUMBIA OFFICE - CALLE 67
  NO 7-35 OF 1108 PH 57 1 7421600
  FAX 57 1 7421780
- CONGO -
POINTE-NOIRE,CONGO OFFICE - B.P.357
  PH 242 2945861 FAX 242 2942818
- ECUADOR -
QUITO,ECUADOR OFFICE - AV AMAZONAS 1014
  AV NACIONES UNIDAS,LA PERVISORA BLDG
  TOWER A,5TH FL OFC 501 PH 593 2 2271 881
  FAX 583 2 2469 940
- EGYPT -
CARIO,EGYPT OFFICE -
  14,RD 280 NEW MAADI PH 202 27545316
  FAX 202 27545315
- EQUATORIAL GUINEA -
MALABO,EQUATORIAL GUINEA OFFICE -
  ARPTDO #713,COCOTEROS CALLE ABILIO
  BALBOA NO 4 PH 240 9 2781
  FAX 240 9 4398
- FRANCE -
AQUITAINE,FRANCE OFFICE - AVE THIMONNIER
  LONS 64140 PH 33 5 59 92 77 09
  FAX 33 5 59 92 89 20
- GABON -
PORT GENTIL,GABON OFFICE - BP 587
  PH 241 55 36 12 FAX 241 55 09 28
- GERMANY -
CELLE,NIEDERSACHSEN GERMANY OFFICE -
  BAKER-HUGHES-STRASSE 1, 29221
  PH 49 5141 203 149 FAX 49 5141 203 144
- HUNGARY -
BUDAPEST,HUNGARY OFFICE - LOVAG ST 8,
  VTH FL,NO 13TH VLTH DISTRICT
  PH 36 30 6262 926 FAX 36 30 6262 926
MAHARASHTRA,INDIA OFFICE - 15 FL PLATINUM
  PLAZA/TECHNOPARK PLOT 17-18,SECTOR 30-A
  VASHI NAVI MUMBAI 400703
  PH 91 22 6154 8500 FAX 91 22 6154 8510
- INDONESIA -
KALIMANTAN TIMUR,INDONESIA OFFICE -
  JL MULAWARMAN KM 16 RT 15 RW 03 NO 63
  BATAKAN BALIKPAPAN 76116
  PH 62 542 764 579 FAX 62 572 764 319
JAKARTA,INDONESIA OFFICE - 6TH FL,GARDEN
  CENTRE CILANDAK COMMERCIAL ESTATE
  PH 62 21 780 0737 FAX 62 21 780 1682
- ITALY -
RAVENNA,ITALY OFFICE - VIA DELLA
  CATALANA 3, 48100 PH 0039 0544424907
  FAX 0039 0854972054
SAN DONATO MILANESE,MILANO,ITALY OFFICE -
  VIA ANGELO,MORO 109,CENTRO COMMERCIALE

L'INCONTRO 20097 PH 39 02 51640503
  FAX 39 02 557 00 630
CEPAGATTI,PESCARA,ITALY OFFICE - S S 602
  CONTRADA DA CALCASACCO DI VILLANOVA,
  KM 52+000, 65012 PH 39 085 497501
  FAX 39 085 4972054
- KAZAKHSTAN -
ALMATY,KAZAKHSTAN OFFICE - 154A,NAURYZBAI
  STR BC KABLAN,4TH FL 050013
  PH 8 7273 30 08 00 FAX 8 7273 30 08 40
ATYRAU,KAZAKHSTAN OFFICE - 2 AZATTYK AVR
  PH 8 7122 90 91 00 FAX 8 7122 90 91 92
AKTAU,MANGISTAU,KAZAKHSTAN OFFICE -
  8 MICRODIST BLDG 39,130000
  PH 8 7292 57 30 53
AKTOBE,KAZAKHSTAN OFFICE - OFFICE 101
  46 BLD,46 MOLDAGULAVA AVE,030000
  PH 8 7132 55 70 44 FAX 8 7132 55 70 25
KYZYLORDA,KAZAKHSTAN OFFICE - 28 AITEKE
  BI ST 120014 PH 8 7242 26 19 29
  FAX 8 7242 26 19 51
- KUWAIT -
EAST AHMADI,KUWAIT OFFICE - OPP AL-RASAI
  GLASS MANUFACTURING AREA 6
  PH 965 398 0720 FAX 965 398 0751
- LIBYA -
TRIPOLI,LIBYA OFFICE - PO BOX 91357
  T4 F1 DAT ELMAD TOWERS
  PH 00218 21 336 0089 93
  FAX 00218 21 335 0014
- MALAYSIA -
KEMAMAN TRENGGANU,MALAYSIA OFFICE -
  PH 609 8623544 FAX 609 8634568
KUALA LUMPUR,WEST MALAYSIA OFFICE -
  MANARA TAN & TAN 207,JALAN TUN RAZAK
  PH 60 3 2164 7888 FAX 60 3 2163 2034
LABUAN FT,MALAYSIA OFFICE - PO BOX 81722
  87027 PH 60 87 411 718 FAX 60 87 412 675
MIRI,SARAWAK,EAST MALAYSIA OFFICE -
  LOT 31 BLK 3 2ND FL,NABA BLDG,PLASSAU
  INDUSTRIAL EST 98000 PH 6 085 658 833
  FAX 6 085 659 944
- MEXICO -
MEXICALI BC,MEXICO OFFICE - CARRETERA
  ESTATAL NO2 KM 23.5 S/N,CP 21705
  PH 52 686 523 09 55 FAX 52 686 523 09 55
MEXICO DF,MEXICO OFFICE - BLV MANUEL
  AVILA CAMACHO NO 138,CP 11560
  PH 52 55 8525 4440 FAX 52 55 8535 4466
REYNOSA,TAMAULIPAS,MEXICO OFFICE -
  AV OCCIDENTAL 1919,CP 88630
  PH 52 899 925 02 03 FAX 52 899 925 02 03
POZA RICA,VERACRUZ,MEXICO OFFICE -
  EZEQUIEL ORDONEZ #105 COL PALMAS,CP 93230
  PH 52 782 111 1735/1736
VERACRUZ,MEXICO OFFICE - JUAN BARRAGAN
  530,ENTRE 1 DE MAYO Y GOMEZ FARIAS
  CP 91900 PH 52 229 931 74 96
  FAX 52 229 931 74 96
VILLAHERMOSA,TABASCO,MEXICO OFFICE -
  COLONIA 1RO DE MAYO,CP 86190
  PH 52 993 187 98 00 FAX 52 993 187 98 31
CUIDAD DEL CARMEN CAMPECHE,MEXICO OFFICE-
  CP 24190 PH 52 938 381 07 70
  FAX 52 938 38 1 07 70 EXT 2191
- THE NETHERLANDS -

NOORD-HOLLAND,THE NETHERLANDS OFFICE -
  WIJKERMEERWEG 7A VELSEN-NOORD,1951 AH
  PH 31 251 260500 FAX 31 251 260555
    - NEW ZEALAND -
NEW ZEALAND OFFICE - 177 COURTENAY ST
  NEW PLYMOUTH 4310 PH 64 6 7580797
  FAX 64 6 7699289
    - NIGERIA -
IKOYI LAGOS,NIGERIA OFFICE - 10B CLUB RD
  PH 234 1 271 8402
PORT HARCOURT,NIGERIA OFFICE - 175 TRANS
  AMADI IND LAYOUT PH 234 84 238 884
  FAX 234 84 236 086
    - NORWAY -
KOKSTAD,NORWAY OFFICE - KOKSTADVEIEN 31A
  N-5061 PH 47 55 986 660 FAX 47 55 227 697
TANANGER,NORWAY OFFICE - EKOFISKVEIEN 1
  4056 PH 47 51 717 900 FAX 47 51 717 901
    - OMAN -
QURUM SULTANTE OF OMAN OFFICE -
  PH 968 571 029 FAX 968 561 856
ISLAMABAD,PAKISTAN OFFICE - PLOT 193 ST 1
  SECTOR L-10/3 PH 92 51 4430791
  FAX 92 51 4430796
    - PERU -
SAN ISIDRO LIMA 27,PERU OFFICE -
  SUCURSAL DEL PERU AV REPUBLICA DE PANAMA
  3055 PISO 9 PH 51 1 441 42 42
  FAX 51 1 442 09 30
TALARA,PERU OFFICE - SUCURSAL DEL PERU
  AV H 55 - A PH 51 74 382955
  FAX 51 74 381167
MUNTINLUPA CITY 1771,PHILIPPINES OFFICE -
  ALABANG HILLS,CUPANG PH 632 842-4081
    - PHILIPPINES -
  FAX 632 842 4194
    - QATAR -
DOHA,QUATAR OFFICE - AAP TOYOTA TWR 2 FL
  C RING RD PH 974 436 5109
  FAX 974 442 2936
    - ROMANIA -
PLOIESTI,PRAHOVA,ROMANIA OFFICE -
  10 CONULUI ST PH 40 244 436 111/2/3/4/5
  FAX 40 0 244 436 117
    - RUSSIA -
MOSCOW,RUSSIA OFFICE - 37 LENINGRADSKY
  PROSPECT,125167 PH 7 495 771 7240
  FAX 7 495 771 7246
    - SAUDI ARABIA -
DAMMAM,SAUDI ARABIA OFFICE - ABQAIQ HWY
  2 INDUSTRIAL CITY PH 966 3 812 1838
  FAX 966 3 812 2057
    - SINGAPORE -
JURONG,SINGAPORE OFFICE - 273 JALAN
  AHMAD IBRAHIM,629150 PH 65 6864 1512
  FAX 65 6863 3800
    - SOUTH AFRICA -
STEENBERG CAPE TOWN,SOUTH AFRICA OFFICE -
  BLK B SILVERWOOD,STEENBERG EST,7945
  PH 27(0)21 702 8100 FAX 27(0)21 701 1110
    - SPAIN -
MADRID,SPAIN OFFICE - CALLE CALERUEGA
  81 MADRID,28033 PH 34 91 515 51 18
  FAX 34 914 672 161
    - THAILAND -
BANGKOK,THAILAND OFFICE - 66 SUKHUMVIT

21 RD,10110 PH 66 2 264 2211
  FAX 66 2 264 2210
SONGKHLA,THAILAND OFFICE - 428 KHOYOR RD
  TAMBOL PHAWONG AMPHUR MUANG,90100
  PH 6674 333977/8 FAX 6674 333979
    - TRINIDAD AND TOBAGO -
TRINIDAD & TOBAGO,W.I. OFFICE -
  3&3A SWEET BRIAR,ST CLAIR,PORT OF SPAIN
    - TUNISIA -
  PH 868 622 3962 FAX 868 622 3993
TUNISIA OFFICE - RUE OKBA LBN NAFAA BP115
  PH 216 74 497 027 FAX 216 74 497 029
TUNIS,TUNISIA OFFICE - IMMEUBLE FAJR
  PH 216 71 515 FAX 216 71 963 005
    - UNITED ARAB EMIRATES -
DUBAI,UNITED ARAB EMIRATES (UAE) OFFICE -
  PH 971 808 2200 FAX 971 4 883 6487
ABERDEENSHIRE,UNITED KINGDOM OFFICE -
  STONEYWOOD PARK N DYCE,ABERDEEN AB21 7EA
  PH 44 1 224 720 000 FAX 44 1 224 720 008
    - VENEZUELA -
ESTADO ZUILIA,VENEZUELA OFFICE -
  PH 58 265 4002 555 FAX 58 265 4002 576
ZUILIA,VENEZUELA OFFICE -
  PH 58 261 7363 244 FAX 58 261 7362 660
ESTADO MONAGAS,VENEZUELA OFFICE -
  PH 58 291 3003000 FAX 50 291 6430959
    - VIETNAM -
HO CHI MINH CITY,S.R. VIETMAN OFFICE -
  19-25 NGUYEN HUE BLVD,DIST 1
  PH 84 8 3 821 3732/3742
  FAX 84 8 3 821 1401
VUNG TAU,S.R. VIETMAN OFFICE -
  8 HOANG DIEU STE 520 PH 84 64 351 0425
  FAX 84 64 351 0426
    - YEMEN -
SANAA,YEMEN OFFICE -
  PH 967 1 414 462 FAX 967 1 417 888

BAKER HUGHES INCORPORATED SEE
  BAKER HUGHES
BAKER HUGHES INTEQ SEE
  BAKER HUGHES
BAKER OIL TOOLS (FISHING DIVISION) SEE
  BAKER HUGHES
BAKER PETROLEUM COMPANY
  PO BOX 2864
  CORPUS CHRISTI,TX 78403-2864
  PH 361 884-0873
    TERSH BAKER,OWNER
BAKER PETROLITE
  3705 INDUSTRIAL BLVD
  LAUREL,MS 39440 PH 601 649-1955
BAKERWELL INC
  10420 COUNTY ROAD 620
  KILLBUCK,OH 44637-9728 PH 330 276-2161
  FAX 330 276-2287
    JEFFREY J A BAKER,SECY/TREAS
    W REX BAKER,PRES
    ROC BAKER,ASST SECY/TREAS
BALCONES ENERGY LIBRARY,INC
  PO BOX 17485,2206 DANBURY DR
  SAN ANTONIO,TX 78217-0485 PH 210 820-0814
  FAX 210 822-3441
    BALCONESENERGY@SBCGLOBAL.NET
    MARY JANE ZOROLA,MGR

BALCONES PRODUCTION CO SEE
  TEXAS AMERICAN RESOURCES COMPANY
BALCONES STARR PIPELINE
  3503 N TAYLOR RD
  MISSION,TX 78573
  PH 956 686-2491 FAX 956 686-7065
    BRUCE G WELCH,FIELD AGENT
BALDWIN DON H OIL CO
  PO BOX 208
  LAWRENCEVILLE,IL 62439-0208
  PH 618 584-3680
BALESTRIERI,MICHAEL V,PETR CONSULTANT
  156 CIRCLE PKWY
  WILLIAMS BAY,WI 53191
  PH 262 348-3244 FAX 262 248-9539
    MICKBALESTRIERI@GMIL.COM
BALIN & ASSOCIATES
  401 AUSTIN HWY STE 209
  SAN ANTONIO,TX 78209 PH 210 829-8080
  FAX 210 829-8008
    DONNA F BALIN,PH D,CONS GEOL
    BALIN@ALUMNI.UTEXAS.NET
BALLANTYNE J ROYALTY CORP SEE
  BLAKE BRUCE W CPL/ESA MGMNT SERVICES
BALLARD EXPLORATION COMPANY INC
  1021 MAIN ST STE 2310
  HOUSTON,TX 77002-6602
  PH 713 651-0181 FAX 713 651-9201
    A L BALLARD,PRES
    JANICE MOSS,ADMIN ASST
    THOMAS G BINIG,EXPL
    DANA ROY,EXPL
    ERIK HARDENBOL,EXPL
    JOHN EDGERTON,EXPL
    BOB FREDERICK,LAND
    SHERRY L CAMPBELL,LAND
    BRIAN CRAVENS,LAND
    STEVE FISCHER,OPERS MGR
    JANE BORTONI,PROD
    NANCY W SNOW,ACCT
    BEN YOESEL,OPERS MGR
BALLENGEE B V
  534 BELLEVIEW DR
  CORPUS CHRISTI,TX 78412-3126
  PH 361 882-5565 361 991-2595
    B V BALLENGEE,OWNER
BALLINGER BOB
  505 ZEPHYR ST
  AUSTIN,TX 78734-5183 PH 512 261-6750
  FAX 512 261-6750
    BOBANN@POSTOFFICE.SWBELL.NET
BALUSEK-FRANKSON & ASSOC,INC
  SURVEYING & CIVIL ENGRG/GPS MEASUREMENTS
  308 E GOODWIN AVE
  VICTORIA,TX 77901-6606 PH 361 578-9956
  FAX 361 573-6991 BFAI@TISD.NET
    GEORGE GANEM,PRES
    GARY J KELLY,VP
BANCORPSOUTH INSURANCE SERVICE
  D/B/A KNOX INSURANCE GROUP
  PO BOX 53406,2014 W PINHOOK RD STE 610
  LAFAYETTE,LA 70505-3406 PH 337 233-0530
  FAX 337 235-0547 WWW.KNOXINSURANCE.COM
    JPRATHER@KNOXINSURANCE.COM
    RANDALL K BONAVENTURE,VP
    P DWAYNE DAVID,VP

BANCROFT RESOURCES COMPANY
1901 N AKARD ST
DALLAS,TX 75201-2305 PH 214 220-9150
WILLIAM E BANCROFT,JR,PRES

BANDA BOATS,INC
PO BOX 2443
MORGAN CITY,LA 70381-2443 PH 504 631-2187
WALLACE M CARLINE,PRES
C P ORTIS,PORT CAPTAIN
AVERY ORTIS,PORT CAPTAIN

BANDON OIL & GAS,LP
1301 MCKINNEY STE 900
HOUSTON,TX 77010 PH 713 728-7840
FAX 713 728-7860 WWW.DYNAMICOSR.COM
G MATT MCCARROL,PRES/CEO
HOWARD TATE,CFO
JAMES BROKMEYER,VP PROD OPERS
GARY JANIK,VP EXPLOITATION & DEV
CAREY NAQUIN,VP WELL OPERS
JOHN H SMITH,VP LAND & BUS DEV
BILL SWINGLE,VP ACCT

BANE & SHUNICK
714 E KALISTE SALOOM RD STE B5
LAFAYETTE,LA 70508-2529 PH 337 235-0740
BSPALEO@COX-INTERNET.COM
WWW.LAFAYETTEPALEO.COM
TOM SHUNICK,PALEONTOLOGIST
BARBARA ALEXANDER,SECY

BANK OF AMERICA,N.A.
OIL & GAS ASSET MANAGEMENT
PO BOX 830308
DALLAS,TX 75283-0308 PH 214 209-2323
FAX 972 728-4456
DICK SADLER,SR VP,NATIONAL MGR
MICHAEL CANALE,SR VP (FT WORTH)
ROBERT D MAXWELL,SR VP,MGR,ENGR
RON E HOOPER,SR VP
VICKIE M ROSE,SR VP
JIMMY PROE,SR VP
KIN PIER,SR VP

BANK ONE,N.A.
SEE J P MORGAN CHASE BANK

BAPTIST FOUNDATION OF OKLAHOMA,THE
C/O BAPTIST FOUNDATION OF TEXAS
1601 ELM ST STE 1700
DALLAS,TX 75201 PH 214 978-3333
WWW.BFTX.ORG
WILLIAM T FRANCIS WILL.FRANCIS@BFTX.ORG

BAR-MAC INVESTMENTS,INC
PO BOX 1227
BRENHAM,TX 77834-1227
PH 979 836-9013 PH 979 277-5526
CHUCK MACHEMEHL,PRES
GLYNN WOOD,PROD SUPT

BARAK OIL CORPORATION
2998 N REMINGTON RD
OLNEY,IL 62450-5121 PH 618 395-8646
JANE TOWNSEND,PRES

BARBEE R L OPERATING,INC
PO BOX 271091
CORPUS CHRISTI,TX 78427-1091
PH 361 854-8805 FAX 361 854-8805
RANDALL LEE BARBEE,PRES

BARBOUR CORPORATION SEE
BARBOUR WELL INC

BARCLAY CRAIG C,PETR GEOL,IND OPER,CONS
522 DUMBARTON DR
SHREVEPORT,LA 71106-6810 PH 318 869-2223
CBARCLAY1@COMCAST.NET

BARCLAY PETROLEUM,INC
PO BOX 81,7400 MARIETTA RD SE
BREMEN,OH 43107-0081
PH 740 569-4327 FAX 740 569-7747
BRUCE W KELLEY,PRES

BARESH ROGER,PETR LDMN
7919 RICHMOND AVE
HOUSTON,TX 77063-6155
PH 713 952-2081 FAX 713 952-2083

BARFIELD WILLIAM G SEE
AQS RECRUITERS

BARGER ENGINEERING,INC
PO BOX 2507,2116 LINCOLN AVE
EVANSVILLE,IN 47728-0507
PH 812 476-3077 FAX 812 476-2622
BARGEREN@BARGERENGINEERING.COM
G J BARGER,PRES
MATTHEW S STONE,CONTRACT ENGINEER
TANEA LYN PRIDDIS,OFC MGR
WAYNE PHILLIPS,PROD SUPT
CINDY OFFERMAN,PROD CLERK

BARNES EXPLORATION COMPANY SEE
B E X,INC

BARNES WILLIAM DRILLING & PRODUCING CO
5334 SPRING BROOK RD
FRIENDSHIP,NY 14739 PH 716 378-3347
WILLIAM BARNES,OWNER

BARNETT SAM,ESTATE
2000 MOSSWOOD CT
ARLINGTON,TX 76015-4002 PH 817 465-4163
D W BARNETT,EXECUTOR

BARNHART CO
2121 SAGE RD STE 333
HOUSTON,TX 77056-4305 PH 713 622-4750
FAX 713 964-3060
PAUL F BARNHART JR,PRES
L IRVIN BARNHART,VP
CONNIE F STEELE,SECY
MIKE MANCHESTER,CFO
KATHY BORAWSKI,CONTROLLER

BARNHART PAUL F,OIL PROD,PETR ENGR
2121 SAGE RD STE 333
HOUSTON,TX 77056-4305 PH 713 622-4750
FAX 713 827-4510
L IRVIN BARNHART,GEOL & LAND

BARNHILL CALVIN
PO BOX 5-A
LAFAYETTE,LA 70505
PH 337 233-0830 FAX 337 233-9772
JACKIE BARNHILL,OFC MGR

BARO
ENGINEERED SOLUTIONS FOR INDUSTRY
4655 WRIGHT RD STE 200
STAFFORD,TX 77477-4133
PH 281 561-0900 OR PH 877 561-0900
FAX 281 561-0826
WWW.BAROCOMPANIES.COM
SALES@BAROCOMPANIES.COM
SAN ANTONIO BRANCH OFFICE -
PO BOX 171284,78217-8284
PH 210 828-0480 FAX 210 828-7050
NORTH TEXAS BRANCH OFFICE -

PH 817 453-9440 FAX 817 453-9449
SOUTH TEXAS BRANCH OFFICE -
PH 361 882-4472 FAX 361 882-4282
GOLDEN TRIANGLE,TX BRANCH OFFICE -
PH 409 838-4900 FAX 409 838-6700
DE SOTO,TX EAST TEXAS BRANCH OFFICE -
PO BOX 1780,75123 PH 972 230-3089
FAX 972 230-2007
WEST TEXAS BRANCH OFFICE -
PH 432 553-7114 FAX 432 618-0628

BAROID DRILLING FLUIDS SEE
HALLIBURTON ENERGY SERVICES

BAROID INDUSTRIAL DRILLING PRODUCTS SEE
HALLIBURTON ENERGY SERVICES

BARON CREST ENERGY COMPANY
601 FIRST ST
APOLLO,PA 15613-8902 PH 724 478-1121
FAX 724 478-3109
FRANK GARUFI,OWNER,PRES
FRANCESCA GARUFI,VP

BARRETT ALVIN M & ASSOCIATES,INC
OIL & GAS PROPERTIES
11202 SANDSTONE ST
HOUSTON,TX 77072-2902 PH 281 498-5878
FAX 281 498-5983
MIKE N BARRETT,PRES
MNBARRETT@SWBELL.NET
PAT A BARRETT,VP
CONNIE T BARRETT,TREAS

BARROW-SHAVER RESOURCES CO,LLC
977 PRUITT PL
TYLER,TX 75703 PH 903 593-5221
FAX 903 593-1692 BARROWSHAVER@TYLER.NET
SCOTT O SHAVER,PRES
JAMES R TURNER,GEOL
RAY KASINO,GEOL

BARSALOU DAVID,LEASES
4635 SOUTHWEST FWY STE 580
HOUSTON,TX 77027 PH 713 652-5044

BARTELL EXPLORATION
5851 SAN FELIPE ST STE 760
HOUSTON,TX 77057-8015 PH 713 781-6974
FAX 713 781-6980
J D BARTELL,MNGNG PRTNR
JDBARTELL@LEGENDSEXPL.COM
LARRY D BARTELL,GEOL
JAMES BARTELL,NEW VENTURES

BARTLETT GEOLOGICAL CONSULTANTS
432 E MAIN ST STE G
ABINGDON,VA 24210-3493 PH 276 628-4136
FAX 276 628-4137
CHARLES BARTLETT,PHD,CHF GEOL
MAY TABOR,GEOL ASST

BARTLING OIL COMPANY
1001 CANYON EDGE DR
AUSTIN,TX 78733-2611 PH 512 795-9593
FAX 512 795-9573
THEODORE A BARTLING,PRES
HARRY FAILING,CONTROLLER
PHYLLIS BARTLING,SECY/TREAS
CHARLYE DAVIS

BARTON ASSOCIATES,INC
701 RICHMOND AVE, STE 226
HOUSTON,TX 77006 PH 713 961-9111
FAX 713 993-9399
GARY R BARTON,PRTNR

SEAN E BARTON,PRTNR

BASIC ENERGY SERVICES,LP
  PERMIAN BASIN REGION
    PO BOX 10460,500 W ILLINOIS
    MIDLAND,TX 79702
    PH 432 620-5500 FAX 432 620-5501
      WWW.BASICENERGYSERVICES.COM
      ROE PATTERSON,PRES/CEO
      ROE.PATTERSON@BASICENERGYSERVICES.COM
      ALAN KRENEK,SR VP/CFO/TRES/SEC
      ALAN.KRENEK@BASICENERGYSERVICES.COM
      DOUG ROGERS,VP MKTG
      DOUG.ROGERS@BASICENERGYSERVICES.COM
      JAMES NEWMAN,GROUP VP/PERMIAN BUS UNIT
      JAMES.NEWMAN@BASICENERGYSERVICES.COM
      RON SCANDOLARI,VP CONTRACT DRLG
      RON.SCANDOLARI@BASICENERGYSERVICES.COM
      MARK RANKIN,VP RISK MGT
      MARK.RANKIN@BASICENERGYSERVICES.COM
      JIM TYNER,VP HR
      JIM.TYNER@BASICENERGYSERVICES.COM
      TRAMPAS POLDRACK,VP SAFETY/OPERS SUPPORT
      TRAMPAS.POLDRACK@BASICENERGYSERVICES.CO
      M
      LYNN WIGINGTON,VP PERMIAN BASIN REGION
      BRANDON MCGUIRE,VP GULF COAST REGION
      ROGER MASSEY,VP ARK/LA/TX REGION
      LANCE GREEN,VP MID-CONTINENT REGION
      TIM DAME,VP PUMPING SERVICES DIV
  VICTORIA,TX OFFICE - GULF COAST REGION
    208 ENTERPRISE DR,77905
    PH 361 574-9512 FAX 361 576-6865
      BRANDON MCGUIRE,VP GULF COAST REGION
  LONGVIEW,TEXAS OFFICE - ARK/LA/TX REGION
    5209 ESTES PKWY,75603
    PH 903 295-0817 FAX 903 295-0517
      ROGER MASSEY,VP ARK/LA/TX REGION
  YUKON,OK OFFICE - MID-CONTINENT REGION
    804 S MUSTANG RD,73099
    PH 405 324-0848 FAX 405 324-0454
      LANCE GREEN,VP MID-CONTINENT REGION
  GRAND JUNCTION,CO OFFICE-ROCKY MTN REGION
    607 25 ROAD STE 200,81505
    PH 970 263-8202 FAX 970 263-8226
      TERRY TUFLY,VP ROCKY MOUNTAIN REGION
  FT WORTH,TEXAS OFFICE - 801 CHERRY ST
    76102,PH 817 334-4100 FAX 817 334-4101
      TIM DAME,VP PUMPING SERVICES DIV
  MIDLAND,TX OFFICE - CONTRACT DRILLING
    4701 S CR 1270,79706
    PH 432 563-2106 FAX 432 563-2136
      RON SCANDOLARI,VP CONTRACT DRILLING

BASIL OILFIELD SERVICE,INC
  PO BOX 93
  SARATOGA,TX 77585-0093 PH 936 274-5311
  FAX 936 274-5079
    B H TOMLINSON,PRES
    T B TOMLINSON,VP

BASIN EXPLORATION,INC
  200 TRAVIS ST STE 201
  LAFAYETTE,LA 70503-2447 PH 337 233-9199
  FAX 337 233-9198 BASIN@BASINEX.COM
    BRADEN C DESPOT,PRES
    JOHN M DUHON,VP
    MARK L DESPOT,VP
    MARLIN ROBERTS,GEOL/GEOPHY

HELEN BRIERRE,OFC MGR

BASIS PETROLEUM,INC
  GATHERING DOMESTIC SUPPLY & TRADING
    PO BOX 696000
    SAN ANTONIO,TX 78269-6000 PH 713 659-3525
    DOMESTIC SUPPLY/TRADING FAX 713 646-5284
      JOHN P VONBERG,VP,GATHERING,DOMESTIC
        SUPPLY & TRADING
      KATHEY ROTHROCK,DOMESTIC CRUDE SCHEDULER
      ED CAIRNS,MGR,DOMESTIC CRUDE
        COMMERCIAL SUPPORT
    GATHERING FAX 713 646-5416
      KEITH JALBERT,GEN MGR,CRUDE OIL ACQS
      BEN RUNNELS,GEN MGR,OPERS
      JOHN S WYCKOFF,GATHERING SCHEDULER
      KEVIN GAMMILL,OPERS ANALYST
      DON LEWIS,MGR,HOUSTON REG
  DALLAS,TX OFFICE - 8080 N CENTRAL STE 400
    75206 PH 214 891-8115 FAX 214 891-8179
      KIRK KITCHENS,MGR,DALLAS METROPLEX
  MIDLAND,TX OFFICE - 415 W WALL STE 816
    79701 PH 432 687-3133 FAX 432 683-6594
      W R REGGIE HOWELL,MGR,W TX/E TX REG
      BILL RIGNEY,MGR,W TX REG
  LAFAYETTE,LA OFFICE - 1313 W PINHOOK RD
    STE 203-B,70503-2902 PH 318 237-6084
    FAX 318 237-6085
      JERRY B BRICE,MGR,S LA

BASS & ASSOCIATES,LLC
  2766 GATES RD
  BASSFIELD,MS 39421-0234
  PH 601 943-5229 FAX 601 943-6671
    BASSASSOCIATESLLC@SOUTHERNSTARLINK.COM
    THOMAS G BASS,MGR

BASS C R
  2500 TANGLEWILDE STE 484
  HOUSTON,TX 77063-2126 PH 713 932-1432
    C R BASS

BASS ENERGY COMPANY INC
  130 MERZ BLVD
  AKRON,OH 44333-2816 PH 330 869-0870
  FAX 330 869-6313 BASSENERGY@NEO.RR.COM
    WILLIAM J HLAVIN,PRES
    LORI BROUGHTON,CONTROLLER
    RALPH GREGORY,VP OPER
    WAYNE HLAVIN,VP LAND ACQUIS
    TIM HLAVIN,PROD SUPT

BASS ENTERPRISES PRODUCTION CO SEE
  BOPCO,LP

BASTROP ENERGY GROUP
  14026 CEDAR ML
  SAN ANTONIO,TX 78231-1951 PH 210 492-3096
    MARK E THOMPSON,OWNER

BATON DAVID & JOHNNYE
  15350 FM 2276 N
  KILGORE,TX 75662-9514 PH 214 983-3676

BATTLE & BATTLE CONSULTANTS
  1314 CHRETIEN POINT RD
  SUNSET,LA 70584-5310 PH 337 662-6660
    JOE BATTLE,GEOL
    JULIA BATTLE,PETR ENGR

BAWDEN DRILLING INC SEE
  NOBLE DRILLING CORP

BAXTER & BAXTER LAND AGENCY
    OIL & GAS LEASING,TITLE SEARCHES
    PERMITS,RIGHT OF WAY

2625 SEQUOIA LN
ROSENBERG,TX 77471 PH 903 436-3333
PH 903 436-5777
  WWW.BAXTERANDBAXTER.EASTTEXASMAIL.COM
  BBLA1@COMCAST.NET
  GORDON BAXTER,DIR
  LINDA BAXTER,MGR

BAY COQUILLE INC
  474 METAIRIE RD STE 203
  METAIRIE,LA 70005-4331 PH 504 834-5559
  FAX 504 834-5554 PRICEENERGY@YAHOO.COM
    RICHARD F PRICE JR,PRES
    S H PRICE,VP
    A P SWANSON,VP
    C H PRICE,ACQ MGR
    T A FERRERA,JT INTEREST ACCT
    S F PRICE,REAL PROPERTY MGR

BAY EXPLORATION,INC
  809 TETE LOURS DR
  MANDEVILLE,LA 70448-1774 PH 504 626-1955
    CHRISTOPHER H BAYNAS,PRES

BAY EXPLORATION,INC
  PO BOX 37
  CASEY,IL 62420-0037 PH 217 932-5721
  FAX 217 932-5706
    J MICHAEL COLLINS,PRES
    JOE COCHONOUR,SECY

BAY GAS LLC
  PO BOX 1634
  FERRIDAY,LA 71334
  PH 318 757-3274 FAX 318 757-8595
    CPNINC1@BELLSOUTH.NET
    CLARK NERREN,GEOL
    JESSE HORTON,PRES
    DEE HORTON,VP

BAY LTD
  PO BOX 9908, 1414 CORN PRODUCTS RD
  CORPUS CHRISTI,TX 78469-9908
  PH 361 693-2100 FAX 361 693-2841
    WWW.BAYLTD.COM
    KEN J LUHAN,PRES
    ROBERT C BLAIR,VP
    BLAIRR@BAYLTD.COM
    W G WHITTINGTON,BUS DEV

BAY ROCK OPERATING COMPANY
  PO BOX 12468
  SAN ANTONIO,TX 78212-0468 PH 210 735-8400
  FAX 210 735-8405
    JOHN P MACDIARMID,PRES

BAY TECH OPERATING CO,INC
  706 FIRST PL
  TYLER,TX 75702-5745 PH 903 597-3741
  FAX 903 526-7058
    BILL C ROSS,GEOL

BAYARD DRILLING TECHNOLOGIES,INC SEE
  NABORS DRILLING USA,LP

BAYOU BOEUF ELECTRIC LLC
  PO BOX 929,334 DEGRAVELLE RD
  AMELIA,LA 70340-0929 PH 985 631-2853
    WWW.BAYOUBOEUF.COM
    CHARLES RICHARD,PRES
    ROBBIE OWENS,GEN MGR
    KEN KETON,BRANCH MGR
  HOUMA,LA OFFICE - 1737 GRAND CALLIOU RD
    70363 PH 985 876-1791
      ROBBIE OWENS, BRANCH MGR

NEW IBERIA,LA OFFICE - PO BOX 10090
1603 E HWY 90,70562 PH 337 364-5411
ROBBIE OWENS,BRANCH MGR

BAYOU CITY EXPLORATION,INC
632 ADAMS ST STE 700
BOWLING GREEN,KY 42101 PH 800 798-3389
FAX 270 842-7362 WWW.BCEXPLORATION.COM
CHARLES T BUKOWSKI,PRES/CEO
STEPHEN C LARKIN,CFO
ROBERT KELLEY,SR VP/COO
JIM STEVENS,SR VP EXPL
ED SUHR,SR VP LAND

BAYOU CITY PETROLEUM COMPANY
1807 ROYAL OAK DR
TYLER,TX 75703-5851 PH 903 216-0189
JOE M MCMAHAN

BAYOU COMPANIES
5200 CURTIS LANE
NEW IBERIA,LA 70560-0449 PH 318 369-3761
FAX 318 365-0774
JERRY E SHEA JR,MNGNG PRTNR COMMERCIAL
STEWART SHEA,MNGNG PRTNR ADMIN
JAMES T SHEA,MNGNG PRTNR OPERS
MIKE KRESS,VP MKTG
JAY SMITH,VP PROD
BURT MUNOZ,VP QHSE
DANNY HEBERT,VP COMMERCIAL
JED LOPEZ,SHIPPING/RECEIVING MGR
CAMILLE LOPEZ,DIR FIN
JOEY LEBLANC,DIR OPERS
DAVID BOULET,DIR BUS DEV
DEBBIE CHAMPAGNE,OFC MGR
RICHARD CLEMENT,VP SLS
MIKE VIATOR,INSIDE SLS

BAYOU GULF MARINE CORP
5036 YALE ST STE 201
METAIRIE,LA 70006-3980 PH 504 394-4921
PH 504 831-8127 FAX 504 831-8145
LARRY J GIBSON,PRES
JEANNE S DUHE',SECY,LEGAL

BAYOU PIPE BENDING COMPANY SEE
BAYOU COMPANIES

BAYOU PIPE COATING COMPANY SEE
BAYOU COMPANIES

BAYOU STATE OIL CORPORATION
PO BOX 7886
SHREVEPORT,LA 71137-7886 PH 318 222-0737
FAX 318 222-0730

BAYSHORE EXPLORATION L.L.C.
PO BOX 429
BELLVILLE,TX 77418-0429 PH 979 865-9924
FAX 979 865-9322
BAYSHOREEXPL@SBCGLOBAL.NET
JAMIN SWANTNER,PRES
JANE SWANTNER,SECY/TREAS

BAYSIDE PETROLEUM COMPANY,INC
PO BOX 2132
ADDISON,TX 75001-2132 PH 972 385-7800
WWW.BAYSIDEPETROLEUM.COM
GORDON H JOHNSON,PRES
JOHN L GRIFFITHS,OPER MGR
HAROLD F LAMBERT,CONTROLLER

BBL OPERATING COMPANY
OIL & GAS OPERATIONS
PO BOX 69,1501 HALL-JOHNSON RD
COLLEYVILLE,TX 76034 PH 817 369-4171

C W WHITMAN KWBBLOC@GMAIL.COM

BC PIPELINE AND FIELD SERVICES SEE
DUKE ENERGY GAS TRANSMISSION

BCF LAND CO,LLC
10201 STUBBS TRL
FORT WORTH,TX 76108 PH 817 366-9985
TED FAY TSFAYS@ATT.NET

BCJ ENERGY COMPANY
3611 W PIONEER PKWY #B
ARLINGTON,TX 76013
PH 817 303-7473 FAX 817 277-7473
BILL VAHRENKAMP,PRES BILL@FWNGING.COM
JOHN VAHRENKAMP,VP FINANCE
CHAD VAHRENKAMP,VP OPERS

BEACON GROUP,THE SEE
BEACON ROYALTY

BEACON RESOURCES CORP
PO BOX 5370
VIENNA,WV 26105-5370 PH 304 295-3333
WALTER H ALLEN,CEO

BEAIRD RESOURCES,INC
PO BOX 1830
TYLER,TX 75710-1830 PH 903 597-1922
FAX 903 531-0056
HAROLD C BEAIRD,PRES

BEAKON OIL & GAS,INC
PO BOX 1264
BROWNWOOD,TX 76804-1264
PH 325 646-5187 FAX 325 646-4841
GROVER BEAKLEY,LAND MGR
ODESSA,TX OFFICE - 68 SHILOH,79762
79762 PH 432 272-3668
BRENT BEAKLEY,PRES
BURLESON,TX OFFICE - 416 JAYME CT
76028 PH 817 426-2250
DAVID O'NEAL,VP

BEAMON ROBERT,BOB
2603 AUGUSTA STE 1050
HOUSTON,TX 77057 PH 713 266-9080

BEAN C F,LLC,DREDGING CONTR
PO BOX 51657
LAFAYETTE,LA 70505-1657 PH 337 234-4501
FAX 337 237-1804 WWW.CFBEAN.COM
GLEN J ASHY,VP,OPERS MGR
GASHY@CFBEAN.COM
JENNIFER FIKE,EXEC SECY

BEAN RESOURCES,INC
PO BOX 52768
LAFAYETTE,LA 70505-2768
PH 337 234-2326 FAX 337 234-2330
THEO B BEAN JR,PRES
D E DOUGHT,CFO
TOMMY HOVIS,ASSOC
ADRIAN ORTLIEB,ASSOC
LORI LANDRY,ACCT
TOM GIOSA,GEOL
LANIE BORDER,EXEC ASST
JENNIFER BROOKS STOUTE,EXEC ASST

BEAR CREEK SERVICES LLC
PO BOX 6687, 425 ASHLEY RIDGE
SHREVEPORT,LA 71136 PH 318 550-0358
WWW.BEARCREEKSERVICES.NET
SCOTT WILHITE
SWILHITE@BEARCREEKSERVICES.NET

BEAR PAW ENERGY LLC SEE
TRANSMONTAIGNE INC

BEAVERS ENERGY LP
PO BOX 10
SANGER,TX 76266-0010 PH 940 458-5496
FAX 940 458-5981 BEAVERSENERGY@GMAIL.COM
JAY BEAVERS,PRES

BECHTEL EXPLORATION COMPANY
1333 HEIGHTS BLVD #200
HOUSTON,TX 77008 PH 713 963-8160
FAX 713 963-8162 WWW.BMEXPL.COM
MICHEL BECHTEL,PRES
SHERRI GUINN,CFO
TOM MCWHORTER,VP EXPL
RON BROCK,VP LAND
WES FIANDT,GEOL
STEVEN DOUGLASS,GEOL
ROBERT DENEHIE,GEOL

BECK C E ASSOC,INC
514 BOUQUIN CIR
OIL CITY,PA 16301-3073 PH 814 676-3682
FAX 814 676-5480
C E BECK,CPL,VP,LAND
CEBECK@MAIL.USACHOICE.NET
SAMUEL J BECK,CPL,VP,LAND
M S BECK,CORP SECY
GAYLE H SMITH,LAND ADMIN

BECK ENERGY CORPORATION
PO BOX 1070,4857 HARDING AVE
RAVENNA,OH 44266-1070 PH 330 297-6891
FAX 330 297-7925 BECKENERGY@HOTMAIL.COM
RAYMOND T BECK,PRES
DAVID E BECK,SECY

BECKER D K,GEOL
600 LEOPARD ST STE 706
CORPUS CHRISTI,TX 78401
PH 361 884-3613
DKBECKER1137@SBCGLOBAL.NET

BECKMAN PRODUCTION SERVICES,INC
PO BOX 670
KALKASKA,MI 49646-0670
PH 231 258-9524 FAX 231 258-4521
DANNY CAGLE,VP
TOM CYBULLA,OPERS MGR
BUTCH PEEPLES,SAFETY DIR

BEEBE & BEEBE,INC
203 NEEL ST
EL DORADO,AR 71730-4219
PH 870 862-1884 FAX 870 863-7451
A V BEEBE
J S BEEBE,JR

BEEBE DRILLING & SUPPLY CO
PO BOX 386,1620 E MAIN ST
EL DORADO,AR 71730-0386 PH 870 862-1377

BEEBE J S,JR,OIL CO
203 NEEL ST
EL DORADO,AR 71730-4219 PH 870 863-7451
FAX 501 862-1319
J S BEEBE,OWNER

BEECH GROVE ENERGY PARTNERS,LLC
952 ECHO LN STE 445
HOUSTON,TX 77024 PH 281 974-5993
JOE KAMINSKI JOE@BEECHGROVEPARTNERS.COM

BEELER OIL CO
11908 GREGORY LN
EVANSVILLE,IN 47712-9017 PH 812 985-5503
DAVID M BEELER,PRES

BEKA DRILLING FLUIDS,INC
152 TRINITY DR
PORTLAND,TX 78374 PH 361 777-3071

BEL MINERAL LLC
PO BOX 1447,500 KIRBY ST
LAKE CHARLES,LA 70602-1447
PH 337 436-9401 FAX 337 436-5266
NICK GUILLORY,CO-MGR
JOHN C THIELEN,CO-MGR

BELCHIC GEORGE JR,IND OPR
PO BOX 5897
SHREVEPORT,LA 71135-5897 PH 318 865-9590

BELGAM OIL COMPANY INC
C/O BOB MATTHEWS
8585 BUSINESS PARK DR
SHREVEPORT,LA 71105
PH 318 798-1880 FAX 318 798-1917
ELLEN BELCHIC,PRES
LAYNE BELCHIC,SECY
MARTHA BELCHIC,TREAS

BELL ROBERT J,PH D,CONSULTING GEOL
3910 SHADY TERRACE DR
KINGWOOD,TX 77345-1184 PH 281 360-9349
PH 713 823-3558
LUCINDA S BELL,SECY
RJBELLMAIL@AOL.COM

BELL SUPPLY I,LP
PO BOX 1299
GAINESVILLE,TX 76241-1299
PH 940 665-1486
DAVID KING,MGR
BOWIE,TX OFFICE - PH 940 872-3066
CHARLEY MARTIN,MGR
JACKSBORO,TX OFFICE - PH 940 567-5586
CARLOS ESPINOZA,MGR
BRIDGEPORT,TX OFFICE - PH 940 683-3577
KENNY HUDSON,MGR
KILGORE,TX OFFICE - PH 903 984-1509
LOWELL MCCOY,MGR
CARTHAGE,TX OFFICE - PH 903 693-7831
MARKEL WALDROP,MGR
BUFFALO,TX OFFICE - PH 903 322-2985
DAVID RIDDLE,MGR
VELMA,OK OFFICE - PH 580 444-2372
KENNY JONES,MGR
FAIRVIEW,OK OFFICE - PH 580 227-2881
WAYNE ELDER,MGR
JENA,LA OFFICE - PH 318 992-2194
SHERMAN GANEY,MGR

BELLAN JOHN A JR,OIL & GAS ATTY
3936 KINGS HWY
JACKSON,MS 39216-3327 PH 601 366-3236
JALEXBELLAN@BELLSOUTH.NET

BELLARD & COMPANY INC
A PROFESSIONAL LAND COMPANY
PO BOX 52007
LAFAYETTE,LA 70505
PH 337 234-2666 FAX 337 234-0305
WWW.BELLARDCOMPANY.COM
JARED P BELLARD,CPL
JBELLARD@BELLARDCOMPANY.COM

BELLE EXPLORATION,INC
PO BOX 952,280 HIGHLAND BLVD
NATCHEZ,MS 39121-0952 PH 601 442-6648
FAX 601 442-3961 BELLEX@BELLSOUTH.NET
ALTON J OGDEN JR,PRES

JEFF L BURKHALTER,VP

BELLE OIL,INC
PO BOX 952,280 HIGHLAND BLVD
NATCHEZ,MS 39121-0952 PH 601 442-6648
FAX 601 442-3961 BELLEX@BELLSOUTH.NET
ALTON J OGDEN,JR,PRES
JEFF L BURKHALTER,VP

BELNORTH PETROLEUM CORPORATION SEE
ENRON OIL & GAS CO

BENCHMARK EXPLORATION INC
6420 HILLCROFT STE 317
HOUSTON,TX 77081-3103
PH 713 974-2880 FAX 713 974-2880
EDWARD F HAYE,PRES

BENCHMARK OIL & GAS CO
9821 KATY FWY STE 450
HOUSTON,TX 77024-1293 PH 281 885-8585
FAX 281 885-7557 BENCHMARKOILANDGAS.COM
ALBERT C GOLDEN,PRES & CEO
BGOLDEN@BMOG.COM

BENGAL GAS TRANSMISSION CO,INC
PO BOX 6027,4940 BROADWAY STE 200
SAN ANTONIO,TX 78209-0027 PH 210 826-0681
CALVIN MICHELSON,PRES
MITCH MICHELSON,VP
ROBERT FANNIN,VP,FIN

BENNETT & WILLIAMS INC,CONS GEOL
98 COUNTY LINE RD WEST STE C
WESTERVILLE,OH 43082-7256 PH 614 882-9122
FAX 614 882-4260
MICHAEL ROBISON,PRES
LINDA ALLER,EXEC VP
KAREN BALOU,SECY/TREAS

BENNETT GEOLOGICAL CONSULTANTS
PO BOX 1
CHERRY CREEK,NY 14723-0001
PH 716 672-1393
BRUCE A BENNETT,PRES

BENOIST LAW OFFICES
329 MARKET ST
NATCHEZ,MS 39120-3465
PH 601 445-4148 FAX 601 445-4428
PAUL H BENOIST,ATTY
PAUL@BENOISTLAW.COM
WWW.BENOISTLAW.COM
BATON ROUGE,LA OFFICE - 5050 HIGHLAND RD
70808 PH 225 938-9140

BENOIST PAUL H,ESQ
ATTY AT LAW - LOUISIANA LITIGATION,
TITLES,UNITIZATION,CONTRACTS
329 MARKET ST
NATCHEZ,MS 39120 PH 601 445-4148
FAX 601 445-4428 WWW.BENOISTLAW.COM
PAUL@BENOISTLAW.COM

BENOIT JOSEPH M MIKE ,CPL & ASSOCIATES
PO BOX 52893
LAFAYETTE,LA 70505-2893 PH 337 237-4436
FAX 337 237-6693 JMIKEBENOIT@CS.COM
JOSEPH M MIKE BENOIT,CPL
RICHARD VINCENT,CPL
MIKHAELA C MELANCON,LEASE ADMIN

BENSON OIL CO
RR 2
SHINGLEHOUSE,PA 16748-9802
PH 814 697-6895
ROBERT D BENSON SR,OWNER

ROBERT D BENSON JR,OWNER

BENT ARROW OPERATING,INC
770 S POST OAK LN STE 630
HOUSTON,TX 77056-1913 PH 713 961-3033
FAX 713 961-9441
BRUCE ARENDALE,PRES

BENT OAK ENERGY,LLC
700 ROCKMEAD DR STE 168
KINGWOOD,TX 77339 PH 713 750-9264
FAX 713 750-9603
JACK PARKS

BENTON ABSTRACT LLC
6701 N MESA
EL PASO,TX 79912 PH 325 853-2600
WWW.BENTONABSTRACT.COM

BENTRE COMPANY,THE
1635 WARREN CHAPEL
FLEMING,OH 45729 PH 740 373-4040
FAX 740 373-2404
EDDY L BIEHL,PRES

BERCEGEAY OIL PROPERTIES,INC
PO BOX 53002
LAFAYETTE,LA 70505-3002
PH 337 235-0662 FAX 337 235-0662
MACBERC@BELLSOUTH.NET
SCOTT L BERCEGEAY,CPL,PRES

BERCEGEAY PAUL,CONS PETR ENGR &
OIL PROPERTY MANAGEMENT
145 LAKEVIEW
BROUSSARD,LA 70578 PH 318 837-1400

BEREN CORPORATION
2020 N BRAMBLEWOOD
WICHITA,KS 67206
PH 316 265-3311 FAX 316 265-8690
ADAM E BEREN,CHRMN/PRES
CHARLES B SPRADLIN JR,VP/SECY
DONNA M STUCKY,ASST SEC

BEREN I B
PO BOX 12827
DALLAS,TX 75225-0827 PH 214 691-0388

BEREN J,ESTATE OF
PO BOX 12827
DALLAS,TX 75225 PH 214 691-0388

BERENTZ DRILLING CO,INC
PO BOX 782228,2345 BROMFIELD
WICHITA,KS 67278-2228
PH 316 685-5908 FAX 316 685-5926
DARREL WALTERS, OWNER
DARRELWALTERS@BERENTZDRILLING.COM
DENNIS LEFTWICH,DRLG SUPT/RIG 5

BERG LANEY & BROWN COMPANY
PO BOX B
CAMDEN,AR 71711-0120 PH 870 836-4121

BERGFELD LAND & MINERALS GROUP,LLC
305 S BROADWAY AVE STE 304
TYLER,TX 75702-7265
PH 903 526-3838 FAX 903 526-3939
BOB BERGFELD BOB@BERGFELDLAND.COM
ROBERT BERGFELD ROBERT@BERGFELDLAND.COM

BERKSHIRE EXPLORATION COMPANY
3030 LAUSAT ST
METAIRIE,LA 70001-5924
PH 504 831-7779 FAX 504 831-8315
MONTE C SHALETT,PRES
MSHALETT@MINDSPRING.COM

BERLIN & DUBUISSON
25207 OAKHURST DR
SPRING,TX 77386
PH 281 367-9199
BRUCE P BERLIN,LDMN
MICHAEL DUBUISSON,LDMN

BERMONT OIL COMPANY
4034 EASTWOOD DR
JACKSON,MS 39211-6443 PH 601 354-1084
B BRYAN JONES III,PRES,DIR
E E LAIRD JR,DIR
H ROBERT EDWARDS,SECY,DIR
C G VAUGHT,TREAS,DIR

BERNARD JR, J PERCY, CPL
PO BOX 51700,217 OAKLEAF DR
LAFAYETTE,LA 70505-1700
PH 337 277-0385 FAX 337 981-2850
J PERCY BERNARD JR,OWNER

BERNARD LEWIS B,INC
120 OIL CENTER DR STE 104
LAFAYETTE,LA 70503 PH 337 261-4746
CAJUNLANDMAN@BELLSOUTH.NET

BERRY BROTHERS GEN CONTRACTORS,INC
PO BOX 253,1414 RIVER RD
BERWICK,LA 70342-0558 PH 985 384-8770
DOYLE G BERRY,PRES

BERRY CONTRACTING INC
PO BOX 4858,1414 CORN PRODUCTS RD
CORPUS CHRISTI,TX 78469-4858
PH 361 289-2100 FAX 361 289-0609
ED MARTIN,PRES,CEO
D J SMITH,VP,ESTIMATING
DAVID GARLIN,VP,HSE
GLEN WHITTINGTON,BUS DEV

BERRY PHILIP B,OPERATING CO,INC
PO BOX 56129
HOUSTON,TX 77256-6129 PH 713 621-2260
FAX 713 621-2920
JOHN B BERRY,OWNER,PRTNR
LAURA MULLINS,ADMIN ASST

BERRY THOMAS N,& COMPANY
PO BOX 1958
STILLWATER,OK 74076-1958
PH 405 372-5252 FAX 405 372-5254
TNBERRYCOMPANY@SBCGLOBAL.NET
JOHN L LOGAN,PRES/CEO
WANDA COOKE,ACCT MGR

BERRY WILLIAM L,OIL PROPERTIES
PO BOX 2726
LEESBURG,VA 20177-7815 PH 703 724-9944
FAX 703 724-9946
WILLIAM L BERRY,OWNER

BERTOLET ROBERT C,GEOL
PO BOX 2090,517 S CANAL ST
NATCHEZ,MS 39121-2090 PH 601 442-0424
FAX 601 442-0365
TODD BERTOLET,GEOL
SUSAN HEWITT,OFC MGR

BERTRAM OIL CO
PO BOX 411
ROBINSON,IL 62454-0411 PH 618 562-1122
DON BERTRAM,OWNER,OPR

BERTRAM,LLC
EXPLORATION & PRODUCTION IN U.S.
1221 RED STONE DR
LEXINGTON,KY 40509 PH 859 264-8330

JAY BERTRAM,MGR JAYBERTRAM@YAHOO.COM

BERTUZZI M A & C L,INDEPENDENT
1818 CARIBBEAN DR
CORPUS CHRISTI,TX 78418-9007
PH 361 937-9234

BESS R C LAND,TITLE,CORROSION
8820 MARYLAND CT
DENTON,TX 76207
PH 817 915-9993 FAX 800 610-9875
RCBESSLANDSERVICES@GMAIL.COM
R C BESS,PHD,MNGNG DIR
MARJORIE N BESS,VP OPERS
JACK BESS,MGR TECH

BEST D M CO INC
PO BOX 311
BELLAIRE,TX 77402-0311 PH 713 641-0323
FAX 713 641-1041
D M BEST,CHRMN OF BD
D M BEST,II,PRES
J SALAZAR,PLT SUPT

BEST HOMER,JR,OIL OPR,OIL,GAS & LAND
PO BOX 1446
JACKSON,MS 39215-1446 PH 601 354-4200
FAX 601 354-4201 HOBOY70@AOL.COM

BEST J M INC
146 IVY LN
VENETIA,PA 15367 PH 724 731-0128
JOHN M BEST,GEOL

BESTOLIFE CORPORATION
2777 N STEMMONS FWY STE 1800
DALLAS,TX 75207 PH 855 243-9164
FAX 214 631-3047 WWW.BESTOLIFE.COM
SHARON WHITE,SLS MGR
WHITE@BESTOLIFE.COM PH 214 583-0312
TOM BRIEVE,DOMESTIC SLS
TBRIEVE@BESTOLIFE.COM PH 214 583-0234
TIM SANDERS,DOMESTIC SALES
TSANDERS@BESTOFLIFE.COM PH 214 583-0343

BESTWAY OILFIELD INC
16030 MARKET ST
CHANNELVIEW,TX 77530-4512
PH 281 452-2525
JENNIFER MAYS

BETA LAND SERVICES LLC
PO BOX 51241
LAFAYETTE,LA 70505-1241 PH 337 371-3601
FAX 337 371-3650
BRYAN J HANKS,PRES
BHANKS@BETALANDSERVICES.COM

BETA OPERATING INC
PO BOX 52443
LAFAYETTE,LA 70505-2443 PH 337 981-7233
DAVID S BERCEGEAY,PRES

BETHEA OIL PROPERTIES LEASES
PO BOX 83
HATTIESBURG,MS 39403-0083 PH 601 520-7976
JOHN J BETHEA,PRES

BETSY PRODUCTION COMPANY,INC
PO BOX 308,1621 COMMERCE ST
MAGNOLIA,AR 71754-0308
PH 870 234-5858 FAX 870 234-2102
MIKE DAVIS,PRES
LEE DAVIS,VP
DEBBIE INSCORE,OFC MGR/BOOKKEEPER
DANA OTWELL,SECY
WINNIE F SMITH,LAND MGR

BETWELL OIL & GAS COMPANY
PO BOX 22577
HIALEAH,FL 33002-2577
PH 305 821-8300 FAX 305 826-9782
LOWELL S DUNN II,PRES
LOWELLII@BETWELL.COM

BEUCLER BROS INC
7237 FLINT RD
DELLROY,OH 44620 PH 216 735-2267
SHEILA MODRANSKI,SECY

BEUSA ENERGY,LLC
4 WATERWAY SQUARE PL STE 900
THE WOODLANDS,TX 77380-2692
PH 281 296-1500 FAX 281 296-1501
JEFF MORRIS,PRES

BEVARD DRILLING
SPECIALIZE IN SHALLOW O&G DRLG (OHIO)
4780 TAVENER RD
NEWARK,OH 43056-9086 PH 740 763-2575

BEYT & BEYT,PLC
PO BOX 52157,700 E UNIVERSITY AVE
LAFAYETTE,LA 70505-2157 PH 318 233-6771
FAX 318 233-6773 BEYTLAW@BELLSOUTH.NET
RAYMOND A BEYT,PRTNR
JANICE DAIGRE BEYT,PRTNR

BGSPE ENERGY,LTD
PO BOX 509
TYLER,TX 75710-0509 PH 903 597-8277
BOBBIE S PRITLE EMBREY,MNGNG PRTNR

BGTT LAND SERVICES,LLC
2814 ROCKY OAK
SAN ANTONIO,TX 78232 PH 210 849-4653
LARRY MOROZ,PRES,REG LDMN
LARRY.MOROZ@BGTTLANDSERVICES.COM

BHATE ENGINEERING CORPORATION
5217 5TH AVE S
BIRMINGHAM,AL 35212-3515 PH 205 591-7062
FAX 205 591-7184
U R BHATE,PRES

BHCH MINERAL,LTD
5111 BROADWAY
SAN ANTONIO,TX 78209 PH 210 828-6565
FAX 210 828-1688

BHP PETROLEUM (AMERICAS) INC
1360 POST OAK BLVD STE 150
HOUSTON,TX 77056-3020 PH 713 961-8500
FAX 713 961-8400
MICHAEL WEILL,VP,STRATEGIC PLANNING &
EXTERNAL AFFAIRS
GARRY WOODHOUSE,VP,EXPL TECHNOLOGY
BERNIE WIRTH,VP,GULF OF MEXICO
ED PARKER,VP,GEN COUNSEL
KEITH SHULL,VP,HUMAN RESOURCES
BILL GRAY,VP,PETR ENGRG
SCOTT SANDERS,VP,SAFETY,HEALTH & ENVIRO
PRESTON MASON,VP,PROJ DEV
GREG CHAPMAN,VP,PROD ASSETS
LARRY KILLION,VP,LATIN AMERICA
LARAY GEIST,CHF GEOPHY
IRENE WANG,MGR,TAX & INSURANCE

BI PETRO INC
3150 EXECUTIVE PARK DR
SPRINGFIELD,IL 62703-4509 PH 217 726-9500
FAX 217 726-9495
JOHN HOMEIER,PRES

BIBLE JOB 38 OIL & GAS LLC
17626 WILD OAK
HOUSTON,TX 77090 PH 713 703-8098
GARY@RCRCORP.COM

BIG COUNTRY PARTNERS LLC
PO BOX 1265
BRENHAM,TX 77834 PH 800 888-7260
WWW.LUTHERPOEHLMANN.COM
BIGCOUNTRYPARTNERS@MSN.COM
LUTHER POEHLMANN,MEMBER MGR
MARK POEHLMANN,MEMBER

BIG JOE OIL CO
PO BOX 1087,61-SOUTH
NATCHEZ,MS 39121-1087 PH 601 442-5481
PH 442-5482 FAX 601 445-7488
JOE FORTUNATO,PRES
NANCY B KUEHNLE,SECY
CATHERINE FORTUNATO,SECY

BIG MAN OIL CO INC
PO BOX 1181
OWENSBORO,KY 42302-1181
PH 270 685-0826 OR 270 925-7499
ROBERT STERGE,PRES

BIG PINEY OIL & GAS CO SEE
NATIONAL ENERGY GROUP INC

BIG SHELL OIL & GAS,INC
500 N SHORELINE BLVD STE 705 N
CORPUS CHRISTI,TX 78471-1013
PH 361 888-9218 FAX 361 883-9566
HARVEY WHITE,PRES

BIG SKY OPERATING
PO BOX 1336, 9065 GOODMAN RD
OLIVE BRANCH,MS 38654 PH 662 890-0050
FAX 662 893-7883
MILTON COX,CEO
GEORGE ROBINSON,LAND MGR
ROCKY MCDONALD,FLD SUPT

BIG TREE LLC
2269 LYELL AVE
ROCHESTER,NY 14606-5723
PH 585 429-6462 FAX 585 429-5511
ALFRED C PROCTON,PRTNR

BIG 4,INC
301 WORTH ST
HEMPHILL,TX 75948 PH 409 787-2733
FAX 409 787-2071 BIG4INC.INFO
BIG4TEXAS@VALORNET.COM
BILLY J MCGEE,OWNER

BIG 6 DRILLING COMPANY
7500 SAN FELIPE ST STE 250
HOUSTON,TX 77063-1707
PH 713 783-2300 WWW.BIG6DRILLING.COM
CHESTER B BENGE JR,PRES
MICHAEL D STONE,VP
MDSTONE@BIG6DRILLING.COM

BIGGS, INGRAM & SOLOP,PLLC
PO BOX 14028
JACKSON,MS 39236-4028 PH 601 713-1192
FAX 601 713-2049 WWW.BISLAWYERS.COM
OTIS JOHNSON JR,ATTY
STAN T INGRAM,ATTY
TRAVIS J CONNER,ATTY

BIGHEART PIPE LINE CORP SEE
KOCH OIL CO

BIGLANE D A,OIL PROD
PO BOX 966,100 PEARL ST

NATCHEZ,MS 39121-0966 PH 601 442-2783
D A BIGLANE
JAMES BIGLANE,GEN MGR

BIGLANE OPERATING COMPANY
PO BOX 988,BIGLANE BLDG 100 PEARL ST
NATCHEZ,MS 39121-0988 PH 601 442-2783
D A BIGLANE,PRES
JAMES BIGLANE,VP
TERESA W MCGEHEE,LDMN
S A NUNN,PROD SUPT

BILETA CORP
1106 FOREST LN
EL DORADO,AR 71730-4110
PH 870 875-1090
W B LINES,PRES

BILINGUAL CONSULTANTS,INC
604 KEES CIR
LAFAYETTE,LA 70506-2922 PH 337 981-8275
FAX 337 981-6628
GLADYS B BRENKE,PRES GBRENKE@COX.NET
C E ED BRENKE,VP

BILLEAUD ROY ABSTRACT CO,INC
106 NOBLEMEN LN
LAFAYETTE,LA 70508-7492 PH 337 988-0450
FAX 337 988-0450
ROY J BILLEAUD III,OWNER

BILLINGSLEY CARL R,PETR LAND SERVICES
PO BOX 1192
HENDERSON,TX 75653 PH 903 649-1882
CARL R BILLINGSLEY,OWNER

BILLINGSLEY DAVID L JR,PETR GEOL SERVICES
400 TRAVIS ST STE 1230
SHREVEPORT,LA 71101-3114 PH 318 222-7123
DAVID L BILLINGSLEY JR,OWNER

BILLUPS T CARLETON
PO BOX 7720
ARLINGTON,VA 22207-0720 PH 662 327-6509

BINTLIFF PROPERTIES LIMITED PARTNERSHIP
1001 FANNIN ST STE 722
HOUSTON,TX 77002-6707 PH 713 652-6113
ROBERT A WEIGLE,MGR,OIL & GAS

BIO CONCEPTS,INC
PO BOX 374
KEMAH,TX 77565-0374
PH 281 339-2222 FAX 281 339-5122
JOHN BARNET,SALES

BIO SI TECHNOLOGY,LLC
P O BOX 784
ARGYLE,TX 76226 PH 940 648-2425
FAX 940 648-5959
WWW.BIOSITECHNOLOGY.COM
INFO@BIOSITECHNOLOGY.COM
WAYNE TUCKER,SALES REP

BIRD CREEK OPERATING
PO BOX 21470,1437 S BOULDER STE 930
TULSA,OK 74121-1470 PH 918 582-7713
FAX 918 592-3232
GARRY SMITH,CFO
GARY ADAMS,PRES
WADE ALEXANDER,OPERS

BIRDSONG GABRIEL OIL CO
121 S BROADWAY STE 728
TYLER,TX 75702-7276 PH 972 592-0826
CARTER GABRIEL,PRTNR

BISBEY AL OIL & GAS LEASING,INC
359 COUNTY ROAD 161

GEORGE WEST,TX 78022-3521 PH 361 701-6611
FAX 361 566-2294 STEXDEERMAN@HOTMAIL.COM
AL BISBEY,PRES

BISETT & ASSOCIATES,LEASES
PO BOX 844
WIMBERLY,TX 78676-0844 PH 409 542-5581

BISHOP LAND SERVICE
PO BOX 366
MESICK,MI 49668
PH 231 885-2405 PH 231 878-0093
FAX 231 885-2439 BLS01@ACEGROUP.CC
WWW.BISHOPLANDSERVICEINC.COM

BISHOP LIFTING PRODUCTS INC
125 MCCARTY DR
HOUSTON,TX 77029 PH 713 674-2266
WWW.LIFTING.COM
DAVID (MO) MOSELEY
DAVID.MOSELEY@LIFTING.COM
- BRANCH OFFICES -
NEW IBERIA,LA
ROCK SPRINGS,WY
BEAUMONT,TX

BISHOP PETROLEUM INC
5900 MEMORIAL DR STE 216B
HOUSTON,TX 77007-8008
PH 713 862-4775 FAX 713 862-4785
R H BISHOP,OWNER/PRES

BISHOP R H
5900 MEMORIAL DR STE 216B
HOUSTON,TX 77007 PH 713 439-1119
FAX 713 439-0735

BISHOP WILLIAM H,CONSULTING GEOL
PO BOX 51797
LAFAYETTE,LA 70505-1797 PH 337 984-0603
WHBISHOP@COX.NET

BISSELL OPERATING LLC
324 W SUNSET
SAN ANTONIO,TX 78209 PH 210 824-3100
FAX 210 824-3114
GENE AMES III,EXEC VP
DAVID CLAY,GEOL

BIVINS ENERGY CORPORATION
4925 GREENVILLE AVE STE 814
DALLAS,TX 75206-4017 PH 214 987-2555
FAX 214 987-2955 BIVCO@SWBELL.NET
CRAIG H BIVINS,PRES
RICK MCCALL,CFO
ANGELA MENDOZA,ACCT MGR
FRANK MCCOLLOCH,LAND MGR
LYNDA ANDERSON,ACCT
JESSICA STEFANIAK,GEOTECH
LOUISE D BIVINS,ADMIN ASST

BJ CHEMICAL SERVICES SEE
BAKER HUGHES

BJ SERVICES COMPANY,USA SEE
BAKER HUGHES

BJ UNICHEM CHEMICAL SERVICES SEE
BJ CHEMICAL SERVICES

BLACK CREEK DRILLING,INC
PO BOX 520
COLUMBUS,TX 78934-0520 PH 979 733-9688
PH 866 897-3188 866 601-9201
FAX 979 733-9901
MIKE WOSTAREK,PRES
CARL WALDRIP,SALES
HOUSTON,TX OFFICE - 515 N SAM HOUSTON

PKWY E,STE 400,77060
PH 281 847-1691 FAX 281 847-2691
CARL WALDRIP,SALES

BLACK CREEK WELL SERVICE,LP
18615 TUSCANY STONE STE 300
SAN ANTONIO,TX 78258 PH 210 495-5577
JOHN WARD,DIR
JOHN.WARD@BLACKCREEKWELLSERVICES.COM
JOSEPH DORN,MGR LEASE SVCS
EDDIE MUNOZ,MGR WELL SVCS

BLACK DIAMOND ENERGY,LLC
PO BOX 127,119 AMERICAN LEGION DR
RAYNE,LA 70578-0127 PH 337 334-0611
FAX 337 334-2309 WWHITEWING@AOL.COM
W K WHITEWING,GEN MGR
BRENDA WINDHAM,OFC MGR
ALDEN WICKSTROM,GEOL

BLACK FALCON EXPLORATION
PO BOX 1267
CORPUS CHRISTI,TX 78403
PH 361 994-8210
CHESTER COKER

BLACK GOLD INTL LLC
DRILLING & DEVELOPMENT - ILLINOIS BASIN
PO BOX 145
NEWBURGH,IN 47630-0145 PH 812 499-6224
MARK KENNEDY ROCKHOUND9125@AOL.COM

BLACK HILLS ENERGY RESOURCES,INC
625 9TH ST STE 200
RAPID CITY,SD 57701-2674 PH 713 942-0595

BLACK LARRY L,CERT PETR GEOL,CONSULTANT
MID CONTINENT REGION
6635 S 76TH EAST AVE
TULSA,OK 74133-1836
PH 918 252-2107 FAX 918 252-2107

BLACK MOUNTAIN EXPLORATION,LP
500 MAIN ST STE 1200
FORT WORTH,TX 76102 PH 817 698-9901
FAX 817 698-9902 WWW.BLACKMTN.COM
RHETT BENNETT,CEO
KYLE BIERY,VP BUS DEV
KYLE BIERY@BLACKMTN.COM
GARRETT LILLIS,VP LAND
LUKE MILDREN,LAND ACQS

BLACK OIL COMPANY,INC
6688 N CENTRAL EXPY STE 1165
DALLAS,TX 75206
PH 972 755-5555 FAX 972 755-5550
ROBERT C BLACK,PRES,SECY
ALEX BLACK,CFO

BLACK PEARL EXPLORATION,LLC
8524 HIGHWAY 6 N
HOUSTON,TX 77095 PH 281 855-4755
FAX 281 855-8452

BLACK RIVER OIL CORPORATION
65 MAPLE ST
MANISTEE,MI 49660-1555 PH 231 723-6502
DENNIS L KELEHER,PRES

BLACK STONE MINERALS COMPANY,LP
1001 FANNIN,STE 2020
HOUSTON,TX 77002-6715
PH 713 658-0647 FAX 713 658-0943
WWW.BLACKSTONEMINERALS.COM
THOMAS L CARTER JR,CEO
TCARTER@BLACKSTONEMINERALS.COM
HALLIE VANDERHIDER,PRES & COO

HVANDERHIDER@BLACKSTONEMINERALS.COM
MARSHALL M EUBANK,VP,BUS DEV
MEUBANK@BLACKSTONEMINERALS.COM
MARK E ROBINSON,VP,LAND & LEGAL
MROBINSON@BLACKSTONEMINERALS.COM
MARC CARROLL,VP/CFO
MCARROLL@BLACKSTONEMINERALS.COM

BLACK STONE OIL COMPANY SEE
COMSTOCK RESOURCES

BLACK STONE OIL COMPANY SEE
BLACK STONE MINERALS COMPANY,L.P.

BLACKBRUSH OIL & GAS LP
18615 TUSCANY STONE STE 300
SAN ANTONIO,TX 78258-4078
PH 210 495-5577 FAX 210 495-0075
BLACKBRUSHENERGY.COM
P SCOTT MARTIN,CO-CEO,CFO
PHILLIP M MEZEY,PE,CO-CEO,COO
DOROTHY MCCOPPIN,JD,VP & GEN COUNSEL,
ASST SECY
MARK A NORVILLE,VP,EXPL & DEV
ERIC FRIEDRICHS,CONTROLLER
ROB LIDDELL,DIR BUS DEV

BLACKDOG OIL & GAS LLC
55 EAGLE WINGS TRL
SILVERTHORNE,CO 80498-8924
PH 713 248-1090 FAX 281 657-7065
SCOTT SILVER,EXPL
SCOTTSILVER@BLACKDOGEXP.COM

BLACKERBY DAVID A
8531 N NEW BRAUNFELS AVE STE 201
SAN ANTONIO,TX 78217-6365 PH 210 820-3009

BLACKWELL BAXTER & MOORE INS SPEC SEE
DON MOORE INSURANCE SERVICES,LLC

BLAIR VREELAND
PO BOX 2603,600 LEOPARD ST STE 1616
CORPUS CHRISTI,TX 78403-2603
PH 361 882-6251 FAX 361 882-9071
JOHN B VREELAND,GEOL & OWNER
JAMES S VREELAND,LAND MGR

BLAKE BERRY-BLAKE CORPORATION
PO BOX 11176,400 N MAIN ST
MIDLAND,TX 79702-8176 PH 432 683-4275
FAX 432 684-4621
JACK E BLAKE JR,PRES
BRUCE W BLAKE,VP,TREAS/LIBERTY,TX
KENNETH R BERRY JR,SECY/DENVER,CO

BLAKE BRUCE W,CPL/ESA MGMNT SERVICES
ENV,AUDIT & LAND SVCS/PETR PROP MGMNT
PO BOX 10105
LIBERTY,TX 77575-2282 PH 936 336-7040
PH 800 453-4275 FAX 936 336-9923
WWW.DRILING-PROSPECTS.COM
BRUCEBLAKE@DRILLING-PROSPECTS.COM
MIDLAND,TX OFFICE - PO BOX 11176,79702
PH 432 683-4275 FAX 432 684-4621

BLAKE PRODUCTION COMPANY,INC
1601 NW EXPRESSWAY STE 777
OKLAHOMA CITY,OK 73118
PH 405 286-9800 FAX 405 286-9799
BLAKE VERNON,PRES
STAN MITCHELL,SR LAND REPR
AMY WRIGHT,SR ACCT
KRISTIN ATTEBERY,GAS REPR
JEFF STAHL,FIELD FRMN
MELVIN POSPISIL,FIELD FRMN

GARY TIBBITS,ENGR
KATHY LIPPERT,GEOL

BLALOCK COMPANY,INC
4433 N 26TH RD
ARLINGTON,VA 22207-4018 PH 703 525-8280
JBLALOCK@COMCAST.NET
WWW.BLALOCKCOMPANY.BIZ
JAMES E BLALOCK,PRES

BLAND MICHAEL R,INC
1525 BINGLE RD
HOUSTON,TX 77055-3226 PH 713 467-4202
FAX 7143 467-4202
MICHAEL R BLAND,LDMN

BLANTON THOMAS A
707 HARDY ST
HATTIESBURG,MS 39401
PH 601 336-5119 FAX 601 336-5142

BLAZER RESOURCES,INC
PO BOX 101,HWY 11
LEESBURG,TX 75451-0101 PH 903 856-2733
FAX 903 856-7820
TOM O HANKS,PRES

BLESSEY ENTERPRISES,INC
PO BOX 23212
HARAHAN,LA 70183-0212 PH 504 734-1156
FAX 504 734-1195 WWW.BLESSEY.COM
LAMARR B HIRSCH,DIR/GOV AFFAIRS
LHIRSCH@BLESSEY.COM

BLESSEY MARINE SERVICES,INC
1515 RIVER OAKS RD E
HARAHAN,LA 70123-2167 PH 504 734-1156
FAX 504 734-1195 WWW.BLESSEY.COM
WALTER E BLESSEY JR, CEO
MITCH JONES,COO
CLARK TODD,PRES
PAT VOSS,CFO
BOB SHEA,SR VP,MKTG

BLESSING OIL & GAS CO,INC
PO BOX 1597,413 S MEADOW LN
EL CAMPO,TX 77437-1597 PH 979 543-6571
PH 800 545-6571 FAX 979 543-8165
C E GENE DOYLE SR,CEO
C E CHUCK DOYLE JR,PRES,PROD EQUIP MGR
CHUCK DOYLE,WELLHEAD MGR
LULA MAE DOYLE,SECY

BLOCK T PETROLEUM,INC
PO BOX 2080
TYLER,TX 75710-2080
PH 903 526-4680 FAX 903 509-4681
WWW.BLOCKT.COM
JOHN M TROSCLAIR,P.E.,PRES
JOHN@BLOCKT.COM
LAUREL A TROSCLAIR,ACCT

BLOCK T OPERATING,LLC
2100 MCKINNEY #1550
DALLAS,TX 75201 PH 214 220-3419
TRAVIS TEAGUE TTEAGUE@STOCKDALEINVEST.COM

BLOCO INC
791 SPRINGWOOD RD
HOT SPRINGS,AR 71913-9214
PH 501 767-9107
COOPER B LAND,PRES
PH 501 538-4836 COOPERLAND1@AOL.COM

BLOUNT OIL PROPERTIES INC
PO BOX 921
KILGORE,TX 75663-0921 PH 903 984-3443

CHARLA ROLPH,AGENT

BLOWOUT TOOLS,INC SEE
SUPERIOR ENERGY SERVICES COMPANY

BLUE DOLPHIN ENERGY COMPANY (BDCO)
801 TRAVIS ST STE 2100
HOUSTON,TX 77002-5705 PH 713 568-4725
FAX 713 227-7626 WWW.BLUE-DOLPHIN.COM
IVAR SIEM,CHRMN,CEO,PRES,SECY
T SCOTT HOWARD,TREAS

BLUE DOLPHIN EXPLORATION COMPANY (BDEX)
801 TRAVIS ST STE 2100
HOUSTON,TX 77002-5705 PH 713 568-4725
FAX 713 227-7626 WWW.BLUE-DOLPHIN.COM
IVAR SIEM,CHRMN,CEO,PRES
T SCOTT HOWARD,VP,TREAS,SECY

BLUE DOLPHIN PETROLEUM COMPANY (BDPC)
801 TRAVIS ST STE 2100
HOUSTON,TX 77002-5705
PH 713 568-4725 FAX 713 227-7626
WWW.BLUE-DOLPHIN.COM
IVAR SIEM,CHRMN,CEO,PRES
T SCOTT HOWARD,VP,TREAS,SECY

BLUE DOLPHIN PIPE LINE COMPANY (BDPL)
801 TRAVIS ST STE 2100
HOUSTON,TX 77002-5705 PH 713 568-4725
FAX 713 227-7626 WWW.BLUE-DOLPHIN.COM
IVAR SIEM,CHRMN,CEO,PRES
T SCOTT HOWARD,VP,TREAS,SECY

BLUE DOLPHIN SERVICES CO (BDSC)
801 TRAVIS ST STE 2100
HOUSTON,TX 77002-5705 PH 713 568-4725
FAX 713 227-7626 WWW.BLUE-DOLPHIN.COM
IVAR SIEM,CHRMN,CEO,PRES
T SCOTT HOWARD,VP,TREAS,SECY

BLUE HERON OIL LLC
PO BOX 1149
COLUMBIA,LA 71418-1149
PH 318 649-6401 FAX 318 649-7703
BOB MEREDITH,PRES

BLUE JAY OIL CO
PO BOX 628
MAGNOLIA,AR 71753-0628 PH 870 234-5511
J FRED JORDAN,OWNER

BLUE MOON EXPLORATION COMPANY LLC
1333 HEIGHTS BLVD #200
HOUSTON,TX 77008 PH 713 963-8160
FAX 713 963-8162 WWW.BMEXPL.COM
MICHEL BECHTEL,PRES
SHERRI GUINN,CFO
TOM MCWHORTER,VP EXPL
WES FIANDT,GEOL
STEVEN DOUGLASS,GEOL

BLUE RIDGE ENERGY INC SEE
BAYOU CITY EXPLORATION,INC

BLUESTAR DIRECTIONAL
1407 NORTHPARK DR
KINGWOOD,TX 77339 PH 281 851-8112
GREG NAZZAL
GNAZZAL@BLUESTARDIRECTIONAL.COM

BLUEWATER CONSTRUCTORS,INC
5337 DOW RD
HOUSTON,TX 77040-6101 PH 713 462-8525
FAX 713 462-4133
J J WELKEY,PRES
ROBERT CARNETT,PROJ COORD ESTIMATOR
TROY CASTLEMAN,PROJ COORD ESTIMATOR

BMP RESOURCES,INC
24619 POTTER RD
OPP,AL 36467-6013 PH 334 493-0420

BMR LAND SERVICES
400 TEXAS ST STE 600
SHREVEPORT,LA 71101 PH 318 429-2345
FAX 318 429-2340 WWW.BRAMMER.COM
ROBERT KYLE,VP LAND/LEGAL
ROBERT.KYLE@BRAMMER.COM
RANDALL J BEAUCLAIR,LAND MGR
CHRIS AYMOND,SR LDMN,PROJ MGR

BNP PARIBAS
333 CLAY ST STE 2500
HOUSTON,TX 77002
PH 713 393-6800 FAX 713 659-3832

BOCK NORMAN A,OIL OPR
5773 WOODWAY DR PMB 182
HOUSTON,TX 77057-1501 PH 713 522-9727
FAX 713 522-3146
JO ANN VERDINA,COMPTROLLER

BOCO OF LOUISIANA,INC SEE
SALAMIS SERVICES,INC

BOEBEL COMPANY THE
PO BOX 53194
NEW ORLEANS,LA 70118-3194 PH 504 866-4313
CAROL.STGERMAIN@BOEBEL.COM

BOERNE LAND COMPANY
PO BOX 118
WARING,TX 78074-0118
PH 210 392-9497 FAX 830 995-3359
BOERNE,TX OFFICE - 439 WARING-WELFARE RD
78006 BDODSON@HCTC.NET
D BARNARD DODSON,PRES

BOERNE MARINE
39316 I-H 10 WEST
BOERNE,TX 78006
PH 830 816-2130 FAX 830 331-9116
WWW.BOERNEMARINE.COM

BOGERT OIL COMPANY SEE
LOUIS DREYFUS NATURAL GAS CORP

BOIS D'ARC ENERGY,INC SEE
STONE ENERGY CORPORATION

BOIS D'ARC OFFSHORE LTD SEE
STONE ENERGY CORPORATION

BOIS D'ARC PROPERTIES LP SEE
STONE ENERGY CORPORATION

BOISE CASCADE CORPORATION SEE
FOREST CAPITAL PARTNERS

BOISE SEE
FOREST CAPITAL PARTNERS

BOLD ENERGY LP,SEE
OXY USA INC

BOMMER ENGINEERING CO
24622 FAIRWAY SPGS
SAN ANTONIO,TX 78260-4802 PH 210 344-0900
FAX 210 344-9856
WWW.BOMMERENGINEERING.COM
INFOABOMMERENGINEERING.COM
PETER A BOMMER,CEO,PRES,ENGR
DAVID R SHRAUNER,OPERS MGR
PAUL M BOMMER,ENGR

BON WIER PRODUCING COMPANY
PO BOX 14213
MONROE,LA 71207-4213 PH 318 323-7626
LOVELL E HAYDEN,III,PRES

BONANZA OIL COMPANY
500 N AKARD STE 1900 LINCOLN PLZ
DALLAS,TX 75201 PH 214 220-1011
LEE FIKES,PRES

BONICA JOHN R,PC
528 THRELKELD ST
HOUSTON,TX 77007 PH 713 659-6500
WWW.BONICA.COM JRBONICA@BONICA.COM.

BONRAY DRILLING CORPORATION SEE
NABORS DRILLING USA,INC

BOO-KER OIL & GAS CORP
826 UNION ST STE 300
NEW ORLEANS,LA 70112-1411 PH 504 581-2430
FAX 504 566-4785
GRAY S PARKER,CHRMN/PRES
INGRID C LAFFONT,VP/TREAS

BOOHER ENGINEERING,INC
PO BOX 7793
TYLER,TX 75711-7793 PH 214 581-7711
TRAVIS L BOOHER

BOONE EXPLORATION,INC
PO BOX 8660,21 WIRE RD
HUNTSVILLE,TX 77340-0011
PH 936 295-4066 FAX 936 295-4042
LYNN D BOONE,PRES
J C CARLISLE,VP
JERRY BLANKENSHIP,OPERS SUPVSR

BOOTH OIL CO,INC
PO BOX 158
FLORA,IL 62839-0158 PH 618 662-7696

BOOTS & COOTS GROUP
EMERGENCY RESPONSE & CONTROL OF OIL & GAS
WELL BLOWOUTS & WELL FIRES
7908 N SAM HOUSTON PKWY W STE 500
HOUSTON,TX 77064-3513 PH 713 621-7911
FAX 713 621-7988 WWW.BNCG.COM
LARRY H RAMMING,CHRMN
JERRY L WINCHESTER,PRES,COO
DEWITT H EDWARDS,EXEC VP
THOMAS L EASLEY,VP,CFO
CHARLES PHILLIPS,GEN COUNSEL
DOMINIQUE BARNETTE,DIR/MKTG & STRATEGIC
PLANNING

BOOTS & COOTS HS&E PRODUCTS
CHEMICAL SPILL RESPONSE,CONTAINMENT EQUIP
MFG/ENV CLEANUP/TRAINING & RELATED SVCS
7908 N SAM HOUSTON PKWY W STE 500
HOUSTON,TX 77064-3513 PH 281 931-4400
FAX 281 931-4406
CHUCK LABOUNTY,PRES

BOOTS & COOTS SPECIAL SERVICES
HAZMAT RESPONSE/INDUSTRIAL FIRE & MARINE
OIL SPILL RESP/IND HYGIENE/NATL RES
DAMAGE ASSMT/CONS,TRNG,RISK CRISIS MGMNT
7908 N SAM HOUSTON PKWY W STE 500
HOUSTON,TX 77064-3513 PH 713 621-7911
FAX 713 621-7988
LEE THOMPSON,PRES

BOOTS & COOTS/IWC INC
FIRE FIGHTING/WELL CAPPING/INSPECTIONS
CONS ENGRG/FIRE FIGHTING EQUIP/WELL
CONTROL TRAINING
7908 N SAM HOUSTON PKWY W STE 500
HOUSTON,TX 77064-3513 PH 713 621-7911
FAX 713 621-7988
BRIAN KRAUSE,PRES

HOUSTON,TX OPERATIONS OFFICE - 11615 N
HOUSTON ROSSLYN RD,77086 PH 281 931-8884
OR 800-BLOWOUT FAX 281 931-8302
JAMES TUPPEN,SR WELL CONTROL SPEC
LARRY H FLAK,VP,ENGRG
RAYMOND HENRY,DIR WELL CONTROL
DANNY CLAYTON,SR VP,WELL CONTROL SPEC
RICHARD HATTEBERG,SR VP,WELL CONTROL SPEC

BOOTS SMITH OILFIELD SERVICES LLC
PO BOX 1987
LAUREL,MS 39441
PH 601 649-1220 FAX 601 649-3533
WWW.BOOTSMITH.NET DISPATCH1@GBBSC.COM
JASON SMITH,PRES
JERRY BROADWAY
KENNY JOHNSON
CURTIS MOYE - FLOMATON,AL
TANYA LIEN - TRENTON,ND
WILLIE BRUMFIELD - BUFFALO,TX
JOEY SKAINS - BRIAR,TX

BOPCO,LP
FORMERLY BASS ENTERPRISES PRODUCTION CO
201 MAIN ST STE 3100
FORT WORTH,TX 76102
PH 817 390-8400 FAX 817 390-8893
MITCHELL R ROPER,PRES
W FRANK MCCREIGHT,SR VP LAND
JOHN R SMITHERMAN,VP OPERS
STEPHEN H NEUSE,VP ENGRG
ERNIE EASLEY,VP EXPL
BRAD BRIGHAM,VP MKTG
KENT ADAMS,VP DRLG
PATRICK JONES,VP CORP DEV & PLNG
COLIN BARRY,VP SPEC SVCS
ROSS SUTTON,DIR OF LAND
MONTY MONTGOMERY,LAND MGR
ANDY MORRISON,DIV LAND MGR
DORSEY D CROUSE,SUPVSR LAND ADMIN
MIDLAND,TX - WEST TEXAS DIV OFFICE -
PO BOX 2760 79702,6 DESTA DR STE 3700
79705 PH 432 683-2277 FAX 432 687-0329
STEVE JOHNSON,PROD MGR
DAVID NELSON,ENGR SUPVSR
CARLOS CRUZ,ENGR SPRVSR
ALAN THOMPSON,SPEC SVCS MGR
STEPHEN MARTINEZ,DRLG & COMP MGR
DAN POE,OFC MGR
KERMIT,TX DIST OFFICE - PO BOX 1019
79745 PH 432 586-2563
CARLSBAD,NM DIST OFFICE - 522 W MERMOD
STE 704,3104 E GREENE ST 88220
PH 575 887-7329 FAX 575 887-7473
NEW ORLEANS,LA - GULF COAST DIV OFFICE -
3850 N CAUSEWAY BLVD,TWO LAKEWAY CNTR
STE 1900 METAIRIE,LA 70002-6970
PH 504 836-7200 FAX 504 836-7250
JOE C DUBRET,PROD MGR

BORDEN F P AND ASSOC
106 W MAIN STE 312
EL DORADO,AR 71730-5636 PH 870 862-7962
FRANCIS P BORDEN,III,OWNER,LDMN
PH 870 863-7691

BORDERLINE VACUUM SERVICE
14619B RUHLMAN DR
LAREDO,TX 78045 PH 915 355-6968
BORDERLINE.VACUUM@YAHOO.COM

HECTOR SAUCEDO

BOREAN OIL COMPANY
615 N UPPER BROADWAY ST STE 613
CORPUS CHRISTI,TX 78401-0790
PH 361 888-4752
C R LEWIS

BOREHOLE CONTROL,LLC
PROVIDES DRLG FLUIDS & SVCS TO OPERATORS
714 E RUTLAND ST
COVINGTON,LA 70433 PH 985 893-6600
BECKY RAMPON BRAMPON@BOREHOLECON-
TROL.COM

BORERO ENTERPRISES,INC
PO BOX 1849
WALLER,TX 77484 PH 405 414-7526
JAMES LEE BEDFORD,PRES
JAMES_B@SBCGLOBAL.NET

BOSS SERVICES
670 HWY 41-A
HENDERSON,KY 42420-4634 PH 270 826-7400
JERRY HOWARD,PROD SUPT
KENNY SHELTON,CEMENTER

BOSTIK WAYNE C,PETR GEOL
418 E RIX ST
TYLER,TX 75701-1928 PH 903 592-1708
FAX 903 593-4481

BOUCHER & SLACK LEASES & ROYALTIES
127 N MAIN ST
SPRINGHILL,LA 71075-3213 PH 318 539-3541

BOUDREAUX DAVID F & ASSOCIATES
11807 WESTHEIMER STE 550 #219
HOUSTON,TX 77077 PH 281 703-7577
DFBOUDREAUX@GMAIL.COM

BOUDREAUX PROPERTIES INC
OIL LEASES,ROYALTIES & ABSTRACTS
PO BOX 1863,102 GREEN ST
THIBODAUX,LA 70302-1863 PH 985 447-5331
FAX 985 447-5332
CALVIN P BOUDREAUX JR,PRES
CALBOUDREAUX@EARTHLINK.NET
REBECCA YATES,SECY,OFC MGR

BOUNDARY OIL CO SEE
AMERICAN EXPLORATION CO

BOURBEAU JIM LAND SERVICE,INC
11106 STATE HWY 18
CONNEAUT LAKE,PA 16316
PH 814 382-2500 FAX 814 382-2550
PH 814 282-3460
JBOURBEAU@JIMBOURBEAU.COM

BOURQUE SALES & SERVICE,INC
PO BOX 51141
LAFAYETTE,LA 70505-1141
PH 337 232-6622 FAX 337 232-6982
RON BOURQUE,PRES
BOURQUE_OILFIELD@YAHOO.COM

BOUTTE ANDRE L
CONSULTING GEOL,SR TECHNICAL WRITER
12122 CARRIAGE HILL DR
HOUSTON,TX 77077-2509 PH 281 772-0593
FAX 281 596-8836
ANDREBOUTTE@GMAIL.COM

BOW PROPERTY AND LAND SERVICES,INC
PO BOX 1818
MONTGOMERY,TX 77356 PH 979 830-0655

BOWIE LUMBER ASSOCIATES
228 ST CHARLES AVE STE 1424

NEW ORLEANS,LA 70130 PH 504 568-1922
FAX 504 568-9438
DOWMANS@DOWNMANSASSOC.COM
LANE M KINCANNON,PRES/CEO
MICHELLE KITTO,EXEC ADMIN ASST
DEBRA ORR-MOONEY,ACCT MGR
SUE SHELLEY,LAND TECH
KEVIN TORRES,LAND MGR

BOWLES ENERGY,INC
PO BOX 3147
LONGVIEW,TX 75606-3147 PH 903 753-7061
FAX 903 753-8572 WWW.BOWLESENERGY.COM
BRADFORD BOWLES,PRES
JEFFREY G BOWLES,VP
PATRICK S BOWLES,VP

BOX ENERGY CORPORATION SEE
REMINGTON OIL AND GAS CORPORATION

BP
501 WESTLAKE PARK BLVD
HOUSTON,TX 77079-2604 PH 281 366-2000
WWW.BP.COM
CARL-HENRIC SVANBERG,CHAIRMAN
BOB DUDLEY,GROUP CHF EXEC
IAIN CONN,CHF EXEC-DOWNSTREAM
DR BRIAN GILVARY,GROUP CFO
PAUL ANDERSON,IND NON-EXEC DIR
ALAN BOECKMANN,IND NON-EXEC DIR
ADMIRAL FRANK BOWMAN,IND NON-EXEC DIR
ANTONY BURGMANS,IND NON-EXEC DIR
CYNTHIA CARROLL,IND NON-EXEC DIR
GEORGE DAVID,IND NON-EXEC DIR
IAN DAVIS,IND NON-EXEC DIR
DAME ANN DOWLING,IND NON-EXEC DIR
BRENDAN NELSON,IND NON-EXEC DIR
PHUTHUMA NHLEKO,IND NON-EXEC DIR
ANDREW SHILSTON,IND NON-EXEC DIR
RUPERT BONDY,GROUP GEN COUNSEL
BOB FRYAR,EXEC VP-SAFETY & OPER RISK
ANDY HOPWOOD,COO/STRATEGY & REGIONS
KATRINA LANDIS,EXEC VP-CORP BUS ACTIVITY
BERNARD LOONEY,COO-PROD
LAMAR MCKAY,CHF EXEC-UPSTREAM
DEV SANYAL,EXEC VP-STRATEGY & REGIONS
HELMUT SCHUSTER,EXEC VP-GROUP HR DIR
NAPERVILLE,IL OFFICE - 150 W WARRENVILLE
RD 60563 PH 630 420-5000
- BP EXPLORATION (ALASKA),INC. -
ANCHORAGE,AK OFFICE - 900 E BENSON BLVD
99508-4254 PH 907 561-5111
- BP CHEMICALS -
NAPERVILLE,IL OFFICE - 150 W WARRENVILLE
RD 60563 PH 630 836-5000
- BP PRODUCTS AND SERVICES -
WARRENVILLE,IL OFFICE - 28301 FERRY RD
60555 PH 800 333-3991 BPCONSUM@BP.COM

BP ALASKA,INC
900 E BENSON BLVD
ANCHORAGE,AK 99508-4254 PH 907 564-5111

BP AMERICA INC SEE
BP

BP AMERICA PRODUCTION COMPANY SEE
BP AMERICA INC

BP AMOCO CORPORATION SEE
BP CORPORATION

BP CORPORATION SEE
BP AMERICA INC

BP EXPLORATION (ALASKA) INC SEE
BP ALASKA,INC

BP EXPLORATION & OIL INC SEE
BP AMERICA,INC

BP EXPLORATION,INC SEE
BP AMERICA,INC

BPL EXPLORATION,LTD
15201 S PADRE ISLAND DR STE 240B
CORPUS CHRISTI,TX 78418
PH 361 949-7711 FAX 361 949-7712
BILL BAKER,MGR

BRACKEN ENERGY COMPANY SEE
BRACKEN OPERATING LLC

BRACKEN OIL COMPANY
PO BOX 6805
TYLER,TX 75711-6805 PH 903 593-7341
FAX 903 593-4008

BRACKEN OPERATING COMPANY
PO BOX 6805
TYLER,TX 75711-6805 PH 903 593-7341
FAX 903 593-4008

BRACKEN PRODUCTION COMPANY
PO BOX 6805
TYLER,TX 75711-6805 PH 903 593-7341
FAX 903 593-4008

BRADDOCK LAND & DEVELOPMENT LLC
PO BOX 14171
MONROE,LA 71207 PH 318 388-3090
WWW.BRADDOCKLND.COM
BRETT T BRADDOCK
BRETT@BRADDOCKLND.COM

BRADEN DALE S,ATTY,PRACTICE LIMITED TO
OIL & GAS ONLY
PO BOX 26,MAIN AT BOULDER
RUSSELLVILLE,AR 72811-0026
PH 479 968-3697 FAX 479 968-5767
BRADEN@CSWNET.COM

BRADEX OIL AND GAS,INC
6513 PERKINS RD
BATON ROUGE,LA 70808-4259 PH 225 769-9555
FAX 225 769-0023 THEBEAV@INTERSURF.COM
JOSEPH P BRANTLEY,PRES,CEO
JPBRANTLEY@GMAIL.COM
SUSAN HAMMETT,OFC MGR

BRADFORD ENERGY CORPORATION
2915 WARREN AVE
MCDONALD,OH 44437-1406 PH
FAX 216 530-6514

BRADFORD MINERALS CORP
2030 W SAINT MARY BLVD
LAFAYETTE,LA 70506 PH 337 269-4654
PH 337 654-9980 FAX 337 269-4654
GEOBRAD@JUNO.COM
BRAD LEBLANC,PRES,EXPL MGR
CHERYL LEBLANC,SECY

BRADLEY BROUSSARD LAND SERVICES,INC
PO BOX 52826,319 AUDUBON BLVD 70503-2610
LAFAYETTE,LA 70505-2826 PH 337 233-3428
FAX 336 233-3427 WWW.BRADLEYBROUSSARD.COM
BRADLEY J BROUSSARD,PRES
BRAD@BRADLEYBROUSSARD.COM
RACHAEL HABETZ,CFO
ALIX COUSIN,LDMN
RICHARD MURFF,OFC MGR/IT
CORY TAYLOR,CAD

BRADLEY LAND SERVICES,INC
4203 NOYES AVE
CHARLESTON,WV 25304
PH 304 545-9012
BRADLEY WM BOWERS,PRES
BRADLEYBOWERS@AOL.COM

BRADLEY LAW FIRM
SPECIALIZE IN TITLE OPINIONS
13 E HENDERSON ST
CLEBURNE,TX 76031 PH 817 645-3993
FAX 817 645-3995 WWW.BRADLEYLAWYERS.COM
KEITH BRADLEY,OWNER/ATTY
KEITH@BRADLEYLAWYERS.COM

BRADLEY OIL PROPERTIES,INC
PO BOX 52521
LAFAYETTE,LA 70505-2521 PH 337 281-2912
PH 877-234-7470 FAX 337 234-7495
WWW.BRADLEYABSTRACTORS.COM
SHAWN BRADLEY,PRES,PETR LDMN
SHAWN@BRADLEYABSTRACTORS.COM

BRADLEY T H,JR,LEASES & ROYALTIES
1215 N WASHINGTON ST
MAGNOLIA,AR 71753-2459 PH 870 234-4036

BRADY OIL,LLC
PO BOX 12631
PENSACOLA,FL 32591 PH 228 697-7819
SCOTT C BRADY,MNGNG MEMBER
SCOTTCBRADY@MAC.COM

BRAMAN WORKING INTERESTS LP
PO BOX 400
VICTORIA,TX 77902-0400 PH 361 578-6271
FAX 361 576-6890
HUBERT BOWERS,ENGR

BRAMMER ENGINEERING INC
400 TEXAS ST STE 600
SHREVEPORT,LA 71101-3546 PH 318 429-2345
FAX 318 429-2340 WWW.BRAMMER.COM
INFO@BRAMMER.COM
KEITH J EVANS,PRES
PAT BROWN,VP OPERS
ELLEN ALLEY,HR/MKTG DIR

BRANDON PETROLEUM PROPERTIES
PO BOX 2766,544 CENTRAL AVE
LAUREL,MS 39442-2766
PH 601 649-2261 FAX 601 649-2264
WWW.BRANDONPETRO.COM PAM@BRANDON-
PETRO.COM
ALEXANDER C LINDSEY,MNGNG AGENT
PAM WALTERS,ADMIN
COLLEEN CAGLE,SECY
CINDY STAKES
STACY PARKER

BRANDT CO,THE SEE
BRANDT,A VARCO CO

BRANDT PETROLEUM INC,SEE
KARBUHN OIL CO

BRANDT/ADVANCED
1202 JANES ST
NEW IBERIA,LA 70563 PH 318 365-7700
PH 800 725-8710 FAX 318 365-0375
WWW.VARCO.COM
JEFFERY E WALKER
RICKY GOTTE
GEORGE ALEXANDER
DAMIAN LEJEUNE

BRANDT/EPI SEE
BRANDT,A VARCO COMPANY

BRANDT,A VARCO COMPANY SEE
NOV BRANDT

BRANT FRANK W AND ASSOCIATES
PO BOX 742,2315 1/2 SPRADLING AVE
FORT SMITH,AR 72904-0742 PH 501 783-5424
FRANK W BRANT,OWNER

BRANTA LLC
2441 HIGH TIMBERS DR STE 120
THE WOODLANDS,TX 77380-1052
PH 832 813-7096 FAX 832 585-0133
BRAD POSEY,LAND & BUS DEV DIR
FRED TRESCA,MNGNG DIR
RANDY BATES,MNGNG DIR
MARTIN SHIELDS,EXPL DIR
CLAYTON KING,LDMN
FELIX ACREE,SR ENGR

BRANTCO ENTERPRISES,LLC
6513 PERKINS RD
BATON ROUGE,LA 70808-4259 PH 225 769-9555
FAX 225 769-0023 JPBRANTLEY@GMAIL.COM
JOSEPH P BRANTLEY,MANAGING DIR

BRASEL OPERATING
1015 BEECHVIEW DR S
WORTHINGTON,OH 43085 PH 740 742-2707
FAX 740 742-2414 BRASELOILGAS@VERIZON.NET
R GENE BRASEL,PRES
DAVID L STRANG,FLD MGR,PETR ENGR

BRASFIELD OIL & GAS
5520 OLD BULLARD RD STE 119
TYLER,TX 75703
PH 903 581-5993 FAX 903 581-6859
GILLIAN BRASFIELD

BRASHER OIL & GAS PROPERTIES,INC
2198 SANDY RANCH RD
HARWOOD,TX 78632 PH 281 392-4499
FAX 281 392-1049
JERRY F BRASHER,PRES

BRAVO NATURAL RESOURCES,INC SEE
CHESAPEAKE ENERGY CORPORATION

BRAVO OIL COMPANY SEE
SANTA FE ENERGY RESOURCES,INC

BRAZOS GAS COMPANY,LLC
4925 GREENVILLE AVE STE 500
DALLAS,TX 75206 PH 214 265-9670
EVERETT COON,JR ECOON98@AOL.COM

BRAZOS NATURAL RESOURCES,INC
PO BOX 24128
WACO,TX 76702-4128
PH 254 292-0962 PMCPETROLEUM@AOL.COM
PHILIP CURRY,DIR

BREARD GARDNER INC
401 WALL ST
LAFAYETTE,LA 70506-3029 PH 318 234-1405
FAX 318 233-8705
JIMMY O'SULLIVAN,BRANCH MGR
LORI PETERSON,INSIDE SALES
RALPH ALEXANDER,INSIDE SALES

BREAZEALE SACHSE & WILSON LLP
PO BOX 3197,ONE AMERICAN PL STE 2300
BATON ROUGE,LA 70821-3197
PH 225 387-4000 FAX 225 387-5397
WWW.BSWLLP.COM
LINTON L MORGAN
NEW ORLEANS,LA OFFICE - FIRST BANK & TWR

STE 1500,909 POYDRAS ST,70112-4004
PH 504 619-1800 FAX 504 584-5452
COVINGTON,LA OFFICE - 506 EAST RUTLAND ST
ST TAMMANY BUSINESS CNTR,70433-3219
PH 985 871-7992 FAX 985 871-7996

BRECHTEL ENERGY CORPORATION
PO BOX 9044
MANDEVILLE,LA 70470-9044 PH 985 792-0822
FAX 985 792-0824 BEC0822@CHARTER.NET
PETER P BRECHTEL,JR,PRES
AL PORRETTO,GEOL
GERRI DESCANT,OFC MGR
JIM FOWLKES,ENGR

BRECK OPERATING CORP
PO BOX 911,300 N BRECKENRIDGE AVE
BRECKENRIDGE,TX 76424-0911
PH 254 559-3355 FAX 254 559-3220
ACCOUNTING FAX 254 559-5862
PRODUCTION FAX 254 559-7066
JOHN H CONNALLY,PRES & DIR
STEVE VEAZEY,CFO,SECY,MGR TAX/ACCT DEPT
ERNIE UNDERWOOD,VP OPERS
MATTHEW THOMPSON,VP ENGNR
P LANE PETTY,VP,SECY
E BRUCE STREET JR,DIR
HARRY C REAUGH,DIR
DAVID L CLARK,DIR
FREDERICK SCOTT DUESER,DIR
BLAKE ESTESS,DIR
- PRODUCTION DIVISIONS & DISTRICTS -
ANDREWS,TX OFFICE - PO BOX 1709,79714
PH 432 523-3650
BOB PIERCE,PROD SUPVSR - PERMIAN DIST
BRECKENRIDGE,TX OFFICE - PO BOX 911,76424
PH 254 559-3355
LARRY BOLES,PROD SUPVSR - EAST DIST
ROBERT LAMBERT,PROD SUPVSR - WEST DIST
ERNIE UNDERWOOD,PROD SUPVSR - MID-CONT
DIST
ERNIE UNDERWOOD,ENGR - SAN JUAN BASIN
MIDLAND,TX OFFICE - 407 N BIG SPRING #240
79701 PH 432 687-3646
HOBBS,NEW MEXICO OFFICE - 5711 S BRONCO
88240 PH 254 559-0881
KEVIN BRECKEL,PROD SUPVR

BREEDLOVE ROBERT W
205 W DEWEY CAMP DR
FLORENCE,MS 39073-8644 PH 601 845-2376
FAX 601 845-4611

BREHM EXPLORATION
PO BOX 52287,322 HEYMANN BLVD STE B
LAFAYETTE,LA 70505-2287 PH 318 233-2823
FAX 318 232-7929
STACY BREHM,PRES
DAVID FIELDS,VP

BREIDENSTEIN DOUGLAS L
C/O C H KING,INC
211 VERANDA DR
LAKELAND,FL 33809-1551 PH 734 844-1816

BREITBURN ENERGY PARTNERS LP
515 S FLOWER ST 48TH FLOOR
LOS ANGELES,CA 90071-2241 PH 213 225-5900
FAX 213 225-5917 WWW.BREITBURN.COM
HAL WASHBURN,CO-FOUNDER,CEO
HOUSTON,TX OFFICE-1401 MCKINNEY STE 2400
77010 PH 713 437-8000 FAX 713 437-8097

THURMON ANDRESS,MNGNG DIR
MARK PEASE,PRES/COO

BRENDEL PRODUCING COMPANY
PO BOX 517
CANTON,OH 44614
PH 330 854-4151 FAX 330 854-4290
FRANK BRENDEL,JR,PRES
ALEXANDER B C BRENDEL,VP

BRETAGNE L P
670 US 41-A
HENDERSON,KY 42420-0537 PH 270 826-7400
JERRY HOWARD,PROD SUPT

BRETT OIL COMPANY
7670 WOODWAY STE 360
HOUSTON,TX 77063-6500 PH 832 251-3800
FAX 832 251-3815 HGAMBLE4@SBCGLOBAL.NET
BRETT C GAMBLE,PRES
HARRY HANK P GAMBLE IV,VP
CAROL MCDOUGAL,SECY/TREAS

BREWER COMPANIES
PO BOX 18010
LAKE CHARLES,LA 70616-8010
PH 337 433-0045 FAX 337 433-0006

BRG ENERGY INC
EXPLORATION & OPERATOR
7134 S YALE AVE STE 600
TULSA,OK 74136-6338 PH 918 496-2626
FAX 918 496-3996 WWW.BRGCORP.COM
WWW.MFOLZ@BRGCORP.COM
J L BURKHART,CHRMN
B J REID,PRES
MIKE W BURKHART,EXEC VP
ROBERT E GEE,VP,MKTG
CLYDE F WOOTTON,VP,EXPL
STEVE WILLIAMS,VP,FIN
SCOTT GRUNS,VP,PROD
ENID,OK OFFICE - 2414 S MONROE ST
73701-8670 PH 580 233-9302
FAX 580 233-9453
MARK NORMAN,OPERS SUPT

BRG LONE STAR LTD SEE
BRG ENERGY INC

BRG PETROLEUM LLC SEE
BRG ENERGY INC

BRG PRODUCTION COMPANY SEE
SEE BRG ENERGY INC

BRIDAS ENERGY USA,INC SEE
BEUSA ENERGY,INC

BRIDEWELL BILLY
PO BOX 789
WILSON,WY 83014-0789 PH 214 597-6693

BRIDGES RON B & ASSOCIATES,INC,CONS ENGRS
4511 COPERNICUS ST
NEW ORLEANS,LA 70131-3617 PH 504 392-5800
FAX 504 392-5801
RON B BRIDGES

BRIDON AMERICAN CORP
3341 NW LOOP 338
ODESSA,TX 79764 PH 432 367-2812
FAX 432 367-1694 WWW.BRIDONAMERICAN.COM
BRIDON@BRIDONAMERICAN.COM
TOM BANNON

BRIDWELL OIL COMPANY
PO BOX 1830,810 8TH ST
WICHITA FALLS,TX 76307-1830
PH 940 723-4351

STEVE GINNINGS,ENGR
MARK HENDERSON,CHIEF GEOL
NEAL MEEKS,OFC MGR
ABILENE,TX OFFICE - PO BOX 2038
79604 PH 325 672-1512
DOUG BOND,SUPT
ARCHER CITY,TX OFFICE - PO BOX 303
76351 PH 940 574-4568
MARK WATSON,SUPT

BRIGGS KERRY,OIL PROD
5452 RIVER THAMES RD
JACKSON,MS 39211-4133 PH 601 956-2235

BRIGGS KIRK M,INC
100 ROBERT DR
LAFAYETTE,LA 70506
PH 337 258-6701 KIRKMBRIGGS@GMAIL.COM
KIRK M BRIGGS,PRES

BRIGHAM EXPLORATION COMPANY
6300 BRIDGE POINT PKWY STE 500 BLDG 2
AUSTIN,TX 78730-5073 PH 512 427-3300
FAX 512 427-3400 WWW.BEXP3D.COM
BEN M BRIGHAM,CEO,COB,PRES
EUGENE B SHEPHERD,CFO,EXEC VP
A LANCE LANGFORD,EXEC VP,OPERS
JEFFERY E LARSON,EXEC VP,EXPL
DAVID T BRIGHAM,EXEC VP/LAND & ADMIN
MALCOM O BROWN,VP,CONTROLLER
KEN TREACCAR,LAND DIR

BRIGHAM OIL & GAS LP
6300 BRIDGEPOINT PKY BLDG 2 STE 500
AUSTIN,TX 78730-5073
PH 512 427-3300 FAX 512 427-3400
WWW.BEXP3D.COM
BEN M BRIGHAM,CEO,PRES
DAVID T BRIGHAM,EXEC VP LAND/ADMIN
A LANCE LANGFORD,EXEC VP,OPERS
JEFFERY E LARSON,EXEC VP,EXPL
KEN C TREACCAR,LAND DIR

BRIGHT & COMPANY,OIL & GAS DIV
2540 KING ARTHUR BLVD STE 234
LEWISVILLE,TX 75056 PH 972 410-5700
FAX 972 410-5769
JACK CARLILE,PRES PH 972 410-6401
BILL ROSAS,CFO PH 972 410-6402
WALLY MANAUGH,LAND MGR PH 972 410-6403
TERRY GRIFFIN,REV/JIB ACCTG
PH 972 410-6404
SHELLY GAGER,LAND ASST PH 972 410-6405
DALLAS,TX OFC-4220 N CENTRAL EXPY STE 300
75206-6534 PH 214 559-9200
FAX 214 559-0021

BRIGHT STAR MANAGEMENT,LLC SEE
CRAFT EXPLORATION COMPANY,LLC

BRINKLEY CHARLES A,OIL & GAS EXPLOR
HIGH STAR OIL & GAS EXPLORATION CO
8007 HURST FOREST LN
HUMBLE,TX 77346-1704 PH 281 852-8919
PH 852-2970 FAX 281 852-8919
CABRINKLEY13@LIVE.COM

BRINKLEY ENTERPRISES INC
410 W MACK
OLNEY,IL 62450 PH 618 392-0791
HAROLD W BRINKLEY,PRES,OWNER
LORAINE BRINKLEY,SECY

BRIS-TEX ENTERPRISES,INC
PO BOX 19130

HOUSTON,TX 77224 PH 713 464-8800
R M ZEID,PRES

BRISITA ENERGY CORPORATION
ACQUISITION OF OIL & GAS PROPERTIES
PO BOX 425
BRIDGEPORT,TX 76426
PH 940 683-4017 FAX 940 683-6360
WWW.BRISITA.COM
JOE E SMALL,PRES JSMALL@BRISATA.COM
B J BREEZE,VP

BRISTOL MUNGER PROP LLC
SEE HUNT OIL COMPANY

BRISTOW U.S.,LLC
FORMERLY AIR LOGISTICS,LLC
PO BOX 13368
NEW IBERIA,LA 70562 PH 337 365-6771
WWW.BRISTOWGROUP.COM
DANNY HOLDER,DIR OF NABU
KADE MONLEZUN,DIR BUS DEV
DOUG FORSLUND,DIR N.I. SUPPORT

BRITOIL U.S. HOLDINGS INC SEE
AMERICAN EXPLORATION CO

BRITOIL VENTURES INC SEE
AMERICAN EXPLORATION CO

BRITT LAND SERVICES LLC
15500 CUTTEN RD # 608
HOUSTON,TX 77070 PH 832 643-9630
BENJAMIN C BRITT,PRES
BENCBRITT@YAHOO.COM
NARISHA SEEMA SYNE,LAND

BROAD OAK ENERGY II,LLC
1707 MARKET PL BLVD STE 320
IRVING,TX 75063
PH 972 444-8808 FAX 972 444-8913
WWW.BROADOAKENERGY.COM
BEN SHELTON,LAND MGR
BEN.SHELTON@BROADOAKENERGY.COM

BROADHEAD PAUL
609 ELMWOOD DR
MERIDIAN,MS 39301-6714
PH 601 693-0602 FAX 601 483-1864

BROCATO CHARLES P,PETR GEOL
615 LEOPARD ST STE 516
CORPUS CHRISTI,TX 78476-2212
PH 361 884-4681 FAX 361 882-5546

BROCK EXPLORATION CORPORATION SEE
KEY PRODUCTION COMPANY,INC

BRODIE EXPLORATION CORP
12 WOODWAY OAKS LN
HOUSTON,TX 77056-1300 PH 713 626-8960
FAX 713 626-8965
JOE E GUYER,PRES

BRONCO OILFIELD SERVICES
4001 W 7TH ST
ELK CITY,OK 73644 PH 580 225-9168
FAX 580 225-5015
QUESTIONS@BRONCOSERVICES.COM
OKLAHOMA CITY,OK OFFICE- 4434 NW EXPY
STE 124,73116 PH 405 823-7931
FAX 405 879-1654
DENVER,CO OFFICE - 621 17TH ST STE 2540
80293 PH 303 519-7998 FAX 303 292-0064
BROUSSARD,LA OFFICE - 1081 AILLET RD
70518 PH 337 359-9960 FAX 337 359-8550
WASHINGTON,PA OFC - 88 E BUFFALO CHURCH
RD 15307 PH 724 222-1219 FAX 724 222-4915

BRYAN,TX OFFICE - 6210 FOURWINDS DR 77806
PH 979 778-0404 FAX 979 778-8385
CORPUS CHRISTI,TX OFFICE - 820 MCBRIDE LN
78408 PH 361 289-7088 FAX 361 289-0953
HOUSTON,TX OFFICE - 2828 TECHNOLOGY
FOREST BLVD 77381 PH 832 295-4770
FAX 832 295-4575
LONGVIEW,TX OFFICE - 5175 WHITEHURST RD
75602 PH 903 553-0037 FAX 903 553-0047
ROCK SPRINGS,WY OFFICE - 369 BLAIRTOWN RD
82901 PH 307 362-5106 FAX 307 362-9706

BROOKLYN UNION EXPLORATION COMPANY SEE
HOUSTON EXPLORATION COMPANY,THE

BROOKS OIL COMPANY
PO BOX 1069
ATLANTA,TX 75551-1069 PH 903 796-2873
FAX 903 796-3358
DR J M BROOKS

BROONER EXPLORATION
2824 NACOGDOCHES RD
SAN ANTONIO,TX 78217-5827 PH 210 828-0384
FAX 210 824-0864
BARRY A BROONER,GEOL

BROUGHTON PETROLEUM INC
PO BOX 1389
SEALY,TX 77474-1389
PH 979 877-0200 FAX 979 877-0031
WTWOKTEX@BPIGAS.COM
CHERYL L MELLEATHIN,PRES
WILLIAM T WILSON,VP

BROUSSARD DENNIS J,& ASSOCIATES,ENGRS
140 EMMA DR
LAFAYETTE,LA 70503-2208 PH 318 234-4660

BROUSSARD MICHAEL J LAND SERVICES,INC
PROFESSIONAL LAND SERVICES
PO BOX 53633
LAFAYETTE,LA 70505-3633 PH 337 233-0168
FAX 337 233-4594
LANDQUEST@BELLSOUTH.NET
MICHAEL J BROUSSARD,PRES

BROWN & ROOT ENERGY SERVICES SEE
KELLOGG BROWN & ROOT,INC

BROWN ARCHIE,OIL CO
PO BOX 644,404 S 5TH ST
CARMI,IL 62821-0644 PH 618 382-7322
FAX 618 382-7324
ARCHIE BROWN,OWNER
TOM MUSE,PROD SUPT

BROWN BRUCE W,GEOLOGIST
23 SPLIT ROCK CT
THE WOODLANDS,TX 77381-2539
PH 281 367-9249

BROWN CONTRACTORS INC
1478 BEAR KNOLL DR
QUITMAN,LA 71268-4504 PH 318 259-4200
FAX 318 259-2336
SCOTT BROWN,PRES
STEVEN BROWN,VP
PAT HEARD,SECY

BROWN DOR W,CONSULTANT
4802 LEEWARD CT
AUSTIN,TX 78731-4506 PH 512 454-1537
DOR W BROWN,III,OWNER

BROWN E W,JR,PROPERTIES
2500 TANGLEWILDE STE 482
HOUSTON,TX 77063-2189 PH 713 782-5320

FAX 713 980-9806
ROCKY ARRELL,AGENT

BROWN G A,OIL PROP SEE
GILA GROUP,LP

BROWN GEO. R PARTNERSHIP,LP,THE
1001 FANNIN ST STE 4700
HOUSTON,TX 77002-6792 PH 713 652-4901
FRED C GIBSON,PRES
ROBERT B BURNHAM,ENGR,RESERVOIR
GEORGE BASKIN,ENGRG,PROD
JAN MOSSBERG,LAND MGR
PAT YERIAN,CONTROLLER
- DISTRICT OFFICES -
POST,TX OFFICE - PO BOX 518
LUBBOCK HWY,79356 PH 806 495-2886
TOMMY HILL,DIST SUPT

BROWN H M,& CO,INC
PO BOX 717
GEORGEWEST,TX 78022 PH 361 449-3371
JAMES D PAWLIK

BROWN KENNETH L,LOG CONS
25747 WESTBOURNE DR
KATY,TX 77494-5149 PH 504 443-1743

BROWN WALTER F
900 NE LOOP 410 #A-107
SAN ANTONIO,TX 78209 PH 210 824-7214

BROWN WARREN L & ASSOCIATES
PO BOX 51124,120 OIL CENTER DR
LAFAYETTE,LA 70503-2442 PH 337 280-8234
WARREN L BROWN III
WARREN@WARRENLBROWN.COM

BROWNING OIL COMPANY,INC
8080 N CENTRAL EXPY STE 780
DALLAS,TX 75206-1806 PH 214 739-3481
FAX 214 739-4458
MICHAEL R MCWILLIAMS,PRES,CEO
JIM BURON,ENGRG
ED STEWART,LAND
BILL PATTERSON,ACCT
GIDDINGS,TX OFFICE - PO BOX 686,78942
PH 409 542-3144
DOUG JATZLAU,PROD SUPT

BRUIN INSTRUMENTS CORP
9001-20TH ST
EDMONTON,ALBERTA,CAN T6P 1K8
PH 780 430-1777 FAX 780 449-5233
WWW.BRUINPUMPS.COM
DARREN PREECE
DPREECE@BRUININSTRUMENTS.AB.CA

BRUMLEY C W,OIL PROD
PO BOX 58
OIL CITY,LA 71061-0058 PH 318 995-7145

BRUMLEY V H,OIL COMPANY
23 JUMILLA LN
HOT SPRINGS,AR 71909 PH 318 256-2851
V H BRUMLEY,OWNER
L D FUNDERBURK,OFC MGR

BRUNINI GRANTHAM GROWER & HEWES,PLLC
PO BOX 119,190 E CAPITOL ST STE 100
JACKSON,MS 39205-0119 PH 601 948-3101
FAX 601 960-6902 WWW.BRUNINI.COM
- ATTORNEYS -
EDMUND L BRUNINI,JR
WATTS C UELTSCHEY
JOHN E MILNER
JAMES L HALFORD

EUGENE R WASSON
J KENNETH HARMON
SHELDON ALSTON
MARCIAL FORESTER
MARCUS C BRYANT

BRUNK BILL,CONS PETR GEOL
PO BOX 63175
PIPE CREEK,TX 78063-3175 PH 512 222-2344

BRUNS PRODUCTION COMPANY INC
1700 THREE MEADOWS RD
GREENSBORO,NC 27455-2821 PH 281 893-1363
H D BRUNS,PRES

BRUNSON & MCKNIGHT INC,SEE
NEW TEX OIL CO

BRUNT LAND GROUP
954 LA VISTA DR
TYLER,TX 75703 PH 903 534-9646
FAX 903 534-7010 BRUNT@GOWER.NET
J FRANK BRUNT,CPL
CHARLOTTE B ARNOLD

BRUSCATO FRANK,CPL,IND LDMN
& JOYCE MCVAY BRUSCATO,RPL
PO BOX 398,255 BRUSCATO PLACE
COLDSPRING,TX 77331-0398
PH 936 653-4267 PH 936 828-7067
OILLEASE@YAHOO.COM
GASLEASE@GMAIL.COM
JOYCE BRUSCATO,OFC MGR,RPL

BRUSCATO LAND & MINERALS,INC
PO BOX 398,255 BRUSCATO PLACE
COLDSPRING,TX 77331-0398
PH 936 653-4267 OILLEASE@YAHOO.COM
GASLEASE@GMAIL.COM
FRANK R BRUSCATO,CPL,IND LDMN
PH 936 653-4267
JOYCE MCVAY BRUSCATO,OFC MGR,RPL
PH 936 828-7067

BRUXOIL INC
PO BOX 16929,1991 LAKELAND DR STE C
JACKSON,MS 39236-6929 PH 601 981-5722
FAX 601 366-9490 BRUXOIL@COMCAST.NET
RAYMOND A HELFRICH,PRES

BRYANT LEONARD C,GEOL
71 MONARCH BLVD
HATTIESBURG,MS 39402 PH 601 579-2931
FAX 601 579-2931

BRYANT-CHASE ENERGY CORPORATION SEE
RIDGE PETROLEUM INC

BTA OIL PRODUCERS,LLC
104 S PECOS
MIDLAND,TX 79701
PH 432 682-3753 FAX 432 683-0311
BARRY BEAL JR,MNGNG PRTNR
STUART BEAL,PRTNR/PROD MGR
BOB DAVENPORT JR,PRTNR/EXPL MGR
CLAY TIPTON - NEW MEXICO OIL
PH 575 369-5814
BRYAN DAVIS - PYOTE AREA OKLA GAS & NEW
MEXICO GAS PH 432 894-1804
HUNTER LATHAM,SWD ANALYST
PH 432 638-0498
JED BUCKMAN,FRMN - NORTH DAKOTA
PH 701 580-0158
EDDY HOLLUMS - GLASSCOCK & SPRABERRY AREA
PH 432 638-5182
JORGE LOPEZ - REAGAN CO AREA

PH 432 894-0953
NICK EATON,DRLG MGR
BEN GRIMES,OPER MGR
WILLIS PRICE,LAND MGR
GREGG GROVES,CONTROLLER
DENVER,CO OFFICE - 600 17TH ST STE 2230 S
80202,PH 303 534-4404 FAX 303 534-4661
TOM TRACEY,ROCKY MTN DIV MGR
LARRY SUGANO,PROD ENGR
HOUSTON,TX OFFICE - 1201 LOUISIANA
STE 570,77002
PH 713 658-0077 FAX 713 655-0346
DAVID CHILDRESS,GULF COAST DIV MGR

BUCHANAN MRS AL
C/O B L HINDS
642 HEDWIG ST
HOUSTON,TX 77024-5311 PH 713 465-6421

BUCHER J J PRODUCING & DRILLING CORPS
108 PLEASANT ST
BOLIVAR,NY 14715 PH 716 928-2728

BUCK GEORGE L,IND OIL PRODUCER
420 W AUSTIN ST
FREDERICKSBURG,TX 78624-3208
PH 956 722-3023 FAX 956 722-3023
GEORGE L BUCK,OWNER
KARL W RITTER,SUPVSR

BUCK WHEAT RESOURCES INC
OIL & GAS PRODUCTION & EXPLORATION
PO BOX 751,2891 E I-20
EASTLAND,TX 76448 PH 254 629-8514
FAX 254 629-8764 BWRES@SBCGLOBAL.NET
CLAY WHEAT,PRES
GARY WHEAT,VP
BUCK WHEAT,SECY/TREAS

BUCKAROO FUEL COMPANY
3756 TANGLEY RD
HOUSTON,TX 77005-2032 PH 713 203-9424
WWW.BUCKAROOFUEL.COM
BUCKAROOFUEL@COMCAST.NET

BUCKEYE OIL PRODUCING CO
PO BOX 129
WOOSTER,OH 44691-0129 PH 330 264-8847
FAX 330 263-4222
R DEAN SMITH,CEO
MARK LYTLE,PRES

BUDDE FRANK J,IND LDMN,LEASES & RLTYS
3412 HEINES DR
TYLER,TX 75701-9033 PH 972 593-1974

BUDMARK OIL CO,INC
106 E OAK ST
WEST FRANKFORT,IL 62896-2741
PH 618 937-2495 FAX 618 937-2496
HIRAM C HUGHES,PRES
JIM DUNSTON,VP
LEAH HUGHES,SECY/TREAS

BUFAY OIL COMPANY,INC
OIL & GAS OPERATION
17649 N COUNTY FARM LN
MOUNT VERNON,IL 62864-8560
PH 618 755-9310
JON R RUE,PRES
WENDY M RUE,TREAS

BULLER ROBERT T
PO BOX 51756
LAFAYETTE,LA 70505-1756 PH 318 232-7399

BULLOCK MCCAULEY O,JR,INC,PETR PROPERTIES
8655 JEFFERSON HWY
9 STONES THROW
BATON ROUGE,LA 70809-2244 PH 225 603-4884
FAX 225 922-9309 MBENR1@AOL.COM
MCCAULEY O BULLOCK JR,PRES

BULLOCK VAN K,EXPLOR,PROD SEE
BULLOCK CORPORATION

BULMER W E (JOHN)
PETROLEUM & NATURAL GAS CONSULTANT
PO BOX 335
BRADFORD,PA 16701-0335
PH 814 362-4844 FAX 814 362-6665
WEBULMER@ATLANTICBB.NET

BUONGIORNO BEN,GEOL
357 N POST OAK LN #111
HOUSTON,TX 77024-5937 PH 713 658-8487
GOODDAYINC@AOL.COM

BURDETTE THOMAS N & ASSOCIATES,INC
OIL & GAS LAND,MGMNT CONSULTING
5022 DARNELL ST
HOUSTON,TX 77096-1511 PH 713 961-3443
FAX 713 961-3443
LOCATED AT: 50 BRIAR HOLLOW,STE 222E
HOUSTON,TX 77027
THOMAS N BURDETTE,PRES,CEO

BUREAU OF ECONOMIC GEOLOGY
WWW.BEG.UTEXAS.EDU

BUREAU OF LAND MANAGEMENT
NEW MEXICO STATE OFFICE
PO BOX 27115
SANTA FE,NM 87502-0115 PH 505 954-2000
FAX 505 954-2015 WWW.NM.BLM.GOV
ALBUQUERQUE,NM DIST OFFICE - 435 MONTANO
RD NE 87107-4935 PH 505 761-8700
FAX 505 761-8911
ED SINGLETON,DIST MGR
LAS CRUCES,NM DIST OFFICE - 1800 MARQUESS
ST 88005 PH 575 525-4300 FAX 575 525-4412
BILL CHILDRESS,DIST MGR
ROSWELL,NM DIST OFFICE - 2909 W 2ND ST
88201-2019 PH 575 627-0272
FAX 575 627-0276
DOUG BURGER,DIST MGR
FARMINGTON,NM DIST OFFICE - 6251 COLLEGE
BLVD STE A 87402 PH 505 564-7600
PH 800 842-3127 FAX 505 599-8998
DAVE EVANS,DIST MGR
SOCORRO,NM FIELD OFFICE - 901 S HWY 85
87801-4168 PH 575 835-0412
FAX 575 835-0223
DANITA BURNS,FIELD MGR
TAOS,NM FIELD OFFICE - 226 CRUZ ALTA RD
87571-5983 PH 575 758-8851
FAX 575 758-1620
SAM DESGEORGES,FIELD MGR
CARLSBAD,NM FIELD OFFICE - 620 E GREENE
ST,88220-6292 PH 575 234-5972
FAX 575 885-9264
JIM STOVALL,FIELD MGR
AMARILLO,TX FIELD OFFICE - 801 S
FILLMORE STE 500,79101 PH 806 356-1000
FAX 806 356-1041
LESLIE THEISS,FIELD MGR
TULSA,OK DIST FIELD OFFICE - 7906 E 33RD
ST STE 101,74145 PH 918 621-4100

FAX 918 621-4130
STEVE TRYON,FIELD MGR
- FEDERAL OFFICE -
WASHINGTON,DC - PUBLIC AFFAIRS OFFICE -
1849 C ST NW RM 5665,20240 WWW.BLM.GOV
PH 202 208-3801
- OTHER STATE OFFICES -
ANCHORAGE,AK OFFICE - 222 W 7TH AVE #13
99513-7504 PH 907 271-5960 WWW.AK.BLM.GOV
PHOENIX,AZ OFFICE - 1 N CENTRAL AVE STE
800,85004 PH 602 417-9200 WWW.AZ.BLM.GOV
SACRAMENTO,CA OFFICE - 2800 COTTAGE WAY
95825 PH 916 978-4400 WWW.CA.BLM.GOV
LAKEWOOD,CO OFFICE - 2850 YOUNGFIELD ST
80215 PH 303 239-3600 WWW.CO.BLM.GOV
SPRINGFIELD,VA (EASTERN STATES) OFFICE -
7450 BOSTON BLVD 22153 PH 703 440-1600
WWW.BLM.GOV/ES/ST/EN.HTML
BOISE,ID OFFICE - 1387 S VINNELL WAY
83709 PH 208 373-4000 FAX 208 373-3889
WWW.ID.BLM.GOV
BILLINGS,MT (MONTANA/DAKOTAS) OFFICE -
5001 SOUTHGATE DR 59101-6800
WWW.MT.BLM.GOV
RENO,NV OFFICE - 1340 FINANCIAL BLVD
89502 PH 775 861-6400 WWW.NV.BLM.GOV
PORTLAND,OR OFFICE - 333 SW 1ST AVE 97204
PH 503 808-6001 WWW.OR.BLM.GOV
SALT LAKE CITY,UT OFFICE - 440 W 200 S
STE 500,84101 PH 801 539-4001
WWW.UT.BLM.GOV
CHEYENNE,WY OFFICE - 5353 YELLOWSTONE RD
82009 PH 307 775-6256 WWW.WY.BLM.GOV

BUREAU OF OCEAN ENERGY MANAGEMENT
WWW.BOEMRE.GOV

BURGIN JIM & ASSOCIATES,INC
PO BOX 395
FULSHEAR,TX 77441-0395 PH 281 346-1584
FAX 281 346-2307 WWW.JIMBURGIN.COM
SALES@JIMBURGIN.COM
JIM BURGIN,PRES

BURK ROYALTY CO,LTD
PO BOX 94903
WICHITA FALLS,TX 76308-0903
PH 940 397-8600
G T TOMMY KIMBELL II,CHMN BD
DAVID KIMBELL JR,PRES
STAN KIMBELL,SR VP,REAL ESTATE/ENVIR
MIKE ELYEA,SR VP,FIN/TREAS
STEVE STULTS,SR VP,OPERS
RICK MORIAN,VP,LAND DEPT
DUSTAN MATHEWS,VP,ACCOUNTING
BILL FINNELL,PROD SUPT
TREY KIMBELL,GEOL
MARK CARTER,CPL,E TX LAND MGR
ROB HYDE,PET ENGR
KILGORE,TX OFFICE - PO BOX 1252
75663 PH 903 984-2018
GEORGE HENSON,DIST SUPT
WICHITA FALLS,TX YARD - 493 US HWY 281
76310 PH 940 322-7248
PERRYTON,TX OFFICE -PO BOX 832 79070
GARY NOGGLE,DIST SUPT

BURKE HARRY PETROLEUM
1817 PINE VILLAGE DR
HOUSTON,TX 77080-7101 PH 713 468-8540

HARRY BURKE,OWNER

BURKE LAND SERVICES
500 SNOW MILL AVE STE 118
TUSCALOOSA,AL 35406 PH 205 345-9861
JAMES E BURKE

BURKETT GERALD G,(GERRY)GEOL
10034 LOCKE LN
HOUSTON,TX 77042-3102 PH 713 782-3857
BURKETT.G@SBCGLOBAL.NET

BURKS OIL & GAS PROPERTIES,INC
PO BOX 680567
HOUSTON,TX 77268-0567
PH 281 580-4590 BURKSOILANDGAS.COM
DONALD H BURKS,CEO
RICHARD Z KLAUZINSKI,EXEC VP
SCOTT G BYRNES,PRES

BURLESON PETROLEUM,INC
PO BOX 2479
MIDLAND,TX 79702-2479 PH 432 683-4747
FAX 432 683-5172 GEOTTECH@PRODIGY.NET
STEVEN L BURLESON,PRES
WAYNE JARVIS,PROD SUPT
GARY L HEADY,PROD FRMN

BURLINGTON RESOURCES OIL AND GAS CO SEE
CONOCOPHILLIPS COMPANY

BURMAN OIL & GAS,INC
27622 HEGAR RD
HOCKLEY,TX 77447-9784
PH 936 931-2119 HHRBOG@ATT.NET
H RICHARD BURMAN,JR,PRES

BURNETT LYNDA FOWLER
PO BOX 413
RED RIVER,NM 87558-0413 PH 575 754-6368
BATON ROUGE,LA (WINTER) OFFICE - 6222
SUMMER LAKE DR 70817 PH 225 753-3400

BURNETT OIL CO,INC
801 CHERRY ST UNIT 9
BURNETT PLAZA STE 1500
FORT WORTH,TX 76102-6881
PH 817 332-5108 FAX 817 332-7832
CHUCK NAGEL,PRES
NEILS AGATHER,VP
DAVID S RHODES,VP LAND
DENNY C WHINERY,VP BUS DEV
MARK A JACOBY,VP ENGRG-NEW VENTURES
DAN TOMLEY,VP PROD & GEN MGR
(APPALACHIAN)
DAVID BRUNETTE,VP NEW VENTURES-LAND
BECKY TUPMAN,VP OPERS PERMIAN BASIN/TX
WALTER GLASGOW,VP OPERS PERMIAN BASIN/NM
MICHAEL MCDOWELL,VP FIN
GEORGE ROTH,VP EXPL
WILLIAM D POLLARD,ADVSR

BURNETT PETROLEUM COMPANY
3811 TURTLE CREEK BLVD STE 1900
DALLAS,TX 75219 PH 214 521-4900
FAX 214 521-4989 WWW.BURNETTPETRO.COM
INFO@BURNETTPETRO.COM
KYLE R BURNETT,PRES
JAMES L MENKE,VP ENGRG
SVETLANA FAMORCA,VP FIN
R J CREE,VP LEGAL & LAND
SHARON CHAMPAGNE,LAND MGR
JOHN P NASH,OPERS SUPT
DEBBE CHABOT,OFC MGR
ROBERT SHANNON,CONTROLLER

RUS RICHARDS,OPERS MGR

BURNETTE RESOURCES INC
37 CAMDEN PL
CORPUS CHRISTI,TX 78412 PH 361 442-2230
C RICHARD BURNETTE,GEOL

BURNS & PERKINS OIL,LLC SEE
BURNS ENERGY CO,LLC

BURNS ENERGY CO,LLC
PO BOX 2808,115 11TH AVE S
MERIDIAN,MS 39302-2808 PH 601 483-3387
FAX 601 483-9851
HENRY D BURNS JR,MGR
BRIAN J SIMS,CONS GEOL,JACKSON,MS

BURNS J I & SON INC
PO BOX 133
SENECAVILLE,OH 43780-0133 PH 740 685-6123
J I BURNS,PRES
JAMES B BURNS,VP

BURNS LAND SERVICES,INC
PROVIDING PROFESSIONAL LANDMEN FOR TEXAS
TITLE RESEARCH,LEASING & PIPELINE ROW
125 BROOKHOLLOW
NEW BRAUNFELS,TX 78132-5200
PH 830 660-2666 WWW.BURNSLANDSERVICES.COM
CHRIS BURNS CHRISBURNS.BLS@GMAIL.COM

BURNSED OIL CO,INC
PO BOX 2298
NATCHEZ,MS 39121-2298 PH 601 442-2596
W B BURNSED JR,PRES

BURT ROY PETROLEUM CONSULTING
17303 BONNARD CIR
SPRING,TX 77379-6282 PH 281 257-3036
ROYBURT1@GMAIL.COM

BURTON DRILLING COMPANY
PO BOX 369
COLUMBIA,KY 42728-8902
PH 270 384-0382 FAX 270 384-0004
WILLIAM W BURTON,PRES

BUTLER ASSOCIATES INC,SEE
WILLBROS ENGINEERS,INC

BUTLER J R AND COMPANY,OIL & GAS CONS
4605 POST OAK PLACE DR STE 107
HOUSTON,TX 77027-9706 PH 713 961-1121
FAX 713 621-3379 CONSULT@JRBUTLER.COM
JRBUTLER.COM
JOHN R BUTLER,JR,SR CHRMN OF BD
BRIAN E AUSBURN,PRES EMERITUS
NELS E VOLDSETH,VP

BUTLER JAMES H,CPL
3842 GREENWAY PL
SHREVEPORT,LA 71105-2016 PH 318 868-2371

BUTTERCUP OIL CORP
PO BOX 2030
ALICE,TX 78333-2030 PH 361 664-0611
R L LYND,PRES
SAN ANTONIO,TX OFFICE - P O BOX 6087
78209 PH 361 826-9667 FAX 361 668-3339
SIDNEY A SPARKS,SECY/TREAS

BW ENERGY CONSULTANTS,INC
516 S SPRING AVE
TYLER,TX 75702 PH 903 593-1173
FAX 903 593-4381 WWW.BWECLAND.COM
BWEC@SUDDENLINKMAIL.COM
BOB WASHMON,PRES
WADE WASHMON,VP

BWB OPERATING INC SEE
 BLAKE BRUCE W CPL/ESA MGMNT SERVICES

BWB PARTNERS I
 PO BOX 51407,500 W TEXAS STE 1100
 MIDLAND,TX 79710-1407 PH 432 682-7818
  WILLIAM H BENNETT
  ANDREW B BURLESON

BYERS COMPANY THE
 3112 ABOVE STRATFORD PL
 AUSTIN,TX 78746-4600 PH 512 328-8564
 FAX 512 328-8584
  ALTON C WHITE JR,PRES

BYRD LAND SERVICES INC
 1801 KINGWOOD DR STE 200
 KINGWOOD,TX 77339-3055
 PH 281 358-4240 FAX 281 358-4280
  JHBYRD@EARTHLINK.NET
  JAMES H BYRD,JR,PRES

BYRD OPERATING COMPANY
 PO BOX 2518,24 SMITH RD STE 130
 MIDLAND,TX 79702-2518
 PH 432 682-6523 FAX 432 682-6626
  JACK L BYRD,PRES JACK@BYRDOPERATING.COM
  LISA SALAZAR,OFC MGR
  GREG BYRD,PROD MGR
  KEN NELSON,SONORA AREA PH 432 650-2216

BYRNE PAUL H,JR
 PO BOX 1227,521 MAIN ST STE U-3
 NATCHEZ,MS 39121-1227 PH 602 445-8091

BYRON OIL INDUSTRIES INC
 154 CLARKSON EXECUTIVE PK
 ELLISVILLE,MO 63011-2114 PH 636 391-8770
 FAX 636 394-0860 BYRONOIL@AOL.COM
  RICHARD A BYRON,PRES
  NANCY WILLIAMS,LAND MGR

C & B SALES & SERVICE INCORPORATED
 119 NOLAN RD
 BROUSSARD,LA 70518-3212 PH 318 837-2701
 FAX 318 837-3250 WWW.CANDBSALES.COM
  BILL COBER,PRINCIPAL
  TROY TRAHAN,SALES

C & C TECHNOLOGIES,INC
  SURVEY SERVICES
 730 E KALISTE SALOOM RD
 LAFAYETTE,LA 70508-2547 PH 337 210-0000
 FAX 337 210-0003 INFO@CCTECHNOL.COM
  WWW.CCTECHNOL.COM
  THOMAS S CHANCE,PRES,CEO
  JAMES A CHANCE,VP
  JEFF SIDES,VP,GEN MGR

C & D LANDS
  PURCHASED MINERAL RIGHTS/PRODUCING &
  NON-PRODUCING
 350 MT UNION CUTOFF
 EL DORADO,AR 71730 PH 870 864-8922
  DBEASLEY@SEARK.NET
  CHUCK BEASLEY

C & E OPERATING,INC
  OIL & GAS OPERATIONS
 345 COMMERCE GREEN BLVD
 SUGAR LAND,TX 77478-3596 PH 281 265-6500
 FAX 281 265-6504
  TERRY BOENING,PRES
  LAURA BURKE,CONTROLLER

C & P OIL & GAS CO
 2202 PRIDE AVE

 CLARKSBURG,WV 26301-1822 PH 304 624-6516
  PETE PERRI,PRTNR
  GUY MORRIS JR,PRTNR

C OIL INC SEE
 CANADAY OIL CORPORATION

C S P ENTERPRISES,INC
  PROFESSIONAL SERVICES PETROLEUM CONS
 122 PALM CIR
 SAN ANTONIO,TX 78213-3353 PH 210 308-9922
  C SCOTT PARKER,PRES/REG PROF ENGR
  CHARLESSCOTTPARKER@YAHOO.COM

C S W CORPORATION
 PO BOX 23087
 OKLAHOMA CITY,OK 73123
 PH 210 860-5325 FAX 405 603-3623
  GREGORY J WINNEKE,CEO
  GREGWINNE@AOL.COM
 OKLAHOMA CITY, OK OFFICE - PO BOX 21655
  73156 PH 405 755-7200 FAX 405 755-5555
  PATRICK COWAN,COO PH 405 503-3884

C X Y ENERGY INC SEE
 NEXEN PETROLEUM U.S.A.,INC

C. REID AND ASSOCIATES
 4750 SHERWOOD COMMON #200
 BATON ROUGE,LA 70816 PH 225 505-7820
  CREIDANDASSOCIATES@GMAIL.COM

C.I. OIL,INC
 PO BOX 44203
 SHREVEPORT,LA 71134-4203 PH 318 572-8810
  JIM M LOVE,PRES CELTOIL@YAHOO.COM

C.T.R. OIL,INC
 PO BOX 659
 JONESVILLE,LA 71343 PH 318 339-6601
 FAX 318 339-8491
  RANDY WHITE,PRES
  PATRICIA WHITE,VP
  BECKY RAMSEY,SECY/TREAS

C.W. MOORE,INC SEE
 INTERNATIONAL DEVELOPMENT CORP

C&D PRODUCTION SPECIALIST CO INC
 PO BOX 1489
 LAROSE,LA 70373 PH 985 693-6872
 FAX 985 693-8100 WWW.CDPROD.NET
 CUT OFF,LA OFFICE - 14090 W MAIN ST 70345
  MICHAEL CROSBY,EXEC VP/OWNER
 HOUMA,LA (OPERS) OFFICE - 4683 W PARK AVE
  70364 PH 985 693-4880 PH 800 250-3873
  FAX 985 693-8156 INFO@CDPROD.NET
 FORT WORTH,TX OFFICE - 2430 GRAVEL DR
  76118 PH 817 595-0781 FAX 817 595-0768
 COUSHATTA,LA OFFICE - PO BOX 374 71019
  6013 HWY 1 71019 PH 318 932-8757
  FAX 318 932-8758
 EVANSTON,WY OFFICE - PO BOX 2160 82930
  724 FRONT ST STE 402 PH 307 789-2702
  FAX 888 833-7694
 WEXFORD,PA OFFICE - 7500 BROOKTREE DR
  STE 300 75090 PH 724 935-1942
  FAX 724 935-1941

CABLE & ASSOCIATES,LP
 545 N UPPER BROADWAY STE 726-B
 CORPUS CHRISTI,TX 78401
 PH 361 883-0970 FAX 361 883-0970
  J DON CABLE,OWNER

CABLE CONSTRUCTORS INC / E-CON DIVISION
 PO BOX 324,4610 PLOVER RD

 WISCONSIN RAPIDS,WI 54494-0324
 PH 715 423-8440 FAX 715 423-8323
  ECON@WCTC.NET
  GARY A UTECH,GEN MGR

CABLE PETROLEUM COMPANY SEE
 CABLE & ASSOCIATES,LP

CABOT ENERGY CORPORATION SEE
 CABOT OIL & GAS CORPROATION

CABOT L N G CORPORATION
 2 SEAPORT LN STE 1300
 BOSTON,MA 02210-2019 PH 617 526-8300
 FAX 617 526-8343
  R GORDON SHEARER,PRES

CABOT OIL & GAS CORPORATION
 - CORPORATE OFFICES -
 840 GESSNER RD STE 1400
 HOUSTON,TX 77024 PH 281 589-4600
 FAX 281 589-4613 WWW.CABOTOG.COM
  DAN DINGES,PRES/CHRMN/CEO
  KEVIN CUNNINGHAM,VP/GEN COUNSEL
  JEFF HUTTON,VP MKTG
  DEIDRE SHEARER,CORP SECY/MANAGING COUNSEL
  ROBERT DRAKE,VP INFORMATION SYSTEMS
  SCOTT SCHROEDER,CFO/VP/TREAS
  JAMES M REID,VP/REG MGR SOUTH REGION
  PHIL L STALNAKER,VP/REG MGR NORTH REGION
  TODD L LIEBL,VP/LAND & BUS DEV
  STEVEN W LINDEMAN,VP/ENGRG & TECH
  TODD M ROEMER,CONTROLLER
 CHARLESTON,WV OFFICE - 900 LEE ST E
  STE 1500 25301 PH 304 347-1600
 BEAVER,OK OFFICE - PO BOX 670,1123 AVE G
  73932 PH 580 625-4589
 DANVILLE,WV OFFICE - 6804 LICK CREEK RD
  25053 PH 304 369-1771
 CORPUS CHRISTI,TX OFFICE - PO BOX 270420
  5926 S STAPLES UNIT D3 78413
  PH 361 986-9266
 GLASGOW,WV OFFICE - PO BOX 450,102 3RD ST
  25086 PH 304 595-5015
 MINDEN,TX OFFICE-PO BOX 120,10069 CR 3125
  75680 PH 903 898-2330
 PINEVILLE,WV OFFICE - PO BOX 1589
  628 RIVER DR 24874 PH 304 732-9219
 ODESSA,TX OFFICE - PO BOX 69569
  4501 W INTERSTATE 20 79763
  PH 432 530-0012
 MONTROSE,PA OFFICE - 8279 S.R. 29 18801
  PH 570 278-3518
 PITTSBURGH,PA OFFICE - 5 PENN CENTER W
  STE 401 15376 PH 412 249-3850

CADDO MANAGEMENT INC
 401 MARKET ST STE 500
 SHREVEPORT,LA 71101-3238 PH 318 222-2720
 FAX 318 222-3688
  JEFFREY D J KALLENBERG,PRES
  KATHY MALONE,VP FIN
  RANDOLPH KALLENBERG,VP EXPL
  CINDY GILES,EXEC SECY
  CAROL LLOYD,LEASE ANALYST/ACCT

CAFITA
 919 MILAM ST STE 1910
 HOUSTON,TX 77002-5066 PH 713 652-5887
 FAX 713 951-0620
  FIELDING L COCKE,MGR
  STEVEN B JENKINS,MGR

GRIER P PATTON,MGR

CAIN LEASING AND TITLE CO
1708 GRIFFITH AVE
OWENSBORO,KY 42301 PH 270 683-0690
DARRY R CAIN,PROF LDMN/OWNER

CAINS WILLIAM T,PETR GEOL
PO BOX 459
ALTUS,AR 72821-0459 PH 501 468-2888
FAX 501 468-2888

CAIRN ENERGY USA,INC SEE
MATRIX PETROLEUM,LLC

CAL-T MANAGEMENT CORP SEE
CAL-T OIL CO

CALAME OIL COMPANY
6337 E HIGHWAY 380
DECATUR,TX 76234 PH 940 627-7040
FAX 940 627-7041
CULLEN F CALAME,OWNER

CALCASIEU RENTALS INC
233 HWY 397
LAKE CHARLES,LA 70615-4702
PH 337 433-5929 FAX 337 433-6887
RAY CROCKET,OWNER,PRES
SHANE CROCKET,OWNER,VP SHANEC@CRILC.COM
LENARD BIHM,SLS

CALDER BRUCE,INC
3303 LEE PKWY STE 420
DALLAS,TX 75219-5116 PH 214 520-7180
FAX 214 520-0688 BRUCECALDER@MSN.COM

CALDWELL GAS VENTURE
1252 JACKSONVILLE RD
HOMER CITY,PA 15748-1129 PH 724 479-2847
JOSEPH DASKIVICH,GEN PRTNR

CALDWELL PETE,DRILLING COMPANY,INC
4007 WHITE'S FERRY RD
WEST MONROE,LA 71291-2048 PH 318 396-6200
WALTER M CALDWELL III,OWNER,PRES
BARBARA T CALDWELL,OWNER,VP
PAUL SMITH,TOOL PUSHER

CALEDONIA LAND SERVICE
1429 NASHVILLE AVE
NEW ORLEANS,LA 70115 PH 504 453-4862
HOUMA,LA OFFICE - P O BOX 283, 70361
JOHN A GORDON JR,MNGNG PRTNR
JAG.CALEDONIA-OIL@ATT.NET

CALHOUN CLAY,OIL OPR
7003 SAINT CHARLES AVE
NEW ORLEANS,LA 70118 PH 504 861-3592
PH 504 866-2529 FAX 504 866-0022

CALHOUN REIMER
PO BOX 732,917 POLK
MANSFIELD,LA 71052-0732 PH 318 872-0835

CALHOUN STEVEN E,PETR LDMN
PO BOX 7621
TYLER,TX 75711-7621 PH 903 597-3954

CALIFORNIA HYDROCARBONS CORPORATION
2280 W HENDERSON RD STE 215
COLUMBUS,OH 43220-7344
PH 614 459-3333 FAX 614 459-3302
RASHMI N YAJNIK,PRES RNYAJNIK@AOL.COM
WOODLAND,CA OFFICE - 433 SECOND ST
#103,95695-4065 PH 530 668-7525
FAX 530 406-1463
JUDY HAMILTON,OFC MGR
JHAMILTON@AAPRODUCTION.COM

CALISTOGA ENERGY RESERVES,LLC
9668 WESTHEIMER RD STE 200-70
HOUSTON,TX 77063 PH 281 734-4579
GLENN T ANDREWS,PRES/COO
GANDREWS@LEFTBEHINDRECOVERY.COM

CALIVA KEVIN & ASSOCIATES,LTD
8121 OAK ST
NEW ORLEANS,LA 70118-2039 PH 504 883-9485
FAX 504 861-3737 KEVINCALIVA@YAHOO.COM
KEVIN H CALIVA,PRES

CALKINS T S & ASSOCIATES,INC
PO BOX 198,9 FORMAN ST
BRADFORD,PA 16701-0198 PH 814 363-9387
FAX 814 363-9389 TSCALKINS@ATLANTICBB.NET
THOMAS S CALKINS,CPL,PRES
C L LORENZO,BUS MGR

CALLON PETROLEUM COMPANY
PO BOX 1287,200 N CANAL ST
NATCHEZ,MS 39121-1287 PH 601 442-1601
FAX 601 446-1410 WWW.CALLON.COM
FRED L CALLON,PRES/CEO/CHRMN OF BD
BOB F WEATHERLY,EXEC VP/CFO
GARY A NEWBERRY,SR VP OPERS
JOHN G WEIHE,VP EXPL
JOSEPH C GATTO,SR VP FIN
H CLARK SMITH,CORPORATE INFO OFCR
RODGER W SMITH,VP TREAS
MITZI P CONN,CONTROLLER

CALSTON EXPLORATION USA
2537 S GESSNER RD STE 246
HOUSTON,TX 77063-2060 PH 832 548-4400
C E HACKSTEDT

CALTO OIL COMPANY
PO BOX 12266,7015 SNIDER PLZ STE 222
DALLAS,TX 75225-0266 PH 214 368-5804
FAX 214 368-5808
JOAN L GERMANY,PRES,TREAS
MARILYN L HUTCHISON,SECY

CALUMET LUBRICANTS CO
2780 WATERFRONT PKY EAST DR
INDIANAPOLIS,IN 46214-2029
PH 317 328-5660 FAX 317 328-5668
BILL GRUBE,PRES
ALLAN MAYES,EXEC VP
PHILIP A CAMPBELL,VP,MKTG

CALVIN RESOURCES,INC
208 RIVULET LN
AUSTIN,TX 78738 PH 713 882-6043
WWW.CALVINRESOURCES.COM
JOHN C GRIFFITHS,PRES
JGRIFF@CALVINRESOURCES.COM

CAMBE GEOLOGICAL SERVICES,INC
6300 WESTPARK DR STE 440
HOUSTON,TX 77057-7206 PH 713 659-8363
FAX 713 757-0179 CAMBE@CAMBE.COM
WWW.CAMBE.COM
REBECCA GORSUCH,PRES/CEO
SUSAN COLLETTE,VP

CAMBRIAN HUNTER,INC
531 E BEECH ST
JEFFERSON,OH 44047-9765 PH 440 576-9177
JEROME A LEMIRE,PRES
JALEMIRE@SUITE224.NET

CAMBRIDGE ENERGY CORPORATION
PO BOX 427
COCOA,FL 32923-0427 PH 321 636-6165

FAX 321 632-7632
PERRY DOUGLAS WEST,CHRMN,CEO
GLENN GILLEY,ENGR

CAMCO COILED TUBING SERVICES SEE
SCHLUMBERGER

CAMCO INTERNATIONAL INC SEE
SCHLUMBERGER

CAMCO PRODUCTS & SERVICES CO SEE
SCHLUMBERGER

CAMCO WIRELINE SEE
CAMCO PRODUCTS & SERVICES COMPANY

CAMERON
DRILLING AND PRODUCTION SYSTEMS
COMPLETE DRLG/PRODUCTION SYSTEMS FOR LAND
SUBSEA APPLICATIONS
PO BOX 1212,4646 W SAM HOUSTON TOLLWAY N
HOUSTON,TX 77251-1212 PH 713 939-2211
FAX 713 939-2620
WWW.C-A-M.COM
- DOMESTIC LOCATIONS -
- ALASKA -
ANCHORAGE,AK CAMSERV FACILITY -
600 E 57TH PL STE A,99518
PH 907 562-2332 FAX 907 562-3880
- CALIFORNIA -
BAKERSFIELD,CA CAMSERV FACILITY -
3004 JEWETT AVE,93301
PH 661 323-8183 FAX 661 323-0946
- COLORADO -
GRAND JUNCTION,CO CAMSERV FACILITY -
2323 LOGOS DR,81505 PH 970 241-5711
FAX 970 241-5730
- LOUISIANA -
BAYOU VISTA,LA MANUFACTURING OFFICE -
3007 HIGHWAY 182,70380
PH 985 395-8697 FAX 985 395-8689
BROUSSARD,LA CAMSERV FACILITY -
120 WELLHEAD RD,70518 PH 337 837-9568
FAX 337 837-2929
NEW ORLEANS,LA SALES OFFICE - 650
POYDRAS ST STE 2310,70130 PH 504 529-7634
FAX 504 522-8837
PATTERSON,LA CAMSERV FACILITY -
585 HIGHWAY 90 EAST,70392
PH 985 395-6171 FAX 985 395-1257
- MISSISSIPPI -
LAUREL,MS CAMSERV FACILITY -
1020 HILLCREST DR,39440
PH 601 649-8900 FAX 601 649-8909
- NEW MEXICO -
FARMINGTON,NM CAMSERV FACILITY -
503 S BEHREND AVE,87401 PH 505 327-3402
FAX 505 327-0454
HOBBS,NM CAMSERV FACILITY -
110 NORTHWEST COUNTY RD,88240
PH 575 397-1325 FAX 575 393-5957
- OKLAHOMA -
OKLAHOMA CITY,OK CAMSERV FACILITY -
4341 SW 33RD ST,73119
PH 405 682-1661 FAX 405 682-1051
OKLAHOMA CITY,OK MANUFACTURING PLANT -
7500 SW 29TH ST,73179
PH 405 745-2715 FAX 405 745-4071
- TEXAS -
BROOKSHIRE,TX MANUFACTURING PLANT -
29501 KATY FREEWAY,77494

PH 281 391-4600 FAX 281 391-4640

CORPUS CHRISTI,TX CAMSERV FACILITY -
6441 I-H 37,78409 PH 361 289-1455
FAX 361 289-6251

HOUSTON,TX DIV HEADQUARTERS OFFICE -
4646 W SAM HOUSTON PKWY N,77041
PH 713 939-2211 FAX 713 939-2019

HOUSTON,TX R&D CENTER -
PO BOX 1212,6750 BINGLE RD,77092
PH 713 369-4110 FAX 713 369-4128

HOUSTON,TX SALES & MFG OFC - 11331 TANNER
RD,77041-6901,PO BOX 1212,77251
PH 713 280-3000 FAX 713 280-3056

HOUSTON,TX MFG PLANT - 6650 BINGLE RD
77092,PO BOX 1212,77251-1212
PH 713 354-1900 FAX 713 354-1923

LIBERTY,TX MANUFACTURING PLANT -
PO BOX 10286,HWY 90 @ FM 1909,77575-0286
PH 936 336-8811 FAX 936 336-2822

LONGVIEW,TX CAMSERV FACILITY -PO BOX 1311
2705 E MARSHALL AVE,75602
PH 903 236-4884 FAX 903 234-0336

ODESSA,TX CAMSERV FACILITY -
270 S GRANDVIEW,79761 PH 432 337-5475
FAX 432 337-3001

- UTAH -

VERNAL,UT CAMSERV FACILITIES -
PO BOX 429,1442 E HWY 40,84078-0429
PH 435 781-0434 FAX 435 789-5656

- WYOMING -

CASPER,WY CAMSERV FACILITY -
7048 ZERO RD,82604
PH 307 472-0222 FAX 307 265-1318

ROCK SPRINGS,WY CAMSERV FACILITY -
102 FOOTHILLS DR,82901
PH 307 382-3134 FAX 307 382-3190

- CANADA OFFICES -

BROOKS,ALBERTA CAMSERV FACILITY -
420 AQUADUCT DR,T1R 1C4
PH 403 793-2700 FAX 403 793-2200

CALGARY,ALBERTA SALES OFC - 600,715-5TH
AVE SW,T2P 2X6 PH 403 261-2800
PH 403 262-5181

EDMONTON,ALBERTA MFG PLANT - 5003 93RD ST
T6E 5S9 PH 780 431-5083 FAX 780 437-7397

RED DEER,AB,CAN CAMSERV FACILITY -
#9,4830 78TH ST,T4P 2B3
PH 403 342-2700 FAX 403 340-0700

SLAVE LAKE,ALBERTA CAMSERV FACILITY -
#6,216 BIRCH ROAD NE,T0G 2A0
PH 780 849-1909 FAX 780 849-1904

FORT NELSON,BRITISH COLUMBIA CAMSERV
FACILITY - 4800 46TH UNIT #7,V0C 1R0
PH 250 774-7394 FAX 250 774-7392

FORT ST JOHN,BRITISH COLUMBIA CAMSERV
FACILITY - 10147 TUNDRA ST,V1J 4H6
PH 250 785-2700 FAX 250 785-0700

GRAND PRAIRIE,ALBERTA CAMSERV FACILITY -
11302 - 89TH AVE,T8V 5V8
PH 780 538-2700 FAX 780 532-0700

MOUNT PEARL,NL CAMSERVE FACILITY -
14 CORISANDE DR
PH 709 748-2600 FAX 709 748-2606

CAMERON MEASUREMENT SYSTEMS
197 EQUITY BLVD
HOUMA,LA 70360-8363 PH 504 868-1514

JOHN.TRAHAN@C-A-M.COM WWW.C-A-M.COM

CAMERON PAUL E,JR,INC,PETR CONSULTANTS
PO BOX 756
MONTGOMERY,TX 77356-0756
PH 713 725-1919 FAX 936 570-0488
PAUL E CAMERON,JR,DIR,PRES
RUTH O CAMERON,SECY/TREAS

CAMERON PETROLEUM INC
PO BOX 487
GRAND SALINE,TX 75140-0487
PH 903 962-8111 FAX 903 962-8111
DOUBLEDUCE@SUDDENLINK.NET
ROBERT LIPPINCOTT,PRES,CEO

CAMEX OPERATING COMPANY
PO BOX 51733,103 EXCHANGE PL STE 100
LAFAYETTE,LA 70505-1733 PH 337 232-0635
FAX 337 232-1609
KEVIN R CAMPBELL,GEOL KEVIN@CAMEXOIL.COM
DONALD H OHEIM,PETR ENGR
ERIC D CAMPBELL,FIN OFCR
CAROLYN D PORCHE,SECY

CAMPANERO ENERGY HOLDINGS LLC
14875 LANDMARK BLVD STE 210
DALLAS,TX 75254
PH 972 386-0571 FAX 972 980-0734
TOMMY J DRESCHER,PRES
MICHAEL ELLIOTT,VP EXPLOITATION
CARL STANG,VP GEOSCIENCES

CAMWEST EXPLORATION LLC SEE
STEPHENS ENERGY COMPANY,LLC

CAN DO,INC
PO BOX 129,103 EAST 57TH ST
CUT OFF,LA 70345-0129 PH 504 632-3733
FAX 504 632-2751
JOEY J ADAMS,PRES

CANADIAN MORAN LTD
3843 N BRAESWOOD BLVD #200
HOUSTON,TX 77025-3001 PH 713 526-4171

CANAL BARGE COMPANY,INC
835 UNION ST
NEW ORLEANS,LA 70112-1401 PH 504 581-2424
FAX 504 584-1505 WWW.CANALBARGE.COM
TDOWIE@CANALBARGE.COM
H MERRITT LANE III,PRES
LEWIS P EAVES III,AREA MGR
TOM DOWIE,VP DECK CARGO
SEAN SMITH,DECK MKTG & OPERS

CANAL REFINING COMPANY
2111 EVANGELINE HWY
EVANGELINE,LA 70537
PH 337 824-2500 FAX 337 824-2565
WWW.CANALCOMPANIES.COM
CANALREFININGCOM@AOL.COM
R MCKEE
JENNINGS,LA CANAL MARINE TERMINAL OFC -
1801 S RIVERSIDE RD 70537
PH 337 824-2500
CHURCH POINT REFINERY
C VILLERMIN PH 337 684-2500
MERMENTAU REFINERY
S EMERSON PH 337 824-3551

CANDIES OTTO,LLC
PO BOX 25,17271 HWY 90
DES ALLEMANDS,LA 70030-0025
PH 504 469-7700 FAX 504 469-7740
OTTOCANDIES.COM INFO@OTTOCANDIES.COM

OTTO CANDIES JR,CHRMN
KEVIN CANDIES,PRES
OTTO CANDIES III,VICE CHMN/COO
BILLY JONES,TRAFFIC
BRETT CANDIES,TRAFFIC MGR
P B CANDIES,SECY
GARY LANDRY,TRAFFIC
DAVE GREVE,MKTG
SHANE CANDIES,SLS/MKTG
SID CANDIES,MAINT MGR
NICKI CANDIES,REG AFFAIRS DIR
GRADY CABLE,HUMAN RELS MGR
DALE PRICE,SFTY DIR
KELLY CANDIES,PROJ MGR
BARRY BLANCHARD,CONTROLLER
ASHLEY CANDIES,SPEC PROJ
RYAN CANDIES,SPEC PROJ
SEAN CANDIES,SPEC PROJ

CANNON OPERATING COMPANY
3200 BROADWAY BLVD STE 520
GARLAND,TX 75043 PH 877 316-7644
FAX 469 209-0780
WWW.CANNONOPERATING.INFO
OFFICE@CANNONOPERATING.INFO
WILLIAM BAKER,PRES
WILLIAM@CANNONOPERATING.INFO

CANRIG DRILLING TECHNOLOGIES
SEE NABORS INDUSTRIES LTD

CANTON OIL WELL SERVICE INC
7793 PITTSBURG AVE NW
N CANTON,OH 44720 PH 330 452-0010
FAX 330 494-1447
R H HUTCHESON,CHRMN
THOMAS R HUTCHESON,CEO
KEVIN W HUTCHESON,PRES,EXPL,DEV
JAMES J PAUMIER,VP,OPERS
MARK YOUNG,FLD OFC MGR

CANTRELL RALPH B,GEOL
800 BERING STE 208
HOUSTON,TX 77057 PH 713 780-2871

CANYON OIL & GAS COMPANY
727 N WACO ST STE 400
WICHITA,KS 67203-3900 PH 316 263-3201
STEVE SLAWSON,PRES

CANYON REEF MINERALS LTD SEE
BRECK OPERATING CORP

CAPITAL EXPLORATION,INC
PO BOX 294671
KERRVILLE,TX 78029-4671 PH 210 771-5451
A E BUD' MARTENS,OWNER
T C MARTENS,VP/OPERS OFCR

CAPITAL ONE,NA
5718 WESTHEIMER 6TH FL
HOUSTON,TX 77057
PH 713 435-5017 FAX 713 706-5499
BILL HERRINGTON,EXEC VP,MGR/ENERGY DEPT

CAPLEX ENERGY,INC
317 TAMPICO ST
IRVING,TX 75062-3947 PH 903 236-3092
FAX 903 757-5719
LEE CAPLE,PRES

CARBIDE BLAST JOINTS INC
PO BOX 90126
HOUSTON,TX 77290-0126
PH 281 353-6750 FAX 281 353-6752
WWW.CARBIDEBLASTJOINTS.COM

CARBIDEBJ@AOL.COM
KARL F KUHNE,GEN MGR

CARBON ENERGY CORPORATION SEE
EVERGREEN RESOURCES,INC

CARDEN OIL & GAS,LLC
3336 N HULLEN
METAIRIE,LA 70002
PH 504 456-8875 FAX 504 456-8883
COG@CARDENOIL.NOCOXMAIL.COM
EDNA M CARDEN,OWNER
L JAY CUCCIA,MGR PH 504 456-8880
LISA ROPER,LAND
JEANNINE CANNATA,ACCT
RHONDA BANEGAS,ACCT

CARDINAL RESOURCES,INC
14 HARWOOD CT STE 225
SCARSDALE,NY 10583-4120 PH 914 472-2090
CARDINALRES@AOL.COM
JAMES J BOYLE,PRES,CHRMN

CARDINAL SERVICES,INC SEE
SUPERIOR ENERGY SERVICES

CARDNEAUX C A,GEOL
PO BOX 18488,151 PROVIDENCE RD
NATCHEZ,MS 39122-8488 PH 601 442-0711
FAX 601 442-2311

CARDNEAUX,INC
PO BOX 18488,151 PROVIDENCE RD
NATCHEZ,MS 39122-8488 PH 601 442-0711
FAX 601 442-2311
C A CARDNEAUX,PRES
ROY M VINES,PROD SUPVSR
ADAM P CARDNEAUX,LAND MGR

CARGILL SALT
1224A SALT MINE RD
BREAUX BRIDGE,LA 70517-7241
PH 800 282-6777 FAX 952 404-6080
NICK SANDSTROM,TERRITORY MGR

CARL/WHITE TRUST
OIL & GAS PROPERTIES
PO BOX 218
WEST COLUMBIA,TX 77486-0218
PH 979 345-5386 FAX 979 345-6664
CARLWHITETRUST@YAHOO.COM

CARLILE DAVID C,ATTY AT LAW
400 S ALAMO BLVD
MARSHALL,TX 75670-4260 PH 903 938-1655
WWW.CARLILELAWFIRM.COM
DCARLILE@CARLILELAWFIRM.COM

CARLINE WALLACE,INC
PO BOX 1286
MORGAN CITY,LA 70381-1286
PH 985 631-2187 FAX 985 631-4564
GENE H DARNELL III,PRES
JULIE MARCOTTE,ADMIN ASST
JULIE@DSCGOM.COM

CARLISLE DUKE
PO BOX 1908
MCCOMB,MS 39649-1908 PH 601 276-2215
FAX 601 276-3027

CARLISLE USA ENERGY COMPANY INC
PO BOX 5383
FRISCO,TX 75035 PH 214 407-8503
FAX 214 407-8116 WWW.USAENERGYCOMPANY.COM
PAUL CARLISLE PAUL@USAENERGYCOMPANY.COM

CARLSON CONSULTING L.L.C.
1966 S SIMON RD

LAKE LEELANAU,MI 49653-9662
PH 231 342-6420
JOHN N CARLSON,MGR
GAIL E CARLSON,SECY/TREAS

CARLTON OIL CORPORATION
38841 STATE ROUTE 7
NEPORT,OH 45768-0671 PH 740 473-2629
DANNY W THOMPSON,PRES
JANET L THOMPSON,SECY/TREAS
JANETTHOMPSON@COMPUSERVE.COM

CARMET OIL INC
PO BOX 1527,5918 FAIRFIELD AVE
SHREVEPORT,LA 71165-1527 PH 318 869-2074
THOMAS G CARMODY,JR,DIR
ANTHONY P CARMODY,DIR

CARNAHAN CORPORATION,CONSULTING ENGRS
PO BOX 42281
HOUSTON,TX 77242-2281 PH 281 493-2600
DR NORMAN F CARNAHAN,PE,PRES
DR LIRIO QUINTERO,VP

CARNES JOHN C SEE
ROCK CHALK ROYALTIES,LTD

CARNES NATURAL GAS,LTD
9320 LAKESIDE BLVD BLDG 2 STE 200
THE WOODLANDS,TX 77381
PH 281 363-8168 FAX 281 363-8191
MICHAEL M CARNES PH 281 451-6789
MICHAELMCARNES@YAHOO.COM

CARPENTER CORPORATION,THE
PO BOX 608
SOUR LAKE,TX 77659-0608 PH 409 287-3511
F H CARPENTER,PRES
R D EDMONDSON,SECY/TREAS

CARPENTER ELECTRICAL EQUIPMENT LLC
ELECTRIC MOTORS,ELECTRICAL SUPPLIES &
DRY-TYPE TRANSFORMERS & 3-PHASE ROTARY
CONVERTERS
PO BOX 307
ANNANDALE,MN 55302 PH 800 543-7435
LOCATED AT: 14518 STATE HWY 55
SOUTH HAVEN,MN 55382
JOHN L CARPENTER,PRES
SHIRLEY CARPENTER,VP
TOM CARPENTER,CONSULTING ENGR
GAIL CARPENTER,CONSULTANT MKTG,ACCT

CARPENTER OIL & GAS COMPANY SEE
ENERGY PRODUCTION CORPORATION

CARR JEFF
PO BOX 576
CORPUS CHRISTI,TX 78403-0576
PH 361 884-9647 FAX 361 884-9672

CARR JOHN P,INC
305 S BROADWAY AVE STE 900
TYLER,TX 75702-7341 PH 903 597-2336
FAX 903 597-1898 JOHN@CARRRESOURCES.COM
JOHN P CARR,PRES

CARR RESOURCES,INC
305 S BROADWAY AVE STE 900
TYLER,TX 75702 PH 903 597-2336
FAX 903 597-1898
JOHN P CARR,PRES JOHN@CARRRESOURCES.COM
RICH ADAMS,GEOL

CARRIZO OIL & GAS,INC
500 DALLAS ST STE 2300
HOUSTON,TX 77002 PH 713 328-1000
FAX 713 358-6437 WWW.CRZO.NET

S P JOHNSON,PRES/CEO
RICHARD SMITH,VP LAND
PAUL BOLING,VP/CFO
BRAD FISHER,VP OPERS
GREGG EVANS,VP EXPL
JEFF HAYDEN,INVESTOR RELS DIR

CARSON GEORGE JOHN
115 E TRAVIS STE 314
SAN ANTONIO,TX 78205-1612
PH 210 225-6586 FAX 210 225-6587

CARSON HELICOPTERS INC
AEROGRAVITY DIVISION
952 BLOOMING GLEN RD
PERKASIE,PA 18944
PH 215 249-3535 FAX 215 249-0726
AEROGRAVITY@CARSONHELICOPTERS.COM
WWW.AEROGRAVITY.COM
FRANKLIN CARSON,PRES
WILLIAM GUMERT,VP,CHF GEOPHY
MARIO PROFETA,VP/LATIN AMERICA OPERS
CANDY TUTTLE,GEOPHY SURVEY COORD
GERALD WASHCALUS,DATA ANALYST
GRACE MORRIS,DATA PROCESSOR
THOMAS PALUSHOCK,GRAPHICS MGR
DURWOOD PHILLIPS,GEOPHY EQUIP MGR
BAGUS SETIAWAN,GEOPHY EQUIP OPER
LARRY GREENBERG,FLD OPERS MGR
CRAIG ZIEGLER,FLD OPERS MGR
JUAN CARLOS MEJIA,SURVEY PILOT
PAUL MCGURR,SURVEY PILOT
ROBERT BOYD,HELICOPTER SURVEY PILOT
JAMES STONEBACK,HELICOPTER SURVEY PILOT
JUAN BOSSA,GEOPHY EQUIP OPER
WILLIAM ARIAS,GEOPHY EQUIP OPER
PEDRO A MORA,GEOPHY EQUIP OPER

CARTER BARNEY ESTATE SEE
MATTYE CARTER FAMILY TRUST

CARTER ENERGY CORPORATION
4925 GREENVILLE AVE STE 1000
DALLAS,TX 75206-4085 PH 214 691-8185

CARTER GABRIAL
121 S BROADWAY STE 728
TYLER,TX 75702-7276 PH 972 592-0826

CARTER JOHN H INC
401 WALL ST
LAFAYETTE,LA 70506-3029 PH 337 233-8331
PH 337 233-8332 PH 337 233-8333
FAX 337 235-5958 WWW.JOHNHCARTER.COM
RON SCHWARZ,ENGR SALES
RONALD.SCHWARZ@JOHNHCARTER.COM
PAUL CALAIS,ENGR SALES
PAUL.CALAIS@JOHNCARTER.COM
PRESTON HEBERT,ENGR SALES
PRESTON.HEBERT@JOHNHCARTER.COM
DAVID LANCLOS,ENGR SALES
DAVID.LANCLOS@JOHNHCARTER.COM
DON GALLAGHER,INSIDE SALES
DON.GALLAGHER@JOHNHCARTER.COM
CARL GUILLORY,INSIDE SALES
CARL.GUILLORY@JOHNHCARTER.COM
DARLENE FUTCH,INSIDE SALES
DARLENE.FUTCH@JOHNHCARTER.COM
JIMMY O'SULLIVAN,BRANCH MGR
JIMMY.O'SULLIVAN@JOHNHCARTER.COM
RON BEST,ENGR SALES
RON.BEST@JOHNHCARTER.COM

ADELE MAYEAU,INSIDE SALES
ADELE.MAYEAU@JOHNHCARTER.COM

CARTER JOHN H,CO,INC
PO BOX 7130,2728 N ARNOULT RD
METAIRIE,LA 70002-7130 PH 504 887-8550
WWW.JOHNHCARTER.COM
MICHAEL SANSOVICH,PRES
CHARLES FOURNIER,EXEC VP
BRUCE LOWREY,DIR OF MKTG
BRUCE.LOWREY@JOHNHCARTER.COM

CARTER L E,DRLG,COMPLETIONS,OPERS
4025 TRIPOLI DR
CORPUS CHRISTI,TX 78411-5022
PH 361 853-9208
L E ED CARTER,PETR CONSULTANT

CARTER LELAND W,OIL OPR
4925 GREENVILLE AVE STE 1000
DALLAS,TX 75206-4085 PH 214 691-8185

CARTER OIL & GAS INC
901 E BYRD ST STE 110
RICHMOND,VA 23219-4069 PH 804 643-1300
FAX 804 644-1448
W KENT CARTER,JR,PRES
ANNE TAYLOR MOORMAN,VP

CARTER RESOURCES
PO BOX 921
KILGORE,TX 75663-0921
PH 903 984-3443 FAX 903 983-2526
DEAN CARTER,OWNER

CARUTHERS PRODUCING COMPANY,INC
400 TRAVIS ST STE 1510
SHREVEPORT,LA 71101-3114 PH 318 222-0285
FAX 318 221-6089
ARTHUR O'Q WALKER,CHRMN
C DEWITT CARUTHERS,PRES
JAMES B AGENT,TREAS,CONTROLLER

CASEROTTI PHILLIP M,CONS GEOL & GEOPHY
15018 N IL HIGHWAY 37
MOUNT VERNON,IL 62864-7803
PH 618 242-2731 FAX 618 242-1361
PH 618 204-6010 PCASEROTTI@JUNO.COM

CASHCO ENERGY CORP SEE
CASHCO OIL CO

CASHCO OIL COMPANY
PO BOX 13017
CHICAGO,IL 60613-0017 PH 713 935-9582
FAX 713 461-4311
RUDY C WILDENSTEIN,VP,ENGRG & OPERS
RICHARD W VETTER,EXEC VP

CASIAS OIL WELL SERVICE,INC
106 ENCINO BLANCO ST
SAN ANTONIO,TX 78232
PH 210 215-5627 FAX 210 334-0375
JIMMIE CASIAS,PRES/OWNER
RACHEL CASIAS,VP/TREAS

CASING JACK RENTALS,INC
FISHING,RENTAL & CASING TOOLS
PO BOX 1489
TOMBALL,TX 77377-1489
PH 800 206-5225 FAX 281 357-4897
CASINGJACKRENTALS@YAHOO.COM
WWW.CASINGJACKRENTAL.COM
MIKE PAYNE,PRES
TOMBALL,TX OFFICE - PO BOX 1489
77377-1489,PH 281 357-4901

CASKIDS OPERATING COMPANY
3637 W ALABAMA ST STE 400
HOUSTON,TX 77027-5999
PH 713 552-1967 FAX 713 552-0631
MICHEAL L CASWELL,PRES
KATHLEEN R SWINSON,SR EXEC OPER/LOGISTICS
TRACY L SWINSON,EXEC ASST,REVENUE ACNTG

CASSELL MRS JUNIA SCHONWALD,OIL PROD
ROYALTY OWNER
3801 VALLEY DR
MIDLAND,MI 48640-6601
PH 517 631-6600 FAX 517 832-0008

CASSIDY SEAN AND ASSOCIATES,PC
118 N MAIN ST
GREENSBURG,PA 15601-2404
PH 724 836-4900 FAX 724 836-2090
SEAN CASSIDY,ATTY
SCASSIDY@CASSIDYPC.COM

CASSITY PAUL E,CONSULTING GEOL
339 LIPPI BLVD
LAFAYETTE,LA 70508-3709 PH 337 237-3172

CASTEX ENERGY,INC
333 CLAY ST STE 2000
HOUSTON,TX 77002-2569 PH 281 447-8601
FAX 281 447-1009
JOHN STOIKA,PRES

CASTLE CRAIG,OIL OPR & OIL PROD
35 AUTUMN HILL DR
JACKSON,MS 39211 PH 601 956-0336
FAX 601 948-5849

CASWELL,INC
625 MARKET ST STE 250
SHREVEPORT,LA 71101-5392 PH 318 221-0761
FAX 318 221-8835
CHARLES H C GERARD,JR,PRES

CAT LIFT TRUCKS
10795 HAMMERLY BLVD STE 350
HOUSTON,TX 77043-2309 PH 713 365-1000
FAX 713 365-1414
JEFF RUFENER,VP MKTG
ASHLEY HELMER,MKTG COMM SPEC
ASHLEY.HELMER@MCFA.COM

CATALYST ENERGY INC
424 S 27TH ST STE 304
PITTSBURGH,PA 15203-2380
PH 724 779-9040 FAX 724 779-9053
PAUL RYAN RODGERS,CEO,PETR ENGR

CATAPULT EXPLORATION,LLC
8889 PELICAN BAY BLVD STE 403
NAPLES,FL 34108-7512
PH 239 597-2136 FAX 239 597-2162
ROBERT N PATRICK,MGR/GEOL
KINGWOOD,TX OFFICE - 600 ROCKMEAD DR
STE 115,77339 PH 281 359-7899
NATE ACOSTA,PRTNR/GEOL
CONRAD J MCGARRY,PRTNR/GEOL
MARK ALSPAUGH,GEOPHY
PAUL YATES,GEOPHY
FOY HARRISON,LDMN
DAN WARD,GEOPHY
RAYMOND FONTENOT,GEOL
TED PIERCE,GEOPHY
BRUCE DAWSON,GEOL

CATARINA PETROLEUM LC
3043 RAMBLING DR
DALLAS,TX 75228-5155

PH 214 537-4469 JCPJR5@GMAIL.COM
JOHN PETTEWAY,GEN MGR

CATES OIL & GAS
1300 TARANSAX DR.
HENDERSON,KY 42420-9657 PH 270 827-0315

CATHEY PETROLEUM,INC
10808 MAUMELLE BLVD
NORTH LITTLE ROCK,AR 72113-6602
PH 501 753-8880
MARK CATHEY,PRES
DIANNE P CATHEY,VP

CAVALLA ENERGY RESOURCES
712 MAIN ST STE 3000
HOUSTON,TX 77002-5751 PH 713 652-0907
FAX 713 225-5995
JAMES A MCCARTHY,PRES,CEO

CAVINS CORPORATION,THE
1800 BERING DR STE 825
HOUSTON,TX 77057
PH 713 523-9214 FAX 713 523-9421
R S ARTERBURY,PRES
HOUSTON,TX OFFICE - 6215 THOMAS RD,77042
PH 713 466-4216
RICK WILLIAMS,DIST MGR
CORPUS CHRISTI,TX OFFICE - PO BOX 308
ODEM,TX 78370 PH 361 883-1331
RICK WILLIAMS,DIST MGR
KILGORE,TX OFFICE - PO BOX 1295,75662
PH 903 984-3624
JAMES MCCOY,DIST MGR
ODESSA,TX OFFICE - PO BOX 2967,79760
PH 432 563-0967
GIOVANNI CASTELAZO,DIST MGR
BILLY CHANDLER,SLS MGR
JACKSBORO,TX OFFICE - PO BOX 516,76056
PH 940 567-5022
RICK TANNER,DIST MGR
HOUMA,LA OFFICE - 20 WELDON RD
70363 PH 985 872-1161
CHRIS TOLAR,DIST MGR
LAFAYETTE,LA OFFICE - PH 337 232-4777
RICK SMITH,DIST MGR
BROOKHAVEN,MS OFFICE - PO BOX 411,39601
PH 601 833-2268
BILL DICKERSON,DIST MGR
GIDDINGS,TX OFFICE - PH 409 542-5432
RICK WILLIAMS,DIST MGR
LAUREL,MS OFFICE - PO BOX 2911,39442
PH 601 428-0670
BILL DICKERSON,MGR
CASPER,WY OFFICE - 5680 W YELLOWSTONE HWY
82604 PH 307 234-9671
NICK CHUDILOWS
OKLAHOMA CITY,OK OFFICE - 6800 PAT AVE
73149,PH 405 503-6455
BRADON SIROKY,MGR

CAVINS OILFIELD SERVICES
280 HIGHLAND BLVD
NATCHEZ,MS 39120 PH 601 660-0710
FAX 601 442-3961

CAWTHON KELLY S,GEOL,
610 MARSHALL ST STE 514
SHREVEPORT,LA 71101-3699 PH 318 424-9737

CAY PRODUCTION LLC SEE
YOAKAM COLER A JR,PETR GEOL

CAZA DRILLING (CA) INC SEE
ENSIGN U.S. DRILLING INC

CAZA DRILLING INC SEE
SEE ENSIGN U.S. DRILLING INC

CBA SERVICES INC
5877 BARNETT RD STE A
KRUM,TX 76249 PH 940 482-9900
FAX 940 482-3457
JANA OSBORN,PRES
JANAO@CBA-CORP.COM
KELSEY MCCAUGHAN,OPERS MGR
CECILY WALKER,SLS,MKTG

CD RESOURCES COMPANY
6104 BROADWAY STE C-1
SAN ANTONIO,TX 78209
PH 210 820-3868 FAX 210 820-3869
JOSEPH F DISHRON,PRES

CEDAR VALLEY ENERGY,INC
PO BOX 726
WOOSTER,OH 44691-0726 PH 330 262-1034
WILLIAM BENNETT,PRES
MARK CONWAY,VP

CELT OIL INC
PO BOX 44203
SHREVEPORT,LA 71134-4203 PH 318 572-8810
CELTOIL@YAHOO.COM
JIM M LOVE,PRES

CEMENTATION (GEMOCO) SEE WEATHERFORD

CENERGY CORP SEE
AMERICAN EXPLORATION CO

CENERGY EXPLORATION CO SEE
AMERICAN EXPLORATION CO

CENTAUR PETROLEUM CORPORATION
PO BOX 270
FORT WORTH,TX 76101-0270 PH 817 335-4821
FAX 817 332-3315
BROOKE A KING,CHRMN OF BD
BONARD D DRAKE,PRES

CENTENNIAL NATURAL GAS CORPORATION SEE
ASSOCIATED NATURAL GAS,INC

CENTENNIAL RESOURCE PRODUCTION LLC
1401 17TH ST STE 1000
DENVER,CO 80202 PH 720 441-5515
WARD POLZIN
WPOLZIN@CENTENNIALRESOURCE.COM
MIDLAND,TX OFFICE - 400 W ILLINOIS AVE
STE 1601 79701

CENTRAL CRUDE,INC
PO BOX 1863
LAKE CHARLES,LA 70602-1863
PH 337 436-1000 FAX 337 436-9602
STEVEN M JORDAN,PRES
JOE MILAZZO,VP,CRUDE SUPPLY

CENTRAL INDUSTRIES INC SEE
STALLION CONSTRUCTION

CENTRAL PETROLEUM,INC
PO BOX 1823
JACKSON,MS 39215-1823 PH 601 856-7613
FAX 601 856-1569
GEORGE S DENNIS,PRES

CENTRAL POWER SYSTEMS & SERVICES,INC
9200 LIBERTY DR
LIBERTY,MO 64068-9396
PH 816 781-8070 FAX 816 781-2207
INFO@CPOWER.COM WWW.CPOWER.COM
SPRINGFIELD,MO OFFICE - 3100 E KEARNEY

65803 PH 417 865-0505
WICHITA,KS OFFICE - 4501 W IRVING
67201 PH 316 943-1231 FAX 316 943-4560
GREAT BEND,KS OFFICE - 625 E 10TH ST
67530 PH 620 792-1361
LIBERAL,KS OFFICE - 1150 EAST HWY 54
67905 PH 620 624-7274
WOODWARD,OK OFFICE - NW HWY 270
73802 PH 580 256-6014
SALINA,KS OFFICE - 1944-B N 9TH
67402 PH 785 825-8291
COLBY,KS OFFICE - 1920 THIELEN AVE
67701 PH 785 462-8211

CENTRAL STALLION SEE
SEE STALLION CONSTRUCTION

CENTREX INC
1001 S DAIRY ASHFORD ST STE 225
HOUSTON,TX 77077 PH 713 781-4292
FAX 713 781-4307
GUILLERMO AMAYA,PRES
CHERYL L DOWELL,EXEC VP

CENTRILIFT - A BAKER HUGHES CO
200 W STUART ROOSA DR
CLAREMORE,OK 74017-3095 PH 918 341-9600
FAX 918 342-0260
JOE BRADY,PRES
PETER CLAYTON,VP,NEW PRODUCTS & MARKET
DEVELOPMENT
LARRY CROW,VP,WESTERN HEMIS OPERS
JERRY HASTINGS,VP,PUMP & CABLE PRODUCT
GROUPS
JULIO LERA,VP,LATIN AMERICA OPERS
JOE MITCHO,VP,HUMAN RESOURCES
STEPHEN PALMER,VP,EASTERN HEMIS OPERS
STEVE THOMPSON,VP,FINANCE & INFO TECH
JOE VANDEVIER,VP,CHF TECHNOLOGY OFCR

CENTROID OF AR,INC
464 BLUEBERRY LN
PARIS,AR 72855 PH 479 518-2703
FAX 479 963-2377
R L JOHNSON,PRES
BUTCHJOHNSON3@HOTMAIL.COM

CENTURY ENERGY LTD
4605 POST OAK PLACE DR STE 250
HOUSTON,TX 77027-9751 PH 713 658-0161
PH 713 725-7291 FAX 713 247-0407
WWW.CENTURYENERGYLTD.COM
JIMMY M MCCARROLL,CHRMN
JMCCARROLL@JHYI.COM
JIMMY MCCARROLL,PRES & CEO

CENTURY EXPLORATION COMPANY SEE
CENTURY EXPLORATION NEW ORLEANS,LLC

CENTURY EXPLORATION HOUSTON,LLC
10210 GROGAN'S MILL RD STE 300
THE WOODLANDS,TX 77380-1144
PH 281 362-7121 FAX 281 362-8671
WWW.CENTURYX.COM
CHRIS LIPARI,LAND MGR

CENTURY EXPLORATION NEW ORLEANS,LLC
3838 N CAUSEWAY BLVD STE 2800
METAIRIE,LA 70002-8319
PH 504 832-3750 FAX 504 832-3760
WWW.CENTURYX.COM INFO@CENTURYX.COM
MICHAEL WILLIS,SR VP
MARK WOJNA,EXPL MGR
TONY RICHARDS,VP RESERVE ENGR

HARVEY KELLEY,PROD MGR
DAVID A SEAY,LAND MGR
LEXINGTON,KY OFFICE - 1537 BULL LEA RD
STE 200,40511
PH 859 253-1300 FAX 859 233-7471
HOWARD SETTLE,PRES
JEFF CRAYCRAFT,CFO

CENTURY OFFSHORE MANAGEMENT CORP SEE
CENTURY EXPLORATION COMPANY

CENTURY ONSHORE EXPLORATION COMPANY SEE
CENTURY EXPLORATION HOUSTON,INC

CETA ENERGY
123 E COMMERCE ST
FAIRFIELD,TX 75840 PH 877 711-2382
FAX 903 389-4988 WWW.CETAENERGY.COM
INFO@CETAENERGY.COM
ROBERT T BULLER,CHF GLOBAL STRATEGIST-DIR
R.BULLER@CETAENERGY.COM
ROY W HILL
TOM ROSE
MICHELLE MOORE
JOANNA FRITZ
SCOTT SCOOTER LONG
CHERYL COCKERELL
GEORGE DAVIS
TRACY THOMPSON

CETCO OILFIELD SERVICES COMPANY
1001 OCHSNER BLVD STE 425
COVINGTON,LA 70433
PH 985 871-4700 FAX 985 871-4701
WWW.CETCOOILFIELDSERVICES.COM
BROUSSARD,LA OFFICE - 309 W 2ND ST 70518
PH 337 839-9944 PH 800 432-0054
FAX 337 839-9279
HOUMA,LA OFFICE - 2059 GRAND CAILLOU RD
70363 PH 985 872-2121 FAX 985 872-3536
HARVEY,LA NITROGEN OFFICE - 2620 8TH ST
70058 PH 504 363-7788 FAX 504 363-1247
LAKE CHARLES,LA OFFICE - 6208 LESLIE LN
70615 PH 337 436-4020 FAX 337 436-0980
NEW IBERIA,LA (COILED TUBING) OFFICE -
2616 W ADMIRAL DOYLE DR 70560
PH 337 364-3117 FAX 337 365-0337
BECKVILLE,TX OFFICE - 3555 FM 124W,75631
PH 903 678-9747 FAX 903 678-9749
SPRINGTOWN,TX OFFICE - 3070 W HWY 199
76082 PH 817 523-5333 FAX 817 523-4333
HOUSTON,TX OFFICE - 16350 PARK TEN PL
STE 217 77084 PH 281 578-8911
FAX 281 578-8873
DRISCOLL,TX OFFICE - 4900 FM 665,78351
PH 361 387-7590 FAX 361 387-7628
JOURJANTON,TX OFFICE - 1515 SIMMONS AVE
78026 PH 830 769-3936 FAX 830 769-2174
HOFFMAN ESTATES,IL OFFICE - 2870 FORBS
AVE 60192 PH 800 527-9948
WESTERVILLE,OH OFFICE - PO BOX 92,43086
PH 281 475-5734
MISSISSAUGA,ONTARIO,CAN OFFICE - 6347
NEUCHATEL RD L5N 2J7 PH 905 821-1914
FAX 847 394-7896

CGG VERITAS
10300 TOWN PARK
HOUSTON,TX 77072-5236 PH 832 351-8300
FAX 832 351-1021 WWW.CGGVERITAS.COM
DENNIS LANGLOIS

CHAINCO TWO,LLC
PO BOX 2058,1308 W PINE
HATTIESBURG,MS 39403-2058 PH 601 545-3800
FAX 601 584-8320
B L CHAIN,PRES
JOYCE J CARTIER,CORP SECY

CHALK HILL RESOURCES,INC
4514 BIRCH ST
BELLAIRE,TX 77401-5508 PH 713 667-8073
FAX 713 667-8073
DIANE G GERLICH,PRES

CHALMERS COLLINS & ALWELL,INC
PO BOX 52287,705 W PINHOOK RD
LAFAYETTE,LA 70505-2287
PH 337 237-2923 FAX 337 232-7929
CCACONSULTANTS.NET
CHALMERS97@AOL.COM
RICHARD W CHALMERS,PRES
MIKE PRIVAT,EXEC VP
JIM DOCHERTY,SR VP,PROJ MGR
BOBBY PRINCE,VP CONSLT OPERS
DAVE MCCUTCHEON,PROJ ENGR
ANDY CART,PROJ ENGR
HORACE HOFFPAUIR,PROD FLD SUPT
PAT SUIRE,OFC MGR
NANCY DOMINGUE,SECY
JAN STELLY,RECPT
PAT ANGERS,DRLNG SUPT
TAYLOR BRAZZEL,DRLG ENGR
MARY POLLARD,SAFETY/SEMS COORD
KIRK STANSBURY,DRLG SUPT
DAVID HANKINS,PROJ ENGR

CHAMA PETROLEUM COMPANY SEE
NEARBURG PRODUCING COMPANY

CHAMBERLAIN,HRDLICKA,WHITE,WILLIAMS AND
MARTIN,ATTORNEYS AT LAW
1200 SMITH ST 1400 TWO ALLEN CTR
HOUSTON,TX 77002 PH 713 658-1818
PH 800-342-5829

CHAMBERS MARK D,CERT PROF LDMN
ENERGY CONSULTING & PRODUCTION FINANCE
4906 KENLAKE GROVE DR
KINGWOOD,TX 77345-1643 PH 713 410-1331
FAX 281 360-0938

CHAMPAGNE G J,CPL
PO BOX 52312
LAFAYETTE,LA 70505-2312 PH 318 988-9141

CHAMPION & CHAMPION
3305 SAINT JAMES CT
TYLER,TX 75701-7747
PH 903 579-9371 FAX 903 579-9399
JOHN G CHAMPION,GEOL
JOHN J CHAMPION,LDMN

CHAMPION CHEMICALS INC/ARKLATEX DIST SEE
CHAMPION TECHNOLOGIES INC

CHAMPION DIRECTIONAL DRLG SERVICES,INC
203 HILLSIDE DR
LAFAYETTE,LA 70503-2840 PH 318 267-4284
FAX 318 261-3164

CHAMPION JOHN J
12559 CR 192
TYLER,TX 75703 PH 903 534-0175

CHAMPION PRODUCTION CO
3305 SAINT JAMES CT
TYLER,TX 75701-7747 PH 903 579-9371
FAX 903 579-9399

CHAMPION TECHNOLOGIES INC
PO BOX 27727,3200 SW FWY STE 2700 (77027)
HOUSTON,TX 77227-7727 PH 713 627-3303
MARKETING@CHAMP-TECH.COM
WWW.CHAMP-TECH.COM
TOM AMONETT,PRES,OILFIELD CHEM DIV
ELWIN MYERS,PRES,SPEC PROD DIV
MABRY THOMAS,VP,AMERICAS
JAMES FISHER,REG MGR/MID-CONTINENT
MIDLAND,TX WESTERN REG OFFICE -
PO BOX 61277,79711-1277 PH 432 563-0142
MIKE ATHEY,REG MGR
HEALDTON,OK DIST SLS OFFICE - HC 64
BOX 875,73438 PH 580 673-2122
TONY WELLS,DIST MGR
HAYS,KS DIST SLS OFFICE - 1019
RESERVATION RD,67601 PH 785 625-3822
TIM RUDER,DIST MGR
VERNAL,UT DIST SLS OFFICE - 2060 S 1500
EAST,84078 PH 435 789-4327
PARTICK CANCIENNE,DIST MGR
DICKINSON,ND DIST SLS OFFICE -
60 40TH ST W,58601 PH 701 225-4619
PERRY KOVASH,DIST MGR
BAKERSFIELD,CA DIST SLS OFFICE -
6321 DISTRICT BLVD,93313
PH 661 834-0454
MATT KNICKREHM,DIST MGR
KILGORE,TX DIST SLS OFFICE - 3306 HWY 135
N,75662 PH 903 984-0591 FAX 903 984-7284
GREG CASKEY,DIST MGR
BIG SPRING,TX DIST SLS OFFICE -
PO BOX 2879,79720 PH 432 267-5586
DAVID CALLISON,DIST MGR
DAYTON,TX DIST SLS OFFICE - PO BOX 1088
77535 PH 936 258-7618
MARK JAMISON,DIST MGR
CORPUS CHRISTI,TX DIST SLS OFFICE -
350 CENTAURUS,78405 PH 361 884-6013
TOBY ZAPLAC,DIST MGR
MONAHANS,TX DIST SLS OFFICE - PO BOX 2070
79756 PH 432 943-4359
DARREN MORRISON,DIST MGR
LAFAYETTE,LA DIST SLS OFFICE - 304 IDA
RD,BROUSSARD,LA 70518 PH 337 839-9920
KENNY VANNESS,DIST MGR
LAFAYETTE,LA GULF COAST REG OFFICE -
PO BOX 92132,70509-2132 PH 337 289-0019
RAYMOND JOHNSON,REG MGR
HOBBS,NM DIST SLS OFFICE - PO BOX 2187
88240 PH 505 393-7726
LARRY HODNETT,DIST MGR

CHAMPION W L,GEOL
1201 MCDUFFIE ST APT 201
HOUSTON,TX 77019-3621 PH 713 779-2575

CHAMPLIN MICHAEL L
PO BOX 782
GULF BREEZE,FL 32562 PH 850 934-5896

CHAMPLIN PETROLEUM COMPANY SEE
UNION PACIFIC RESOURCES CO (UPRC)

CHANOCO CORP
PO BOX 490,15008 MAIN ST
LYTLE,TX 78052-0490 PH 830 772-3262
FAX 830 772-3629
TOM CHANEY,PRES

CHANSE PETROLEUM CORP
60 E 42ND ST STE 1134
NEW YORK,NY 10165-1134
PH 212 682-3789 FAX 212 687-5360
KAI S CHANG,PRES
SHREVEPORT,LA OFFICE - 315 FANNIN ST
71101

CHAPARRAL ENERGY,LLC
701 CEDAR LAKE BLVD
OKLAHOMA CITY,OK 73114-7806
PH 405 478-8770,ACTG FAX 405 478-5863
LAND FAX 405 478-1890
ENGRG FAX 405 478-1947
WWW.CHAPARRALENERGY.COM
MARK A FISCHER,PRES,CEO
EARL REYNOLDS,EXEC VP,COO
JOSEPH EVANS,EXEC VP,CFO
ROBERT KELLY,SR VP,GEN COUNSEL

CHAPARRAL ROYALTY COMPANY
PO BOX 66687
HOUSTON,TX 77266-6687 PH 713 529-9949
FAX 713 529-9702
VIRGINIA P RORSCHACH,MNGNG PRTNR
RICHARD T MCCOMMON,JR,CPA
GAY HILLMAN,ASST

CHAPMAN A D DEAN ,ATTORNEY AT LAW
1021 EAST SE LOOP 323 STE 200
TYLER,TX 75701
PH 903 534-8063 FAX 903 534-1650
ADC@FLOWERSDAVIS.COM

CHAPPARAL OPERATING CO
PO BOX 121788
FORT WORTH,TX 76121 PH 817 738-2177

CHARBONNET CRAIG S,INC
5 GROGANS PARK DR STE 101
SPRING,TX 77380-2969 PH 281 363-3217
FAX 281 363-4422 CRAIG@CHARBONNET.CC

CHARIS ENERGY,INC
PO BOX 290469
KERRVILLE,TX 78028 PH 830 792-5154
FAX 830 792-3343

CHARIS OIL AND GAS
PO BOX 670842
DALLAS,TX 75367 PH 214 702-8177
FAX 214 615-6564

CHASE MANHATTAN BANK SEE
J P MORGAN CHASE BANK

CHEAIRS,SUSAN FEAGIN TRUST
JP MORGAN (OIL & GAS LEASING)
2200 ROSS AVE 7TH FL
DALLAS,TX 75201-2787 PH 214 965-3257

CHENIERE ENERGY,INC
700 MILAM ST STE 1900
HOUSTON,TX 77002
PH 713 375-5000 FAX 713 375-6000
INFO@CHENIERE.COM WWW.CHENIERE.COM
CHARIF SOUKI,CHRMN,CEO,DIR

CHEROHALL RESOURCES CORP
PO BOX 8796
TYLER,TX 75711-8796 PH 903 521-0625
STANLY K HARRIS,PRES
STANKHARRIS@YAHOO.COM

CHEROKEE RESOURCES INCORPORATED SEE
WYNN-CROSBY ENERGY INC

CHERRY OIL COMPANY,INC
PO BOX 444

OIL CITY,PA 16301-0444 PH 814 676-8234
 JON R RYBAK,PRES
  JONRYBAK@YAHOO.COM
 DAVID J RYBAK,VP
  RYBAK.DAVID@YMAIL.COM

CHESAPEAKE ENERGY CORPORATION
 PO BOX 18496,6100 N WESTERN AVE
 OKLAHOMA CITY,OK 73154-0496
 PH 405 848-8000 WWW.CHK.COM
  ROBERT D LAWLER,PRES/CEO & DIR
  DOMENIC J DELL JR,EXEC VP/CFO
  DOUGLAS J JACOBSON,EXEC VP/ACQUISITIONS
   & DIVESTITURES
  M CHRIS DOYLE,SR VP/OPERS NORTHERN DIV
  JAMES C JOHNSON,SR VP/MARKETING
  MICHAEL A JOHNSON,SR VP/ACCTG,CONTROLLER
   & CHIEF ACCTG OFFICER
  JOHN M KAPCHINSKE,SR VP/EXPL & SUBSURFACE
   TECHNOLOGY
  MIKELL J PIGOTT,SR VP/OPERS SOUTHERN DIV
  CATHY L TOMPKINS,SR VP/IT & CIO
  JAMES R WEBB,SR VP/GEN COUNSEL & CORP SEC
  JERRY L WINCHESTER,CEO OF SEVENTY SEVEN
   OPERATING,LLC

CHESAPEAKE ENERGY MARKETING,INC
 PO BOX 18496,6100 N WESTERN AVE
 OKLAHOMA CITY,OK 73154-0496
 PH 405 848-8000 WWW.CHK.COM
  NICK DELL'OSSO,EXEC VP/CFO
   NICK.DELLOSSO.COM
  JAMES C JOHNSON,SR VP MKTG
   JIM.JOHNSON@CHK.COM
   PH 405 935-9163 FAX 405 849-9163

CHESAPEAKE OPERATING,INC SEE
 CHESAPEAKE ENERGY CORPORATION
CHESAPEAKE PANHANDLE,INC SEE
 CHESAPEAKE ENERGY CORPORATION
CHESAPEAKE PETROLEUM,LLC
 2803 GULF TO BAY BLVD STE 424
 CLEARWATER,FL 33759
 PH 813 287-2643 FAX 813 287-2904
  ROBERT ROBINSON,CHRMN
CHEVRON
 6001 BOLLINGER CANYON RD
 SAN RAMON,CA 94583
 PH 925 842-1000
  JOHN S WATSON,CHAIRMAN/CEO
  GEORGE L KIRKLAND,VICE CHAIRMAN/EXEC VP
  LYDIA I BEEBE,CORP SECY/CGO
  PAUL BENNETT,VP/TREASURER
  JAMES R BLACKWELL,SENIOR ADVISOR
  MATTHEW J FOEHR,VP COMPTROLLER
  JOSEPH C GEAGEA,CORP VP/TECH,PROJ,& SVCS
  STEPHEN W GREEN,VP/POLICY,GOVT & PUBLIC
   AFFAIRS
  JOE W LAYMON,VP/HR,MED,SECURITY,DIVERSITY
   OMBUDS
  WESLEY E LOHEC,VP/HEALTH,ENVIRO SAFETY
  CN SANDY MACFARLANE,VP/GEN TAX COUNSEL
  JOHN W MCDONALD,VP/CTO
  JOSEPH M NAYLOR,VP/STRATEGIC PLANNING
  R HEWITT PATE,VP GEN COUNSEL
  JAY R PRYOR,VP/BUS DEV
  MICHAEL K WIRTH,EXEC VP/DOWNSTREAM &
   CHEMICALS
  PATRICIA E YARRINGTON,VP/CFO

  RHONDA ZYGOCKI,EXEC VP/POLICY & PLANNING
CHEVRON U S A INC SEE
 CHEVRONTEXACO EXPLORATION & PRODUCTION CO
CHEVRONTEXACO EXPLORATION & PRODUCTION
 SEE CHEVRON
CHEYENNE PETROLEUM COMPANY
 14000 QUAIL SPRINGS PKWY STE 2200
 OKLAHOMA CITY,OK 73134-2617
 PH 405 936-6220 FAX 405 936-6221
  STEPHEN A IVES,PRES
  WILLIAM (BILL) SPURGEON,VP,ENGRG &
   BUS DEV
 CHEYENNE ENERGY SERVICES OFFICE -
 14000 QUAIL SPRINGS PKWY STE 2200
 OKLAHOMA CITY,OK 73134-2617
 PH 405 936-6220 EXT 201 FAX 405 936-6241
  WADE FERGUSON,PRES
CHIASSON CARL D IND LDMN
 PO BOX 53414
 209 SUNNY LN STE 1
 LAFAYETTE,LA 70505-3414 PH 337 981-3767
 FAX 337 981-3768
CHIEFTAIN EXPLORATION CO,INC
 ROYALTY INVESTMENTS
 PO BOX 19566
 HOUSTON,TX 77224-9566 PH 832 358-1201
CHIEFTAIN INTERNATIONAL (U.S.) INC
 SEE HUNT OIL COMPANY
CHIYODA INTERNATIONAL CORP
 1177 WEST LOOP S STE 680
 HOUSTON,TX 77027-9007 PH 713 965-9005
 FAX 713 965-0075
  Y TORII,GEN MGR
  E RIBAUDO,PURCH MGR
CHOCTAW CORPORATION
 808 TRAVIS ST STE 1700
 HOUSTON,TX 77002-5703 PH 281 632-0222
 FAX 713 227-1007,CHOCTAW@CHOCTAWCORP.COM
  BLAKE T LIEDTKE,CEO
  W RUSSELL BROWN,JR,PRES
  JOHN N BLACK,VP,COO
  KARL H HERKERT,VP
  PEGGY A GILBERT,LAND MGR
  TIM C LECHNER,MGR/RKY MTN
  GREG FOX,ENGR MGR
CHOCTAW RESOURCES,INC
 14614 FALLING CREEK DR STE 243
 HOUSTON,TX 77068 PH 281 586-7900
 FAX 281 586-8747
  CHARLES H ASBILL,PRES
CHOICE TRAILER MANUFACTURING,LTD
 25825 FM 529 RD
 KATY,TX 77493-7922 PH 281 395-8000
  SALES@CHOICETRAILERS.COM
CHRISTENSEN & MATTHEWS
 6989 W LITTLE YORK RD STE L
 HOUSTON,TX 77040-4821 PH 713 896-8082
  S H CHRISTENSEN,OWNER
  M S KEY,ADMIN MGR
  S M CHRISTENSEN,PETR ENGR
CHRISTENSEN P J,OIL OPR
 6989 W LITTLE YORK RD STE L
 HOUSTON,TX 77040-4821 PH 713 896-8082
CHRISTENSEN STEVEN M,GEOL
 6989 W LITTLE YORK RD STE L
 HOUSTON,TX 77040-4821 PH 713 896-8082

CHRISTEVE OIL CO,INC
 4422 FM 1960 RD W STE 105
 HOUSTON,TX 77068-3417 PH 281 580-8708
 FAX 281 580-5900
  CCULLINS.CHRISTEVE@SBCGLOBAL.NET
  HENRY L CULLINS,CHRMN
  CHRIS L CULLINS,PRES
CHRISTIE INTERESTS,INC
 11800 GERKE RD
 BRENHAM,TX 77833-6361
 PH 979 421-9915
  RONALD D CHRISTIE,PRES
  RONCHRISTIE@HUGHES.NET
CHRISTIE PETROLEUM LLC
 1981 TWIN SISTERS DR
 SPRING BRANCH,TX 78070-6639
 PH 830 885-6550 FAX 830 885-6550
  ROBERT BOB CHRISTIE JR,OWNER/LDMN
  RCHRISTIEJ@AOL.COM
CHRISTOPHER OIL & GAS INC
 PO BOX 5717
 FRISCO,TX 75035
 PH 254 744-3334 CHRISOIL@MSN.COM
  STEPHEN L CALLAWAY,PRES
  ROBERT J SCHROCK,VP
  VIRGIL W CLEVELAND,VP,LAND
  ROSS FORD,EXPL MGR
CICO OIL & GAS CO,OIL PROD
 750 BERING DR STE 650
 HOUSTON,TX 77057-2132 PH 713 783-0400
  DALE C CHEESMAN,CEO
  DALE C CHEESMAN III,PRES,TREAS
  MARILYN CHEESMAN ERWIN,LAND MGR,SECY/TREA
CIMA ENERGY,LTD
 100 WAUGH DRIVE STE 500
 HOUSTON,TX 77007-5962 PH 713 209-1112
 FAX 713 759-1186 WWW.CIMA-ENERGY.COM
  CHARLES M OGLESBY,CEO
  THOMAS K EDWARDS,PRES
  MICHAEL D RUPE,CFO
  FRANK J MORENO,DIR NATURAL GAS MKTG
  JOHN E CODRINGTON,NAT GAS TRANSPORATION
   & EXCHANGE
  DAVID K TANOUS,ACCT
CIMA EXPLORATION CO SEE
 BARNEBURG,INC
CIMAREX ENERGY CO
 1700 LINCOLN ST STE 3700
 DENVER,CO 80203 PH 303 295-3995
 FAX 303 295-3494 WWW.CIMAREX.COM
  THOMAS E JORDEN,PRES & CEO
  PAUL KORUS,SR VP & CFO
  JIM SHONSEY,VP
  JOSEPH R ALBI,EXEC VP/COO
  STEVE P BELL,EXEC VP BUS DEV
  FRANCIS BARRON,SR VP-GEN COUNSEL
  JOHN LAMBUTH,VP EXPL
  DICK DINKINS,VP HUMAN RESOURCES
  GARY ABBOTT,VP CORP ENGRG
 TULSA,OK OFFICE - 202 S CHEYENNE AVE
 STE 1000 74103-4367 PH 918 585-1100
 FAX 432 571-7832
  JERRY NAGEL,VP/PROD
  JERRY MCLAUGHLIN,VP/MKTG
  JIM PAINTER,REG MGR/GULF COAST EXPL REG
  TONY CRISTELLI,REG MGR MID-CONT EXPL

ROBERT NEWMAN,REG MGR CANADA EXPL

MIDLAND,TX OFFICE - 600 N MARIENFELD ST

STE 600 79701 PH 432 571-7800

FAX 432 571-7832

ROGER ALEXANDER,REG MGR/PERMIAN BASIN

EXPL REGION

RICK WHITE,PROD MGR

CIMARRON ENGINEERING,LLC

PO BOX 1536

KINGSVILLE,TX 78364-1536 PH 361 592-4766

FAX 361 592-5090 CECJLG@SBCGLOBAL.NET

JAMES L GERYK,PRES

CAROL O GERYK,VP,TREAS

CIMARRON OPERATING COMPANY SEE

LOMAK PETROLEUM INC

CIMARRON PETROLEUM CORPORATION

1616 S VOSS RD STE 650

HOUSTON,TX 77057-2696

PH 713 337-1440 FAX 713 781-4065

S K BRADSHAW,PRES

K S BRADSHAW,VP

M A FOSTER,CONTROLLER

CIMMARON FIELD SERVICES,INC

PROFESSIONAL LAND & RIGHT OF WAY SERVICES

303 W WALL ST STE 600

MIDLAND,TX 79701 PH 432 242-4542

PH 877 944-2705 FAX 877 677-5553

WWW.CIMMARON.COM

INFO@CIMMARON.COM

CHRISTIAN PATRY,OPERS DIR-WESTERN DIV

TULSA,OK (MID-CONT) OFFICE - 7134 S YALE

AVE 74136

PAUL F WHITMIRE,CEO/PRES

PAUL@CIMMARON.COM

CAMBRIDGE,OH (UTICA SHALE) OFFICE -

PO BOX 1506, 43725

MEMPHIS,TN (ACCT & ADMIN) OFFICE -

PO BOX 171179, 38187

ELLEN HELDT,CFO/VP ELLEN@CIMMARON.COM

MEMPHIS,TN (CONTRACTOR RELS) OFFICE -

7700 POPLAR AVE STE 208, 38138

DELAINE ROTT,CONTRACT ADMIN

DELAINE@COMMARON.COM

CINCO ENERGY LAND SERVICES

CINCO COMMUNICATIONS LAND SERVICES

8811 GAYLORD DR STE 400

HOUSTON,TX 77024-3046 PH 713 463-6009

FAX 713 463-5304

RANDY H NICHOLS,PRES

CINCO EQUIS OIL COMPANY

314 E COMMERCE ST STE 400

SAN ANTONIO,TX 78205-2907 PH 210 223-5564

CINERGY MARKETING & TRADING,LP SEE

BNP PARIBAS

CIRCLE INCORPORATED

1204 A ENGINEERS RD

BELLE CHASSE,LA 70037 PH 504 394-7611

FAX 504 394-7626

M J WOLFE,JR,PRES

CIRCLE STAR ENERGY CORP

7065 CONFEDERATE PARK RD STE 102

FORT WORTH,TX 76108 PH 817 744-8502

WWW.CIRCLESTARENERGY.COM

INFO@CIRCLESTARENERGY.COM

S JEFFREY JOHNSON,CEO

JAYME WOLLISON,VP OPERS

CISCO ENERGY,LLC

6900 N DALLAS PKWY STE 740

PLANO,TX 75024 PH 214 291-9987

FAX 214 291-9985

DAVID MYERS,CEO

RANDALL K CLICK,PRES

CITADEL ENERGY INC

PO BOX 41106

HOUSTON,TX 77241-1106 PH 713 759-1185

PHIL STEFFANO,PRES

CITATION OIL & GAS CORP

14077 CUTTEN ROAD

HOUSTON,TX 77069-2212 PH 281 891-1000

FAX 281 891-1298

F E HARRELL,CHRMN OF BD

CURTIS F HARRELL,PRES,CFO

WAYNE WIESEN,SR VP,GEN COUNSEL,SECY

STEVEN C PEARSON,SR VP OPERS

STEVE K ANNA,SR VP ENGRG

ROBERT T KENNEDY,SR VP LAND-BUS DEV

CITGO PETROLEUM CORPORATION

PO BOX 4689

HOUSTON,TX 77210-4689 PH 832 486-4000

WWW.CITGO.COM INFO@CITGO.COM

- KEY EXECUTIVES -

FELIX RODRIGUEZ,PRES,CEO

JERRY THOMPSON,COO

FREDDY CARABALLO,PRES/CITGO ASPHALT

REFINING COMPANY

JIM MCCOY,VP,CORP PLANNING & ECONOMICS

FRANK GYGAX,VP,REFINING

RIVIO MEDINA,VP,HEALTH,SAFETY,SECURITY

OF ASSETS & ENVIRONMENTAL PROTECTION

RAFAEL GOMEZ,VP,GOV/PUBLIC AFFAIRS

HECTOR BIVERO,VP LEGAL AFFAIRS &

GEN COUNSEL

AL PREBULA,VP,LAKE CHARLES MFG COMPLEX

MARK J SMITH,VP,GEN MGR/LEMONT REFINERY

RANDY CARBO,VP,GEN MGR/CORPUS CHRISTI

REFINERY

BOB KOSTELNIK,VP,SHARED SERVICES

LARRY KRIEG,CORP CONTROLLER

PHIL REEDY,CORP TREAS

WLADIMIR NORIEGA,GEN AUDITOR

MARTY SEDLACEK,GEN MGR,MKTG

ALBERTO RAMIREZ,GEN MGR,HUMAN RESOURCES

BOB MAREBURGER,GEN MGR,INFO TECHNOLOGY

MARSHALL BUZAN,GEN MGR,TAX

JEANNE STURGES,GEN MGR,SPECIAL PROJ

ALAN SYLVESTER,GEN MGR,NON-REFINING OPERS

STEVE LATTION,GEN MGR,PRODUCT SUPPLY

DISTRIBUTION & TRADING

HERB WHITNEY,GEN MGR,MARINE TRANS

BARRY FULDA,GEN MGR,BUS ANALYSIS &

ENHANCEMENT

PAUL RUDOLPH,GEN MGR,LUBRICANTS MKTG

GUSTAVO VELASQUEZ,GEN MGR,CRUDE SUPPLY

BILL HATCH,VP,SUPPLY & DISTRIBUTION

DICK GOOLEY,GEN MGR,RISK MGMNT

TULSA,OK OFFICE - PO BOX 3758,74102

PH 918 495-4000

CORPUS CHRISTI,TX REFINERY -

PO BOX 9176,78469 PH 361 844-4000

LAKE CHARLES,LA MANUFACTURING COMPLEX -

4401 HIGHWAY 108,70601 PH 337 708-6011

LEMONT,IL REFINERY - 135TH & NEW AVE

60439-3659 PH 630-257-7761

CITIZENS RESOURCE DEVELOPMENT CORPORATION

RR 2 BOX 180

WORTHINGTON,IN 47471-9754

PH 812 659-4134 FAX 812 659-4135

MIKE J MORLEY,VP,OPERS

JERRY D ROBINSON,MGR,FLD OPERS

CITY EXPLORATION CO SEE

CENTRAL UNIVERSAL CO

CIVIL CONSTRUCTION CONTRACTORS,INC

AGGREGATE SLS & HEAVY EQUIPMENT SVCS

PO BOX 394

HAHNVILLE,LA 70057-0394 PH 504 783-6893

FAX 504 783-6894

CJS OIL & GAS PROPERTIES,LLC

11467 HOLLYRIDGE

TYLER,TX 75703 PH 903 509-2106

CHARLES J SAUL,MNGNG PRTNR

CHUCKSAUL@MSN.COM

FLYNN,TX OFFICE - PO BOX 201

77855 PH 936 396-1312

CJW CORPORATION

PO BOX 1598,103-A S MECHANIC

EL CAMPO,TX 77437 PH 979 541-5454

CJ WOFFORD

CL&F RESOURCES

16945 NORTHCHASE DR STE 1500

HOUSTON,TX 77060 PH 281 873-9378

R PAUL LOVELESS,PRES

MARK K STOVER,SR VP HARDROCK EXPL/BUS DEV

GARY A DOBBS,VP LAND

ROBERT D MURRAH,VP EXPL

MARK H PARROTT,EXPL MGR/BUS DEV

TAMMY K WILLIS,SR OFFSHORE LDMN

ALLISON M GILL,ONSHORE LDMN

ACCT/FIN OFFICE - 111 VETERANS MEMORIAL

BLVD STE 500 METAIRIE,LA 70005-3099

PH 504 378-9378

MIDLAND,TX OFFICE - 303 W WALL STE 1000

79701 PH 432 664-8144

CLANTON JOHN L,IND GEOL

FROST BANK STE 1220

CORPUS CHRISTI,TX 78401 PH 361 884-2927

CLARCO GAS CO,INC

PO BOX 1278

WESTMONT,IL 60559-3878

PH 630 655-2209 FAX 630 655-2260

KENT H WELTMER,PRES

EARL J JOYCE,TREAS

CLARK ENERGY COMPANY,INC,OIL,GAS PROP

401 EDWARDS ST STE 2106

SHREVEPORT,LA 71101-5505

PH 318 424-0813 FAX 318 222-1432

JEFFREY F CLARK,PRES

CLARK JEFFREY F

PO BOX 1841

SHREVEPORT,LA 71166 PH 318 424-0813

CLARK NOLAN FAMILY TRUST

PO BOX 530

WAYNESBORO,MS 39367-0530 PH 601 735-2062

CLARK PROPERTIES,LTD

2335 OAK ALLEY

TYLER,TX 75703

PH 903 561-4041 EXT:223

CLARK R B,OIL & GAS

RR 2 BOX 1212,# 828 FAIR FOUNDATION BLDG

BULLARD,TX 75757 PH 214 597-9139

CLARKE JOE B,JR,OIL & GAS PROPERTIES
PO BOX 51224,217 E KALISTE SALOOM RD #104
LAFAYETTE,LA 70505-1224
PH 318 233-0711 FAX 233-0713

CLARKSTON OIL CORPORATION,INC
5980 S MAIN ST STE 101
CLARKSTON,MI 48346-2377 PH 248 673-1099
  LARRY BARNETT,CEO,PRES
  ERIC TAYLOR,GEOL
  RUSSELL BATES,LAND MGR
  PETER WILES,OPERS MGR
  SUSAN L KNOPPE,OFC MGR

CLARUS ENERGY PARTNER LP SEE
HUNT OIL COMPANY

CLASSEN EXPLORATION INC
PO BOX 140637
BOISE,ID 83714-0637 PH 208 854-1037
FAX 208 854-1029 CLASSENLLC@MSN.COM
  J S CLASSEN,PRES
NEW ORLEANS,LA OFFICE - 124 ROSA AVE
METAIRIE,LA 70005 PH 504 837-7185
  PAUL JURIK,VP EXPL

CLASSIC HYDROCARBONS INC
6500 W FRWY STE 222
FORT WORTH,TX 76116
PH 817 731-4100 FAX 817 731-4103
  ROB JACOBS,PRES
  DON GANN,COO
  MARK DOERING,CHRMN
  MARK CARTER,LAND MGR
SHREVEPORT,LA OFFICE - 400 TEXAS ST
STE 950,71101 PH 318 676-9943
FAX 318 676-3687
  MARK T WARREN,VP,LAND

CLAY ENERGY
PO BOX 9603
THE WOODLANDS,TX 77387-6603
PH 281 367-9907
  GARY CORZINE,PRES
  CHRISTIE L BARNES,OFC MGR

CLAYTON ENERGY COMPANY
PO BOX 301
JACKSON,MI 49204-0301 PH 517 782-8240
FAX 517 782-8205
  GARY N HACKWORTH,PRES
    GNH.CLAYTONENERGY@SBCGLOBAL.NET

CLEAR FORK ROYALTY
309 W 7TH ST STE 500
FORT WORTH,TX 76102 PH 817 370-7540
FAX 866 580-6364 WWW.CLEARFORKROYALTY.COM
    OFFER@CLEARFORKROYALTY.COM
  JOSEPH P DEWOODY,PRES
  RYAN HAGGERTY,PRTNR
  MICHAEL DEWOODY,PRTNR
  DOUG KING,GEOL
  LOGAN KING,ACQS
  JOHN A MONCRIEF,ACQS
  CHASE BECHTEL,BUS DEV
  TERESA TEAGUE,DIV ORDERS

CLEARFIELD COUNTY ECONOMIC DEVELOPMENT
CORPORATION (CCEDC)
511 SPRUCE ST STE 5
CLEARFIELD,PA 16830 PH 877 768-7838
  ROB SWALES RSWALES@CLEARLYAHEAD.COM
  WWW.CLEARLYAHEAD.COM WWW.RIGMON-

KEYAPP.COM

CLEMCO INC
6211 BANDERA AVE APT A
DALLAS,TX 75225-3603 PH 601 946-8828

CLEMENTS ENERGY GROUP,INC
JIMMY L CLEMENTS LEASES & ROYALTY
PO BOX 160
BUDE,MS 39630-0160 PH 601 384-4010
PH 601 384-2007 OR 601 384-6800
    ORTHOKENNETH@NETSCAPE.NET

CLEMENTS THOMAS H,JR,CONS GEOPHYS
6211 BANDERA AVE APT A
DALLAS,TX 75225-3603 PH 601 259-1111

CLESI SCOUTING SERVICE INC
4208 NEWTON ST
METAIRIE,LA 70001 PH 504 886-1100
FAX 504 886-1102
  JOHN J CLESI,JR,PRES

CLEVELAND VIRGIL W,OIL & GAS EXPLORATION
9505 NORTHPOINTE BLVD APT 2036
SPRING,TX 77379-3527 PH 830 249-9730
FAX 830 249-9730

CLIMAX EXPLORATION,LLC
1062 ADDO BARNES RD
MCCOMB,MS 39648 PH 601 684-0001
    CCHALE@BELLSOUTH.NET

CLOUSE RICHARD E,RECO,LEASES & ROYALTIES
4010 FRY AVE
TYLER,TX 75701-9604 PH 903 561-8255

CLOVELLY OIL CO,LLC
650 POYDRAS ST STE 2350
NEW ORLEANS,LA 70130-6194
PH 504 522-7496 FAX 504 523-6302
    NEWORLEANS@CLOVELLYOIL.COM
  JEFF J JANDEGIAN,PRES/MGR
  D IRWIN MACKENROTH JR,VP LAND

CML EXPLORATION, LLC
900 ROCKMEAD DR STE 260
KINGWOOD,TX 77339-2180
PH 281 358-2695 FAX 281 358-6931
  LEE W STAIGER,OPER MGR

CMP AMERICA
SPECIALISTS IN FIELD OF HAZARDOUS
LOCATION CABLE CONNECTORS DESIGN & MFG
1813 ROTARY DR
HOUSTON,TX 77338 PH 281 540-7575
    CMP@CMP-AMERICA WWW.CMP-PRODUCTS.COM

CMR ENERGY,LP
4265 SAN FELIPE STE 1040
HOUSTON,TX 77027-2929 PH 713 580-7200
  CARTER OVERTON

CMS OIL AND GAS COMPANY SEE
PERENCO LLC

CNG PRODUCING COMPANY SEE
DOMINION EXPLORATION & PRODUCTION,INC

COASTAL BEND GEOLOGICAL LIBRARY,INC
600 LEOPARD ST STE 1200
CORPUS CHRISTI,TX 78401-0431
PH 361 883-2736
  SEBASTIAN WIEDMANN,PRES
  SCOTT HINES,BD DIR
  TONY HAUGIUM,VP
  DAVID BECKER,TREAS
  JEFF KIRBY,SECY

COASTAL CHEMICAL CO,LLC
PO BOX 820

ABBEVILLE,LA 70511-0820 PH 337 898-0001
FAX 337 892-1185
  JIM DOYLE,PRES
  KERRY WILTS,VP FIN
  LANA G ROGERS,CORP ADMIN ASST
  DAVID G ROGERS,N-SPEC SFTY MGR
  THERESA STEEN,ACCT MGR
  BONNIE BROUSSARD,CONTROLLER
  MICHAEL KOERNER,ACCT CLERK
  DONNA ROBICHEAUX,ACCT CLERK
  DELORIS CABROL,ACCT CLERK
  MONA TRAHAN,ACCT CLERK
  VICKY MENARD,ACCT CLERK
  CINDY MEAUX,ACCT CLERK
  PATRICIA PRIMEAUX,ACCT
  NEWBY COMEAUX,ACCT PAYABLE CLERK
  JENNY SUIRE,ACCT PAYABLE CLERK
  CARRIE DURKE,ACCT REC
  MARY DETRAZ,ACCT REC
  PUNKIE TATE,ACCT REC
  RENEE ROMERO,ACCT REC
  LAURA BAUGH,ACCT REC
  SHEILA HEBERT,ACCT REC
HOUSTON,TX SALES & TECHNICAL OFFICE -
5300 MEMORIAL DR 77007
PH 713 865-8787 FAX 713 865-8788
  CARTER NESS,NATL ACCT
  STAN DORAK,SLS MGR
  CRAIG SORENSEN,VP SLS
  LORENE WIRTH,FLEET MGR
  THOMAS LIIKE,SLS-CHICAGO AREA
  DWIGHT FRUGE,SUPPLIER RELS MGR
  DEBI SHARP,ADMIN ASST
  BRYANT MILLER,PRIN PROCESS ENGR
  BARBARA MABRY,CUSTOMER SVC
  WILL BRIDGES,SLS MGR
BEAUMONT,TX OFFICE - 6534 INDUSTRIAL
77705 PH 409 842-0777 FAX 409 842-8114
  SCOTT RAGGIO,REG OPERS MGR
  BRAD THIBODEAUX,FACILITY MGR
  STEVE KNIGHT,CUSTOMER SVC REP
ABBEVILLE,LA OFFICE - 3520 CHARITY ST
70511 PH 318 893-3862
  KEVIN NERO,FACILITY MGR
  JIM BAZAR,OPERS MGR
  CARL BROUSSARD,GDU SLS COORD
  SHELLIE MARTINEZ,CUSTOMER SVC
  JODY CASTILLE,PUR AGENT
  BECKY SONGNE,OFC MGR
  BABETTE LANDRY,CUSTOMER SVC MGR
  CRAIG DOYLE,SLS
  MIKE CRISMON,SLS
  CARL DUPUY,BLEND PLANT MGR
BROUSSARD,LA OFFICE - 6133 HWY 90 EAST
PH 337 261-0796
  TOMMY DUPUIS,PROD GROUP MGR
  CARLISS ALMANZA,ADMIN ASST
  MIKE GROTEFEND,SLS MGR
  TYSON DUPUIS,N-SPEC GROUP MGR
  DANNY CORMIER,LAB MGR
  RICKY LATIOLAIS,SLS
  PAUL CHOATE,SLS
  DWAYNE CHAUMONT,SLS
RUSTON,LA OFFICE - 1700 INDUSTRIAL DR
71270 PH 318 255-1010 FAX 318 255-1089
  TAMMY LEBRUN,FACILITY MGR

ODESSA,TX OFFICE - 1800 E 2ND ST
79761 PH 432 332-1457
JERRY DUNLAP,DIST OPERS MGR
MIKE MOORE,FACILITY MGR
GORDON L WARREN,TECH MGR
DAVE WALKER,SLS
MARC NELSON,SLS
PASADENA,TX OFFICE - 3205 PASADENA BLVD
77503 PH 713 477-1561 FAX 713 477-3438
BRIAN SORENSEN,FACILITY MGR
GINA EINKOFF,ADMIN ASST
KILGORE,TX OFFICE - 1312 INDUSTRIAL BLVD
75662 PH 903 984-5005 FAX 903 984-2708
JAY SENTERFITT,FUEL MGR/PROJ MGMNT SUPVSR
GARY HARDIN,SLS MGR
TROY WATSON,REG SLS MGR
BON BOATWRIGHT,MATERIAL MGR
FRED MCKETHAN,REG OPERS MGR
JOHN PAUL,SLS MGR-FUELS
SUGG NIBLETT,FACILITY MGR
MELISSA WORTHAM,ADMIN ASST
BRYAN,TX OFFICE - 1613 GOOSENECK DR
77806 PH 409 778-5010 FAX 409 778-0889
STEVE MCBRIDE,FAC MGR
JOEY HOGAN,REG OPERS MGR
ALICE,TX OFFICE - PO BOX 539
AGUA DULCE,TX 78330 PH 361 664-8488
SCOTT SULSER,FACILITY MGR
ROBBIE TOMLIN,SLS MGR
JIMMY GUANA,SLS
WAYNE GALLIA,SLS
KURT KUEL,SLS
EVANSTON,WY OFFICE - PO BOX 1671
82930 PH 307 789-7122
DANE HUTCHINGS,FACILITY MGR
PATTI STIGLITZ,CUSTOMER SVC
DAN KNOX,SLS
FARMINGTON,NM OFFICE - #10 COUNTY RD 5911
87401 PH 505 327-9280
ADRIAN BLUMBERG,FACILITY MGR
MASON WARREN,SLS

COASTAL COOLERS, LLP
PO BOX 10740
CORPUS CHRISTI,TX 78460 PH 361-289-2895
JIMMIE MILLER,MNGNG PRTNR

COASTAL COORDINATION COUNCIL
WWW.GLO.STATE.TX.US/COASTAL/CCC.HTML

COASTAL CORPORATION AND SUBSIDIARIES SEE
EL PASO PIPELINE GROUP

COASTAL DRILLING FLUIDS,INC
DRILLFLUIDS CONSULTING
632 RANCHO BAUER DR
HOUSTON,TX 77079-6826
PH 281 493-9993
W E BOOKER,PRES BILLBOOKER@AOL.COM

COASTAL ENVIRONMENTS INC,ARCHAEOLOGY
WETLAND DELINEATION,NEPA COMPLIANCE,
GEOPHY SURVEY,COMPLIANCE MONITORING
WETLAND RESTOR/MITIGATION,PERMITTING
1260 MAIN ST
BATON ROUGE,LA 70802-4695
PH 225 383-7455 FAX 225 383-7925
WWW.COASTALENV.COM KWICKER@COASTAL-
ENV.COM
MARK GAGLIANO,PRES

COASTAL EXPLORATION INC
PO BOX 195,701 AVIGNON DR STE 101 39157
RIDGELAND,MS 39158
PH 601 427-5388 FAX 601 427-5393
JULIUS RIDGWAY,PRES
ANITA HEMPHILL,OFC MGR

COASTAL GULF & INTERNATIONAL,INC
PO BOX 429
KENNER,LA 70063-0429 PH 985 785-0765
FAX 985 785-1328 KCOLLURA@COASTALGULF.COM
WWW.COASTALGULF.COM
MICHAEL CARAVELLA,PRES
ROBERT KENNEDY,OPERS MGR
KEITH COLLURA,VP

COASTAL INVESTMENTS,INC
DBA/ COASTAL PRODUCTION COMPANY
PO BOX 1364
EL CAMPO,TX 77437-1364
PH 979 543-7951 FAX 979 543-2920
HEFNER APPLING JR,PRES
CINDY GARRETT,VP

COASTAL LAND SERVICES,INC
102 ASMA BLVD STE 200
LAFAYETTE,LA 70508
PH 337 291-2910 FAX 337 291-2914
WWW.CLS-US.COM
MAC A GUARINO,PRES
KEVIN R GUARINO,LDMN/SUPVSR
DAVID J CORNAY,LDMN/SUPVSR
STACEY A CARRIERE,OFC MGR
DOUG ALSPAUGH,ABSTRACTOR/SUPERVISOR
CARON MYLES,ABSTRACTOR
KEVIN DUGAS,CAD OPERATOR
TOBY CORMIER,CAD OPERATOR

COASTAL MANAGEMENT CORPORATION SEE
SCHLUMBERGER-IPM

COASTAL OIL & GAS CORPORATION SEE
EL PASO PIPELINE GROUP

COASTAL PIPE OF LOUISIANA,INC
PO BOX 99,4831 NW EVANGLEINE THRUWAY
CARENCRO,LA 70520
PH 337 896-8462 FAX 337 896-8465
DOUGLAS M YENTZEN,OWNER/SALES
TERRI BRASSEAUX,SALES/MKT COORD
JAKE YENTZEN,SALES
JONATHAN YENTZEN,SALES
RANDY WILLIAMS,OPERS MGR
KENDLE BROWN,YARD FRMN
JEANNEL VALLOT,ACCTS MGR
TANYA YENTZEN,OFFICE MGR
JERREN MALBROU,QC,SAFETY
R A RICHARD,FLD SUPT
ROSE CORMIER,SECY/RECPT

COASTLAND ENERGY,INC
PO BOX 1799
CONROE,TX 77305-1799
PH 936 539-2036 FAX 936 539-2036
RUSTY CARLSON,PRES
RUSTYCARLSON2002@YAHOO.COM

COATES FIELD SERVICE INC,LAND & RIGHT OF
WAY ACQUISITION & RELATED SERVICES
4800 N SANTA FE
OKLAHOMA CITY,OK 73118-7910
PH 405 528-5676 FAX 405 557-0433
WWW.COATESFIELDSERVICE.COM
CFS4800@COATESFIELDSERVICE.COM

JOE COATES JOE@COATESFIELDSERVICE.COM
ALBANY,NY NE DIV OFFICE - PO BOX 992
950 NEW LOUDON RD #240 LATHAM,NY 12110
PH 518 782-1506 FAX 518 782-1507
BILL DOW,VP BILL@COATESFIELDSERVICE.COM
TALLAHASSEE,FL SE DIV OFFICE -
1311 EXECUTIVE CENTER DR STE 103,32301
PH 850 668-0525 FAX 850 580-5333
MARK HANDLEY,VP
MHANDLEY@COATESFIELDSERVICE.COM
WALNUT CREEK,CA W DIV OFFICE -
3021 CITRUS CIR STE 160,94598
PH 925 935-5101 FAX 925 935-8367
SUE EVANS,VP
SREVANS@COATESFIELDSERVICE.COM
ELAINE LIPON,VP
ELAINE@COATESFIELDSERVICE.COM
HOUSTON,TX TX DIV OFFICE - 14550 TORREY
CHASE BLVD,#257,77014
PH 281 583-7300 FAX 281 583-2759
MARK ROBY,VP MROBY@COATESFIELDSERVICE.COM

COATS J L COMPANY,INC
P O BOX 745,RT 40 EAST
CAMBRIDGE,OH 43725-0745 PH 740 439-2391
CAROL COATS GOFF,PRES

COBIA OIL & GAS,LLC
PO BOX 5423
BEAUMONT,TX 77726-5423
PH 409 892-3710 FAX 409 892-3716
JOHN B SELMAN,PRES
SUSAN L SELMAN,CFO & TREAS
SANDRA CARRINGTON,SECY & GEN COUNSEL

COBRA OIL & GAS CORPORATION
PO BOX 8206
WICHITA FALLS,TX 76307-8206
PH 940 716-5100 PROD FAX 940 716-5110
LAND FAX 940 716-5210
JEFF R DILLARD,PRES,CPL
ROBERT W OSBORNE,VP,EXPL & DEV
RICHARD W HASKIN JR,CPA,SECY/TREAS
RORY EDWARDS,MGR,DRLG & PROD
PHIL RUGELEY,CPL,LAND MGR
CHARLES H GIBSON,OPERS MGR
CRAIG W REYNOLDS,EXPL MGR

COCHRAN F B,JR,IND OIL OPR
101 N SHORELINE BLVD STE 600
CORPUS CHRISTI,TX 78401-2826
PH 361 882-5435 FAX 361 884-4296

COCKBURN OIL CORP
PO BOX 1340
PINEHURST,TX 77362 PH 713 208-4400
WADE H COCKBURN,PRES
SUSANNAH W COCKBURN,SECY

COCKE FIELDING LEWIS
919 MILAM ST STE 1910
HOUSTON,TX 77002-5811 PH 713 652-5887

COCO PRODUCTION CO
PO BOX 524
LONGVIEW,TX 75606-0524
PH 903 753-4522 FAX 903 753-9717

CODA ENERGY INC SEE
BELCO OIL & GAS CORP

COFFEY MURRAY,IND GEOL/GEOPHY
PO BOX 53606
LAFAYETTE,LA 70505-3606 PH 337 235-8983

COFFEY OIL COMPANY
PO BOX 53606,510 E UNIVERSITY AVE
LAFAYETTE,LA 70505 PH 337 235-8983
GLENN H COFFEY,GEOL
COFFEYGLENN@BELLSOUTH.NET

COHORT ENERGY COMPANY
15508 WRIGHT BROTHERS DR
ADDISON,TX 75001
PH 972 233-8191 FAX 972 991-0704
COHORT@JWOPERATING.COM
LONGVIEW,TX DISTRICT OFFICE -
122 DOVEL RD,75607 PH 800 436-7808
PH 903 643-3413 FAX 903 643-3586
CENTENNIAL,CO DISTRICT OFFICE -
7074 S REVERE PKWY,80112
PH 800 333-4990 303 422-4990
FAX 303 422-0178
FRIERSON,LA FIELD OFFICE -
2601 STONEWALL-FRIERSON RD,71027
PH 800 274-0033 318 925-8088
FAX 318 925-8058
HAUGHTON,LA FIELD OFFICE -
4555 HWY 527,71037
PH 318 987-8003 FAX 318 987-3373
ROANOKE,TX FIELD OFFICE -
11350 CLEVELAND GIBBS RD,STE 107
76262 PH 682 831-0228 FAX 682 831-0230
ARP,TX FIELD OFFICE - 11956 COUNTY RD
2222,75750 PH 903 566-8651

COILED TUBING CORP SEE
CUDD PRESSURE CONTROL,INC

COKER JERRY L,OIL LAND LEASES
5823 CROSS CREEK CIR
TYLER,TX 75703 PH 972 561-6174

COLE EDWIN D
23646 COUNTY ROAD 7
ALVADA,OH 44802-9610 PH 419 387-7382
ED COLE,OWNER

COLE J M CO
11668 ARROWOOD CIR
HOUSTON,TX 77063-1402 PH 713 780-4164
FAX 713 780-4165 JIMMCOLE@SWBELL.NET
J M COLE,PRES

COLLARINI ENERGY STAFFING INC
1500 S DAIRY ASHFORD RD STE 350
HOUSTON,TX 77077 PH 832 251-0553
FAX 832 251-0157 WWW.COLLARINI.COM
CHERYL R COLLARINI,CHRMN
VOLKER RATHMANN,PRES

COLLARINI ENGINEERING INC
3100 WILCREST DR STE 140
HOUSTON,TX 77042-3549 PH 832 251-0160
NANCY REECE NREECE@COLLARINI.COM
HOUSTON,TX OFFICE - 11111 RICHMOND
STE 126,77063 PH 832 251-0160
FAX 832 251-0157

COLLIER & ELY,L.P. SEE
EBR ENERGY,LP

COLLIER RESOURCES CO
2600 GOLDEN GATE PKWY STE 112
NAPLES,FL 34105-3227 PH 239 262-0900
FAX 239 262-7378

COLLIER-WHEELER PETROLEUM COMPANY
P O BOX 191
OBLONG,IL 62449-0191 PH 618 592-4136
R L WHEELER,PRES

C S COLLIER,VP

COLLINS BROTHERS OIL COMPANY
PO BOX 689,805 BROADWAY
MOUNT VERNON,IL 62864-0014
PH 618 244-1093 FAX 618 244-1096
MIKE O'DEA,GENERAL MGR

COLLINS DAN S,CPL & ASSOCIATES,INC
OIL & GAS PROPERTIES
PO BOX 66773
BATON ROUGE,LA 70896-6773 PH 225 927-1323
PH 225 241-7122 FAX 225 927-1325
DAN S COLLINS,CPL,DIR,PRES
COLLINSDANS@AOL.COM

COLLINS ED INC,OIL PRODUCERS
PO BOX 51443
LAFAYETTE,LA 70505-1443
PH 337 216-0155 FAX 337 216-0155
A E COLLINS,PRES
ED@MAMMOTHCOMPUTERS.COM

COLLINS JOHN R
OIL AND GAS ATTORNEY
PO BOX 5616,6818 WESTOVER DR
GRANBURY,TX 76049 PH 432 296-8800
PH 817 894-7225 FAX 817 886-8648

COLOGNE PRODUCTION CO
PO BOX 6049,900 NE LOOP 410 STE E-109
SAN ANTONIO,TX 78209-0049 PH 210 824-0131
WILLIAM HAUSSER,PRES
WILLIAM THOMAS,VP

COLOMES RICHARD P,CONS GEOL
432 HECTOR AVE
METAIRIE,LA 70005 PH 504 522-8246

COLONY ENERGY CORPORATION SEE
ASSOCIATED NATURAL GAS,INC

COLORADO CRUDE CO SEE
GULF ENERGY EXPLORATION CORP

COLORADO INTERSTATE GAS COMPANY SEE
EL PASO PIPELINE GROUP

COLUMBIA ENERGY GROUP
PARENT CO OF COLUMBIA GULF TRANSMISSION
200 CIVIC CENTER DR
COLUMBUS,OH 43215-4157 PH 703 561-6000
FAX 703 561-7324

COLUMBIA ENTERPRISES,A LA PARTNERSHIP
416 TRAVIS ST STE 612
SHREVEPORT,LA 71101-5502 PH 318 221-6143
FAX 318 221-6186 CVINC@BELLSOUTH.NET
PEARLA T DESPOT,PRTNR
CAMILLE C DESPOT,PRTNR
KATINA RIOS,OFC MGR

COLUMBIA GAS DEVELOPMENT CORPORATION SEE
AVIARA ENERGY CORPORATION

COLUMBIA GULF TRANSMISSION COMPANY
5151 SAN FELIPE STE 2500
HOUSTON,TX 77056 PH 713 267-4100
FAX 713 267-4110
GLEN KETTERING,PRES,PIPELINES
JAMES W HART,SR COMM CONSLT
ELISE CORT,MARKETING MGR

COLUMBIA OIL COMPANY,INC
PO BOX 763
MAGNOLIA,AR 71754-0763 PH 870 234-7992
FAX 870 234-8354 COLOIL@YAHOO.COM
GARY DAVIS,PRES

COLUMBIA VENTURES INCORPORATED
416 TRAVIS ST STE 612

SHREVEPORT,LA 71101-5502 PH 318 221-6143
FAX 318 221-6186 CVINC@BELLSOUTH.NET
CAMILLE C DESPOT,PRES
KATINA RIOS,OFC MGR

COLUMBUS ENERGY CORP SEE
CIMAREX ENERGY CO

COLUMBUS EXPLORATION & LAND SERVICES,INC
4280 BALL GROUND RD
BALL GROUND,GA 30107-4371 PH 662 434-8959
FAX 662 434-8959
CHESTER L MEAUX,PRES

COMANCHE OIL & GAS CO
505 N BIG SPRING ST STE 303
MIDLAND,TX 79701-4346 PH 432 686-7744
FAX 432 686-0627
W H GILMORE,JR,PRTNR
SAM F HURT,JR,PRTNR

COMANCHERIA ENERGY RESOURCES,LLC
14027 MEMORIAL DR #165
HOUSTON,TX 77079 PH 713 419-8013
FAX 281 847-0781 THILLIARD@BBLMCF.COM
THERESA HILLARD,VP & CFO

COMBINED RESOURCES GROUP
401 SONTERRA BLVD STE 215
SAN ANTONIO,TX 78258
PH 210 490-4910 EXT 110
HARVEY GARTLEY,PRES

COMBS AND COMPANY
P O BOX 5074
BEAUMONT,TX 77706-5074 PH 713 833-1440
DONALD L COMBS,PRTNR
ROBERT F COMBS,PRTNR
TALMADGE COMBS,AGT
VILLAGE MILLS,TX OFFICE - P O BOX 38
77663

COMBS TALMADGE,TRUSTEE
P O BOX 5074
BEAUMONT,TX 77706-5074 PH 409 833-1440

COMCO
PO BOX 1425,435 W WASHINGTON ST
SPRINGFIELD,IL 62705-1425 PH 217 522-5407
FAX 217 522-8785
LES COLLINS,PRES
FRANK VALA,VP

COMDISCO EXPLORATION,INC SEE
DUNCAN ENERGY COMPANY

COMEAUX LEON & ASSOCIATES
PO BOX 53922,305 LA RUE FRANCE (70508)
LAFAYETTE,LA 70505-3922
PH 337 233-9839 FAX 337 233-2131
LCOMEAUX@COX-INTERNET.COM
WILLIAM S MCALISTER JR,GEOL
DAVID W COMEAUX,GEOL
RANDY MCALISTER,GEOL
AMANDA FISHER,GEOTECH
CHERYL UMSTEAD,OFC MGR

COMEGYS W M,JR,IND OPR
333 TEXAS ST STE 825
SHREVEPORT,LA 71101 PH 318 221-5201

COMERICA BANK-TEXAS
PO BOX 650282
DALLAS,TX 75265-0282 PH 713 722-6540
FAX 713 722-6550
CHARLES E HALL

COMGO,LLC
6855 OAK HILL BLVD

TYLER,TX 75703 PH 903 534-8811

COMMONWEALTH CREDIT SERVICES,INC
TITLE SEARCH/APPRAISALS/LAND TITLE INS
PO BOX 761,27 N MAIN ST
GREENSBURG,PA 15601-0027
PH 724 834-0817 FAX 724 836-6596
DONALD WAXTER,PRES,CEO
STEPHEN WAXTER,EXEC VP

COMMUNITY ENERGY CO
76 MAPLE ST
MANCHESTER,NH 03103-5616 PH 603 669-5713
WILLIAM TROMBLEY,PRES

COMPASS BANK
SUCCESSOR TO RIVER OAKS TRUST CO
PO BOX 4886,2001 KIRBY DR STE 311
HOUSTON,TX 77210-4886 PH 713 831-5878
FAX 713 831-5773 COMPASSWEB.COM
JANA.REYNOLDS@COMPASSBANK.COM
JANA REYNOLDS,VP,MGR,TRUST OIL,GAS &
REAL ESTATE

COMPASS DRILLING SERVICES INC
15754 TUCKERTON RD
HOUSTON,TX 77095 PH 281 856-8735
FAX 281 856-9432
WWW.COMPASSDIRECTIONAL.COM
JASON MCCALL,REG SALES TECH SUPPORT
PH 832 392-8335 JMCCALL@COMPASSDSI.COM
ALICE,TX OFFICE - SOUTH TEXAS OPERS
4495 S HWY 281,78332 PH 361 664-5100
FAX 361 664-2123
CARMICHAELS,PA OFFICE - NORTHEAST OPERS
2018 E ROY FURMAN HWY,15320
PH 724 966-2370 724 966-2371
FAX 724 966-2372

COMPASS ROYALTY MANAGMENT
15601 N DALLAS PKWY STE 900
ADDISON,TX 75001-6098
PH 972 720-1888 FAX 972 720-1899
WWW.COMPASSROYALTYMANAGEMENT.COM
FRED O HULL,SR COUNSEL
DENNIS SUTTON,INV REL

COMPLETION SERVICES INC
PO BOX 179,210 SECOND ST
SAINT MARYS,WV 26170-0179 PH 304 684-7686
PAUL WILLIAMS,PRES

COMPLETION TOOL COMPANY SEE
CTC INTERNATIONAL

COMPRESSCO PARTNERS L.P.
101 PARK AVENUE, STE 1200
OKLAHOMA CITY,OK 73102
PH 800 259-2714 PH 405 677-0221
FAX 405 677-0605
WWW.COMPRESSCO.COM
SALES@COMPRESSCO.COM
RONALD J FOSTER,PRES/CEO
RFOSTER@COMPRESSCO.COM
SHERI VANHOOSER,SR VP,SLS & BUS DEV
SVANHOOSER@COMPRESSCO.COM
TED GARNER,VP,ENGINEERING
TGARNER@COMPRESSCO.COM
KEVIN BOOK,VP INTL OPERS
KBOOK@COMPRESSCO.COM
PERMIAN BASIN OFFICE- PH 432 556-7499
CLAY GOOD,SALES ENGR CGOOD@COMPRESS-
CO.COM
OKLAHOMA CITY,OK OFFICE-

TYLER STUCKS,REG SALES MGR
BSTUCKS@COMPRESSCO.COM
KS-OK PANHANDLE - TX OFFICE
PH 580 370-0886
EVERETT (JR) LONG,SALES ENGR
ELONG@COMPRESSCO.COM
ARKOMA BASIN - NE OK - E KS SALES OFFICE
PH 918 509-0403
RANDY NEAL,SALES ENGR
RNEAL@COMPRESSCO.COM
LLOYD CROWNOVER,SLS ENGR
KEN REAGAN,SLS ENGR
LCROWNOVER@COMPRESSCO.COM
APPALACHAIN REGION OFFICE-PH 814 323-2354
JEREMY JACOBY,SALES ENGR
JJACOBY@COMPRESSCO.COM
EAST TX SALES OFFICE-
SEAN MCARDLE,SALES ENGR
SMCARDLE@COMPRESSCO.COM
ARK-LA-TX OFFICE- PH 318 470-0411
MARK HEDGES,REG SLS MGR
MHEDGES@COMPRESSCO.COM
MS & SO LA SALES OFFICE - PH 337 962-6569
MIKE BURTON,SALES ENGR
MBURTON@COMPRESSCO.COM
FT WORTH BASIN SALES OFFICE -
PH 817 239-4633
JOE SUGREK,SALES ENGR
JSUGAREK@COMPRESSCO.COM
HOUSTON,TX OFFICE - PH 713 408-4202
ROBERT DEAL,SALES ENGR
RDEAL@COMPRESSCO.COM
SOUTH TX OFFICE- PH 361 533-4535
THOMAS MANN,SALES ENGR
TMANN@COMPRESSCO.COM
CALIFORNIA OFFICE- PH 510 501-2606
LYNDY AFFELD,SALES ENGR
LAFFELD@COMPRESSCO.COM
N ROCKIES-WY & UT OFFICE -
PH 303 903-4301
CRAIG MOORE,REG SALES MGR
CMOORE@COMPRESSCO.COM
SAN JUAN BASIN-W CO OFFICE -
PH 505 486-3924
STEVE MAGEE,SALES ENGR
SMAGEE@COMPRESSCO.COM
CANADA SALES OFFICE - 5050 76TH AVE SE
CALGARY,AB,T2C 2X2 PH 403 991-2707
ALEX FLOURNY,TECH SALES REP
BFLOURNOY@COMPRESSCO.COM

COMPRESSOR SYSTEMS,INC
PO BOX 60760,3809 S FM 1788
MIDLAND,TX 79711-0760
PH 432 563-1170 FAX 432 563-0820
WWW.COMPRESSOR-SYSTEMS.COM
FIRSTNAME.LASTNAME@COMPRESSOR-SYS-
TEMS.COM
TIM KNOX,PRES,COO
LLOYD ROBERTS,VP,TECH SUPPORT SVCS
HANK SHEERAN,VP SALES
NINA VALLES,VP ACCT & IT
ERICH HARDAWAY,REG SLS MGR SVCS
ANTHONY SPEARS,MANUFACTURING MGR
- PERMIAN BASIN BUSINESS UNIT -
MIDLAND,TX OFFICE - PO BOX 60760
79711 PH 432 563-1170

MARK RILEY,BUS UNIT MGR
JOHN HAYNES,ACCT MGR
DAVID STONE,ACCT MGR
- GULF COAST BUSINESS UNIT -
VICTORIA,TX OFFICE - PO BOX 3425,77903
11503 US HWY 59 N,77905 PH 361 576-6827
BRANDON IMMENHAUSER,BUS UNIT MGR
BECKY HAYNES,ACCT MGR
HOUSTON,TX OFFICE - 17171 PARK ROW
STE 175,77084 PH 281 599-3900
ROY JACOBS,VP BUS DEV
BRAD BENGE,VP COMPRESSION SVCS
CHRIS JACOBS,ACCT MGR
RUSS DWORKSHAK,REG SLS MGR
JIM WADE,ACCT MGR
JOHN DAUER,GULF COAST BUS UNIT MGR
MANUEL MORALES,MGR INTERNATIONAL
RICHARD LOBRECHT,SR SALES COORD
LARRY NAYLOR,STRATEGIC ACCT MGR
JIM REGITZ,STRATEGIC ACCT MGR
JON WILLIAMS,ACCT MGR
TIM SMITH,ACCT MGR
THE WOODLANDS,TX OFFICE - 2203 TIMBERLOCH
PL,STE 218A,77380 PH 281 298-8875
JEFF LEE,ACCT MGR
WILLIAM HOLLOWAY,MGR INT BUS DEV
MCALLEN,TX OFFICE - 36868-B FM 490
EDINBURG,TX 78541 PH 956 842-3606
RANDY WHITE,ACCT MGR
UNION CITY,PA OFFICE - 7900 CLEMENS RD
16438 PH 814 438-2115
KARL BALLOG,ACCT MGR
- MID-CONTINENT BUSINESS UNIT -
OKLAHOMA CITY,OK OFFICE - 5300 S
ROCKWELL,73179-1076 PH 405 745-4274
STEVE O'BRIEN,BUS UNIT MGR
RYAN COCKLIN,ACCT MGR
MATTHEW PITCOCK,ACCT MGR
TULSA,OK OFFICE - 6140 S 104TH EAST AVE
STE 500,74133 PH 918 250-9471
MIKE STUBENHOFER,ACCT MGR
WEATHERFORD,TX OFFICE - 4030 W I-20,76088
PH 817 596-3306
JEFF LUTKE,ACCT MGR
PERRYTON,TX OFFICE - PO BOX 967
79070-0967,917 S LOOP 143 WEST,79070
PH 806 435-4274
LONGVIEW,TX OFFICE - 3670 EAST LOOP DR
75602 PH 903 757-3857
MIKE KINARD,ACCT MGR
- SAN JUAN BUSINESS UNIT -
FARMINGTON,NM OFFICE - 5995 US HWY 64
87499 PH 505 632-5501
DOUG DEAREN,BUS UNIT MGR
- ROCKY MOUNTAIN BUSINESS UNIT -
WESTMINSTER,CO OFFICE - 1400 W 122 AVE
STE 260,80234 PH 720 887-9023
BRAD BOYLES,SR ACCT MGR
SCOTT OLTROGGE,BUS UNIT MGR
KIP MARCH,ACCT MGR
LANCE PEREZ,ACCT MGR
VERNAL,UT OFFICE - PO BOX 640,84078
4764 S & 4625 EAST,84078 PH 435 789-8190
JIM LUBE,ACCT MGR

COMPUTALOG USA SEE
SEE WEATHERFORD

COMPUTER PLACE
52205 WAREHIME RD
CUMBERLAND,OH 43732-9717
PH 740 826-2667 WWW.HELPCOMPUTING.COM
FRANK DONIA

COMSTOCK OIL AND GAS,LP
5300 TOWN & COUNTRY BLVD STE 500
FRISCO,TX 75034-6881 PH 972 668-8800
FAX 972 668-8822
M JAY ALLISON,PRES,CEO
ROLAND BURNS,SR VP,CFO
MARK WILLIAMS,VP OPERS
DAN PRESLEY,VP,ACCT & CONTROLLER
STEVE NEUKOM,VP,MKTG
D DALE GILLETTE,VP LAND & GEN COUNSEL
RICK SINGER,VP FIN REPORTING
WALTER BURKS,ETX DIST MGR
BLAINE STRIBLING,CORP DEV MGR
GERRY BLACKSHEAR,G&G MGR
LANCE LAMONS,DRLG MGR
DAN HARRISON,NLA DIST MGR
RHONDA KASCHMITTER,REGULATORY MGR
JAY CALLARMAN,STX DIST MGR
LARAE SANDERS,LDMN MGR
VICKI SNIDER,LDMN
MARSHALL,TX (EAST TX) DIST OFFICE -
705 COX RD 75672 PH 903 927-1100
FAX 903 927-1133
BILL DONEGHUE,PROD SUPT
LIVINGSTON,TX (SOUTH TX) DIST OFFICE -
623 THREE BRIDGE RD 77351
PH 936 563-2868 FAX 936 563-2882
CHAM KING,PROD SUPT
ARCADIA,LA (NORTH LA) DIST OFFICE -
PO BOX 723 71001 PH 318 263-8322
GARY GOODSON,PROD FRMN

COMSTOCK RESOURCES,INC
5300 TOWN & COUNTRY BLVD STE 500
FRISCO,TX 75034-6881 PH 972 668-8800
FAX 972 668-8822
M JAY ALLISON,PRES,CEO
ROLAND BURNS,SR VP,CFO
MARK WILLIAMS,VP OPERS
DAN PRESLEY,VP,ACCT & CONTROLLER
STEVE NEUKOM,VP,MKTG
D DALE GILLETTE,VP LAND & GEN COUNSEL
RICK SINGER,VP FIN REPORTING
WALTER BURKS,ETX DIST ENGR
BLAINE STRIBLING,CORP DEV MGR
GERRY BLACKSHEAR,G&G MGR
LANCE LAMONS,DRLG MGR
DAN HARRISON,NLA DIST MGR
RHONDA KASCHMITTER,REGULATORY MGR
JAY CALLARMAN,STX DISTR MGR
LARAE SANDERS,LDMN MGR
VICKI SNIDER,LDMN
MARSHALL,TX (EAST TX) DIST OFFICE -
705 COX RD,75672 PH 903 927-1100
FAX 903 927-1133
BILL DONEGHUE,PROD SUPT
LIVINGSTON,TX (SOUTH TX) DIST OFFICE -
625 THREE BRIDGE RD,77351
PH 936 563-2868 FAX 936 563-2882
CHAM KING,PROD SUPT
ARCADIA (NORTH LA) DIST OFFICE -
PO BOX 723,71001 PH 318 263-8322

GARY GOODSON,PROD FRMN

CONATSER W E,CO,INC
17 CHATEAU MAGDELAINE DR
KENNER,LA 70065-2026 PH 504 469-2496
WECONATSER@AOL.COM

CONCENTRIC PIPE & TOOL RENTALS SEE
SUPERIOR ENERGY SERVICES COMPANY

CONCHO EQUITY HOLDING CORP SEE
COG OPERATING LLC

CONCHO OIL & GAS CORP SEE
COG OPERATING LLC

CONCHO OILFIELD SERVICES
P&A SPECIALISTS,WELL SVCS,CEMENTING
PO BOX 2710
ALBANY,TX 76430 PH 325 762-3300
FAX 325 762-3992 WWW.CONCHOOILFIELD.COM
INFO@CONCHOOILFIELD.COM
KYLE BRYAN,OPERS MGR PH 325 762-4594
RANDY HUDSON,PRES PH 325 762-5026
PAULA TORREZ,HR/OFC MGR PH 325 762-3300

CONCORD LAND & MINERALS,LLC
PO BOX 671099
DALLAS,TX 75367-1099 PH 214 707-7535
FAX 214 572-2699 WWW.TRUNKBAY.NET
BENNY DUNCAN,MGR
BDUNCAN@TRUNKBAY.NET

CONCORD OIL COMPANY
100 W HOUSTON ST STE 1500
SAN ANTONIO,TX 78205-1424 PH 210 224-4455
FAX 210 224-6430
REAGAN S MCCOY,VP

CONCORD OPERATING,INC
PO BOX 1897
ROCKPORT,TX 78381-1897
PH 830 769-3955 FAX 830 769-2261
BARRY LAIDLAW,PRES

CONCORDE RESOURCES,LLC
820 GESSNER RD STE 1650
HOUSTON,TX 77024 PH 713 224-2500
FAX 713 224-6096
WWW.CONCORDERESOURCES.COM
CARL D CAMPBELL,PRES
CARL@CONCORDERESOURCES.COM

CONDOR PETROLEUM CORP
PO BOX 80901,714 E KALISTE SALOOM #D-3
LAFAYETTE,LA 70508-0901 PH 318 261-0190
FAX 318 269-1155
W WAYNE EVITT,SECY/TREAS
CHRISTI JORDAN,BOOKKEEPER
GIL SMITH,GEOL

CONLEY & ASSOCIATES,INC
1304 E 2ND ST
BLOOMINGTON,IN 47401 PH 213 947-3838
JACK F CONLEY,PRES
W Z HOLDEN,SECY/TREAS
JOHN CONLEY,GEOL

CONMACO
1602 ENGINEERS RD
BELLE CHASSE,LA 70037-3127
PH 504 394-7330 FAX 504 393-8715
WWW.CONMACO.COM
SALES@CONMACO.COM
DUANE P SMITH,CEO
RALPH ROSS,PRES
MICHAEL G FAVALARO,GEN MGR

CONN ENERGY INC
5 SANCTUARY BLVD STE 201
MANDEVILLE,LA 70471
PH 504 835-4546 FAX 504 835-4351
WILEY CONN,PRES
RACHEL MILLER,ACCT MGR

CONNECTION TECHNOLOGY SEE
SUPERIOR ENERGY SERVICES

CONOCOPHILLIPS COMPANY
PO BOX 2197,600 N DAIRY ASHFORD (77079)
HOUSTON,TX 77252-2197 PH 281 293-1000
WWW.CONOCOPHILLIPS.COM
- EXECUTIVES -
RYAN LANCE,CHRMN/CEO
MATT FOX,EXEC VP EXPL & PROD
AL HIRSHBERG,EXEC VP TECH & PROJECTS
JEFF SHEETS,EXEC VP FIN & CFO
DON WALLETTE,EXEC VP BUS DEV & COMMERCIAL
ANDREW LUNDQUIST,SR VP/GOVT AFFAIRS
JANET LANGFORD KELLY,SR VP LEGAL,GEN
COUNSEL & CORP SECY
ELLEN DESANCTIS,VP INVESTOR RELS &
COMMUNICATIONS
SHEILA FELDMAN,VP HUMAN RESOURCES
T.E JOHANSEN,PRES/CONOCOPHILLIPS ALASKA
BIJ AGARWAL,VP/COMMERCIAL ASSETS
BILLIE R KORSUNSKIY,MGR HR
JOE A FARRELL,VP/CHIEF COUNSEL
WES HEINOLD,HSE MGR/ALASKA
BOB HEINRICH,VP FIN/ALASKA
NICK OLDS,VP/NORTH SLOPE OPERS & DEV
SCOTT JEPSEN,VP/EXTERNAL AFFAIRS
- CONOCOPHILLIPS ALASKA -
ANCHORAGE,AK OFFICE - 700 G ST 99501
PH 907 276-1215
COPALASKAINFO@CONOCOPHILLIPS.COM

CONQUEST DRILLING FLUIDS,INC
9200 LEONIDAS HORTON RD
CONROE,TX 77304-2448 PH 936 539-1777
FAX 936 539-1983
CONQUEST@CONSOLIDATED.NET
GRANT L PETERSON

CONQUEST EXPLORATION COMPANY SEE
AMERICAN EXPLORATION COMPANY

CONSOLIDATED PIPE & SUPPLY
15810 PARK TEN PLACE STE 180
HOUSTON,TX 77084 PH 281 558-4413

CONSOLIDATED RESOURCES OF AMERICA
898 PINE VALLEY LN
CINCINNATI,OH 45245-3323 PH 513 721-8802

CONTANGO OIL & GAS COMPANY
717 TEXAS AVE STE 2900
HOUSTON,TX 77002 PH 713 236-7400
FAX 713 236-4424 WWW.CONTANGO.COM
ALLAN KEEL,PRES/CEO
JOE GRADY,SR VP/CFO
STEVE MENGLE,SR VP ENGRG
TOMMY ATKINS,SR VP EXPL
CARL ISAAC,SR VP OPERS

CONTINENTAL LABORATORIES
6600 FAIRBANKS N HOUSTON RD
HOUSTON,TX 77040-4309 PH 713 460-0780
FAX 713 460-0788 CONTINENTALLABS.COM
CONTLAB@CONTINENTALLABS.COM
PATRICK REMMERS,PRES

(800) 375-1838
WWW.ARMSTRONGOIL.COM

If your company is not listed in our directory, we would like to list it in the next edition of our directory - absolutely FREE. To be listed, we need it in writing. Please fill out the form below or visit our website and fill out the listing form there. If you wish to use the form below, just mail it or fax it to us at (800) 375-1838.

Company Name _____

Physical Address _____

Mailing address if different _____

Phone # _____ Fax # _____

Email address _____

Key personnel and their titles:

_____

_____

_____

_____

If you need to list additional offices, please include on letterhead

To Order Call (800) 375-1838 or
www.armstrongoil.com

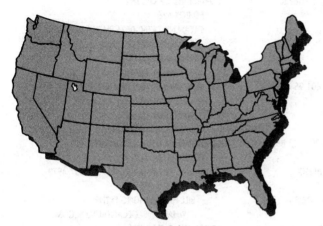

Nationwide Office Directory
Full 8 1/2" x 11" book size
Entire Nation
over 16,000 companies listed

$ 225 (no discount available)

Nationwide Mini Directory (Briefcase)
Small Size 5 1/4" x 8 1/4"
Same complete nationwide information
over 16,000 companies listed
$ 140 w / discount*

Texas Directory
Includes
Texas and S.E. New Mexico

$ 80 w / discount*

Louisana / Gulf Coast Directory
Includes the following states:
Gulf coast of Texas, Louisana
Arkansas, Mississippi,
Alabama, Georgia, Florida
N.E. states
$80 w / discount*

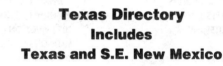

Rocky Mountain / Central U.S. Directory
Includes the following states:
West Texas and Panhandle of Texas
Oklahoma, New Mexico
Colorado, Alaska and all
Western U.S. states

$80 w / discount*

* discount applies when invoice is paid within 30 days after receipt of order.

ANTHONY WELKA,VP

STEVE PRIMOFF,SALES MGR

CONTINENTAL RESOURCES INC-ILLINOIS DIV

PO BOX 749

MOUNT VERNON,IL 62864-0749

PH 618 242-1717 FAX 618 242-7056

RICHARD STRAETER,PRES

MICHAEL PAYNE,VP,OPERS

LEW MURRAY,GEOL

WAYNE PRESSON,LDMN

NIDA WOODFALL,HUM RES MGR

OWENSBORO,KY OFFICE - PO BOX 21626

42304-0626 PH 270 926-4656

RICK KENCZKA,PROD SUPT

ED KOHLER,SR ENGR,DRLG

CONTINENTAL RESOURCES,INC

OIL & GAS EXPLORATION

PO BOX 26900

OKLAHOMA CITY,OK 73126 PH 405 234-9000

WWW.CLR.COM

HAROLD G HAMM,CHRMN OF BD/CEO

JOHN HART,SR VP/CFO/TREAS

RICK BOTT,PRES/COO

STEVE OWEN,SR VP LAND

JACK STARK,SR VP EXPL

RICHARD MUNCRIEF,SR VP OPERS

CHRIS HAUGEN,VP RESO DEV

CONTINENTAL SPECIALTIES,INC

PO BOX 69

FRESNO,TX 77545-0069 PH 281 431-0502

FAX 281 431-1441 CONTINENTAL@WT.NET

OLEN OVERSTREET,PRES

JAMES MOFFITT,VP

ROBBIE OVERSTREET,SECY/TREAS

CONTOUR ENERGY CO SEE

SAMSON COMPANIES

CONTRACT ENERGY,LLC

OIL & GAS OPERATING SERVICES

2015 CROCKER ST

HOUSTON,TX 77006-1303 PH 713 278-9100

FAX 713 278-9111

OFFICE@CONTRACTENERGY.COM

WWW.CONTRACTENERGY.COM

CONTRACT LAND STAFF,LLC

2245 TEXAS DR STE 200

SUGAR LAND,TX 77479-1468

PH 281 240-3370 FAX 281 240-5009

BRENT LEFTWICH,CEO

LAURIE MARKOE,PRES & COO

CONVERGENT ENERGY GROUP,LLC

PO BOX 885

TOMBALL,TX 77377-0885

PH 713 683-9969 FAX 713 683-9940

ERIC ADAMS

DAVID COCHRAN

JOHN HAYNES

LUC CHABOT

CONVEXX OIL & GAS,INC

3861 AMBASSADOR CAFFRY STE 400

LAFAYETTE,LA 70503-5267

PH 337 735-3300 FAX 337 237-5158

DAVID ETIENNE,VP EXPL

ARTHUR J PRICE,VP

JERRY YUNKER,GEOL

DON SOBBA,GEOL

LANNY JACKSON,GEOL

JAMES CRANE,GEOPHY

MARK HILLIARD,GEOL

COOK A M

510 BUENA VISTA BLVD

HOUMA,LA 70360-7522 PH 504 879-1363

COOK DRILLING COMPANY

805 HILLCREST ST

FORT WORTH,TX 76107 PH 817 732-6730

FAX 817 731-2149

EDWARD COOK,PRES

GAYLE WEBB COOK,SECY

COOK ENERGY,INC

105 LIVINGSTON DR

MADISON,MS 39110-7772 PH 601 954-7689

PHILIP L COOK,JR,OWNER

COOK EXPLORATION COMPANY

P O BOX 2643

LONGVIEW,TX 75606-2643 PH 903 753-8661

JAY COOK,PRES

COOK INVESTMENTS,A PARTNERSHIP

PO BOX 460,225 N LAFAYETTE ST

GREENVILLE,MI 48838-0460 PH 616 754-7149

754-7140 FAX 616 754-5947

BYRON J COOK,CO-OWNER

WILLIAM F COOK,CO-OWNER

JEFFREY D COOK,LDMN

COOK PHILIP L,JR,CONS PETR GEOL

105 LIVINGSTON DR

MADISON,MS 39110 PH 601 954-7689

COOK ROYALTIES

C/O LYNNE J BALDWIN,GEN PRTNR

P O BOX 241093

OMAHA,NE 68124 PH 402 333-3300

FAX 402 333-5770 LBALDWIN@BHMI.COM

COOKE ENERGY CO

OIL & GAS PRODUCTION

5019 ROUNDHILL

SAN ANTONIO,TX 78250-4743 PH 210 681-1606

E E COOKE

COOPER GREGORY H

PETROLEUM LAND SERVICES

PO BOX 1263

GULFPORT,MS 39502-1263 PH 251 610-1501

GCOOP@GRONTIERNET.NET

COOPER MANUFACTURING & SUPPLY,INC

PO BOX 16573,4931 E BROAD ST

LAKE CHARLES,LA 70616-6573

PH 337 436-1318 FAX 337 436-1223

WWW.COOPMFG.COM COOPERMFG@AOL.COM

LARRY COOPER,PRES

COOPER OIL TOOL SEE

CAMERON

COOPERATIVE REFINING,LLC SEE

NATIONAL COOPERATIVE REFINERY ASSOC(NCRA)

COPAR INC

138 CEDAR LN

STARKVILLE,MS 39759-2618 PH 601 553-8306

FAX 601 924-1303 JTMCKEE27@GMAIL.COM

JAY T MCKEE,PRES

COPAS INTERPRETATIONS SEE

AUDITORS - OIL & GAS

COPELAND COOK TAYLOR & BUSH

A PROFESSIONAL ASSOC/ATTORNEYS AT LAW

PO BOX 6020,1076 HIGHLAND COLONY PKY

RIDGELAND,MS 39158-6020 PH 601 856-7200

FAX 601 856-7626 WWW.CCTB.COM

GLENN GATES TAYLOR GTAYLOR@CCTB.COM

C GLEN BUSH GBUSH@CCTB.COM

IAN AUSTIN IAUSTIN@CCTB.COM

C DALE SHEARER DSHEARER@CCTB.COM

JOHN N GEARY JR JGEARY@CCTB.COM

ALEXANDER L BONDURANT

ABONDURANT@CCTB.COM

COPPER RIDGE OIL,INC

PO BOX 626

OLEAN,NY 14760-0626 PH 716 372-4021

GREGORY J THROPP,PRES

COPPERFIELD ENERGY,LLC

6609 FALCON RIDGE LN

MCKINNEY,TX 75071 PH 972 984-1811

FAX 972 984-1812 QUICKCO@SBCGLOBAL.NET

ALAN D QUICK,MGR

WANDA K QUICK,MGR

COPPERHEAD OIL AND GAS LTD

PO BOX 414

LULING,TX 78648-0414 PH 512 557-4972

FAX 830 875-5301

BILL HALES,MNGNG PRTNR

WHALES@SAGECAPITALBANK.COM

CORAL OIL & GAS INC

5600 SAN FELIPE STE 4

HOUSTON,TX 77056 PH 713 222-7304

FAX 713 224-8101

DAVID B CHALMERS,CHRMN,CEO,PRES

MARY B JENKINS,SECY

CORBAN EXPLORER,INC

PO BOX 52368

LAFAYETTE,LA 70505-2368

PH 337 962-8439 JWALKERCORBAN@ATT.NET

CORBUT & ASSOCIATES LLC

1235 ANTOINE DR

HOUSTON,TX 77055-6920

PH 713 688-6266 FAX 713 688-6566

STEPHEN A CORBUT,CPL

CORBUT@CORBUTANDASSOCIATES.COM

CORDELE DEVELOPMENT CORPORATION

314 E COMMERCE ST STE 400

SAN ANTONIO,TX 78205-2907 PH 210 223-5564

FAX 210 223-9050

CORDELL OIL CO

PO BOX 921

KILGORE,TX 75663-0921

PH 903 984-3443 FAX 903 983-2526

PANCHO CORDELL,PRES

CORDOVA ENERGY SERVICES

1151 CROOKED STICK

PROSPER,TX 75078 PH 972 347-2835

GARY THOMAS

CORLEY TRUST,LLC

PO BOX 65

SMACKOVER,AR 71762-0065 PH 870 725-3928

CORMIER FRANK A AND ASSOCIATES,INC

120 HUGGINS RD

LAFAYETTE,LA 70506-5802

PH 337 984-5550 FAX 337 984-7215

FRANK A CORMIER,PRES,RES ENGR

CORNAY-LOWRY LAND & ABSTRACT,INC

PO BOX 52426

LAFAYETTE,LA 70505-2426 PH 337 235-9982

FAX 337 235-9335 WWW.CORNAY-LOWRY.COM

JAMES D CORNAY,PRES

DENNIS B LOWRY,VP

CORNE-LEMAIRE GROUP,AN ARCHITECTURAL CORP
111 RUE JEAN LAFITE STE 105
LAFAYETTE,LA 70508-3141 PH 318 232-0773
WAYNE L CORNE,ARCHITECT
PAUL D LEMAIRE,ARCHITECT

CORNELIUS,EDDIE & ASSOCIATES
15448 COUNTRY MANOR RD
LINDALE,TX 75771-2424 PH 903 882-1997
E E CORNELIUS III,PETR LDMN
ECORNELIUS@SUDDENLINK.NET

CORNERSTONE ENERGY,INC
12941 N FREEWAY STE 510
HOUSTON,TX 77060-1242 PH 281 872-9700
LARRY HOLT,PRES
JIM FOX,FIN & ADMIN
RON NEWBERRY,OPERS

CORNERSTONE RESOURCES, L.L.C.
2476 HWY 8 EAST
HOUSTON,MS 38851 PH 601 842-3539
ROX52DOC@AOL.COM
STANLEY KING,MGR

CORNWELL WELL SERVICE,INC
PO BOX 647,SMITHDALE RD
SUMMIT,MS 39666-0647 PH 601 684-4951
SUE CORNWELL,PRES
ROBERT DUNAWAY PH 601 248-8317
LANNY HURT PH 601 249-7943

CORONA CHARLES J,GEOL
7215 STONELEIGH DR
HARAHAN,LA 70123-4821 PH 504 737-6101
FAX 504 738-9653 CJCORONA@COX.NET

CORONADO ENERGY E&P COMPANY LLC SEE
EL PASO PRODUCTION & EXPLORATION

CORONADO MINING & MINERALS,INC
P O BOX 66312
BATON ROUGE,LA 70896-6312 PH 225 928-1822
FAX 225 927-9982
J B HANKS,PRES

CORPENING ENTERPRISES
4109 GLENWOOD DR
FORT WORTH,TX 76109-1633 PH 817 336-8126
JOSEPH D CORPENING
A V SCOTT CORPENING

CORPRO
COMPLETE CORING SERVICES & SYSTEMS
14103 INTERDRIVE W
HOUSTON,TX 77032 PH 281 776-5300
PH 888 436-9326 FAX 281 227-3115
WWW.CORPRO-GROUP.COM
NICHOLE HAMMONS,FIN CONTROLLER
KINMERLY BURNETT,A/P & MKTG
MICHELLE COUPE,A/R
LEANNE CZYRNIK,SR FIN ANALYST
TREVOR WHALEN,US OPERS MGR
DOUG BERRETT,CORE BIT DESIGN MGR
MISTY PARKER,SLS REPR
DAN WINDHAM,FLD SVCS MGR
- CORE MANUFACTURING DIVISION -
MIDLAND,TX OFFICE - 2003 COMMERCE DR
79703 PH 432 563-0775 FAX 432 563-4752
CLIFF PETERSON,SR FLD SVCS REPR
JOHN WOOD,SR FLD SRVC REPR
ZADE ZYR,FLD SRVC REPR
JESSE MARTIN,FLD SRVC REPR
RANDY MARTINEZ,CORING DEPT COORD
CLIFF VAN CUREN,FLD SRVC REPR

JAMES HARRISON,CORE HANDLING TECH
OKLAHOMA CITY,OK OFFICE - PO BOX 94007
1545 SE 39TH ST 73143 PH 405 672-3013
FAX 405 672-5025
KIRBY MCADAMS,US SLS MGR
RICHARD CORLEY,SLS MGR
DENVER,CO OFFICE - 600 17TH ST STE 2800S
PH 303 634-2233 FAX 303 260-6401
MARK WOOD,ROCKY MTN ACCT MGR
KURT HUEHL,US SALES MGR
NICK PERRY,TECH SALES ENGNR
INDIANA,PA OFFICE - 1700 SLEEPY HOLLOW RD
15701 PH 724 801-8015 FAX 724 801-8056
AARON MARTIN,FLD SRVC REPR
SCOTT ESGRO,FLD SRVC REPR
MIKE JENDRAL,NE SLS REPR

CORPUS CHRISTI AREA OIL SPILL CONTL ASSOC
OIL SPILL CLEAN UP & SUPPLIES SINCE 1971
PO BOX 717,1231 NAVIGATION BLVD
CORPUS CHRISTI,TX 78403-0717
PH 361 882-2656
TONY ALEJANDRO,PRES

CORPUS CHRISTI GEOLOGICAL LIBRARY,INC
615 LEOPARD ST STE 530
CORPUS CHRISTI,TX 78401-0628
PH 361 884-1362 WWW.CCGLDATA.ORG
CCGL@CCGL-CC.ORG

CORPUS CHRISTI LEASEHOLDS,INC
PO BOX 779
CORPUS CHRISTI,TX 78403-0779
PH 361 882-2001 FAX 361 883-5992
PAUL R HAAS,PRES
L A MCNEIL,VP
LESLIE W DUNN,SECY/TREAS

CORTEZ RESOURCES LLC
3131 MCKINNEY AVE STE 430
DALLAS,TX 75204 PH 214 628-9155
FAX 214 628-9160 WWW.CORTEZOIL.COM
INFO@CORTEZOIL.COM
J PATRICK COLLINS,PRES/CEO
MICHAEL F CATRINO,EX VP/COO
RYAN P ALLEN,VP-CONTROLLER/FIN
PEGGY S LOYD,VP ADMIN & BUS SVCS

CORUM PRODUCTION COMPANY
1212 ANTOINE DR
HOUSTON,TX 77055 PH 713 973-0525
CORUMPRODUCTION@ATT.NET
KEMP MCMILLAN,PRTNR
SCOTT STEPHENS,PRTNR
MARK DECKER,EXPL MGR
EILEEN DOEHRING,CONTROLLER
ANDREW YORK,PROJ MGR
JOHN MCMILLAN,REAL ESTATE MGR

CORY KENNETH W,LTD
6750 WEST LOOP S STE 1050
BELLAIRE,TX 77401-4198 PH 713 661-5911
FAX 713 661-2679
KENNETH W CORY,OWNER
MARK CORY,GEOL
PAT CHESNUT,LAND MGR
WALTER W WILLIS,CONTROLLER
SCOTT CORY,GAS MKTG
MARSHA TYREE,PROD ANALYST
DANIEL CORY, ENGR

COSARA ENERGY COMPANY,INC
12003 AUCKLAND PT

CYPRESS,TX 77429 PH 281 370-7807
RAYMOND N BLACKHALL,PRES

COSDEN OIL & CHEMICAL CO SEE
FINA OIL AND CHEMICAL CO

COSSUM ROBERT W,GEOL
2137 BRANARD ST
HOUSTON,TX 77098-2405 PH 713 759-2042

COTTON PETROLEUM CORPORATION SEE
APACHE CORPORATION

COTTON VALLEY PRODUCTIONS,INC/
COTTON VALLEY OPERATIONS,INC & COTTON
VALLEY INVESTMENTS,INC
2401 JUDSON RD STE 404
LONGVIEW,TX 75605 PH 903 295-8028
FAX 903 295-2068
H C WOOLSEY,PRES
C E THOMPSON,VP,OPERS
H CRAIG WOOLSEY,VP,INVESTMENTS
S A WOOLSEY,SECY/TREAS

COUGAR LAND SERVICES LLC
1600 HWY 6 STE 260
SUGAR LAND,TX 77478 PH 281 242-2244
BRUCE FULKER
BFULKER@COUGARLANDSERVICES.NET

COURTNEY CONTRACTING CORP
320 SPRINGDALE RD
VENETIA,PA 15367-1322 PH 724 941-5099
FAX 724 941-5121
ED COURTNEY,PRES

COUTRET AND ASSOCIATES,INC,PETR RES ENGRS
401 EDWARDS ST STE 810
SHREVEPORT,LA 71101-3148 PH 318 221-0482
FAX 318 221-3202 WWW.COUTRET.COM
ROBERT M MCGOWEN,PRES
HENRY C COUTRET JR,VP
TIMOTHY BROWN,ENGR
ROBET D LATHAM,ENGRG TECH

COVENANT OIL COMPANY,INC
P O BOX 5127
LAKE WYLIE,SC 29710-5001 PH 803 831-7441
FAX 803 831-7441
E NEIL MATHESON,PRES

COVEY RESOURCES COMPANY
1010 LAMAR ST STE 800
HOUSTON,TX 77002 PH 713 851-3555
STEVEN M COVEY SCOVEY8288@AOL.COM

COVINGTON AND ASSOCIATES CORPORATION
FULL SVC ENVIRON ENGRG & CONSULTING FIRM
2510 14TH ST STE 1010
GULFPORT,MS 39501-1984
PH 228 396-0486 FAX 228 396-0487
JOHN F SZABO,PE
RIMMER COVINGTON,CPL/ESA
LARS LARSON,PG
TONY DAMIANO

COVINGTON MICHAEL L,IND LDMN
501 W CHAPEL LN
MIDLAND,MI 48640-2912 PH 989 513-1404

COW CREEK CORPORATION
PO BOX 9832
THE WOODLANDS,TX 77387-9832
PH 281 364-7355 FAX 281 292-0801
M B B FRANTES,PRES

COWBOY ENERGY,INC
1624 WINDING VIEW
SAN ANTONIO,TX 78260 PH 210 364-4361

STEPHEN WORMSER,PRES

DAVID WORMSER,VP

COWBOY PIPELINE SERVICE COMPANY

1415 LOUISIANA STE 3800

HOUSTON,TX 77002

PH 713 652-5700 FAX 713 652-5720

A C SONNY DUBOSE,PRES

COWGILL & ASSOCIATES,LLC

PO BOX 72180

BOSSIER CITY,LA 71172-2180

PH 318 429-2170 FAX 318 429-1170

COWGILL@SUDDENLINK.NET

STEPHEN C COWGILL,MNGNG PRTNR

TERRIE WEILAND,OFC MGR

COWGILL ENERGY RESOURCES,LLC

PO BOX 72180

BOSSIER CITY,LA 71172-2180

PH 318 429-2170 FAX 318 429-1170

COWGILL@SUDDENLINK.NET

STEPHEN C COWGILL,MNGNG PRTNR

TERRIE WEILAND,OFC MGR

COWGIRL ENERGY,INC

1624 WINDING VIEW

SAN ANTONIO,TX 78260 PH 210 364-4361

DAVID WORMSER,PRES

CHARLSIE GOURE,VP

COX SMITH MATTHEWS,INC

112 E PECAN ST STE 1800

SAN ANTONIO,TX 78205 PH 210 554-5500

FAX 210 226-8395 WWW.COXSMITH.COM

KATY MOORE,SHRHLDR/TITLES

DAVID H O ROTH,SHRHLDR/LEASES

JAMES MARTY TRUSS,SHRHLDR/TITLES

PAUL SANTOYO,SHRHLDR/TITLES

COREY F WEHMEYER,SHRHLDR/TITLES

COX WELTON E,INDEPENDENT

PO BOX 1105

LULING,TX 78648-1105 PH 830 424-3508

WECOX@GVEC.NET

SEQUIN,TX OFFICE - PO BOX 1262,78156

PH 830 445-1119

COY OIL,INC

PO BOX 575

MOUNT VERNON,IN 47620-0575

PH 812 838-3146

MICHAEL G CASH,PRES

COYLE CONCORD OIL CO,LTD

615 BELKNAP PL

SAN ANTONIO,TX 78212-3413 PH 210 735-6181

PAT LANGE PAT@LPCPA.COM

CP INTERNATIONAL,INC (A CPTDC COMPANY)

OILFIELD EQUIPMENTS SUPPLIER

10681 HADDINTON DR STE 130

HOUSTON,TX 77043

PH 713 464-8890 FAX 713 464-5537

CHRIS LI,GEN MGR LICM@CPTDCUSA.COM

CPAC SEE

COMPACT PUMPING & COIL SPECIALISTS,INC

CPN,INC

NATIONWIDE GEOLOGICAL DRAFTING SVC/EXPL

115 TRACESIDE DR

NATCHEZ,MS 39120 PH 601 445-5026

CPNINC1@BELLSOUTH.NET

JAMES CLARK NERREN,CERTIFIED PETR GEOL

CRABTREE OPERATING CO

2510 CRESTVIEW

MAGNOLIA,AR 71753-4336

PH 870 234-6020 FAX 870 234-1831

SAMMYCRABTREE@ATT.NET

CRAFT EXPLORATION COMPANY,LLC

7720 OLD CANTON RD,STE C-1

MADISON,MS 39110

PH 601 427-9009 FAX 601 427-9119

STEVEN H CRAFT,MGR STEVECRAFT@ATT.NET

TYE DENSFORD,GEO PH 601 427-9009

TYEDENSFORD@THECRAFTCOMPANIES.COM

CRAFT PAUL H,CPL

110 EASTHAVEN CIR

BRANDON,MS 39042-2806 PH 601 825-7905

CRAIG JACK

PO BOX 921

KILGORE,TX 75663-0921 PH 903 984-3443

CHARLA ROLPH,AGENT

CRAIG OIL COMPANY OIL PROD

105 N NEWTON AVE

EL DORADO,AR 71730 PH 870 863-6337

CRAIG ROBERT TUT

PO BOX 6873

TYLER,TX 75701-6873 PH 903 561-6242

FAX 903 561-6250

CRAIG WILLIAM L,IND GEOL & ENGR

PO BOX 51225

LAFAYETTE,LA 70505-1225 PH 337 234-4288

CRATON ENERGY CORP SEE

ARCHON RESOURCES LLC

CRAWFORD ENERGY INC

770 S POST OAK LN STE 520

HOUSTON,TX 77056-1938 PH 713 626-2637

FAX 713 626-9698

A GAIL CRAWFORD,PRES

CRAWFORD HUGHES ENERGY,LLC

770 S POST OAK LN #520

HOUSTON,TX 77056 PH 713 626-2627

FAX 713 626-9698

A GAIL CRAWFORD,PRES

TOM HUGHES,EXEC VP-OPERS

LYNDA MOCZYGEMBA,VP OPERS

PAM DOWNING,ACCT

STEPHEN HILL,LDMN

CRAWFORD MARK L

PO BOX 23005

CORPUS CHRISTI,TX 78403-3005

PH 361 815-2660

CRAWFORD WEYMAN W,PETROLEUM CONSULTANT

10026 SUGAR HILL

HOUSTON,TX 77042-1540 PH 713 782-0595

CRC-EVANS

7011 HIGH LIFE DR

HOUSTON,TX 77066 PH 800 664-9224

PH 832 249-3100 FAX 832 249-3292

HOUSTON,TX OPERATIONS ONSHORE-WEST

7011 HIGH LIFE DR 77066 PH 800 664-9224

PH 832 249-3100 FAX 832 249-3292

SALES@CRC-EVANS.COM

HOUSTON,TX OFFSHORE AMERICAS - 7011 HIGH

LIFE DR 77066 PH 832 249-3100

CATHERINE.WENDE@SBDINC.COM

HOUSTON,TX STANLEY INSPECTION - 9977 WEST

SAM HOUSTON PKWY N STE 140 77064

PH 713 771-5446 FAX 713 771-5457

SALES@MICROALLOYING.COM

TULSA,OK-MANUFACTURING ONSHORE

10700 E INDEPENDENCE 74116

PH 918 438-2100 FAX 918 438-6913

SALES@CRC-EVANS.COM

TULSA OK-PIPELINE SUPPLY STORE

1134 N GARNETT RD 74116 PH 918 438-1050

DAVID.KIMBALL@SBDINC.COM

MONTOURSVILLE,PA-PIPELINE SUPPLY STORE

232 HOWARD ST STE 1,17754 PH 570 505-7450

BRIAN.CARLIN@SBDINC.COM

CALGARY,ALBERTA-STANLEY INSPECTION

5025 51 ST S.E. T2B 3S7

EDMONTON,CANADA-CANADA LTD

2005-80 AVE AB T6P 1P8

PH 1 780 440-2005 FAX 1 780 440-4952

KEN.NETTER@SBDINC.COM

WESTHILL,ABERDEEN,U K - OFFSHORE

3 ABERCROMBIE COURT,AMALL BUSINESS PARK

AB32 6FE PH 44 1224 766660

INFO@CRCOFFSHORE.COM

JOHN.WATSON@CRCOFFSHORE.COM

INVERGORDON ROSS-SHIRE,SCB-OFFSHORE

OPERATIONAL BASE - 18-21 SUPPLY BASE

SHORE ROAD 1V18 0EX PH 44 1349 855 150

INFO@CRCOFFSHORE.COM

BURNLEY,UK - FIELD JOINT COATING PIPELINE

PIPELINE INDUCTION HEAT

THE PIPELINE CENTRE FARRINGTON ROAD

ROSSENDALE RD INDUSTRIAL ESTATE BB11 5SW

PH 44 1282 415 323 FAX 44 1282 415 326

SALES@PIH.CO.UK DBELL@PIH.CO.UK

ALNESS,ROSS-SHIRE,UK - OFFSHORE HEADQTRS

PIPELINES HOUSE,3 DAIL NAN ROCAS

TEANINICH INDUSTRIAL ESTATE 1V17 OPH

PH 44 1349 887 200 INFO@CRCOFFSHORE.COM

SAO PAULO,BRAZIL - LATIN AMERICAN SALES

ALAMEDA SANTOS,1940 13' FIR,01418-200

PH 55(15)3342-4510 FAX 55(11)3149-7414

ANDRE.DECASTRO@SBDINC.COM

IVRY SUR SEINE,FRANCE - SOMICO

IMMEUBLE CAP DE SEINE

45/47 BOULEVARD PAUL VAILIANT COUTURIER

94200 PH 33 1 49 87 23 54

FAX 33 1 49 87 20 75

SOMICO-SALE@SBDINC.COM

ZEEWOLDE,NETHERLANDS - ONSHORE EAST

FABRICAGEWEG 28,3899 AV

PH 31 36 711 7500 FAX 31 36 711 7501

NLSALES@SBDINC.COM

PASIR GUDANG,MALAYASIA-INTERNATIONAL

SDN BHD OFFSHORE

PTD 188731,JALAN KONTENA 3

KAWASAN PELABUHAN JOHOR,81750

PH 60 7 254 9000 FAX 60 7 252 3594

IAN.DIXON@CRCOFFSHORE.COM

JOHANNESBURG,SOUTH AFRICA - INSPECTIONS

121 KOOMHOF RD % FLEMING STR

POWERHOUSE UNIT A,MEADOWDALE EXT 2,2008

PH 27(0)11 453 4115 FAX 27(0)11 453 0738

DUBAI,U.A.E. - MIDDLE EAST INSPECTIONS

AL QUSAIS,PO BOX 62574

PH 971 4 267 9989 FAX 971 4 267 9585

ABU DHABI,UAE - PIH SERVICES ME

% AL KHAJA PIMEX LLC

ICAD 1,MUSAFFAH,PO BOX 42766

PH 971 2 697 6100 FAX 971 2 551 2296

SALES@PIHME.COM

MADINAT QABOOS,SULTANATE OF OMA
PIH SERVICES ME LLC,PO BOX 289,CODE # 115
 PH 968 24 595 766 FAX 968 24 595 073
 SALES@PIHME.COM
CREAGER R H,INC
 PO BOX 1149
 MANDEVILLE,LA 70470-1149 PH 504 469-6432
 DAVID MCDONALD,PRES
 WWW.RHCREAGER.COM
 SALES@RHCREAGER.COM
CREDO OIL COMPANY
 524 E PASCAGOULA ST
 JACKSON,MS 39201-4309 PH 601 354-8755
 JAMES L CUMMINGS JR,PRES
 ANN HALL,SECY
CREE OIL COMPANY
 PO BOX 53902
 LAFAYETTE,LA 70505-3902 PH 337 261-0800
 FAX 337 261-0803
 HARDY F EDMISTON JR,PRES
 EDNA MECHE,ADMIN ASST
CREEDE MINERALS LTD DBA CREEDE,LTD
 PO BOX 781555
 SAN ANTONIO,TX 78278 PH 210 415-5795
 STANLEY L PERKINS,PRES OF UTOPIEA OIL CO
 GEN PRTNR SPERKINSAG@PRODIGY.NET
 STANLEY L PERKINS SR,LTD & MNGNG PRTNR
 SPERKINSAG@HOTMAIL.COM
 SAN ANTONIO,TX DISTRICT OFFICE
 1800 NE LOOP 410 STE 305,78217
 PH 210 828-3889 FAX 210 821-3795
 STANLEY L PERKINS JR,PETR GEOL
 STANPERKINS@SBCGLOBAL.NET
 CREEDE,CO DISTRICT OFFICE -PO BOX 492
 81130 PH 719 658-0320 FAX 719 658-0320
CREEDE,LTD SEE
 CREEDE MINERALS LTD
CRENSHAW ROYALTY CORP,OIL ROYALTIES
 8700 CROWNHILL BLVD STE 605
 SAN ANTONIO,TX 78209
 PH 210 930-4999 FAX 210 930-9271
 THOMAS L MCGEHEE,PRES
 FLO JAMESON,VP/SECY
CREOLE ENGINEERING SALES CO
 PO BOX 23159
 NEW ORLEANS,LA 70183-0159 PH 504 733-0176
 WWW.CREOLEENGINEERING.COM
 BEN LOUVIERE,OWNER,PRES
 R L GRAHAM,SALES MGR
CREOLE GAS COMPANY
 416 TRAVIS ST STE 1106
 SHREVEPORT,LA 71101-5504 PH 318 227-8944
 FAX 318 221-6401
CREOLE PETROLEUM COMPANY,LLC
 PO BOX 452
 SHREVEPORT,LA 71162-0452
 PH 318 747-1998 FAX 318 747-6739
 CHARLES PAUL GEORGE,MGR
CRESCENDO RESOURCES,L.P. SEE
 BP AMOCO CORPORATION
CRESCENT ENERGY SERVICES,LLC
 1304 ENGINEERS RD
 BELLE CHASSE,LA 70037
 PH 504 433-4188 FAX 504 433-9159
 WWW.CRESCENTES.COM
 TOMMY JAHNCKE,VP ADMIN

TJAHNCKE@CRESCENTES.COM
CREW LAND RESEARCH,OIL & GAS LEASING
 2400 AUGUSTA DR STE 360
 HOUSTON,TX 77057-5034
 PH 713 784-5263 FAX 713 784-1711
 JACK W WOMACK,CPL
 JACK@CREWLANDRESEARCH.COM
 MATTHEW L ZANDER,CPL
 MZANDER@CREWLANDRESEARCH.COM
CRIM J T
 P O BOX 1250,200 SABINE
 KILGORE,TX 75663 PH 903 984-2433
CRIMSON EXPLORATION OPERATING INC SEE
 CONTANGO OIL & GAS COMPANY
CROCKER JAMES A,ATTORNEY AT LAW
 2723 WALLINGFORD PINES
 HOUSTON,TX 77042-3568
 PH 225 262-2297
CROCKETT OIL PRODUCERS
 109 LINDA DR
 CLINTON,MS 39056-3105 PH 601 924-5552
 THERON A CROCKETT,OWNER,GEOL
 T A CROCKETT JR,OWNER,LDMN
CROCKETT THERON A,GEOL
 109 LINDA DR
 CLINTON,MS 39056-3105 PH 601 924-5552
CROFT EXPLORATION
 5021 GRAFORD PL
 CORPUS CHRISTI,TX 78413-5355
 PH 361 991-7450 FAX 361 991-5790
CROOM BOB,INC
 DIRECTIONAL DRILLING RENTAL SERVICE
 PO BOX 533
 BROUSSARD,LA 70518-0533 PH 337 837-6677
 FAX 337 837-5911
 ALLEN CROOM,CEO
 RYAN T WILTZ,OPER MGR
 CORBERT LEE,WIRELINE TECH
CROSBIE & MACOMBER PALEONTOLOGICAL
 LAB,INC,PALEONTOLOGISTS
 125 CHARLESTON PARK
 METAIRIE,LA 70005-3967 PH 504 885-3930
 WM A BRANTLEY,JR,PRES
 DONALD MACOMBER JR,VP
 THOMAS REILLY,VP,SECY
 WM GRANT BLACK,JR
 FRANK K LOOR,III
CROSBYS CREEK OIL & GAS,LLC
 605 NORTHPARK DR STE A
 RIDGELAND,MS 39157-4843 PH 601 898-0051
 FAX 601 898-0233
 EMIL H PAWLIK,MGR
 JAMES O STEPHENS,MGR
CROSS BORDER RESOURCES
 2515 MCKINNEY AVE STE 900
 DALLAS,TX 75201-1976
 PH 210 226-6700 FAX 210 930-3967
 WILL GRAY,CEO
 LAWRENCE J RISLEY,PRES
CROSS OIL & WELL SERVICE INC
 104 E MISSOURI ST
 OBLONG,IL 62449 PH 618 592-4609
 JOHN O CROSS,OWNER
CROSS OIL REFINING & MARKETING,INC
 484 E 6TH ST
 SMACKOVER,AR 71762

PH 870 725-3611 FAX 870 725-3405
 DENNY MCCONATHY,PRES,CEOMGR
 BILLY NEAL,V P,PETR,SUPPLY & DISTR
CROSS TIMBERS ENERGY SERVICES
 AFFILIATED WITH CROSS TIMBERS OIL CO
 810 HOUSTON ST STE 2000
 FORT WORTH,TX 76102-6298 PH 817 870-2800
 FAX 817 882-7259
 TERRY SCHULTZ,CHRMN,PRES
 JIM PENDERGRASS,DIR,GAS MKTG
 NICKIE BRENNAN,MGR,CONTRACT ADMINS
 JAY LAUDERDALE,MGR,MKT DEV
 KIM ROTHA,SUPVSR,GAS MKTG
CROSS TIMBERS OIL COMPANY SEE
 XTO ENERGY INC
CROSS TIMBERS OPERATING COMPANY SEE
 XTO ENERGY INC
CROSSOVER RESOURCES LLC
 16225 PARK TEN PL STE 830
 HOUSTON,TX 77084-5155
 PH 281 646-2600 FAX 281 646-2610
 WWW.CROSSOVERRESOURCES.COM
 INFO@CROSSOVERRESOURCES.COM
 RANDALL COUCH,PRIN
 WILLIAM WHITTINGTON,PRIN
 BILLWHITTINGTON@CROSSOVERRESOURCES.CO
 M
CROSSROADS ENERGY LP
 20333 STATE HWY 249 STE 380
 HOUSTON,TX 77070 PH 713 665-0321
 FAX 713 654-2139
 BYRON YEATMAN,MGR
 MIKE GIBSON,LAND MGR
CROSSROADS VACUUM SERVICE
 PO BOX 71
 LULING,TX 78648 PH 830 875-2453
 FAX 830 875-5930
 LLOYD NEWTON,OWNER
 BOB GRANTHAM,MGR
CROSSTEX ENERGY SERVICES,LP SEE
 ENLINK MIDSTREAM OPERATING LP
CROSSTEX LIG LIQUIDS,LLC SEE
 ENLINK LIG,LLP
CROSSTEX LIG,LLC SEE ENLINK LLG,LLC
CROUCH GENE INVESTMENTS
 PO BOX 8
 LOCKHART,TX 78644 PH 512 398-5814
 EUGENE L CROUCH,OWNER
CROW DAVID,TRUSTEE
 900 PIERREMONT RD STE 221
 SHREVEPORT,LA 71106-2055
 PH 318 861-6040 FAX 318 861-0039
 JOHN D CROW,PRTNR
 BALLARD L SMITH,OFC MGR
 JAMES THOMAS,LDMN
CROWN DRILLING,INC
 PO BOX 51433
 LAFAYETTE,LA 70505-1433
 PH 337 332-8563 FAX 337 332-8598
 WWW.CROWNDRILLING.NET
 ANDY C SIMON,PRES
 MATTHEW A TURLAK,VP
CROWN ENERGY,LLC
 PO BOX 1788
 BUTLER,PA 16003-1788 PH 724 625-9548
 GARY G GRIWATZ,CEO

PH 724 312-1900 GGG3@NAUTICOM.NET

CROWN OIL COMPANY
PO BOX 2929
MADISON,MS 39130 PH 601 605-4921

CROWNPOINTE RESOURCES,INC
PO BOX 539
RIDGELAND,MS 39158-0539 PH 601 353-4971
FAX 601 948-6060
NAT W PRESTAGE,PRES
J BRUNS CLEMENT,VP

CRS SEE
COMPRESSOR RENEWAL SERVICES LTD

CRUDEWELL DRILLING,INC
PO BOX 10
ALBANY,KY 42602-0010 PH 606 387-7083
JOE GARMON,PRES

CRUTCHER-TUFTS CORPORATION
EXPLORATION & DEVELOPMENT
PO BOX 8180,2750 LAKE VILLA DR STE 200
METAIRIE,LA 70011-8180 PH 504 887-9327
FAX 504 887-9373
FREDERICK J TUFTS,VP

CRYSTAL RIVER OIL & GAS,LLC
PO BOX 6749
SNOWMASS VILLAGE,CO 81615-6749
PH 970 920-0245 FAX 970 920-2610
REINER KLAWITER,PRES

CSA EXPLORATION COMPANY,INC
770 S POST OAK LN STE 415
HOUSTON,TX 77056-1964 PH 713 622-5080
FAX 713 622-5083
CHARLES ATCHISON,PRES
DON S SAMPLE,LAND & LEGAL

CSC ENERGY CORP
401 EDWARDS ST STE 820
SHREVEPORT,LA 71101-5506
PH 318 221-5625 FAX 318 459-1650
JOEL B CHEVALIER,PRES

CTC INTERNATIONAL
PO BOX 40129
HOUSTON,TX 77240-0129 PH 713 961-3336
GEORGE O SUMAN,JR,PRES

CTC MINERALS,INC SEE
BANK OF AMERICA

CTR RESOURCES CORP
1844 W STATE ST STE A
ALLIANCE,OH 44601-5713 PH 330 821-1430
FAX 330 821-2217

CUDD ENERGY SERVICES
2828 TECHNOLOGY FOREST BLVD
THE WOODLANDS,TX 77381 PH 832 295-5555
FAX 832 295-4555 WWW.CUDD.COM
VILONIA,AR OFFICE - PH 501 796-2870
FRUITA,CO OFFICE - PH 970 244-5560
DENVER,CO OFFICE - PH 303 260-6422
BROUSSARD,LA OFFICE - PH 877 283-3363
HOBBS,NM OFFICE - PH 575 393-4111
BILLINGS,MT OFFICE - PH 406 530-4068
WILLISTON,ND OFFICE - PH 701 572-0147
ELK CITY,OK OFFICE - PH 580 243-5890
PH 580 225-6922
LINDSAY,OK OFFICE - PH 405 756-4337
MCALESTER,OK OFFICE - PH 918 423-0160
OKLAHOMA CITY,OK OFFICE - PH 405 842-2800
SEMINOLE,OK OFFICE - PH 405 382-2803
TULSA,OK OFFICE - PH 918 585-9860

WOODWARD,OK OFFICE - PH 580 254-3393
WASHINGTON,PA OFFICE - PH 724 222-4430
CORPUS CHRISTI,TX OFFICE- PH 361 387-8521
SAN ANTONIO,TX OFFICE - PH 210 310-1330
CHANNELVIEW,TX OFFICE - PH 281 452-2800
DALLAS,TX OFFICE - PH 972 377-0055
FT WORTH,TX OFFICE - PH 817 439-4142
IRAAN,TX OFFICE - PH 432 639-6101
KILGORE,TX OFFICE - PH 903 988-2161
MIDLAND,TX OFFICE - PH 432 570-5300
PH 432 689-5700
ODESSA,TX OFFICE - PH 432 563-3356
PH 432 580-3544
SNYDER,TX OFFICE - PH 325 573-7022
TYLER,TX OFFICE - PH 903 939-2833
VERNAL,UT OFFICE - PH 435 789-0757
CANTON,PA OFFICE - PH 570 673-5965
PITTSBURGH,PA OFFICE - PH 412 928-3651
INTERNATIONAL LOCATIONS HEADQUARTER OFC -
PH 832 295-5555

CUDD PRESSURE CONTROL,INC
WELL INTERVENTION SVCS/LIVE WELL SVCS
ENGRG & CONS SVCS/TRAINING & EDUCATION
2828 TECHNOLOGY FOREST BLVD
THE WOODLANDS,TX 77381-3907
PH 832 295-5555 FAX 832 295-4567
WWW.CUDD.COM CPCINFO@CUDD.COM
OKLAHOMA CITY,OK OFFICE - 4334 NW EXPWY
STE 124,73116 PH 405 842-2800
FAX 405 879-0653
TULSA,OK OFFICE - PH 918 585-9807
WOODWARD,OK OFFICE - PO BOX 1047
73802 PH 580 254-3393
ELK CITY,OK OFFICE - PO BOX 1801
73648 PH 580 225-6922
ELK CITY,OK SPECIAL SERVICES OFFICE -
RT 2,BOX 145,73644 PH 580 243-5890
MCALESTER,OK OFFICE - PO BOX 3265
74502 PH 918 423-0160
DALLAS/FORT WORTH SALES OFFICE -
PH 972 377-0000
CORPUS CHRISTI,TX OFFICE - PO BOX 10405
78460-0405 PH 361 387-8521
ODESSA,TX OFFICE - PO BOX 4618
79760 PH 432 563-3356
MIDLAND,TX OFFICE - PH 432 570-5300
DENVER,CO OFFICE - 303 260-6422
VERNAL,UT OFFICE - 1382 E HWY 40,84078
PH 435 789-0757
WILLISTON,ND OFFICE - 13902 SUNSET BLVD
58801 PH 701 572-0147
CANTON,PA OFFICE - 2897 RT 414,17724
PH 570 673-5965

CUDD PUMPING SERVICES
10 DESTA DR STE 420-E
MIDLAND,TX 79705 PH 432 570-5300
WWW.CUDD.COM
IRAAN,TX OFFICE - PH 432 639-6101
KILGORE,TX OFFICE - PO BOX 1447
75663-1447 PH 903 988-2161
HOBBS,NM OFFICE - PH 505 393-4111
ODESSA,TX OFFICE - PH 432 580-3544
SEMINOLE,OK OFFICE - PH 405 382-2803
SNYDER,TX OFFICE - PH 325 573-7022
TYLER,TX OFFICE - PH 903 939-2833

CUDD WELL CONTROL
2828 TECHNOLOGY FOREST BLVD
THE WOODLANDS,TX 77381-3907
PH 713 849-2769

CULBERTSON RESOURCES,LTD
770 S POST OAK LANE STE 220
HOUSTON,TX 77056 PH 713 275-4312
SHARI MORENO
SMORENO@CULBERTSONRESOURCES.COM

CULOCO,INC
3500 GREYSTONE CT
MCKINNEY,TX 75070-4191 PH 972 479-1006
FAX 972 231-6520
CYNTHIA M CULWELL,PRES

CULVER & CAIN PRODUCTION
121 S BROADWAY STE 760
TYLER,TX 75702 PH 903 533-0091
FAX 903 597-6850
CALVIN CAIN,PRES
CCAIN@CULVERANDCAIN.COM
MATT CULVER,MNGNG DIR
MCULVER@CULVERANDCAIN.COM

CULVER OIL & GAS LP
PO BOX 7666,121 S BROADWAY STE 760
TYLER,TX 75711 PH 903 592-7993
JIM CULVER,PRES
JCULVER@CULVEROILANDGAS.COM
MAT CULVER,VP
MCULVER@CULVEROILANDGAS.COM

CUMBURLAND PETROLEUM COMPANY,INC
PO BOX 2929
MADISON,MS 39130 PH 601 605-4921
HOMER N CUMMINGS,MGR

CUMMINGS HOMER N
430 ST AUGUSTINE DR
MADISON,MS 39110 PH 601 605-4921

CUMMINGS J L,JR,IND GEOL
524 E PASCAGOULA ST
JACKSON,MS 39201-4309 PH 601 354-8755
ANN HALL,SECY

CUMMINS RANDY
704 LAURA AVE
CORSICANA,TX 75110-2037 PH 903 654-3937

CUNNINGHAM MARK S CPL INC
309 LA RUE FRANCE STE 204
LAFAYETTE,LA 70508-2528
PH 337 593-0900 FAX 337 534-4295
MARK S CUNNINGHAM,PRES
MSCUNNINGHAM@OUTLOOK.COM

CURFMAN PERRY G,PETROLEUM LAND SERVICES
5014 WALNUT HILLS DR
KINGWOOD,TX 77345-2411 PH 318 233 8840
PH 318 233-8840

CURRIE V MONTA JR,IND OPER,OIL & GAS PROP
PO BOX 18789,118 LOWER WOODVILLE RD
NATCHEZ,MS 39122-8789 PH 601 442-4701
FAX 601 442-4804
TOM CLEMENTS,CONSLT GEOL
JIM LANDREM,CONSLT GEOPHY
PATSY BROWN,ACCT
RITA MARTIN,SECY

CURTIS & SON VACUUM SERVICE,INC
PO BOX 767
LIBERTY,TX 77575-0767
PH 936 334-1188 FAX 936 334-8838
CSVC@TXUCOM.NET

CURTIS HUDNALL,PRES
JOHN HUDNALL,VP

CUSACK CHARLES E,JR,PETR GEOL
8304 COUNTY RD 192
GONZALES,TX 78629 PH 830 437-2259
FAX 830 437-2259 CEC@GVEC.NET

CUSTOM DRILL PIPE
PO BOX 471523
FORT WORTH,TX 76147 PH 817 735-9174
PH 817 735-4913 PH 877 735-9174

CUTTER OIL CO
9270 CEDAR VALLEY RD
WEST SALEM,OH 44287-9533 PH 419 846-3850
FAX 419 846-3878 WWW.CUTTEROIL.COM
ELIZABETH CUTTER,PRES

CUTTING IRON,LLC
4512A COTEAU RD
NEW IBERIA,LA 70560-8795 PH 337 365-2110
JAMES E FATHEREE JIMF@CUTTINGIRON.NET

CVS OIL & GAS
PO BOX 143
MILLERSBURG,OH 44654-0143 PH 330 674-8536
FAX 330 674-6373
CHARLES V STRAITS,CEO

CWJ OPERATING CO,INC
2124 FAIRFIELD AVE
SHREVEPORT,LA 71104 PH 318 221-1657
FAX 318 221-1894
CARL W JONES,PRES
ANN MONTGOMERY,SECY/TREAS

CYCLONE EXPLORATION,INC
1300 BAY AREA BLVD STE 275-1
HOUSTON,TX 77058-2505 PH 281 280-0941
DONALD E HENKEL,PRES

CYPRESS ENERGY CORPORATION
PO BOX 66769
BATON ROUGE,LA 70896-6769 PH 225 343-1311
FAX 225 343-2841 CYPRESS@CYPRESSLA.COM
CYRIL J LANDRY III,PRTNR
N PETER DAVIS,PRTNR

CYPRESS OPERATING,INC
330 MARSHALL ST STE 930
SHREVEPORT,LA 71101-3018
PH 318 424-2031 FAX 318 425-8140
PHIL ISRAEL,PRES
BEN ISRAEL,ENGR
STEVE SINGLETARY,GEOL
SCOTT MORGAN,LAND
SANDY MATTESON,ACCT
MIKE ROSENZWEIG,PROD MGR

D & D DRILLING & EXPLORATION INC
PO BOX 1634
FERRIDAY,LA 71334
PH 318 757-3274 FAX 318 757-8595
DEE HORTON,PRES
JESSE HORTON,VP
CASEY ASHLEY,TOOLPUSHER
DENNIS NICHOLS,DRLG SUPT
BILLY KIMBALL,TOOLPUSHER
MIKE DAVIS,TOOLPUSHER
GARY JUNEAU,TOOLPUSHER
JAMES CLEM,TOOLPUSHER
DUSTIN TILLMAN,TOOLPUSHER

D & D SWABBING,LLC
3471 E HWY 84
PALESTINE,TX 75801 PH 903 729-7922

D & D VACUUM SERVICE
10730 NEEDVILLE-FAIRCHILD RD
NEEDVILLE,TX 77461 PH 979 481-2062
FAX 979 793-4541
DERAY GOODRUM

D & D WELL SERVICE
203 STORY LN
CORSICANA,TX 75109 PH 903 654-2873
FAX 903 874-1838
RICHARD KELLY,OWNER
PATRICIA KELLY,OWNER
WELLSWEEP3711@SBCGLOBAL.NET

D & E ENERGY,INC
1010 LAMAR ST STE 1020
HOUSTON,TX 77002-6313
PH 713 739-9700 FAX 713 739-9701
PROSPECTS@DE-ENERGY.COM
DANIEL L DOSS,MNGNG PRTNR
MICHAEL W ENGLERT,MNGNG PRTNR

D & J PIPE
4560 JUNCTION CITY HWY
EL DORADO,AR 71730-6154 PH 870 863-7990
FAX 870 863-7294

D & K SUPPLY & EQUIPMENT INC
4700 RAVENNA AVE SE
EAST CANTON,OH 44730-9730
PH 330 488-1294 FAX 330 488-8209
JAKE LESHER,PRES
JLESHER@D-KSUPPLY.COM WWW.D-KSUPPLY.COM
CATHY LESHER,TREAS

D & V PETROLEUM CORPORATION
P O BOX 1432,5201 INDIAN HILLS ROAD
DUBLIN,OH 43017-6432 PH 614 761-8559
JOHN V VANKREVEL,PRES
KIM S STEMEN,CONS GEOL

D D C OIL COMPANY
PO BOX 1034
MATTOON,IL 61938-0393
PH 217 235-9191 FAX 217 235-9192
DEBRA HELLER,PRES
CAROL ZUHONE,VP
DIANE SHORE,SECY/TREAS

D L MUD INC SEE
AMBAR LONE STAR TECHNOLOGY

D R DRILLING RECORDS SEE
DIVESTCO USA INC

D V I
2601 CENTENARY BLVD
SHREVEPORT,LA 71104-3329
PH 318 226-1773 FAX 318 425-2592
EUGENE DUCHARME,PRES
JAMES K VOZZELLA,VP

D.J. ENERGYCOM
PO BOX 730,261 MANUEL RD
SHEPHERD,TX 77371-0730
PH 936 628-3832 FAX 936 628-2097
WWW.DJENERGYCOM.COM
DANIEL J JEFF JONES,PRTNR
JEFFJONES@CONSOLIDATED.NET

D-A-M SERVICES,INC
PO BOX 611
EL CAMPO,TX 77437-0611 PH 979 543-7041
FAX 979 543-6086 WWW.ALLGAYER-DAM.COM
DAVID ALLGAYER,PRES

D-J OIL CO
PO BOX 337
BEVERLY,OH 45715-0337
PH 740 984-2320 FAX 740 984-4080
JERRY WELCH,PRTNR
HARRY WELCH,PRTNR

D-J OPERATIONS,INC
4435 THUNDER RD
DALLAS,TX 75244-6436 PH 972 239-4040
DE B BROOKS,PRES,CO-OWNER,LAND MGR
JAMES L STEPHENSON,VP,CO-OWNER,GEOL

D-O-R LEASE SERVICE,INC
PO BOX 51707
LAFAYETTE,LA 70505-1707
PH 337 233-2378 FAX 337 366-1727
M F MCKENZIE,PRES
DON BAZER,SR ADVISOR
DEBBIE SAVAGE,OFC MGR

D-S-B PROPERTIES,LLC
PO BOX 1050
KILGORE,TX 75703 PH 903 984-3050
FAX 903 984-0850 BHANCOCK@DSBHEI.COM
BRIAN P HANCOCK,PRES

DACAT TRUCKING,LLC
1411 STONEBRIAR DR
CARTHAGE,TX 75633 PH 903 693-7313
FAX 903 693-3712
DACATTRUCKING@PRODIGY.NET
DAVID WELBORN,OWNER

DAEDALUS DESIGN CORP
AIR/GAS COMPRESSORS
6142 S FOSTER RD
SAN ANTONIO,TX 78222-4406
PH 210 648-9478 FAX 210 648-7298
TOMWHITTENBURG@CS.COM
TOM ED WHITTENBURG,VP,SALES

DAIGLE,WILLIAM J
PO BOX 53602
LAFAYETTE,LA 70505 PH 337 269-1799
FAX 337 269-1794
BILL DAIGLE,OWNER

DAILEY DAMCO SEE WEATHERFORD

DAILEY DWS SEE WEATHERFORD

DAILEY INTERNATIONAL INC SEE WEATHERFORD

DAILEY PETROLEUM SERVICES CORP SEE
DAILEY INTERNATIONAL,INC

DAKOTA ENERGY,L.C.
13331 SE 97TH TERRACE RD
SUMMERFIELD,FL 34491-5786
PH 352 245-5088
THOMAS L MYERS,MNGNG MEMBER

DALE OPERATING COMPANY
2100 ROSS AVE STE 1870
DALLAS,TX 75201
PH 214 979-9010 FAX 214 969-9394
LAWRENCE B DALE,PRES
BRYCE MOEN,CONTROLLER

DALE RESOURCES,INC
2100 ROSS AVE STE 1870
DALLAS,TX 75201 PH 214 979-9010
FAX 214 969-9394
LAWRENCE B DALE,PRES
WWW.DALE-ENERGY.COM

DALE WILTON R,BILL,JR
PO BOX 53063,103 EXCHANGE PL
LAFAYETTE,LA 70505-3063 PH 318 237-2612

DALE-ANN ENTERPRISES SEE
DALE-ANN CO,INC

DALE-ANN GAS SPECIALISTS
SEE DALE-ANN CO,INC

DALE-ANN INDUSTRIAL SEE
DALE-ANN CO,INC

DALE-ANN UTILITIES SEE
DALE-ANN CO,INC

DALECO RESOURCES CORP
17 WILMONT MEWS 5TH FL
WEST CHESTER,PA 19382 PH 610 429-0181
GARY NOVINSKIE,PRES

DALEN RESOURCES OIL & GAS CO SEE
ENSERCH EXPLORATION,INC

DALLAS CONTRACTING COMPANY,INC
PROVIDING OILFIELD SERVICES
1260 NEW MARKET AVE
SOUTH PLAINFIELD,NJ 07080
PH 908 668-0600
INFO@DALLASCONTRACTING.COM
CARL FRANZETTI,OFC MGR

DALLAS EXPLORATION,INC
1580 S MAIN ST STE 102
BOERNE,TX 78006-3312 PH 830 331-1224
JOE E ALLEN,PRES

DALLAS PETROLEUM PARTNERS
9540 GARLAND RD STE 381-380
DALLAS,TX 75218 PH 214 343-2721
FAX 214 594-8790
SUSAN IRBY

DALY WOODROW W & ASSOCIATES,INC
PO BOX 53125
LAFAYETTE,LA 70505-3125 PH 337 233-5858

DAMAC DRILLING INC SEE
MCKOWN OIL INC

DAMIAN OIL & SUPPLY,INC
1008 OLD EVANGELINE HWY
EVANGELINE,LA 70546
PH 337 824-6470 FAX 337 824-6672
DAMIAN1008@AOL.COM
EDWIN L SIMAR,PRES
D P SIMAR,VP

DAMSON OIL CORPORATION SEE
PARKER & PARSLEY PETROLEUM CO

DANIEL MEASUREMENT AND CONTROL,INC
11100 BRITTMOORE PARK DR
HOUSTON,TX 77041
PH 713 467-6000 FAX 713 827-4360

DANNA EXPLORATION
PO BOX 53734
BLDG HC 4-5,STE 209,1126 COOLIDGE BLVD
LAFAYETTE,LA 70505-3734 PH 337 232-9861
FAX 337 232-9861
FRANK P DANNA,OWNER,GEOL

DANNIC ENERGY CORPORATION
164 MILL RUN RD
INDIANA,PA 15701-1532
PH 724 465-6663 FAX 724 465-7375
DANIEL SINCLAIR,PRES

DAR OIL & GAS,INC
5905 CHURCHILL DR
TYLER,TX 75703-4568 PH 903 530-9352
RICHARD L KRAFVE,VP

DAR-WAY INC
PO BOX 448
KALKASKA,MI 49646-0448 PH 231 258-9053

FAX 231 258-9740
DERRELL W ELDRIDGE,OWNER,PRES
DWANE ELDRIDGE,VP
WANDA ELDRIDGE,SECY/TREAS

DARST CREEK OIL CORP
PO BOX 1026
LOCKHART,TX 78644-1026 PH 512 398-5180
J SANFORD HELLUMS,JR,PRES
ALBERT ROSE JR,VP
BETTY HELLUMS,SECY/TREAS

DART OIL & GAS CORPORATION
PO BOX 177,600 DART RD
MASON,MI 48854-0177
PH 517 676-2900 WWW.DARTOILANDGAS.COM
RICHARD HINKLEY,PRES
DAVE FARNER,SR VP/ENGR & OPERS
ROGER MCKINLEY,VP,LAND

DART RESOURCES,INC
PO BOX 51842, 1001 W PINHOOK RD STE 104
LAFAYETTE,LA 70505 PH 337 234-1601
DAMON R WEGER DAMON@DARTRESOURCES.COM

DATAGAS,INC SEE
ATHENA ENERGY,INC

DATALAND RESOURCES
PO BOX 266
SEALY,TX 77474-0266 PH 713 307-1995
FAX 713 307-1994 BILL@DATALANDUSA.COM
WILLIAM A REAY II,CPL,PRES
ANN REAY,LAND ADMIN

DAUBERT OIL & GAS
4040 BROADWAY ST STE 515
SAN ANTONIO,TX 78209-6352
PH 210 822-0686 X3 FAX 210 822-0912
C ROBERT DAUBERT,OWNER

DAUGHERTY PETROLEUM INC SEE
NGAS RESOURCES,INC.

DAUGHERTY TRUCKING SERVICE,INC
PO BOX 533
MADISONVILLE,KY 42431-0533
PH 270 825-1746
JIMMIE G DAUGHERTY

DAUTERIVE DAVID L,PETR LAND SRVS
PO BOX 82285
LAFAYETTE,LA 70598 PH 337 706-8650
PH 337 344-8059
DDAUTERIVE@PENTERRASERVICES.COM

DAUTERIVE EDWARD J,OIL PROP
P O BOX 52408,1116 COOLIDGE BLDG HC2
LAFAYETTE,LA 70505-2408 PH 318 232-0651

DAVID G MATTHEW,CPL & ASSOCIATES,LTD
PROFESSIONAL PETROLEUM LAND SERVICES
PO BOX 51231
LAFAYETTE,LA 70505-1231 PH 318 264-9299
FAX 318 264-1122
G MATTHEW DAVID,CPL,PRES
PAUL A GAUTREAOX,LDMN
AIMEE' CHERIE' VANICOR,SECY
DAVID VANICOR,LDMN
MARY ANNE LYNCH,LDMN

DAVIDSON CHARLIE,INC
OIL & GAS LAND SERVICES
12910 BUTTERFLY
HOUSTON,TX 77024 PH 281 384-0857
CHAS.DAVIDSON@ATT.NET

DAVIDSON JAKE,INC
12330 COBBLESTONE DR

HOUSTON,TX 77024-4903 PH 713 907-9757
FAX 713 932-9703
JAKE DAVIDSON,PRES
CHARLES DAVIDSON,LAND MGR
TOM NOGLE,PETR ENGR
ROY WHITMAN,LEGAL

DAVIDSON OIL AND GAS
SATELLITE DATA,GEO CHEMS,LIMITED SEISMIC
& RADIOMETRICS IN DRILL SITE DEV
110 HILL CREST DR
BYRDSTOWN,TN 38549 PH 931 864-3166
KENDLED@TWLAKES.NET
ERIK DAVIDSON
KENDLE DAVIDSON

DAVIDSON TOM,GEOL
28550 IH-10 WEST STE 4
BOERNE,TX 78006 PH 830 981-8138
FAX 830 981-8138 PH 210 844-8962
TOMGEO@TELEWRX.NET

DAVIS A VIDAL,OIL LAND LEASES
PO BOX 614,118 N COMMERCE ST
NATCHEZ,MS 39121-0614 PH 601 442-9888
FAX 601 442-9866 WWW.Q-HOPE.COM
VDAVIS@CABLEONE.NET

DAVIS AND LANDRY INC
37518 DUPLESSIS RD
PRAIRIEVILLE,LA 70769 PH 225 673-9632
FAX 225 925-1237
MACKIE LANDRY,PRES
MATT LANDRY,VP,LDMN

DAVIS BROS,LLC
ROYALTIES,EXPLORATION
110 W 7TH ST STE 1000
TULSA,OK 74119-1031
PH 918 584-3581 FAX 918 582-3403
LEE H DAVIS
BARRY M DAVIS
HOUSTON,TX OFFICE - 1221 MCKINNEY
STE 3100,77010 PH 713 659-3131
FAX 713 659-8070
ROSS M DAVIS

DAVIS BROS,OIL PRODUCERS,INC
OPERATOR,DRILLING CO
110 WEST 7TH ST STE 1000
TULSA,OK 74119 PH 918 584-3581
FAX 918 582-3403
LEE H DAVIS,OIL/GAS DIV MGR
BARRY M DAVIS,MGR,OPERS
HOUSTON,TX OFFICE - 1221 MCKINNEY
STE 3100,77010 PH 713 659-3131
ROSS DAVIS

DAVIS BROTHERS SEE
BENSON & SCHOEN OIL CO,INC

DAVIS CLYDE L,JR
3008 STANFORD CT
TYLER,TX 75701-7624 PH 903 597-4872
CLYDELDAVIS@SBCGLOBAL.NET

DAVIS DON OIL CO
311 DALLAS ST
NOCONA,TX 76255-2614 PH 940 841-2786
DON DAVIS DAVISCATTLE@AOL.COM

DAVIS INC (DAVIS INTERESTS) SEE
DAVIS BROS,LLC

DAVIS LAND & MINERALS,INC
PO BOX 79188
HOUSTON,TX 77279-9188 PH 713 553-6913

FAX 713 461-4403
  A RAY DAVIS,PRES
  ANDREW C DAVIS,VP
DAVIS N PETER,INDEPENDENT
  PO BOX 66769
  BATON ROUGE,LA 70896-6769 PH 225 343-1311
  FAX 225 343-2841 PDAVIS@CYPRESSLA.COM
DAVIS OIL COMPANY SEE
  DAVIS PETROLEUM CORPORATION
DAVIS PETROLEUM CORP
  1330 POST OAK BLVD STE 600
  HOUSTON,TX 77056
  PH 713 626-7766 FAX 713 626-7775
    WWW.DAVISPETROLEUMCORP.COM
DAVIS R H,OIL PROD
  P O BOX 31,ROBERTS BLDG
  OIL CITY,LA 71061-0031 PH 318 995-7366
DAVIS RALPH E,ASSOCIATES,INC
    CONSULTANTS - PETR & NATL GAS
  1717 ST JAMES PL STE 460
  HOUSTON,TX 77056-3496 PH 713 622-8955
  FAX 713 626-3664 RALPHEDAVIS.COM
DAVIS RESOURCES SEE
  DAVIS BROS,LLC
DAWS BEN C,OIL PROPERTIES
  PO BOX 323
  WAYNESBORO,MS 39367-0323
  PH 601 735-4891 FAX 601 735-5346
  BEN C DAWS,OWNER
DAWSON & DAWSON CONSULTANTS,INC
  2000 BERING DR STE 460
  HOUSTON,TX 77057-3746 PH 713 784-3197
  PH 800 422-7540 FAX 713 784-3190
    WWW.DAWSON-DAWSON.COM
    SDAWSON@DAWSON-DAWSON.COM
  SHERYL N DAWSON,PRES
DAWSON ENERGY,LLC
  307 W 7TH ST STE 912
  FORT WORTH,TX 76102-5101 PH 817 744-8010
  JIM DAWSON,MNGNG PRTNR
    JDAWSON@DAWSONENERGY.COM
  MIDLAND,TX OFFICE - 415 W WALL STE 1710
  79701 PH 432 218-9935
  HOUSTON,TX OFFICE - 521 N SAM HOUSTON
  PKWAY E STE 635 77060 PH 832 300-3664
  DENVER,CO OFFICE - 110 16TH ST STE 905
  80202 PH 720 259-9925
  OKLAHOMA CITY,OK OFFICE - 309 NW 13ST
  73103 PH 405 231-2108
  FRANKLIN,TN OFFICE - 509 NEW HWY 96 WEST
  STE 102B 37064 PH 615 807-1710
  FAX 615 807-1712
DAWSON GARY J
  312 E ILLINOIS AVE STE 7
  MIDLAND,TX 79701-4892 PH 432 686-7070
  GARY J DAWSON,IND GEOL
    GJDJOSHUA24.15@GMAIL.COM
DAY DREAMS RESOURCES,LLC
  PO BOX 101,14 HEATHER DR
  NATCHEZ,MS 39121-0101
  PH 601 446-8105 FAX 601 446-8844
    JERRY P OGDEN,MGR/PE/GEOL
DAY GENE,INC,OIL & GAS CONS
  115 E TRAVIS ST STE 1115
  SAN ANTONIO,TX 78205-1678 PH 210 222-9576
  GENE DAY

DAY PAUL,GEOL
  119 DOGWOOD CT
  MADISON,MS 39110-9246 PH 601 856-1028
  FAX 601 898-0979
DAYLIGHT ENGINEERING,INC
  11022 ELBERFELD RD
  ELBERFELD,IN 47613-9449 PH 812 983-2518
  FAX 812 983-2515
    WWW.DAYLIGHTENGINEERING.COM
    THOMAS SAWYER,PRES
    JESSE DELAP,PROD MGR
DAYSON GEOLOGICAL CONSULTING LLC
  501 CARANZA CT
  EVANSVILLE,IN 47711-1627 PH 812 868-0957
  ROBERT C DAYSON,GEOL
DCP MIDSTREAM
  370 17TH ST STE 2500
  DENVER,CO 80202-5644 PH 303 595-3331
  FAX 303 255-0480
  FORT WORTH,TX OFFICE - 201 MAIN ST
  STE 1000,76102 PH 817 255-8000
  FAX 817 255-5578
  TULSA,OK OFFICE - 6120 S YALE STE 600
  74136 PH 918 492-3331 FAX 918 492-3375
    BILL GIFFORD,VP,MID-CONT REG
DCW TRANSPORT,LLC
  1825 HWY 80
  HAUGHTON,LA 71037 PH 318 377-8861
  FELICIA GUILLORY FGUILLORY-DCW@ATT.NET
DEARING H COMPANY
  120 RIVERWOOD DR
  COVINGTON,LA 70433-4723 PH 504 892-7630
    MARK DEARING,PRES
    HOWARD DEARING,VP
    R D DEARING,SECY/TREAS
DECKER EXPLORATION,INC
  3701 KIRBY DR STE 514
  HOUSTON,TX 77098 PH 713 759-1925
    MARK DECKER,GEOL
DECKER OPERATING COMPANY,LLC
  1706 SEAMIST DR STE 590
  HOUSTON,TX 77008-8417
  PH 713 880-4343 FAX 713 880-1553
    L S STAN DECKER,MGR
    JOHN DECKER,FIN
    STEVE HILL,EXPL MGR
    DELBERT BRUNS,ACCT
    GERALD LOFTON,MKTG & REGLATORY
    PAT MCINTURFF,ENGRG
DEDICA ENERGY CORPORATION
  PO BOX 1034,1317 WABASH AVE
  MATTOON,IL 61938-1034 PH 217 235-9192
    DEBRA HELLER,PRES
    WILLIAM H ZUHONE,MGR
    DIANE SHORE,SECY/TREAS
DEEP GULF ENERGY LP
  738 HIGHWAY 6 SOUTH STE 800
  HOUSTON,TX 77079-4048
  PH 832 327-1325 FAX 281 596-0939
    TYOUNG@DEEPGULFENERGY.COM
    TOM E YOUNG,VP,BUS DEV
DEEPKO LEASE & ROYALTY CO SEE
  REVARD OIL AND GAS PROPERTIES,INC
DEGOLYER AND MACNAUGHTON
    GEOL & PETR ENGRG CONS
  5001 SPRING VALLEY RD STE 800 EAST

DALLAS,TX 75244-3946
  PH 214 368-6391 FAX 214 369-4061
    DEGOLYER@DEMAC.COM WWW.DEMAC.COM
    JAMES W HAIL,JR,CEO
  HOUSTON,TX OFFICE - 5151 SAN FELIPE
  STE 950,77056 PH 713 273-8300
  FAX 713 784-1972
    GREG GRAVES,MGR
  CALGARY,ALTA,CAN OFFICE - 311 6TH AVE SW
  STE 1430,ENERGY PLAZA,EAST TOWER
  T2P 3H2 PH 403 266-8680 FAX 403 266-1887
    DOUG CHRISTIE,MGR
DEGUELLO CORPORATION,THE
  PO BOX 42429
  HOUSTON,TX 77242-2429 PH 713 782-3831
  FAX 713 782-6439 LFY@OILGASCONSULT.COM
    LEIGHTON F YOUNG JR,PRES/GEOL
DEGUIRE OIL & GAS INC
  8940 CHATSWORTH DR
  HOUSTON,TX 77024-3710 PH 713 681-5138
  JOE A DEGUIRE,PRES
DEHY-TECH
  13426 OAK HOLLOW DR
  CYPRESS,TX 77429-2922 PH 281 469-4930
  J R BOWLIN,OWNER
DEI OIL & GAS,LLC
  PO BOX 53963
  LAFAYETTE,LA 70505-3963 PH 337 232-9485
  JACK W LARIMER,OWNER
  RUTH T LARIMER,LDMN
DEIBEL COMPANIES,INC
  P O BOX 5476
  TYLER,TX 75712-5476 PH 972 593-4904
  800 777-1483
  JOHN F DEIBEL,LDMN
    P O BOX 2296,ATHENS,TX 75751
DEISTER W JAMES,JR,PETR GEOL
  4604 LAKE BORGNE AVE
  METAIRIE,LA 70006-2424 PH 504 455-9984
DEISTER WARD & WITCHER,INC
    ABSTRACT AND LAND TITLE INFORMATION
  2620 S PARKER RD STE 310
  AURORA,CO 80014 PH 303 671-9043
  PH 800 829-8426 FAX 303 671-9086
    MITCH COWAN,PRES
    WILLIAM BILL M WEDDLE,DIST MGR
  CASPER,WY DIST OFFICE - 777 OVERLAND
  TRAIL STE 124,82601 PH 307 472-3514
  PH 800 829-8427
    JACK LAMB,DIST MGR
  BILLINGS,MT DIST OFFICE - 1130 16TH ST W
  STE 4,59102 PH 406 248-8751
  PH 800 443-7874 FAX 406 248-6478
    LARRY KENNEDY,DIST MGR
  DICKINSON,ND DIST OFFICE - 235 SIMS ST
  STE 16,58601 PH 701 225-6439
  PH 800-829-8427
    PATRICK PAT J SCHMALZ,VP,DIST MGR
DEJEAN JAMES A,CPL
  915 KIM DR
  LAFAYETTE,LA 70503-4025 PH 318 984-2229
DELACROIX CORPORATION
  206 DECATUR ST
  NEW ORLEANS,LA 70130-1016
  PH 504 523-2245 FAX 504 523-2254
    DOROTHY L BENGE,CHRMN OF THE BD

H HUNTER WHITE JR,VP
ROBERT MIKE BENGE,PRES/GEN MGR
MARY B HALEY,SECY/TREAS
MELINDA B BROWN,CORPORATE ATTORNEY
DONALD ANSARDI,LDMN
MICHAEL FARIZO,LDMN

DELANEY FRANK G,ATTORNEY AT LAW
615 UPPER N BROADWAY STE 725 MT 47
CORPUS CHRISTI,TX 78401
PH 361 888-4088 FAX 361 884-7921

DELANEY R W,CONSTRUCTION CO
PO BOX 264,155 RIVER TERMINAL RD
NATCHEZ,MS 39121-0264 PH 601 442-0352
PH 800-541-7189 FAX 601 442-0491
RWDELCC@YAHOO.COM
WWW.RWDELANEY.COM
RANDY IRVIN,PRES
JIMMY DELANEY,SEC/TREAS
PRENTISS HARVESTON,DISPATCHER
VERA MESSER,OFC MGR
MAX MONTGOMERY,DISPATCHER

DELAWARE ROYALTY CO INC
3009 POST OAK BLVD STE 1212
HOUSTON,TX 77056 PH 713 658-1142
FAX 713 658-0739
ROBERT W KENT,VP LAND/ACQS

DELCAR,INC
PO BOX 6534
SAN ANTONIO,TX 78209-0534 PH 210 828-2215
CARL D LANG,PRES

DELHI GAS PIPELINE CORPORATION SEE
KOCH MIDSTREAM SERVICES COMPANY

DELMAR SYSTEMS, INC
P O BOX 129
BROUSSARD,LA 70518-0129 PH 337 365-0180
FAX 337 365-0037 WWW.DELMARUS.COM
SALES@DELMARUS.COM
SHERMAN A SCOTT,PRES

DELRAY OIL INC
900 NE LOOP 410 STE A107
SAN ANTONIO,TX 78209-1482
PH 210 824-7214 FAX 210 824-7229
WALTER F BROWN JR,PRES,CEO
GLENDA F CASTRO,VP,TREAS
MARY LEA RYON,SECY
LULING,TX OFFICE - PO BOX 944
78648 PH 830 875-3210
ROY HEBBE,PROD FRMN

DELTA DEVELOPMENT CO INC
P O BOX 430
BELLE CHASSE,LA 70037-0430 PH 656-7371
WILLIAM J KILNEMAN,PRES & CEO

DELTA MINERALS,LLC
PO BOX 741300
NEW ORLEANS,LA 70174-1300 PH 504 393-8659
LOUIS E LEMARIE,MGR LEMARIE6@COX.NET

DELTA OPERATING CORPORATION
2424 EDENBORN AVE STE 454
METAIRIE,LA 70001 PH 504 831-7600
FAX 504 831-7768
EUGENE J YOUNG,PRES

DELTA PRODUCTION CORP
919 MILAM ST STE 1965
HOUSTON,TX 77002 PH 713 659-4463
FAX 713 659-4463
ROBERT W ANDERSON,PRES

N L ANDERSON,PUR AGT

DELTA ROYALTY COMPANY,INC
4450 OLD CANTON RD STE 203
JACKSON,MS 39211-5991 PH 601 354-2479
W D MOUNGER,PRES

DELTA/SEABOARD WELL SERVICE,INC
1212 W SAM HOUSTON PKWY N
HOUSTON,TX 77043-4009 PH 713 782-1468
FAX 713 782-8357 WWW.DELTASEABOARD.COM
RDERRICK@DELTASEABOARD.COM
ROB DERRICK,PRES,CEO
LAFAYETTE,LA OFFICE - PO BOX 53817
70505 PH 337 235-4545 FAX 337 235-4408
RON BURLEIGH,VP
RBURLEIGH@BELLSOUTH.NET

DEMCO DIVISION COOPER INDUSTRIES,INC SEE
CAMERON,A DIV OF COOPER CAMERON CORP

DEMINEX U S OIL COMPANY SEE
SOUTHWEST ROYALTIES,INC

DEMONTROND GEORGE,SR,ESTATE
PO BOX 6688
TYLER,TX 75711-6688 PH 903 561-8122
FAX 903 561-0919

DEMONTROND OIL CORP OIL PROD
PO BOX 6688
TYLER,TX 75711-6688 PH 903 561-8122
FAX 903 561-0919

DENALI OIL & GAS MANAGEMENT,LLC
650 N SAM HOUSTON PKWY E STE 500
HOUSTON,TX 77060-5918
PH 281 847-1888 FAX 281 847-1898
RLOUDEN@DENALIOG.COM
WWW.DENALIOG.COM
RICK LOUDEN,PRES,CEO
JOHN ELZNER,SR VP,BUS DEV
JOHN BRIM,VP/LAND
JEFF WAYBRIGHT,CFO
DAVID MONTZ,VP/DRLG

DENBURY RESOURCES INC/OIL & GAS OPERATOR
5320 LEGACY DR
PLANO,TX 75024 PH 972 673-2000
PHIL RYKHOEK,PRES/CEO
MARK C ALLEN,SVP/CFO
BRAD KERR,SVP/DEV,TECH & INNOVATION
JAMES MATTHEWS,SVP/GEN COUNSEL & SECY
JOHN FILIATRAULT,VP/CO2 SUPPLY/PL OPERS
STEVE MCLAURIN,VP/CIO
ALAN RHOADES,VP/CAO
WHITNEY SHELLY,VP/CHRO
MATTHEW ELMER,VP/GULF COAST
DAN E COLE,VP/MKTG & BUS DEV
MATTHEW DAHAN,VP/NORTH
CORY WEINBEL,VP/PROJECTS & FACILITIES

DENEX PETROLEUM CORPORATION
RR 5 BOX 560
BUCKHANNON,WV 26201-9126 PH 304 472-2186
FAX 304 472-2187
R DENNIS XANDER,PRES
DALE CURRENCE,PROD SUPT

DENISON CARRIE R,INC
533 VETERINARIAN RD
LAFAYETTE,LA 70507-3207
PH 337 237-5418 FAX 337 237-5418
CRDENISON@AOL.COM
CARRIE R DENISON,PRES

DENKMANN INTERESTS
PO BOX 320579
FLOWOOD,MS 39232-0579 PH 601 919-3677
FAX 601 919-3762

DENMON'S H2S SAFETY SERVICE INC
18569 COUNTY RD 139
FLINT,TX 75762-9103 PH 903 561-5706
FAX 903 561-6516

DENNIS,BATES & BULEN,LLP
318 SAINT CHARLES ST
BATON ROUGE,LA 70802-0201
PH 225 343-0100 FAX 225 343-0344
JAMES C BATES
THOMAS C MCKOWEN,IV
DON R BEARD
JAMES L WILLIAMS,IV
LAFAYETTE,LA OFFICE - 130 S AUDUBON
70503 PH 337 237-5900 FAX 337 233-9095
HOWELL A DENNIS,JR
JAMES L BULLEN BULLEN@DBLAW.NET

DENNY STEPHEN K,OIL LAND LEASES
PO BOX 53364
LAFAYETTE,LA 70505-3364 PH 337 988-7722
FAX 337 988-7739

DERAY'S PUMPING,GAUGING & LEASE SERVICE
10730 NEEDVILLE-FAIRCHILD RD
NEEDVILLE,TX 77461 PH 979 481-2062
FAX 979 793-4541
DERAY GOODRUM

DERBY ENERGY,LLC
7500 SAN FELIPE ST STE 475
HOUSTON,TX 77063
PH 713 706-3090 FAX 713 706-3490
WARREN MCFATTER,PRES

DERRICK CONSTRUCTION COMPANY,INC
250 COVE HARBOR SOUTH
ROCKPORT,TX 78382 PH 361 729-2423
FAX 361 729-1218
WWW.DERRICKCONSTRUCTION.NET
ROY M JOHNSON,EXEC DIR OF OPER
DERRICK JOHNSON,SR DIR OF OPER
SHANE JOHNSON,SUPT MECH & MAINT
SERENITY ALLEN,ACCT RECEIVABLE/
CONTRACTS ADMIN

DESCO OIL COMPANY
800 BERING DR STE 430
HOUSTON,TX 77057 PH 713 461-3566
FAX 713 984-0844
R L DAVIS,PRES

DESORMEAUX E R INC
P O BOX 52194,1454 SURREY ST
LAFAYETTE,LA 70505-2194 PH 318 237-0404
E RAYMOND DESORMEAUX,PRES
JANICE RICHARD,OFC MGR
JIM OPITZ,GEN SUPT
SHEILA BARRAS,ACCT MGR

DESOTO OIL & GAS CORP
3010 KNIGHT ST STE 270
SHREVEPORT,LA 71105-2541 PH 318 636-6666

DESOTO PIPELINE CO,INC
2584 TED TROUT DR
LUFKIN,TX 75904-8320 PH 936 632-1440
FAX 936 632-2201
CHRISTOPHER C SMITH,MGR,P/L OPS

DESPOT LAND COMPANY,INC
BROKERAGE,CONTRACTS,JOINT VENTURES

1716 LUBBOCK
HOUSTON,TX 77007-7718
PH 713 228-3577 FAX 713 228-3599
JDESPOT@FRONTLINEENERGY.COM
JUSTIN G DESPOT,PRES

DESPOT OIL COMPANY
PO BOX 52944,200 TRAVIS STE 201
LAFAYETTE,LA 70505-2944 PH 318 233-9199
FAX 318 233-9198
MARK DESPOT,PRES

DESTIN OPERATING COMPANY,INC
PO BOX 51386
LAFAYETTE,LA 70505-1386
PH 337 237-6022 FAX 337 237-6021
DENIS H BAILLARGEON,PRES
DOTTIE M COUGHLIN,OFC MGR/PROD ANALYST

DEVON ENERGY CORPORATION
333 WEST SHERIDAN AVE
OKLAHOMA CITY,OK 73102
PH 405 235-3611 FAX 405 552-4550
WWW.DEVONENERGY.COM
JOHN RICHELS,PRES & CEO
DAVID A HAGER,COO
R ALAN MARCUM,EXEC VP,ADMIN
JEFF A AGOSTA,EXEC VP & CFO
FRANK W RUDOLPH,EXEC VP,HUMAN RESOURCES
TONY D VAUGHN,SR VP,EXPL & PROD
STRATEGIC SVCS
DARRYL G SMETTE,EXEC VP,MKTG,MIDSTREAM &
SUPPLY CHAIN
LYNDON C TAYLOR,EXEC VP,GEN COUNSEL
BRADLEY A FOSTER,SR VP US OPERS
SUE ALBERTI,SR VP,MKTG
CARLA BROCKMAN,VP, CORP GOV & SECY
DAVID G HARRIS,VP,CORP FIN & TREASURER
GREGG L HENSON,VP,CORP CONTROLLER
STEVE HOPPE,SR VP,MIDSTREAM
JEREMY D HUMPHERS,VP,ACCTG
JEFFREY L RITENOUR,SR VP,INV REL
CHRIS SEASONS,SR VP,CANADIAN DIV & DEVON
CANADA PRES
GINA E SEWELL,VP, TAX
VINCENT W WHITE,SR VP,COMM & INV REL
ALLEN WRIGHT,VP,PUBLIC & GOVT AFFAIRS
DEVON CANADA CORPORATION - 400 3RD AVE SW
CALGARY,ALBERTA T2P 4H2 PH 403 232-7100

DEVON PETROLEUM CORPORATION
1635 WARREN CHAPEL
FLEMING,OH 45729 PH 740 373-2500
FAX 740 373-2404
EDDY L BIEHL,PRES

DEVON SFS OPERATING,INC SEE
DEVON ENERGY CORPORATION

DEWAR ROBERT L,INVESTMENTS
PO BOX 1442
FULTON,TX 78358-1442 PH 361 729-9496
BDEWAR79@GMAIL.COM

DEWARE RUSH,
PO BOX 668
JEFFERSON,TX 75657-0668 PH 972 758-5636

DEWBRE PETROLEUM CORPORATION
EXPLORATION, DEVELOPMENT & PRODUCTION
802 N CARANCHUA ST STE 1800
CORPUS CHRISTI,TX 78470-0352
PH 361 888-7978 FAX 361 888-7980
DEWBRE.COM PBRAND@DEWBRE.COM

JERRY C DEWBRE,PRES
JACK P DAY,VP,OPERS

DFM PROPERTIES,LTD
PO BOX 271968
HOUSTON,TX 77277 PH 713 269-4788
DAVID M FRIEDMAN FRIEDMAN100@COMCAST.NET

DFW SEISMIC BROKERAGE SERVICES
5310 HARVEST HILL RD STE 172 LB-174
DALLAS,TX 75230 PH 972 661-1471
JAMES FULLER,PRES/OWNER
JFULLER@DFWSEISMIC.COM

DHC ENERGY SERVICES,LLC
19003 TIMBER TRACE DR
HUMBLE,TX 77346
PH 281 852-2722 FAX 281 852-2722

DI CHEM/DRESSER
135 INDUSTRIAL DR
RAYNE,LA 70578
PH 318 235-2461 318 334-9633
DAVID TRAHAN,DIST MGR
TRACY KEHRER,SLS ENGR
RANDY GUILBEAUX,SLS ENGR
PAUL CHOATE,SLS ENGR
MIKE PHILLIPS,SLS ENGR
HOLLIE CORLEY,SLS ENGR
DON BOUDREAUX,SLS ENGR
AUDIE ANDRUS,DIST MGR

DI INDUSTRIES,INC SEE
DRILLERS INC

DIA LOG COMPANY SEE
WEDGE DIA-LOG,INC

DIAMOND CORE/TESTCO,INC
6674 FM 2767
TYLER,TX 75708
PH 903 593-3458 FAX 903 593-9757
WWW.DIAMONDCORETESTCOINC.COM
JASON SHAVER,PRES/OWNER
JASONSHAVER.DIAMONDCORETESTCO@GMAIL.C
OM

DIAMOND ENERGY CORPORATION
PO BOX 8
CANTON,MS 39046-0008 PH 601 859-5251
FAX 601 859-5258 WILDCATTER@AOL.COM
LLOYD G SPIVEY,JR,PRES

DIAMOND L INC
801 LOUISIANA STE 700
HOUSTON,TX 77002
PH 713 780-9599 FAX 713 781-7493
JAMES GREGG LEA,PRES

DIAMOND M - ODECO DRILLING INC SEE
DIAMOND OFFSHORE DRILLING INC

DIAMOND OFFSHORE DRILLING,INC
PO BOX 4558
HOUSTON,TX 77210-4558 PH 281 492-5300
FAX 281 492-5316
ROBERT E ROSE,PRES,CEO
MARK A CHILDERS,SR VP,TECH SVCS
R C JOHNSON,SR VP,EUROPEAN OPERS
THOMAS P RICHARDS,SR VP,DOMESTIC
OFFSHORE OPERS
LAWRENCE R DICKERSON,SR VP,CFO
ROBERT G BLAIR,VP,CONTRACTS,MKTG
AUSTRALIA & FAR EAST
JOHN L GABRIEL,VP,CONTRACTS,MKTG
GARY D LEE,VP,HUMAN RESOURCES
RICHARD L LIONBERGER,VP,GEN COUNSEL,SECY

ROBERT M MACLEOD,VP,NORTH SEA OPERS
RONNIE E MCBRIDE,VP,ONSHORE OPERS
ARTHUR M MEARS,VP,BUS DEV
GLEN E MERRIFIELD,VP,FOREIGN OPERS
DAVID W WILLIAMS,VP,GEN MGR,CONTRACTS
& MKTG
LARRY BOBBITT,MGR,CONTRACTS,MKTG
BODLEY THORNTON,MGR,CONTRACTS,MKTG
MORRISON PLAISANCE,MGR,OPERS,SPECIAL PROJ
LESTER L THOMAS,TREAS
METAIRIE,LA OFFICE - 111 VETERANS BLVD
HERITAGE PL STE 1030,70005
PH 504 834-9040 FAX 504 834-8153
KENNETH A BRADLEY,DIR,CLAIMS
CHRIS DAUTREUIL,CLAIMS REPR
VANCE T GREENE,MGR,CONTRACTS,MKTG

DIAMOND PRODUCTION ENERGY CO,LLC
PO BOX 167853
IRVING,TX 75016 PH 405 203-3500
FAX 972 409-9639

DIAMOND S MASADA LLC
4740 INGERSOLL ST STE 205
HOUSTON,TX 77027 PH 713 882-1777
PETE LIPPINCOTT PETE99@SBCGLOBAL.NET

DIAMOND SERVICES CORP
PO BOX 1286
MORGAN CITY,LA 70381-1286
PH 985 631-2187 FAX 985 631-4564
WWW.DIAMONDSERVICESCORP.COM
AMELIA,LA OFFICE - 503 S DEGRAVELLE RD
70340
GENE H DARNELL III,PRES
JULIE MARCOTTE,ADMIN ASST
JULIE@DSCGOM.COM
WESLEY DAIGLE,DREDGING,PILE DRIVING SUPT
MIKE SWIBER,PUR AGT
MEL SWIBER,PUR AGT
KENNY GUIDRY,MARINE TRANS DEPT
(TUGS & CREWBOATS)
JIM FURLETTE,ENGR,PIPELINE/SALVAGE SUPT
DEXTER BABIN,SLS

DIAMOND SERVICES WHT CORP
PO BOX 1286
MORGAN CITY,LA 70381-1286 PH 985 631-2187
FAX 985 631-4564 DIAMONDSERVICESCORP.COM
WALLACE CARLINE,PRES
JULIE MARCOTTE,ADMIN ASST
EARL HEBERT,CONTROLLER

DIAMOND SHAMROCK EXPLORATION COMPANY SEE
MAXUS EXPLORATION COMPANY

DIAMOND SHAMROCK INC SEE
ULTRAMAR DIAMOND SHAMROCK CORPORATION

DIAMOND SHAMROCK PIPELINE COMPANY SEE
ULTRAMAR DIAMOND SHAMROCK CORPORATION

DIAMOND SOUTH OPERATING LLC
PO BOX 65
SHREVEPORT,LA 71161-0065
PH 318 222-3119 FAX 318 222-0566
HARRY L AVANT,PRES
DEBRA B WALTERS,SECY/TREAS

DIAMONDBACK OPERATING,LP SEE
PATRICK ENERGY GROUP

DIASU OIL & GAS CO,INC
1000 LOUISIANA STE 1500
HOUSTON,TX 77002 PH 713 580-6600

DIBLER GEOPHYSICAL & INVENTORY SERVICES
1815 POLLEY CT
RICHMOND,TX 77469-2134 PH 281 341-1705
CHRIS DIBLER,PRES

DICKERSON & ASSOCIATES
PO BOX 52919
LAFAYETTE,LA 70505-2919
PH 337 264-1700 FAX 337 264-1700
LARRY DICKERSON,GEOL
MASON DICKERSON,AGRONOMIST,GEOL

DICKERSON LARRY N & ASSOC,PETR GEOL
PO BOX 52919
LAFAYETTE,LA 70505-2919
PH 337 264-1700 FAX 337 264-1700

DICKERSON MASON M,CONS,AGRONOMIST,GEOL
PO BOX 52919
LAFAYETTE,LA 70505-2919 PH 337 264-1700
PH 337 593-8104 FAX 337 234-0961

DICKERSON W B JR
PO BOX 9
OCEAN SPRINGS,MS 39566-0009
PH 228 324-2245 WBDJR@BELLSOUTH.NET

DIEHL LAND SERVICES
PO BOX 51874
LAFAYETTE,LA 70505-1874 PH 337 237-4842
FAX 337 237-4847 DIEHLLAND@AOL.COM
JAMES G DIEHL,PRES

DIFCO INC
PO BOX 151
CORPUS CHRISTI,TX 78403-0151
PH 361 882-3625
TABOR BROOKS,OWNER,PRES

DIGICON GEOPHYSICAL CORPORATION SEE
VERITAS DGC INC

DILLARD A R,INC
PO BOX 8206
WICHITA FALLS,TX 76307-8206
PH 940 716-5100 FAX 940 716-5110
JEFF R DILLARD,PRES
ROBERT W OSBORNE,VP
RICHARD W HASKIN,JR,SECY,DIR

DILLEY DISPOSAL COMPANY,INC
PO BOX 17203
SAN ANTONIO,TX 78217-0203 PH 210 828-8602
G A JEFF STONE,PRES

DIMENSION ENERGY CO,LLC
OIL & GAS EXPLORATION
1010 LAMAR ST STE 720
HOUSTON,TX 77002-6394
PH 713 651-1588 FAX 713 651-1853
CHARLES A O'NIELL III,PRES
CAON@FLASH.NET
JAMES H TINDALL
NEW IBERIA,LA OPERS OFFICE - 223 WEEKS ST
70560,PH 337 367-0121
DAVID D DALY
HOUMA,LA FLD OFFICE - 309 GOODE ST STE 3B
PH 985 262-1216 FAX 985 262-1028
MICHAEL DUGAS

DINERO OIL CORP SEE
ANDERSON OIL LTD

DIRECTIONAL TECHNOLOGIES,INC SEE
RYAN ENERGY TECHNOLOGIES USA,INC

DIRKS PETROLEUM COMPANY
PO BOX 29
BEEVILLE,TX 78104-0029 PH 361 358-9938

WAYNE D DIRKS,OWNER PH 361 362-7888
WAYNEDDIRKS@YAHOO.COM

DIRKS R W PETROLEUM ENGINEER,INC
PO BOX 200,8785 HWY 181
TULETA,TX 78162-0200
PH 361 375-2194 FAX 361 375-2100
JFISCHER@RWDIRKSPETROLEUM.COM
WWW.RWDIRKSPETROLEUM.COM
LAURA FISCHER,PRES
SUSAN A DIRKS,VP
JON R FISCHER,GEN MGR
RUSSELL MUSGROVE,PROJ COORD
CLIFF DAVIS,ENGR

DIRNETT,INC
PO BOX 200,HWY 181
TULETA,TX 78162-0200
PH 361 375-2194 FAX 361 375-2100
SUSAN DIRKS,PRES
J R FISCHER,VP OPERS
JFISCHER@RWDIRKSPETROLEUM.COM
LAURA FISCHER,VP

DISCORBIS OIL COMPANY
8620 N NEW BRAUNFELS AVE STE 620
SAN ANTONIO,TX 78217-6363
PH 210 828-8250 FAX 210 828-3170
GEORGE D WEATHERSTON,PRES
NICHOLAS WEATHERSTON,GEOL

DISCOVER E&P LLC
820 GESSNER RD STE 1375
HOUSTON,TX 77024-4461
PH 713 973-1820 FAX 713 650-6421
BILL HOWARD,PRES

DISCOVERY ACQUISITION SERVICES LLC
4141 KATY HOCKLEY RD
KATY,TX 77493
PH 281 371-2800 FAX 281 371-2744
WWW.DISCOVERYACQUISITION.COM
JOHN ODETTE,COO & PRES-DRILL OPERS
TERRY A GORDON,PRES-PERMIT OPERS
JIM PIGGOTT,PRES-SURVEY OPERS
JEFF SLEDER,VP-PERMIT OPERS
TAMMY SMALLEY,HSE

DISCOVERY ENERGY CORPORATION
PO BOX 2996
CORPUS CHRISTI,TX 78403-2996
PH 361 887-8331
BORDEN JENKINS,PRES

DISCUS OIL CORPORATION
PO BOX 458
PLAIN DEALING,LA 71064-0458
PH 318 326-4652 FAX 318 326-5015
WAYNE T DAVIS,PRES
MAI L DOLES,VP
JUDITH PITTMAN,SECY/TREAS

DISHMAN GEORGE A,JR
6820 COLLEGE ST
BEAUMONT,TX 77707-3203 PH 713 892-4461

DISHMAN H E,LEASES & ROYALTIES
6820 COLLEGE ST
BEAUMONT,TX 77707-3203 PH 409 892-6662
H E DISHMAN,OWNER
GEORGE A DISHMAN,JR
JAMES C DISHMAN

DISHMAN-MITCHELL-GORIN,INC
3165 OLD LEBANON RD
CAMPBELLSVILLE,KY 42718

PH 270 789-2341
GEORGE MITCHELL,PRES

DIVERSE ENERGY MANAGEMENT
840 GESSNER RD STE 700
HOUSTON,TX 77024
PH 713 571-9212 FAX 713 571-1877
BBASHAM@DIVERSEGP.COM
B TRAVIS BASHAM,MGR
THOMAS R FULLER,MGR
DONALD H WIESE,MGR
BRYAN BASHAM,MGR

DIVERSIFIED CHEMICALS OF CALIFORNIA
C/O BAKER PERFORMANCE CHEMICALS
135 INDUSTRIAL DR
RAYNE,LA 70578 PH 318 235-2461
JOHN BIBAEFF,DIV MGR
DAVID TRAHAN,SALES ENGR
CALVIN HARGRAVE,SALES ENGR
HOLLIE CORLEY,SALES ENGR
AUDEE ANDRUS,SALES

DIVERSIFIED LAND MANAGEMENT,INC
SEISMIC PERMITTING/PROJECT MGT
2-D & 3-D PROJ MGMNT
405 FONTAINE PLACE STE 102
RIDGELAND,MS 39157 PH 601 898-0024
FAX 601 898-0079 DLMINCONLINE.COM
JACK TATE,PRES PH 601 259-1366
JEAN TATE,VP PH 601 259-1366
DWAYNE TATE,SECY/TREAS/GIS MAPPING
PH 601 898-0024
GEORGE TATE,OPERS MGR/MKTG
PH 601 898-0024
GLYN KING,LAND/TITLE MGR PH 601 898-0024
TIM MCCANN,MINERAL AGT PH 601 898-0024
LITA TROXLER,AP/AR PH 601 898-0024
TONY POWELL,HSE MGR PH 601 898-0024
LAFAYETTE,LA REGIONAL OFFICE - 505 LOIRE
STE G,70507 PH 337 886-0060
FAX 337 886-0064
DEE COBB,ADMIN/REGULATORY
BRISTOL BROUSSARD,GIS MAPPING SUPVSR
EDNA,TEXAS REGIONAL OFFICE - 5633 US 59 S
77957,PH 361 400-3219
SHANE SKLAR,OPERS MGR/BUS DEVLP
PH 409 750-1161

DIVERSIFIED OIL & GAS
PO BOX 572136
HOUSTON,TX 77257-2136 PH 713 349-0841
FAX 713 349-0945
ROGER TICKNOR,PRES
ALAN GOODWILL,EXEC VP
KEN KULIK,SR VP

DIVINE'S SERVICE & REPAIRS,INC
6945 JEFFERSON PAIGE ROAD
SHREVEPORT,LA 71119-8850 PH 318 635-7806

DIVISIONORDERS.COM
3333 LEE PKWY STE 667
DALLAS,TX 75219 PH 844 462-6600
CHRIS SCHWIND
CSCHWIND@DIVISIONORDERS.COM

DIXIE DRILLING CO
3354 HWY 541 N
MENDENHALL,MS 39114-8825
PH 662 847-0735
J LARRY KENNEDY,PRES

DIXIE LAND & EXPLORATION,INC
3538 HIGHWAY 282
VAN BUREN,AR 72956-8728 PH 479 782-0694
JUANITA L PATTERSON,EXEC VP
NPATTERSON42542@YAHOO.COM

DIXIE RESOURCES,INC/WELLSITE CONSULTING
DRLG,COMPL,(INTL,STATESIDE,ON/OFFSHORE)
5222 S LAKESHORE DR
SHREVEPORT,LA 71109-1810
PH 318 631-0817 FAX 318 631-0817
DEAN BANKER,PRES DEANWBAKER@GMAIL.COM

DIXON EXPLORATION INC SEE
DXN INTERESTS,LLC & DXN ASSOCIATES

DIXON LANE H,PETR GEOL
4010 SPARTANBURG
TYLER,TX 75701
PH 903 747-3738 LANEDIXON7@YAHOO.COM

DIXON RAYMOND J,JR
101 CAMLAN CIR
LAFAYETTE,LA 70503-3085 PH 318 234-6986

DIXON SERVICES,INC
PO BOX 6602
TYLER,TX 75711
PH 903 579-9300 PH 800-283-1696
WWW.DSITYLER.COM
LARRY R DIXON,PRES

DIXON-DEARMORE OIL COMPANY,INC SEE
DIXON ENERGY,INC

DLB OIL & GAS,INC SEE
CHESAPEAKE OPERATING,INC

DM PETROLEUM OPERATIONS CO
850 S CLEARVIEW PKWY
NEW ORLEANS,LA 70123-3401
PH 504 734-4000 FAX 504 734-4121
ROBERT MCGOUGH,PROJ MGR

DMS OIL COMPANY
3000 WILCREST DR STE 250
HOUSTON,TX 77042-3390 PH 713 953-7718
FAX 713 953-7719
DOUGLASS M STEWART,PRES
GARY RAKER,VP
MARIA PAPPAS,OFC MGR

DOAN ANNA JUNIA
OIL PROD,ROYALTY OWNER
3801 VALLEY DR
MIDLAND,MI 48640-6601
PH 517 631-6600 FAX 517 832-0008

DOBIE C WALTER,GEOL
PO BOX 51682,106 OIL CENTER DR STE 106
LAFAYETTE,LA 70505-1682
PH 337 237-0647 FAX 337 232-1707

DODD C M,III,PETR ENGR
5642 FRESNO DR
CORPUS CHRISTI,TX 78411 PH 361 853-6007

DOEHRING CARL D
PO BOX 160774
MOBILE,AL 36616 PH 205 344-3344

DOGWOOD OPERATING COMPANY,INC
35 CHAMPIONS COURT PL
HOUSTON,TX 77069 PH 281 830-7571
DAVID KNEPPER,PRES DAVKNEP@SBCGLOBAL.NET

DOLLISON ROBERT S,IND GEOL
3333 CUMMINS #705
HOUSTON,TX 77027-5816 PH 713 825-5214

DOLPHIN ENERGY LLC
2699 STIRLING RD STE C102

FT LAUDERDALE,FL 33312 PH 954 981-1441
FAX 954 981-4841
NEAL RUDDER,MGR MEMBER

DOLPHIN ENERGY,INC
PO BOX 79190
HOUSTON,TX 77279-9190 PH 713 932-1735
FAX 713 932-1007 CAPTNZEB@INFOHWY.COM
ZEB D ALFORD,PRES

DOME ENERGICORP
2001 CROCKER RD STE 420,GEMINI II
CLEVELAND,OH 44145-6967 PH 440 892-9434
JOHN J CARNEY,PRINCIPAL
JAMES A CARNEY,PRINCIPAL
JON O NEWTON,PRINCIPAL
JAMES E GESSEL,PRINCIPAL

DOMESTIC FINANCIAL SERVICES INC
5220 HOLLYWOOD AVE
SHREVEPORT,LA 71109-7717 PH 318 636-6811
BETTY WILLIAMS,PRES
MARK F PREDDY,VP/SECY

DOMESTIC OIL AND GAS CO
19600 ROCKSIDE RD
BEDFORD,OH 44146-2079 PH 440 232-3150
FAX 440 232-0616
GLENN SIEGLER,PRES,TREAS

DOMINGUE FLOYD J
101 MOCKINGBIRD LN
LAFAYETTE,LA 70506-3119 PH 337 344-4840
DMNGFLYD@AOL.COM

DOMINGUE PAUL T,CPL
208 SANDALWOOD DR
LAFAYETTE,LA 70507
PH 337 501-3333 PAULDOMINGUE@COX.NET

DOMINGUE ROBERT C,OIL LAND LEASES
PO BOX 51668,133 S AUDUBON BLVD
LAFAYETTE,LA 70505-1668
PH 337 232-1291

DOMINICK PAT & ASSOCIATES
PO BOX 1706
DAPHNE,AL 36526-1706 PH 205 432-9028
FAX 205 432-9029
PATRICK R DOMINICK,CPL,PETR LDMN

DOMINION CORP,OIL OPR
PO BOX 491,1330 POST OAK BLVD #2850
HOUSTON,TX 77001-0491 PH 713 961-9699

DOMINION MINERALS CORPORATION
14505 TORREY CHASE BLVD STE 205
HOUSTON,TX 77014 PH 281 397-0091
FAX 281 397-0093
RANDALL K LOWRY,JR,PRES

DOMINION OKLAHOMA TEXAS EXPL & PROD,INC
(DOTEPI) SEE HIGH MOUNT E&P

DOMINO JOSEPH C INC
PO BOX 6,5520 RIVER RD
MARRERO,LA 70073-0006 PH 504 341-1122
FAX 504 341-1258 PATRICK@DOMINOTOWING.COM

DON MANLEY & ASSOCIATES
766 OAKDALE DR
AUSTIN,TX 78745 PH 970 406-8312
MANLEYDON@YAHOO.COM

DONNELL PIPE & SUPPLY COMPANY
PO BOX 1265
KILGORE,TX 75663-1265 PH 903 984-5055
FAX 903 984-3703 POWELL@CABLELYNX.COM
POWELL@CABLELYNX.COM

DONNER PROPERTIES
PO BOX 1346
SHREVEPORT,LA 71164-1346 PH 318 227-2131
FAX 318 222-5832
WWW.DONNERPROPERTIES.COM
PATTI HARTLEY,ADMIN ASST
DIANA CHANCE,MNGNG DIRECTOR
DCHANCE@DONNERPROPERTIES.COM

DONOHUE PATRICK L PETR PROPERTIES,INC
221 S MAIN ST
ABBEVILLE,LA 70510-5907
PH 337 264-1151 FAX 337 264-1152
PATRICK L DONOHUE,PRES PLDCPL@AOL.COM

DORAN CHARLES,E,OIL EXPLOR
PO BOX 1264
BENTON,LA 71006-1264 PH 318 222-2647

DORE' ENTERPRISES INC
PO BOX 626,333 WILLOW OAK DR
CROWLEY,LA 70527 PH 337 581-4684
AL DORE' DOREINC@MSN.COM

DORFMAN PRODUCTION COMPANY
8144 WALNUT HILL LN STE 1060 LB 64
DALLAS,TX 75231 PH 214 361-1660
FAX 214 361-2016
SAM Y DORFMAN,JR,PRES
GREG NEW,VP
BOB BRANDENBERGER,OPERS MGR

DORSEY WILLIAM D,CPL
PO BOX 643,610 MARSHALL ST STE 1030
SHREVEPORT,LA 71162-0643 PH 318 424-0100
WDDORSEY@AOL.COM

DORWARD ENERGY CORPORATION
447 3RD AVE N STE 400
ST PETERSBURG,FL 33701-3255
PH 727 490-1778 FAX 727 490-1780
DAVE@DORWARDENERGY.COM
DAVID A DORWARD,JR,PRES

DOUBLE M INC
PO BOX 1086
BENTON,LA 71006-1086 PH 318 326-4563
T R MCCLELLAN,PRES
DAN R MCCLELLAN,GEOL

DOUBLE-D-DRILLING,INC
206 SOUTHLAND DR E
LONDON,KY 40744-8180 PH 606 878-0905
FAX 606 877-7833
RICHARD PARKS,PRES

DOUGHERTY JAMES R,PROPERTIES
PO BOX 640,201 N WASHINGTON ST
BEEVILLE,TX 78104-0640 PH 361 358-3560
FAX 361 358-9693
BEN F VAUGHAN III,ATTY
J F SULIK,GEOL

DOUGHERTY LAW FIRM,P.C.
1106 FIRST PLACE
TYLER,TX 75702-5745 PH 903 597-5524
FAX 903 597-5367 DLFPC@SBCGLOBAL.NET
ROBERT P DOUGHERTY,JR
THOMAS K DOUGHERTY
KENNETH P DOUGHERTY

DOUGHTIE EXPLORATION COMPANY
13313 SOUTHWEST FWY STE 150
SUGAR LAND,TX 77478-3571 PH 281 494-5575
DAVID DOUGHTIE
DAVIDD@DOUGHTIEEXPLORATION.BIZ
BOB SPEER

BILL STIRLING

DOUGHTY ERIK,OIL PRODUCER
711 N CARANCAHUA ST STE 1600
CORPUS CHRISTI,TX 78401 PH 361 884-9437

DOUGLAS DALE OIL & GAS PROPERTIES SEE
DZ RESOURCES,LLC

DOUGLASS BOB EXPLORATION CO
PO BOX 1059
DESTREHAN,LA 70047-1059
PH 985 764-7463 BOBDOUGLASS@COX.NET
M R DOUGLASS,PRES PH 225 247-0600

DOUGLASS M R
PO BOX 1059
DESTREHAN,LA 70047 PH 985 764-7463
M R DOUGLASS,IND PETR GEOL
BOBDOUGLASS@COX.NET PH 225 247-0600

DOVE DRILLING INC
PO BOX 921
KILGORE,TX 75663-0921 PH 903 984-3443
CHARLA ROLPH,AGENT

DOVER TIM,CPL
9410 BRIAR FOREST DR
HOUSTON,TX 77063 PH 832 693-4515
TIM DOVER TIM-DOVER@COMCAST.NET

DOW CHEMICAL USA OIL & GAS DIV SEE
APACHE CORPORATION

DOWDCO/DIAMOND OIL WELL DRILLING CO,INC
SEE CORPRO

DOWELL
300 SCHLUMBERGER DR
SUGAR LAND,TX 77478-3155 PH 281 275-8400
F A OSBORN,VP,GEN MGR
D PFERDEHIRT,VP,MKTG
HOUSTON,TX SALES OFFICE - 1325 S DAIRY
ASHFORD STE 300,77077 PH 281 556-7270
J RICHARDS,VP,NAM SALES

DOWNHOLE SEISMIC SERVICES SEE
ATLAS WIRELINE SERVICES

DOWNHOLE SYSTEMS AND TECHNOLOGY
6911 SIGNAT RD
HOUSTON,TX 77041 PH 281 498-7399
FAX 281 498-7286
GLENN GRIMES,SR ENGR
GLENNGRIMES@MSN.COM

DOWNING WELL SERVICE
411 MOCKINGBIRD LN
DEVINE,TX 78016-1309 PH 830 665-4923
FAX 830 665-4923
MARK DOWNING,PRES

DOWNMAN JONES OIL OPER,INC
7210 FALCON DR
BROOKSHIRE,TX 77423-9155 PH 281 375-8757

DOYLE LAND SERVICES,INC
400 LAFAYETTE ST
NEW ORLEANS,LA 70130-3206 PH 504 620-5051
FAX 504 818-1138 WWW.DOYLELAND.COM
JOHN WARREN DOYLE,PRES
JWDOYLE@DOYLELAND.COM
TERESA E MATHESON,VP BUS DEV
TEMATHESON@DOYLELAND.COM PH 504 620-5054
A D DEL BARNES JR,GEN COUNSEL
ADBARNES@DOYLELAND.COM PH 504 818-1118

DRACO SPRING MFG CO INC
9002 CHIMNEY ROCK RD
HOUSTON,TX 77096-2509 PH 713 645-4973

BARRY DRAGER,PRES
BOB VELAZQUEZ,SHOP FRMN
DANNY ROSS,OFC MGR

DRAGON ENERGY CORPORATION
650 POYDRAS ST STE 2828
NEW ORLEANS,LA 70130-6155
PH 504 586-1717 FAX 504 586-0017
DRAGONENERGY@BELLSOUTH.NET

DRAKE DENNIS R,OIL INVESTMENTS
2 CHAMPIONS COURT TRL
HOUSTON,TX 77069-1794 PH 281 880-8580
DRAKERES@AOL.COM

DRAKE ENERGY CORP
PO BOX 4567
MONROE,LA 71211-4567 PH 318 322-5289
S G HARRINGTON,PRES
C A FARRINGTON,VP,OPERS

DRAKE WELL MUSEUM & PARK
MUSEUM OF THE PETR INDUSTRY & ITS GROWTH
202 MUSEUM LN
TITUSVILLE,PA 16354-8902 PH 814 827-2797
WWW.DRAKEWELL.ORG
DRAKEWELL@VERIZON.NET

DRAVES DOUGLAS A,PETR GEOL
10 GRONEWOLD LN
TONASKET,WA 98855-9570 PH 509 486-1015

DREAMERS LAND & MINERALS,INC
PO BOX 2910
BRYAN,TX 77805-2910 PH 979 589-3774

DRESSER ATLAS,DRESSER INDUSTRIES SEE
ATLAS WIRELINE SERVICES

DRESSER OIL TOOLS SEE
HALLIBURTON ENERGY SERVICES

DRILCO OIL & GAS INC
APPALACIAN BASIN - O&G IND PRODUCER
PO BOX 385
GRANTSVILLE,WV 26147 PH 304 354-9516
FAX 304 354-6809
HUGH DALE,PRES
CYNTHIA DALE,VP

DRILEX SYSTEMS,INC
DIRECTIONAL DRLG,WELL PLANNING SERVICES
DOWNHOLE DRLG TOOLS/MUD MOTORS
PO BOX 670968
HOUSTON,TX 77267-0968 PH 713 937-8888
FAX 713 849-2390
JOHN FORREST,PRES,CEO
BRUCE BROUSSARD,VP,FIN,ADMIN
DENNY KERR,VP,ENERGY SVCS/PROD SALES
ANCHORAGE,AK OFFICE - 6300 PETERSBURG
99507 PH 907 562-3312 FAX 907 562-4452
BRIAN BINGHAM,OPERS COORD
BAKERSFIELD,CA OFFICE - 3109 ANTONIO
93301 PH 661 328-0234 FAX 661 328-0246
TOM GIBSON,OPERS COORD
CASPER,WY OFFICE - 1283 N DERRICK DR
82604,PO BOX 1750 MILLS,WY 82644
PH 307 234-8888 FAX 307 234-8884
JEFF BENNETT,REG MGR
BRUCE COATES,OPERS COORD
DENVER,CO OFFICE - 1675 BROADWAY,STE 1800
80202 PH 303 623-1933 FAX 303 892-9299
JIM BALOCK,APPL SPEC
TERRY KERR,APPL SPEC
FORT WORTH,TX OFFICE - 115 W 7TH ST
STE 1322,76102 PH 817 336-9609

FAX 817 336-9609
DEDE TERVEEN,APPL SPEC
HOUSTON,TX OFFICE - PO BOX 801114
15151 SOMMERMEYER,77280-1114
PH 713 466-8784 FAX 713 849-4370
BO GODFREY,REG MGR
GABBY BENOIT,DIR COORD
JIM SANDERS,APPL SPEC
RANDY SPRINGER,APPL SPEC
LAFAYETTE,LA OFFICE - PO BOX 51410
102 CASON RD,70505
PH 318 837-2901 FAX 318 837-3927
JAY BELLAMY,REG MGR
NICK BERWICK,DIR COORD
RON HETHCOX,APPL SPEC
NEW ORLEANS,LA OFFICE - 201 SAINT CHARLES
AVE STE 2530,70170 PH 504 522-4293
FAX 504 524-7979
DAVID CLEMENT,APPL SPEC
MIKE TERREBONNE,APPL SPEC
OKLAHOMA CITY,OK OFFICE - 6209 S SOONER
RD,73135 PH 405 495-3671 FAX 405 495-3673
DANNY WARD,REG MGR
GERRE VODEN,OPERS COORD
STEVE HOOPER,APPL SPEC

DRILL GAS,LLC
29335 NO LE HACE DR
BOERNE,TX 78015 PH 830 249-6860
PH 210 535-3745 FAX 830 230-5103
BENNOWOTNY@GMAIL.COM
WWW.DRILLGAS.COM
M BEN NOWOTNY
PAUL MAGUIRE,DRLG SUPT
CHARLES DUNCAN,MAINT SUPT/LULING,TX

DRILL LABS INC
915 TALBOT AVE
THIBODAUX,LA 70301 PH 800 256-8432
PH 985 446-8432 WWW.DRILLLABS.COM
MERRILL UTLEY,OPERS-PETROLEUM CTR
LAFAYETTE,LA OFFICE - 1030 E ST MARY
BLDG 3 70505 PH 337 237-6110
PH 337 781-6421 DRILLLAB@BELLSOUTH.NET
PAUL L DAVIS
HOUSTON,TX OFFICE - PH 832 247-7805
GARY J BURKETT GARYJBURKETT@YAHOO.COM

DRILLERS ELECTRIC CORPORATION
PO BOX 51262
LAFAYETTE,LA 70505-1262 PH 337 232-3993
FAX 337 232-6767 DECORP@COX-INTERNET.COM
NORMAN R CURTIS,VP
KENNY CURTIS,SECY/TREAS
KATIE LALANDE,OFC MGR
DANNY ROACH,FIELD FRMN
TODD BROUSSARD,REWINDER
LAWRENCE TEE CORMIER
GLENN ALLEMAND

DRILLERS,INC SEE
GREY WOLF DRILLING CO

DRILLING APPALACHIAN CORPORATION (D.A.C.)
PO BOX 99
ALMA,WV 26320-0099 PH 304 758-4638
FAX 304 758-2433
KENNETH R MASON,PRES

DRILLING INFO INC
PO BOX 5545
AUSTIN,TX 78763 PH 888 477-7667

WWW.DRILLINGINFO.COM

DRILLING PARTNERS,INC
PO BOX 52006,110 RUE JEAN LAFITTE
LAFAYETTE,LA 70505 PH 337 233-6871
FAX 337 233-7198
WWW.STOKESANDSPIEHLER.COM
MAIL.STOKESANDSPIEHLER.COM
BRUCE M JORDAN,DRLG & COMP ENGR
BJORDAN@STOKESANDSPIEHLER.COM
GEORGE W STOKES,DRLG & COMP ENGR
GSTOKES@STOKESANDSPIEHLER.COM
JOHN LONG,DRLG & COMP ENGR
JLONG@STOKESANDSPIEHLER.COM
MARK STRINGER,CONTR MGR
MSTRINGER@STOKESANDSPIEHLER.COM
LARRY FOWLER,EXEC SLS REPR
LFOWLER@STOKESANDSPIEHLER.COM

DRILLING RECORDS,DIV OF CANAMERA CORP SEE
DIVESTCO USA INC

DRILLING SPECIALTIES COMPANY
DIVISION CHEVRON PHILLIPS CHEMICAL CO,LP
PO BOX 4910
THE WOODLANDS,TX 77387-4910
PH 800 423-3985 FAX 832 813-4910
WWW.DRILLINGSPECIALTIES.COM
BILL HOLVEY,SLS MGR,WEST HEMIS
PRESTON ALFORD,DISTRICT SLS

DRILLING-PROSPECTS.COM SEE
BLAKE BRUCE W CPL/ESA MGMNT SERVICES

DRILTECH LLC
PO BOX 80097
LAFAYETTE,LA 70598 PH 337 837-1219
FAX 337 837-9019 WWW.DRILTECH.NET
PATRICK S KILLEEN,PRES/OWNER
BRADLEY J VINCENT SR,VP/OWNER
MARK PATIN,SALES
MARK.PATIN@DRILTECH.NET
WILLIAM BLANCHET,CFO
CASEY POCHE',SHOP MGR
TANYA S ABSHIRE,OFC MGR

DRLS,INC
PO BOX 51711
LAFAYETTE,LA 70505-1711
PH 337 237-3650 FAX 337 234-2163
NODSOR3@AOL.COM
DONALD P ROSS III,CPL,PRES

DRONET KEITH A
PO BOX 53411
LAFAYETTE,LA 70505-3411
PH 337 233-9099 FAX 337 237-4912

DRURY VENTURES,LLC
5500 DAVID DR
KENNER,LA 70065 PH 504 905-9540
FAX 504 582-4155 DRURYLLC@GMAIL.COM
L LEONARD DRURY,JR,ATTY/CONSULTANT

DU PONT COMPANY
1007 MARKET ST
WILMINGTON,DE 19898-0001 PH 302 774-1000

DUAL PRODUCTION PARTNERS LLC
PO BOX 631508
NACOGDOCHES,TX 75963 PH 936 560-6477
FAX 936 569-8128

DUBOIS PAUL,PETROLEUM GEOL
1919 EATON AVE
OWENSBORO,KY 42301 PH 270 926-9063
FAX 270 926-9133 KEYANACOMPANY@JUNO.COM

DUCHIN OIL AND GAS LLC
4424 E LA PALOMA DR
TUCSON,AZ 85718-1500 PH 520 577-8879
FAX 520 577-1812
RALPH C DUCHIN,OWNER,GEOL

DUCHIN RALPH C,PETR GEOL
4424 E LA PALOMA DR
TUCSON,AZ 85718-1500 PH 520 577-8879
FAX 520 577-1812

DUERR PETROLEUM CONSULTANTS
64 TOWNHOUSE LN
CORPUS CHRISTI,TX 78412-4271
PH 361 986-9933 FAX 361 986-9933
S E DUERR,PETR ENGR,CONS
SEDUERR@SBCGLOBAL.NET
NEW BRAUNFELS,TX OFFICE - 155 RIDGE
COUNTRY DR 78132 PH 830 237-6240
MICHAEL D DUERR,PETR GEOL,CONS
MDUERR@GVTC.COM PH 830 956-5008

DUFFY & MCGOVERN INC - ACCOMMODATION SVCS
SUPPLIER OF TEMPORARY CABINS FOR OIL IND
5813 HIGHWAY 90 E
BROUSSARD,LA 70518-5914 PH 504 392 9455
PH 504 392-9411 FAX 504 392-9455

DUFOUR PETROLEUM,INC
PO BOX 1184
PETAL,MS 39465-1184
PH 601 583-9991 FAX 601 583-9881
CURTIS J DUFOUR III,CEO
MIKE HOWELL,PRES
BOB FULLEN,SALES REPR

DUGAN A W
3009 POST OAK BLVD STE 1212
HOUSTON,TX 77056 PH 713 658-1142
FAX 713 658-0739
ROBERT W KENT,LAND MGR

DUGAN DRILLING,INC
27238 NEW GUILFORD RD
WALHONDING,OH 43843-9612 PH 740 668-3811
FAX 740 668-3811
GUY E DUGAN,PRES
LINDA DUGAN,TREAS

DUGAN OIL AND GAS LLC
27238 NEW GUILFORD ROAD
WALHONDING,OH 43843-9612
PH 740 668-3811 FAX 740 668-3811
GUY E DUGAN,CO-OWNER/AGENT
LINDA D DUGAN,CO-OWNER

DUGGAN DAN EARL
PO BOX 174
FT WORTH,TX 76101 PH 817 347-9300

DUGGAN ENERGY COMPANY
PO BOX 837
INDIANA,PA 15701-0837 PH 724 357-9862
MICHAEL P DUGGAN,PRES

DUGGAN MACHINE CO,AN ANGLO ENERGY CO
P O BOX 7333,1509 GRIMMET DR
SHREVEPORT,LA 71137-7333
PH 318 222-8371
DON DUGGAN,PRES
JACK JEROME,VP

DUGGER GLENN,OIL OPR
1915 ENCINO AVE
ALICE,TX 78332-4115 PH 361 664-5807
FAX 361 664-4905

DUKE ENERGY FIELD SERVICES,INC SEE
DCP MIDSTREAM

DUKE ENERGY NATURAL GAS CORPORATION
370 17TH ST STE 2500
DENVER,CO 80202-5644 PH 303 595-3331
FAX 303 595-0480
JIM W MOGG,CHRMN

DULA JAMES E JR
PO BOX 921
KILGORE,TX 75663-0921 PH 903 984-3443
CHARLA ROLPH,AGENT

DULL JOE A,OIL PROD
15885 N IL HWY 37
MOUNT VERNON,IL 62864-1818
PH 618 244-1266,242-0753
BARBARA MCBRIDE,SECY
DOROTHY W JOHNSON,SECY
JAMES E DULL,ATTY
BOX 1583,1116 MAIN ST
MOUNT VERNON,IL 62864 PH 618 244-6611

DUMONT DAN
3901 MCGREGOR AVE S
MOBILE,AL 36608 PH 251 433-2372
FAX 251 433-2374 ALFRC@BELLSOUTH.NET
WWW.ALFRC.ORG

DUNCAN ENERGY COMPANY SEE
BABCOCK & BROWN ENERGY,INC

DUNCAN LAND SERVICES,LLC
147 NOBLE AVE STE 100
PITTSBURGH,PA 15214
PH 412 922-0900 FAX 412 922-0901
INFO@DUNCANLAND-ENERGY.COM
WWW.DUNCANLANDSERVICES.COM
GUY A TRULLI,PRES
BRADLEE W TEBBS,VP,CPL

DUNCAN OIL PROPERTIES INC
100 PARK AVE STE 1200
OKLAHOMA CITY,OK 73102-8006
PH 405 272-1800 FAX 405 272-1875
WALT DUNCAN IV,PRES
NICHOLAS V DUNCAN,VP
DENNIS DAN,CFO
JACK MURLIN,SR GEOL
NICK HUMPHREY,PROD MGR
JOHN MYLES,GEN COUNSEL
BRIAN BRANESKY,LDMN
TIFFANY STEPHENS,SR GEOL

DUNCAN WALTER,OIL PROPERTIES SEE
DUNCAN OIL PROPERTIES INC

DUNDEE PETROLEUM,INC SEE
SCOTT ROYCE ARNOLD

DUNDEE RESOURCES INC SEE
SCOTT ROYCE ARNOLD

DUNE ENERGY,INC
777 WALKER ST STE 2300
HOUSTON,TX 77002-5314 PH 713 888-0895
HAL BETTIS,EXEC VP/COO
HBETTIS@DUNEENERGY.COM
JAMES GAGLIARDI,SR VP EXPL MGR
JGAGLIARDI@DUNEENERGY.COM
GREGORY J FOX,MGR OPERS
GFOX@DUNEENERGY.COM

DUNIGAN OPERATING CO,INC
PO BOX 30080
AUSTIN,TX 78755-3080 PH 512 334-9467
FAX 512 334-9467

DUNNE EQUITIES INC
5773 WOODWAY DR STE 408
HOUSTON,TX 77057 PH 713 266-0110
DUNSON E C,GEOPHY
100 E WADLEY
MIDLAND,TX 79701 PH 432 682-2993
DUNWOODY CHARLES G,JR
2001 KIRBY DR STE 810
HOUSTON,TX 77019-6033 PH 713 652-2949
DUNWOODY HOLDINGS LP
PO BOX 770668,2500 TANGLEWILDE STE 150
HOUSTON,TX 77215-0668 PH 713 784-4000
FAX 713 784-4040
R SCOTT DUNWOODY,PRES
MICHAEL G PITZER,EXPL MGR
DUPLANTIS RESOURCES LLC
820 CEDARWOOD DR
MANDEVILLE,LA 70471-6728
PH 504 236-4650
MERLEJ@BELLSOUTH.NET
MD@ALPINEXCI.COM
MERLE J DUPLANTIS,PRES/OWNER
DUPRE' SUPPLY CO
101 COMMISSION BLVD
LAFAYETTE,LA 70508 PH 318 237-8078
FAX 318 233-9032
CORNELIUS DUPRE' II,CEO
JOHN R DUPRE',JR,CFO
RONNIE JOSEPH,SALES MGR
TIM WILLIAMS,OPERS MGR
DAVID KNIGHT,OPERS MGR
LAFAYETTE,LA DIV OFFICE - PH 318 237-6400
FAX 318 232-3620
RON DAIGLE,OUTSIDE SALESMAN
KEN ROMERO,OUTSIDE SALESMAN
BRANDON BROUSSARD,OUTSIDE SALESMAN
KEN GUIDRY,OUTSIDE SALESMAN
LONNIE CARRIERE,OUTSIDE SALESMAN
SHREVEPORT,LA DIV OFFICE - 1728 N MARKET
71107 PH 318 221-3658 FAX 318 221-3684
TIMMY BOUDREAUX,STORE MGR
DON LEE,OUTSIDE SALESMAN
PAUL WILSON,OUTSIDE SALESMAN
JOE PEACH,OUTSIDE SALESMAN
DEWAYNE KLIENPETER,OUTSIDE SALESMAN
HOUMA,LA DIV OFFICE - 1824 GRAND
CAILLOU RD,70363 PH 504 872-5400
FAX 504 872-0032
DAVID OLIVIER,PIPING PRODUCTS MGR
FRITZ DRYDEN,OUTSIDE SALESMAN
JAMES SPEARMAN,OUTSIDE SALESMAN
MARK TALBOT,OUTSIDE SALESMAN
TONY STEWART,STORE MGR
VENICE,LA DIV OFFICE - 41268 HWY 23
70038 PH 504 534-4100 FAX 504 534-4107
DAVID RICHOUX,STORE MGR
MIKE MEANS,OUTSIDE SALESMAN
JIM EDGERTON,OUTSIDE SALESMAN
DERIDDER,LA OFFICE - 18651 CENTRAL AVE
ROSEPINE,LA 70659 PH 318 463-2499
JOHN REAVES,STORE MGR
FOURCHON,LA OFFICE - 103 N J DOUCET DR
PORT OF FOURCHON,GOLDEN MEADOW,LA
70357 PH 504 396-3978
NEIL RICHARD,STORE MGR
LAUREL,MS OFFICE - 290 VICTORY RD

39440 PH 601 425-2333
ATLEY LEDLOW,STORE MGR
BEAUMONT,TX DIV OFFICE - 2206 W CARDINAL
DR,77705 PH 409 842-5858 FAX 409 842-9645
BILL POWERS,STORE MGR
RANDY FEVERJEAN,OUTSIDE SALESMAN
GENE ELKINS,OUTSIDE SALESMAN
ALVIN,TX DIV OFFICE - 8411A INDUSTRIAL DR
PEARLAND,TX 77584 PH 281 992-1900
FAX 281 992-1920
STAN HILTON,STORE MGR
WAYNE BROUSSARD,OUTSIDE SALESMAN
ODESSA,TX DIV OFFICE - 2135 W I-20
79763 PH 432 332-6272 FAX 432 332-9955
RICK MOBLEY,STORE MGR
HOUSTON,TX SALES OFFICE - 2400 AUGUSTA DR
STE 410,77057 PH 713 787-6900
FAX 713 787-6661
RONNIE JOSEPH,SALES MGR
CHARLES LEE,SALESMAN
PALESTINE,TX OFFICE - 5335 W OAK ST
75801 PH 903 723-3338
EDDIE COOKSEY,STORE MGR
CORPUS CHRISTI,TX OFFICE - 1202 SOUTHERN
MINERALS RD,78409 PH 361 289-1233
LINDA WHITLEY,STORE MGR
MCALLEN,TX OFFICE - 7 MI N CONWAY/1 MI W
681,MISSION,TX 78572 PH 956 584-1440
ROY MORIN,STORE MGR
- PIPING PRODUCTS DIVISION -
LAFAYETTE,LA OFFICE - 101 COMMISSION BLVD
70508 PH 318 237-0056 FAX 318 237-8752
JORGE DIAZ,STORE MGR
HOUMA,LA OFFICE - 1824 GRAND CAILLOU RD
70508 PH 504 851-2236
DAVID OLIVIER,STORE MGR
HARVEY,LA OFFICE - 1225 PETERS RD
70059 PH 504 363-9404
JIM EDGERTON,STORE MGR
CORPUS CHRISTI,TX OFFICE - 1202 SOUTHERN
MINERALS RD,78409 PH 361 289-1233
LINDA WHITLEY,STORE MGR
BEAUMONT,TX OFFICE - 2203 W CARDINAL DR
77705 PH 409 842-5858
BILL POWERS,STORE MGR
KEITH BRIST,REGL TEAM LEADER
ODESSA,TX OFFICE - 2135 W I-20
79763 PH 432 332-6272
RICK MOBLEY,STORE MGR
- DUPRE' VALVE -
HOUSTON,TX OFFICE - 6531 PETROPARK DR
77041 PH 713 849-3468 FAX 713 849-9618
CARL AXELSON,SALES
LENNY GARY,OUTSIDE SALES
MARTIN WILLMORE,OUTSIDE SALES
LAFAYETTE,LA OFFICE - 307 MECCA DR
70508 PH 318 237-8878 FAX 318 237-2995
MIKE REYNOLDS,STORE MGR
DUPRIEST LIMITED PARTNERSHIP
PO BOX 2006
MAGNOLIA,AR 71754-2006 PH 870 234-4090
KEITH A DUPRIEST,GEOL
DURANGO RESOURCES CORP
1147 BRITTMOORE RD STE 1
HOUSTON,TX 77043 PH 281 558-7998
FAX 281 558-3323

JEFF SWANSON,PRES
DONALD C SWANSON,CHIEF GEOSCIENTIST
GREG STEVENS,VP OPERS
ROD HALL,VP MKTG
DURST OIL COMPANY
615 N UPPER BROADWAY ST STE 1900
CORPUS CHRISTI,TX 78477-0042
PH 361 888-4741 FAX 361 888-4744
LEE A DURST,JR,PRES
DUSTY DRILLING & PRODUCING CORPORATION
960 S MAIN ST
NEW LEXINGTON,OH 43764-1552
PH 740 342-2050 FAX 740 342-4498
STEVEN L ALTIER,PRES
DUVAL GAS GATHERING CORPORATION
1915 ENCINO AVE
ALICE,TX 78332-4115 PH 361 664-5807
FAX 361 664-4905
GLENN DUGGER,PRES
KENNETH MARKGRAF,VP
MARYLOU DUGGER,SECY
DUVICS INCORPORATED
PO BOX 1237,3650 W BANK EXPWY
HARVEY,LA 70058-1237 PH 504 341-1654
FAX 504 341-1654
M DUVIC,JR,PRES
JAMES M DUVIC,VP
HARRIET HOLDER
DWIGHTS ENERGY DATA SEE
PETROLEUM INFORMATION/DWIGHTS LLC
DYAD PETROLEUM COMPANY
505 N BIG SPRING ST STE 603
MIDLAND,TX 79701-4396 PH 432 683-9290
FAX 432 684-4775
TOM D DYCHES,PRES
CHARLES A ADKISSON,VP,ENGR
LINDA BRADSHAW,ACCT MGR
AMY BUSHONG,EXEC ASST
THE WOODLANDS,TX OFFICE - 2204 TIMBERLOCH
PL,STE 140,77380 PH 281 465-0842
FAX 281 298-2294
DYASON LINDA F
PO BOX 413
RED RIVER,NM 87558-0413 PH 575 754-6368
BATON ROUGE,LA (WINTER) OFFICE - 6222
SUMMER LAKE DR 70817-4326 PH 225 753-3400
DYCO PETROLEUM CORPORATION SEE
SAMSON RESOURCES CO
DYKES WELL SERVICES
5329 SHREVEPORT-BLANCHARD HWY
SHREVEPORT,LA 71107 PH 318 929-2929
FAX 318 929-3498
BRYAN DYKES,VP OPERS
B.DYKES@DYKESWELLSERVICES.COM
MIKE MORGAN,SLS
DYN MCDERMOTT PETROLEUM OPERATIONS CO SEE
DM PETROLEUM OPERATIONS CO
DYNAMIC EXPLORATION PARTNERS,LLC
PO BOX 52889,126 HEYMANN BLVD
LAFAYETTE,LA 70505-2889 PH 337 232-6841
FAX 337 235-6355 DYNAMIC@126COMPANY.COM
W K RAINBOLT,JR,MGR
DAVID G JONES,MGR
SANTA FE,NM OFFICE-524 CAMINOS LOS ALTOS
87501-8305 PH 505 982-0075
ROY MELTON,EXPL MGR

DYNAMIC OFFSHORE RESOURCES LLC
  1301 MCKINNEY STE 900
  HOUSTON,TX 77010 PH 713 728-7840
  FAX 713 728-7860 WWW.DYNAMICOSR.COM
    G MATT MCCARROLL,PRES/CEO
    HOWARD TATE,SR VP,CFO
    JOHN Y JO,SR VP,ACQ & ENG
    THOMAS R LAMME,SR VP & GEN COUNSEL
    JAMES BROKMEYER,VP PROD OPERS
    GARY JANIK,VP EXPLOITATION & DEV
    CAREY NAQUIN,VP WELL OPERS
    JOHN SMITH,VP LAND & BUS DEV
    BILL SWINGLE,VP ACCT

DYNAMIC OFFSHORE RESOURCES NS,LLC
  1301 MCKINNEY STE 900
  HOUSTON,TX 77010 PH 713 728-7840
  FAX 713 728-7860 WWW.DYNAMICOSR.COM
    G MATT MCCARROLL,PRES/CEO
    HOWARD TATE,CFO
    JAMES BROKMEYER,VP PROD OPERS
    GARY JANIK,VP EXPLOITATION & DEV
    CAREY NAQUIN,VP WELL OPERS
    JOHN H SMITH,VP LAND & BUS DEV
    BILL SWINGLE,VP ACCT

DYNEGY MIDSTREAM SERVICES,LP
  601 TRAVIS ST STE 1400
  HOUSTON,TX 77002 PH 713 507-6400
  FAX 713 507-6740
    STEVE FURBACHER,PRES
    BRAD FARNSWORTH,VP,CONTROLLER
    MARC BREITLING,VP,BUS DEV
      STRATEGIC PLANNING
    MARK STUBBE,PRES,LIQUIDS MKTG & TRADE
    JOHN GAWRONSKI,VP,WHOLESALE NGL MKTG
      & TRANSPORTATION
    BILL PUCKETT,VP,LIQUIDS MKTG ASSETS
    VINNY MCCONNELL,SR VP,LIQUIDS MKTG
      & TRADE
    JOHN O'SHEA,MGR,TECH SERVICES
  HOUSTON,TX ARK-LA-TX REGION OFFICE -
    LEN HESSELTINE,REG MGR
    DAVID ADAMS,GAS SUPPLY/BUS DEV (E TEX)
    RICK JOHNSON,GAS SUPPLY/BUS DEV (N TEX)
    BOBBY MCGUIRE,GAS SUPPLY/BUS DEV (N TEX)
    BERNIE THOMAS,GAS SUPPLY/BUS DEV (E TEX)
  GULF COAST REG OFFICE - PH 504 676-2200
    FAX 504 676-2204
    ALEX BUCHER,REG MGR
    TIM BALASKIN,GAS SUPPLY/BUS DEV
    DONNIE BROWN,GAS SUPPLY/BUS DEV
    KEVIN COXON,GAS SUPPLY/BUS DEV
    MIKE SPIES,GAS SUPPLY/BUS DEV
  TULSA,OK MID-CONT REG OFFICE -
    320 S BOSTON,STE 701,74103
    PH 918 699-2400 FAX 918 587-5878
    MIKE GRAY,REG MGR
    CESAR ESPINO,GAS SUPPLY/BUS DEV
    MIKE MARLOW,GAS SUPPLY/BUS DEV
    STEVE MARSH,GAS SUPPLY/BUS DEV
    BILL GRANTHAM,GAS SUPPLY/BUS DEV
    LEFTY SMITH,GAS SUPPLY/BUS DEV
  MIDLAND,TX PERMIAN BASIN REG OFFICE -
    6 DESTA DR,STE 3300,79705
    PH/FAX 432 688-0555
    CLARK WHITE,REG MGR
    JEROME GEGELMON,GAS SUPPLY/BUS DEV

    STEVE MCCOWN,GAS SUPPLY/BUS DEV
    TERRY PARRISH,GAS SUPPLY/BUS DEV
    JOHN WILLIAMS,GAS SUPPLY/BUS DEV
  EUNICE,NM OFFICE - PO BOX 1909,88231-1909
    PH 505 394-2534 FAX 505 394-2714

D90 ENERGY LLC
  202 TRAVIS STE 402
  HOUSTON,TX 77002
  PH 713 227-0391 DSILVERMAN@D90ENERGY

E & B NATURAL RESOURCES
  1984 HIGHWAY 190 N
  COVINGTON,LA 70433-5158 PH 713 703-8607
    WILLIAM MOODY C JR,SR VP GULF COAST

E & E PRODUCTION CO,INC
  PO BOX 13840
  NEW IBERIA,LA 70562-3840 PH 337 369-3853
  FAX 337 364-6429
    JOHNNY ESTIS,PRES
    JAMELL ESTIS,SECY/TREAS

E & H DRILLING CO
  PO BOX 1058,NEW CASTLE HWY
  GRAHAM,TX 76450-1058 PH 940 549-0370
  FAX 940 549-8191 RHO@WF.NET
    RAY HERRING,PRES
    RONNIE ROBERTSON,VP
    EARLENE ROGERS,OFC MGR
    JODIE HOOD,DRLG SUPT

E & H OIL OPR
  125 LAKEWOOD PT
  BOSSIER CITY,LA 71111-2073
  PH 318 424-2556
    HUEY P STROTHER

E R C WELLHEAD
  100 KOL DR
  BROUSSARD,LA 70518-3874
  PH 318 837-3156

E.D.I. (ELECTRONIC DESIGN FOR INDUSTRY)
  MFG OF ELECTRONIC CONTROLLERS FOR OIL &
  GAS INDUSTRY
    100 AYERS BLVD
    BELPRE,OH 45714-9303 PH 740 401-4000
    FAX 740 401-4005 WWW.EDIPLUNGERLIFT.COM
    RICH WYNN,PRES

E.G.S.I. ENVIRONMENTAL GAS SERVICES,INC
  5019 ROUNDHILL
  SAN ANTONIO,TX 78250 PH 210 681-1606
  FAX 210 520-9220
    E E COOKE,PRES

EADS LYNN C,GEOLOGIST
  OIL & GAS EXPLORATION
    545 N UPPER BROADWAY STE 508 WILSON PLZ E
    CORPUS CHRISTI,TX 78476
    PH 361 884-8430 FAX 361 883-9566

EAG SERVICES,INC
  19 BRIAR HOLLOW LN STE 200
  HOUSTON,TX 77027-2820
  PH 832 485-5800 FAX 832 485-5899
    WWW.EAGSERVICES.COM
    INFO@EAGSERVICES.COM

EAGLE ENERGY DEVELOPMENT COMPANY
  153 S BROADWAY ST
  LA PORTE,TX 77571-5305
  PH 281 474-3379 FAX 281 474-7118
    DOUGLAS W SHOWS,PRES
    KEITH MACIVOR,VP
    TERI GOEBEL,MGR

    CYNDI FROHLING,ACCT MGR
    LAURA BAUGHMAN,REV SPEC

EAGLE ENERGY INC
  20 ORCHARD CT
  PALM HARBOR,FL 34683-3725 PH 727 492-3300
    W J WILSON,PRES

EAGLE INVESTMENTS,INC
  PO BOX 348
  TRAVERSE CITY,MI 49685-0348
  PH 231 933-3233 FAX 231 933-3253
    KELLY E MILLER,PRES,CEO
    CURTISS R YEITER,CONTROLLER

EAGLE MINERALS,LP
  PO BOX 671099
  DALLAS,TX 75367 PH 214 707-7535
  FAX 214 572-2699 WWW.TRUNKBAY.NET
    BENNY DUNCAN,MGR
    BDUNCAN@TRUNKBAY.NET

EAGLE OILFIELD INSPECTION SERVICE,INC
  PO BOX 695,307 HWY 96
  BROUSSARD,LA 70518-0695
  PH 337 837-4230 EAGLEOILFIELD@AOL.COM
    MIKE JOHNSON

EAGLE OPERATING COMPANY,LLC
  PO BOX 849
  BROOKHAVEN,MS 39602-0849
  PH 601 833-1323 FAX 601 833-1247
    D W MAXWELL,MGR

EAGLE PIPE & SUPPLY,INC
  PO BOX 53202,1808 HWY 89
  LAFAYETTE,LA 70505
  PH 337 837-4004 FAX 337 837-5832
    GEORGE R RIVES,PRES
    KEEL BOUDREAUX,YARD SUPT/PURCH AGT
    DAVID ROMERO,YARD SUPT/PURCH AGT

EAGLE RESOURCES,LLC
  PO BOX 849
  BROOKHAVEN,MS 39602-0849
  PH 601 833-1323 FAX 601 833-1247
    D W MAXWELL,MGR DWMAXWELL@BELLSOUTH.NET

EAGLE ROCK ACQS PARTNERSHIP II SEE
  EAGLE ROCK OPERATING COMPANY LLC

EARNEST PRODUCING CORPORATION
  310 W WALL STE 802
  MIDLAND,TX 79701 PH 432 685-1940
  FAX 432 685-1949 EPC1949@SBCGLOBAL.NET
    BRIAN LINGARD,PRES
    ART WIEBUSCH,VP
  HOUSTON,TX OFFICE - 1001 MCKINNEY STE 804
    77002 PH 281 822-7777

EARTH TECHNOLOGY CONSULTANTS,INC
  10810 OLD KATY RD STE 201
  HOUSTON,TX 77043-5013 PH 713 465-9090
    MAAIKE G VAN BEMMEL,PRES

EARTHI.ORG
  11079 WITT AVE
  BUTLER,IL 62015-2128
  PH 314 378-2464 WWW.EARTHI.ORG
    H L PRICE,REMOTE SEMSING

EASON PETROLEUM
  OIL & GAS PRODUCTION/EXPLORATION
    PO BOX 957,318 EASON LN
    ATLANTA,TX 75551 PH 903 799-7372
    BILL EASON EASON@BOWIE-CASS.COM

EASON PRODUCTION COMPANY
  PO BOX 957

ATLANTA,TX 75551-0957 PH 903 799-7372
FAX 903 799-7595 EASON@TXK.NET
WILLIAM W EASON,PRES

EAST TENNESSEE NATURAL GAS SEE
DUKE ENERGY GAS TRANSMISSION

EASTERN AMERICAN ENERGY CORPORATION
501 56TH ST SE
CHARLESTON,WV 25304-2393 PH 304 925-6100
FAX 304 925-3285
DONALD C SUPCOE,PRES
GEORGE O'MALLEY,VP,ACCT
RANDALL C FARKOSH,VP,MKTG
ROBERT M ADKINS,SECY
J MICHAEL FORBES,TREAS
INDIANA,PA OFFICE - 1380 ROUTE 286 HWY E
STE 211,15701-9240
PH 724 463-8400 FAX 724 463-9750
MARK FRY,DIST MGR
AL ELKIN,PROD FRMN
MATT WILLIAMS,PROD FRMN
DEB MCKEE,PROD ANALYST

EASTERN GEOPHYSICAL INC SEE
SEISMIC EXCHANGE,INC

EASTERN LAND SERVICE
P O BOX 1700
NATCHEZ,MS 39121-1700 PH 601 446-6229
RICHARD L RICHARDSON,LDMN
JODY L STEVENS,LDMN
CARL D RICHARDSON,LDMN
PETER T BURNS,JR,LDMN
DEBBIE L WILLSON,SECY/TREAS,LAND MGR

EASTERN MOUNTAIN FUEL INC
103 SENECA DR
MARIETTA,OH 45750
PH 740 376-9662 FAX 740 376-9667
ROBERT B THOMAS,PRES
RTHOMAS@EASTMTNFUEL.COM

EASTEX CRUDE COMPANY
10907 STATE HWY 11 WEST
LEESBURG,TX 75451-2524 PH 903 856-2401
FAX 903 856-7820 WWW.EASTEXCRUDE.COM
TOM O HANKS TOM.HANKS@EASTEXCRUDE.COM
TIM HANKS
DON HOYT
CALLIE HANKS

EASTEX GEOLOGICAL CONSULTANTS
2011 S BECKHAM AVE
TYLER,TX 75701 PH 903 533-9990
FAX 903 533-9980
KENT S CASTAGNO,CONS GEOL

EASTEX OPERATING,INC
2011 S BECKHAM AVE
TYLER,TX 75701-4455 PH 903 561-9947
FAX 903 561-9947
KENT S CASTAGNO,PRES

EASTMAN TELECO SEE
BAKER HUGHES INTEQ

EASY DRILLING INC
1095 BOLD HILL RD
ZANESVILLE,OH 43701 PH 740 826-4600
H DEAN BRADFORD,PRES
JAMES E BERRY,VP
PEARL A BRADFORD,SECY/TREAS

EBR ENERGY LP
345 COMMERCE GREEN BLVD
SUGAR LAND,TX 77478-3596

PH 281 265-6500 FAX 281 265-6504
MARK H ELY,PRES
CHARLES LOBUE,EXPL MGR
DONNA DEES,LAND MGR
LAURA BURKE,CONTROLLER
GREG BOWEN,GEOL
JOE MCREYNOLDS,GEOPHY

EBY AND PETRUS SURVEY SEE EBY SURVEY INC

EBY SURVEY INC
PO BOX 1284,600 2ND ST
WOODBORO,TX 78393-1284
PH 361 543-8161 WWW.EBYSURVEY.COM
NATHAN EBY,RPLS NATHAN@EBYSURVEY.COM
KAY ALTHEIDE,CFO

ECCO PETROLEUM,INC
PO BOX 2017
ROCKWALL,TX 75087-4417 PH 972 771-6007
FAX 972 772-9005 ECCO1@SBCGLOBAL.NET
ECCOPETROLEUM.COM
LEVENT KECIK,PRES
DOMINIQUE M ROBINSON,OFC MGR

ECKEL INTERNATIONAL
PO BOX 1375
8035 N COUNTY RD WEST 79794
ODESSA,TX 79760 PH 432 362-4336
FAX 432 362-1827 WWW.ECKEL.COM
SALES@ECKEL.COM

ECKEL MANUFACTURING CO INC
HYDRAULIC POWER TONGS/POWER UNITS
PO BOX 1375
ODESSA,TX 79760-1375 PH 432 362-4336
800 654-4779 FAX 432 362-1827
WWW.ECKEL.COM SALES@ECKEL.COM
TECHNICAL SUPPORT - SUPPORT@ECKEL.COM
TERRY L ECKEL,CEO/PRES
TERRY@ECKEL.COM
LANCE HEMPHILL,GULF COAST SALES
LANCE@ECKEL.COM

ECKELS CHRISTOPHER R F
P O BOX 30
CEDAREDGE,CO 81413-0030 PH 970 856-7366

ECKERT W F,JR,GEOL
PO BOX 1339
CORPUS CHRISTI,TX 78403-1339
PH 361 883-2831 EXT 130 FAX 361 883-9628

ECKISS LOIS A LAND SERVICES
6223 E ILLINOIS 250
OLNEY,IL 62450-4868
PH 618 392-2651 FAX 877 811-5175
RLEKS@ILLINIWIRELESS.COM
LOIS A ECKISS,RPL

EDCO PRODUCING,INC
PO BOX 329
MOUNT GILEAD,OH 43338-0329
PH 419 947-2515 FAX 419 947-2535
ALAN W JONES,PRES

EDGE RESOURCES,L.L.C.
4388 VICKERY BLVD STE 100
FORT WORTH,TX 76107 PH 817 870-0130
FAX 817 870-0133
CHRIS@EDGERESOURCESLLC.COM
WWW.EDGERESOURCESLLC.COM

EDGEWOOD EXPLORATION,INC
13803 SWEETWOODS HOLLOW
ST FRANCISVILLE,LA 70775
PH 225 921-4582 FAX 225 634-9910

RCAMPBELL@EDGEWOODEXPLORATION.COM
RICHARD A CAMPBELL,JR,PRES

EDKO OIL PROPERTIES
P O BOX 757
SALEM,IL 62881-0757 PH 618 548-1616
EDWARD C KOCH,OWNER

EDMISTON HARDY F,JR,OIL & GAS EXPLOR
PO BOX 52321
LAFAYETTE,LA 70505-2321 PH 337 261-0800
FAX 337 261-0803
HARDY F EDMISTON,JR,PRES
EDNA MECHE,ADMIN ASST

EDMUNDSON & ASSOCIATES,INC SEE
UNITSOURCE INCORPORATED

EDP MANAGEMENT COMPANY
5100 WESTHEIMER RD STE 122
HOUSTON,TX 77056-5598
PH 713 621-6223 FAX 713 627-7007
ERIK C MILLER,PRES

EDWARD OIL COMPANY
PO BOX 202
YOUNGSVILLE,PA 16371-0202 PH 814 726-9576
FAX 814 723-0987
JOHN E MCCOOL,OWNER

EDWARDS ROY D,ABSTRACT CO
108 N MARKET ST
OPELOUSAS,LA 70570-5262 PH 318 942-2116
REX EDWARDS,ABSTRACTER

EEX CORPORATION SEE
NEWFIELD EXPLORATION COMPANY

EGAN RESOURCES INC
4518 IRON RIVER DR
CORPUS CHRISTI,TX 78410-5821
PH 361 387-3587
LOIS BUEHRING,PRES
AL BUEHRING,SECY/TREAS

EGYPTIAN ENERGIES
PO BOX 127
WEST FRANKFORT,IL 62896-0127
PH 618 937-4663 FAX 618 937-4662
J SCOTT WILLIAMS,OWNER

EICHE MAPES AND COMPANY,INC
PO BOX 7992,1025 PRUITT PL
TYLER,TX 75711-7992 PH 903 581-1674
FAX 903 581-2634
JOHN M EICHE JR,PRES
JOHN_EICHE@EICHEMAPES.COM

EIGHTY EIGHT PETROLEUM CO INC SEE
88 PETROLEUM CO,INC (END OF ALPHA)

EISEMAN CHEMICAL SEE
BAKER HUGHES INTEQ

EL CAN EXPLORATION,INC
19 S REGENT OAK
THE WOODLANDS,TX 77381-6444
PH 281 221-8556
EDAVIS@EL-CAN.COM
EDWARD L DAVIS,PRES
THOMAS C KLEKAMP,VP,GEOL

EL PASO CORPORATION SEE
KINDER MORGAN

EL PASO ENERGY CORPORATION SEE
KINDER MORGAN

EL PASO NATURAL GAS COMPANY SEE
KINDER MORGAN

EL PASO PIPELINE GROUP SEE
KINDER MORGAN

EL PASO PRODUCTION & EXPLORATION SEE
EP ENERGY

EL TORO OIL COMPANY OIL OPRS
PO BOX M,202 FRY BLDG
NATCHEZ,MS 39121-1057 PH 601 446-6651
FAX 601 446-5041
PHIL W VASSER,OWNER
PAGE BLACKWELL,OFC MGR

EL TORO PETROLEUM CORP
PO BOX 52241,OCS 133 S AUDUBON BLVD
LAFAYETTE,LA 70505-2241 PH 337 235-5288
ROLAND D LIBERDA,PRES
GINGER BLANCHET,OFC MGR

EL TORO PRODUCTION CO INC
PO BOX M,202 FRY BLDG
NATCHEZ,MS 39121-1057 PH 601 446-6651
FAX 601 446-5041
PHIL W VASSER,PRES
PAGE BLACKWELL,SECY/TREAS

EL-OIL,LTD
PO BOX 52282,1602 W PINHOOK RD STE 200
LAFAYETTE,LA 70505-2282
PH 337 232-7572 FAX 337 233-3743
ENERGYGUY@COX-INTERNET.COM
GUY C ELLISON,JR,PRES

ELAD PETROLEUM CORPORATION
PO BOX 53063,103 EXCHANGE PL
LAFAYETTE,LA 70505-3063 PH 318 237-2612
WILTON R BILL DALE JR,EXPL GEOL

ELAND ENERGY,INC
KNOLL TRAIL PLAZA
16400 DALLAS PKWY STE 100
DALLAS,TX 75248-2609 PH 214 368-6100
FAX 214 365-9695

ELCO OIL,LLC
PO BOX 130
BULL SHOALS,AR 72619-0130
PH 870 445-6528 FAX 870 445-6529
WILLIAM ELDER,MGR
JESSE HOLLAND,OFC MGR
SARAH SILLS,SECY
DENNIS STUTES,SALES
DAVE BROWN,ILLINOIS FIELD OPERS
TERRY MADDEN,KANSAS FIELD OPERS
JAKE STEWART,OKLAHOMA FIELD OPERS

ELDER AND ASSOCIATES,INC
4407 OWENS CREEK
SPRING,TX 77388 PH 281 353-6615
W H ELDER,JR,PRES
ROBIN WOOD ELDER,VP

ELECTROCHEM LITHIUM BATTERIES
10000 WEHRLE DR
CLARENCE,NY 14031-2033 PH 716 759-5395
FAX 716 759-2562 WWW.GREATBATCH.COM
BWEBBER@GREATBATCH.COM
BRIAN WEBBER,MKT MGR,PETR APPLICATIONS

ELEPHANT EXPLORATION
PO BOX 1026
HARTVILLE,OH 44632-1026
PH 330 877-4219 LUQY@MSN.COM
LUQ YACUB,PRES

ELEPHANT OIL & GAS,LLC
3131 MCKINNEY AVE STE 750
DALLAS,TX 75204-2457 PH 214 323-8360
FAX 214 323-8379
BRADLEY WILLIAMS,MNGNG MEMBER

NICK VAREL,MNGNG MEMBER
RICK ARMSTRONG,OPERS MGR
DAVE ALDERKS,GEOL
ERICA MERKEY,REGULATORY/OFC ADMIN
PHILIP THOMPSON,LAND MGR
JADYN GINGRAS,IN-HOUSE LAND & LGL MGR
LAUREN FREEMAN,ACCT
JOSH STRANGE,LDMN

ELEXCO LAND SERVICES,INC
PO BOX 313,106 HURON BLVD STE A
MARYSVILLE,MI 48040-0313
PH 810 364-7940 FAX 810 364-8120
WWW.ELEXCO.COM ELEXCO@AONE-
ELEXCO.COM
RANDALL L HANSEN,PRES,CPL
LYNN P HALL,LAND AGENT

ELF AQUITAINE PETROLEUM SEE
ELF EXPLORATION INC

ELF EXPLORATION,INC SEE
TOTALFINAELF E&P USA,INC

ELIZABETH ALLISON OIL COMPANY,LLC
PO BOX 452
SHREVEPORT,LA 71162-0452
PH 318 747-1998 FAX 318 747-6739
CHARLES PAUL GEORGE,MGR

ELLCO RESOURCES,INC
4960 S GILBERT RD STE 1-479
CHANDLER,AZ 85249 PH 281 620-4042
ELLCORESOURCES@YAHOO.COM
STEVEN M ELLIOTT

ELLIOTT COMPANY,SUB UNITED TECHNOLOGIES
5901 JEFFERSON HWY
HARAHAN,LA 70123-5116 PH 504 733-2108

ELLIOTT GARY C,CPL
PO BOX 53586
LAFAYETTE,LA 70505-3586 PH 337 234-4537
FAX 337 234-0586

ELLIOTT JAMES W,JR,OIL OPR
PO BOX 774,306 S JACKSON
BROOKHAVEN,MS 39602-0774 PH 601 833-6201
AMANDA WARREN,LDMN,ACCT

ELLIOTT TURBOCHARGER GROUP INC
1648 W MAGNOLIA RD
SALINA,KS 67401-8148 PH 785 823-9211
PH 800 972-7612 FAX 785 826-4970
WWW.ELLIOTT-TURBOCHARGER.COM
HARVEY,LA FACILITY - 1900 INDUSTRIAL BLVD
70058 PH 504 348-4462 800 237-2393
FAX 504 348-1522
YORKTOWN,VA FACILITY - 201 PRODUCTION DR
23693 PH 757 596-3100 FAX 757 596-9109
- REPRESENTATIVES -
MARILYN ROBB,MID-CONT SLS
KEVIN EINHAUS,N CENTRAL SLS
JUDY CHARRIER,SE SLS
ALLEN PERRY,SW SLS
DAVE DAILY,W SLS
ANDY SCHUBERT,EASTERN SLS

ELLIS EXPLORATION INC
121 S BROADWAY AVE STE 478
TYLER,TX 75702-7275 PH 903 592-9955
JIM S ELLIS,PRES

ELLISON ENGINEERING
PO BOX 421565
HOUSTON,TX 77242-1565 PH 713 398-5445
DONRELLISON@HOTMAIL.COM

ELLISON EVARD P GEOL
150 GESSNER RD UNIT 4A
HOUSTON,TX 77024-6137 PH 713 465-3076
EPSSS@EARTHLINK.COM

ELLSWORTH H P OIL & GAS PROPERTIES
615 UPPER N BROADWAY STE 1910
CORPUS CHRISTI,TX 78477 PH 361 887-0994
FAX 361 887-9726

ELM CORPORATION
PO BOX 2845
MOBILE,AL 36652-2845 PH 251 621-9699
FAX 251 621-6778
WILLARD B SIMMONS JR,CPL

ELSBURY JOE W,INDEPENDENT
PO BOX 51284
LAFAYETTE,LA 70505-1284 PH 337 232-1662
FAX 337 235-9125 PH 337 322-0389

ELTEX WASH RACK SERVICES INC
PO BOX 370,1208 FM 1353
KARNES CITY,TX 78118 PH 337 945-7988
GARY LAVERGNE GARY@ELTEXSERVICES.COM

ELYSIUM ENERGY,LLC
2494 EDGERLY-DEQUINCY RD
VINTON,LA 70668
PH 337 589-2336 FAX 337 589-2492
WWW.ELYSIUMENERGY.COM
JAMES M TRIMBLE,PRES,COO
STEPHEN D LAYTON,EXEC VP
L BRUCE CURRIE,VP,LAND
STEVE M PERRY,SPECIAL PROJ/COMPLIANCE
MIKE LEMROND,OPERS MGR
MARTHA M HARMAN,CONTROLLER
E KEITH CLAGHORN,RESERVOIR ENG MGR
BRYAN DICUS,DIV MGR/ILLINOIS BASIN
DAVE STAHL,KS DIST PROD MGR
JERRY SMITH,LA DIST PROD MGR
GARY MOCK,CA DIV PROD MGR

EMERALD OIL COMPANY
PO BOX 50
RICHBURG,NY 14774 PH 585 234-5500
EMERALDOIL@JUNO.COM
ROBERT EBERLING,OWNER

EMISON CHRISTINE RYAN,ATTY
7522 CLIPPING CROSS RD
LOUISVILLE,KY 40241-1060 PH 502 228-2418
FAX 502 228-2493 SCEMISON@AOL.COM

EMPIRE ENERGY E&P,LLC
380 SOUTHPOINTE BLVD STE 130
CANONSBURG,PA 15317-8561 PH 724 483-2070
WWW.EMPIREENERGYGROUP.NET
INFO@EMPIREENERGYUSA.COM
MAYVILLE,NY OFFICE - 100 E CHATAUGUA ST
14757 PH 716 708-1493
TIM HULL,VP
WICHITA,KS OFFICE - 345 RIVERVIEW DR
67203 PH 316 313-4394
ROB KRAMER,VP

EMPIRE ENERGY,LTD
12600 HILL COUNTRY BLVD #R-270
AUSTIN,TX 78738-6723 PH 713 655-1221
FAX 713 951-0079

EMPIRICAL DATA SOLUTIONS LLC
1232 CAMELLIA BLVD STE C
LAFAYETTE,LA 70508 PH 855 433-7328
INFO@EDS-MONOTORING.COM
JASON R MILAM

EMPRESA ENERGY
9821 KATY FRWY STE 910
HOUSTON,TX 77024-1228
PH 713 468-0121 FAX 713 468-0122
WWW.EMPRESAENERGY.COM
JEFF ELKIN,PRES,COO
JELKIN@EMPRESAENERGY.COM
PH 713 468-0119
DALE BOWERING,CEO
DBOWERING@EMPRESAENERGY.COM
PH 713 468-0120
RICKY HARRIS,VP,OPERS
RHARRIS@EMPRESAENERGY.COM
PH 713 463-3924
JOHN DEAN,VP,CHF GEOL
JRD@EMPRESAENERGY.COM
PH 713 463-3921
BOBBY CAMPBELL,VP,CONTROLLER
BCAMPBELL@EMPRESAENERGY.COM
PH 713 463-3920
SEAN KEENAN,EXEC VP & CFO
SKEENAN@EMPRESAENERGY.COM
PH 713 463-3925
DAVID HOOPER,VP BUS DEV
DHOOPER@EMPRESAENERGY.COM
PH 713 463-3933
DEIDRA DIERKS,MGR,LAND
DDIERKS@EMPRESAENERGY.COM
PH 713 463-3929

ENBRIDGE ENERGY PARTNERS,LP
1100 LOUISIANA ST STE 3300
HOUSTON,TX 77002-5216
PH 713 821-2000 FAX 713 653-6711
WWW.ENBRIDGEPARTNERS.COM
TERRY MCGILL,PRES
- SUBSIDIARIES -
ENBRIDGE PIPELINES(NORTH DAKOTA)LLC
ENBRIDGE MIDCOAST ENERGY,LP
ENBRIDGE PIPELINES(EAST TEXAS)LP
ENBRIDGE PIPELINES(LOUISIANA LIQUIDS)LLC
ENBRIDGE PIPELINES(TEXAS GATHERING)LP
ENBRIDGE PIPELINES(TEXAS INTRASTATE)LP

ENCANA CORPORATION
- HEAD OFFICE -
PO BOX 2850,1800 855 - 2ND ST SW
CALGARY,AB CAN T2P 2S5
PH 403 645-2000 FAX 403 645-3400
EMERGENCY CONTACTS FOR CANADA:
PH 902 422-4500 - EAST
PH 403 645-7777 - WEST
EMERGENCY CONTACTS FOR U.S.:
PH 1 877 386-2200
FLORENCE MURPHY,V P,PUBLIC & COMMUNITY
RELS PH 403 645-4748
ALAN BORAS,MGR,MEDIA RELS
PH 403 645-4747
- ENCANA OIL & GAS (USA) INC OFFICES -
BRIDGEPORT,TX OFFICE - 306 HWY 380
76426 PH 940 683-8600 FAX 940 683-8637
MIDLAND,TX OFFICE - PO BOX 10829,79702
6750 E HWY 80,79706
PH 432 682-9944 FAX 432 682-9643
DALLAS,TX OFFICE - 14001 N DALLAS PKWY
75240 PH 214 987-3650 FAX 214 242-7345
MOAB (LISBON),UT OFFICE - PO BOX 760
7 RANKINE RD,84532-0760

PH 435 686-0760 FAX 435 686-2341
DENVER,CO OFFICE - REPUBLIC PLZ
370 17TH ST,STE 1700,80202
PH 303 623-2300 FAX 303 623-2400
COCOMMUNITY@ENCANA.COM
PARACHUTE,CO OFFICE - 2717 COUNTY RD 215
STE 100,81635 PH 970 285-2600
FAX 970 285-2619

ENCINO EXPLORATION INC
BOX 1589
GEORGE WEST,TX 78022-1589 PH 361 449-3011
LEE ROY HOSKINS,JR,PRES

ENCO EXPLORATION COMPANY
500 N SHORELINE BLVD STE 910
CORPUS CHRISTI,TX 78401 PH 361 882-6100
FRED E LONG,PRES,CEO
MARTIN MADRO,VP
KEN KAY,GEOL TECH

ENCO RESOURCES,INC
PO BOX 5738
HUMBLE,TX 77325-5738 PH 281 358-1732
FAX 281 358-1732
DOUGLAS H BURGESS BURGESSD@CEBRIDGE.NET

ENCORE ACQUISITION COMPANY SEE
DENBURY RESOURCES INC

ENDEAVOR OIL,LLC
PO BOX 131955
THE WOODLANDS,TX 77393-1955
PH 281 362-2807 FAX 281 362-2808
PHIL BARBER,MGR CRUDE OIL PUR
AMY LACROIX,MGR ADMIN

ENERFIN RESOURCES COMPANY
2500 CITY WEST BLVD STE 400
HOUSTON,TX 77042 PH 713 888-8600
FAX 713 888-8629 WWW.ENERFIN.COM
DCREMER@ENERFIN.COM
DAVE C CREMER,MNGNG DIR,PRTNR
TOM M IMRE,MNGNG DIR,PRTNR
PATTY ABRAHAM,MGR HUMAN RESOURCES

ENERGEN RESOURCES CORPORATION
605 RICHARD ARRINGTON JR BLVD N
BIRMINGHAM,AL 35203-2707
PH 205 326-2710 FAX 205 326-1858
WWW.ENERGEN.COM
JOHN S RICHARDSON,PRES & COO
HOLLEY S LAGRONE,VP,MKTG
D PAUL SPARKS,SR VP,OPERS
JOE E RUSTY COOK,VP,LEGAL & LAND
PAUL ROTE,VP,LAND
RONALD M TISDALE,VP GEOL
HENRY E GENE CASH,VP,ACQ & ENGRG
ARCADIA,LA OFFICE - 601 HWY 147,71001
MIDLAND,TX OFFICE - 3510 NORTH A ST
BLDG A & B, 79705 PH 432 687-1155
FAX 432 687-1796
JOE NIEDERHOFER,VP/PERMIAN BASIN
FARMINGTON,NM OFFICE - 2010 AFTON PL
87401 PH 505 325-6800 FAX 505 326-6112
GARY BRINK,VP/SAN JUAN
DON GRAHAM,SUPT,PROD/DRLG
ADGER,AL OFFICE - 10740 LOCK 17 RD,35006
COTTONDALE,AL OFFICE - 10899 TAURUS RD
35453

ENERGETICS INC,MINING,O & G EXPL & DEV
PO BOX 5038
ENGLEWOOD,CO 80155-5038 PH 303 790-7870

FAX 303 790-8525
JORDAN R SMITH,CHRMN,CEO
ROBERT L MEHL,PRES,TREAS
JOHN MARVIN,MGR OF ENGRG

ENERGISTS THE
10260 WESTHEIMER RD STE 300
HOUSTON,TX 77042-3108 PH 713 781-6881
FAX 713 781-2998 WWW.ENERGISTS.COM
ALEX@ENERGISTS.COM
ALEX PRESTON,PRES

ENERGY & ENVIRONMENTAL SERVICES INC
PO BOX 14726
OKLAHOMA CITY,OK 73113 PH 405 843-8996
PH 800 635-7716 FAX 405 843-0819
MELVIN B SMITH,VP PH 405 642-9354
TYLER,TX OFFICE - 915 W CONNALLY ST
75701-1404 PH 903 595-2044 888 977-2044
FAX 903 595-2684
BOB ISENHOWER,SLS REP PH 903 752-2159
BOBI5407@YAHOO.COM

ENERGY & EXPLORATION SOLUTIONS,LLC
PO BOX 1594
COVINGTON,LA 70434
PH 985 807-7921
DEBRADFORD@GMAIL.COM
DOUGLAS BRADFORD

ENERGY ACQUISITIONS,INC
10878 WESTHEIMER STE 267
HOUSTON,TX 77042 PH 713 789-5977
FAX 713 780-0761
J MILTON CRAFT,PRES
J LAWSON FANCHER,VP
W D EDWARDS,VP

ENERGY CONNECTION
WWW.ENERGYCONNECT.COM

ENERGY CORPORATION OF AMERICA
500 CORPORATE LANDING
CHARLESTON,WV 25311 PH 304 925-6100
FAX 304 925-3285 WWW.ECA.COM INFO@ECA.COM

ENERGY CRANES
279 THOMPSON RD
HOUMA,LA 70363-7320
PH 985 873-7969 FAX 985 873-8932
HOUSTON,TX (MFG) OFFICE -
6707 NORTHWINDS DR 77041
PH 713 896-0002 FAX 713 896-8688

ENERGY DEVELOPMENT CORPORATION SEE
SAMEDAN OIL CORPORATION

ENERGY DRILLING COMPANY
PO BOX 905,413 LIBERTY RD (39120)
NATCHEZ,MS 39121-0905
PH 601 446-5259 FAX 601 446-8607
JODY HELBLING,DRLG MGR
WESLEY CALVERT,DRLG SUPT

ENERGY ENTERPRISES INC SEE
REH ENERGY

ENERGY FUTURES - I
PO BOX 51321
LAFAYETTE,LA 70505-1321 PH 337 237-4292
FAX 337 237-0577
JOHN O HARRIS,PRTNR/GEOL

ENERGY GRAPHICS
9039 KATY FWY STE 516
HOUSTON,TX 77024-1608 PH 281 558-2061
FAX 281 558-7340 WWW.ENERGYGRAPHICS.COM
INFO@ENERGYGRAPHICS.COM

A DALE MCCALLUM,PRES
ANN SCHROEDER,VP,CFO
STEVE TRUXAL,VP,TECH
RICH GERMANO,VP,SALES
PATTI STEFEK,TRAINING & SUPPORT
MARTY LINGNER,DATABASE MGR

ENERGY INDUSTRIES SEE
WEATHERFORD ENTERRA COMPRESSION CO

ENERGY INFORMATION ADMINISTRATION
WWW.EIA.DOE.GOV

ENERGY INTERNATIONAL CORP
PO BOX 6690
KINGWOOD,TX 77325-6690 PH 281 360-7100
FAX 281 360-7014
WWW.EIGENERGY.COM
J Q DELAP,JR,PRES
PH 713 824-6631 JQDELAP@FLASH.NET

ENERGY INVESTMENT PARTNERS,LLC
PO BOX 225878,400 N ST PAUL ST STE 720
DALLAS,TX 75222 PH 214 978-2500
WWW.ENERGYINVESTMENTPARTNERS.COM
BOB FLOURNOY,PRES
BOBFLOURNOY@ATT.NET
DENNY ALLISON,VP GEOL RKY MTN DIV
SAM EMBRAS,VP GEOL TX/OK
TANNER FLOURNOY,LDMN
J R FLOURNOY,LDMN
DAN PFEIFFER,VP GEOL MICHIGAN

ENERGY INVESTMENTS COMPANY SEE
LOUISIANA ONSHORE EXPLORATION,LLC

ENERGY LAND SERVICES
PO BOX 302
WEEMS,VA 22576
PH 804 438-5852 PH 713 705-7235
FAX 804 438-9043
I MEADE HUFFORD,OWNER
HUFFORD1913@AOL.COM

ENERGY LAND SERVICES,LLC
PO BOX 3495
FORT SMITH,AR 72913-3495
PH 479 452-8617 FAX 479 452-4758
PATRICK.SPINDLER@ENERGYLANDSERVICES.COM
PATRICK L SPINDLER,CPL,MGR

ENERGY MACHINE,LLC
360 RT 34 NORTH
WAVERLY,NY 14892
PH 607 249-6019 FAX 607 249-6025
DEAN DAYE PH 337 254-6986
DDAYE_EXP@YAHOO.COM
STEVE BLACK PH 432 553-2065
BLACK.STEVE1960@YAHOO.COM

ENERGY MANAGEMENT COMPANY
3546 CARUTH BLVD
DALLAS,TX 75225-5001 PH 972 803-3520
JOE VAUGHAN,PRES
DAVID VAUGHAN,VP/GEN COUNSEL
HAROLD RATCLIFF,ACCT

ENERGY MANAGEMENT CORP SEE
TELLUS OPERATING GROUP,LLC

ENERGY MARKETING EXCHANGE INC SEE
KCS ENERGY,INC

ENERGY MINERALS,INC SEE
DAVIS BROS,LLC

ENERGY MINERALS,LLC SEE
DAVIS BROS,LLC

ENERGY OMEGA INC
1635 WARREN CHAPEL
FLEMING,OH 45729 PH 740 373-2083
EDDY L BIEHL,PRES

ENERGY PARTNERS,LTD SEE EPL OIL & GAS,INC

ENERGY PROPERTIES
121 S BROADWAY STE 300
TYLER,TX 75702 PH 214 597-8022

ENERGY RESERVES GROUP INC SEE
BHP PETROLEUM (AMERICAS) INC

ENERGY RESOURCES MANAGEMENT LLC SEE
KBL E&P LIMITED COMPANY

ENERGY RESOURCES OF AMERICA INC
5211 MAHONING AVE STE 125
AUSTINTOWN,OH 44515 PH 330 953-1813
FAX 330 953-1815 NATSOIL@ZOOMINTERNET.NET
JOSEPH S GLISTA,CEO
KELLY A KOVAL,VP,LAND

ENERGY SEARCH PERSONNEL CONSULTANTS
6523 INWOOD WEST
HOUSTON,TX 77088-2249 PH 713 680-9943
LYN WILSON,PRES

ENERGY SEARCH,INC,NATURAL GAS DISTR SYSTM
PO BOX 435,500 SHORTCUT RD
ALBANY,KY 42602-0435
PH 606 387-5016 FAX 606 387-5775
WHADDIX1@WINDSTREAM.NET
JOHN W HADDIX,PRES
WALTON R HADDIX,VP

ENERGY TECHNICAL SERVICES,INC
23106 PARK LN
TOMBALL,TX 77377-3941 PH 318 233-5082
FAX 318 269-0293
JUDY R ALLEN,CEO
ALFRED A ALLEN,PRES
BRETT ALLEN,ADMIN ASST
BILL VIDRINE,MKTG
STEVE HENLEY,PROD OPER
JESUS GINO PEREZ,INTL COORD
CRAIG BOUDREAUX,ELECTRICAL & MECHANICAL
KENNETH SMITH,INT'L OPERS
RICHARD MARTIN,MGMNT,TECH SVC ADMIN

ENERGY TRANSFER COMPANY
800 E SONTERRA BLVD STE 400
SAN ANTONIO,TX 78258-3941 PH 210 403-7300

ENERGY TRANSFER PARTNERS,LP
1300 MAIN
HOUSTON,TX 77002 PH 713 989-7000
DALLAS,TX OFFICE - 3738 OAK LAWN AVE
75219 PH 214 981-0700 FAX 214 981-0703
SAN ANTONIO OFFICE - 800 E SONTERRA BLVD
STE 400 78258 PH 210 403-7300
FAX 210 403-7500

ENERGY UNLIMITED
PO BOX 1185
BUCKHANNON,WV 26201-1185
PH 304 472-9172
RICHARD L SCHULTZ

ENERGY XXI
1021 MAIN STE 2626
HOUSTON,TX 77002 PH 713 351-3000
FAX 713 351-3300 WWW.ENERGYXXI.COM
JOHN SCHILLER,CHRMN,PRES & CEO
BRUCE BUSMIRE,CFO
ANTONIO D PINHO,COO
HUGH MENOWN,EXEC VP,CAO

KEITH ACKER,SR VP-PROD
GRANGER ANDERSON,SR VP-LAND
BO BOYD,SR VP/LEGAL & CORP SECY
ANDRE BROUSSARD,SR VP-EXPLOIT & EXPL

ENERGYNET.COM,INC.
7201 I-40 WEST STE 319
AMARILLO,TX 79106
PH 806 351-2953 FAX 806 354-2835
ENERGY@ENERGYNET.COM
WWW.ENERGYNET.COM
HOUSTON,TX - GULF COAST & EASTERN US
PH 713 861-1866 FAX 832 201-9598
CHRIS ATHERTON PH 832 654-6612
CHRIS.ATHERTON@ENERGYNET.COM
CODY FELTON PH 281 221-3042
CODY.FELTON@ENERGYNET.COM
PLANO,TX - ARK-LA-TEX/PERMIAN OFFICE -
PH 972 265-7980 FAX 972 268-7982
MICHAEL BAKER PH 972 898-5358
MICHAEL.BAKER@ENERGYNET.COM
OKLAHOMA CITY,OK - MID-CONTINENT/TEXAS
PANHANDLE OFFICE - PH 405 759-8437
ETHAN HOUSE PH 806 433-5501
ETHAN.HOUSE@ENERGYNET.COM
HOUSTON,TX - VP ENGINEERING/GOVERNMENT
AFFAIRS OFFICE - PH 832 403-3122
PH 713 582-7755
JOHN S MUNROE
JOHN.MUNROE@ENERGYNET.COM
EVERGREEN,CO - WESTERN US
PH 303 500-3063 FAX 303 500-3063
RYAN P DOBBS PH 720 549-2072
RYAN.DOBBS@ENERGYNET.COM

ENERGYQUEST,INC
10814 CARISSA DR
DALLAS,TX 75218-1218 PH 214 364-6416
FAX 214 368-8375
BOBBY C BEILUE,PRES

ENERPIPE LTD
REHABILITATION,LEAK LOCATING,PIPELINE/
OILFIELD CONSTR,TESTING
PO BOX 2329
AMARILLO,TX 79105-2329
PH 806 371-8851 FAX 806 371-8856
MIKE R BRISTER,CEO,PRES
G H RIFFE,VP
PERRYTON,TX CONSTRUCTION OFFICE -
PO BOX 1260,79070 PH 806 435-7644
FAX 806 435-7164
JOE NIVENS,MGR
MUNITH,MI REGIONAL OFFICE - PO BOX 218
49259 PH 517 596-2629 FAX 517 596-3172
PAUL T MOONEY,VP
CHANNELVIEW,TX OFFICE - 15937 RIDLON
77530 PH 281 457-6600 FAX 281 457-6641
LEE MCINTIRE,REG MGR

ENERPOL
2040 N LOOP 336 W STE 123
CONROE,TX 77304 PH 512 422-6411
BRIAN SMILEY BSMILEY@ENER-POL.COM

ENERVEST LTD
1001 FANNIN ST STE 800
HOUSTON,TX 77002-6707 PH 713 659-3500
FAX 713 659-3556 WWW.ENERVEST.NET
JOHN B WALKER,PRES,CEO
MARK A HOUSER,EXEC VP,COO

JAMES M VANDERHIDER,EXEC VP,CFO
PHIL C DELOZIER,SR VP,BUS DEV
PDELOZIER@ENERVEST.NET
STEPHEN A MCDANIEL,EVP/COO,ENERVEST OPER
KEN MARIANI,PRES/CEO,ENERVEST OPERATING

ENERVEST OPERATING,LLC
EASTERN DIV OIL & GAS OPERS
1064 OLD ROUTE 33
WESTON,WV 26452-7722
PH 304 622-1102 FAX 304 622-1698
GREGORY A SHOCKLEY,VP/EASTERN DIV MGR
JERRY L JACKSON,LAND MGR
KIMBERLY A GEORGE,ACCT SUPVSR
SCOTT ANDREW,PROD FRMN
HOWARD DUNN,PROD FRMN
RICK HANIFAN,PROD FRMN

ENGINEERING SERVICE
PO BOX 180429,115 AEROSMITH DR
RICHLAND,MS 39218 PH 601 939-8737
WWW.ENGSERVICE.COM PMARTIN@ENGSER-
VICE.COM
CHARLES S PARKER,PRES
ALLEN SCOTT,VP
PAT A MARTIN,VP
TIM PARKER,SECY/TREAS
- BRANCH OFFICE -
MOBILE,AL OFFICE - 2468 COMMERCIAL PARK
DR 36606 PH 251 479-7383
RUSSELL MCDILL,OFC MGR

ENGLAND ENERGY LLC
PRODUCTION/ACQUISITIONS
PO BOX 888
LITTLETON,CO 80160-0888
PH 303 347-2600 FAX 303 347-0196
RONALD HORNIG,MGR
ALLAN HEINLE,MGR
BROOK PHIFER,MGR

ENGLAND OPERATING LLC
PRODUCTION OPERATIONS
1490 W CANAL CT STE 3000
LITTLETON,CO 80120-5648 PH 303 730-7373
FAX 303 794-9261
BROOK J PHIFER,PRES
RONALD E HORNIG,VP
PERRY,OK OFFICE - PO BOX 384,73077
PH 580 336-3156
DERROLD BOLAY,PROD FRMN

ENGLAND RESOURCES CORPORATION
EXPLORATION/PRODUCTION/ACQUISITIONS
PO BOX 280
LARAMIE,WY 82073-0280 PH 303 861-3000
RONALD E HORNIG,PRES
BROOK J PHIFER,PROD DIV
ALLAN R HEINLE,ENGR
JEREMY K HORNIG,LDMN

ENGLAND ROBERT W,IND PETR LDMN
5527 RIDGEWOOD RD
JACKSON,MS 39211-4025 PH 601 956-8250

ENGLISH JR, ESTATE OF W.C.
PO BOX 22580
HOUSTON,TX 77227-2580 PH 713 851-9753
C/O WALTER BERING
WBERING@MARTHATURNER.COM

ENHANCED EXPLORATION,LLC
PO BOX 820
COVINGTON,LA 70434-0820

PH 985 626-5562 OILMANLA@AOL.COM
KEITH A LONG,PRES

ENHANCED OIL RESOURCES INC
1 RIVERWAY, STE 610
HOUSTON,TX 77056 PH 832 485-8526
FAX 832 485-8506 WWW.ENHANCEDOILRES.COM
BARRY LASKER,CEO,PRES
W KYLE WILLIS,CFO,VP FIN
BARRY PORTMAN,MGR,WELL OPERS
JIM SKORNER,MGR,RESERVIOR ENGRG
RUSSELL C LONGMIRE,MGR,LAND
CYNTHIA NEWMAN,CAO
DON CURRIE,VP,INVESTOR RELS

ENLINK MIDSTREAM OPERATING LP
2501 CEDAR SPRINGS RD STE 100
DALLAS,TX 75201-1432 PH 214 721-9355
FAX 214 721-9485 WWW.ENLINK.COM
BARRY E DAVIS,PRES/CEO
JOE A DAVIS,EXEC VP/GEN COUNSEL
WILLIAM W DAVIS, EXEC VP/CFO
JENNIFER K JOHNSON,SR VP/HR-ORG DEV
MICHAEL J GARBERDING,SR VP-FIN
STAN GOLEMON, SR VP/ENGRG-OPERS
MIKE BURDETT,SR VP-COMMERCIAL

ENMARK GAS CORP
17430 CAMPBELL RD STE 230
DALLAS,TX 75252 PH 214 368-5050
FAX 214 368-0999
R G MILLER,PRES
BRIAN SWIGERT,CONTROLLER
SHARON CONRAD,TRANS

ENRON OIL & GAS CO SEE
EOG RESOURCES,INC

ENRON OIL TRADING & TRANSPORTATION CO SEE
EOTT ENERGY OPERATING LTD PRTNR

ENSCO INTERNATIONAL INCORPORATED
5847 SAN FELIPE ST STE 3300
HOUSTON,TX 77057-3195 PH 214 397-3000
DAN RABUN,CHRMN,PRES & CEO
BILL CHADWICK JR,EXEC VP,COO
JAY SWENT III,SR VP,CFO
JEFF SAILE,SR VP,OPERS
SEAN O'NEILL,VP,INVESTOR RELS
DAVE ARMOUR,VP,FIN
MARK BURNS,PRES,EOIC
MIKE WILEY,GEN MGR,HR & SECURITY
CARY MOOMJIAN JR,VP,GEN COUNSEL
DOUG MANKO,CONTROLLER
MICHAEL HOWE,TREAS

ENSERCH EXPLORATION,INC SEE
EEX CORPORATION

ENSIGN OPERATING CO SEE
EL PASO EXPLORATION & PRODUCTION

ENSLEY PROPERTIES INC
550 POST OAK BLVD STE 540
HOUSTON,TX 77027-9410 PH 713 622-7332
FAX 713 622-0030 WWW.ENSLEYPROPERTIES.COM
ART ENSLEY,PRES ART@ENSLEYPROPERTIES.COM
LINDA ENSLEY,VP
LINDA@ENSLEYPROPERTIES.COM
LARRY LATCH,VP OPERS
LARRY@ENSLEYPROPERTIES.COM

ENSOURCE INC SEE
U M C PETROLEUM CORP

ENTERRA OIL FIELD RENTAL SEE
WEATHERFORD COMPRESSION

ENTRADE CORPORATION SEE
TENNECO GAS MARKETING COMPANY

ENVIRO SHIELD,INC
222 SIDNEY BAKER SOUTH STE 325
KERRVILLE,TX 78028-6080 PH 830 895-7877
FAX 830 896-7727 INFO@ENVIROSHIELD.BIZ
DONALD P DORSEY,PRES
JOYCE E RUTAN,VP,ADMIN

ENVIRONMENTAL DYNAMICS,INC
102 COPPER JCT
LAFAYETTE,LA 70508 PH 318 264-9810
FAX 318 233-9198
BRADEN C DESPOT,PRES
HANK J KIZER,VP,REG MGR
KERN C ROULY,OPERS MGR
MICHAEL P GUIDRY,PROJ ENGR
SANDRA L MARTIN,ADMIN ASST,CORP SECY
MARK L DESPOT,CONS
JOHN M DUHON,CONS

ENVIRONMENTAL GAS SERVICES,INC (E.G.S.I.)
GAS GATHERING,TREATING PROCESSING & MKTG
5019 ROUNDHILL
SAN ANTONIO,TX 78250-4743 PH 210 681-1606
E E COOKE

ENVIRONMENTAL MANAGEMENT SERVICE LLC
1600 SMITH ST #48 FLOOR
HOUSTON,TX 77002 PH 713 600-9006
FAX 713 650-0840 WWW.EMSOILANDGAS.COM
INFO@OILFIELDMGNTSVC.COM
JOHN L GRAVES,PRES
GRANT DARNELL II,VP

ENVIRONMENTAL OIL CO
OHIO OIL & GAS PRODUCER
PO BOX 495
THORNVILLE,OH 43076-0495 PH 740 928-7549
RAYMOND BAUMAN

ENVIRONMENTAL PROTECTION AGENCY
WWW.EPA.GOV

ENVIRONMENTAL TREATMENT TEAM (ETT) SEE
SUPERIOR ENERGY SERVICES COMPANY

ENVISION ENERGY RESOURCES,INC SEE
SIGNATURE OIL & GAS LLC

EOG OKLAHOMA INC SEE
ENSIGN OPERATING CO

EOG RESOURCES,INC
PO BOX 4362,1111 BAGBY SKY LOBBY 2
HOUSTON,TX 77210-4362 PH 713 651-7000
PH 877 363-3647 FAX 713 651-6995
MARK G PAPA,EXEC CHRMN OF THE BOARD
WILLIAM R THOMAS,PRES/CEO
GARY L THOMAS,COO
LLOYD W HELMS JR,EXEC VP-EXPL & PROD
DAVID W TRICE,EXEC VP-EXPL & PROD
TIMOTHY K DRIGGERS,VP/CFO
MICHAEL P DONALDSON,VP/GEN COUNSEL &
CORP SECY
KURT D DOERR,EXEC VP/GEN MGR-DENVER
ROBERT K GARRISON,EXEC VP/GEN MGR-
SAN ANTONIO
MAIRE A BALDWIN,VP-INVESTOR RELS
SANDEEP BHAKHRI,VP/CIO
KENNETH E DUNN,VP/GEN MGR-CORPUS CHRISTI
PATRICIA L EDWARDS,VP-HR & ADMIN
MARC R ESCHENBURG,VP-MKTG & REGULATORY
AFFAIRS
DAVID J GRIFFITHS,GEN MGR-EOG RESOURCES

UNITED KINGDOM LIMITED
KEVIN S HANZEL,VP-AUDIT
RAYMOND L INGLE,VP/GEN MGR-SUPPORT SVCS
ANN D JANSSEN,VP-ACCOUNTING
ERNEST J LAFLURE,VP/GEN MGR-TYLER
HELEN Y LIM,VP/TREAS
LINDELL L LOOGER,VP/GEN MGR/INTL PRES-
EOG RESOURCES INTERNATIONAL,INC
TONY C MARANTO,VP/GEN MGR-OKLAHOMA CITY
COLLEEN A MARPLES,VP/GEN MGR-CANADA
RICHARD A OTT,VP-TAX
SAMMY G PICKERING,MNGNG DIR-EOG
RESOURCES
TRINIDAD LIMITED
AMOS J OELKING III,DEPUTY CORP SECY
GARY L PITTS,VP/GEN MGR-MIDLAND
FREDERICK J PLAEGER II,VP-GOV RELS
GARY L SMITH,VP/GEN MGR-PITTSBURGH
ROBERT C SMITH,VP-DRLG
JAMES C FLETCHER,CONTROLLER-LAND ADMIN
JOSEPH C LANDRY,CONTROLLER-OPERS ACCT
JANET B JOHNSON,CONTROLLER,COMPLIANCE &
CONTROLS
GARY Y PENG,CONTROLLER-FIN REPORTING
ROBERT L WEST,CONTROLLER-FIN PLANNING
GEORGE A ALCORN,DIR
CHARLES R CRISP,DIR
JAMES C DAY,DIR
MARK G PAPA,DIR
H LEIGHTON STEWARD,DIR
DONALD F TEXTOR,DIR
FRANK G WISNER,DIR
WILLIAM R THOMAS,DIR
- DISTRICT OFFICES -
CORPUS CHRISTI,TX OFFICE -
539 N CARANCAHUA STE 900,78478
PH 361 883-9231 FAX 361 902-2801
FORT WORTH,TX OFFICE - 421 W 3RD ST
STE 150,76102 PH 817 339-9380
FAX 817 339-9327
MIDLAND,TX OFFICE - PO BOX 2267,79702
4000 N BIG SPRING STE 500,79705
PH 432 686-3600 FAX 432 686-3686
TYLER,TX OFFICE - 6101 S BROADWAY STE 200
75703 PH 903 509-7100 FAX 903 509-4726
SAN ANTONIO,TX OFFICE - 19100 RIDGEWOOD
PKWY BLDG 2,78259 PH 210 403-7700
DENVER,CO OFFICE - 600 17TH ST STE 1000N
80202 PH 303 572-9000 FAX 303 824-5400
OKLAHOMA CITY,OK OFFICE - 3817 NW EXPY
STE 500 73112-1483 PH 405 246-3100
PITTSBURGH,PA OFFICE - SOUTHPOINTE
PLAZA I,400 SOUTHPOINTE BLVD STE 300
CANONSBURG,PA 15317 PH 724 745-1102
FAX 724 745-0956
BIG PINEY,WY OFFICE - PO BOX 250,83113
1540 BELCO DR PH 307 276-3331
FAX 307 276-3335

- EOG RESOURCES CANADA INC -
CALGARY,ALBERTA,CANADA OFFICE - 700 9TH
AVE SW STE 1300 T2P 3V4 PH 403 297-9100
FAX 403 297-9199

- EOGR TRINIDAD LIMITED -
ST CLAIR PORT OF SPAIN TRINIDAD, W.I.

OFFICE - BRIAR PLACE,10-12 SWEET BRIAR RD
PH 868 622-8653 FAX 868 628-4215

- EOG RESOURCES UNITED KINGDOM LTD -
GUILDFORD SURREY,UNITED KINGDOM OFFICE -
ANDREWS HOUSE,COLLEGE RD,GU1 4QB
PH +44 0 1483 462360
FAX +44 0 1483 451133
EOI EAGLE OPERATING INC
8419 SHAKESPEAKE LN
FRISCO,TX 75034
PH 214 407-8503 FAX 214 407-8116
PAUL CARLISLE
EOS ENERGY,LLC
PO BOX 52
BELLAIRE,TX 77402-0052
PH 713 218-6931 FAX 713 218-6932
LARRY RAIRDEN,PRES
GLEN GEE,LDMN
JANDI SUTEDJA,GEOL
VERONICA STEVENSON,ENGR
EOS SERVICES
PO BOX 2315
SUGAR LAND,TX 77487-2315 PH 281 793-4358
FAX 281 344-0307
EOS WELL SERVICE,INC
1860 FM 359 RD #328
RICHMOND,TX 77406
PH 281 914-2191 FAX 281 344-0307
EOSWS@SBCGLOBAL.NET
JESS MOORE,PRES
RONALD MOORE,VP
PATRICIA MOORE,OFFICE MGR
EOTT ENERGY OPERATING LIMITED PRTNR SEE
LINK ENERGY LIMITED PARTNERSHIP
EP ENERGY
1001 LOUISIANA ST
HOUSTON,TX 77002 PH 713 997-1000
WWW.EPENERGY.COM
BRENT SMOLIK,PRES/CEO
CLAY CARRELL,EXEC VP/COO
DANE WHITEHEAD,EXEC VP/CFO
JOHN JENSEN,EXEC VP OPERS
MARGUERITE WOUNG-CHAPMAN,SR VP/
GEN COUNSEL
JOAN M GALLAGHER,SR VP HUMAN RESOURCES
FRANK FALLERI,SR VP-CENTRAL DIV
GREGORY GIVENS,VP-EAGLE FORD DIV
RICHARD LITTLE,VP-SOUTHERN DIV
SCOTT ANDERSON,VP BUS DEV
DENNIS PRICE,VP MKTG
DELANEY BELLINGER,VP/CIO
KYLE MCCUEN,VP PLANNING & TREASURY
FRANK OLMSTEAD III,VP/CONTROLLER
EPI CONSULTANTS
2828 TECHNOLOGY FOREST BLVD
THE WOODLANDS,TX 77381 PH 281 719-2828
FAX 713 849-3861
JESSE CARASSCO,DIV MGR
MIDLAND,TX OFFICE-10 DESTA DR STE 420 E
79705 PH 432 570-5708 FAX 432 570-7878
LAFAYETTE,LA OFFICE-
3639 AMBASSADOR CAFFERY PRKWY STE 325
70503 PH 337 322-8599
MILBURN DUCOTE,REG SLS MGR

EPL OIL & GAS,INC SEE ENERGY XXI
EPOCH RESOURCES,INC
1316 LADELLE ST
WHARTON,TX 77488 PH 210 349-9169
FAX 210 525-0496
MARY E MCDONNELL,PRES
SHAWN TELLANDER,OFC MGR
EPOCH WELL SERVICES,INC SEE
CANRIG DRILLING TECHNOLOGIES
EQUILON PIPELINE COMPANY SEE
SHELL PIPELINE COMPANY,LP
EQUION CORPORATION,THE
FORMERLY TRINITY RESOURCES,INC
4514 BIRCH ST
BELLAIRE,TX 77401-5508 PH 713 667-8073
FAX 713 667-8073
MICHAEL A GERLICH,OIL & GAS MGR
EQUITY COMPRESSORS,INC SEE
OUACHITA ENERGY CORPORATION
EQUITY OIL & GAS FUNDS,INC
343 W BAGLEY RD STE 410
BEREA,OH 44017-1357 PH 440 234-4202
FAX 440 234-4260 AKING@EQUITYOIL.COM
RICHARD DESICH,PRES
ALANE M KING,SECY
EQUITY OIL COMPANY
PO BOX 1605
SHREVEPORT,LA 71165-1605
PH 318 221-7196 FAX 317 221-7217
FRANK HOOD GOLDSBERRY III,PRES/EXPL MGR
G G NESBITT III,VP
CLAYTON GLENN PRICE,PETR ENGR
ERCO-ENERGY RESOURCES COMPANY
25602 PECAN VALLEY CIR
THE WOODLANDS,TX 77380-2229
PH 281 962-0400
WWW.ERCO-ENERGYRESOURCES.COM
BILL OLSON,CEO
CESAR ABEIGNE,PHD-GEOPH CONSLT
DAVID H MANGUM,PRES,PE,GEOL,MBA
GERALD AVERY,VP,ADMIN
CHAS MANGUM,ENGR CONSLT,PE
DARIN MANGUM,LEGAL COUNSEL
ERGON EXPLORATION INC
PO BOX 14476,2461 TOWER DR
MONROE,LA 71207-4476 PH 318 322-1414
L B LAMPTON,SR,PRES
C D KITCHINGHAM,VP
JACKSON,MS OFFICE - PO BOX 1639
39205 PH 601 933-3000
ROBERT PRITCHARD,VP,LAND & LEGAL
GEORGE BECK,VP OPERS
ERGON OIL PURCHASING INC
PO BOX 1639,2829 LAKELAND DR
JACKSON,MS 39215-1639 PH 601 933-3000
FAX 601 933-3352 WWW.ERGON.COM
ROBERT H LAMPTON,PRES
J LARRY HARTNESS,SR VP
LARRY.HARTNESS@ERGON.COM
BARTON LAMPTON,GEN MGR-DOM CRUDE
BARTON.LAMPTON@ERGON.COM
CHRIS ELDRIDGE,OPER MGR
CHRIS.ELDRIDGE@ERGON.COM
JERA HOOD,CONTRACTS MGR
JERA.HOOD@ERGON.COM
HOUSTON,TX OFFICE - PH 281 660-4094

DARDEN BOURNE DARDEN.BOURNE@ERGON.COM

ERIE OIL & GAS,INC
1105 SCHROCK RD STE 602
COLUMBUS,OH 43229 PH 614 885-1901
FAX 614 885-3006
GERALD S JACOBS,PRES
DONNA L SANGER,VP

ERIN OIL COMPANY
PO BOX 308
HIGH ISLAND,TX 77623-0308 PH 409 286-5511
FAX 409 286-5512
FRANK E HATCHER,OWNER

ERM-ENVIROCLEAN-SOUTH,INC
SITE REMEDIATION CONTRACTOR
10210 HIGHLAND MANOR DR STE 140
TAMPA,FL 33610 PH 813 622-8727
FAX 813 621-0160
PAUL GRUBER,PRES

ERM-SOUTHEAST INC,ENVIRONMENTAL ENGRG CO
10210 HIGHLAND MANOR DR STE 140
TAMPA,FL 33610 PH 813 622-8727
FAX 813 621-8504 WWW.ERM.COM
MICHAEL J STARKS,PG,PRINCIPAL

ERMIS VACUUM & PUMP TRUCK SERVICE
PO BOX 1543, CR 351
EL CAMPO,TX 77437-1543
PH 979 543-7144 979 543-1227
DAVID ERMIS,OWNER
TONY ERMIS,OWNER
JENNIFER EGGEMEYER,SECY

ERSKINE ENERGY,LLC
2200 WEST LOOP S SSTE 400
HOUSTON,TX 77027-3531
PH 713 974-3322 FAX 713 400-9201
RODNEY D ERKSINE,CEO
GREGORY W HUTSON,PRES
GWHUTSON@ERSKINEOG.COM

ESCONDIDO PETROLEUM,INC
7700 SAN FELIPE ST STE 106
HOUSTON,TX 77063-1604 PH 713 978-7631
FAX 713 978-6108
KURT J WISEMAN,PRES

ESENJAY PETROLEUM CORPORATION
500 N WATER ST STE 1100 S
CORPUS CHRISTI,TX 78401-0236
PH 361 883-7464 FAX 361 883-3244
MICHAEL E JOHNSON,PRES
LINDA D SCHIBI,VP LAND SCHIBI@EPC-CC.COM
ERIC GARDNER,VP EXPL
DALE ALEXANDER,COO/EXPLOITATION
HOWARD WILLIAMS,TREAS
SIL BOSCH,GEOL
ROLF WOODS,GEOL

ESSFUNDS,LLC
1801 PATTERSOM
HOUSTON,TX 77007 PH 713 869-0077
TIM SULLIVANT TSULLIVANT@ESSFUNDS.COM

ESSI CORPORATION
200 CUMMINGS RD
BROUSSARD,LA 70518
PH 337 837-3774 FAX 337 837-3712
KADAMS@ESSICORP.COM WWW.ESSICORP.COM
KIM A ADAMS,PRES,CEO
KEVIN M DELCAMBRE,VP,OPERS
MARTIN L PONTIFF,VP,ELECTRONICS

ESTATE OIL & GAS CORP
4625 GREENVILLE AVE STE 305
DALLAS,TX 75206-5036
PH 214 691-5465 FAX 214 691-5843
RAY H EUBANK,PRES
NORMAN DEPEW,OFC MGR

ESTILL-SHEFFIELD GROUP INC
PO BOX 2631
BIG SPRING,TX 79721-2631 PH 817 408-6522
DON B BRAD ESTILL,CPL/PRES
BRAD_ESTILL@HOTMAIL.COM

ESTIS COMPRESSION
545 HUEY LENARD LOOP
WEST MONROE,LA 71292 PH 318 397-5557
BRESTIS@ESTISCOMPRESSION.COM
DENNIS ESTIS
BRETT ESTIS

ESTIS WELL SERVICE,LLC
PO BOX 13840,1414 GRAND PRAIRIE RD
NEW IBERIA,LA 70562-3840
PH 337 369-3853 FAX 337 364-6429
ESTIS@ESTISWELLSERVICE.COM
WWW.ESTISWELLSERVICE.COM
JOHNNY L ESTIS,CO-OWNER
JAMELL J ESTIS,CO-OWNER
DEBBIE ESTIS,OFC MGR
JOHN NAPIER,PORT SUPT
KIM HEBERT,RIG SUPT
JOHN ESTIS,SALES

ETCO OIL OPERATIONS,INC
PO BOX 668
OLNEY,IL 62450-0668 PH 618 395-4865

ETERNITY EXPLORATION,LLC
338 SPYGLASS DR
COPPELL,TX 75019 PH 469 464-3849
CARLO A UGOLINI
CUGOLINI@TX.RR.COM

ETHYL PETROLEUM ADDITIVES,INC SEE
AFTON CHEMICAL CORPORATION

ETOCO, L.P.
1600 SMITH ST STE 3910
HOUSTON,TX 77002-7357 PH 713 654-5010
FAX 713 654-5025 ETOCO.COM
WALTER H COCHRAN,PRES
THOM FARVER,TREAS
HAL BOZEMAN,LAND MGR
CAROL HALL,OFC MGR

EV ENERGY PARTNERS,L.P.
1001 FANNIN ST STE 800
HOUSTON,TX 77002-6707
PH 713 651-1144 FAX 713 651-1260
WWW.EVENERGYPARTNERS.COM
JOHN B WALKER,EXEC CHRMN
MARK A HOUSER,PRES,CEO
RONALD J GAJDICA,SR VP ACQS
MICHAEL E MERCER,SR VP,CFO

EVANS A R SEE
A.R. EVANS & ASOCIATES

EVANS BROS
P O BOX 35,U S HWY 171
CONVERSE,LA 71419-0035 PH 318 567-3180
R H EVANS,PRES & GEN MGR
S B EVANS JR,VP

EVANS JULIAN,OIL OPR
14651 PHILIPPINE ST APT 9103
HOUSTON,TX 77040-6984 PH 713 464-2492

EVANS MINERALS,LLC
OIL & GAS PROPERTIES
5321 CHESTNUT ST
NEW ORLEANS,LA 70115 PH 337 828-1955
FAX 337 828-4319 JPE3@COX.NET
JAMES P EVANS III,MGR

EVANS ROBERT H
INDEPENDENT LDMN,RPL
PO BOX 6531
TYLER,TX 75711-6531 PH 903 825-3827
RHEVANS@EMBARQMAIL.COM

EVANS S LAVON JR,OPERATING CO INC
PO BOX 2336
LAUREL,MS 39442-2336 PH 601 649-7639
FAX 601 649-3139 LAVONINC@BELLSOUTH.NET
S LAVON EVANS,JR,PRES
RONALD R TAYLOR,OPERATIONS CONTROLLER
BRIAN BUNNELL,OFC MGR

EVEREST RESOURCE COMPANY
PO BOX 1339,500 N SHORELINE STE 400-N
CORPUS CHRISTI,TX 78403-1339
PH 361 883-2831 FAX 361 883-9628
INFO@EVERESTCOS.COM
JAMES T CLARK,PRES
THOMAS M CRAIN JR,VP
TCRAIN@EVERESTCOS.COM
DAVID P DESENBERG,VP EXPL
KEITH H BAKER,SR GEO SCIENTIST
CODY BALL,CONSLT GEOL
ELLA C BAKER,CORP SECY

EVERETT JACK T,LLC
416 TRAVIS ST STE 1012
SHREVEPORT,LA 71101-3282 PH 318 222-0941

EVERSBERG H WALLACE,PETR ENGR
353 NAPOLEON
BATON ROUGE,LA 70802-5955 PH 225 344-9995

EVERSBERG JON R & CO
2248 SWIFT BLVD
HOUSTON,TX 77030-1125
PH 713 542-1143 FAX 713 664-8031
JON EVERSBERG,OWNER
JONEVERSBERG@MSN.COM

EVOLUTION PETROLEUM CORPORATION
2500 CITYWEST BLVD STE 1300
HOUSTON,TX 77042 PH 713 935-0122
FAX 713 935-0199
WWW.EVOLUTIONPETROLEUM.COM
INFO@EVOLUTIONPETROLEUM.COM
ROBERT S HERLIN,PRES
STERLING MCDONALD,CFO
DARYL MAZZANTI,VP OPERS
EDDIE SCHELL,GEN MGR,UNCONVENTIONAL
DRILLING & DEVELOPMENT
JEFFREY VINCENT,LDMN

EX-CEL RESOURCES,LLC
737 CR 209
BRECKENRIDGE,TX 76424 PH 254 559-7222
FAX 254 559-9651
JAMIE V WHITLEY,PRES

EXARO ENERGY III LLC
1800 BERING DR STE 540
HOUSTON,TX 77057 PH 832 730-4440
FAX 866 309-7299 WWW.EXAROENERGY.COM
CHRISTOPHER L BEATO,PRES
JOHN P ATWOOD,SR VP
J.ATWOOD@EXAROENERGY.COM

SCOTT R CLARK,SR VP
    S.CLARK@EXAROENERGY.COM

EXCALIBUR EXPLORATION INC
  PO BOX 362,9720 CLEVELAND AVE NW
  GREENTOWN,OH 44630-0362 PH 330 966-7003
  FAX 330 966-4818 EXCALOIL@AOL.COM
    DAVID HARKER,PRES,CEO
    JENNIFER HARKER,VP
    SUSAN COZBY,ADMIN ASST

EXCEL ENGINEERING,INC SEE
  RAMBOLL OIL & GAS US,INC

EXCELL SERVICES,INC
  DRILLING & WORKOVER HEADQUARTERS
  36629 US HIGHWAY 385
  WRAY,CO 80758-9667
  PH 800 876-0258 970 332-3151
  FAX 970 332-5821 DRILLING@JWOPERATING.COM
  CENTENNIAL,CO DRLG & WORKOVER SALES OFC -
  7074 S REVERE PKWY,80112
  PH 800 333-4900 303 422-4990
  FAX 303 422-0178
  ROOSEVELT,UT WORKOVER DIST OFFICE -
  210 W 1760 S,84066
  PH 435 725-0136 FAX 435 725-0138

EXCHANGE EXPLORATION & PRODUCTION CO
  844 BARONNE ST
  NEW ORLEANS,LA 70113
  PH 504 529-5100 FAX 504 529-3700
    JOHN M WAID,PRES

EXCO MIDCONTINENT DIVISION SEE
  SHERIDAN PRODUCTION COMPANY,LLC

EXCO RESOURCES
  PO BOX 8
  RAVENSWOOD,WV 26164
  PH 304 273-5371 FAX 304 273-5379
    RANDALL SHEETS,PROD SUPT

EXETER DRILLING COMPANY SEE
  NABORS DRILLING USA,INC

EXL PETROLEUM OPERATING,INC
  6 DESTA DR STE 2800
  MIDLAND,TX 79705 PH 432 686-8080
  FAX 432 686-8087

EXOTHERM CORPORATION
  888 WILCREST DR
  HOUSTON,TX 77042 PH 713 981-9100

EXPERITEC INC
  8863 E 34TH ST N
  WICHITA,KS 67226-2624 PH 316 838-1111
    WWW.EXPERITEC.COM
    RANDY RUBENTHALER,SLS MGR
    KEITH SOWALSKIE,SLS MGR
  LIBERAL,KS OFFICE - 2001 W THIRD,67901
  PH 620 624-3821
    TOM WHITE,SLS MGR

EXPLORATION COMPANY,THE
  PO BOX 160727
  SAN ANTONIO,TX 78280-2927
  PH 210 496-5000 FAX 210 496-3232
    WWW.TXCO.COM TXCO@TXCO.COM
    JAMES E SIGMON,CEO
    JEFF BOOKOUT,COO
    P MARK STARK,CFO
    ROBERT LEE,LAND MGR
    GARY GRINSFRIDER,VP,EXPL
    STEVE CRUSE,PIPELINE MGR

EXPLORATION FUNDS INC SEE
  MCCOY OIL & GAS CO

EXPLORATION INVESTMENTS,INC SEE
  WYNNE PETROLEUM CO

EXPLORATION LAND SERVICES,LLC
  4021-B AMBASSADOR CAFFERY PKWY STE 200
  LAFAYETTE,LA 70503-5281
  PH 337 234-3500 FAX 337 234-3525
    CONTACT@EXPLORATIONLAND.COM
    BURTON T ZAUNBRECHER,MGR
    MARK SIMON,MGR

EXPLORATION PARTNERS,LLC
  PO BOX 930
  BRIDGEPORT,WV 26330-0930 PH 304 842-8777
  FAX 304 842-8786 LAF@IOLINC.NET
    THOMAS A DINGLEDINE,PRES
    LOUIS A FERRARI,VP,LAND
    BRADLEY THOMAS,VP,GEOL

EXPLORATION SURVEYS INC
  101 E PARK BLVD STE 955
  PLANO,TX 75074 PH 972 423-3544
  FAX 972 424-3943 WWW.TGCSEISMIC.COM
    INFO@TGCSEISMIC.COM
    WAYNE WHITENER,PRES,CEO
    TOM PIERCE,MKTG MGR

EXPLORATION TECHNIQUES,INC
  3100 TIMMONS LN STE 200
  HOUSTON,TX 77027-5904
  PH 713 526-0828 FAX 713 523-0145
    RICHARD O'DONNELL,PRES
    WES PUSTEJOVSKY,VP

EXPLORATION TECHNOLOGIES INC
  7755 SYNOTT RD
  HOUSTON,TX 77083-5115 PH 713 785-0393
  FAX 713 785-1550
    VICTOR T JONES III,PRES
    PATRICK N AGOSTINO,VP
    FRANK E LEVY,BUS DEV MGR
  CASPER,WY OFFICE - 104 S WOLCOTT STE 724
  82602 PH 307 266-4409 FAX 307 266-9406
    WALTER R MERSCHAT,MGR
  LITTLETON,CO OFFICE - 7800 S ELATI ST
  STE 302,80120 PH 303 797-6477
    MARCUS K BATEMAN,CO-MGR
  JAMESTOWN,PA OFC - 403 LIBERTY,PO BOX 531
  16134 PH 724 932-3202
    DR ROBERT A HODGSON,MGR

EXPLORE ENERGY CORPORATION
  PO BOX 1890
  WESTERVILLE,OH 43086 PH 614 286-5454
  FAX 614 898-9373
    EDWARD KNEZEVICH,PRES
    EDKNEZEVICH@GMAIL.COM

EXPLORECO INTERNATIONAL,LLC
  11930 S SAM HOUSTON PKWY E
  HOUSTON,TX 77089-4778 PH 713 796-6000
  FAX 281 922-7363 WWW.EXPLORECO.COM
    W BARRY MILNER,PRES
    DON K MILNER,VP

EXPRESS ENERGY SERVICES OPERATING LP
  9800 RICHMOND AVE STE 700
  HOUSTON,TX 77042 PH 713 625-7400
  FAX 713 625-7403 WWW.EESLP.COM
    INFO@EESLP.COM

EXPRESS OIL COMPANY
  PO BOX 432

HALLETTSVILLE,TX 77964-0432
  PH 361 798-4031 FAX 361 798-2839
    DON R JONES,OWNER

EXPRO AMERICAS,LLC
  738 HWY 6 SOUTH STE 1000
  HOUSTON,TX 77079 PH 713 643-9776
    WWW.EXPROGROUP.COM
    RODNEY.KORCZYNSKI@EXPROGROUP.COM

EXTERRAN
  16666 NORTHCHASE DR
  HOUSTON,TX 77060 PH 281 836-7000
    WWW.EXTERRAN.COM
    ERNIE L DANNER,PRES/CEO
    J MICHAEL ANDERSON,SR VP/CFO
    KENNETH R BICKETT,VP FIN & ACCT
    D BRADLEY CHILDERS,PRES-NORTH AMERICA
    OPERS
    RONALDO REIMER,PRES-LATIN AMERICA OPERS
    JOSEPH KISHKILL,PRES-EASTERN HEMISPHERE
    OPERS
    DAVID MILLER,VP/CFO-EASTERN HEMISPHERE
    DANIEL K SCHLANGER,SR VP OPERS SVCS
    DONALD C WAYNE,SR VP/GEN COUNSEL & SECY
  BROOKWOOD,AL DISTRICT OFFICE -
  15690 WALDEN POND,35444 PH 205 556-8552
  FAX 205 553-5087
  FORT SMITH,AR OFFICE - PO BOX 6338,72906
  PH 877 732-7052 PH 918 732-7000
  FAX 866 633-9832
  SEARCY,AR DISTRICT OFFICE - 710 E BOOTH
  72143
  BAKERSFIELD,CA OFFICE - 3333 GIBSON ST
  93308 PH 661 321-0271 FAX 661 321-0859
  STOCKTON,CA OFFICE - 2000 W CHARTER
  WAY,95206
  DENVER,CO SALES OFC-600 17TH ST STE 1950
  80202 PH 303 633-0880 FAX 303 792-5711
  GREELEY,CO OFFICE - 915 E 18TH ST
  BLDG 4,80631
  RIFLE,CO (AFTERMARKET SERVICES) OFFICE -
  762 BUCKHORN DR 81650 PH 970 625-5138
  WRAY,CO (AFTERMARKET SERVICES) OFFICE -
  29360 HWY 34,80758 PH 303 892-1302
  MERIDIAN,ID (EMIT) OFFICE - 705 N RALSTIN
  ST 83642 PH 208 887-4631
  MCPHERSON,KS (TURBOCHARGER GROUP) OFFICE-
  PO BOX 187,1404 MOHAWK RD 67460
  PH 620 241-8740 PH 800 526-4347
  FAX 620 241-8744
  THAYER,KS (DEPOT) OFFICE -
  501 N GALVESTON,66776
  ARCADIA,LA (DEPOT) OFFICE - 750 FIRST ST
  71001 PH 381 263-2999 FAX 318 263-7837
  BELLE CHASSE,LA - MACH SHOP & REPAIR
  FACILITY - 2206 ENGINEERS RD
  70037 PH 504 392-2600 FAX 661 322-5911
  BROUSSARD,LA (BASIN MAKE READY) OFFICE -
  1114 HUGHES RD,70518 PH 337 359-3400
  HOUMA,LA - MACH SHOP & REPAIR FACILITY -
  3664 SOUTHDOWN MANDALAY BLVD 70360
  PH 985 868-7232
  BROUSSARD,LA (ENERGY SOLUTIONS) OFFICE -
  PO BOX 40,1114 HUGHES RD,70518
  PH 337 359-3400 FAX 337 560-5739
    BOBBY IVY,SOUTHEAST BASIN DIRECTOR
    RICKY LANDRY,SOUTHEAST BASIN SALES DIR

LYNDON LEJEUNE,SOUTHEAST OPERS MGR

GLEN BOYKIN,SOUTHEAST DIST MGR-OFFSHORE

MIKE EARLEY,SOUTHEAST DIST MGR-LAND

DANIEL QUINTANA,SOUTHEAST BASIN AMS MGR

STACY GREEN,SOUTHEAST BASIN DIST MGR

GREG DOMINGUE,MANUFACTURING MGR

BRIAN LANDRY,SOUTHEAST BASIN SVCS MGR

JENNINGS,LA (DEPOT) OFFICE - 1510 HWY
90 WEST 70546 PH 337 824-8376

MANSFIELD,LA OFFICE - MARTINEZ RD 71052

PORT SULPHUR,LA (DEPOT) OFFICE -
29838 HWY 23,70083

PORT SULPHUR,LA OFFICE - 29280 HWY 11
70083

SHREVEPORT,LA OFFICE - 475 IDEMA ST

SHREVEPORT,LA OFFICE - 1401 WELLS
ISLAND RD,71107

GAYLORD,MI (BASIN MAKE READY) OFFICE -
1850 ENGEL AVE 49735 PH 800 898-4824
PH 989 732-6078 FAX 877 732-9358

GAYLORD,MI (PARTS WAREHOUSE) -
1553 CAULKINS DR 49735 PH 866 732-0491
PH 989 732-0491 FAX 866 688-2800

COLUMBIA,MS (STORAGE) - 60 COLUMBIA
PURVIS RD 39429 PH 337 359-3400

RIDGELAND,MS OFFICE - 574 HIGHLAND COLONY
PKWY BLDG 3 39157

HAVRE,MT (DEPOT) OFFICE - 1038 32ND AVE E
59501 PH 406 265-6649

CARLSBAD,NM (BASIN MAKE READY) OFFICE -
3204 E GREENE 88220 PH 505 887-5258

FARMINGTON,NM (MANUFACTURING) OFFICE -
358 LA PLATA HWY,87401

FARMINGTON,NM (BASIN MAKE READY) OFFICE -
1280 TROY KING RD 87401 PH 505 325-3220
FAX 505 325-4242

FARMINGTON,NM REGIONAL OFFICE -
3440 MORNINGSTAR DR,87401 PH 505 326-6525

LAKEWOOD,NY (DEPOT) - 4477 GLEASON RD
14750 PH 716 763-1553 FAX 716 763-1584

WILLISTON,ND OFFICE - 4936 HWY 85,58801

SUMMERFIELD,OH (INTEGRATED PROJ) OFFICE -
27480 PUMP STATION RD 43788

ALDERSON,OK OFFICE - 401 1/2 HWY 270
EAST,74501

BARTLESVILLE,OK OFFICE - 115 N ADELINE
74003

BROKEN ARROW,OK OFFICE - 3460 E HOUSTON
ST 74014

BROKEN ARROW,OK (MANUFACTURING/
FABRICATION OFFICE) - 20602 E 81ST ST
74014 PH 918 251-8571 FAX 918 259-2337

CHICKASHA,OK OFFICE - 6 HONDA LN 73018

DAVIS,OK OFFICE - 112 BLACKBERRY RD 73030

DAVIS,OK (MANUFACTURING/FABRICATION)
OFFICE - 801 INDUSTRIAL PARK S 73030
PH 580 369-2646 FAX 580 369-7724

ELK CITY,OK DISTRICT OFFICE -
1306 AIRPORT INDUSTRIAL RD 73644
PH 580 225-9303

OKLAHOMA CITY,OK (MANUFACTURING/
FABRICATION) OFFICE - 5400 SW 33RD ST
73179

OKLAHOMA CITY,OK WAREHOUSE -
14301 CALIBER DR,1 CALIBER PARK 73134

POCOLA,OK DISTRICT OFFICE - 301 CUMMINGS

AVE 74902,PO BOX 6338 FORT SMITH,AR 72906
PH 877 732-7052 PH 918 732-7000
FAX 866 633-9832

TULSA,OK SALES OFFICE - 9410 E 51ST ST S
STE K,74145

YUKON,OK (BASIN MAKE READY) OFFICE -
11000 NW 10TH ST 73099 PH 800 523-2854
PH 405 324-8787 FAX 405 324-8414

WOODWARD,OK DISTRICT OFFICE -
801 JIMAR WAY,73801

INDIANA,PA (DEPOT) OFFICE -
157 STORMER RD,15701

WEXFORD,PA SALES OFFICE - 3000 STONEWOOD
DR STE 310,15090 PH 724 935-7660

WILLIAMSPORT,PA OFFICE- 316 ROSE ST 17701

ALEDO,TX DISTRICT OFFICE -
119 S RANCH HOUSE RD,76008

ALLEYTON,TX (COLUMBUS - MANUFACTURING/
FABRICATION) OFFICE - 2207 FM 949,78935
PH 979 732-2327 FA 979 732-0056

BRENHAM,TX DISTRICT OFFICE - 3030 NORTH
PARK ST,77833 PH 979 289-5990

BRIDGEPORT,TX DISTRICT OFFICE -
103 INDUSTRIAL PARK,76426 PH 940 683-8383

BURTON,TX OFFICE - 10959 HWY 290 W

CENTER,TX OFFICE - 145 CATCO DR 75935

CLEBURNE,TX OFFICE - 3600 E HWY 67 76031

CARRIZO SPRINGS,TX OFFICE - 2979 SOUTH
HWY 83 78834

CORPUS CHRISTI,TX (BASIN MAKE READY) OFC
232 NORTH PADRE ISLAND DR,78406
PH 361 939-6800 FAX 361 289-0724
FAX 800 664-3516

DALLAS,TX REGIONAL OFFICE -
8150 N CENTRAL EXPY STE 1550,75206
PH 214 369-5554

DICKINSON,TX OFFICE - 3828 HUGHES
CT 77539

FAIRFIELD,TX DISTRICT OFFICE -
105 BAILIFF DR,75840

FORT STOCKTON,TX (MANUFACTURING/
FABRICATION) OFFICE - 3105 W 9TH ST
79735 PH 915 336-5949

GRAPEVINE,TX OFFICE - 1701 W NORTHWEST
HWY,MERIDIAN BUSINESS CENTER 76051

HOUSTON,TX CORPORATE GPS OFFICE -
GREENSPOINT SOUTH,263 N SAM HOUSTON PKWY
77060 PH 281 836-7000

HOUSTON,TX (MANUFACTURING/FABRICATION)
OFFICE - 4444/4510/4517 BRITTMOORE RD
77041 PH 281 854-3000

HOUSTON,TX (MANUFACTURING/FABRICATION)
OFFICE - 12001 N HOUSTON ROSSLYN,77086
PH 281 477-8787

JASPER,TX (DEPOT) OFFICE - 891 HWY 63 W
STE 3 & 4,75951 PH 409 384-3200

JEWETT,TX OFFICE - 613 W MEXIA HWY 75846

KILGORE,TX (BASIN MAKE READY) OFFICE -
2019 HWY 135,75662 PH 903 986-9007

LAREDO,TX (DEPOT) OFFICE -
101 OILPATCH RD,78043

LIBERTY,TX DISTRICT OFFICE - 1700 HWY
146 BYPASS 77575

LONGVIEW,TX OFFICE - 911 NW LOOP 281
MULTI-TENANT OFFICE BLDG 75604

MANVEL,TX (DEPOT) OFFICE -

18235 COUNTRY RD 143,77578

MCALLEN,TX DISTRICT OFFICE -
1200 E HACKBERRY AVE STE D,78501

MIDLAND,TX SALES OFFICE - 9704 W I-20
79706 PH 732 567-7050

MIDLAND,TX (BASIN MAKE READY) OFFICE -
5200 I-20 W,79703

MINERAL WELLS,TX OFFICE - 506 N GRANT
76067

MONAHANS,TX (DEPOT) OFFICE -
900 S STOCKTON HWY 79756

PAMPA,TX (BASIN MAKE READY) OFFICE -
PO BOX 861,79066-0861,305 S PRICE RD
79065 PH 800 790-3378 PH 806 669-3378
FAX 806 669-9652

ROSENBURG,TX OFFICE - 211 F2 RANDON
DRYER RD 77471

SCHULENBURG,TX (MANUFACTURING/
FABRICATION) OFFICE - 150 E AVE 78956

SONORA,TX (DEPOT) OFFICE -
105 SPUR RD,2ND FL 76950

TYLER,TX OFFICE - 100 E FERGUSON 75702

VICTORIA,TX (BASIN MAKE READY) OFFICE -
8193-8198 LONE TREE RD 77905
PH 361 572-9904

ZAPATA,TX OFFICE - 779 FR 496 W

ROOSEVELT,UT (AFTERMARKET SERVICES) OFC -
2005 W 1760 S,84066 PH 435 722-3471
FAX 435 722-0281

OAK HILL,WV (BASIN MAKE READY) OFFICE -
337 INDUSTRIAL DR,25901 PH 304 250-6100

CASPER,WY OFFICE - 3364 SQUAW CREEK
RD 82604

EVANSTON,WY (AFTERMARKET SERVICES) OFC -
76 IMPERIAL LN STE N,82930
PH 307 789-5331

GILLETTE,WY (AFTERMARKET SERVICES) OFC -
4988 N HWY 14-16 NORTH,82718

MILLS,WY (AFTERMARKET SERVICES) OFFICE -
1010 FALCON AVE,82644 PH 307 266-6373

ROCK SPRINGS,WY (MANUFACTURING/
FABRICATION) OFFICE -
519,608 & 622 WINTOON CIRCLE 82901

ROCK SPRINGS,WY (AFTERMARKET SVCS) OFC -
152 INDUSTRIAL DR 82901

SHERIDAN,WY (EMIT) OFFICE - 2665 AVIATION
DR 82801 PH 307 673-0805

SHERIDAN,WY (EMIT) OFFICE - 2688 & 2708
AVIATION DR,82801

WAMSUTTER,WY OFFICE - 621 LATHAM 82336

CALGARY,ALBERTA,CANADA OFFICE - 736 8TH
AVE STE 910 T2P 1H4 PH 800 661-5252
PH 403 236-5252 FAX 403 236-5253

CALGARY,ALBERTA,CANADA OFFICE -
1721 - 27TH AVE NE,T2E 7E1

EDMONTON,ALBERTA,CANADA OFFICE -
5325 93 ST,T5Y 6E9 PH 800 661-3610
PH 780 433-8484 FAX 780 433-8656

EDSON,ALBERTA,CANADA OFFICE -
SE CORNER INTERSECTION TRANSCANADA HWY
16 & 44TH ST PH 877 209-5000
PH 780 712-5500 FAX 780 712-2368

GRANDE PRAIRIE,ALBERTA,CANADA OFFICE -
11401 98 AVE,T8V5S5 PH 877 898-3535
PH 780 539-3535 FAX 780 538-0659

PEACE RIVER,ALBERTA,CANADA OFFICE -

8002E 102 AVE,T8S 1S3 PH 780 624-8767
FAX 780 624-8867
REDCLIFF,ALBERTA,CANADA OFFICE - 2150 S
HWY DR SE,T0J 2P0 PH 888 526-3220
PH 403 526-3220 FAX 403 528-2530
ROCKY MOUNTAIN HOUSE,ALBERTA,CANADA OFC -
BAY 4 LOT 9 BLK 2 PIDHERNEYS INDUSTRIAL
SUBDIV PH 403 845-7615 PH 403 845-7391
PH 250 788-1298 FAX 250 788-1053
KINDERSLEY,SASKATCHEWAN,CANADA OFFICE -
1319 11 AVE WEST,BAY 1,S0L 1S0
PH 306 463-5909 FAX 306 463-5908
BUENOS AIRES,ARGENTINA MAIN OFFICE
TALCAHUANO 833,PISO 11A,C1013AAQ
PH +54 11 4814 4430 FAX +54 11 4814 0158
BUENOS AIRES,ARGENTINA REGIONAL OFFICE
TALCAHUANO 833,PISO 7F,C1013AAQ
PH +54 11 5169 3000 FAX +54 11 5169 3001
COMODORO RIVADAVIA,CHUBUT 9000,ARGENTINA
OFFICE - MACIZO 3-PARQUE INDUSTRIAL
PH +54 297 448 1890 FAX +54 297 448 1892
COMODORO RIVADAVIA,CHUBUT 9000,ARGENTINA
OFFICE - MARIA CORCOY 170 BARRIO
INDUSTRIAL PH +54 297 448 6840
NEUQUEN 8300 ARGENTINA OFFICE - PARQUE
INDUSTRIAL ESTE S/NRO PH +54 299 441 3118
PLOTTIER 8316 ARGENTINA OFFICE - RUTA 22
KILOMETRO 1234 PH +54 299 493 7899
FAX 54 299 493 3299
RIO GALLEGOS,SANTA CRUZ 9400,ARGENTINA
OFFICE - JUAN A BARK N 180
PH +54 296 644 2247
RIO GALLEGOS,SANTA CRUZ 9400,ARGENTINA
CALLE AVELLANEDA N 408 PH +54 2966 423022

EXTEX OPERATING COMPANY
5065 WESTHEIMER RD STE 625
HOUSTON,TX 77056-5606
PH 713 953-0824 FAX 713 952-2564
WWW.EXTEX.NET
WALLIS MARSH

EXTRA ENERGY
309 W 7TH ST STE 500
FT WORTH,TX 76102 PH 817 335-9393
FAX 817 335-7776 WWW.EXTRAENERGY.NET
ROBERT L GAUDIN,MNGNG PRTNR
RGAUDIN@EXTRAENERGY.NET
GREG SHARP,PROJ MGR
GSHARP@EXTRAENERGY.NET

EXTREME TRUCKING
DIRECTIONAL TOOLS TRANSPORTING COMPANY
12502 CR 2907
EUSTACE,TX 75124
PH 903 675-4006 FAX 903 675-4414
MATT ANDING,OWNER
TIM RUTTER,OPERS MGR
BROUSSARD,LA OFFICE - PO BOX 689,70518

EXXON MOBIL CORPORATION
5959 LAS COLINAS BLVD
IRVING,TX 75039-4202 PH 972 444-1000
FAX 972 444-1350 WWW.EXXONMOBIL.COM
HOUSTON,TX OFFICE - 800 BELL ST,77002
PH 713 656-3636 FAX 713 656-6267
HOUSTON,TX BRANCH OFFICE -
12450 GREENSPOINT DR,77060-1991
PH 713 656-3636
FAIRFAX,VA OFFICE - 3225 GALLOWS RD 22037

PH 703 846-3000
EXXONMOBIL PRODUCTION COMPANY
PO BOX 4610
HOUSTON,TX 77210-4610 PH 832 625-4487
ROBERT E WEITZEL,LAND MGR
JAROD M ROLLAND,REG LAND MGR
PH 832 624-6203
BETH R DAVIS,PTA MGR PH 832 624-5688
EZ HULL,LLC SEE
LCM SOLUTIONS,LLC
EZELLE EZELLE & ASSOC,INC
OIL & GAS INTERESTS
PO BOX 2368
MARRERO,LA 70072-2368
PH 504 341-3325 FAX 504 341-3326
R WAYNE EZELLE JR,PRES
SHEILA BARNETT,VP
WENDY CARTO,VP
DAVID ALSEVER,VP
JAN HOLLOWAY,VP
F & F WIRELINE SERVICES,INC SEE
SUPERIOR ENERGY SERVICES
F & H PRODUCTION
P O BOX 489
OIL CITY,LA 71061 PH 318 995-7910
A C FRIZZELL,OWNER
F EXPLORATION LLC
8107 SIDNEY GAUTREAUX RD
ABBEVILLE,LA 70510-4362 PH 337 893-2800
RAYMOND FONTENOT,IND GEOL
F.L. BEARD SERVICE CORP
800 STOKES ST
MOUNT CARMEL,IL 62863
PH 618 262-5193 FAX 618 262-5194
RICK LINCOLN,PRES
DARRELL DEISHER,GEN MGR
F.T.G. PROPERTIES
PO BOX 921
KILGORE,TX 75663-0921
PH 903 984-3443 FAX 903 983-2526
DOUG RAY,OWNER
F-OIL PROPERTIES,INC
810 N RAILROAD AVE
TYLERTOWN,MS 39667
PH 601 876-9678 FAX 601 510-9193
FOIL J BRANTON,IND LDMN/CPL
JBFOIL.FOILPROPERTIES@GMAIL.COM
FAGADAU ENERGY CORPORATION SEE
PRIMEXX OPERATING CORPORATION
FAIR OIL,LTD
PO BOX 689,225 S COLLEGE
TYLER,TX 75710-0689 PH 903 592-3811
FAX 903 597-3587 LAND@FAIROIL.COM
JOHN R BOB GARRETT,PRES
RODNEY K THOMSON,PROD MGR
JAY BYNUM,FIELD OPERS MGR
RACHEL LARSON,ACCT MGR
SHERRI HARRIS,LDMN
FAIRCHASE ASSOCIATES,LLC
LAND SERVICES
551 CREST AVE
BENTON,PA 17814 PH 570 477-3524
FAX 570 477-2749
GREGORY S GASS,CPL/ESA-OWNER
GGASS@FRONTIERNET.NET

FAIRFIELD INDUSTRIES INC SEE
FAIRFIELDNODAL
FAIRFIELDNODAL
1111 GILLINGHAM LN
SUGAR LAND,TX 77478-2865 PH 281 275-7500
FAX 281 275-7550 WWW.FAIRFIELDNODAL.COM
WALTER PHARRIS,PRES/CEO
ROY DUFF,VP/CFO
JOE DRYER,VP-DATA LICENSING DIV
STEVE MITCHELL,VP-DATA ACQ DIV
JOHN SMYTHE,DATA PROC DIV MGR
DR CLIFFORD H RAY,SR VP
DAVID HAYS,VP TECH GROUP
FALCON BAY ENERGY,LLC SEE
CAZA OPERATING LLC
FALCON BAY OPERATIONS,LLC SEE
CAZA OPERATING,LLC
FALCON GAS STORAGE COMPANY,INC
1201 LOUISIANA ST STE 700
HOUSTON,TX 77002-5603 PH 713 961-3204
FAX 713 961-2676 WWW.FALCONGASSTORAGE.COM
JOHN M HOPPER,PRES,CEO
STEVEN B TOON,CFO
JEFFREY H FOUTCH,EXEC VP
EDMUND A KNOLLE,EXEC VP
THOMAS B WYNNE,VP,LAND
CARL OELZE,VP,ENGRG & OPERS
MARK D COURTNEY,VP,ORIGINATION
KEITH CHANDLER,VP,EARTH SCIENCES
DAVID MATTHES,CONTROLLER & TREAS
FALCON RESOURCES,INC
PO BOX 2640
KILGORE,TX 75663-2640
PH 903 983-5333 FAX 903 983-1298
BRAD FAULKNER,PRES
TOM SARTOR,VP
FALK CARL,JR,OIL LEASES
4813 OLYMPIA
CORPUS CHRISTI,TX 78413-2721
PH 361 991-5285
FALLON PETROLEUM,LTD
PO BOX 671099
DALLAS,TX 75367-1099 PH 214 707-7535
FAX 214 572-2699 WWW.TRUNKBAY.NET
BENNY DUNCAN,MGR
BDUNCAN@TRUNKBAY.NET
FAMBROUGH JAMES W,PETR GEOL
101 OAKWOOD DR
LAFAYETTE,LA 70503-4434 PH 337 984-6985
FAMCOR OIL INC
7887 SAN FELIPE ST STE 250
HOUSTON,TX 77063-1621 PH 713 974-0002
FAX 713 974-0148
JAMES M RAY,PRES
JERRY DRAKE,GEOL
LARRY A DRAKE,GEOPHY
FARMERS OIL COMPANY
211 HIGHLAND CROSS DR STE 100
HOUSTON,TX 77073-1700 PH 281 874-2101
FAX 281 874-2107
FARRINGTON WALTER L,JR
3415 FRY AVE
TYLER,TX 75701-9061 PH 903 593-8617
FAX 903 593-8643
FASTORG,INC SEE
SUPERIOR ENERGY SERVICES

FAULCONER VERNON E INC
PO BOX 7995,1001 ESE LOOP 323 STE 160
TYLER,TX 75711-7995
PH 903 581-4382 FAX 903 581-5072
JIB@VEFINC.COM WWW.VEFINC.COM
VERNON E FAULCONER,CEO
TOM MARKEL,VP,FIN
JEAN CRAWLEY,VP,LAND & ADMIN
ROY BUDDY SLOAN,ENGR
LANCE MATHIS,ACQ MGR
BREAUX BRIDGE,LA OFFICE - 1803-H MILLS
HWY,70517 PH 337 332-1726
DAVID ENRIGHT,PRES
GERALD LAGNEAUX,ACQ MGR
DALLAS,TX OFFICE - 8117 PRESTON RD
75225, PH 214 706-9010
JULIE LIPPMAN,MKTG REP

FAVALORO G J,& ASSOC
P O BOX 53928,1128 COOLIDGE
LAFAYETTE,LA 70505-3928 PH 318 232-1121

FAYETTE EXPLORATION COMPANY
PO DRAWER J
SCHULENBURG,TX 78956-0330 PH 979 561-8700
FAX 979 561-8710 FAYEXPLO@CVTV.NET
STEWART CHUBER,PRES & GEOL

FEAGIN PARTNERSHIP
3302 SUFFOLK DR
HOUSTON,TX 77027 PH 832 498-4781
MICHAEL FEAGIN,PRTNR
LUISA FEAGIN LORD,PRTNR

FEDERAL ENERGY REGULATORY COMMISSION
WWW.FERC.GOV

FEDERAL PETROLEUM CORPORATION
PO BOX 670386
DALLAS,TX 75367-0386 PH 972 484-3400
FAX 972 484-3420 JCHADSELL@SBCGLOBAL.NET
JAMES C HADSELL,PRES,CEO

FEDERAL RAILROAD ADMINISTRATION
WWW.FRA.DOT.GOV

FEDERAL ROYALTY PARTNERS,LTD/PROPERTIES
2001 KIRBY DR STE 1210
HOUSTON,TX 77019-6081 PH 713 529-3729
FAX 713 529-8166
ROLF WOODS,GEOL

FEDERATED OIL & GAS PROPERTIES,INC
12719 S WEST BAY SHORE DR STE 5
TRAVERSE CITY,MI 49684-5489
PH 231 929-4466 FAX 231 929-4678
J G KOSTRZEWA,CHRMN
THERESE M MENTZER,VP

FEHRENBACHER PETROLEUM LAND SERVICES
737 E 3RD ST
FLORA,IL 62839-2521 PH 618 662-2516
FAX 618 662-2516
JAMES L FEHRENBACHER,OWNER

FELMONT OIL CORPORATION SEE
TORCH ENERGY ADVISORS,INC

FENDER EXPLORATION & PRODUCTION CO LLC
116 E FRONT ST
TYLER,TX 75702-8120 PH 903 533-9111
FAX 903 593-5881
DAVID M FENDER,PRES
BOB LEE,CONTROLLER
SHELBY MASSEY,PROD SUPT
BAILEY FENDER,LDMN

FENNER ROBERT D
1543 GRIMMETT DR
SHREVEPORT,LA 71107 PH 318 425-0400
FAX 318 222-2650
RFENNER@FENNERCONSULTING.NET

FENSTERMAKER
CIVIL ENGRS,LAND SURVEYORS,ENVIRO CONSLTS
135 REGENCY SQ
LAFAYETTE,LA 70508 PH 337 237-2200
FAX 337 232-3299,WWW.FENSTERMAKER.COM
WILLIAM H FENSTERMAKER,CEO,CHRMN
KAM MOVASSAGHI,PH.D,P.E.,PRES
R J BOUTTE,CAO & VP,OPERS
JOHN FENSTERMAKER,VP,SURVEY DIV
RAYMOND REAUX,P.E.,VP,ENGRG DIV
NEW ORLEANS,LA OFFICE - 1100 POYDRAS
STE 1550,70163 PH 504 582-2201
FAX 504 582-2210
SHREVEPORT,LA OFFICE - 401 MARKET ST
STE 1300,71101 PH 318 222-0040
FAX 318 222-0042
HOUSTON,TX OFFICE - 5005 RIVER WAY
STE 300,77056 PH 713 840-9995
FAX 713 840-9997
BATON ROUGE,LA OFFICE - 327 NORTH BLVD
STE 210,70801 PH 225 344-6701
FAX 337 232-3299

FERGUSON A J,GEOL
204 SOMERSET DR
NATCHEZ,MS 39120-3718 PH 601 445-8022
FAX 601 442-3117

FERGUSON DISPATCHING SERVICE
OILFIELD DISPATCHERS/SHOREBASE RIG CLERKS
PO BOX 548
BUNKIE,LA 71322-0548 PH 318 346-2826
FAX 318 346-2826
CIEL FERGUSON,OWNER
CLAUDE FERGUSON,CO-OWNER
DAVID FERGUSON,FIELD REP

FESCO LTD
PROD TESTING,WIRELINE SVCS,LAB & PVT SVCS
1000 FESCO AVE
ALICE,TX 78332-7318 PH 361 661-7000
BILL FINDLEY,CEO
BOBBY MANDEL,VP ENGRG
JAIME GONZALEZ,DIST MGR
ALICE,TX DIST OFFICE - PH 361 664-3479
EDINBURG,TX OFFICE - 4501 UNIVERSITY DR
78539-7921 PH 956 383-8378
JAMES DEVRIES,DIST MGR
REFUGIO,TX OFFICE - 207 PLASUELA ST
78377 PH 361 526-4644
BRAD GILLESPIE,DIST MGR
VICTORIA,TX OFFICE - 2102-C HOUSTON
HWY,77901-5735 PH 361 575-7533
ROBERT MOLINA,DIST MGR
CORPUS CHRISTI,TX OFFICE - 627 OMAHA
DR,78408-2952 PH 361 882-4124
JOEL MORRIS,DIST MGR
EL CAMPO,TX OFFICE - 310 N WHARTON
77437-4655 PH 979 543-9451
RANDY TARVER,DIST MGR
LAREDO,TX OFFICE - RR 1,BOX 9B
78043-9801 PH 956 724-7501
JAVIER GARCIA,DIST MGR
OZONA,TX OFFICE - 105 MEDICAL DR

76943 PH 325 392-3773
TOM ANDERSON,DIST MGR
KILGORE,TX OFFICE - 206 BEALL ST
75662-5002 PH 903 984-4814
ERNIE POOLE,DIST MGR
BRYAN,TX OFFICE - 400 INDUSTRIAL BLVD
77803-2030 PH 979 775-1825
JAMES GALLEGO,DIST MGR
BEAUMONT,TX OFFICE - 2205 W FLORIDA ST
77705-6352 PH 409 842-3000
SCOTT DAVIS,DIST MGR
SUGAR LAND,TX OFFICE - PH 281 565-1115
JEFF BOWMAN,TECH SLS REPR
ODESSA,TX OFFICE - 2600 EINSTEIN AVE
79763 PH 432 332-3211
JON JACKSON,DIST MGR
LAFAYETTE,LA OFFICE - 4484 NORTH EAST
EVANGELINE THRUWAY,CARENCRO,LA 70520
PH 337 896-3838
TONY SMITH,DIST MGR
WOODWARD,OK OFFICE - HWY 270 & WESTERN
AVE,73802 PH 580 256-1314
BRYAN HULL,REG MGR
CANADIAN,TX OFFICE - PH 806 323-5050
BRYAN HULL,REG MGR
SHINNSTON,WV OFFICE - PH 304 592-3366
JACK COOPER,REG MGR
PECOS,TX OFFICE - PH 432 445-1993
ROBERT ALFORD,DIST MGR

FIBER GLASS SYSTEMS
PO BOX 37389
SAN ANTONIO,TX 78237-0389 PH 210 434-5043
FAX 210 434-7543 WWW.STARFIBERGLASS.COM
INFO@STARFIBERGLASS.COM
W G BILL BURNETT,PRES
STEVE HEINTZ,VP,SALES & MKTG
- AREA SALES OFFICES -
HOUSTON,TX OFFICE - PH 903 521-9208
LARRY STANFORD,REG SLS MGR
MIDLAND,TX OFFICE - PH 432 425-7985
DENNIS GRAHAM,REG SLS MGR
SAN ANTONIO,TX OFFICE - PH 210 434-5043
TONI CLINE,CSTM SVC MGR
OKLAHOMA CITY,OK OFFICE - PH 405 642-2334
DON VITELLO,REG SLS MGR

FIELDING HOWARD K,JR,PETROLEUM GEOL
306 ROBIN HOOD CIR
LAFAYETTE,LA 70508-4032 PH 318 233-7200

FIELDS BERT,JR
11835 PRESTON RD
DALLAS,TX 75230-2708
PH 972 661-3330 FAX 972 991-3584
BERT FIELDS,JR,OWNER
JUDY LEONHART,CHF ACCT

FIELDS BYRON W PETROLEUM LDMN & CONS
545 N UPPER BROADWAY ST STE 1100
CORPUS CHRISTI,TX 78476-1401
PH 361 883-4721 FAX 361 883-4715
P ARCHIBALD,SECY

FIELDS EXPLORATION,INC
545 N UPPER BROADWAY ST STE 1100
CORPUS CHRISTI,TX 78401-0678
PH 361 883-4721 FAX 361 883-4715
BYRON W FIELDS,PRES,LDMN
CRAIG B FIELDS,VP,PETR GEOL

FIELDSTONE J V
6104 GREENBRIAR DR
HOUSTON,TX 77030 PH 832 693-8782
LARRY S SANDERS,SOLE PROPRIETOR

FIELDWOOD ENERGY
ACQS & DEV - CONV OIL & GAS ASSETS
2000 W SAM HOUSTON PKWY S STE 1200
HOUSTON,TX 77042 PH 713 969-1000
FAX 713 969-1099 WWW.FIELDWOODENERGY.COM
MATT MCCARROLL,PRES & CEO
RICHARD BLACK,SR VP & GEN COUNSEL
JOHN SMITH,SR VP-BUS DEV
JIM ULM,SR VP & CFO
PAUL GLUTH,SR VP-PROD/OPERS
GARY JANIK,SR VP-ASSET MGMNT
JIM BRYSCH,VP-PROD MKTG
JILL CURRY,VP-HUMAN RELS
MIKE DANE,VP-FIN
TREY GILMORE,VP-RES ENGRG
INGRID HILLHOUSE,VP-ACQS
DOUG MACAFEE,VP-DRLG
JOHN NICHOLSON,VP-GEOL/GEOPHY
SHANNON SAVOY,VP-PROD
JOHN SEEGER,VP-DECOMMISSIONING OPERS
CRIS SHERMAN,CAO
LAFAYETTE,LA OFFICE - 2014 W PINHOOK RD
STE 800 70508 PH 337 354-8000
FAX 337 354-8052

FILGO JESSE E,OIL & GAS EXPLOR
3404 COMANCHE TRACE DR
KERRVILLE,TX 78028 PH 830 896-2546

FIN OIL INC SEE
TOTALFINAELF E&P USA,INC

FINA LA TERRE SEE
TOTALFINAELF E&P USA,INC

FINA OIL AND CHEMICAL COMPANY SEE
TOTALFINAELF E&P USA INC

FINGER OIL & GAS INC
PO BOX 543
CASTROVILLE,TX 78009
PH 210 710-1133 FAX 830 931-0550
JOE FINGER,PRES
FINGEROILANDGAS@YAHOO.COM

FINISH THOMPSON INC
921 GREENGARDEN RD
ERIE,PA 16501-1525 PH 800 934-9384
FAX 814 455-8518 WWW.FINISHTHOMPSON.COM
FTI@FINISHTHOMPSON.COM
TROY HURLEY,SLS MGR

FINITE RESOURCES LTD
PO BOX 536
HARRISBURG,IL 62946-0536 PH 618 252-3733
FAX 618 252-0641
KEVIN W REIMER,PRES
ROBERT C WILSON,SECY
ARIANNE PHELPS,ACCT
LIN PAYNE,OFC MGR

FINK DARRELL M,CONS PETR ENGR,IND OPR
1 CHATEAU AUSONE DR
KENNER,LA 70065-2005 PH 504 456-8884

FINKELSTEIN PARTNERS,LTD
PO BOX 1101
HOUSTON,TX 77251-1101 PH 713 654-0144
FAX 713 654-1524
JEMC@MEDGRP.COM WWW.MEDGRP.COM
ROBERT J PILEGGE,EXEC DIR

JERELD E MCQUEEN,DIR OIL & GAS

FIRE BOSS OF LA/SAFETY & HEALTH ASSOC
7905 HIGHWAY 90 W
NEW IBERIA,LA 70560-7651 PH 318 365-6729
PH 318 233-3110 800-737-7233
FAX 318 367-6655
DEBBIE ROMERO,PRES
ANGELA BROUSSARD,PURCHASING/SLS
KIMBERLY BROUSSARD,ACCT
BLAINE ROMERO,VP,MGR
CHRIS FORE,SALES

FIRESIDE OIL & GAS INC
PO BOX 127
WEST MONROE,LA 71294-0127
PH 318 366-8465 FAX 318 387-4702
RICHARD D NORMAN SR
RICHARD D NORMAN JR

FIRST ENERGY CORP
PO BOX 799,2ND & MAURY STS
RICHMOND,VA 23206-0799 PH 804 233-8370
FAX 804 232-9347
LEWIS W PARKER JR,PRES
LOFTON D ALLEN,VP
WM E STEARNS III,GEN MGR

FIRST ROCK INC
600 LEOPARD ST STE 1800,THE 600 BLDG
CORPUS CHRISTI,TX 78401
PH 361 884-0791 FAX 361 884-0863
FIRSTROCKINC@MSN.COM

FIRST SOUTH INVESTMENTS
PO BOX 1769
RIDGELAND,MS 39158 PH 601 278-6088
WILLIAM (BILL) B MCHENRY,JR,PRES/BD CHMN
WBMCJR@FIRSTSOUTHINVESTMENTS.COM

FISCHER PETROLEUM CORPORATION
PO BOX 2982
VICTORIA,TX 77902-2982 PH 361 570-6556
FAX 361 570-6553
JOHN A ZIMMERMAN,PRES
I BROCK,SECY/TREAS

FISHER THOMAS JOHN,LAW OFFICE
ATTORNEY AT LAW
600 LEOPARD STE 1720
CORPUS CHRISTI,TX 78401
PH 361 882-2091 FAX 815 927-0298
WWW.TOMFISHERLAW.COM TOM@TOMFISHER-
LAW.COM

FISHER-SHEEHAN ENTERPRISES
31 LAKEVIEW CIR
CANFIELD,OH 44406 PH 330 206-9028
JJSPVNY@AOL.COM
JEFF FISHER-SHEEHAN,PRTNR
SUSAN FISHER-SHEEHAN,PRTNR

FISK/MEI INSPECTION SERVICES,INC
2 NORTHPOINT DR STE 700
HOUSTON,TX 77060-3200 PH 281 913-1700
FAX 281 548-0909 SALES@FISKMEI.COM
WWW.FISKMEI.COM
ROBERT G DAVIS,PRES
SCOTT BOSTON,EXEC VP
ROBERT L WOODUM,GEN MGR
GLENDA WARMAN,OPS MGR
RITA ADCOCK,ACCT MGR

FITE DAVID E,NATL GAS CONS & IND LDMN
PO BOX 1231
SHREVEPORT,LA 71163-1231 PH 318 424-0544

FITE OIL & GAS,INC
PO BOX 1231
SHREVEPORT,LA 71163-1231 PH 318 424-0544
FAX 318 424-1057
DAVID E FITE,PRES
WALT PIPKIN,VP

FIVE J.A.B. INC
PO BOX 1063
TOMBALL,TX 77377-1063
PH 281 356-7767 FAX 281 252-0575
WWW.FIVEJAB.COM
JAMES A BOHANNON JR,PRES
JAMES A BOHANNON III,VP
JENNIFER BOHANNON,SECY/TREAS
JENNIFERBOHANNON@FIVEJAB.COM

FLAG REDFERN OIL COMPANY SEE
KERR-MCGEE CORPORATION

FLANAGAN AND WILEY,CONSULTING ENGRS SEE
WINTER GARDEN ENGINEERING

FLARE RESOURCES,INC SEE DISCOVER E&P LLC

FLASH GAS & OIL SOUTHWEST,INC
19341 N 10TH ST
COVINGTON,LA 70433
PH 985 626-8758 FAX 985 626-8767
FLITCHLITER@FLASHGASANDOIL.COM
STEVEN G HALLER,PRES
FRED LITCHLITER,BUS DEV MGR

FLECK MATHER & STRUTZ,PLLP SEE
CROWLEY FLECK,PLLP

FLEET ENERGY,LLC
PO BOX 1475
ANGLETON,TX 77516-1475 PH 214 354-5224
JACK FLEET,MNGNG PRTNR

FLEET OIL & GAS LLC
PO BOX 703908
DALLAS,TX 75370 PH 214 668-5646
JOHN FLEET   JF@FLEETCO.COM

FLEETWOOD RESOURCES
PO BOX 51874, 233 LA RUE FRANCE
LAFAYETTE,LA 70505 PH 337 237-4842
FAX 337 237-4847
JIM DIEHL DIEHLLAND@AOL.COM

FLETCHER PETROLEUM CORP
PO BOX 2147,101 LOTTIE LN STE 5
FAIRHOPE,AL 36533-2147 PH 251 990-0733
FAX 251 990-0737
WWW.FLETCHERPETROLEUM.COM
INFO@FLETCHERPETROLEUM.COM
DANIEL P SLOAN,PRES/COO
RICK FLETCHER,CHRMN/CEO
CHRISTEN BURKETT,OFC MGR

FLINT BERLIN CO.
PO BOX 7238
SHREVEPORT,LA 71137 PH 318 424-2153
FAX 318 425-3550 CHOCTAW1@SHREVE.NET
FLINT BERLIN,OWNER,PRES
BUCKIE BERLIN,VP,SECY
ROCKY BERLIN,PROD ENGR
SPORT,LA OFFICE - PO BOX 7238,71137

FLINT HILLS RESOURCES,LP
CORPUS CHRISTI,TX REFINING COMPLEX
PO BOX 2608
CORPUS CHRISTI,TX 78403-2608
PH 361 241-4811

FLINTROCK RESOURCES MANAGEMENT,INC
2802 FLINTROCK TRACE STE B-102

AUSTIN,TX 78738 PH 512 371-4150
FAX 512 371-4101
WWW.FLINTROCKRESOURCES.COM
CHRIS BERRY,PRES/CEO
JIM DARWIN,VP
CATHIE DARWIN,ADMIN DIR
CATHIE@FLINTROCKRESOURCES.COM

FLORES & RUCKS,INC SEE
OCEAN ENERGY,INC

FLORES WILLIAM S,GEOLOGIST
5501 LONGMONT DR
HOUSTON,TX 77056 PH 337 232-2305
FAX 337 232-4243 PH 337 278-7536
WSFLORES@AOL.COM

FLOW SPECIALTIES INC
1262 GRIMMET DR
SHREVEPORT,LA 71107-6604 PH 318 425-5862
FAX 318 221-1321
G M KELLEY,PRES
MINDEN,LA OFFICE - PO BOX 1340,71058-1340
PH 318 377-5161

FLOWERS DAVIS LAW FIRM
1021 ESE LOOP 323 STE 200
TYLER,TX 75701
PH 903 534-8063 FAX 903 534-1650
WWW.FLOWERSDAVIS.COM
WWW.ETEXTITLE.COM
CELIA C FLOWERS CCF@FLOWERSDAVIS.COM

FLOWERS MICHAEL W,LAND LEASES
121 S BROADWAY STE 671
TYLER,TX 75702 PH 903 597-7299
FAX 903 657-8326

FLOYD ENERGY LTD
PO BOX 52107
MIDLAND,TX 79710 PH 432 683-3553
ROBERT W FLOYD,MGR

FLOYD HERSHEL,JR,IND PETR LDMN
PO BOX 975
RUSTON,LA 71273-0975
PH 318 255-1779 EHFLOYD@SUDDENLINK.NET

FLOYD OIL COMPANY
863 WASHINGTON ST
RALEIGH,NC 27605 PH 919 832-7560
FAX 919 832-7678
ALEXFLOYD@FLOYDOILCOMPANY.COM
ALEXANDER G FLOYD,PRES
ALEXANDER G FLOYD JR,VP
CHRISTINA W FLOYD,VP

FLUID CRANE & CONSTRUCTION,INC
PO BOX 9586,HWY 90 & ROSS RD
NEW IBERIA,LA 70562-9586 PH 318 364-6191
800 447-2384 FAX 318 364-0410
ED DOMINGUES,PRES

FLUID RECOVERY SERVICES,LLC
DISPOSAL OF PRODUCTION BRINES &
FRACURING FLUIDS
PO BOX 232,5035 RT 110
CREEKSIDE,PA 15732-0232 PH 724 349-8600
FAX 724 349-8601 HARTP@FLUIDRECOVERY.COM
PAUL HART,PRES
BECKY SNYDER,OPERS MGR

FLUOR CANADA LTD
55 SUNPARK PLAZA SE
CALGARY,AB,CAN T2X 3R4
PH 403 537-4000 FAX 403 537-4222
GARY DONOVAN,V P,BUSINESS DEV & SALES

FLUOR CONSTRUCTORS INTERNATIONAL,INC
6700 LAS COLINAS BLVD
IRVING,TX 75039 PH 469 398-7000
RIC CARTER,PRES

FLUOR CORPORATION
1 FLUOR DANIEL DR
ALISO VIEJO,CA 92698-1000 PH 714 975-2000
DAVID S TAPPAN,JR,CHRMN OF BD
L G MCCRAW,PRES,CEO
NAD A PETERSON,SR VP,SECY
P JOSEPH TRIMBLE,SR VP,LAW
ROBERT L GUYETT,SR VP,CFO
CHARLES J BRADLEY,VP,HUMAN RESOURCES
JAMES O ROLLANS,VP,CORP COMMUNICATIONS
J ROBERT FLUOR II,VP,CORP RELS
WILLIAM M HOFACRE,VP,FIN PLNG,ANALYSIS

FLUOR HOUSTON OPERATIONS CENTER
PO BOX 5014,ONE FLUOR DANIEL DR
SUGAR LAND,TX 77487-5014 PH 281 263-1000
JIM HEAVNER,SR VP,UPSTREAM BUS LINE
DAVID SEATON,GROUP PRES/ENERGY &
CHEMICALS
TOM ZACHMAN,VP,OPERS
DAN PALOMINO,GEN MGR,HOUSTON OPERS
CHARLIE SANDS,SR VP,UPSTREAM OPERS
MIKE PIWETZ,MGR,HOUSTON PROCESS OPERS

FMC INVALCO SEE
INVALCO PRODUCTS

FMC TECHNOLOGIES
1602 WAGNER AVE
ERIE,PA 16514 PH 814 898-5000
FAX 814 899-8927
MEASUREMENT.SOLUTIONS@FMCTI.COM
WWW.FMCTECHNOLOGIES.COM/
MEASUREMENTSOLUTIONS

FOCUS ENERGY INC
PO BOX 18496
OKLAHOMA CITY,OK 73154-0496
PH 713 787-0024 FAX 713 787-9224
DERRY D ESSARY,CEO
SAMUEL G MOSELEY,PRES
TOM FANNING,CFO
DAVID DALE,ENGRG MGR
KEVIN PFISTER,LAND MGR
OKLAHOMA CITY,OK OPERATIONS OFFICE - 4100
PERIMETER CENTER DR STE 202,73112-2311
PH 405 951-7545 FAX 405 951-7548
RICK HART,VP,OPERS

FOLEY OIL PROPERTIES
P O BOX 1465,406 LIBERTY RD
NATCHEZ,MS 39121-1465 PH 601 442-8072

FONDREN OIL COMPANY
3 RIVERWAY STE 120
HOUSTON,TX 77056-1910 PH 713 623-0809
FAX 713 960-8128
W W FONDREN,III,PRES

FONTENOT PETROLEUM LAND SERVICES,INC SEE
ACADIAN LAND SERVICES,LLC

FONTENOT RAYMOND,IND GEOL
8107 SIDNEY GAUTREAUX RD
ABBEVILLE,LA 70510-4362 PH 337 893-2800

FORAN BILL,EXPLORATION
PO BOX 311595,899 EDGEWATER TERRACE
NEW BRAUNFELS,TX 78131-1595
PH 830 625-6225 FAX 830 625-0262
BFORAN@SATX.RR.COM

FORAN MICHAEL C
200 LAMONT ST
SAN ANTONIO,TX 78209
PH 210 804-1244 FAX 210 804-1677
MMCF34@SBCGLOBAL.NET

FORAN OIL COMPANY SEE
MATADOR RESOURCES COMPANY

FORAYS OIL & GAS COMPANY
12122 CARRIAGE HILL DR
HOUSTON,TX 77077-2509 PH 281 772-0593
FAX 281 596-8836
ANDRE BOUTTE,CONSLT GEOL
ANDREBOUTTE@GMAIL.COM

FORCENERGY INC SEE
FOREST OIL CORPORATION

FOREST OIL CORPORATION SEE
SABINE OIL AND GAS LLC

FORESTAR MINERALS LLC
1801 BROADWAY STE 600
DENVER,CO 80202 PH 303 297-2200
FAX 303 297-2204 WWW.FORESTARGROUP.COM

FORMAN ENERGY,LTD
PO BOX 340346
COLUMBUS,OH 43234-0346 PH 614 717-9262
FAX 614 717-9262
AMY L LANG,PRTNR
JOHN L FORMAN,PRTNR JLFORMAN@ATT.NET

FORNEY & COMPANY
600 LEOPARD ST STE 1614
CORPUS CHRISTI,TX 78401 PH 361 884-7721
FAX 361 887-9012 FORNEY01@SPRYNET.COM
CHARLES R FORNEY,PRES

FORNEY & MCCOMBS SEE
MCCOMBS ENERGY

FORNEY OIL CORP SEE
FORNEY & MCCOMBS

FORT WORTH NATURAL GAS,INC
3611 WEST PIONEER PKWY #B
ARLINGTON,TX 76013
PH 817 303-7473 FAX 817 277-7473
BILL VAHRENKAMP,PRES
BILL@FWNGINC.COM
JOSH VAHRENKAMP,VP FINANCE
CHAD VAHRENKAMP,VP OPERS

FORTENBERY OPERATING COMPANY,INC
PO BOX 1183
NATCHEZ,MS 39121 PH 601 442-6011
MARK FORTENBERY,PRES
LANIUS R FORTENBERY,SECY/TREAS

FORTITUDE EXPLORATION COMPANY
PO BOX 5417
NAVARRE,FL 32566-0417 PH 850 939-6966
FAX 281 749-8108
GREGORY P DILLON,PRES

FORTUNE NATURAL RESOURCES CORPORATION
16400 DALLAS PKWY STE 100
DALLAS,TX 75248-2609
PH 214 368-6100 FAX 214 365-9695

FOSSIL OIL COMPANY, LLC
2500 WILCREST DR STE 405-415
HOUSTON,TX 77042 PH 713 978-7986
FAX 713 715-6227 WWW.FOSSILOIL.COM
DENNIS R KITTLER,PRES/FOUNDER
DENNIS@FOSSILOIL.COM
DONALD J TIMKO,GEOL
LES H KITTLER,OPERS

LISA KITTLER,CLIENT & PR
SHARON NORSCH KITTLER,HR
JOSEPH G SOLIZ,CORP ATTY
JAMES E FULP JR,MKTG/WEBMSTR CONSLT
E J GILBER,DRLG ENGR
KEVIN B HILL,GEOPHY

FOSTER & ASSOCIATES,INC
675 BERING DR STE 800
HOUSTON,TX 77057-2129 PH 713 266-2883
FAX 713 266-4296
FOSTERINC@JUSTDRILLIT.COM
LARRY D CORBIN,PRES
L M CORKY ATKINS,VP
GEORGE NEMETZ
RANDALL RIEPE
KURT SOMMER
HUBERT TETT

FOSTER & HARVEY,P.C.
3586 HWY 181 N
FLORESVILLE,TX 78114-5921 PH 830 393-6496
FAX 830 393-9426 FOSTERANDHARVEY.COM
ROBBY@FOSTERANDHARVEY.COM
ROBERT E HARVEY IV,PRTNR
KRYSTA A BARING,PRTNR
MIDLAND,TX OFFICE - 3300 N A ST BLDG 7
STE 120,79705
PH 432 704-5040 FAX 432 704-5043
RICHARD W FOSTER JR,PRTNR
RICHARD@FOSTERANDHARVEY.COM
LABECCA S BUSELLI,PRTNR
TIMOTHY W FOSTER,PRTNR

FOSTER BRAYTON P,CONSULTING GEOL
4442 LOWER COVERT RD
TRUMANSBURG,NY 14886-9305 PH 607 387-5958
FAX 607 387-5958 BFOSTER4442@AOL.COM

FOSTER J L
4106 W HILLSBORO
EL DORADO,AR 71730-6757 PH 870 863-7980

FOSTER NEWTON
25206 E 30TH ST S
BLUE SPRINGS,MO 64015 PH 806 249-4605

FOSTER-BROWN COMPANY
PO BOX 15208, 1888 HUDSON CIRCLE STE 12
MONROE,LA 71207-5208
PH 318 325-5840 FAX 318 325-5841
W DENIS BROWN,PRES DENIS@FOBROCO.COM

FOTIADES MINERAL INTERESTS
2434 ST CHARLES AVE APT 401
NEW ORLEANS,LA 70130 PH 504 895-1694
A E ARMBRUSTER,JR,MGR

FOUNDATION OIL CO,INC
PO BOX 131357
HOUSTON,TX 77219 PH 713 807-9200
FAX 713 513-5671
STEPHEN M WINDLE,PRES
SMWINDLE@FOUNDATIONOIL.COM

FOUR CORNERS DRILLING CO SEE
BIG A WELL SERVICE

FOUR H OIL FIELD RENTAL
PO BOX 2344
SPRING,TX 77383-2344 PH 281 260-0880
A R HENDON,OWNER
FREDA HENDON,TREAS

FOUR RIVERS EXPLORATION,INC
PO BOX 18400
NATCHEZ,MS 39122-8400 PH 318 339-6003

FAX 318 339-4999
CURTIS P BEARD,PRES
C BRET BEARD,VP
M KEVIN FLOWERS,SECY/TREAS

FOUR SANDS PRODUCTION CO
1201 BROOKWOOD DR
EL DORADO,AR 71730 PH 870 814-7627
MIKE MEEKS,PROD

FOUR STAR DEVELOPMENT CORP
6208 HIGHWAY 134
EPPS,LA 71237-9362 PH 318 388-0728

FOUR STAR OIL COMPANY
BOX 308
OIL CITY,LA 71061-0308 PH 318 995-7198
G M GANT,OWNER
MAURY WOOLDRIDGE,SUPT

FOUR STARR PRODUCTION,LLC
8235 DOUGLAS AVE STE 525
DALLAS,TX 75225-6093 PH 214 691-9436
FAX 214 360-7455
FRANK PAUL KING,CEO
DON MALLORY,FLD OPERS-KAUFMAN CO
JOEY HERNANDEZ,FLD OPERS-CROCKETT CO

FOUR WINDS LOGISTICS LLC
COMPLETE FRAC SAND LOGISTICS COMPANY
13719 SAN PEDRO AVE STE 140
SAN ANTONIO,TX 78232 PH 210 593-3290
WWW.FOURWINDSLOGISTICS.COM
SHANNON SMITH
SSMITH@FOURWINDSLOGISTICS.COM

FOURNET JOHN D,SR
102 ROYAL GARDEN TER
MADISON,MS 39110-7637 PH 601 707-3189

FOWLER CLARA OR REFORD
PO BOX 413
RED RIVER,NM 87558-0413 PH 575 754-6368
BATON ROUGE,LA (WINTER) OFFICE - 6222
SUMMER LAKE DR 70817 PH 225 753-3400

FOX BRUCE W,PETR GEOL
121 S BROADWAY AVE STE 710
TYLER,TX 75702-7284 PH 903 592-1301
FAX 903 531-2302

FOX HAMLIN G,GEOL
1115 BARBARA
TYLER,TX 75701-7133 PH 972 593-6960

FOX HEWITT B,INC,OIL & GAS EXPLOR & PROD
545 N UPPER BROADWAY ST STE 1101
CORPUS CHRISTI,TX 78401-0678
PH 361 882-1021 FAX 361 884-4622
DOUGLAS S STAN FOX,VP LAND,SECY
OPER MGR
STANFOXLANDMAN@YAHOO.COM

FOX PETROLEUM ENGINEERING
1064 GREENSVIEW DR
WOOSTER,OH 44691-1617 PH 330 264-5965
FOX@SSSNET.COM
WALTER F FOX,PE

FP INC SEE
LOMAK PETROLEUM INC.

FRANCIS DRILLING FLUIDS
PO BOX 1694
CROWLEY,LA 70527 PH 337 783-8685
PH 800 252-3104 FAX 337 783-0059
WWW.FDFLTD.COM INFO@FDFLTD.COM
CROWLEY,LA OFFICE - 240 JASMINE RD 70526
DOUG CHAPPLE,PRES,COO

JUDE GREGGORY,CFO
BARRY CHARPENTIER,VP FLUIDS & CLEANING
FREDDIE RICHARD,VP PNEUMATICS MGR
JOHN FRANCIS,VP SALES/MARKETING
RAY BROWN,VP BUS DEV
INTRACOASTAL CITY,LA OFFICE - 9711 EXXON
(PVT) RD 70510 PH 800 252-3104
LAFAYETTE,LA OFFICE - 100 ASMA BLVD
STE 151,70508 PH 337 521-6825
SUSAN BOUDREAUX,CONTROLLER
STEVE SCHAAF,IT MGR
LAKE CHARLES,LA OFFICE - 3220 METRIC DR
70665 PH 866 960-4333
BERWICK,LA OFFICE - 2600 2ND ST 70342
PH 800 960-6630
FERELL STROTHER,PLANT MGR
CAMERON,LA OFFICE - 120 REX ST 70631
PH 800 960-6640
FOURCHON,LA OFFICE - 180 17TH ST
FOURCHON E,GOLDEN MEADOW,LA 70352
PH 800 638-3893
ALICE,TX OFFICE - 208 W MAIN 78332
PH 800 960-6685
FAUSTINO VILLARREAL,PLANT MGR
ODESSA,TX OFFICE - 3215 W MURPHY 79763
PH 800 960-6685
FREDDIE ARRIOLA,PLANT MGR
DAYTON,TX OFFICE - 7311 HWY 321
77535 PH 800 960-6670
DARREN DORSEY,PLANT MGR
KERMIT,TX OFFICE - 1149 W AUSTIN ST 79745
PH 800 960-6685
WARD WOODARD,PLANT MGR
VICTORIA,TX OFFICE - 47 BLUE QUAIL CT
77903 PH 866 711-4995
CLINTON,OK OFFICE - 1101 SMITH INDUSTRIAL
PARK 73601 PH 866 378-4531
ROBERT LEBLANC,PLANT MGR
SALLISAW,OK OFFICE - 1615 W LENNINGTON RD
74955 PH 800 756-5602
ROCK SPRINGS,WY OFFICE - 3029 KILLPECKER
82901 PH 866 982-2829
ALVIN SPRINGS,PLANT MGR

FRANCIS ENERGY CORPORATION
P O BOX 16752
JACKSON,MS 39236-6752 PH 601 956-0328
JOSEPH F FRANCIS,JR,PRES

FRANCISCO J W,OIL OPR
100 OAKWOOD DR
LAFAYETTE,LA 70503-4434 PH 318 232-1720

FRANKE INTERESTS,INC
C/O THE FROST NATIONAL BANK
PO BOX 1600
SAN ANTONIO,TX 78296-1600 PH 210 220-4901
FAX 210 220-4377

FRANKEL,FRANK,ESTATE OF
5701 WOODWAY DR STE 200
HOUSTON,TX 77057-1505 PH 713 623-4646
FAX 713 623-4648 HARDINGFRANKEL@AOL.COM
HARDING S FRANKEL,EXECUTOR

FRANKEL,HARDING S,IND OIL PROD
5701 WOODWAY DR STE 200
HOUSTON,TX 77056-5785 PH 713 623-4646
FAX 713 623-4648 HARDINGFRANKEL@AOL.COM
HARDING S FRANKEL,OWNER

FRANKLIN CONSULTING
1102 GREENBRIAR RD
LAFAYETTE,LA 70503-3654
PH 337 984-8207 FAX 337 984-4341
JOSEPH FRANKLIN FRANKLINGEO@COX.NET

FRANKLIN GAS & OIL CO,LLC
PO BOX 1005
WOOSTER,OH 44691-7005 PH 330 264-8739
FAX 330 264-0796
J C MORGAN SR,PRES
J C MORGAN JR,VP,EXPL,DEV

FRANKS CASING CREW & RENTAL TOOLS,INC
PO BOX 51729,700 E VEROT SCHOOL RD
LAFAYETTE,LA 70505-1729
PH 337 233-0303 PH 800 833-7265
WWW.FRANKSINTERNATIONAL.COM
KEITH MOSING,PRES/CEO
ROBERT GILBERT,EXEC VP/COO
MIKE WEBRE,VP ENGRG
BRUCE COULOMBE,CORP COUNSEL
JOHN GUARISCO,CONTROLLER
ADRIENNE FONTENOT,EXEC ASST
JOAN CRAFT,LEGAL/EXEC ASST
- ENGINEERING DEPT -
REESE COMEAUX,ENGRG DEPT MGR
JEREMY ANGELLE,SPEC OPERS DEPT MGR
ROBBIE THIBODEAUX,SPECIAL OPERS ENGRG MGR
- OPERATIONS -
CORY COLE,OPERS MGR
RAY BARRILLEAUX,ASST OPERS MGR
BRAD MOSING,OPERS MGR-KILGORE/LAUREL
STACY CHARLEVILLE,COMPLETIONS DEPT MGR
DEWAYNE ARCENEAUX,OPERS DISPATCH MGR
JOE QUEBEDEAUX,CASING OPERS MGR
RANDY MENARD,CASING SHOP DEPT MGR
WAYNE CHAMPAGNE,LAYDOWN DEPT MGR
ELI PREJEAN,VEHICLE MAINT MGR
RUSTY HERRING,FLEET MGR
VOORHIES SHORT,MAINT MGR
BRAD BREAUD,HAMMER DEPT MGR
KARL MCGEE,STAB RITE DEPT MGR
LANE BOUDREAUX,FILL UP TOOL DEPT MGR
BRANDON SPELL,CRT DEPT MGR
CODY BOUILLION,INSP & REPAIR DEPT SUPV
JOHN LETHBRIDGE,INTL ASSETS MGR
PHILLIP CHAMPAGNE,DOMESTIC ASSETS MGR
SHANE ARCENEAUX,DEEPWATER COOR
DONALD FONTENOT,DEEPWATER COOR
BRYAN ISTRE,DEEPWATER COOR
- ADMINISTRATION DEPT -
MARK SIBILLE,DIR STRATEGIC PLANNING
BRANDI LEDET,HR DEPT MGR
RYAN LEMAIRE,CONTRACTS DEPT MGR
SAM WHITE,CONTRACTS/BIDS COOR
ERICH MOSING,MRKTNG DEPT MGR
JACKE WEST,TRAINING DIR
- SAFETY -
CLIFF ROBERTS,SAFETY DIR
- QA -
JUDE BOUDREAUX,QUALITY ASSURANCE DIR
- MANUFACTURING -
CURT JONES,MANUFACTURING DIR
JUDE PATIN,MANUFACTURING DEPT MGR
CRAIG GREGORY,PROD DEPT MGR
BJ TASSIN,SOG PRODUCTION DEPT MGR
- PIPE -

DONNIE CAIN,PIPE DEPT MGR
JOHNNIE STINSON,PIPE YARD MGR
CRIS MORGAN,ACCT REP
JEREL WEST,ACCT REP
DEBBIE ZANETTI,ACCT REP
KILEY CUSIMANO,ACCT REP
MIKE BOUDREAUX,ACCT REP
- SALES -
LEONARD CASTILLE,VP SALES
TOM HEBERT,ACCT REP
CULLEN RICHARD,ACCT REP
LENNETTE CAS CASTEX,ACCT REP
BUDDY GUILLORY,ACCT REP
RAY RICHARD,ACCT REP
CRAIG ROMERO,ACCT REP
LUCAS MARKS,ACCT REP
DAVID HELMICK,TECH SUPT
PORT OF IBERIA OFFICE - 3500 SEGURA RD
70560 PH 337 560-5552
KUMAR MALLENHALI,RISER FAB MGR
MARTY CANNON,POI OPERS MGR
HOUMA,LA OFFICE - 1727 COTEAU RD 70364
PH 985 876-2392
BROOKS BLAKEMAN,LOCATION MGR
NEW ORLEANS,LA OFFICE - 1010 COMMON ST
STE 2410 70417 PH 504 525-3421
COVINGTON,LA OFFICE -1011 N CAUSEWAY BLVD
STE 14 70417 PH 985 951-7980
JIM ABLES,LOCATION MGR
RANDY RAYMOND,ACCT REP
JASON BOURG,ACCT REP
LAUREL,MS OFC-59 MANAGEMENT RD,ELLISVILLE
39437 PH 601 649-9555
DAVID SCOTT,LOCATION MGR
ALVIN,TX OFFICE - 3735 E HWY 6 77511
PH 281 331-1501
TERRY BARTUSKA,LOCATION MGR
BRYAN,TX OFFICE - 4100 CARRABBA RD 77808
PH 979 778-8700
JUSTIN CONRAD,LOCATION MGR
BURLESON,TX OFFICE - 2324 S IH 35 W 76028
PH 817 447-6000
RICHARD BOLTON,LOCATION MGR
CORPUS CHRISTI,TX OFFICE -6605 LEOPARD ST
78469 PH 361 289-1955
TODD ALFORD,LOCATION MGR
HOUSTON,TX OFFICE - 10260 WESTHEIMER RD
STE 700 77042 PH 281 966-7300
KEITH MOSING,PRES/CEO/CHAIRMAN
JON VEVERICA,VP TX OPERS
MIKE MATHER,PIPE ACCT MGR
TOMMY LEBLANC,SLS MGR
LEWIS JONES,PIPE ACCT REP
BILL SEAGROVES,ACCT REP/BID COOR
TOBY PITRE,ACCT REP
DREW URUSKI,ACCT REP
JOHN PITTS,ACCT REP
SIDNEY LONGMAN,TECH SUPT
SCOTT SHERROD,TECH SUPT
KILGORE,TX OFFICE - 2405 HWY 135 N 75662
PH 903 984-0261
RODNEY TURMAN,LOCATION MGR
LAREDO,TX OFFICE - 122 OIL PATCH RD 78041
PH 956 717-8500
RICK JARVIS,LOCATION MGR
GREENSBORO,PA OFC-153 DORA VILLAGE MAIN

ST,15338 PH 724 943-3243
MONTGOMERY,PA OFFICE - 234 PARK DR 17752
PH 570 547-0525
JEFF REYNOLDS,REGIONAL MGR
MASSILLON,OH OFFICE - 607 1ST ST SW 44646
PH 330 236-4264
MANUEL BARRIGA,LOCATION MGR

FRANKS EXPLORATION COMPANY,LLC
PO BOX 7665,1312 N HEARNE
SHREVEPORT,LA 71137-7665
PH 318 221-2688 FAX 318 221-7720
BOBBY E JELKS,PRES
F DRAKE LEE,GEN COUNSEL
FAITH N GILBERT,SECY/TREAS
- EXPLORATION DEPARTMENT -
PH 318 221-2688 FAX 318 459-2935
EDWARD YARBROUGH,EXPL MGR
JAMES LIGHT,LAND MGR

FRANKS INTERNATIONAL
10260 WESTHEIMER STE 700
HOUSTON,TX 77042 PH 281 966-7300
PH 800 827-6020 FAX 281 558-3348
WWW.FRANKSINTERNATIONAL.COM
KEITH MOSING,CHRMN,CEO
JOHN WHEELER,VP & COO
ALAIN MIRAMON,VP/LATIN AMERICA
JOHN WALKER,VP/NORTH AMERICA
MARK MARGAVIO,VP,FIN
JENNY REED,HUMAN RESOURCES MGR
DICK RADER,VP,BUS DEV

FRANKS TONG SERVICE,INC
PO BOX 94580
OKLAHOMA CITY,OK 73143-4580
PH 405 672-8064 800 522-4687
FAX 405 677-9872
JON VEVERICA,VP
GREG PARRISH,AREA MGR
HENRY LANTZ,OPERS MGR
PHIL NORTON,SLS REP
DANIEL ROBERTS,SLS REP
JIMMY ARNOLD,SLS REPR
SCOTT BEACH,SAFETY COORD
ELK CITY,OK OFFICE - RT 4,BOX 277
73644 PH 580 225-0028 FAX 580 225-0027
JERRY HEMINGWAY,MGR
SCOTT CLOYD,SLS REP
MCALESTER,OK OFFICE - RT 6,BOX 285
74501 PH 918 423-0688 FAX 918 423-0961
GREG PARISH,AREA MGR
JOHNNY NICHOLS,MGR

FRANKS WESTATES SERVICES,INC
PO BOX 5,1304 SOUTH 1220 EAST
VERNAL,UT 84078-0005
PH 435 789-1698 FAX 435 789-1007
KEITH MOSING,CHRMN,CEO
JIM BREAUX,VP,COO
LARRY STEVENSON,MGR
EVANSTON,WY OFFICE - PO BOX 1514
105 MEADOW DR,82930
PH 307 789-1801 FAX 307 789-1754
STEVE MENSING,MGR
CASPER,WY OFFICE - 2110 PYRITE RD,82604
PH 307 234-1796 FAX 307 235-8122
STEVE GRISWOLD,MGR
ROCK SPRINGS,WY OFFICE - PO BOX 1018
82902 PH 307 382-0930 FAX 307 382-0699

BOB FINK,MGR
GRAND JUNCTION,CO OFFICE - 2785 RIVERSIDE
PKWY 81501 PH 970 245-5365
FAX 970 241-9045
JIM RAPOSA,MGR
CHEYENNE,WY OFFICE - 8140 HUTCHINS DR
82007 PH 307 634-2090 FAX 307 634-2101
PAUL NELSON,MGR

FRANTZEN DAN R,CONS GEOL
15 HEATHERSTONE DR
LAFAYETTE,LA 70508
PH 337 269-9135 PH 337 654-4140
WWW.ODEOFANOILMAN.COM
DANR.FRANTZEN@LUSFIBER.NET

FRAZIER KENNETH W,PETR ENGR
P O BOX 7338,434 APACHE TRAIL
SHREVEPORT,LA 71137-7338 PH 318 221-0605
PH 318 227-2212

FRAZIER OIL & GAS CO,INC
8720 RIVER RD
ABBEVILLE,LA 70510 PH 713 772-9910
T H FRAZIER JR

FRAZIER OIL PROPERTIES,LLC
800 BERING DR STE 150
HOUSTON,TX 77057-2181
PH 713 789-0008 FAX 713 782-9967
WWW.FRAZIEROILPROPERTIES.COM
GREGORY R FRAZIER,CPL,PRTNR
GFRAZIER@FRAZIEROILPROPERTIES.COM
DAVID J FRAZIER,PRTNR
DFRAZIER@FRAZIEROILPROPERTIES.COM

FREDDY'S WELL SERVICE,INC
PO BOX 124
VICTORIA,TX 77902-0124 PH 361 578-4559
FAX 361 578-6062
RICHARD FLORES,PRES
JOHN FUENTEZ,VP
FEDERICO P FLORES,OPERS MGR

FREEDOM WELL SERVICES,LLC
3100 S GESSNER RD STE 210
HOUSTON,TX 77063 PH 832 379-2300
JEFF SHULSE,GEN MGR
PATRICK PAT HUDSON,MGR SLS/MKTG
PHUDSON@FREEDOMWELLS.COM
SKIPPER JOHNSTON,SLS
HOUMA,LA OFFICE - 161 THOMPSON RD 70363
PH 985 346-8089
HARVEY BERTINOT,MGR WIRELINE SVCS
GRANT BORNE,MGR P&A OPERS

FREEMAN J EARLE
12207 OVERCUP DR
HOUSTON,TX 77024-4229 PH 713 465-2165
EARLEFREEMAN@SBCGLOBAL.NET

FREEMAN JOHN C,ESTATE SEE
FREEMAN LIVING TRUST,JEAN L

FREEPORT-MCMORAN OIL & GAS COMPANY
700 MILAM ST STE 3100
HOUSTON,TX 77002 PH 800 934-6083
PH 713 579-6000 FAX 713 579-6611
WWW.FCX.COM

FREEZE TECHNOLOGY INTERNATIONAL LTD
PIPE FREEZING,LEAK LOCATING,PIPELINE MTNC
PO BOX 2329
AMARILLO,TX 79105-2329 PH 806 371-8854
800-321-7584 FAX 806 371-8856
WWW.FREEZE-PLUG.COM

MIKE R BRISTER,CEO
G H RIFFE,VP
HOUSTON,TX REG OFFICE - 15937 RIDLON
CHANNELVIEW,TX 77530 PH 281 452-1800
FAX 281 457-6641
TOM PARKER,GEN MGR
MUNITH,MI REG OFFICE - PO BOX 218
49259 PH 517 596-2629 FAX 517 596-3172
PAUL T MOONEY,VP

FRENCH ENERGY,INC SEE
BISON INVESTMENTS,LLC

FRIEDSON LAW GROUP
2043 KENDON DR E
PITTSBURG,PA 15221 PH 412 519-8527
DANIEL T FRIEDSON
DANIELFRIEDSON@GMAIL.COM

FRIERSON VON R,GEOL
6211 W NORTHWEST HWY APT 1807
DALLAS,TX 75225-3426 PH 281 497-0290

FRISCO OIL CORPORATION SEE
KEW DRILLING

FRITZ JOSEPH F,CONS GEOL
P O BOX 3467
JACKSON,MS 39207-3467 PH 601 354-1134

FRITZ OPERATING CO
P O BOX 3467
JACKSON,MS 39207-3467 PH 601 354-1134
JOSEPH F FRITZ,OWNER

FRMAJA CAPITOL GROUP
1000 DOBBINS RD
CORSICANA,TX 75110-2218 PH 214 874-7331
JAMES H GILL,ATTY AT LAW

FRONTERA EXPLORATION CONSULTANTS,INC
19240 REDLAND RD STE 250
SAN ANTONIO,TX 78259
PH 210 410-9587 FAX 210 824-6423
THOMAS E EWING,PRES,GEOL
TEWING@FRONTERAEXPLORATION.COM

FRONTIER LAND INC
601 S BOULDER AVE STE 810
TULSA,OK 74119-1308
PH 918 584-2050 FAX 918 584-2034
BRUCE BLEVINS,PRES
HEATHER BLEVINS,CFO
KURT W ZUMWALT,LAND MGR
DEANNA GLEESON,OFC MGR
SANDY SPRINGS,OK OFFICE - 1520 S 129TH
WEST AVE 74063 PH 918 514-4405
FAX 918 514-4409

FRONTIER RESOURCES INC
26 E OVERDALE DR
TALLMADGE,OH 44278-1932
PH 330 923-2900 FAX 330 923-4322
RONALD W MANUS,PRES
THOMAS R WOOD,VP

FRONTLINE ENERGY,INC
BROKERAGE,CONTRACTS,JOINT VENTURES
1716 LUBBOCK ST
HOUSTON,TX 77007-7718
PH 713 228-3577 FAX 713 228-3599
JDESPOT@FRONTLINEENERGY.COM
JUSTIN G DESPOT,PRES
JEFF VO,INFO OFCR

FROST NATIONAL BANK-OIL AND GAS TRUST
PO BOX 1600
SAN ANTONIO,TX 78296-1499 PH 210 220-4901

FAX 210 220-4377
BAKER DUNCAN,VP
PATRICIA ORMOND,ASST VP
TIM TERRY,ASST VP

FUGRO CHANCE INC
CIVIL ENGINEERINGS & SURVEYORS
PO BOX 52029,200 DULLES DR
LAFAYETTE,LA 70505-2029
PH 337 237-1300 FAX 337 237-0011
WWW.FUGROCHANCE.COM
INFO@FUGROCHANCE.COM
CHARLES G RHINEHART,PRES
BLAINE THIBODEAUX,CEO
J RIALS,EXEC MKTG MGR
GARRY FORESTIER,EXEC MKTG MGR
LARRY PREWITT,GEN MGR,MARINE
FINN RICHARD,MARINE OPERS MGR
RALPH HERIG,HUMAN RESOURCES MGR
HOUSTON,TX OFFICE - PH 713 346-3700
GARY MCKENZIE,INTL MARINE MGR
TONY GRAY,MARINE CONSTRUCTION MGR
J RASBERRY,QUALITY MGR

FUGRO CONSULTANTS,INC
916 SAMPSON ST STE E
WESTLAKE,LA 70669-5311 PH 337 439-1731
FAX 337 433-3313 DDUGAS@FUGRO.COM
WWW.FUGROCONSULTANTS.COM
DON DUGAS,III,BRANCH MGR

FUGRO GEOSERVICES,INC
200 DULLES DR
LAFAYETTE,LA 70506-3006 PH 337 237-2636
FAX 337 268-3221 WWW.FUGRO-USA.COM
THAMPTON@FUGRO.COM
TED D HAMPTON,VP

FUGRO-MCCLELLAND MARINE GEOSCIENCES,INC
P O BOX 740010
HOUSTON,TX 77274-0010 PH 713 778-5500
FAX 713 778-5573

FULLWOOD P D
119 N BEATON
CORSICANA,TX 75110-5216 PH 214 874-4546

FULTON MANAGEMENT CORPORATION
PO BOX 66802
HOUSTON,TX 77266-6802 PH 713 526-8919
FAX 713 526-9108
G M ROWE,III,PRES

FUQUA WILLIAM H,LEASE BROKER & LDMN
22 KINGS LAKE ESTATES BLVD
HUMBLE,TX 77346-4035 PH 337 232-6615
F2QQ@AOL.COM

FUTURA PETROLEUM INC
P O BOX 4792, 1509 LAMY LANE
MONROE,LA 71211-4792 PH 318 387-2458
JIM C STEELE,III,PRES
MIKE TOFT,LDMN

FUTURE ACQUISITION COMPANY LLC
PO BOX 1129
FULSHEAR,TX 77441 PH 832 831-3700
WWW.FUTUREACQ.COM
CARL PRICE,MNGNG DIR

FUTURE OIL & GAS,INC
204 WILDWOOD DRIVE
LAFAYETTE,LA 70503-4383 PH 318 981-1621
TIMOTHY R O'CONNOR,PRES

G & A INTERNATIONAL,INC
1686 GENERAL MOUTON

LAFAYETTE,LA 70508-3729 PH 337 266-9970
FAX 337 264-9908 GANDAINT@AOL.COM
GLENN E GILLEY,PRES,PROF ENGR
RON K ZILAR,STAFF ENGR

G & C CONSTRUCTION INTERNATIONAL,LLC
DBA G & C ENERGY SERVICES - EXPLORATION &
PRODUCTION FLUID TRANSPORT/DISPOSAL
222 ROAD CAMP RD
RUSTON,LA 71270 PH 318 202-5924
GANDC.CONSTRUCTION.INT@GMAIL.COM
JOHN MORGAN

G & H ASSOCIATES,INC
PO BOX 7931
TYLER,TX 75711-7931 PH 903 581-4050
FAX 903 581-2145 BGROUND@AOL.COM
BOB GROUND,CPL,PRES
AMANDA TRAMMELL,ADMIN LDMN

G & L WELL SERVICE,INC
PO BOX 2673
LAFAYETTE,LA 70502-2673 PH 337 886-2919
PH 800 848-4501
JOE LANDRY,PRES

G-R CONTRACTING INC
35479 SR 78
LEWISVILLE,OH 43754
PH 740 567-3217 FAX 740 567-3107
GARY A RUBEL,PRES
RICHARD SULSBERGER
JORDAN JONES

G-SQUARE PRODUCTION,INC
PO BOX 6304
TYLER,TX 75711-6304 PH 903 561-8289
FAX 903 581-4001
ANDY GUINN,PRES

GAEA SERVICES INC
622 W RHAPSODY STE A
SAN ANTONIO,TX 78216-2607
PH 210 341-5749 FAX 210 341-8285
JOHN DAVID PATTERSON,PRES
RAY C DUBOSE,PROD ENGR
SUSAN PALMER,CONTROLLER

GAEDEKE OIL & GAS OPERATING,LLC
3710 RAWLINS ST STE 1000
DALLAS,TX 75219 PH 214 373-3350
FAX 214 521-4680 WWW.GAEDEKE.COM

GAFFNEY CLINE & ASSOCIATES
5555 SAN FELIPE ST STE 550
HOUSTON,TX 77056 PH 713 850-9955
FAX 713 850-9966 GCAH@GAFFNEY-CLINE.COM
WWW.GAFFNEY-CLINE.COM
BILL CLINE,GRP CHIEF EXEC WH
RAWDON SEAGER,DEPUTY REG MGR

GAFFNEY MICHAEL O,IND LDMN,CPL
700 SHANNON DR
TYLER,TX 75701-8874 PH 903 581-6668

GAINCO INC
PO BOX 309
PORTLAND,TX 78374-0509 PH 361 777-0465
THERESA GAINES NIX

GAITHER PETROLEUM CORPORATION
16600 PARK ROW
HOUSTON,TX 77084-5019
PH 281 994-5400 FAX 281 994-5410
WWW.GPCOIL.CO GPC@GPCOIL.CO
O DUANE GAITHER,CEO
JOHN WYATT,CAO

DOUGLAS W GAITHER,PRES
JIM HAMMELMAN,VP FIN

GALAXY BRUSHES
MFG OF PIPELINE & DOWNHOLE BRUSHES
500 GLEASON DR
AVOCA,PA 18641 PH 570 457-5199
DOUGLAS BATZEL DOUGB@GALAXYBRUSHES.COM

GALLAGHER DRILLING,INC
PO BOX 3046
EVANSVILLE,IN 47730-3046 PH 812 425-8256
VICTOR R GALLAGHER,PRES
VICTOR R GALLAGHER JR,VP
MICHAEL S GALLAGHER,VP
SHAWN G GALLAGHER,VP
DANIEL G GALLAGHER,ASST SECY
THOMAS R BAILEY,SECY,CONTROLLER
THOMAS R BAILEY,TREAS
JAY A RITTER,LAND MGR

GALLAGHER GREGORY J
8955 KATY FWY, STE 204
HOUSTON,TX 77024-1626 PH 713 827-7051

GALLAGHER J ALAN,INC OIL & GAS PROPERTIES
208 COLE AVE
MONROE,LA 71203-3814 PH 318 343-9000
J ALAN GALLAGHER,PRES

GALLASPY IRVIN L,GEOL
1033 ROSELAWN DR
LAFAYETTE,LA 70503-4137 PH 318 984-4261

GALLATIN FUELS,INC
250 W MAIN ST
UNIONTOWN,PA 15401 PH 724 437-6234
FAX 724 437-1963
JOSEPH P TASSONE,CHRMN
JOHN R HART,PRES/CEO
JHART.GFI@ATLANTICBB.NET
EDWARD REBITCH,VP
JEFFREY M STRAUCH,SECY
JOANNE BURNS,TREAS

GALLOWAY ENERGY COMPANY
PO BOX 956
TOMBALL,TX 77377-0956 PH 281 356-9589
FAX 281 259-9671
MICHAEL L GALLOWAY,PRES

GALTWAY INDUSTRIES
650 N SAM HOUSTON PKWY E STE 550
HOUSTON,TX 77060 PH 713 364-8443
JOSH LOWREY JOSH@GALTWAYINDUSTRIES.COM

GAMMALOY HOLDINGS LP
201 IDA RD
BROUSSARD,LA 70518 PH 337 232-3475
FAX 337 234-9046
WWW.GAMMALOYHOLDINGS.COM
KENNY HIGGINBOTHAM,SLS
JASON HOBBS,SLS
JIMMY HARGRAVE,OPERS MGR

GARBER BROS INC
P O BOX 815
MORGAN CITY,LA 70381-0815
PH 504 384-4511 800-877-5667
CHARLES M GARBER,PRES
KENNETH R GARBER,VP
ROY GARBER,MGR
KIM FOLSE,INLAND OPERS
DUDLEY GASPAR,INLAND OPERS
BOBBY FALGOUT,OFFSHORE OPERS
HOUSTON,TX OFFICE - PH 281 999-0081

ROLF KRUGER
MORGAN CITY,LA OFFICE - PH 504 384-4511
KENNETH GARBER
KIM FOLSE

GARCIA R T & CO,INC
723 MAIN ST STE 506
HOUSTON,TX 77002 PH 713 654-8053
FAX 713 654-9047 WWW.RAYMONDTGARCIA.COM
RAYMOND T GARCIA,PRES/PE
RTGARCIA@SBCGLOBAL.NET

GARDES ENERGY SERVICES,INC
PO BOX 92593,301 FAIRLANE DR
LAFAYETTE,LA 70509-2593 PH 337 234-6544
FAX 337 235-4138 WWW.GARDESENERGY.COM
ROBERT A GARDES,PRES
RGARDES@GARDESENERGY.COM

GARDNER CONSULTANTS INC
TESTING GAS & OIL WELLS,GAS & OIL
ANALYSIS & MEASUREMENT
5927 FAIRFIELD AVE
SHREVEPORT,LA 71106-1913 PH 318 865-1449
PH 318 865-2666,FAX 318 865-0493
GARDNERCONSULTANTS@GMAIL.COM
MARK GARDNER,PRES
THOMAS GARDNER,VP

GARDNER DENVER
1800 GARDNER EXPY
QUINCY,IL 62305-9464 PH 217 222-5400
PH 800 682-9868 FAX 217 228-8243
WWW.GARDNERDENVER.COM
MAGGIE@GARDNERDENVER.COM
BARRY PENNYPACKER,PRES,CEO
J DENNIS SHULL,VP,GEN MGR
KENT MASON,GEN SLS MGR

GARDNER DENVER WATER JETTING SYSTEMS,INC
12300 N HOUSTON-ROSSLYN RD
HOUSTON,TX 77086-3219
PH 281 448-5800 FAX 281 448-7500
MKTG.WJS@GARDNERDENVER.COM
WWW.WATERJETTING.COM
CRAIG STAPLES,SALES MGR
JOHN SNYDER,MGR AFTERMARKET SALES

GARGIULO BROS OIL INC
PO BOX 9461
NEW HAVEN,CT 06534-0461 PH 203 865-0072
MARY LOU GARGIULO,PRES
HENRY A GARGIULO,MGR,SECY

GARRISON JONES AND SONS MACHINE WORKS,INC
PO BOX 274,BOX 274 HIGHWAY 15 WEST
FAIRFIELD,IL 62837 PH 618 847-2161
ROBERT P JONES,CO-OWNER
CARROLL E GARRISON,CO-OWNER

GARY A MONROE & ASSOCIATES PETROLEUM
LAND SERVICES SEE MONROE GARY A & ASSOC

GARY ANDREW E
14534 BROADGREEN DR
HOUSTON,TX 77079-6506 PH 281 496-6867

GAS & OIL MANAGEMENT ASSOC,INC
601 ROUSE AVE
YOUNGSVILLE,PA 16371 PH 814 563-4601
R J CLARK,PRES
ROBERT E CLARK,SECY/TREAS

GAS AND OIL COMPANY,THE
209A S 2ND ST
APOLLO,PA 15613-1108
PH 724 478-4108 FAX 724 478-3160

TOM@GASANDOILCOMPANY.COM
WWW.GASANDOILCOMPANY.COM
ANDRON KAVOURAS,GEN PRTNR

GAS DYNAMICS,LLC
1980 160TH AVENUE
MORA,MN 55051-7413
PH 320 679-1220 FAX 320 679-1220
WWW.GASDYNAMICSCORP.COM
RENGBERG@AOL.COM
ROBERT E ENGBERG,PE,PRES & OWNER

GAS MASTERS OF AMERICA
4150-C OLD STERLINGTON RD
MONROE,LA 71203 PH 318 323-4007
FAX 318 345-4937
HELEN GABLE,CONTROLLER

GAS PROCESSORS ASSOCIATION
WWW.GASPROCESSORS.COM

GAS RESEARCH INSTITUTE
WWW.GASTECHNOLOGY.ORG

GAS TURBINE CONTROLS CORPORATION
CIRCUIT BOARDS & SPARE PARTS FOR ALL GE
SPEEDTRONIC TURBINE CONTROL SYSTEMS
466 SAW MILL RIVER RD
ARDSLEY,NY 10502-2112 PH 914 693-0830
SALES@GASTURBINECONTROLS.COM
J SIMMS

GASPER RICE RESOURCES,LTD
4201 CYPRESS CREEK PKWY STE 400
HOUSTON,TX 77068-3447 PH 281 828-1112
FAX 281 828-2214
GRANT F RICE,PRES,GRAI(GP)
PAT BUDRO,VP,SECY/TREAS

GASTEX INC
PO BOX 2326
VICTORIA,TX 77902-2326 PH 361 645-2455
FAX 361 645-8128
O S HAHN,PRES
M K HAHN,SECY/TREAS

GASTON ROBERT W,PROF LDMN
5314 HULEN DR
CORPUS CHRISTI,TX 78413-2247
PH 361 215-7728 GASTYBUG@GMAIL.COM

GATES CHARLES G,OIL PROD
PO BOX 22787
JACKSON,MS 39225-2787
PH 601 948-7400 FAX 601 948-7412

GATEWAY ENERGY CORPORATION
1415 LOUISIANA ST
HOUSTON,TX 77002-7360 PH 713 336-0844
BOB PANICO,PRES,CEO

GATEWAY EXPLORATION,LLC
3040 POST OAK STE 525
HOUSTON,TX 77056 PH 713 750-9485
FAX 713 750-9418
WWW.GATEWAYEXPLORATION.COM
JOHN P (JAY) MOFFITT,PRES
JMOFFITT@GATEWAYEXP.COM
GEORGE E JOCHETZ III,VP

GATEWAY GATHERING AND MARKETING COMPANY
16200 PARK ROW STE 300
HOUSTON,TX 77084 PH 281 829-3206
FAX 281 829-2143 WWW.GATEWAYGATHERING.COM
KEITH STEPHENSON,MGR PH 281 675-3476

GATOR HAWK/TUBOSCOPE NOV
18660 E HARDY RD
HOUSTON,TX 77073-3706 PH 281 443-3343

FAX 281 443-7019 WWW.NOV.COM
DAVID HASHA,BUS MGR
STEVE BAKER,GEN MGR

GATSCHENBERGER DIANNE,CPL
152 KINGS XING
SHREVEPORT,LA 71105-3361 PH 225 272-3705
FAX 225 273-9442

GAUNTT JOHN D
18323 SONTERRA PL #2308
SAN ANTONIO,TX 78258-4374
PH 210 493-1653 FAX 210 493-1653

GAUTHIER BROTHERS INC SEE
BRANDT,A VARCO CO

GAUTHIER BROTHERS RECOVERY SYSTEMS SEE
BRANDT,A VARCO CO

GCO MINERALS COMPANY SEE
IP PETROLEUM COMPANY,INC

GE OIL & GAS SEE
HYDRIL PRESSURE CONTROL

GEAR PETROLEUM CO INC SEE
PETROLEUM PROPERTY SERVICES,INC

GEARENCH INC
PO BOX 192
CLIFTON,TX 76634-0192 PH 254 675-8651
FAX 254 675-6100
BOB POSEY,PRES
RANDAL BURDEN,SALES MGR
JOE LEDLOW,INSIDE SLS MGR
PAT JOHNSON,CHF ENGR

GEARHART INDUSTRIES,INC SEE
HALLIBURTON LOGGING SERVICES,INC

GEAUGA GAS & OIL LLC
7558 MAYFIELD RD
CHESTERLAND,OH 44026 PH 440 708-3742
FAX 440 729-6234
DAVID MAPES DMAPES1998@AOL.COM
PAMELA MAPES

GECO-PRAKLA SEE
WESTERNGECO LLC

GEDD INC
802 N CARANCAHUA STE 1010
CORPUS CHRISTI,TX 78470
PH 361 882-5999 FAX 361 882-5997
GEDD@GEDDTEXAS.COM
JAMES M HARMON,PRES
BRENT HOPKINS,EXPL MGR
WILLIAM C JOHNSON,CONSULTING GEOPHY

GEDNETZ DON E,CONS GEOL
564 OCKLEY DR
SHREVEPORT,LA 71106-1252 PH 318 221-8904

GEE WILLIAM E,GEOPHY
1401 NW 191ST ST
EDMOND,OK 73012-8968 PH 405 285-2022
WEGEEMSN@MSN.COM

GEIGER TEEPLE SMITH & HAHN
1844 W STATE ST STE A
ALLIANCE,OH 44601-5713 PH 330 821-1430
FAX 330 821-2217 WWW.GTSHLAW.COM
THOMAS P MOUSHEY,ATTY
BRUCE E SMITH,ATTY
B SCOTT HAHN,ATTY
KEITH RANDALL,ATTY
MICHAEL A OGLINE,ATTY
BRENT A BARNES,ATTY

GEISER OPERATING INC
PO BOX 1303

PORTLAND,TX 78374-1185
PH 361 643-1539 FAX 361 643-3926
D ALLEN GEISER
ALLENGEISER@CHARTER.NET

GELTEMEYER GWEN BUSH
203 ROSEHEART
SAN ANTONIO,TX 78259-2377
PH 210 277-0922 210 464-4484
GWENDOLYN B GELTEMEYER,OWNER/EXECUTRIX

GEMINI EXPLORATIONS,INC,OPR & PROD
2601 CENTENARY BLVD
SHREVEPORT,LA 71104-3398 PH 318 226-1773
FAX 318 425-2592
EUGENE DUCHARME,PRES
JAMES K VOZZELLA,VP

GEMINI INTERESTS,INC
PO BOX 396
FAIRHOPE,AL 36533-0396 PH 251 928-3200
JIM THOMPSON JR,PRTNR,CPL
ROBERT M NEWSOME,PRTNR

GEMOCO SEE
WEATHERFORD ENTERRA

GENERAL ATLANTIC RESOURCES,INC SEE
U M C PETROLEUM CORPORATION

GENERAL ENGINEERING & CONSTRUCTION,INC
114 OAK GLEN DR
LAFAYETTE,LA 70503-4709 PH 318 233-7046
A ANDRE AMY,PRES
JULES BABINEAUX,VP
J KELLY FREDERICK,SUPT

GENERAL PRODUCING COMPANY SEE
U M C PETROLEUM CORPORATION

GENERAL SERVICES CO OF NEW IBERIA,INC
PO BOX 10029
NEW IBERIA,LA 70562-0029 PH 318 369-9353
FAX 318 365-2126
W L GUILLORY,PRES
JOHN GUILLORY,VP

GENERATION LAND RESOURCES LLC
7101 BRYANT IRVIN RD #16361
FT WORTH,TX 76162
PH 817 715-8393 GLANDRESOURCES@YAHOO.COM
ERIC SMITH

GENERON IGS
16250 TOMBALL PKWY
HOUSTON,TX 77086 PH 713 937-5200
WWW.IGS-GLOBAL.COM
JOHN FONT,SALES/RNTL MGR PH 713 937-5236

GENESIS LAND & MINERAL RESOURCES
5503 LOUETTA RD STE D
SPRING,TX 77379 PH 281 370-7772
FAX 281 376-1001
WWW.GENESISLANDONLINE.COM
DON HUEBNER,OWNER
DON@GENESISLANDONLINE.COM

GENESIS LIMITED PARTNERSHIP
PRODUCTION,GEOLOGIST
PO BOX 1363
MT PLEASANT,SC 29465-1363 PH 843 884-0011
FAX 843 884-0011 SPEEREX@COMCAST.NET
STEPHEN W SPEER,GEN PRTNR

GENESIS OILFIELD PIPE & SUPPLY,INC
4414 HIGHWAY 90 WEST
NEW IBERIA,LA 70560-7640
PH 337 359-8750 FAX 337 359-8797
GENESISOILQUIP.COM

E C GABEHART,PRES EC@GENESISOILQUIP.COM
BRANDY RICHARD,MAIN OFFICE
SARAH GABEHART,SALES
BILLY BERTRAND,MAINT DIR
PAUL DOMINGUE,YARD FRMN

GENESIS PRODUCING COMPANY
1413 BRITTMOORE RD
HOUSTON,TX 77043-4005
PH 361 884-7241 FAX 361 884-7413
PNBELLGENESIS@AOL.COM
J MORGAN SMITH,OWNER
JAMES V RICHARDS,CONSLT GEOL
PHILIP N BELL,LDMN

GENOVA POWER COMPANY LP SEE
HUNT OIL COMPANY

GEO-CONSULTANTS INC
22607 BOBOLINK CIR
TOMBALL,TX 77377-3550 PH 281 351-8499
B E CREASY,PRES

GEO-WISE,INC
7700 SAN FELIPE ST STE 106
HOUSTON,TX 77063-1604 PH 713 978-7631
FAX 713 978-6108
KURT J WISEMAN,PRES
BETTY B WISEMAN,VP

GEOCENTER EXPLORATION
4805 WESTWAY PARK BLVD
HOUSTON,TX 77041-2003 PH 281 443-8150
FAX 281 443-8010
SUKHIE HYARE,PRES

GEOCHEM LABORATORIES,INC
1143-C BRITTMORE RD
HOUSTON,TX 77043-5003 PH 713 467-7011
FAX 713 467-7639
DR G S BAYLISS,PRES
R S BAYLISS,VP

GEOCHEM RESEARCH,INC
1143-C BRITTMORE RD
HOUSTON,TX 77043-5003 PH 713 467-7011
FAX 713 467-7639

GEOCORE LABORATORIES,INC
3230 G E DR
TYLER,TX 75701-0138 PH 903 566-0255
PH 800 256-5801

GEODOMINION PETROLEUM
PO BOX 2761
CORPUS CHRISTI,TX 78403-2761
PH 361 887-2134 FAX 361 884-1943
GEODOMINION@SBCGLOBAL.NET
RICHARD C GEISLER,PRTNR
KINNEY E SIMON,GEOL,PRTNR
DENNIS KOLMEIER,CONTROLLER

GEOFAX INC
161 POPLAR DR
MORGANTOWN,WV 26505-2540
PH 304 599-5024 FAX 304 599-5024
RONALD PERRY,PRES
HERMAN RIEKE,VP

GEOKINETICS INC
P O BOX 421129,1500 CITYWEST BLVD STE 800
HOUSTON,TX 77242
PH 713 850-7600 FAX 713 850-7330
WWW.GEOKINETICS.COM SALES@GEOKINET-ICS.COM
DAVID J CROWLEY,PRES/CEO
GARY L PITTMAN,EXEC VP/CFO

LEE PARKER,EXEC VP N AMERICA/E HEMISPHERE
BILL MOLL,GEN COUNSEL/CORP SECY
JOSE TAMAYO,VP QHSE
GLENN SNIEZEK,VP/TREASURER
ALEJANDRA VELTMANN,VP/CAO
ARNAUD PHAM,VP TAX
DR M LEE BELL,CHEIF GEOPHYSICIST
BILL PRAMIK,VP AQUISITION TECH
EWAN NEILL,VP SUPPORT
AUGUSTO YANEZ,MGR GLOBAL SUPPORT
HUGH SHIELDS,OBC/TZ MGR
JOHN ARCHER,GLOBAL MGR BUS DEV
BRENDA TAQUINO,DIR HUMAN RESOURCES

- DATA PROCESSING AND INTERPRETATION -

HOUSTON, TX OFFICE - 1500 CITYWEST BLVD
77042 PH 713 850-7600 FAX 713 782-1829
WALT RITCHIE,VP PROCESSING & INTEGRATED
RESERVOIR GEOSCIENCES
FRED HILTERMAN,CHF SCIENTIST
RICHARD VERM,VP RESEARCH & TECH
BARRY LAROSE,MGR MULTI-CLIENT & LAND
PROCESSING
IRA RODNEY,SR SLS EXEC

- NORTH AMERICA DATA ACQUISITION -

HOUSTON, TX OFFICE - 1500 CITYWEST BLVD
77042 PH 281 398-9503 FAX 281 398-9996
LYNN TURNER,VP NORTH AMERICA
D HUGH FRASER JR,MGR SUBCONTRACTOR
COMPLIANCE
HENRY BIGGART,AREA MGR WESTERN US
TOMMY MILLER,AREA MGR,MID-CON/NS TEXAS
KEITH STEVENS,AREA MGR EASTERN US
OPERS,US
DAVE YACCO,GEN MGR,NA CREW SUPPORT
DANIEL GROBERG,QHSE MGR,N.A. OPERS,US
RICK IRVING,SURVEY SUPVSR
PENNSYLVANIA,PA OFFICE - 101 HILLPOINTE
DR STE 120 CANNONSBURG,PA 15317
PH 724 745-3067 FAX 724 745-3068
DON KECK,NE REG SLS MGR/MULTI-CLIENT SVCS
DENVER,CO OFFICE - 1675 BROADWAY STE 1800
80202 PH 303 888 8885 FAX 303 892-9299
MARTY HALL,MULTI-CLIENT PROGRAM DEV MGR
KIM NORDBERG,SLS/MKTG US ACQUISITION
CALGARY,ALBERTA,CANADA OFFICE -
3815 32ND ST NE T1Y 7C1 PH 403 255-9388
FAX 403 265-1693
PAUL NOSEWORTHY,OPERS MGR/CANADA
TIM CARRY,TECHNICAL MGR/CANADA
MARVIN LEBEAU,QHSE MGR/CANADA

- LATIN AMERICA DATA ACQUISITION -

RIO DE JANEIRO,BRAZIL OFFICE -
AV. DAS AMERICAS,3.500-6 ANDAR
SALAS 601A605E634A638, BARRA DA TIJUCA
22640 PH 55 21 3094 7268
FAX 55 21 3094 7269
MAURICIO GOMEZ,MGR BRAZIL REGION
MIGUEL HIDALGO,MEXICO OFFICE -
GENERAL GARCIA CONDE PALOMAS 64
REFORMA SOCIAL 11650 PH 52 55 5282 4301

FAX 52 55 5520 4049
IGNACIO OROZCO,MGR MEXICO REGION
ARTURO VILLANUEVA,OPERS MGR
ARIOC LOPEZ,QHSE MGR
GILBERTO ROBLEDO,OPERS SUPERVISOR
FRANCISCO CABALLERO,OPERS SUPERVISOR
HOUSTON,TX OFFICE - 1500 CITYWEST BLVD
77042 PH 713 850-7600 FAX 713 782-1829
FRANCISCO DUCAS,QHSE MGR LATIN AMERICA
NESTOR SANABRIA,REGIONAL GEOPHYSICIST

- EUROPE,AFRICA,AND MIDDLE EAST -

GLASGOW, SCOTLAND OFFICE - 93 W GEORGE ST
6TH FLOOR G2 1PB PH 44 141 204 3004
FRASER ERKSINE,REG MGR/EAME INT'L OPERS

- ASIA PACIFIC -

SINGAPORE OFFICE - MSL BLDG 27 UBI RD 4
#03-01, 408618 PH 65 6841 2015
FAX 65 6841 7763
CRAIG WALKER,REG MGR FAR EAST
BRISBANE,AUSTRALIA OFC-601 CURTIN AVE E
PINKENBA,QUEENSLAND 4008 PH 617 326 85611
FAX 61 7 326 85622
RICK DUNLOP,SR VP ASIA PACIFIC
GREG DUNLOP,REG MGR AUSTRALIA
DAVE STEGEMANN,OPERS MGR ASIA/PACIFIC
PAUL HUMMEL,BUS DEV & MKTG MGR
PETER CRAWFORD,ASIA PACIFIC QHSE MGR

- MULTI-CLIENT SERVICES -

HOUSTON,TX OFFICE - 1500 CITYWEST BLVD
77042 PH 281 398-9503 FAX 281 398-9996
JAMES BOGARDUS,VP MULTI-CLIENT SVCS &
COPORATE MKTG
LEO SNOWMAN,INTL PROGRAM DEV MGR
JOE ROSAS,MGR/MID-CON
ARTURO M LUNA,MULTI-CLIENT OPERS SUPVSR

GEOLAND GRAPHICS,LLC
1101 HUGH WALLIS RD S STE 106
LAFAYETTE,LA 70508-2544 PH 318 233-1887
FAX 318 235-8385
JASON C STEWART,DIR OF GRAPHICS

GEOLOGICAL CONSULTING SERVICES,INC SEE
IHS INTERPRETED FORMATION TOPS

GEOLOGICAL DATA LIBRARY
811 DALLAS ST STE 930
HOUSTON,TX 77002-5911 PH 713 658-0033
FAX 713 658-0401 WWW.GEOLOGICALDATA.COM

GEOLOGICAL DATA SERVICES SEE
IHS INTERPRETED FORMATION TOPS

GEOLOGICAL RESEARCH CENTERS LLC
601 W TEXAS AVE
MIDLAND,TX 79701-4231
PH 432 682-7773 FAX 432 686-8251
GRCMIDLAND@MIDLANDMAP.COM
WWW.GRCLIBRARY.COM
ROBERT W EAGLE,PRES
ERIC OLIVER,VP
ABILENE,TX OFFICE - 1157 N 5TH,79601
PH 325 673-5057 FAX 325 672-2579
GRCABILENE@MIDLANDMAP.COM
WWW.GRCLIBRARY.COM

GEOLOGICAL SURVEY OF ALABAMA
PO BOX 869999
TUSCALOOSA,AL 35486-6999
PH 205 349-2852 FAX 205 349-2861
WWW.GSA.STATE.AL.US
DR BERRY H TEW JR,STATE GEOL,OIL/GAS SUPR
PATRICK O'NEIL,DEP DIR
SETH NEWTON,COUNSEL
IRENE BURGESS,EXEC SECY
- DIVISION DIRECTORS -
SANDY EBERSOLE,GEOL INVESTIGATIONS
STUART MCGREGOR,ECOSYSTEMS INVESTIGATION
DENISE HILLS,ACTING ENERGY INVESTIGATIONS
MARLON COOK,GROUNDWATER ASSESSMENTS

GEOLOGRAPH PIONEER SEE
SWACO,A DIV OF M-I

GEOMAP COMPANY
GEOLOGICAL/DIGITAL GIS MAPPING/LIBRARY
1100 GEOMAP LN
PLANO,TX 75074-7116 PH 972 578-0571
PH 800 527-2626 FAX 972 424 5533
SALES@GEOMAP.COM WWW.GEOMAP.COM
KATHERINE BREWER,CHRMN,CEO
REED VAN VALIN,VP,OPERS
BRIAN REDLIN,SLS REP
TREY MORGAN,SLS REPR
BIBI KHAN,CUSTOMER SVC
HOUSTON,TX BRANCH OFFICE LIBRARY - 3701
KIRBY DR,STE 750,77098 PH 713 520-8989
FAX 713 520-8376
DELORES HARRISON,OFC MGR,CUSTOMER SVC

GEOMICROFILM DATA INCORPORATED
DATA MKTG SERV,GEOPHY
10633 SHADOW WOOD DR
HOUSTON,TX 77043-2825 PH 713 973-9790

GEOPETRO LLC
7100 N HIGH ST STE 303
WORTHINGTON,OH 43085
PH 614 885-9350 FAX 614 885-1082
PAUL L ARCHER,MGR PAUL@GEOPETROLLC.COM

GEOPHYNQUE INTERNATIONAL SEE
HYDROGEOPHYSICS,INC

GEOPHYSICAL DEVELOPMENT CORPORATION SEE
GEOKINETICS INC

GEOPHYSICAL PURSUIT,INC
1740 WESTHEIMER STE 200
HOUSTON,TX 77098
PH 713 529-3000 FAX 713 529-5805
WWW.GEOPURSUIT.COM
GPI@GEOPURSUIT.COM
JEFF SPRINGMEYER,PRES
LARRY GALLOWAY,VP
RICK DRAKE,FLD MGR
KEVIN JONES,IT MGR
MARTIN STUPEL,GEOPHY MGR
JIM BROTHERS,SALES
REID SPRINGMEYER,SALES
TAYLOR GALLOWAY,SALES
SCOTT BRANNAN,SALES
SCOTT LAYNE,SALES
LIZETTE RUMOHR,ACCT
PATTY HAUGEN,ACCT
JULIE YANCEY,GEO TECH ASST
BELINDA COOPER,EXEC ASST
NEW ORLEANS,LA OFFICE - 2895 HWY 190
STE 227,MANDEVILLE,LA 70471

PH 985 727-6720 FAX 985 727-6719

GEOPHYSICAL SERVICE INC SEE
HALLIBURTON GEOPHYSICAL SERVICES,INC

GEOPROBE,INC
EXPLORATION VENTURES SPECIALISTS
7600 BURGOYNE RD STE 202
HOUSTON,TX 77063-3144
PH 713 443-5577 FAX 713 974-3025
P KRONFIELD,PRES PK@GEOPROBE.ORG

GEOQUEST/SCHLUMBERGER SEE
SCHLUMBERGER

GEORGE ASSOCIATES DRILLING SEE
GEORGE ENTERPRISES

GEORGE ENTERPRISES,INC
512 PRINCETON AVE
MORGANTOWN,WV 26505-2120 PH 304 599-3243
FAX 304 599-5996
LEONARD GEORGE,PRES
JOSEPH M GEORGE,VP

GEORGE MIKE E
C/O CRAIG M LUITJEN
9280 DIETZ ELKHORN RD
BOERNE,TX 78015-4900 PH 210 313-9963

GEORGE,CHARLES PAUL,INDEPENDENT LANDMAN
PO BOX 452
SHREVEPORT,LA 71162-0452 PH 318 747-1998

GEORGETOWN EXPLORATION INC
712 MAIN ST STE 1700
HOUSTON,TX 77002
PH 713 223-5730 FAX 713 223-5379
MICHAEL M FOWLER,PRES,DIR

GEORGETOWN MINERALS INC
PO BOX 897
GEORGETOWN,TX 78627
PH 512 863-3503 FAX 512 863-5617
GLYNN D BUIE,PRES

GEOSERVICES INC
MUDLOGGING & PRODUCTION SVCS
1325 S DAIRY ASHFORD ST
HOUSTON,TX 77077-2307 PH 713 365-0592
FAX 713 461-0976 WWWGEOSERVICES.COM
PIERRE BARADAT-LIRO,PRES
CHRIS PLATT,CORP BUS DEV MGR
RICHARD PARKER,CORP BUS DEV MGR
- MUDLOGGING -
TREVOR PACKER,REG OPERS MGR
GEORGE GIL HAINES,TRAING/RECRUITMENT
MGR

GEOSONICS/VIBRA-TECH
359 NORTHGATE DR STE 200
WARRENDALE,PA 15086-7597 PH 800 992-9395
PH 724 934-2900 FAX 724 934-2999
SALES@GEOSONICS.COM
WWW.GEOSONICSVIBRATECH.COM
JOY L GRIFFIN,SALES & SVC MGR

GEOSOUTHERN ENERGY CORPORATION
1425 LAKE FRONT CIRCLE STE 200
THE WOODLANDS,TX 77380
PH 281 363-9161 FAX 281 363-9181
GEORGE BISHOP,PRES & SOLE DIR
MARGARET WOODWARD MOLLESTON,VP
MMOLLESTON@AFIGEO.COM
RICHARD BORSTMAYER,GEN MGR,OPERS
BRENHAM,TX PRODUCTION OFFICE - 5416 HWY
290 W 77834 PH 979 836-5203

GEOSPECTRA CORP
122 N MAPLE ST
BOWLING GREEN,OH 43402-2209
PH 419 353-9706
DR ROBERT K VINCENT,PRES

GEOSYSTEMS LLP
1410 STONEHOLLOW DR
KINGWOOD,TX 77339-2070 PH 281 358-2662
FAX 281 358-3276
DR DICK VESSELL,OPERS MGR
RVESSELL@GEOSYSTEMSLLP.COM
CHUCK SEGREST,SALES MGR
CSEGREST@GEOSYSTEMSLLP.COM
RUTH DAVIES,OFC MGR
RDAVIES@GEOSYSTEMSLLP.COM

GEOVEND INTERNATIONAL
8834 STROUD DR
HOUSTON,TX 77036-5352 PH 713 272-9280
FAX 713 272-8981
PETER P CARRICO,CONS

GERARD ASSOCIATES,LC
625 MARKET ST STE 250
SHREVEPORT,LA 71101-5392
PH 318 221-0761 FAX 318 221-8835
LAND@CHCGERARD.COM
CHARLES GERARD,MGR
J A WOJTKIEWICZ,LDMN
HELEN D CAUSEY,ACCT

GERARD ROYALTY PARTNERSHIP
625 MARKET ST STE 250
SHREVEPORT,LA 71101-5392 PH 318 221-0761
FAX 318 221-8835 LAND@CHCGERARD.COM
ESTATE OF C H COSTER GERARD
HELEN D CAUSEY,ACCT

GERMANY ENERGY COMPANY
PO BOX 5198,975 NORTH ST STE 207 39202
JACKSON,MS 39296-5198 PH 601 968-8015
FORREST GERMANY
FORREST@GERMANYENERGY.NET

GERMANY EXPLORATION COMPANY
PO BOX 5198
JACKSON,MS 39296 PH 601 969-6090
NORMAN G GERMANY,PRES
N FORREST GERMANY,VP
MARJORIE F GERMANY,SECY

GIBRALTAR ENERGY COMPANY
200 N WASHINGTON ST
EL DORADO,AR 71730-5620 PH 870 862-5155
FAX 870 862-5251 GIBRALTARENERGY.COM
RANDY@GIBRALTARENERGY.COM
RICHARD H MASON,PRES
RANDALL M THOMPSON,LAND MGR

GIDDENS LESLIE W,JR,GEOL
600 LEOPARD ST STE 1506
CORPUS CHRISTI,TX 78473-0046
PH 361 888-8382 FAX 361 887-8636

GILA GROUP (LEASING)
PO BOX 140460
DALLAS,TX 75214-0460 PH 214 240-3054
FAX 214 823-5545 WWW.GILAGROUPLP.COM
LANGFORD KEITH III,PRES
FORD.KEITH@GILAGROUPLP.COM
LISA BRIGGS,CONTROLLER
LISA.BRIGGS@GILAGROUPLP.COM

GILBERT A A,ARKANSAS ACCOUNT
PO BOX 3985

SHREVEPORT,LA 71133 PH 318 861-6974
RON NIERMAN,MGR
OVERTON,TX OFFICE - PO BOX 430
75684 PH 903 834-3661
RICHARD M MAY,MGR

GILBERT A A,TEXAS ACCOUNT
PO BOX 3985
SHREVEPORT,LA 71133 PH 318 861-6974
RON NIERMAN,MGR
OVERTON,TX OFFICE - PO BOX 430
75684 PH 903 834-3661
RICHARD M MAY,MGR

GILBREATH LONNIE B,CONSULTING GEOL
PO BOX 1478
GREENWOOD,AR 72936-1478 PH 479 806-1742

GILL PRESTON O OPERATING CO,INC
133 OSCAR BOND RD
PURVIS,MS 39475-4473
PH 601 731-4700 JANETHGILL@YAHOO.COM
PRESTON O GILL,PRES

GILLEY JOHN R,LDMN,LEASES,TITLES,RYLTS
1500 EVERGLADES DR
TYLER,TX 75703 PH 903 561-6725

GILLILAND & ASSOCIATES
PO BOX 8318
HORSESHOE BAY,TX 78657 PH 512 217-8852
ROYCE GILLILAND,PRES

GINGER OIL COMPANY
1400 WOODLOCH FORREST DR STE 425
THE WOODLANDS,TX 77380
PH 281 681-8600 FAX 281 681-8604
WWW.GINGEROIL.COM
WILLIAM DON NEVILLE,PRES
DNEVILLE@GINGEROIL.COM
HANS G BLIXT,CEO
HBLIXT@GINGEROIL.COM
SCOTT ROBINSON,VP ENGRG
SROBINSON@GINGEROIL.COM

GIRARD INDUSTRIES
6531 N ELDRIDGE PKWY
HOUSTON,TX 77041-3507 PH 713 466-3100
PH 800 231-2861 FAX 713 466-8050
WWW.GIRARDIND.COM EMAIL@GIRARDIND.COM
DAVID HENRY,PRES
MICHAEL HENRY,GM

GLADE PRODUCTION,INC
PO BOX 921
KILGORE,TX 75663-0921
PH 903 984-3443 FAX 903 983-2526
BOB CLOER,PRES

GLASSCOCK C GUS,JR,INVESTMENTS
PO BOX 519
COLUMBUS,TX 70934-0519 PH 979 732-6968

GLASSELL PRODUCING COMPANY,INC
919 MILAM ST STE 2010
HOUSTON,TX 77002 PH 713 652-3103
FAX 713 658-0009
ALFRED C GLASSELL,III,PRES
J B COX,GEOL
PAM LINDBERG,OFC MGR
ANNIE HARDIN,PERSONAL ASST

GLENCLIFT OIL CO
BOX 308
NEWPORT,OH 45768-0308 PH 740 473-1341
JACK CLIFT,SECY/TREAS

GLENDALE GAS VENTURE
1252 JACKSONVILLE RD
HOMER CITY,PA 15748-1129 PH 724 479-2847
JOSEPH DASKIVICH,GEN PRTNR

GLENN & LOGUE ATTYS
PO BOX 146,901 CHARLESTON AVE
MATTOON,IL 61938-0146
PH 217 234-7461 FAX 217 258-6556
THOMAS J LOGUE,PRTNR
TLOGUE1@CONSOLIDATED.NET

GLENN WAYNE E ASSOC INC
PO BOX 1326
DICKINSON,TX 77539-1326 PH 281 534-4980
DON M LLOYD,PRES
RICHARD LLOYD,VP/SECY

GLICKENHAUS ENERGY CORP
4605 POST OAK PLACE DR STE 221
HOUSTON,TX 77027-6731 PH 713 225-4400
FAX 225-6279
JAMES D RIEKER,JR,PRES

GLOBAL GEOPHYSICAL SERVICES
13927 SOUTH GESSNER ROAD
MISSOURI CITY,TX 77489 PH 713 972-9200
FAX 713 972-1008
WWW.GLOBALGEOPHYSICAL.COM
CONTACT@GLOBALGEOPHYSICAL.COM
RICHARD WHITE,PRES & CEO
SEAN GORE,SR VP & CFO
TOM FLEURE,SR VP-GEOPHY TECHNOLOGY
DALLAS,TX OFFICE - 17103 PRESTON RD
STE 200 75248 PH 972 818-2550
FAX 972 818-2553
DENVER,CO OFFICE - 1625 BROADWAY ST
STE 1150,80202 PH 720 279-3600
FAX 720 279-3605
- INTERNATIONAL OFFICES -
BUENOS AIRES,ARGENTINA OFFICE - ALICIA
MOREAU DE JUSTO 1848,OFICINA 317 C1107AFL
PH 4311 2680
DUBAI,UNITED AREB EMIRATES OFFICE - STE
3302 PLATINUM TOWER PH 971 4 361 2278
ERBIL,IRAQ OFFICE - HOUSE 22 DREAM CITY
GULAN STREET
WAIYAKI WAY,NAIROBI,KENYA OFFICE - WEST
END TOWERS 6TH FL PH 254 2042 14133
TRIPOLI,LIBYA OFFICE - PO BOX 92045
PH 218911701679 PH 218944353528
BAUSHER,MUSCAT,OMAN OFFICE - DOLPHIN
COMPLEX BLDG 2568 (FLAT 3C),BLK 255
WAY 5533 PH 968 96570560
CALGARY,ALBERTA,CANADA OFFICE (SENSOR
GEOPHYSICAL) - 1300,736 - 6 AVE SW
T2P 3T7 PH 403 237-7711 FAX 403 237-7881
WWW.SENSORGEO.COM
INFO@SENSORGEO.COM

GLOBAL GEOPHYSICAL SERVICES LTD
SEE GLOBAL GEOPHYSICAL SERVICES INC

GLOBAL MILLENNIUM ENERGY INC SEE
GMX RESOURCES INC

GLOBAL NATURAL RESOURCES INC SEE
SEAGULL ENERGY CORPORATION

GLOBAL NITROGEN SERVICES
16250 TOMBALL PKWY
HOUSTON,TX 77086
PH 713 937-5200 PH 713 304-8584
WWW.GLOBALNITROGENSERVICES.COM

JOHN FONT,PRES
GLOBAL POWER SYSTEMS
5410 KENNON LN
BOSSIER CITY,LA 71112
PH 318 741-1073

GLOBAL/WEINMAN GEOSCIENCE
SEE GLOBAL GEOPHYSICAL SERVICES INC

GLOBE ENERGY SERVICES
3204 W HWY 180
SNYDER,TX 79549 PH 325 573-1310
FAX 325 573-1313
AMARILLO,TX (FISHING & RENTAL) OFFICE -
4616 N WESTERN 79124 PH 806 374-5623
FAX 806 435-2596
AMARILLO,TX (FLUID SVCS) OFFICE - 4616 N
FAX 325 436-0315
WESTERN 79124 PH 806 228-6123
FAX 806 435-2596
ANDREWS,TX (FLUID SVCS) OFFICE - 900 W
BROADWAY 79714 PH 432 355-4291
ANDREWS,TX (WELL SVCS) OFFICE - 900 W
BROADWAY 79714 PH 432 557-7043
FAX 432 557-7043
ARTESIA,NM (COMPL SYSTEMS) OFFICE - 6465
SEVEN RIVERS HWY 88210 PH 575 736-7370
FAX 575 735-7271
ARTESIA,NM (FLUID SVCS) OFFICE - 7296 N
HWY 285 88211 PH 575 365-2033
FAX 575 365-2195
BIG LAKE,TX (FLUID SVCS) OFFICE - 159
SANTA RITA RD 76932 PH 325 884-3091
FAX 325 884-3494
BIG SPRING,TX (FLUID SVCS) OFFICE - 3112
N HWY 87 79720 PH 432 264-9100
FAX 432 264-9101
CANADIAN,TX (FLUID SVCS) OFFICE - 14975
RED DEER RD 79014 PH 806 228-6573
FAX 806 435-2596
CARLSBAD,NM (FLUID SVCS) OFFICE - 512 E
GREEN 88221 PH 575 234-9887
FAX 575 236-6647
DENVER CITY,TX (FLUID SVCS) OFFICE - 1855
WAGON TRAIL RD 79323 PH 806 592-4808
FAX 806 592-4809
EUNICE,NM (FLUID SVCS) OFFICE - 113 TEXAS
AVE 88231 PH 575 390-6549
FAX 575 394-2049
GUYMON,OK (PROD CHEMICALS) OFFICE - 5220
PATRICIA 73942 PH 432 684-4939
FAX 432 684-7610
HOBBS,NM (FISHING & RENTAL) OFFICE - 2113
FRENCH DR 88240 PH 575 391-8858
FAX 575 738-0055
HOBBS,NM (FLUID SVCS) OFFICE - 2113
FRENCH DR 88240 PH 575 391-8858
FAX 575 738-0055
KERMIT,TX (WELL SVCS) OFFICE - 2275 HWY
380 W 79745 PH 432 634-5249
KILGORE,TX (FLUID SVCS) OFFICE - 3010
MAVERICK DR 75603 PH 903 984-5300
FAX 903 984-5337
KILGORE,TX (WELL SVCS) OFFICE - 3010
MAVERICK DR 75603 PH 903 984-5300
FAX 903 984-5337
LAMESA,TX (FLUID SVCS) OFFICE - 2112 S
HWY 87 79339 PH 806 872-2165

FAX 806 872-2616

LEVELLAND,TX (COMPL SYSTEMS) OFFICE -
1827 W FM 300,79336 PH 806 897-0117
FAX 806 897-0106

LEVELLAND,TX (FLUID SVCS) OFFICE - 1700
10TH ST 79336 PH 806 894-3151
FAX 806 894-1291

LIBERAL,KS (FLUID SVCS) OFFICE - 1702 W
1702 W 2ND ST 67901 PH 620 624-5579
FAX 620 624-5578

MARSHALL,TX (FLUID SVCS) OFFICE - 4877 FM
2199 S,75672 PH 903 927-1219
FAX 903 927-1429

MARSHALL,TX (WELL SVCS) OFFICE - 4877 FM
2199 S,75672 PH 903 984-5300
FAX 903 984-5337

MIDLAND,TX (FISHING & RENTAL) OFFICE -
2901 E I-20 79706 PH 432 682-0349
FAX 432 685-3393

MIDLAND,TX (FLUID SVCS) OFFICE - 2905 E
I-20,79706 PH 432 682-2882
FAX 432 628-2883

MIDLAND,TX (PROD CHEMICALS) OFFICE - 1706
S MIDKIFF 79710 PH 432 684-4939
FAX 432 684-7610

MIDLAND,TX (WATER SYSTEMS) OFFICE - 306 W
WALL ST STE 900,79701 PH 432 218-7888
FAX 432 682-7889

MIDLAND,TX (WELL SVCS) OFFICE - 2905 E
I-20,79706 PH 432 682-2882
FAX 432 682-2883

MONAHANS,TX (FLUID SVCS) OFFICE - 4501 S
STOCKTON 79756 PH 432 943-5000
FAX 432 943-5001

ODESSA,TX (COMPL SYSTEMS) OFFICE - 3900
KERMIT HWY 79760 PH 432 366-2121
FAX 432 366-9451

ODESSA,TX (FISHING & RENTAL) OFFICE -
3101 N FM 1936,79763 PH 432 385-0740

ODESSA,TX (FLUID SVCS) OFFICE - 2394 W
CATLIN ST 79766 PH 432 333-8177
FAX 432 333-2553

ODESSA,TX (WELL SVCS) OFFICE - 3101 N FM
1936,79763 PH 432 385-0740
FAX 432 381-5598

PERRYTON,TX (FISHING & RENTAL) OFFICE -
422 INDUSTRIAL 79070 PH 806 648-0561
FAX 806 648-0563

PERRYTON,TX (FLUID SVCS) OFFICE - 102 S
JUNIPER ST 79070 PH 806 435-2380
FAX 806 435-2596

PERRYTON,TX (WELL SVCS) OFFICE - 14415 E
LOOP 143 79070 PH 806 435-6541
FAX 806 435-2014

SAN ANGELO,TX (FLUID SVCS) OFFICE - 4825
N CHADBOURNE 76903 PH 325 653-7800
FAX 325 952-5460

SAN ANGELO,TX (WELL SVCS) OFFICE - 4825 N
CHADBOURNE 76903 PH 325 942-5750
FAX 325 942-5460

SNYDER,TX (COMPL SYSTEMS) OFFICE - 3646 W
HWY 180 79549 PH 325 436-0314
FAX 325 436-0315

SNYDER,TX (FISHING & RENTAL) OFFICE -
5401 HWY 350 79549 PH 325 573-1700
FAX 325 573-1800

SNYDER,TX (FLUID SVCS) OFFICE - 1015 N
COLLEGE AVE 79549 PH 325 574-2111
FAX 325 574-2639

SWEETWATER,OK (FLUID SVCS) OFFICE - 12024
N HWY 1750 ERICK,OK 73745 PH 580 526-3200
FAX 580 526-3230

WESTBROOK,TX (FLUID SVCS) OFFICE - 306 W
THORNE ST 79565 PH 325 644-5600
FAX 325 644-5601

GLOBE EXPLORATION,INC
PO BOX 12
GREAT BEND,KS 67530-0012 PH 620 792-7607
RICHARD STALCUP,COO

GMX RESOURCES INC
9400 N BROADWAY EXT STE 600
OKLAHOMA CITY,OK 73114-7401
PH 405 600-0711 FAX 405 600-0600
KEN L KENWORTHY,JR,PRTNR
KEN L KENWORTHY,PRTNR
MARSHALL,TX BLOCKER YARD FLD OFFICE -
PH 903 935-5954

GOFF D C REVOCABLE ENERGY TRUST
PO BOX 1465,114 S COLLEGE STE B
FAYETTEVILLE,AR 72702-1465
PH 479 521-5307 FAX 479 521-4047
DASH GOFF,OWNER DASHGOFF@SBCGLOBAL.NET
BOB ADKINS,ENGR RCADKINS@HOTMAIL.COM
NEIL MOSS,GEOL

GOINS OIL & GAS INC
1400 S D ST
FORT SMITH,AR 72901-4620 PH 479 782-8597
FAX 479 782-4375
MARTY GOINS
ERNEST C GOINS

GOLDAK DAVID J,CONSULTING GEOL
155 N MARKET STE 710
WICHITA,KS 67202-1821 PH 316 263-5785
FAX 316 263-1851

GOLDCO ENERGY
333 TEXAS ST STE 521
SHREVEPORT,LA 71101 PH 318 221-7196
FAX 318 221-7217
FRANK H GOLDSBERRY III,PRES
G G NESBITT III,VP

GOLDCO OPERATING LLC
333 TEXAS ST STE 521
SHREVEPORT,LA 71101 PH 318 221-7196
FAX 318 221-7217
GOLDSBERRYOPS@BELLSOUTH.NET
FRANK HOLD GOLDSBERRY III,CEO
G G NESBITT III,COO
CLAYTON GLENN PRICE,PETR ENGR

GOLDEN ENGINEERING,LP
1001 NANTUCKET DR APT 5
HOUSTON,TX 77057-1980
PH 713 201-3798 FAX 713 465-0084
WWW.GOLDENENGR.COM BGOLDEN@GOLDE-
NENGR.COM
ALBERT C GOLDEN,PRES
MIRA GOLDEN,CORP SECY

GOLDEN STATE PETROLEUM CORP
PO BOX 51756
LAFAYETTE,LA 70505-1756 PH 318 232-7399
ROBERT T BULLER,PRES
ROBERT BULLER@GMAIL.COM
FAIRFIELD,TX OFFICE - 123 E COMMERCE ST

75840 PH 877 711-2382

GOLDKING ENERGY PARTNERS I,LP
PO BOX 671099
DALLAS,TX 75367-1099 PH 214 707-7535
FAX 214 572-2699 WWW.TRUNKBAY.NET
BENNY DUNCAN,MGR
BDUNCAN@TRUNKBAY.NET

GOLDKING ONSHORE OPERATING,LLC
777 WALKER ST STE 2500
HOUSTON,TX 77002-5322
PH 713 222-2800 FAX 713 222-2824
EDDIE HEBERT,CEO
KEN CLEVELAND,CONTROLLER
JAMES ANHAISER,SUPT OPERS

GOLDKING RESOURCES
777 WALKER ST STE 2500
HOUSTON,TX 77002
PH 713 222-2800 FAX 713 222-2824
EDDIE HEBERT,CEO
KEN CLEVELAND,CONTROLLER
JAMES ANHAISER,SUPT OPERS

GOLDRUS PRODUCING COMPANY
PO BOX 8758
THE WOODLANDS,TX 77387-8758
PH 281 807 6114
PATRICK WARREN,PRES

GOLDSMITH J PAUL OIL OPR
P O BOX 6014,2311 EAST SE LOOP 323
TYLER,TX 75711-6014 PH 972 561-0001

GOLDSTON OIL CORPORATION
PO BOX 570365,1819 ST JAMES PL
HOUSTON,TX 77257-0365 PH 713 355-3408
WALTER G MAYFIELD,COO,PRES
RODNEY E HENCKEL,EXEC VP
GREG COLBURN,PROD MGR
KENT M JOHNSTON,LAND MGR

GOLSTON-OSBORN INVESTMENTS
PO BOX 118316
CARROLLTON,TX 75011 PH 979 775-3545
FAX 979 775-3545
BILL OSBORN,GEN PRTNR

GONZOIL,INC
5260 FULTON DR NW
CANTON,OH 44718-1806 PH 330 497-5888
FAX 330 497-8010 GONZOIL1@AOL.COM
DOUGLAS W GONZALEZ,PRES
FRANK W GONZALEZ,SECY/TREAS

GOOD DAY ENERGY INC
357 N POST OAK LANE #111
HOUSTON,TX 77024 PH 713 658-8487
GOODDAYINC@AOL.COM
BEN BUONGIORNO,PRES

GOODGAME ASSOCIATES OIL & GAS EXPLORATION
PO BOX 7344
TYLER,TX 75711-7344 PH 903 581-5998
JAMES A GOODGAME,PRES,OWNER

GOODRICH EXPLORATION INC
1001 FANNIN STE 4670
HOUSTON,TX 77002 PH 713 659-3680
FAX 713 659-8606

GOODRICH OPERATING CO INC
1001 FANNIN STE 4670
HOUSTON,TX 77002 PH 713 659-3680
FAX 713 659-8606
DOUGLAS ANDERSON,PRES

GOODRICH PETROLEUM CORPORATION
EXPLORATION,PRODUCTION,LAND
801 LOUISIANA STE 700
HOUSTON,TX 77002 PH 713 780-9494
FAX 713 780-9254
WWW.GOODRICHPETROLEUM.COM
WALTER G GOODRICH,V CHRMN/CEO
ROBERT C TURNHAM JR,PRES/COO
JAN SCHOTT,EXEC VP/CFO
MARK E FERCHAU,EXEC VP
BRET HAMMETT,SR VP EXPL
TOM NEMEC,VP/PROJ MGR
TIMOTHY D LANE,VP LAND

GOODWIN C GUY,III,CPL
7134 MAPLERIDGE ST UNIT 4A
HOUSTON,TX 77081-6631 PH 713 665-5155

GOOSE CREEK OIL COMPANY INC
PO BOX 453
SALEM,IL 62881-0453 PH 618 548-0915
ROBERT D HOLSAPPLE,PRES
BRIAN L HOLSAPPLE,VP

GORDA SOUND ROYALTIES,LP
PO BOX 671099
DALLAS,TX 75367-1099 PH 214 707-7535
FAX 214 572-2699 WWW.TRUNKBAY.NET
BENNY DUNCAN,MGR BDUNCAN@TRUNKBAY.NET
BDUNCAN@TRUNKBAY.NET

GORDON ARATA MCCOLLAM DUPLANTIS &
EAGAN,L.L.P.
201 ST CHARLES AVE FL 40
NEW ORLEANS,LA 70170-4000 PH 504 582-1111
FAX 504 582-1121 WWW.GORDONARATA.COM
JGORDON@GORDONARATA.COM
BLAKE G ARATA,APLC
EWELL E EAGAN,JR,APLC
CYNTHIA A NICHOLSON,ATTY
MARCEL GARSAUD,JR,ATTY
PATRICK M SHELBY,ATTY
STEVEN W COPLEY,ATTY
MARION WELBORN WEINSTOCK,ATTY
MARTIN E LANDRIEU,ATTY
A GREGORY GRIMSAL,ATTY
DONNA PHILLIPS CURRAULT,ATTY
SCOTT A O'CONNOR,ATTY
C PECK HAYNE JR,ATTY
HOWARD E SINOR JR,ATTY
TINA CRAWFORD WHITE,ATTY
DAVID J MESSINA,ATTY
TERRENCE K KNISTER,ATTY
FERNAND L LAUDUMIEY IV,ATTY
KELLY D PERRIER,ATTY
MICHAEL E BOTNICK,ATTY
V M WHEELER,ATTY
PHILLIP J ANTIS JR,ATTY
NINA W ENGLISH,ATTY
DAVID M ROSS,ATTY
JAMES D RHORER,ATTY
STEPHANIE C TOUPS,ATTY
MEREDITH S GRABILL,ATTY
ALEX B ROTHENBERG,ATTY
PEGGY M WELSH,ATTY
LAFAYETTE,LA OFFICE - PO BOX 81829
400 E KALISTE SALOOM RD,#4200,70508-8517
PH 337 237-0132 FAX 337 237-3451
B J DUPLANTIS,APLC
SAMUEL E MASUR,ATTY

GREGORY G DUPLANTIS,ATTY
GERALD H SCHIFF,ATTY
PAUL B SIMON,ATTY
JULIE D JARDELL,ATTY
J MICHAEL FUSSELL JR,ATTY
AMISTEAD M LONG,ATTY
AMY GAUTREAUX,ATTY
DAVID J ROGERS,ATTY
BATON ROUGE,LA OFFICE - 301 MAIN ST,ONE
AMERICAN PL STE 1600,70801-1916
PH 225 381-9643 FAX 225 336-9763
LOUIS M PHILLIPS,ATTY
PETER A KOPFINGER,ATTY
HOUSTON,TX OFFICE - 1980 POST OAK BLVD
STE 1800 77056 PH 713 333-5500
FAX 713 333-5501
TEANNA WEST NESKORA,ATTY
CHARLES L STINNEFORD,ATTY
CATHY E CHESSIN,ATTY
MELISSA A LOVELL,ATTY
WILLIAM A SHERWOOD,ATTY

GORDON J E,JIM
7311 OSWEGO DR
SAN ANTONIO,TX 78250-5287
PH 361 437-5706

GORDON TULANE
5930 STAR LN STE A
HOUSTON,TX 77057-7130 PH 713 785-4995

GOTCO INTERNATIONAL INC
DRILLING BITS & TOOLS INCLUDING FISHING
14421 CHRISMAN RD
HOUSTON,TX 77039 PH 281 591-1874
PH 800 683-7746 FAX 281 999-4251
ROGER D PARRISH,PRES
JACK WALLACE,OPERS MGR
LARRY ROUSH,SR VP,MFG
SHEILA WARE,CONTROLLER
BART MCSHERRY,QUALITY ASSURANCE ADMIN
KEVIN WYBLE,QUALITY ASSURANCE ADMIN
JAMES SOWELL,PLT MGR
DIAN BENTLEY,PURCH AGENT
JOHN BOALS,EXEC SLS
JOANN KOSTER,INSIDE SLS
SANDY SIROIS,INSIDE SLS
JB ROBERSON,DOMESTIC SLS MGR
BOB ROBERTS,DOMESTIC SLS
BUDDY MCNABB,DOMESTIC SLS
HOUSTON,TX MFG OFFICE - PO BOX 691245
77269-1245 LOCATED AT 11410 SPRING
CYPRESS RD,TOMBALL,TX 77375
PH 281 376-3784 FAX 281 370-8343

GOUGER OIL CO
PO BOX 17925
SAN ANTONIO,TX 78217-0925 PH 210 824-5957
FAX 210 824-6973
TOM M GOUGER,III,OWNER

GOUGH & COMPANY
1630 N 10TH ST
MCALLEN,TX 78501-4103
PH 956 687-6288 FAX 956 687-2665
ROBERT W GOUGH,OWNER
RWGOGCO@AOL.COM

GOUIN FRANK L,GEOL
PO BOX 6223
BRANSON,MO 65615-6223
PH 580 255-5375

GOVETT RAY,CONSULTING GEOL
4146 HARRY ST
CORPUS CHRISTI,TX 78411-1921
PH 361 855-0134

GPM GAS CORPORATION SEE
PHILLIPS PETROLEUM COMPANY

GRACE PETROLEUM CORPORATION SEE
SAMSON INVESTMENT COMPANY

GRAGE ALLAN P
3408 AMHERST AVE
DALLAS,TX 75225-7624 PH 318 868-4135

GRAHAM BILL J OIL AND GAS CORP SEE
INCLINE ENERGY,INC

GRAHAM CEMENTING CO
PO BOX 119,220 OAK ST
GRAHAM,TX 76450-0119 PH 940 549-5267
GORDON S NEES III

GRAHAM MANER
PO BOX 8880
TYLER,TX 75711 PH 903 561-6870
FAX 903 561-9604 TEXASOIL42@YAHOO.COM

GRAHAM MARGARET B
PO BOX 8880
TYLER,TX 75711 PH 903 561-6870
FAX 903 561-9604 TEXASOIL42@YAHOO.COM

GRAHAM R J OIL CO
PO BOX 474
SALEM,IL 62881-0474 PH 618 548-5544
FAX 618 548-3736
RONNIE JOE GRAHAM,OWNER

GRAHAM TEX M
3320 HINTON RD
ATHENS,WV 24712 PH 304 384-7254
FAX 304 384-9468 TEXASOIL42@YAHOO.COM
TYLER,TX OFFICE - PO BOX 8880, 75711
PH 903 561-6870 FAX 903 561-9404

GRAND OPERATING,INC
15303 DALLAS PKWY STE 1010
ADDISON,TX 75001 PH 972 788-2080
FAX 972 788-0176 WWW.GRANDENERGY.COM
INFO@GRANDENERGY.COM
JAMES L HARRIS,PRES
TERRY MACKEY,OPERS MGR
MARCH MCRUIZ,LAND MGR/ATTY
MARK STANISLAV,GEOL
CLAUDIA YOUNG,CONTROLLER
CAROL G PIKE,SR REV ACCT
LARIANN HINTON,ACCT PAYABLE

GRANDIN ENERGY LLC
7920 FM 1489 STE B
SIMONTON,TX 77476 PH 281 533-0733
WWW.GRANDINENERGY.COM
KIMM L COSTANZO,PRES
KCOSTANZO@GRANDINENERGY.COM

GRANT BETTY C,IND OIL & GAS OPR
10990 BELLE COUR WAY
SHREVEPORT,LA 71106-7706 PH 318 222-4950

GRANT GEOPHYSICAL SEE
GEOKINETICS INC

GRANT PRIDECO/ATLAS BRADFORD
410 COMMERCIAL BLVD
BROUSSARD,LA 70518-3630 PH 318 232-3098
PH 866 840-5750 FAX 318 261-1066
JIM DAVIDSON,FLD SVC MGR,LA & EASTERN US
KEN TAUZIN,FLD SVC
BRYAN ISTRE,FLD SVC

QUINTON ABSHIRE,FLD SVC
CLAY RANDOLPH,FLD SVC
JAMES PITTINGER,FLD SVC
CARL MORGAN,FLD SVC
MICHAEL REGAN,FLD SVC

GRANT RUSSELL P JR,ATTY AT LAW/CPL
36 WINTERGREEN RD
MADISON,MS 39110
PH 601 898-9587 FAX 601 898-9635
RUSSELL P GRANT JR,OIL & GAS LAND SVCS
RPGRANTJR@COMCAST.NET

GRAPHIC CONTROLS,LLC
PO BOX 1271,400 EXCHANGE ST
BUFFALO,NY 14240-1271 PH 716 853-7500
MARGEE WILLE,MKTG MGR

GRATTA DAVID M OIL & GAS PROPERTIES
PO BOX 15334
HATTIESBURG,MS 39404-5334 PH 601 520-1455
DAVID M GRATTA DAVIDMGRATTA@MAC.COM

GRAVES & CO
OIL & GAS CONSULTANTS
1600 SMITH ST 48TH FLR
HOUSTON,TX 77002
PH 713 650-0811 FAX 713 650-0840
WWW.GRAVES-CO.COM INFO@GRAVES-
CO.COM
JOHN L GRAVES,PRES JGRAVES@GRAVES-CO.COM
GRANT S DARNELL II,VP
CHRISTIAN OGDEN,ATTORNEY
HEATHER WOLF,LDMN
VANESSA SCOBIE,MKTG MGR
SHELLY HESS,BOOKKEEPER
JERI PETTEY,OFC MGR

GRAVITY EXPLORATION TECHNIQUES INC
3100 TIMMONS LN STE 200
HOUSTON,TX 77027-5904
PH 713 526-0828 FAX 713 523-0145

GRAVITY MAP SERVICE
GRAVITY DATA & INTERPRETATIONS
2116 THOMPSON RD STE H-1
RICHMOND,TX 77469-5428
PH 281 342-2884 WWW.GRAVITYSERVICES.COM
ROBERT NEESE,PRES
B.NEESE@GRAVITYSERVICES.COM
DENNIS ROHAN,GEOL STAFF MGR
PENNY NEESE,OFC MGR
JOHNNY NEESE,MKTG
J.NEESE@GRAVITYSERVICES.COM

GRAVTRO INC
13814 ANGEL FIRE LN
HOUSTON,TX 77070-2825 PH 713 781-6774

GRAWARD OPERATING INC
227 S COLLEGE
TYLER,TX 75702 PH 903 593-8858
FAX 903 535-9902
JOHN GRAHAM,OWNER,PRES
CHARLOTTE GRAHAM,VP
BECKY HUFFMAN,SECY

GRAY J A,ESTATE
PO BOX 45
HOUSTON,TX 77001-0045 PH 713 623-4514

GRAY OIL COMPANY
P O BOX 638,707 MEMORIAL DR
BAYTOWN,TX 77520 PH 281 422-3677
EDDIE V GRAY,OWNER

GRAY THOMAS C,CPL & ASSOCIATES
LEASING
724 N AVENUE H
CROWLEY,LA 70526 PH 337 288-3841
THOMAS C GRAY,CPL/OWNER
TCGRAY@BELLSOUTH.NET

GRAY WIRELINE (PART OF ARCHER)
CASED-HOLE WIRELINE SERVICES
10613 W SAM HOUSTON PKWY N STE 600
HOUSTON,TX 77064 PH 713 856-4222
WWW.GRAYWIRELINE.COM
- PERMIAN BASIN REGION -
MIDLAND,TX SALES OFFICE - 306 W WALL ST
STE 600 79701 PH 432 620-0008
JEFF WELCH JEFF.WELCH@GRAYWIRELINE.COM
DENVER CITY,TX DIST OFFICE - 601 W
BROADWAY 79323 PH 806 592-3060
ANDREWS,TX DIST OFFICE - 190 SE 1000
79714 PH 432 523-5436
ODESSA,TX DIST OFFICE - 2400 E I-20 79760
PH 432 580-0040
LEVELLAND,TX DIST OFFICE - 1912 W AVE
79336 PH 806 894-6008
HOBBS,NM DIST OFFICE - 2610 W MARYLAND
88240 PH 575 393-8295 OR 575 392-8300
- MID CONTINENT NORTH REGION -
WOODWARD,OK DIST OFFICE - 25 CEDARDALE
ADDITION 73802 PH 580 256-3775
KREBS,OK (MCALESTER) DIST OFFICE - 1100
W WASHINGTON AVE 74554 PH 918 423-1900
DICKINSON,ND (NORTH DAKOTA) DIST OFFICE -
925 37TH AVE E 58601 PH 701 483-9412
NEW KENSINGTON,PA (PENN) DIST OFFICE -
2154 GREENSBURG RD PH 724 334-1822
- MID CONTINENT SOUTH REGION -
WICHITA FALLS,TX DIST OFFICE - 9478
SEYMOUR HWY 76130 PH 940 691-1256
REFUGIO,TX DIST OFFICE - 711 E EMPRESARIO
ST 78377 PH 361 526-4729
CRESSON,TX (GRANBURY) DIST OFFICE - 12060
CELBURNE HWY 171,76035 PH 817 396-0210
GIDDINGS,TX DIST OFFICE - 5400 HWY 290
78942 PH 979 542-4729
- EAST REGION -
YOUNGSVILLE,LA (LAFAYETTE LAND &
OFFSHORE) DIST OFFICE - 4530 DECON RD
70592 PH 337 232-6101
SHREVEPORT,LA DIST OFFICE - 820 HAVENS RD
71107 PH 318 221-7599
LONGVIEW,TX DIST OFFICE - 291 JOHNNY
CLARK RD 75603 PH 903 643-3120
LAUREL,MS DIST OFFICE - 258 VICTORY RD
39443 PH 601 426-0990
OTHER FIELD OFFICES -
ALICE,TX - PH 361 661-0488
ROSHARON,TX - PH 281 431-9900
LONGVIEW,TX - PH 903 643-3120
BUCKHANNON,WV - PH 304 472-3640

GRAYHAWK ENERGY/GRAYHAWK OPERATING SEE
CHESAPEAKE ENERGY CORPORATION

GRAYLYNNE PROPERTIES
10110 BURGOYNE RD
HOUSTON,TX 77042-2936 PH 713 520-0642
ROBERT M GRAY,IND LDMN & PRODUCER
RMDONGRAY@COMCAST.NET

GREAT OAK ENERGY
PO BOX 445,637 ALLEGHENY AVE
OAKMONT,PA 15139-0445
PH 412 828-2900 FAX 412 828-8942
TERRY HOLT
ROBERT CLAY
EDWARD KLAMMER

GREAT PLAINS OPERATING LLC
611 S MAIN ST STE 400
GRAPEVINE,TX 76051 PH 817 416-4856
JAMES SMITH
JSMITH@GPENERGYLLC.COM

GREAT SOUTHERN DRILLING SERVICE SEE
DAILEY PETROLEUM SERVICES,INC

GREAT WESTERN DRILLING,LTD
PO BOX 1659,700 W LOUISIANA
MIDLAND,TX 79702 PH 432 682-5241
FAX 432 684-3702 FAX 432 682-4348 (LAND)
WWW.GWDC.COM
BRUCE M BRADY,PRES
BECKY WILLIAMS,CONTROLLER
DENNIS HENDRIX,VP & OPERS MGR
RUSSELL RICHARDS,EXPL MGR
F CARTER MUIRE,LAND MGR
RANDY HARDIN,MGR INFORM SVC
SANDY KEPPLE,HR MGR
LOVINGTON,N M OFFICE - PO BOX 515
88260 PH 505 396-5538
RALPH SKINNER JR,PROD SUPVSR
SUNDOWN,TX OFFICE - PO BOX 828
79372 PH 806 229-2011
MARK FORD,DRLG & PROD SUPVSR
ODESSA,TX OFFICE - 9186 W I-20,79763
PH 432 381-6433
KEITH KING,DRLG & PROD SUPVSR
GEORGE SMITH,PROD SUPVSR
FARMINGTON,NM OFFICE - 115 W AZTEC BLVD
AZTEC,NM 87410 PH 505 334-7550
CULLAN KELLER,ASST PROD SUPVSR
MENTONE,TX OFFICE - PO BOX 807
PECOS,TX 79772 PH 432 634-0828

GREAT WESTERN RESOURCES INC SEE
FORCENERGY,INC

GREEHEY & COMPANY
506 SANDAU RD STE 100
SAN ANTONIO,TX 78216-3600
PH 210 384-0117 FAX 210 384-0075
SIDNEY J GREEHEY,PRES

GREENBRIER OPERATING CO SEE
CAMDEN RESOURCES INC

GREER C BARRY,PRES VOYAGER PETROLEUM INC
406 WORTH AVE
LAFAYETTE,LA 70508
PH 337 232-7745 FAX 337 232-0409

GREGG OPERATING INC
PO BOX 921
KILGORE,TX 75663-0921 PH 903 984-3443
CHARLA ROLPH,AGENT

GREGORY & COOK CONSTRUCTION INC SEE
PRICE GREGORY CONSTRUCTION INC

GREIG GERALD P,JR,OIL PROPERTIES
56 MAR REE DR
LAUREL,MS 39440-1129 PH 601 428-0126
GERALD P GREIG,JR,CERT PROF LDMN

GRESHAM J MARK,CMM,CDOA
OIL & GAS ROYALTIES

PO BOX 662
WHARTON,TX 77488-0662
PH 979 532-1485 PH 979 533-2120
J MARK GRESHAM,OWNER
HOUSTON,TX OFFICE - PO BOX 27234,77227

GRESHAM PETROLEUM COMPANY
PO BOX 690,415 PERSHING AVE
INDIANOLA,MS 38751-0690 PH 662 887-2160
FAX 662 887-6873 WWW.GRESHAMPETROLEUM.COM
W W GRESHAM III,PRES
CHARLES R VEAZEY,VP SALES
RVEAZEY@GRESHAMPETROLEUM.COM
J W MCPHERSON JR,VP
T G GRESHAM,SECY/TREAS

GRESHAM ROYALTIES
PURCHASERS OF OIL & GAS ROYALTIES
PO BOX 662
WHARTON,TX 77488-0662
PH 979 532-1485
J MARK GRESHAM,OWNER JMG992@PRODIGY.NET
CAROL K GRESHAM,OFC MGR

GREY WOLF DRILLING COMPANY,LP SEE
PRECISION DRILLING OILFIELD SERVICES CORP

GREYSTAR CORPORATION
10375 RICHMOND AVE STE 900
HOUSTON,TX 77042-4170 PH 713 953-7007
FAX 713 953-7015 WWW.GREYSTAR-CORP.COM
GREYSTAR@GREYSTAR-CORP.COM
DAVE PATTON,PRES
MIKE KNEALE,VP
BRUCE TAYLOR,HS&E MGR

GREYSTONE OIL & GAS LLP
1616 S VOSS RD STE 400
HOUSTON,TX 77057-2620
PH 832 333-4000 FAX 832 333-4029
MICHAEL A GEFFERT,MNGNG PRTNR
CARL F DREWS,SR VP LAND
J MICHAEL BLACK,SR VP RESERVOIR ENGRG
MICHAEL R SHOURD,VP GEOL
RUBLE CLARK,SR VP GEOPHY
TIM WOODS,CFO

GRIBAS PAUL J,EXPLOR,DEV & GEOL
1857 FARRIDGE DR
JACKSON,MS 39211-6002 PH 601 362-8378

GRIBBLE CONSULTING
250 W MAIN
BELLVILLE,TX 77418-1351 PH 979 865-4377
KRUSE GRIBBLE,PE,OWNER

GRICE JOEL S
5416 SUFFOLK DR
JACKSON,MS 39211-4506 PH 601 956-6965

GRIFFIN & GRIFFIN EXPLORATION,LLC
1904 LAKELAND DR STE F
JACKSON,MS 39216 PH 601 713-1146
FAX 601 713-1175
WILLIAM K GRIFFIN,III,PRES
JOHN ANDREW GRIFFIN,VP
JIM ANLGE,CFO
KENNEDY GRIFFIN,LAND
LORRI PARKERSON,LAND
KATHY MIDDLETON,ACCT
BOB BOYETT,DRLG MGR
JACK CARONA,ENGR
ANNA CALLENDAR,ASST

GRIFFIN CONSULTING
PO BOX 218257

HOUSTON,TX 77218-8257
PH 281 347-9551 BILLYENGR@AOL.COM
PHYSICAL ADD:22327 BUCKTROUT LN
KATY,TX 77449
W D BILL GRIFFIN,REG PROF PETR ENGR

GRIFFIN RESOURCES INC
OIL & GAS EXPL/DRLG CONTRACTOR/OIL &
GAS OPERATOR
PO BOX 37,14703 S 53RD E AVE
BIXBY,OK 74008
PH 918 366-3148 FAX 918 366-3152
GRI1@COX.NET
VAN F RICK GRIFFIN,PRES
HAMILTON,AL DIST OFFICE - PO BOX 609
114 7TH ST SW,35570-0609

GRIFFIS & SMALL,LLC
1001 FANNIN ST #1900
HOUSTON,TX 77002-6712
PH 713 650-8600 FAX 713 650-8602
RGRIFFIS@RGRIFFIS.COM WWW.RGRIFFIS.COM
RICHARD D GRIFFIS,PRES
JOSEPH SMALL,COO
STEVE PHILLIPS,SR VP,ENGRG
JOEL SABER,VP FINANCE
ERIC LIEKE,VP ENGR
ANGELA POLANSKY,GEOSCIENCE TECH
GRANT BUTKUS,ENGR MGR
MARK NELSON,FINANCIAL ANALYST
MARK MAHLOW,RESERVOIR ENGR
PAUL MAICAH,ENGR TECH

GRIFFITH & SPRAGGINS OIL PRODUCERS
RR 1,BOX 131
YALE,IL 62481 PH 618 793-2057
JIM SPRAGGINS,PARTNER
MARION GRIFFITH,PARTNER

GRIFFITH LAND SERVICES,INC
11060 TIMBERLINE RD
HOUSTON,TX 77043-3804
PH 713 465-3273 FAX 713 647-7270
MARTY L GRIFFITH,PRES
VICTORIA,TX OFFICE - 118 N MAIN ST,STE B
77901 PH 361 575-4577 FAX 361 575-5811

GRIFFITH WESLEY
PO BOX 160
MENTONE,AL 35984-0160 PH 256 634-9411
FAX 256 634-9411

GRIFFON & ASSOCIATES,LLC
4649 DIXIE FARM RD
PEARLAND,TX 77581
PH 281 482-1247 GRIFFONASSOCIATES@MSN.COM
ROBERT J GRIFFON

GRIGSBY PETROLEUM INC
333 TEXAS ST STE 2285
SHREVEPORT,LA 71101-3665 PH 318 425-5306
FAX 318 425-3733
TERRY M WATSON,PRES
TERRY@GRIGSBYPETRO.COM

GRIMES ENERGY COMPANY
11 GREENWAY PLAZA STE 2902
HOUSTON,TX 77046 PH 713 651-7855
FAX 713 655-0018
MIKE GRIMES,PRES
HOUSTON,TX OFFICE - FAX 713 655-0018
DAVID M GRIMES,VP

GRIVICH MINERALS & MINING CORP
600 LEOPARD ST STE 807A

CORPUS CHRISTI,TX 78401 PH 361 884-3100
FAX 361 884-3100 GMMCORP@ATT.NET
PAUL GRIVECH,PRES

GROENDYKE TRANSPORT,INC
2510 ROCK ISLAND BLVD
ENID,OK 73701 PH 580 234-4663
FAX 580 234-1216 WWW.GROENDYKE.COM
GTI.RECEPTION@GROENDYKE.COM
PHOENIX,AZ OFFICE - 4907 S 35TH AVE 85041
PH 620 272-2785
LITTLE ROCK,AR OFFICE - 401 DELTA DR
72206 PH 501 490-0440
FOUNTAIN,CO OFFICE - 910 S SANTA FE 80817
PH 719 391-9855
HENDERSON,CO OFFICE - 9751 E 104TH AVE
80640 PH 303 289-3373
GRAND JUNCTION,CO OFFICE - 2796 HWY 50
SOUTH 81503 PH 970 241-4411
WINDER,GA OFFICE - 68 PEARL PENTECOST RD
30680 PH 770 868-8246
CHANNAHON,IL OFFICE - 23140A W EAMES
60410 PH 815 521-1080
GRANITE CITY,IL OFFICE - 3145 W CHAIN OF
ROCKS RD 63138 PH 618 797-4028
HUTCHINSON,KS OFFICE - 2701 E 4TH 67501
PH 620 662-7281
KANSAS CITY,KS OFFICE - 299 E DONOVAN
66115 PH 913 621-2200
LIBERAL,KS OFFICE - 2124 HWY 83 67901
PH 620 624-2572
PHILLIPSBURG,KS OFFICE - 1566 N HWY 183
67661 PH 620 662-7281
WICHITA,KS OFFICE - 3350 N OHIO 67219
PH 316 755-1266
PT ALLEN,LA OFFICE - 2723 S WESTPORT DR
70767 PH 225 338-1191
LAKE CHARLES,LA OFFICE - 6273 HWY 90 E
70615 PH 337 436-3315
ALBUQUERQUE,NM OFFICE - 5555 BROADWAY SE
87105 PH 505 873-4030
ARTESIA,NM OFFICE - 2401 N FREEMAN ST
88210 PH 575 746-2741
ENID,OK OFFICE - 810 N 54TH ST 73701
PH 580 234-6763
PONCA CITY,OK OFFICE - 1946 W HWY 60
74601 PH 580 765-6202
TULSA,OK OFFICE - 2223 S 57TH W AVE
74107 PH 918 446-1871
BENSALEM,PA OFFICE - 1000 IMPERIAL CT
19020 PH 215 639-6415
AMARILLO,TX OFFICE - 10201 TRIANGLE DR
79108 PH 806 335-1686
ANGLETON,TX OFFICE - 1600 S HWY 288B
77515 PH 979 848-0816
BORGER,TX OFFICE - 2415 FAIRLANES BLVD
79008 PH 806 274-6388
CORPUS CHRISTI,TX OFFICE - 5503 AGNES ST
78405 PH 361 289-1699
EL PASO,TX OFFICE - 830 TONY LAMA 79915
PH 915 772-1922
FORT WORTH,TX OFFICE - 1101 CANTRELL-
SANSOM RD 76131 PH 817 847-6700
CHANNELVIEW,TX OFFICE - 8503 SHELDON RD
77049 PH 281 456-8958
LONGVIEW,TX OFFICE - 820 RYDER DR 75603
PH 903 753-5741

LUBBOCK,TX OFFICE - 6907 N INTERSTATE 27
79403 PH 806 765-5609
RIVERTON,WY OFFICE - 620 RAILROAD AVE
82501 PH 307 857-5881

GROFF PETROLEUM
2200 BANDERA RD
SAN ANTONIO,TX 78228-2166 PH 210 434-2200
FAX 210 432-3755
JOE E GROFF,PRES
ROGER ZICKEFOOSE JR,LAND MGR
JOE E GROFF JR,ENGR
MOLLY GROFF,EXEC SECY
THERESA GROFF,SECY

GROUNDS TIMOTHY L,OIL PRODUCER
PO BOX 44
ALLENDALE,IL 62410-0044 PH 618 299-5291

GROVES BRYAN S,INDEPENDENT GEOL
RAINIER MINERALS CORPORATION
PO BOX 53887,110 OIL CENTER DR
LAFAYETTE,LA 70505-3887
PH 337 233-8032 FAX 337 233-8066
WWW.BRYANGROVESGEOLOGY.COM
GEOGROVES@GMAIL.COM

GRSA CONSULTANTS AND ENGINEERS
14661 S HARRELLS FERRY RD
BATON ROUGE,LA 70816
PH 225 291-9988 WWW.GRSAENG.COM
G W CADBY,PRES GARY.CADBY@GRSAENG.COM

GRUY PETROLEUM MANAGEMENT CO,LLC SEE
CIMAREX ENERGY CO

GRX,INC
PO BOX 1843
CORPUS CHRISTI,TX 78403
PH 361 882-7681 FAX 361 882-7685
GREXPLORATION@GMAIL.COM
ROBERT N GRAHAM,PRES
R C GRAHAM,VP

GS PETROLEUM
PO BOX 767
LIBERTY,TX 77575-0767
PH 936 336-4114 FAX 936 334-8838
CURTIS HUDNALL,PRES
TERRY TURBEVILLE,VP

GSE ENVIRONMENTAL
19103 GUNDLE RD
HOUSTON,TX 77073-3598 PH 800 435-2008
WWW.GSEWORLD.COM
ROD KIRCH,UPSTREAM O&G MGR
RKIRCH@GSEWORLD.COM PH 281 723-2036

GSI OIL & GAS,INC
PO BOX 663
BRYAN,TX 77806-0663 PH 979 778-8850
FAX 979 778-8802
DAVID S CARRABBA,PRES
MARK J CARRABBA,VP
JAMES D LAMPLEY JR,OPERS MGR
JENNIFER R GOTT,SECY,OFC MGR

GUADALUPE OIL & GAS CO
P O BOX 3811
VICTORIA,TX 77903-3811 PH 361 575-3531
JOE N PRATT SR,CHRMN OF BD,PRES
ROBERT C MCKAY,SECY/TREAS

GUDERIAN EMMETT C,JR,GEOPHY CONS
17011 MILLION DOLLAR RD
COVINGTON,LA 70435-7943 PH 985 285-0483
EMMETT C GUDERIAN JR,OWNER

EGUDERIAN@GMAIL.COM

GUERRA ENGINEERING INC SEE
HANOVER COMPRESSOR COMPANY

GUIBERSON AVA SEE
DRESSER OIL TOOLS

GUICHARD OPERATING CO,INC
PO BOX 2000
CROWLEY,LA 70527-2000 PH 337 334-8301
PH 800 738-4645 FAX 337 334-8378
DRILLING@GUICHARDCO.COM
WWW.GUICHARDOPERATING.COM
JOEL GUICHARD,PRES
LANCE GUICHARD,ENGR
CLYDE SIMON,PERSONNEL

GUIDO ENERGY COMPANY
P O BOX 951
NATCHEZ,MS 39121-0951 PH 601 445-9451
AL GUIDO,PARTNER
PAUL GUIDO,PARTNER

GUIDO PRODUCTION COMPANY,INC
PO BOX 1813
NATCHEZ,MS 39121-1813 PH 601 445-9451
PAUL GUIDO,PRES
SUZANNE GUIDO,VP

GUIDRY W W BILL , IND CERT PETR LDMN
PO BOX 71
ABBEVILLE,LA 70511-0071 PH 318 893-4098

GUINN GREG D
P O BOX 7782
TYLER,TX 75711-7782 PH 903 581-1365

GULF CANADA RESOURCES LIMITED SEE
CONOCOPHILLIPS CANADA RESOURCES CORP

GULF CAPITAL RESOURCES,LLC
952 ECHO LN STE 322
HOUSTON,TX 77024-2774 PH 713 984-9525
WWW.GULFCAP.COM
KIRBY H ATWOOD HKATWOOD@GULFCAP.COM

GULF COAST ENERGY INC
615 N UPPER BROADWAY STE 925
CORPUS CHRISTI,TX 78401-0024
PH 361 883-3883 FAX 361 883-3888
GCE@GULFCOASTENERGYINC.COM
MARK STEEN,PRES
BARBARA S SMITH,VP,TREAS

GULF COAST GAS GATHERING LLC
615 N UPPER BROADWAY STE 925
CORPUS CHRISTI,TX 78401-0774
PH 361 883-3883 FAX 361 883-3888
GCE@GULFCOASTENERGYINC.COM
MARK C STEEN,PRES
W S STEVE MAUCH,VP
GARY L MCATEE,VP
BARBARA S SMITH,SECY/TREAS

GULF COAST GEOLOGICAL LIBRARY,INC
1001 MCKINNEY ST STE 800
HOUSTON,TX 77002-6406 PH 713 658-8449
FAX 713 652-6190
BRENDA COMEAUX,MGR

GULF COAST HYDROCARBONS INC
PO BOX 5417
NAVARRE,FL 32566-0417 PH 850 939-6966
FAX 281 749-8108
GREGORY P DILLON,PRES

GULF COAST PIPELINE COMPANY,INC
PO BOX 925204
HOUSTON,TX 77292-5204 PH 713 650-3200

FAX 713 650-3200
THOMAS P CONES,PRES

GULF COAST PRODUCTION COMPANY,INC
402 WHITEBARK DR
LAFAYETTE,LA 70508-6360 PH 318 237-1162
FAX 318 237-1163
GLENN H COFFEY,GEOL
M STEVE REED,LDMN
MARK MUSSO,LDMN
A MURRAY COFFEY,CONS GEOPHY
PATTI REED,OFC MGR

GULF COAST RENTAL TOOL SERVICE,INC
PO BOX 2010
SCOTT,LA 70583-2010 PH 318 234-4571
FAX 318 234-9603 GCRT@BELLSOUTH.NET
HOUSTON,TX OFFICE - 2503 MCCUE STE 9
77056 PH 713 622-1686
BEN R BUSBY,PRES

GULF COAST TUBULARS,INC
3825 BEE CAVE RD
AUSTIN,TX 78746 PH 512 328-6000
FAX 512 328-6070
STEVEN P MASSEY,CHRMN,CEO
CASEY MASSEY,PRES
HOUSTON,TX OFFICE - 650 N SAM HOUSTON
PKY E STE 301,77060 PH 281 759-0700
FAX 281 759-0800

GULF COAST WELL TESTERS,INC
P O BOX 53909,315 MECA DR
LAFAYETTE,LA 70505-3909 PH 337 233-0303
FAX 337 233-2629
DONALD MOSING,CEO
HOUSTON,TX OFFICE - PH 281 558-5226
KEITH MOSING,PRES
HOUSTON,TX OFFICE - PH 281 558-5226
KEITH MOSING,PRES

GULF COAST 3-D INC
114 CLIPPER CV
LAFAYETTE,LA 70508-7024
PH 337 989-7144 FAX 337 989-7079
JAMES CRANE,GEOPHY

GULF CRESCENT RESOURCES,INC
7245 FLOOD REEF
PENSACOLA,FL 32507 PH 850 492-7414
FAX 850 492-7423
CHARLES C LANDRUM,PRES

GULF ENERGY EXPLORATION CORP
PO BOX 161914
AUSTIN,TX 78716-1914
PH 512 335-4800 FAX 512 335-4802
WWW.GULFEXP.COM
STEVE BAILEY,PRES SBAILEY@GULFEXP.COM

GULF ENGINEERING CO,LLC
615 HILL ST
JEFFERSON,LA 70121 PH 504 733-4868
PH 800 821-9574 WWW.GULFENGINEERING.COM
S V MASSIMINI,PRES
N MASSIMINI,CFO
A SPEAKER VELEZ,SALES/MKTG DIR

GULF EXPLORER,L.L.C.
PO BOX 1645
COVINGTON,LA 70434-1645 PH 504 893-3431
PH 504 893-9820 FAX 504 893-9821

GULF GAS UTILITIES CO
3027 MARINA BAY DR STE 205
LEAGUE CITY,TX 77573-2700 PH 281 334-6335

FAX 281 334-5976
R W BROWN,PRES
RBROWN@GULFGASUTILITIES.COM

GULF INTERSTATE ENGINEERING COMPANY
16010 BARKERS POINT LN STE 600
HOUSTON,TX 77079-9000 PH 713 850-3400
FAX 713 850-3579 WWW.GIE.COM
INFO@GIE.COM
H D EVANS,PRES,CEO
B SMITH,CFO
C SHIPMAN,SR VP
R BARNARD,SR VP
B TAKSA,VP INTL DEV
B SPRICK,VP GI FLD SVCS

GULF OIL EXPLORATION & PRODUCTION CO SEE
CHEVRON U S A,INC

GULF PRODUCTION COMPANY,INC
PO BOX 1645
COVINGTON,LA 70434-1645 PH 504 893-9820
PH 504 893-3431 FAX 504 893-9821

GULF SANDS ENERGY,LLC
PO BOX 271091
CORPUS CHRISTI,TX 78427-1091
PH 361 854-8805 FAX 361 854-8805
BARBEECOMP@AOL.COM
PAUL P BARBEE,MNGNG MEMBER
RANDALL L BARBEE,MEMBER

GULF SOUTH ENERGY LLC
PO BOX 1769,HIGHLAND COLONY PARKWAY
RIDGELAND,MS 39158
PH 601 853-2315 FAX 601 853-6625
WILLIAM (BILL) B MCHENRY,JR,PRES

GULF SOUTH OPERATORS,INC
650 POYDRAS ST STE 2660
NEW ORLEANS,LA 70130-6158 PH 504 566-9802
FAX 504 566-9804
DAVID M METTZ
REESE B PINNEY
ROBERT A BORIES

GULF STATES OIL & GAS INVITATIONAL,INC
GOLF & FISHING TOURNAMENT
PO BOX 863
NATCHEZ,MS 39121-0863 PH 601 446-7651
ANNUAL DATES: LAST WEEKEND OF JUNE
IN BILOXI,MS WWW.GSOGI.COM
EDDIE STUTTS,CHRMN/GENESIS CRUDE OIL
GARY PARKER,PAST PRES/W T DRILLING
DEE HORTON,PRES/D & D DRILLING
BRUCE HIGHTOWER,VP/RAPAD DRILLING
COURTNEY ALDRIDGE,SECY/ALDRIDGE OPERATING
BOB M DEARING,EXEC SECY/AFLAC
BOBMDEARING@YAHOO.COM

GULFLAND INSURANCE SERVICES,INC
1066 WEST TUNNEL BLVD
HOUMA,LA 70360-4071 PH 504 868-2577
FAX 504 851-3983

GULFLINK LLC
9302 CHARTER PINE ST
HOUSTON,TX 77070-2053
PH 281 413-4015 FAX 281 257-9466
MYRON KORPAN

GULFMARK ENERGY INC
PO BOX 844
HOUSTON,TX 77001-0844
PH 713 881-3602 FAX 713 881-3491
GEOFF GRIFFITH,PRES

MARK THIBAUT,VP CRUDE OIL PUR

GULFSTREAM NATURAL GAS SYSTEM SEE
DUKE ENERGY GAS TRANSMISSION

GULFSTREAM SERVICES INC
103 DICKSON RD
HOUMA,LA 70363-7306 PH 800 821-8454
PH 985 868-0303 FAX 985 872-3423
WWW.GULFSTREAMSERVICES.COM
GSI@GULFSTREAMSERVICES.COM
MIKE MIRE,CEO/PRES
BOBBY BOND,VP OPER
STEVE ARCENEAUX,COMPTROLLER
KIM GIROIR,WIRELINE OPERS
GREG LANDRY,OPERS MGR
MIKE DUPONT,AP/AR MGR
HAROLD GUIDRY,SLS - HOUSTON/NEW ORLEANS
JULIE KITZIGER,SLS - HOUSTON/NEW ORLEANS
RONNIE LUQUETTE,SLS - HOUSTON
KEN WESTBROOK,SLS/TECH SUPPORT - HOUSTON
AMY LYONS,SLS - HOUSTON
BRADLEY BARKURN,SLS - HOUSTON
EMERIC WATSON,SLS
HAYES GARRETT,SLS
JERRY RUSSO,FLD SLS
ROBERT CHAMPAGNE,FLD SLS
HOUMA,LA OFFICE - HYDRAULIC TOOLS/SHEAR
215 N HOLLYWOOD RD,70364 PH 888 822-8664
PH 985 876-8615 FAX 985 876-8715
BILLY MARCEL,OPERS
ROGER DAVIS,OPERS
SCOTT ADAMS,SLS
HOUMA,LA OFFICE - SPECIAL SVCS/BALL-DART
105 W WOODLAWN RANCH RD,70363
PH 888 876-1384 985 876-1384
FAX 985 876-1766
KYLE SADLER,GLOBAL MGR,CEMENT HEAD SYSTEM
GLEN DARCEY,REG MGR-GOM
KILGORE,TX OFFICE - 3200 HWY 135 N,75662
PH 866 983-2469 PH 903 983-2469
FAX 903 983-2950
JESSIE VIATOR,OPERS MGR
LAFAYETTE,LA OFFICE - 107 ROW 2,70508
PH 866 218-0590 PH 337 704-0091
FAX 337 704-0096
RONNIE MICHEL,OPERS MGR
MALCOLM KRAUS,SLS MGR
BRIAN BORDELON,QUAL ASSUR MGR
WILLIAMSPORT,PA OFFICE - 1330 DIX ST
17701 PH 877 901-8471 PH 570 320-2882
FAX 570 320-1885
FRED BAILEY,OPERS MGR

GUMBO OIL COMPANY
PO BOX 1060
BREAUX BRIDGE,LA 70517 PH 337 332-5987
DANIEL J REDMOND,PRES

GUNN W L BILL,& ASSOCIATES,OIL OPR
PO BOX 232
LUFKIN,TX 75902-0232 PH 409 634-9196
FAX 409 634-8821

GUPTON REALTY CO
P O BOX 725,301 S BROAD ST
WEST COLUMBIA,TX 77486-0725
PH 409 345-4657
S D GUPTON,REALTOR

GUSTAFSON R B,JR,IND GEOL,OIL PROD
PO BOX 865,705 AZALEA DR

WAYNESBORO,MS 39367-0865 PH 601 735-2731
R B GUSTAFSON,JR,OWNER

GUTHREY HARVEY R,C.P.L.
PO BOX 53844
LAFAYETTE,LA 70505-3844 PH 337 233-2111
PH 233-2123 FAX 337 234-0586
HARVEY R GUTHREY,CERT PROF LDMN

GWALTNEY DRILLING INC
PO BOX 520,107 SE 3RD ST
WASHINGTON,IN 47501-0520 PH 812 254-5085
MICHAEL CROUCH,PRES
LEE CAMPBELL,DRLG SUPT
BILL MCCAIN,OPERS MGR

GYRO EXPLORATION,INC
1237 WOODCLIFF DR
BATON ROUGE,LA 70815-6856 PH 225 921-1659
FAX 225 275-1978 GYROX33@GMAIL.COM
DAVID D TETTLETON,PRES

GYRODATA WELLBORE SURVEYORS
23000 NW LAKE DR
HOUSTON,TX 77095 5344 PH 713 461-3146
FAX 713 461-0920 WWW.GYRODATA.COM
R S MACMAHAN,PRES

H & A DRILLING
SPECIALIZE IN SHALLOW O&G DRLG (OHIO)
4780 TAVENER RD
NEWARK,OH 43056-9086 PH 740 763-2575

H & D OPERATING COMPANY
807 OSAGE ST
REFUGIO,TX 78377 PH 361 526-4691
FLOYD R BOEN,PRES

H & H DEVELOPMENT CO
705 HODGE RD
FARMERVILLE,LA 71241 PH 318 726-5477
B J HODGE,PRES

H & H ENTERPRISES
DIRECTIONAL DRLG/PIPELINE CONTRACTOR
4578 JOHNSON RD
BEMUS POINT,NY 14712-9744 PH 440 293-8911
FAX 440 293-5498 JASON@HANDHENT.COM
HANDHENT.COM
THOMAS A HOCKRAN,PRES

H & N OPERATING COMPANY,INC SEE
NEW DAVID OPERATING CO,INC

H & S DRILLING COMPANY,THE,DRLG CONTR
320 S BOSTON AVE STE 1910
TULSA,OK 74103-4734
PH 918 587-8163 FAX 918 587-8164
BILL R SNOW,PRES
ROBERT R SNOW,VP & LEGAL COUNSEL
DOROTHY DEBORDE,SECY

H B RENTALS,LC
PO BOX 190,5813 HWY 90 E
BROUSSARD,LA 70518-0190 PH 337 839-1641
PH 800 262-6790 WWW.HBRENTAL.COM
DEIDRE TOUPS,SR VP
DAVID CAILLIER,VP,OFFSHORE
JUDE PRIMEAUX,OFFSHORE OPERS MGR
BYRON BRASSEAUX,ONSHORE MGR
MIKE BLAKELY,REG OPER MGR
SCOTT LEBLANC,REG SALES MGR
GLENN AGUILAR,DIR OFFSHORE SALES
JIM CLIBURN,SALES
CYNDEE POTTER,CORP SALES
HOUSTON,TX OFFICE - 523 N SAM HOUSTON PKY
EAST,STE 175,77060 PH 281 999-0047

PH 866 999-0040
MAURICE BLEDSOE,PRES
GARY BLEDSOE,VP,LAND OPER
MIKE ROPER,CORP SALES
ROBERT NEAL,CORP SALES
ALVIN,TX OFFICE - 8525 S HWY 35
LIVERPOOL,TX 77577 PH 281 393-1210
PH 800 237-6062
RICKY RICHARD,REG OPERS MGR
GREG REINSCH,MGR
DUSTIN JONES,SALES
ALICE,TX OFFICE - 4637 S HWY 281
78332 PH 361 664-8591 888 464-8591
ALBERT GARZA,MGR
BILL BLACKBURN,SALES
FAIRFIELD,TX OFFICE - 130 HWY 75 S
75840 PH 903 389-9230 866 552-9230
BRIAN SIMPSON,REG OPERS MGR
LESS LODEN,SALES
MIDLAND,TX OFFICE - 3319 HWY 158 E,79706
PH 432 570-0975 866 874-3362
TONY DELAROSA,MGR
JAKE KEPPLE,SALES
EL RENO,OK OFFICE - 3701 S CHOCTAW,73036
PH 405 422-1062 877 422-1062
BRIAN CHILTON,MGR
DAVID THUMMEL,SALES
DECATUR,TX OFFICE - 149 W BYPASS 287
76225 PH 940 427-9673 866 710-9673
MIKE CROSS,MGR
DELMER STANKO,SALES
RIVERTON,WY OFFICE - 12674 US HWY 26
82501 PH 307 856-9761 800 850-9761
ANDY DAVIDSON,REG OPER MGR
JIM BOLING,MGR
KENT CROOKS,SALES
MENIFEE,AR OFFICE - 31 BELL MOUNTAIN RD
72107 PH 501 977-1900 877 931-1900
MIKE MONTGOMERY,MGR
JANSON SEACH,SALES

H G B LAND SERVICES COMPANY,INC SEE
H G B OIL CORPORATION

H H & R ENTERPRISES
P O BOX 51233,920 PINHOOK RD STE 313
LAFAYETTE,LA 70505-1233 PH 318 235-0475
L A,MICKEY,HOLLIER,GEOPHYS

H H C DRILLING CO,INC
16749 HWY 62 SOUTH
ORANGE,TX 77630-8499 PH 409 886-3297
HARRY CORBETT II,PRES

H J GRUY AND ASSOCIATES,INC,RESERVOIR
ENGRG,GEOL ASSET EVAL,RESERVE ESTIMATES
333 CLAY ST STE 3850
HOUSTON,TX 77002-4108 PH 713 739-1000
FAX 713 739-6112 WWW.HJGRUY.COM
HOUGRUY@HJGRUY.COM
MARILYN WILSON,CHRMN & PRES
ROBERT RASOR,EXEC VP,ENGRG MGR
BOB SARTAIN,SR VP,MGR/GEO

H R H OPERATING,INC
PO BOX 127
BRUNI,TX 78344-0127 PH 361 747-5341
RON HERSCHAP,PRES
HOWARD HERSCHAP,VP

H R H PARTNERS LTD
PO BOX 127

BRUNI,TX 78344-0127 PH 361 747-5341
RON HERSCHAP,PRES
HOWARD HERSCHAP,VP

H S I GEOTRANS,INC
45610 WOODLAND RD STE 400
STERLING,VA 20166-4221
PH 703 444-7000 FAX 703 444-1685
TEMPE,AZ OFFICE - 4665 S ASH AVE STE G-1
85282 PH 480 839-2800 FAX 480 839-2828
RANCHO CORDOVA,CA OFFICE - 3035 PROSPECT
PARK DR STE 40,95670
PH 916 853-1800 FAX 916 853-1860
COSTA MESA,CA OFFICE - 3150 BRISTOL ST
STE 500,92626 PH 714 513-1415
FAX 714 513-1278
WESTMINSTER,CO OFFICE - 9101 HARLAN ST
STE 210,80030 PH 303 426-7501
FAX 303 426-7780
ROSWELL,GA OFFICE - 1080 HOLCOMB BRIDGE
RD,BLDG 100,STE 190,30076
PH 770 642-1000 FAX 770 642-8808
HARVARD,MA OFFICE - 6 LANCASTER COUNTY RD
01451 PH 978 772-7557 FAX 978 772-6183
RENO,NV OFFICE - 50 W LIBERTY ST STE 580
89501 PH 775 324-5900 FAX 775 324-5924
NORTH LAS VEGAS,NV OFFICE - 2621 LOSEE RD
BLDG B-1,RM 3050,M S 439,89030
PH 702 295-2033 FAX 702 295-2025
FREEHOLD,NJ OFFICE - 2 PARAGON WAY
07728 PH 732 409-0344 FAX 732 409-3020
SAN JUAN,PUERTO RICO OFFICE - IL BLDG
KENNEDY AVE,MARGINAL RD 10,STE 307
00920 PH 787 774-8776 FAX 787 783-8799
GLEN ALLEN,VA OFFICE - 5030 SADLER RD
STE 103,23060 PH 804 346-5433
FAX 804 346-5432
BROOKFIELD,WI OFFICE - 175 N CORPORATE DR
STE 100,53045 PH 262 792-1282
FAX 262 792-1310

H T S,INC
416 PICKERING ST
HOUSTON,TX 77091-3312 PH 713 692-8373
R E LANGSTON,PRES

H-M OIL COMPANY
8554 KATY FWY STE 320
HOUSTON,TX 77024-1849 PH 713 827-0405
FAX 713 827-0426 HMOIL.COM
JACK LITTLE,PRES
TRACY LITTLE,VP
RANDY LITTLE,VP

H-M RESOURCE MANAGEMENT,INC
8554 KATY FWY STE 320
HOUSTON,TX 77024-1849 PH 713 827-0405
FAX 713 827-0426 HMOIL.COM
TRACY L LITTLE,PRES
JACK W LITTLE,VP

HAAS C F,OIL AND GAS,INC
PO BOX 1026
CORPUS CHRISTI,TX 78403-1026
PH 361 855-9306 FAX 361 855-9309
CHARLES F HAAS,OWNER,CFO
RICHARD A HAAS,PRES

HACKNEY L FRANKLIN,CPA,PLLC
5090 RICHMOND AVE #119
HOUSTON,TX 77056 PH 713 888-0645
INFO@LFHACKNEYCPA.COM

LAWRENCE F HACKNEY,CPA

HAD INC
9797 BENNER RD
RITTMAN,OH 44270 PH 330 925-1000
FAX 330 925-1105 WWW.HADINC.COM
JASON HATFIELD,VP JASON@HADINC.COM

HADCO INTERNATIONAL
GEN EQUIP APPRAISERS,O&G PROP,D & WS RIGS
O&G EQUIP,COMMERCIAL APPRAISALS
PO BOX 1465
CONROE,TX 77305-1465 PH 409 760-1220
FAX 409 760-1121
HARVEY A DAVIS,PRES,APPRAISER
DUKE COON,VP

HADDAD GEORGE A,JR,OIL & GAS PRODUCER
P O BOX 7847
SHREVEPORT,LA 71137-7847 PH 318 425-2090

HADDOCK FRED & DEBORAH FREDERICKS TRUST
3935 HOLDEN DR
ANN ARBOR,MI 48103 PH 734 663-7046
FRED.DEB.HADDOCK@GMAIL.COM

HADDOCK FRED & HELEN
3935 HOLDEN DR
ANN ARBOR,MI 48103 PH 734 663-7046
FRED.DEB.HADDOCK@GMAIL.COM

HAGGARD ID WIPER,INC
PO BOX 27906
HOUSTON,TX 77227 PH 281 330-6016
FAX 936 321-8490 WWW.HAGGARD-MUDDOG.COM
HAGMUDDOG@AIRMAIL.NET

HAHN ENGINEERING,INC
PO BOX 190251
SAINT LOUIS,MO 63119-0251 PH 314 968-3656
JOSEPH K HAHN,PRES

HAIL RESOURCES,LLC
800 BERING DR STE 209
HOUSTON,TX 77057-0213 PH 713 658-8590
TOM L HAIL,PRES

HAIL TOM L
800 BERING DR STE 209
HOUSTON,TX 77057-0213 PH 713 658-8590

HAL SYSTEMS CORPORATION
8111 LBJ FRWY #860
DALLAS,TX 75251 PH 214 691-4700
PH 800 442-9273 FAX 214 691-4730
WWW.HALFILE.COM
WWW.COUNTYRECORDS.COM
SALES@HALFILE.COM
GREGORY J HAHN,CEO,PRES
AUSTIN,TX OFFICE - 1301 S CAPITAL OF TX
HWY,#231,78746 PH 512 892-0972
FAX 512 892-1829 877 425-3453
TOM HOKANSON,VP,SOFTWARE DEV

HALBERT ROYALTIES,INCORPORATED
PURCHASER OF PRODUCING OIL/GAS ROYALTIES
PO BOX 6990
TYLER,TX 75711-6990 PH 903 592-0578
FAX 903 561-4254
KEVIN HALBERT,PRES
CHARLOTTE HALBERT,VP,TREAS
LINDA B DORSEY,SECY/TREAS

HALCON ENERGY PROPERTIES,INC SEE
HALCON RESOURCES CORPORATION

HALCON HOLDINGS,INC SEE
HALCON RESOURCES CORPORATION

(800) 375-1838
WWW.ARMSTRONGOIL.COM

If your company is not listed in our directory, we would like to list it in the next edition of our directory - absolutely FREE. To be listed, we need it in writing. Please fill out the form below or visit our website and fill out the listing form there. If you wish to use the form below, just mail it or fax it to us at (800) 375-1838.

Company Name _____

Physical Address _____

Mailing address if different _____

Phone # _____ Fax # _____

Email address _____

Key personnel and their titles:

_____

_____

_____

_____

If you need to list additional offices, please include on letterhead

To Order Call (800) 375-1838 or
www.armstrongoil.com

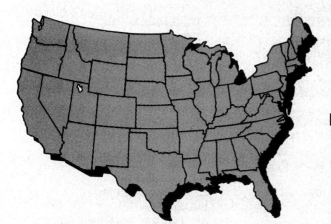

Nationwide Office Directory
Full 8 1/2" x 11" book size
Entire Nation
over 16,000 companies listed

$ 225 (no discount available)

Nationwide Mini Directory (Briefcase)
Small Size 5 1/4" x 8 1/4"
Same complete nationwide information
over 16,000 companies listed

$ 140 w / discount*

Texas Directory
Includes
Texas and S.E. New Mexico

$ 80 w / discount*

Louisana / Gulf Coast Directory
Includes the following states:
Gulf coast of Texas, Louisana
Arkansas, Mississippi,
Alabama, Georgia, Florida
N.E. states

$80 w / discount*

Rocky Mountain / Central U.S. Directory
Includes the following states:
West Texas and Panhandle of Texas
Oklahoma, New Mexico
Colorado, Alaska and all
Western U.S. states

$80 w / discount*

* discount applies when invoice is paid within 30 days after receipt of order.

HALCON OPERATING CO.,INC SEE
  HALCON RESOURCES CORPORATION
HALCON RESOURCES CORPORATION
  5100 E SKELLY DR STE 650
  TULSA,OK 74135-6559 PH 918 663-2800
  FAX 918 663-9540
    LARRY E LEE,PRES/CEO
    LARRY G RAMPEY,SR VP OPERS
    DRAKE N SMILEY,SR VP LAND & LEGAL
    G LES AUSTIN,SR VP FIN
    JOHN FRICK,VP OPERS
HALCON RESOURCES OPERATING,INC SEE
  HALCON RESOURCES CORPORATION
HALE C CLARK,OIL & GAS PROPERTIES
  1062 ADDO BARNES RD
  MCCOMB,MS 39648 PH 601 684-0001
    CCHALE@BELLSOUTH.NET
HALE ROBERT C & ASSOCS INC
  PO BOX 825,430 CELINA RD
  BURKESVILLE,KY 42717-0825 PH 270 864-3111
  FAX 270 864-3111
    ROBERT C HALE,PRES
HALEX OIL CORPORATION
  1940 FOUNTAIN VIEW #165
  HOUSTON,TX 77057
  PH 713 850-1220 FAX 888 850-1442
    MIKE HALE,PRES MHALE@HALEXOIL.COM
HALL E G,OIL COMPANY
  159 PRIVATE ROAD 5489
  MEXIA,TX 76667 PH 903 874-0855
    D P MITCHELL,OWNER
HALL ENERGY INC
  PO BOX 218
  MAGNETIC SPRINGS,OH 43036-0218
  PH 937 348-2244 FAX 937 348-2244
    JON HALL,PRES
HALL FRANK J
  400 TRAVIS ST STE 320
  SHREVEPORT,LA 71101-3119 PH 318 424-5236
HALL RESOURCES CORP
  1721 S AZTEC AVE
  INDEPENDENCE,MO 64057
  PH 816 796-2906
  SEMINOLE,OK OFFICE - RT 1,BOX 251-A1
  74868
    BO CLYMER,PROD SUPT
HALLIBURTON ENERGY SERVICES
    A HALLIBURTON COMPANY
  10200 BELLAIRE BLVD
  HOUSTON,TX 77072-5206 PH 281 575-3000
    WWW.HALLIBURTON.COM
    DAVID J LESAR,BOARD CHRMN/PRES/CEO
    JEFF MILLER,EXEC VP/COO
    MARK A MCCOLLUM,EXEC VP/CFO
    ALBERT O CORNELISON JR,EXEC VP/GEN
      COUNSEL
    LAWRENCE J POPE,ADMIN EXEC VP/CHF HR OFCR
    TIM PROBERT,PRES-STRAGEGY & CORP DEV
    JIM BROWN,PRES-WESTERN HEMISPHERE
    JOE D RAINEY,PRES-EASTERN HEMISPHERE
    SHERRY D WILLIAMS,SR VP-CHF ETHICS &
      COMPLIANCE OFCR
    EVELYN M ANGELLE,SR VP/CAO
    CHRISTIAN GARCIA,SR VP/TREAS INVEST RELS
    CHRISTINA M IBRAHIM,VP/CORP SECY
    ROBERT MORAN,VP-GOV AFFAIRS

    ROBERT L HAYTER,ASST SECY/ASST GEN
      COUNSEL
    BRUCE A METZINGER,ASST SECY/SR DIR
    - SOUTH TEXAS -
  HOUSTON,TX TECH CENTER OFFICE - 15081
    1/2 MILNER RD 77032 PH 281 871-4000
  HOUSTON,TX OFFICE - 3000 N SAM HOUSTON
    PKWY E 77032 PH 281 871-4000
  ALICE,TX OFFICE - 850 COMMERCE RD 78332
    PH 361 660-1200
  CORPUS CHRISTI,TX OFFICE - 555 N
    CARANCHUA ST TOWER II STE 775
    78478 PH 361 888-8153
  FRESNO,TX OFFICE - 330 SYCAMORE RD
    77545 PH 281 431-2531
  SAN ANTONIO,TX OFFICE - 8610 N NEW
    BRAUNFELS STE 614 78217 PH 210 824-2471
    - GULF OF MEXICO -
  LAFAYETTE,LA OFFICE - 110 CAPITAL DR
    70508 PH 337 232-7831
  NEW ORLEANS,LA OFFICE - 601 POYDRAS ST
    70130 PH 504 593-6700
    - WEST COAST -
  BAKERSFIELD,CA OFFICE - 34722 7TH
    STANDARD RD 93314 PH 661 393-8111
    - MID-CONTINENT -
  OKLAHOMA CITY,OK OFFICE - 210 PARK AVE
    STE 2000 73102 PH 405 231-1800
    - NORTHEAST -
  CANONSBURG,PA OFFICE - 121 CHAMPION WAY
    STE 110 15317-5817 PH 724 743-8100
    - PERMIAN BASIN -
  MIDLAND,TX OFFICE - 125 W MISSOURI
    79701 PH 432 682-4305
    - ROCKY MOUNTAINS -
  DENVER,CO OFFICE - 1125 17TH ST STE 1900
    80202 PH 303 308-4200
    - SOUTHEAST -
  SHREVEPORT,LA OFFICE - 416 TRAVIS ST
    STE 505 71101-3282 PH 318 673-4400
  TYLER,TX OFFICE - 3800 PALUXY DR STE 210
    75703 PH 903 581-5263
    - ALASKA -
  ANCHORAGE,AK OFFICE - 6900 ARCTIC BLVD
    99518 PH 907 275-2600
    - CANADA -
  CALGARY,ALBERTA,CANADA - 645 7TH AVE SW
    T2P 4G8 PH 403 231-9300
    - MEXICO -
  VILLAHERMOSA,MEXICO OFFICE -
    PH 52 9933101100
HALLIBURTON GEODATA SEE
  HALLIBURTON ENERGY SERVICES
HALLIBURTON GEOPHYSICAL SERVICES,INC SEE
  HALLIBURTON ENERGY SERVICES
HALLIBURTON LOGGING SERVICES,INC SEE
  HALLIBURTON ENERGY SERVICES
HALLIBURTON OPERATING COMPANY
  2108 DALLAS PKWY STE 214
  PLANO,TX 75093 PH 214 373-8840
    COLE HALLIBURTON
    COLEHALLIBURTON@HOTMAIL.COM
HALLIBURTON RESERVOIR SERVICES SEE
  HALLIBURTON ENERGY SERVICES
HALLIBURTON RESOURCE MANAGEMENT SEE
  HALLIBURTON ENERGY SERVICES

HALLIBURTON SERVICES SEE
  HALLIBURTON ENERGY SERVICES
HALLYSON,INC
  PO BOX 52919
  LAFAYETTE,LA 70505-2919
  PH 337 264-1700 FAX 337 264-1700
    MASON M DICKERSON,PRES
    ALLIE F DICKERSON,VP
    COLLEEN DICKERSON,SECY
    LARRY DICKERSON,TREAS
HALSTEAD CHARLES R,PETR GEOL
  803 ASHFORD CT
  TYLER,TX 75703-1408 PH 903 593-6067
HALWELL COMPANY,INC
  1635 WARREN CHAPEL
  FLEMING,OH 45729 PH 740 373-6134
  FAX 740 373-2404
    EDDY L BIEHL,PRES
    GEORGE D BAILEY,JR,EXEC VP
HAMILTON & SQUIBB,LLP
  8235 DOUGLAS AVE STE 1040
  DALLAS,TX 75225
  PH 214 987-1483   WWW.HAMILTONSQUIBB.COM
    RHODES W HAMILTON,PTNR
      RHAMILTON@HAMILTONSQUIBB.COM
    CLIFTON A SQUIBB,PTNR
HAMILTON BUTLER RIDDICK TARLTON &
    SULLIVAN,PC
  PO BOX 70185
  MOBILE,AL 36670-1185 PH 251 432-7517
HAMILTON ENGINEERING INC,DRLG CONS
  777 POST OAK BLBVD STE 400
  HOUSTON,TX 77056-3222 PH 713 956-0956
  FAX 713 956-0365
    WWW.HAMILTONENGINEERING.NET
    KEITH GRIMES,CEO
    KEN THOMAS,CFO
    CHARLES CHUCK BROWN,PRES ENGRG
    CLAUDE THORP,VP-ATLANTIS
    CLYDE NEELY,VP SLS
    KRISTOPHER LABLUE,SLS
    LORI GUTIERREZ,OFC MGR
    HUNTER SANDRIDGE,CONSLT COORD
    JOE BARNES,DRLG FLUIDS MGR
    DIANE MORENO,INVOICING
    JOYCE BARBAZETTE
    LAUREL BLAKE,RECPT
HAMILTON HARRY W
  HAMILTON RANCH
  PO BOX 1099
  SINTON,TX 78387 PH 361 364-1515
HAMILTON-TEDFORD OPERATING CO,LLC
  900 8TH ST STE 710
  WICHITA FALLS,TX 76301-6892
  PH 940 322-1124
HAMMAN OIL & REFINING COMPANY,OIL OPR
  PO BOX 130028
  HOUSTON,TX 77219 PH 713 526-7417
  FAX 713 526-3068 BGOODWIN@HAMMANOIL.COM
    HENRY HAMMAN,PRES
    BILL GOODWIN,OPERS MGR
HAMON OIL & GAS RESOURCE CENTER
    WWW.DALLASLIBRARY2.ORG
HANCOCK J M
  P O BOX 68
  BEEVILLE,TX 78104 PH 361 358-4262

HANKAMER CURTIS CORPORATION,THE
9039 KATY FWY STE 530
HOUSTON,TX 77024-1608 PH 713 461-8140
JAMES RANDOLPH HANKAMER,PRES
GREGORY A HERBST,SECY/TREAS

HANKEY OIL COMPANY
4265 SAN FELIPE ST STE 1050
HOUSTON,TX 77027-2938
PH 713 960-9795 FAX 713 960-0334

HANLAD OIL CORP SEE
MCBRIDE OIL & GAS CORP

HANLEY LAND SERVICES
14404 COUNTY ROAD 452
LYNDALE,TX 75771 PH 903 533-1060
DAVID HANLEY,CPL,OWNER

HANLON-TOWNES ROYALTY COMPANY
401 S BOSTON AVE STE 1850
TULSA,OK 74103-4060 PH 918 583-7434
FAX 918 583-7451
WM DENNIS INGRAM,PRES
VIRGINIA INGRAM,SPEC PROJ

HANNA OIL AND GAS COMPANY
PO BOX 1356,60 S 6TH ST
FORT SMITH,AR 72902-1356 PH 479 782-8808
FAX 479 782-1343 WWW.HANNAOILANDGAS.COM
BILL HANNA,PRES
RON ROBBINS,VP
RANDY STRICKLAND,CFO
MIKE CARDWELL,LDMN
JIM EDGIN,DRLG SUPVSR

HANNAH & HANNAH,GEOLS
PO BOX 49314
ALGOOD,TN 38506-0314 PH 931 526-7806
DEBORAH A HANNAH,PRES

HANOVER COMPANY,THE
12001 N HOUSTON ROSSLYN
HOUSTON,TX 77086-3212 PH 281 447-8787
FAX 281 447-0821 (CORP) OR 447-8790 (SLS)
HANOVER-CO.COM
MICHAEL J MCGHAN,PRES,CEO
WILLIAM S GOLDBERG,CFO/TREAS
WILLIAM S GOLDBERG,EXEC VP
CHARLES D ERWIN,SR VP/SLS & MKTG
JOE BRADFORD,SR VP,WORLDWIDE OPERS DEV
ROBERT O PIERCE,SR VP,OPERS FABRICATION
STEVE GILL,VP,INTL SLS
MARK STORY,VP,SLS-SOUTHERN REG
AL LAVENUE,VP,SLS-NORTHERN REG
WILLIAM C BRYANT,VP,OPERS-MID CONTINENT
MAXWELL C MCDONALD,VP,OPERS-SE REGION
JERRY BOB MCCOLLOM,VP,OPERS-WESTERN REG
TEDDY J HEAD,VP,OPERS-SOUTH TEXAS
DON DEVILLE,VP,OPERS-SUPPORT
ROGER WAGNER,VP,FLEET MGMNT
MATT GASIOR,VP,ACCT
TODD RUTHERFORD,VP,INTL OPERS
CAL CAHILL,VP,BUS DEV
DALLAS,TX OFFICE - 8150 N CENTRAL EXPWY
STE 1550,75206-1883 PH 214 369-5554
FAX 214 369-6972

HANOVER COMPRESSOR COMPANY SEE
HANOVER COMPANY,THE

HARBISON-FISCHER,INC
901 N CROWLEY RD
CROWLEY,TX 76036 PH 817 297-2211
FAX 817 297-4248 WWW.HFPUMPS.COM

H-F_SALES@HFPUMPS.COM
DAVID MARTIN,SR VP/MNGNG DIR
JOHN PERKINS,VP SLS
GIL APPELHANS,MID-CONT REG MGR
JOEL KEETER,WESTERN REG MGR
RANDY DE WERFF,EASTERN REG MGR
SCOTT ALTENBERN,FLD SYSTEMS MGR
JUSTIN CONYERS,REG MGR/TECH SVCS/EXPORT
SLS
- CALIFORNIA WAREHOUSES -
SANTA PAULA,CA OFFICE - 224 W SANTA MARIA
ST STE E 93060 PH 805 525-7900
FAX 805 525-7911
TOM DEMOS,DIST MGR PH 661 577-2092
BOB DOERING,ASST DIST MGR
PH 661 577-2098
BAKERSFIELD,CA - 2801 PEGASUS DR
93308 PH 661 387-0166 FAX 661 387-0165
TOM DEMOS,DIST MGR PH 661 577-2092
BOB DOERING,ASST DIST MGR
PH 661 577-2098
FREDDIE HERNANDEZ,SLS PH 661 979-5366
PAT PETERSEN,SLS PH 661 577-2101
TAFT,CA - PO BOX 1015,116 E MAIN 93268
PH 661 765-7792 FAX 661 765-5569
TOM DEMOS,DIST MGR PH 661 577-2092
BOB DOERING,ASST DIST MGR
PH 661 577-2098
- ILLINOIS WAREHOUSE -
GRAYVILLE,IL - 1421 N COURT ST
62844 PH 618 375-3841 FAX 618 375-6121
H-F_GRAYVILLE@HFPUMPS.COM
WAYNE MIDDLETON,DIST MGR PH 812 568-6383
JOHNNY RAVELLETTE,SLS PH 618 599-0127
ROBERT O'DANIEL,SLS PH 618 384-7615
- KANSAS WAREHOUSES -
EL DORADO,KS - PO BOX 978,615 STATE ST
67042-0978 PH 316 321-5940
FAX 316 321-5525 H-F_ELDORADO@HFPUMPS.COM
BILL O'DELL,DIST MGR PH 580 254-0919
BOB ROGERS,SLS PH 316 322-0444
BENNY SMITH,SLS PH 316 258-7358
GARDEN CITY,KS - PO BOX 1837,2410 W JONES
67846 PH 620 275-1095 FAX 620 275-8543
H-F_GARDENCITY@HFPUMPS.COM
JUSTIN GREEN,DIST MGR PH 713 483-4064
EARL AVALON,SLS PH 620 271-3998
GREAT BEND,KS - 5820 ANCHOR WAY
67530 PH 620 793-5091 FAX 620 793-5911
H-F_GREATBEND@HFPUMPS.COM
JUSTIN GREEN,DIST MGR PH 713 483-4064
ROB BOOTH,SLS PH 620 546-1544
TOM FREDERKING,SLS PH 785 650-4499
LIBERAL,KS - PO BOX 796,67905
1470 GENERAL WELCH 67901 PH 620 624-9042
FAX 620 624-9059 H-F_LIBERAL@HFPUMPS.COM
JUSTIN GREEN,DIST MGR PH 713 483-4064
RICK GOKEY,SLS PH 620 482-2642
- LOUISIANA WAREHOUSE -
SHREVEPORT,LA (BOSSIER CITY,LA 71111) -
PO BOX 7761,4415 VIKING LOOP 71137
PH 318 742-2942 FAX 318 742-2942
H-F_SHREVEPORT@HFPUMPS.COM
ROGER JOHNSON,DIST MGR PH 903 987-0629
SONNY EZELLE,SLS PH 903 720-4957
- MICHIGAN WAREHOUSE -

MT PLEASANT,MI - 1280 N FANCHER
48858 PH 989 773-1032 FAX 989 773-1411
H-F_MTPLEASANT@HFPUMPS.COM
WAYNE MIDDLETON,DIST MGR PH 812 568-6383
ANDREW MASSARO,SLS PH 989 289-4363
- MISSISSIPPI WAREHOUSES -
LAUREL,MS (ELLISVILLE,MS 39437) -
PO BOX 4297,5417 HWY 11 N
39441 PH 601 428-7919 FAX 601 428-7919
H-F_LAUREL@HFPUMPS.COM
ROGER JOHNSON,DIST MGR PH 903 987-0629
KEITH WESTMORELAND,SLS PH 601 433-0525
NATCHEZ,MS - 24 FELTUS
39120 PH 601 442-7961 FAX 601 446-9090
H-F_NATCHEZ@HFPUMPS.COM
ROGER JOHNSON,DIST MGR PH 903 897-0629
MARK MCANDREWS,SLS PH 601 870-6420
- NEW MEXICO WAREHOUSES -
FARMINGTON,NM - PO BOX 2082,87499
2000 TROY KING RD,87401
PH 505 327-1398 FAX 505 327-1666
H-F_FARMINGTON@HFPUMPS.COM
JIMMY KEMP,DIST MGR PH 806 891-4917
STEVE COCHRAN,SLS PH 505 258-3338
MIKE DAME,SLS PH 505 258-3338
HOBBS,NM - PO BOX 1257,2015 W MARLAND
88241 PH 575 393-9618 FAX 575 397-7797
H-F_HOBBS@HFPUMPS.COM
JIMMY KEMP,DIST MGR PH 806 891-4917
MARK LEE,SLS PH 575 390-6020
JAMES OWENS,SLS PH 575 390-6009
- NORTH DAKOTA WAREHOUSES -
DICKINSON,ND - PO BOX 1694,4123 W VILLARD
58602 PH 701 483-0422 FAX 701 483-1626
JON COBB,DIST MGR PH 307 259-8033
PEDER SCHILLO,SLS PH 701 218-0145
TIOGA,ND - PO BOX 188,203 SECOND ST SE
58852 PH 701 664-4300 FAX 701 664-4301
H-F_TIOGA@HFPUMPS.COM
JON COBB,DIST MGR PH 307 259-8033
DICK MONSON,SLS PH 701 570-0197
WILLISTON,ND - 4991 140TH AVE NW
58801 PH 701 774-0276 FAX 701 572-6268
H-F_WILLISTON@HFPUMPS.COM
JON COBB,DIST MGR PH 307 259-8033
JEREMY RAGLEY,SLS PH 701 570-0198
- OHIO WAREHOUSES -
WOOSTER,OH - 3934 BURBANK RD #H
44691 PH 330 345-2055 FAX 330 345-2460
H-F_WOOSTER@HFPUMPS.COM
WAYNE MIDDLETON,DIST MGR PH 812 568-6383
STEVE PETTIJOHN,SLS PH 330 465-9841
ZANESVILLE,OH - 3470 OLD WHEELING RD
43701 PH 740 453-5991 FAX 740 453-5374
H-F_ZANESVILLE@HFPUMPS.COM
WAYNE MIDDLETON,DIST MGR PH 812 568-6383
SCOTT GILLESPIE,SLS PH 740 408-0611
- OKLAHOMA WAREHOUSES -
ENID,OK - PO BOX 532,73702-0532
2620 WRISTON CIR,73701 PH 580 237-7558
FAX 580 237-8268 H-F_ENID@HFPUMPS.COM
BILL O'DELL,DIST MGR PH 580 254-0919
JOSH BUGG,SLS PH 580 278-6525
OKLAHOMA CITY,OK - PO BOX 95127,73143
1606 S JORDAN 73129 PH 405 677-3393
FAX 405 677-8793

H-F_OKLAHOMACITY@HFPUMPS.COM
BILL O'DELL,DIST MGR PH 580 254-0919
KEVIN MATTHEWS,SLS PH 918 223-6039
DUSTIN SLOAT,SLS PH 405 627-7785
BOB WILLIAMS,SLS PH 405 830-0633
POTEAU,OK - PO BOX 363,909 TARBY RD
74953 PH 918 649-0750 FAX 918 649-0758
H-F_POTEAU@HFPUMPS.COM
BILL O'DELL,DIST MGR PH 580 254-0919
CHRIS KEENER,SLS PH 918 413-2659
RATLIFF CITY,OK - PO BOX 268
11142 STATE HWY 7,73481 PH 580 856-4058
FAX 580 856-3778
H-F_RATLIFFCITY@HFPUMPS.COM
BILL O'DELL,DIST MGR PH 580 254-0919
LARRY HOWARD,SLS PH 580 313-0752
- TEXAS WAREHOUSES -
ABILENE,TX - PO BOX 3094,79604
550 S 11TH,79602 PH 325 673-8274
FAX 325 673-8276 H-F_ABILENE@HFPUMPS.COM
DAVID KRUGER,DIST MGR PH 940 550-8050
JOE BOB PATE,SLS PH 325 338-2905
JIMMY PITTCOCK,SLS PH 940 256-3961
GREG BUNCH,SLS PH 432 212-3051
SETH POTTER,SLS PH 325 428-6692
BROWNFIELD,TX - PO BOX 1355,602 W WEBB
79316 PH 806 637-7142 FAX 806 637-3216
H-F_BROWNFIELD@HFPUMPS.COM
JIMMY KEMP,DIST MGR PH 806 891-4917
JAMES PIERCE,SLS PH 806 759-9595
CRANE,TX - PO BOX 818,416 GASTON ST
79731 PH 432 558-7155 FAX 432 558-7552
H-F_CRANE@HFPUMPS.COM
RODNEY SANDS,DIST MGR PH 432 661-5442
AARON SMITH,SLS PH 432 558-7155
FREER,TX - PO BOX 390 602 N NORTON
78357 PH 361 394-6040 FAX 361 394-7861
H-F_FREER@HFPUMPS.COM
JAY DAMRON,DIST MGR PH 432 661-5673
ROBERT CARSON,SLS PH 432 693-6837
SCOTT CARSON,SLS PH 830 570-9246
GRAHAM,TX - PO BOX 575,405 5TH ST
76450 PH 940 549-4544 FAX 940 549-8865
H-F_GRAHAM@HFPUMPS.COM
DAVID KRUGER,DIST MGR PH 940 550-8050
REAGAN KELLEY,SLS PH 940 521-2523
JIMMY BRUTON,SLS PH 940 867-9521
HOUSTON,TX - 14100 ASTON
77040 PH 713 690-8378 FAX 713 460-2769
H-F_HOUSTON@HFPUMPS.COM
JAY DAMRON,DIST MGR PH 432 661-5673
TANER GARDNER,SLS PH 713 859-7219
SCOTT FULLER,CITY SLS PH 713 818-8719
KILGORE,TX - PO BOX 916,102 KNOWLES
75662 PH 903 984-8695 FAX 903 984-2184
H-F_KILGORE@HFPUMPS.COM
ROGER JOHNSON,DIST MGR PH 505 793-3223
MATT GATES,SLS PH 817 888-7320
LULING,TX - PO BOX 107,827 HWY 183 N
78648 PH 830 875-2305 FAX 830 875-9577
H-F_LULING@HFPUMPS.COM
JAY DAMRON,DIST MGR PH 432 661-5673
A B RODRIGUEZ,SLS PH 432 296-8295
ODESSA,TX - PO BOX 7557 79760
1311 POOLE I-20,79766 PH 432 337-3592
FAX 432 337-0742 H-F_ODESSA@HFPUMPS.COM

RODNEY SANDS,DIST MGR PH 432 661-5442
CHAD TUBB,SLS PH 432 813-3807
BENJAMIN VILLARREAL,SLS PH 432 337-3592
MICHAEL SMITH,SLS PH 432 337-3592
PERRYTON,TX - PO BOX 1003 14510 US HWY 83
79070 PH 806 435-6569 FAX 806 435-3992
H-F_PERRYTON@HFPUMPS.COM
JUSTIN GREEN,DIST MGR PH 713 483-4064
BRUCE HINES,SLS PH 580 334-4215
BRADY SCHWALK,SLS PH 806 202-7530
SONORA,TX - 611 US HWY 277 N
76950 PH 325 387-5600 FAX 325 387-6300
H-F_SONORA@HFPUMPS.COM
DAVID KURGER,DIST MGR PH 940 550-8050
GREG BUNCH,SLS PH 432 212-3031
WICHITA FALLS,TX - PO BOX 2151 76307
327 US HWY 281,76310
PH 940 766-4259 FAX 940 766-3387
H-F_WICHITAFALLS@HFPUMPS.COM
DAVID KRUGER,DIST MGR PH 940 550-8050
HARVEY GARVIN,SLS PH 940 613-5656
GENE NEEPER,SLS PH 940 210-1424
- WYOMING WAREHOUSES -
CASPER,WY - 6701 W YELLOWSTONE HWY,82604
PO BOX 417 MILLS,WY 82644
PH 307 472-7518 FAX 307 472-0132
H-F_CASPER@HFPUMPS.COM
JON COBB,DIST MGR PH 307 259-8033
REX BELL,SLS PH 307 277-0855
DICK BRIDGES,SLS PH 307 351-9156
DANIEL FLORES,SLS BRIGHTON,CO
PH 806 336-3940
GILLETTE,WY - PO BOX 4125,82717
903 HANNUM RD,82716 PH 307 686-4050
FAX 307 686-2117 H-F_GILLETTE@HFPUMPS.COM
JON COBB,DIST MGR PH 307 259-8033
LINDY ROBERTS,SLS PH 307 680-9535

HARBOR PETROLEUM,LLC
6217 JOSEPH DR
GRANBURY,TX 76049 PH 817 579-8260
WWW.HARBORPETROLEUM.COM
CECIL GRITZ GRITZCD@HARBORPETROLEUM.COM

HARBOUR ENERGY,INC
LAND SERVICE COMPANY
PO BOX 968
FLORA,MS 39071-0968 PH 601 992-2277
EDMOND,OK OFFICE - PO BOX 8311,73012
PH 405 513-4140 FAX 405 341-8600
JAMES A BRYAN,PRES JIMBRYAN4@AOL.COM

HARDEN AGR LIME & RECLAMATION SERVICE,INC
13865 NICKEL PLATE RD
LOGAN,OH 43138 PH 740 603-4045
SCOTT R HARDEN,OWNER
SCOTTHARDEN4020@GMAIL.COM

HARDING H W
1322 AMBERGATE DR
HOUSTON,TX 77077-2521 PH 281 920-3698

HARDWICK JAMES F & ASSOCIATES
PO BOX 80972,1101 S HUGH WALLIS RD #101
LAFAYETTE,LA 70598-0972 PH 337 232-7756
FAX 337 232-7797 GEOUNIT@COX-INTERNET.COM
JAMES HARDWICK,GEOL
JOHN MELANCON,GEOL

HARDY OIL & GAS USA,INC SEE
MARINER ENERGY,INC

HARGROVE OIL COMPANY,LLC
PO BOX 53036,725 COOLIDGE ST
LAFAYETTE,LA 70505-3036
PH 337 232-7559 FAX 337 232-9811
ROBERT B HARGROVE,MNGNG MEMBER
BRENDA B HARGROVE,LAND
TONNI MAW,OFC MGR

HARING ENERGY COMPANY
PO BOX 12468
SAN ANTONIO,TX 78212-0468
PH 210 735-8400
JOHN MACDIARMID,ENGR

HARLETON OIL AND GAS INC
PO BOX 345
TYLER,TX 75710-0345 PH 903 531-0033
597-0918,597-1505 FAX 903 533-8671
BRUCE A WOOLDRIDGE,PRES
JERRY E IRWIN,VP,EXPL

HARLEY DRILLING & PRODUCING,LTD
9955 AVON LAKE RD
BURBANK,OH 44214-9629
PH 330 948-1054 FAX 330 948-5102
HARLEYDRILLING2@NEO.RR.COM
DON R HARLEY,CEO
STEVE HARLEY,MEMBER

HARLOW ROYALTIES LTD
FORMERLY HARLOW ROYALTIES,INC
22499 IMPERIAL VALLEY DR
HOUSTON,TX 77073-1173
PH 281 209-1150 FAX 281 209-1154
GEORGE S WEBB,VP LAND

HARMAN OPERATING CO,INC
121 S BROADWAY STE 757
TYLER,TX 75702-7207 PH 903 595-2691

HARMAN STEPHEN H & ASSOCIATES,LLC
LDMN & RIGHT OF WAY AGENTS FOR OIL & GAS/
TELECOMMUNICATINS INDUSTRIES
6028 S MILL CREEK RD
PETERSBURG,WV 26847-9725 PH 304 257-2385
PH 304 668-2778 FAX 304 257-9439
STEPHEN H HARMAN,PETR LDMN

HARMON DAVID E,GEOLOGIST
PO BOX 1
NEW CONCORD,OH 43762-0001 PH 740 826-7000
FAX 740 826-7197 DEHARMON@SPEMAIL.ORG
INTL EMAIL: HARMON@WEBMAIL.CO.ZA

HARMON OIL & GAS COMPANY
PO BOX 5875
FORT SMITH,AR 72913-5875 PH 501 783-2244
BOB HARMON,PRES

HARMONY PRODUCING CO,INC
PO BOX 1902
LAUREL,MS 39441-1902 PH 601 649-4461
FAX 601 649-4468
HERSCHEL LANE,PRES
ROBERT M STONE SR,SECY/TREAS

HARPER HEFTE,INC.
13434 LEOPARD ST STE A29B
CORPUS CHRISTI,TX 78410-4466
PH 361 242-9149 FAX 361 242-9153
KENNETH HEFTE,PRES
K T HEFTE,VP

HARPER JOSEPH R,INDEPENDENT LANDMAN
1401 PECAN AVE
METAIRIE,LA 70001 PH 504 887-7695

HARPER PETROLEUM COMPANY
1401 PECAN AVE
METAIRIE,LA 70001 PH 504 887-7695
JOSEPH R HARPER,PRES
JUDY D HARPER,SECY/TREAS

HARPER PETROLEUM ENGINEERING
4330 W ALABAMA ST
HOUSTON,TX 77027-4904 PH 713 622-4344
TED N HARPER,P.E.,OWNER
TED.HARPER22@GMAIL.COM

HARRELL OIL CO,INC
9493 HWY 15
MOUNT CARMEL,IL 62863-9804
PH 618 263-3900 618 262-8257
B R HARRELL,PRES
ROBERT L LEWIS III,VP,DIR
HELEN HARRELL,SECY/TREAS

HARRIGAN ENERGY PARTNERS,INC
16821 BUCCANEER STE 218
HOUSTON,TX 77058
PH 281 286-4100 FAX 281 677-4262
HARRIGANT@HARRIGANENERGY.COM
TOM HARRIGAN

HARRIS & COMPANY
PO BOX 191
HAMILTON,TX 76531 PH 254 223-1888
CHERYL HARRIS LINNI39@YAHOO.COM

HARRIS ENERGY,INC
102 ALPHA DR
LAFAYETTE,LA 70506 PH 337 984-6302
GEORGE W HARRIS,PROF LDMN

HARRIS GEORGE,LEASES & MINERALS
102 ALPHA DR
LAFAYETTE,LA 70506 PH 337 984-6302
PH 337 344-7039 ELSTONGUNN@COX.NET
GEORGE HARRIS

HARRIS JOHN O,GEOL
PO BOX 51321
LAFAYETTE,LA 70505-1321 PH 337 237-4292
PH 337 984-6322 FAX 337 237-0577

HARRIS OIL CO
RR 3 BOX 799
VADALIA,IL 62471-9391
PH 618 423-2822 MCHARRIS@MADISONTELCO.COM
CLIFF HARRIS,OWNER
MICHELLE HARRIS,FIELD SUPVSR

HARRIS STAN,OIL AND GAS EXPLORATION
PO BOX 8796
TYLER,TX 75711-8796 PH 903 521-0625
STAN HARRIS,OWNER,GEOL
STANKHARRIS@YAHOO.COM

HARRIS, WILLIAM P OIL & GAS PROP SEE
TASCOSA LAND RESOURCES,LLC

HARRISBURG/WOOLEY SEE
NATIONAL OILWELL VARCO

HARRISON COUNTY LAND RECORDS INC
305 E PINECREST DR
MARSHALL,TX 75672 PH 903 935-5268
LESLIE CHAMBERS LESLIE@HCLR.COM

HARRISON DAN J,III & BRUCE F EST
712 MAIN ST STE 1900
HOUSTON,TX 77002-3224 PH 713 228-5911
FAX 713 225-1565

HARRISON FRANK W,JR,CONS GEOL
PO BOX 51943,200 AUDUBON BLVD OIL CTR
LAFAYETTE,LA 70505-1943 PH 337 232-4031

FAX 337 235-5333
FRANKH@OPTIMISTICOIL.COM

HARRISON INTERESTS LTD
712 MAIN ST STE 1900
HOUSTON,TX 77002-3220
PH 713 632-1341 FAX 713 225-1565
JIM SCHOERGER,LAND MGR
JSCHOERGER@HARRISONINTERESTS.COM
EDWIN KNIGHT,GEN MGR
DAVID BURKETT,GEOL,GEOPHY
DALE MUELLER,GEOL

HARRISON SAM G OIL,INC
24 GREENWAY PLAZA STE 555
HOUSTON,TX 77046-2401
PH 713 526-8888 FAX 713 526-8839
MATILDA H BROWN,PROD AGT
HENRY OLSOUSKY,FLD SUPT PH 361 588-6981

HARRISON WALLACE OIL PROPERTIES
180 SEA DUNES DR
MELBOURNE BEACH,FL 32951-3312
PH 321 676-2431

HARRISON WELL SERVICE INC
PO BOX 421,908 1/2 W 9TH ST
MOUNT CARMEL,IL 62863 PH 618 262-7722
KENT HARRISON,PRES
RICK HARRISON,VP

HARRISS RICHARD T,III,GEOL
112 NORTHAMPTON RD
NATCHEZ,MS 39120-5241 PH 601 442-2114

HARROGATE ENERGY,LLC
5902 CORINTHIAN PARK LANE
SPRING,TX 77379
PH 281 531-9903
GARY D GILES,OWNER/MGR
DONALD D PATTON,OWNER

HART & MCFARLAND OIL PRODS
PO BOX 725
VIVIAN,LA 71082-0725 PH 318 375-3536
JAMES F SLAGLE,PUR AGT

HART RESOURCE TECHNOLOGIES,INC SEE
FLUID RECOVERY SERVICES,LLC

HARTER E M,JR
PO BOX 52327
SHREVEPORT,LA 71135-2327 PH 318 869-3535

HARTSHORNE & ASSOCIATES ENGINEERING,INC
PO BOX 214
DECKER,IN 47524 PH 812 499-1616
JAMES M HARTSHORNE,PRES

HARVEST NATURAL RESOURCES,INC
1177 ENCLAVE PKWY STE 300
HOUSTON,TX 77077-1885 PH 281 899-5700
FAX 281 899-5702 WWW.HARVESTNR.COM
JAMES EDMISTON,PRES,CEO
STEVEN HAYNES,VP,CFO
KEITH HEAD,VP,GEN COUNSEL

HARVEY BROTHERS OIL & GAS
P O BOX 750
CORPUS CHRISTI,TX 78403-0750
PH 361 882-3981 FAX 361 882-1808
FAX 361 882-1808

HARVEY ENERGY SEE
HARVEY MINERAL PARTNERS,LP

HARVEY K S,CO
PO BOX 750
CORPUS CHRISTI,TX 78403 PH 361 358-5205

HARVEY LYNCH INC
12718 CENTURY DR
STAFFORD,TX 77477-4202 PH 281 240-5441
FAX 281 240-0932 WWW.HARVEY-LYNCH.COM
ABOUDA@HARVEY-LYNCH.COM
PHIL HOWELLS,PRES

HARVEY MIKE W,OIL & GAS
P O BOX 750
CORPUS CHRISTI,TX 78403-0750
PH 361 882-3981
MIKE W HARVEY,OWNER

HARVEY MINERAL PARTNERS,LP SEE
HARVEY VENTURES GROUP,LLC

HARVEY ROYALTY PARTNERS,LP SEE
HARVEY VENTURES GROUP,LLC

HARVEY VENTURES GROUP,LLC
1875 LAWS ST
DALLAS,TX 75202-1700
PH 214 363-7380 FAX 214 559-6142
M J HARVEY III,MANAGING PTNR
MHARVEY@HARVEYVENTURES.COM

HARWOOD EXPLORATION INC
PO BOX 620
CORPUS CHRISTI,TX 78403-0620
PH 361 882-9221
W E HARWOOD,PRES

HAT CREEK EXPLORATION,LTD
2900 WESLAYAN STE 430
HOUSTON,TX 77027
PH 713 871-1106 FAX 713 871-1616
JOHN DORN JOHNDORN@MSN.COM

HAT CREEK PRODUCTION,LP
2900 WESLAYAN STE 430
HOUSTON,TX 77027
PH 713 871-1106 FAX 713 871 1616
JOHN DORN JOHNDORN@MSN.COM

HATTOX & FEATHERSTON
24 VILLAGE GREEN CIR
JACKSON,MS 39211 PH 601 978-3537
DEBRA HATTOX FEATHERSTON,MGR

HAVARD JACK E,OIL & GAS PROPERTIES
3003 SHADOWDALE DR
HOUSTON,TX 77043-1315 PH 713 465-8586
PH 713 460-9933
JACK E HAVARD,OWNER

HAVERLAH WILLIAM C,OIL PROPERTIES
PO BOX 416
LLANO,TX 78643 PH 325 247-3624

HAWES COMPANY
PO BOX 1186,614 E MILAM ST
WHARTON,TX 77488-1186
PH 979 532-1321
JOAN G HAWES,AGENT

HAWK OILFIELD SERVICE,INC
PO BOX 812
ZAPATA,TX 78076 PH 956 765-6080
FAX 866 472-0426 INFO@HAWKOILFIELD.COM

HAWKE INC
PURCHASE PRODUCTION/DEVELOP SHALE WELLS
3203 ETHAN ALLEN RD
BARBERTON,OH 44203 PH 330 858-0202
WWW.WWWOOODDD@SBCGLOBAL.NET
GREGORY L WOOD
GREG@UTICASHALEINVESTING.COM

HAWKEYE OIL & GAS,INC
PO BOX 1459

TUSCALOOSA,AL 35403-1459
PH 205 758-0462 FAX 205 758-6566
DAYTON F HALE,JR,PRES

HAWKEYE RESOURCES,LP
4809 COLE AVE STE 245,LB-136
DALLAS,TX 75205 PH 214 987-2602
FAX 214 987-2669

HAWKEYE STRATIGRAPHIC,INC
5300 MEMORIAL DR STE 610
HOUSTON,TX 77007 PH 713 951-0096
FAX 713 951-0147
BEN BARNES,PRES
BEN@HAWKEYESTRATIGRAPHIC.COM

HAWKINS OIL,LLC
427 S BOSTON AVE STE 915
TULSA,OK 74103-4114 PH 918 382-7743
FAX 918 584-6050
JAMES F HAWKINS,JR,GEN MGR
- FIELD OFFICES -
EL DORADO,KS OFFICE - PH 316 322-3506
DON LARUE,DIST OPERS FRMN

HAWKINS PETROLEUM CONSULTING AND
INVESTMENTS,INC
PO BOX 1574
AFTON,WY 83110 PH 479 636-7851
FAX 479 636-7851 PH 479 621-3622
WAREHOUSE MGR PH 479 636-9498
WWW.HAWKINSWORLD.COM
HAWKPCI@IPA.NET
HAROLD HAWKINS,VP
W HERB HAWKINS,CHRMN,PRES

HAWKINS PETROLEUM,INC
207 CRESTHILL DR
YOUNGSVILLE,LA 70592 PH 337 856-2893
CHUCK HAWKINS

HAWKINS REMOTE SENSING & EXPLORATION
8531 N NEW BRAUNFELS AVE STE 201
SAN ANTONIO,TX 78217-6366 PH 210 829-5330
ALF HAWKINS,OWNER

HAWN BROTHERS COMPANY
101 N SHORELINE BLVD STE 600
CORPUS CHRISTI,TX 78401-2826
PH 361 882-5435 FAX 361 884-4296
GEORGE S HAWN,PRES
ED JENSEN,TAX MGR
R ACOCK,PE,ENGR

HAYDEN ENERGY CORP
406 WOODVALE AVE
LAFAYETTE,LA 70503 PH 318 873-3565
FAX 318 873-0284
WM H KENNY,PRES
HUGH CORNAY,VP

HAYDEN LEE,JR,ATTORNEY/LANDMAN
PO BOX 3555
BAY ST LOUIS,MS 39521-3555
PH 228 467-2596 LEEHAYDEN@AOL.COM

HAYES CHAS F & ASSOCIATES,INC
714 CHICKASAW AVE
JACKSON,MS 39206-5809 PH 601 981-0225
FAX 601 981-0226
CHARLES F HAYES,PRES

HAYES JAMES F & COMPANY
PO BOX 1004
CENTER POINT,TX 78010-1004
PH 806 874-3546

HAYES RAYMOND B,OIL & GAS CONS,
6152 CLEARWATER DR
SLIDELL,LA 70460-3922 PH 504 242-5377

HAYMANS GEORGE S,III,GEOL
83 BLACK BEAR RD
NATCHEZ,MS 39120-9532 PH 601 445-4052

HAYMANS JEANNE FAMILY TRUST
83 BLACK BEAR RD
NATCHEZ,MS 39120-9532 PH 601 445-4052
DAVID M SMITH,ATTY/TRUSTEE

HAYNES PRODUCTION CO,INC SEE
CREEK ENERGY,INC

HAYNIE RICHARD,IND LDMN
7807 VIRGINIA WATER LN
HOUSTON,TX 77095-3479 PH 281 463-1266
FAX 281 463-4833 RHRHRH@BIGPLANET.COM

HB RENTALS LC
- WORLD HEADQUARTERS -
5813 HWY 90 E
BROUSSARD,LA 70518 PH 337 839-1641
PH 800 262-6790 FAX 337 839-1628
WWW.HBRENTAL.COM
- WESTERN HEMISPHERE HQ -
HOUSTON,TX OFFICE - 11000 EQUITY DR
STE 150 77041 PH 281 999-0047
PH 866 999-0040 FAX 281 999-6505
GLENN AGUILAR,SR VP-GLOBAL OPERS
BRIAN CHILTON,BUS UNIT DIR (SOUTH)
TIM MURPHY,CORP SLS DIR
JILL ADAMS,CORP SLS MGR
JEB BELLARD,CORP SLS
ROBERT NEAL,CORP SLS
TONI PORRETTO,CORP SLS
TULLY BLANCHARD,CORP SLS
YVETTE FORET,CORP SLS
MIKE ROPER,REG SLS MGR
- DISTRICT OFFICES -
ALICE,TX OFFICE - 4976 HWY 281 S 78332
PH 361 664-8591 FAX 361 664-8762
PH 888 464-8591
BRIAN CHILTON,BUS UNIT DIR (SOUTH)
MIKE ROPER,REG SLS MGR
CANADIAN,TX OFFICE - 10951 US HWY 83
79014 PH 806 323-9311
BRIAN CHILTON,BUS UNIT DIR (SOUTH)
COLIN JOHNSTON,REG SLS MGR
MIDLAND,TX OFFICE - 3319 E HWY 158 79706
PH 432 570-0975 FAX 432 570-0973
PH 866 874-3362
BRIAN CHILTON,BUS UNIT DIR (SOUTH)
MIKE ROPER,REG SLS MGR
YANCEY,TX OFFICE - 10065 FM 462 S,78886
PH 830 741-6576
BRIAN CHILTON,BUS UNIT DIR
MIKE ROPER,REG SLS MGR
LIVERPOOL,TX OFFICE - 8525 HWY 35 S 77577
PH 281 393-1210 FAX 281 581-9034
PH 800 237-6062
BRIAN CHILTON,BUS UNIT DIR (SOUTH)
MIKE ROPER,REG SLS MGR
FAIRFIELD,TX OFFICE - 130 HWY 75 S 75840
PH 903 389-9230 FAX 909 389-7961
PH 866 552-9230
BRIAN CHILTON,BUS UNIT DIR (SOUTH)
MIKE ROPER,REG SLS MGR
EL RENO,OK OFFICE - 3701 S CHOCTAW 73036

PH 405 422-1062 FAX 405 422-1064
PH 877 422-1062
BRIAN CHILTON,BUS UNIT DIR
COLIN JOHNSTON,REG SLS MGR
RIVERTON,WY OFFICE - 12674 US HWY 26
82501 PH 307 856-9761 FAX 307 856-7916
PH 800 850-9761
JOHN SKIDMORE,BUS UNIT DIR (NORTH)
KENT CROOKS,REG SLS MGR
MILL HALL,PA OFFICE - 7484 NITTANY VALLEY
DR 17751 PH 570 726-8034 FAX 570 726-8247
JOHN SKIDMORE,BUS UNIT DIR (NORTH)
AARON JOHNSON,REG SLS MGR
MENIFEE,AR OFFICE - 31 BELL MOUNTAIN RD
72107 PH 501 977-1900 FAX 501 977-1904
PH 877 931-1900
BRIAN CHILTON,BUS UNIT DIR (SOUTH)
COLIN JOHNSTON,REG SLS MGR
GRAND JUNCTION,CO OFFICE - 598 23 1/2 RD
81505 PH 970 242-4555 FAX 970 242-4556
PH 877 288 4555
JOHN SKIDMORE,BUS UNIT DIR (NORTH)
KENT CROOKS,REG SLS MGR
FREDERICK,CO OFFICE - 7750 JOHNSON DR
80504 PH 720 494-8877
JOHN SKIDMORE,BUS UNIT DIR
KENT CROOKS,REG SLS MGR
SHREVEPORT,LA OFFICE - 8279 W ANTOINE
LOOP 71129 PH 318 603-0740
FAX 318 603-0742
BRIAN CHILTON,BUS UNIT DIR (SOUTH)
MIKE ROPER,REG SLS MGR
CANONSBURG,PA OFFICE - 257 JOHNSON RD
15317 PH 724 916-4215 FAX 724 916-4592
JOHN SKIDMORE,BUS UNIT DIR (NORTH)
AARON JOHNSON,REG SLS MGR
WILLISTON,ND OFFICE - 4934 HWY 85 BLDG
300,58001 PH 701 752-5029
JOHN SKIDMORE,BUS UNIT DIR (NORTH)
KENT CROOKS,REG SLS MGR
CARLSBAD,NM OFFICE - 903H AIRPORT RD
88220 PH 575 628-8389 FAX 575 628-8397
BRIAN CHILTON,BUS UNIT DIR (SOUTH)
MIKE ROPER,REG SLS MGR
- GLOBAL LOCATIONS -
MACAE,RIO DE JANEIRO BRAZIL OFFICE -
PH 55 22 3723-0100 PH 55 22 2773-6284
JUDE PRIMEAUX,BUS UNIT DIR (LATIN/SOUTH
AMERICA OPERS)
LUCIANO N P SIQUEIRA,OPERS COORD
LA ROMAINE,SAN FERNANDO,TRINIDAD OFFICE -
PH 868 657-7039 FAX 868 697-7719
JUDE PRIMEAUX,BUS UNIT DIR(LATIN/SOUTH
AMERICA OPERS)
JASON COX,SLS REPR
SURIN PALTOO,PROJ/ENGRG MGR
ABERDEENSHIRE SCOTLAND,UK OFFICE -
PH 44 1224 772304 FAX 44 1224 772641
NORMAN PORTER,BUS UNIT DIR (EASTERN
HEMISPHERE)
BRAD HIRST,SLS/MKTG MGR
ASHLEIGH BRAND,SLS COORD
DUBAI,UAE OFFICE - PH 971 (0) 4339 7017
FAX 971 (0) 4339 7851
NORMAN PORTER,BUS UNIT DIR (E HEMISPERE)
RAMI MILED,BUS DEV

BRAD HIRST,SLS/MKTG MGR
STAVANGER,NORWAY OFFICE - PH 47 5154 2248
PH 0047 924 58752
NORMAN PORTER,BUS UNIT DIR (E HEMISPHERE)
BRAD HIRST,SLS/MKTG MGR
ASHLEIGH BRAND,SLS COORD

HB RENTALS SEE
SUPERIOR ENERGY SERVICES

HCI COASTAL CHEMICAL COMPANY,LLC SEE
COASTAL CHEMICAL CO,LLC

HDBC INVESTMENTS,LIMITED
PO BOX 12766
DALLAS,TX 75225-0766
PH 214 692-7785 FAX 214 692-7820
HAROLD D CARTER
B K SLOAN

HDC ENERGY COMPANY SEE
HDBC INVESTMENTS,LIMITED

HEAD & KING EXPLORATION,INC
314 GENTILLY CIR
SHREVEPORT,LA 71106 PH 318 861-2580
WILLIAM T HEAD,PRES
JOHN B KING,CPL,VP

HEADINGTON OIL COMPANY LLC
1700 N REDBUD BLVD STE 400
MCKINNEY,TX 75069 PH 214 307-5400
FAX 972 529-9557 WWW.HEADINGTON.COM
TIMOTHY C HEADINGTON,PRES/CEO
PAT SMITH,EXEC VP
MICHAEL TREGONING,VP/CFO
GARY MCKAY,VP LAND
SCOTT MAHAND,VP
SANDRA REED,ACCT MGR
CORPUS CHRISTI,TX OFFICE - 500 N
SHORELINE BLVD STE 902,78401-0343
PH 361 885-0110 FAX 361 885-0120
BILL JOHNSTON
DALLAS,TX OFFICE - 2711 N HASKELL AVE
STE 2800 75204 PH 214 696-0606

HEAPE EXPLORATION INC
16200 ADDISON RD STE 155
ADDISON,TX 75001 PH 972 407-6030
FAX 972 407-9392
HEAPEOIL@SBCGLOBAL.NET

HEARD J A,OIL OPR
PO BOX 193
ARANSAS PASS,TX 78335 PH 361 758-2642

HEBERT HENRY P,JR,OIL PROP
PO BOX 52712,1030 E ST MARY BLVD BLDG 3
LAFAYETTE,LA 70505-2712 PH 337 235-1727
FAX 337 235-1740 HPHEBERT@BELLSOUTH.NET
HENRY P HEBERT,JR,CPL

HEBERT VALVE & CONTROLS
17630 PERKINS RD WEST
BATON ROUGE,LA 70810-3827 PH 225 751-0000
MIKE NICAUD,PROD MGR
DAVE SNELL,INSIDE SLS
BRIAN LAYMAN,INSIDE SLS
STEVE SMITH,INSIDE SLS
DON DUFOUR,INSIDE SLS

HECI EXPLORATION COMPANY SEE
BROWNING OIL COMPANY,INC

HEDBERG OIL COMPANY
PO BOX 470337
FORT WORTH,TX 76147-0337 PH 817 763-9500
FAX 817 377-3539 WWW.HEDBERGOIL.COM

JOHN GEORGE,PRES JOHN@HEDBERGOIL.COM
ANNE DUNLAP,ACCT MGR
ANNE@HEDBERGOIL.COM
AMY BRITTAIN,OFC MGR AMY@HEDBERGOIL.COM
AUSTIN MOTHERAL,LAND MGR

HEDGECO,INC
1963 COUNTY ROAD 3133
TYLER,TX 75708-2705 PH 903 531-9594
FAX 903 531-9389 HEDGECO@TYLER.NET
STEVEN D HEDGES,PRES
J L HEDGES,OFC MGR

HEDGEHOG LLC
PO BOX 4284
BATON ROUGE,LA 70821-4284 PH 225 343-5713
HEDGEHOGLLC@COX.NET
DOC L'HERISSON,MGR
BILL DURIO,LEGAL COUNSEL
KEVIN KEMMERLY,AGT

HEEMANN JOHN A,PETR CONS OIL OPR
5227 BIRD WOOD
HOUSTON,TX 77096-2503 PH 713 665-2782

HEEREMA MARINE CONTRACTORS US,INC
15600 JFK BLVD 3RD FLOOR
HOUSTON,TX 77032-2349 PH 281 880-1600

HEGGEMAN REALTY CO,INC
725 EXECUTIVE PARK DR
MOBILE,AL 36606-2843 PH 334 479-8606
FAX 334 479-8630 HEGGEMAN.COM
HEGGEMAN@HEGGEMAN.COM
B J HEGGEMAN,III,PRES

HEI-VENTURES ENGLAND LP SEE
HUNT OIL COMPANY

HEID JAMES G,PETR ENGR
12122 OVERCUP DR
HOUSTON,TX 77024-4228 PH 713 468-3983

HEIGHTS ENERGY CORPORATION
5801 TENNYSON PKWY STE 300
PLANO,TX 75024 PH 972 378-0304
ERNEST S SIRAKI ERNIE@HEIGHTSENERGY.COM

HEIL MICHAEL M
6618 OPENGATE
CORPUS CHRISTI,TX 78413 PH 361 887-2609

HEINRICH ENTERPRISES INC
PO BOX 305
RENO,OH 45773-0305 PH 740 373-5302
FAX 740 373-6208
CARL HEINRICH,VP

HEINTZ COMPANY,THE
PO BOX 498
CORPUS CHRISTI,TX 78403 PH 361 888-6382
WILLIAM A HEINTZ JR,PRES,GEOL

HEISEY VENTURES,INC
OIL & GAS,MINING
1302 WAUGH DR STE 903
HOUSTON,TX 77019-3908 PH 713 533-9908
PH 713 254-1528 FAX 713 533-9996
HEISEY@SWBELL.NET
H MICHAEL HEISEY,P.E.,PRES

HELIS OIL & GAS COMPANY,L.L.C.
228 ST CHARLES AVE STE 912
NEW ORLEANS,LA 70130-2685 PH 504 523-1831
FAX 504 522-6486
DAVID A KERSTEIN,PRES
MICHAEL F SCHOTT,VP
JAMES P STOYANOFF,EXPL MGR

HELIX ENERGY SOLUTION GROUP SEE
SEE ENERGY RESOURCE TECHNOLOGY GOM INC

HELMER DIRECTIONAL DRILLING
PO BOX 1670
GRETNA,LA 70053-1670 PH 504 367-0774
PH 800-749-7578
H W HELMER,CEO
RICHARD HELMER,PRES
YOUNGSVILLE,LA OFFICE - PO BOX 170
70592 PH 318 837-2435 800-435-8983
SAMUEL PRATKA,SUPVSR
ROBERT SAVOIE,SUPVSR
ARNOLD SMITH,SUPVSR
HOUSTON,TX OFFICE - 2424 S VOSS RD,#L208
77057 PH 713 267-3432

HELMERICH & PAYNE INC
1437 S BOULDER AVE STE 1400
TULSA,OK 74119
PH 918 742-5531 FAX 918 742-0237
HANS HELMERICH,CHRMN & CEO
STEVE R MACKEY,EXEC VP/CAO/SECY/GEN COUN
JUAN PABLO TARDIO,VP & CFO
GORDON HELM,VP & CONTROLLER

HELMERICH & PAYNE INTERNATIONAL DRLG CO
1437 S BOULDER AVE STE 1400
TULSA,OK 74119-3623 PH 918 742-5531
FAX 918 742-0237 WWW.HPIDC.COM
JOHN LINDSAY,PRES/COO
JEFF FLAHERTY,SR VP-US LAND OPERS
ROB STAUDER,SR VP/CHF ENGR
GEORGE MICHALOPULOS,REG VP-US LAND OPS
RON FULLERTON,VP-US OFFSHORE OPERS
WARREN HUBLER,VP-HSE/TRAINING
DAVID MILLWEE,REG VP-US LAND OPERS
JIM BISHOP,VP-ADMIN
STEVE SPARKS,VP-INTERNATIONAL OPERS
WADE CLARK,REG VP-US LAND OPERS
SHANE MARCHAND,VP-MARKETING & BUS DEV
OKLAHOMA CITY,OK NORTHERN DIVISION
OFFICE - 5401 S HATTIE 73129
PH 405 677-8882 FAX 405 670-2667
JOHN BAER,DIST MGR
PEARL,MS OFFICE - 102 WARE ST 39208
PH 601 939-1589 FAX 601 939-9122
BAKERSFIELD,CA OFFICE - 10360 ENOS LN
SHAFTER,CA 93263 PH 661 746-0579
FAX 661 746-6046
WAYNE VOWELL,OPERS MGR
HOUSTON,TX SALES OFFICE - 2930 W SAM
HOUSTON PKWY N STE 250,77043
PH 832 782-6800 FAX 832 782-6849
ALLEN WILLIAMS,REG VP-US LAND OPERS
SCOTT GORDON,MKTG REPR
DAVID EVANS,MKTG REPR
CLYDE HEBERT,MKTG REPR
TOM DOUGHERTY,MKTG REPR
CRISTI HARRINGTON,MKTG REPR
CHRISTOPHER GALLIO,MKTG REPR
BULLARD,TX OFFICE-52133 US HWY 69 N 75757
PH 903 894-1500 FAX 903 894-8260
JOEL RUARK,DIST MGR
ROSS RITTENOURE,ADMIN MGR
ODESSA,TX OFFICE - 7951 E I-20,79765
PH 432 563-5757 FAX 432 563-2727
MIKE LENNOX,DIST MGR
CONLY PRITCHARD,OPS MGR

TREY ADAMS, OPS MGR
DANNY LAME,ADMIN MGR
ANDY DALE,ADMIN
CHASE SALATIA,ADMIN
ALICE,TX OFFICE - PO BOX 1700
   78333 PH 361 664-0114 FAX 361 664-8534
   ERIC ROBERSON,DIST MGR
   ANDREW HYATT,ADMIN
COVINGTON,LA OFFICE - 106 PARK PL STE 100
   70433 PH 985 871-4071 FAX 985 871-4072
   J T DOHM,DIST MGR
GRAND JUNCTION,CO OFFICE - 2360 G ROAD
   81505 PH 970 263-0872 FAX 970 263-0876
   DUSTIN HORNOK,DIST MGR
   JOHN POTTORD,ADMIN
DICKINSON,ND OFFICE - 3214 110K AVE SW
   58601 PH 701 225-7005 FAX 701 225-9651
   STEVEN ESTROLD,DIST MGR
   JOSEPH INMAN,ADMIN
HOWARD,PA OFFICE- 912 N EAGLE VALLEY RD
   16841 PH 814 353-3450 FAX 814 353-3454
   RICKY SHOALMIRE,DIST MGR
   SEAN CORSO,ADMIN

HELMS DRILLING CO
   70 CURTIS LANE
   FORDSVILLE,KY 42343-0113 PH 270 276-5108
   ARNOLD HELMS,PROPRIETOR

HELTON PAT A & ALBERTA
   PO BOX 154
   ALLISON,TX 79003 PH 806 663-6334
   FAX 806 353-2490 ALBERTAHELTON@ATT.NET

HELTON PROPERTIES,INC
   PO BOX 1229
   PEARLAND,TX 77588-1229
   PH 281 993-1424 FAX 281 993-1424
   ARCH W HELTON,PRES

HEMERA LAND,INC SEE
   JACKFORK LAND,INC

HEMPEL COATINGS,USA,INC
   600 CONROE PARK NORTH DR
   CONROE,TX 77303-2207 PH 713 672-6641
   FAX 713 672-0616
   JOEL BENETTI,GEN MGR

HENDERSON CARL S,LANDMAN
   18919 ROBIN LN
   TOMBALL,TX 77377-3543 PH 281 460-6709
   FAX 281 357-4365

HENDERSON CHARLOTTE L
   PRES OF LYNCH LANDS LIMITED
   PO BOX 667455
   HOUSTON,TX 77266-7455 PH 281 812-7977

HENDERSON PETROLEUM CORPORATION
   PO BOX 62704
   SAN ANGELO,TX 76906-2704 PH 325 944-1924
   W PETER HENDERSON,PRES
CROZET,VA OFFICE - PO BOX 340,22932-0340
   PH 434 823-8608 FAX 434 823-8612

HENIGMAN ALAN F,GEOL
   404 W NEVADA ST
   URBANA,IL 61801-4111 PH 217 344-5883

HENLEY AND ASSOCIATES
   5523 LOUETTA RD STE B
   SPRING,TX 77379 PH 281 257-4731
   WWW.HENLEY-ASSOC.COM
   NEIL HENLEY NEILHENLEY@HENLEY-ASSOC.COM

HENLEY BILLY,OIL & GAS EXPL
   12203 RIP VAN WINKLE
   HOUSTON,TX 77024 PH 713 465-3777

HENLEY TITLE COMPANY,LLC
   1706 22ND AVE
   GULFPORT,MS 39501 PH 228 575-9099
   HENLEYTITLE@CABLEONE.NET
   THAD HENLEY,MGR & COUNSEL

HENRY & SANDOZ,INC SEE
   SANDOZ & ASSOC,INC

HENRY OIL CO,INC
   675 HARTFORD AVE
   PROVIDENCE,RI 02909-5920 PH 401 521-0200
   FAX 401 521-5709
   HENRYOILCO@VERIZON.NET
   CARMINE H DISANTO,PRES
   CARMINE DISANTO III,VP

HENRY PRODUCTION COMPANY,INC
   PO BOX 53492
   LAFAYETTE,LA 70505-3492 PH 337 233-6547
   FAX 337 232-5717
   ROBERT C HENRY,PRES
   MARSHA O CAHILL,OFC MGR

HENSARLING L R,OIL OPR
   320 PRINCETON WOODS LOOP
   LAFAYETTE,LA 70508-6602 PH 210 804-2054

HERBERT BOB & ASSOCIATES,INC
   MANUFACTURERS REPRESENTATIVES
   2213 ALDINE BENDER RD
   HOUSTON,TX 77032-3123 PH 281 449-1010
   FAX 281 449-0809
   WWW.BHDE.COM WWW.BHERBERT.COM
   BOB HERBERT,PRES
ALICE,TX OFFICE - 1801 S HWY 281,78332
   PH 361 664-0472
VICTORIA,TX OFFICE - 8104 LONE TREE RD
   77901 PH 361 578-7956
FT WORTH,TX OFC - 6627 CORPORATION PKWY
   STE 200, 76126 PH 817 696-0101

HERCULES TRANSPORT INC
   PO BOX 536
   CHOUDRANT,LA 71227-0536 PH 318 768-2534
   FAX 318 768-2050
   TOM O'NEAL,PRES

HERD PRODUCING CO INC
   3901 MANHATTAN DR
   TYLER,TX 75701-9403 PH 903 509-3456
   BOB L HERD,PRES,OWNER

HERINGER ENERGY RESOURCES CO SEE
   HERCO

HERITAGE ENERGY COMPANY
   401 EDWARDS ST STE 2110
   SHREVEPORT,LA 71101-5535
   PH 318 222-1545 FAX 318-222-1432
   JOHN KINNEBREW,PRES/LDMN
   KEVIN M BYRAM,VP/GEOL

HERLIHY JOHN D
   419A NORTHPARK DR
   RIDGELAND,MS 39157
   PH 601 420-2525 FAX 601 420-2524
   JOHN D HERLIHY,OWNER

HEROLD JOHN S INC SEE
   IHS HEROLD

HERPIN JOHN E,CPL & ASSOCIATES
   302 HALCOTT DR
   LAFAYETTE,LA 70503-4624

PH 337 984-3060 HERPINSR@YAHOO.COM
   JOHN E HERPIN,PRTNR
   JOHN E HERPIN JR,PRTNR

HERR ROBERT C,III,CONS PETR ENGR
   PO BOX 885
   MOUNT VERNON,IL 62864-0885
   PH 616 244-5541

HERRINGTON T R,JR, OIL PROPERTIES
   P O BOX 364
   CORSICANA,TX 75110-0364 PH 214 345-2861

HERSCHBACH PETROLEUM CO, LTD.
   LEASES,ROYALTIES
   121 S BROADWAY STE 753
   TYLER,TX 75702 PH 903 595-1575

HERSHEY OIL CORP (U.S. PROPERTIES) SEE
   AMERICAN EXPLORATION CO

HESS CORPORATION
   1501 MCKINNEY ST
   HOUSTON,TX 77010 PH 713 496-4000
   JOHN B HESS,CEO
   GREGORY P HILL,PRES & COO
   GARY BOUBEL,SR VP-DEVELOPMENTS
   ZHANNA GOLODRYGA,SR VP-SVCS & CIO
   TIMOTHY B GOODELL,SR VP & GEN COUNSEL
   RICHARD LYNCH,SR VP-DRLG & COMPLETIONS
   HOWARD PAVER,SR VP-STRATEGY,COMM & NEW
      BUS DEV
   JOHN P RIELLY,SR VP & CFO
   BRIAN TRUELOVE,SR VP-OFFSHORE
   MICHAEL R TURNER,SR VP-ONSHORE
   BARBARA YILMAZ,SR VP-EXPL
   MYKEL ZIOLO,SR VP-HUMAN RELATIONS
   GEORGE C BARRY,VP/SECY/DEPUTY GEN COUNSEL
   C MARTIN DUNAGIN,VP-CORP TAX
   ERIC FISHMAN,VP/TREAS
   INDRANI FRANCHINI,VP/CCO
   DREW MALONEY,VP-GOV AFFAIRS &
      PUBLIC POLICY
   JONATHAN C STEIN,VP & CHF RISK OFCR
   KEVIN B WILCOX,VP & EXPL/PROD CONTROLLER
   JAY R WILSON,VP-INVESTOR RELS
NEW YORK CITY,NY OFFICE - 1185 AVE OF THE
   AMERICAS,40TH FL 10036 PH 212 997-8500
KUALA LUMPUR,MALAYSIA OFFICE - LEVEL 14
   MENARA 3 PETRONAS,KUALA LUMPUR CITY
   CENTRE 50088 PH 60-3-2788-7000

HESS OIL & CHEMICAL,A DIV OF AMERADA
   PO BOX N,HESS ST
   HEIDELBERG,MS 39439-1013
   PH 601 425-1496,787-2341
   LEON HESS,CHRMN OF BD,AMERADA
   H W MCCOLLUM,PRES,HESS OIL &
      CHEMICAL DIV,WOODBRIDGE,NJ
   RENE BOURG,GEN MGR
   HARRY J PERKINS,PROD SUPT
   M G SLAID,COORD

HESS PIPELINE COMPANY
   P O DRAWER N
   HEIDELBERG,MS 39439-1013 PH 601 787-3441
   L A STRICKLIN,VP,JACKSON,MS
   M G SLAID,MGR
   B J KITCHENS,MGR OF OPERS
   W R GREEN, JR,GATHERING SYSTEM SUPT
   W MCCLELLAN,CHF DISPATCHER

HESTER B M
   P O BOX 2588

WICHITA FALLS,TX 76307-2588
PH 940 322-1868

HESTER LOUIS
82 S REGAN MEAD CIR
THE WOODLANDS,TX 77382 PH 832 444-3937
LOUIS_HESTER@ATT.NET

HESTERLY JAMES P,JR,INC
PO BOX 51322
LAFAYETTE,LA 70505-1322 PH 337 406-9829
FAX 337 406-9831
JAMES P HESTERLY,JR,PRES

HEW-TEX OIL & GAS CORPORATION
11222 RICHMOND AVE STE 190
HOUSTON,TX 77082-2646 PH 281 558-7686
FAX 281 558-7907
PETER H HEWETT,PRES
WILLIAM L RONEY,VP

HFP ACOUSTICAL CONSULTANTS INC SEE
SLR CONSULTING (CANADA) LTD

HHC EXPLORATION INC
601 JEFFERSON 40TH FLR
HOUSTON,TX 77002-7904 PH 713 651-8951

HHE COMPANY SEE
SEE XTO ENERGY

HIDALGO OIL & EXPLORATION CORP
PO BOX 312439
NEW BRAUNFELS,TX 78131-0115
PH 501 665-2599
R DEAN MCMANICLE,PRES

HIGGASON C L ESTATE,OIL & GAS PROPERTIES
151 GOODLOE RD
CANTON,MS 39046-8731 PH 601 859-3468

HIGH PLAINS GAS SYSTEMS,INC
PO BOX 541053
HOUSTON,TX 77254-1053 PH 713 524-9960
FAX 713 522-9239 WWW.MCALESTERFUEL.COM
EDWARD G WALLACE JR,PRES/CEO
J T FRIDLEY,SECY/TREAS
JOSIE@MCALESTEFUEL.COM
WALTER H WALNE III,ASST SECY/GEN COUNSEL

HIGH STAR OIL & GAS EXPLORATION COMPANY
8007 HURST FOREST LN
HUMBLE,TX 77346-1704 PH 281 852-8919
PH 281 852-2970 FAX 281 852-8919
CHARLES A BRINKLEY,CO-OWNER,MGR,GEOL
CABRINKLEY13@LIVE.COM

HIGHLAND (TEXAS) ENERGY COMPANY
7557 RAMBLER RD STE 918 LB 72
DALLAS,TX 75231 PH 214 369-2020
FAX 214 369-2058
STEVEN M BURR,PRES & CFO
STEVE@HIGHLANDTXENERGY.COM
TRUITT MATTHEWS,VP EXPL
TRUITT@HIGHLANDTXENERGY.COM

HIGHLAND ENERGY COMPANY SEE
CALPINE PRODUCER SERVICES,LP

HIGHLAND MINERALS,INC
615 LEOPARD ST STE 215
CORPUS CHRISTI,TX 78476-2228
PH 361 884-1906 FAX 361 884-4514
JOHN P MCBROOM,PRES

HIGHLANDS PIPELINE COMPANY LC
1600 SMITH ST STE 3910
HOUSTON,TX 77002 PH 713 654-5010
FAX 713 654-5025 WWW.ETOCO.COM
WATER COCHRAN,PRES WCOCHRAN@ETOCO.COM

HIGHTOWER OIL & GAS CO,OIL OPR
800 BERING DR STE 460
HOUSTON,TX 77057-2131 PH 713 780-7722
FAX 713 780-8833
WAYNE HIGHTOWER,CEO
H W HIGHTOWER,JR,PRES

HIGMAN BARGE LINES
PO BOX 908,JACKSON & WATER
ORANGE,TX 77631-0908 PH 409 883-5636
FAX 409 883-5661
PRESTON N SHUFORD

HIGMAN MARINE
1980 POST OAK BLVD STE 1101
HOUSTON,TX 77056-3877
PH 713 552-1101 FAX 713 552-0732
MARKF@HIGMAN.NET
MARK FLYNN,VP,SALES
JOHN MCMAHAN,E VP
SARAH BAUCHER,SALES/SCHEDULING

HILCORP ENERGY COMPANY
PO BOX 61229
HOUSTON,TX 77208-1229 PH 713 209-2400
FAX 713 209-2475
HOUSTON,TX OFFICE - 1201 LOUISIANA ST
STE 1400,77002
JEFFERY D HILDEBRAND,CHRMN & CEO
GREG R LALICKER,PRES
SHELBIE DEZELL,CFO
JASON REBROOK,EXEC VP A&D
GREG HOFFMAN,VP BUS DEV
CURTIS SMITH,VP LAND

HILL A G
47 HIGHLAND PARK VILLAGE STE 200
DALLAS,TX 75205 PH 214 922-1000
TY MILLER,CEO

HILL ABSTRACTING COMPANY,INC
231 KENILWORTH PKWY
BATON ROUGE,LA 70808
PH 225 925-9796 FAX 225 302-7094
KENNETH S HILL,PRES
KENNETHHILL07@ATT.NET

HILL HOUSTON,ESTATE
500 W 7TH ST STE 1802
FORT WORTH,TX 76102-4740 PH 817 336-8252
FAX 817 336-8216
BOB HILL,CO-OWNER
GLENN HILL LATTIMORE,CO-OWNER
BILL SCALES,MGR
NANCY WOODS,EXEC SECY
SHEILA RICHARDS,LDMN
JOHN A STYRSKY,CPA CONTROLLER
HOUSTON HILL,ACCT MGR
MICHAEL H LATTIMORE,ACCT MGR

HILL JERRY G
1770 SAINT JAMES PL STE 340
HOUSTON,TX 77056-3426 PH 713 688-6318

HILL KENNETH S PROPERTIES,INC
KENNETH S HILL,ATTORNEY AT LAW
231 KENILWORTH PKWY
BATON ROUGE,LA 70808 PH 225 925-9796
FAX 225 302-7094 KENNETHHILL07@ATT.NET
KENNETH S HILL,PRES

HILL MARC OIL & GAS
1770 SAINT JAMES PL STE 115
HOUSTON,TX 77056-3426 PH 713 688-6318
MARC HILL,PRES

HILL ROBERT B,GEOPHY
P O BOX 51233,404 MARILYN DR
LAFAYETTE,LA 70505-1233 PH 318 984-7525

HILLER HERBERT S,CORP
PO BOX 23770
HARAHAN,LA 70183-3770 PH 504 736-0008
FAX 504 736-0030
HERBERTS.HILLER@HILLERCOMPANIES.COM

HILLIARD C PAUL,OIL OPER
PO BOX 52745,3861 AMBASSADOR CAFFERY #400
LAFAYETTE,LA 70505-2745 PH 337 233-9200
FAX 337 233-5785

HILLIARD OIL & GAS,INC
601 POYDRAS STE 1900
NEW ORLEANS,LA 70130 PH 504 568-1010
H E NORTHCOTT,PRES,CEO

HILLIN T A
222 SIDNEY BAKER S STE 202
KERRVILLE,TX 78028
PH 830 896-0432 FAX 830 896-0433
LEIGH ANN POLSER,REG/ACCT

HILMAN ROLLERS
WELL-TO-WELL SKIDDING LAND RIGS/HILMAN
LIFT & ROLL SYSTEMS ON OFFSHORE JACKUPS
PO BOX 45,12 TIMBER LN
MARLBORO,NJ 07746 PH 732 462-6277
SALES@HILMANROLLERS.COM
WWW.HILMANROLLERS.COM
JEFF HILL

HILTY INTERESTS INC
7965 RANGER CK RD
BOERNE,TX 78006 PH 830 537-5430
FAX 830 537-5431
R E HILTY,PRES

HINES E R,JR,GEOL SEE MOON & HINES,LLC

HINTON WELL SERVICING INC
P O BOX 133
LISBON,LA 71048-0133 PH 318 353-6677
C B SIMPSON,PRES
E A SIMPSON,VP
JERRY D DEVORE,SECY/TREAS & OFC MGR
B G SIMPSON,GEN MGR

HIPKE DALE A,GEOL
121 S BROADWAY AVE STE 875
TYLER,TX 75702-7282 PH 903 597-3228

HISE COMPANY,THE
PO BOX 64806
BATON ROUGE,LA 70896-4806 PH 225 381-9252
RICHARD W HISE,PRES
BILL R HISE,VP
ANNE W HISE,SECY/TREAS
LAFAYETTE,LA OFFICE - 230 HEYMANN
BLVD,70503 PH 318 235-0590

HITE & ASSOCIATES,INC
712 MAIN ST #1701
HOUSTON,TX 77002 PH 713 654-4141
FAX 713 654-4404 HITEINC.COM
GEORGE C HITE,PRES

HITE COALBED METHANE OPERTING LLC
PO BOX 5168
EVANSVILLE,IN 47716-5168 PH 812 480-4625
PH 436-4475 FAX 812 428-6782
THITE@SIGECOM.NET
MICHAEL HITE,FIELD SUPVSR
ANDY MYERS,LAND MGR
PAUL RIDDLE,GAS MKTG MGR

THOMAS HITE,PROJ MGR

HNC-CFC HEIRS,LLC
PO BOX 51487
LAFAYETTE,LA 70505-1487 PH 318 984-1841
FAX 318 984-1841 HNCRAWFORD@YAHOO.COM

HNG OIL COMPANY SEE
ENRON OIL & GAS CO

HNG/INTERNORTH INC SEE
ENRON OIL & GAS CO

HOC FAR EAST VENTURES INC SEE
HUNT OIL COMPANY

HOCKING OIL CO,INC
PO BOX 162,123 W 4TH ST
MOUNT CARMEL,IL 62863-0162
PH 618 263-3258
ANDY G HOCKING,PRES

HODGDEN H JERRY,GEOL
408 18TH ST
GOLDEN,CO 80401-2433
PH 303 279-8199 PH 720 312-1208
FAX 303 279-8233 GEODOGS@COMCAST.NET

HODGDEN OIL COMPANY
408 18TH ST
GOLDEN,CO 80401-2433 PH 303 279-8199
FAX 303 279-8233 GEODOGS@COMCAST.NET
H JERRY HODGDEN,PRES PH 720 312-1208
DR LEWIS KLEINHANS,VP EXPL 720 273-9233

HODGES A J,INDUSTRIES,INC
PO BOX 1817
SHREVEPORT,LA 71166-1817 PH 318 221-7167
ANDREW J HODGES III,PRES
W L HODGES,VP

HOERMANN S E
830 CURRY RD
SEGUIN,TX 78155-9803 PH 830 379-7722
S E HOERMANN,OWNER,OPR

HOG OIL
11079 WITT AVE
BUTLER,IL 62015-2128
PH 314 378-2464
S WELLER,PRES XCORP,G P OF
GREAT HOG LTD PARTNERSHIP

HOGBACK EXPLORATION INC
PO BOX 180368
FORT SMITH,AR 72918-0368
PH 479 709-9014 FAX 479 709-0200
GERALD W LUNDY,PRES
KEVIN DELUNG,LDMN
SARAH FULLER,ACCT

HOLDEN ENERGY CORP SEE
UNO,INC

HOLDITCH-RESERVOIR TECHNOLOGIES SEE
SCHLUMBERGER

HOLEX ENERGY CORP
2131 PARKDALE
KINGWOOD,TX 77339-2352 PH 281 358-9588
FRED R HOLASEK,PRES

HOLLAND OIL CO,EST. 1933
138 CANYON CREEK DR
SAN ANTONIO,TX 78232-1304 PH 210 494-2901
SAM VAN DER WEIDE,CEO

HOLLEMAN & PARKS OIL & GAS,INC
1108 MAXWELL
TUPELO,MS 38804 PH 662 791-1707
LANDANDMINERAL@BELLSOUTH.NET
JACK P HOLLEMAN,PRES

RAYBURN PARKS,VP

HOLLEMAN ROBERT T,IND GEOL
PO BOX 51745,BLDG 10 HEYMANN BLVD
LAFAYETTE,LA 70505-1745 PH 318 234-5611
FAX 318 235-7709

HOLLENKAMP R J CORPORATION
800 LOVELL ST
SALEM,IL 62881-1433 PH 973 713-3927
FAX 618 548-2474 RJH710@MSN.COM
RODNEY J HOLLENKAMP,PRES
ROBERT D HOLLENKAMP,LDMN
RANDY M HOLLENKAMP,LDMN

HOLLIDAYSBURG OIL & GAS CO INC
5217 4TH AVE
ALTOONA,PA 16602-1428
PH 814 944-3302
MR KRAFT,PRODUCT & SALES
MR DRILL,NATURAL GAS ENGR/CONSLT

HOLLIMON OIL CORPORATION
8610 N NEW BRAUNFELS AVE STE 705
SAN ANTONIO,TX 78217
PH 210 829-8822 FAX 210 829-8833
J CHARLES HOLLIMON
REEVES HOLLIMON,PRES
ARMANDO MEDINA,VP
SCOTT BROWN,GEOL

HOLLIS ENERGY RESOURCE SERVICES
106 S ST CHARLES
BRENHAM,TX 77833
PH 713 461-5556 PH 713 256-0550
JULIE HOLLIS,PRES
JULHERS598@AOL.COM

HOLLOWAY PERRY G,GEOL
142 MAXIMILIAN LN
SHREVEPORT,LA 71105-3351 PH 318 865-3736
FAX 318 869-0936

HOLLY CORP
2828 N HARWOOD ST STE 1300
DALLAS,TX 75201-1507 PH 214 871-3555
WWW.HOLLYCORP.COM
LAMAR NORSWORTHY,CHRMN OF BD
MATTHEW P CLIFTON,CEO
DAVE LAMP,EXEC VP,REFINING & MKTG
JOHN GLANCY,SR VP,GEN COUNSEL
STEVE MCDONNELL,VP,CFO
DAVID G BLAIR,VP,MKTG,ASPHALT & LPG SLS
GREG WHITE,VP,REFINING & MKTG
TOM CREERY,VP,CRUDE SUPPLY & REFINERY
ECONOMICS

HOLMAN BERNARD A,OIL PROD
PO BOX 4672,120 N CONGRESS STE 608
JACKSON,MS 39296-4672 PH 601 948-2056

HOLT CAT
2001 N LOOP 12
IRVING,TX 75061 PH 972 721-5800
FAX 972 721-5844
BOB STRATTON,GEN MGR,HOLT PWR SYS
JIM HUGHES,SALES MGR
MIKE MEEKS,PRODUCT SUPPORT MGR

HOLTOM A HARRY,INC
4998 SMOKETALK LANE
WESTERVILLE,OH 43081-4433 PH 614 882-7147
HARRY A HOLTOM,PRES

HOMBRE OIL CO LTD
PO BOX 130070
TYLER,TX 75713-0070 PH 903 581-7100

FAX 903 581-7102
KELLY E RICHEY,GEN PRTNR

HOMCO CORING SERVICES SEE
WEATHERFORD INTERNATIONAL INCORPORATED

HOMCO INTERNATIONAL,INC SEE
WEATHERFORD ENTERRA

HONEYWELL SENSOTEC
2080 ARLINGATE LN
COLUMBUS,OH 43228-4112
PH 614 850-5000 800 848-6564
FAX 614 850-1111
WWW.SENSOTEC.COM SALES@SENSOTEC.COM

HOOD PETROLEUM INC
PO BOX 1592
RUSTON,LA 71273-1592 PH 318 251-2720
FAX 318 251-2030 JOHN@HOODCOMPANIES.NET
JOHN M HOOD,PRES,CEO
SETH HOOD,VP,COO
MATT WOODARD,SECY,TREAS,CFO
RENE DAVIDSON,OFC MGR

HOODOO LAND AND CATTLE COMPANY SEE
HUNT OIL COMPANY

HOOKER GREG D,GEOL
211 HIGHLAND CROSS DR STE 103
HOUSTON,TX 77073-1700 PH 281 784-1100
GHOOKER@SBCGLOBAL.NET

HOOKS CHAS G & SON
820 GESSNER RD STE 1300
HOUSTON,TX 77024-4296
PH 713 984-9891 FAX 713 984-9893
CHARLES G HOOKS III,MNGNG PRTNR
CGHANDSON@AOL.COM

HOOKS RUFUS H,GEOPHY
P O BOX 73
KOUNTZE,TX 77625-0073 PH 409 246-4814

HOOPER J HOWARD,OIL PROD
5828 CRESWELL AVE
SHREVEPORT,LA 71106-2202 PH 318 221-6841

HOOVER ENERGY PARTNERS LP
333 CLAY ST STE 3650 THREE ALLEN CENTER
HOUSTON,TX 77002 PH 832 582-7200
FAX 832 582-8146 WWW.HOOVERENERGY.COM
RANDY HOOVER,PRES
RHOOVER@HOOVERENERGY.COM

HOPE PRODUCTION,INC
PO BOX 3277
EDINBURG,TX 78540-3277 PH 956 584-8281
FAX 956 583-6640
KEN BUSS,PRES
JUNE BUSS,SECY-TREAS

HOPEWELL OIL AND GAS DEVELOPMENT CO
PO BOX 2776
ZANESVILLE,OH 43702-2776 PH 740 452-9326
JERRY S HENDERSON,PRES

HORGOS F A ASSOCIATES,INC
PETROLEUM ENGINEERING CONSULTANTS
PO BOX 135
WARREN,MA 01083-0135
PH 413 436-9586 FAX 413 436-9586
FRANK HORGOS,PRES

HORIZON EXPLORATION COMPANY
2727 ALLEN PKWY STE 1900
HOUSTON,TX 77019-2153
PH 713 522-5800 FAX 713 522-1881
SCOTT ROTHWELL,CO-MANAGING DIR
RICK L STEPHENS,VP,GEOPHY

MARK ROTHWELL,CO-MANAGING DIR
DOUG MANSKE,EXPL GEOL
STEPHEN POTH,EXPL GEOL

HORNE CURTIS D & ASSOCIATES,LLC
PETROLEUM LAND CONSULTANTS
2404 GRAND BLVD STE 140
PEARLAND,TX 77581-4270 PH 281 412-3777
WWW.CDHLAND.COM
CURTIS D HORNE,CPL,PRES

HORNING GROVE HULETT & THOMPSON SEE
GROVE & HULETT,P.C.

HORSESHOE ENERGY INC
PO BOX 653
FAIRFIELD,TX 75840-3132
PH 903 389-2320 FAX 903 389-4542
DSTEWARD3@GMAIL.COM
PAM STEWARD,PRES
DAVID STEWARD,VP LDMN PH 512 415-9490
MIKE D STEWARD,LDMN

HORTON JAMES V OIL & GAS
PO BOX 1219
SHREVEPORT,LA 71163-1219
PH 318 213-9413
JAMES V HORTON,LDMN

HORTON PAUL A,OIL LEASES
PO BOX 536
BLANCHARD,LA 71009-0536 PH 870 234-5504

HORTON PETROLEUM CORPORATION
5795 DOLIVER DR
HOUSTON,TX 77057-2493 PH 713 974-1607
LOREN G HORTON,OWNER,PRES

HOSKINS PETROLEUM CORPORATION
P O BOX 400
GEORGE WEST,TX 78022-0400
PH 361 449-1591 361 449-1618
CLIFF HOSKINS,PRES
LEONARD HOSKINS,VP

HOTCO ENERGY CO
PO BOX 51171,1030 E ST MARY BLVD BLDG 3
LAFAYETTE,LA 70505 PH 337 233-8866
JAMES HUNT HUNT@HOTCOENERGY.COM

HOUFF ENERGY CORPORATION
PO BOX 55768
HOUSTON,TX 77255-5768 PH 713 652-9626
BRUCE H HOUFF,PRES

HOUFF EXPLORATION COMPANY
PO BOX 55768
HOUSTON,TX 77255-5768 PH 713 652-9626
BRUCE H HOUFF,IND GEOL

HOUMA SALT WATER DISPOSAL CORPORATION
1034 COTEAU ROAD
HOUMA,LA 70364-4511 PH 504 868-2477
FAX 504 857-9004
U J FOURNIER,PRES
BRIAN J FOURNIER,GEN MGR
DEAN P FOURNIER,PLANT MGR

HOUSE RICHARD D & ASSOCIATES
PO BOX 52561,3024 PINHOOK
LAFAYETTE,LA 70505-2561 PH 337 232-2252
FAX 337 237-1087
RICHARD D HOUSE,OWNER,GEOL
RICHARD D HOUSE,JR,PROGRAMMER

HOUSER PHILIP S,INDEPENDENT
PO BOX 61941
SAN ANGELO,TX 76906-1941 PH 325 944-0844

HOUSTON ENERGY,L.P.
1200 SMITH ST STE 2400,TWO ALLEN CENTER
HOUSTON,TX 77002 PH 713 650-8008
FAX 713 650-8305 HEI@HOUSTONENERGYINC.COM
WWW.HOUSTONENERGYINC.COM
RONALD E NEAL,PRES OF ITS GEN PRTNR
FRANK W HARRISON,PRES OF ITS GEN PRTNR
P DAVID AMEND,SR EXEC VP
ALLEN WILHITE,VP LAND
DALE COUTHARD,VP ONSHORE EXPL
BILL FLORES,SR VP ENGRG
STACEY GUYNES,OFC MGR

HOUSTON GEOPHYSICAL SERVICES
5503 LYMBAR DR
HOUSTON,TX 77096-5000 PH 713 729-1348
EMILE A BUSSEMEY,GEOPHY

HOUSTON OIL PRODUCING ENTERPRISES,INC
1106 BERTHEA ST
HOUSTON,TX 77006-6410
PH 713 522-4673 FAX 713 522-7273
WILLIAM J HILL,PRES
HIGH ISLAND,TX OFFICE - PO BOX 298
77623 PH 409 286-5516
P R SATTLER,FRMN

HOUSTON PETROLEUM COMPANY
3100 TIMMONS LN STE 200
HOUSTON,TX 77027-5904 PH 713 521-0704
FAX 713 523-0145 HPC3000@SWBELL.NET
RICHARD O'DONNELL,PRES
WESLEY PUSTEJOVSKY,VP
THOMAS L PETERSON,GEOL

HOUSTON PIPE LINE COMPANY LP SEE
ENERGY TRANSFER PARTNERS,LP

HOUSTON PUBLIC LIBRARY/BST
1050 QUITMAN
HOUSTON,TX 77009 PH 832 393-1612
FAX 832 393-1590 WWW.HOUSTONLIBRARY.ORG

HOUSTON RESOURCES CORP
3009 POST OAK BLVD STE 1212
HOUSTON,TX 77056 PH 713 658-1142
FAX 713 658-0739 WWW.NORTEXCORP.COM
ROBERT W KENT,VP LAND/ACQS

HOWARD DOUGLAS J,GEOL
7915 FM 1960 W STE 203
HOUSTON,TX 77070-5716 PH 281 477-9200
FAX 281 477-9299

HOWARD ENERGY CORP
PO BOX 693,519 WEST THIRD ST
MOUNT CARMEL,IL 62863-0693
PH 618 263-3000 FAX 618 262-7085
CRAIG@HOWARDENERGYCORP.COM

HOWARD EXPLORATION,INC
7915 FM 1960 W STE 203
HOUSTON,TX 77070-5716
PH 281 477-9200 FAX 281 477-9299
DOUGLAS J HOWARD,CEO
ALAN W HOWARD,PRES

HOWARD GEORGE E,IND LDMN,LEASE BROKER
112 A LAUREL ST
WEBER CITY,VA 24290 PH 276 386-6015
FAX 276 386-2804

HOWELL & SANDLIN INC SEE
HOWELL OIL & GAS,INC

HOWELL CRUDE OIL COMPANY
SUBSIDIARY OF HOWELL CORPORATION
PO BOX 1330

HOUSTON,TX 77251-1330 PH 713 658-4000
FAX 713 658-4153
MARK J GORMAN,PRES
JOHN M FETZER,SR VP,CRUDE OIL
JAMES JIM C BUFORD,VP,CRUDE OIL
JEFFREY JEFF C LEE,GEN MGR,OPERS & SUP
JEFF D INGLISH,JR,AREA MGR
BOBBY L KELM,CRUDE OIL REPR
DEBRA DEBBIE L STAGE,SCHEDULER
YOAKUM,TX CENTRAL TX AREA OFFICE -
412 FORREST ST,77995 PH 361 293-2778
LOWELL MARTIN,CRUDE OIL REPR
CORPUS CHRISTI,TX SOUTH TX AREA OFFICE -
711 N CARANCAHUA,STE 700-D,78475
PH 361 888-6622 FAX 361 884-5219
GARY R TAUB,AREA MGR
BRANDON,MS AREA OFFICE -
PO BOX 1438,39043-1438
PH 601 352-0037 FAX 601 354-7900
DON CHAMPLIN,CRUDE OIL REP

HOWELL OIL & GAS,INC
PO BOX 1228,3700 EAST END BLVD SOUTH
MARSHALL,TX 75671-1228 PH 903 935-0999
FAX 903 938-9833 STEVE@HOWELLOIL-GAS.COM
STEVE HOWELL,PRES
LESLIE CHAMBERS,VP
RON WALSH,VP/FIN & TAXATION
SAM HOWELL,GEN COUNSEL
RUSH HARRIS,LAND MGR

HOWELL PETROLEUM CORPORATION
PO BOX 1330
HOUSTON,TX 77251-1330 PH 713 658-4000
FAX 713 658-4114
RICHARD K HEBERT,PRES,COO
DAVID IVY,VP,EXPL
JOSEPH M SMALL,VP,OPERS & ENGRG
SALLY J MCELROY,SR LDMN,MIN CONTACT

HPS OIL & GAS PROPERTIES INC
PO BOX 52149,118 DEMANADE BLVD
LAFAYETTE,LA 70505-2149 PH 337 232-1200
FAX 337 233-0793
GARY L SALMON,PRES
C ANN PELTIER,SECY

HRACHOVY OIL & GAS,L.C.
PO BOX 267
STAFFORD,TX 77497-0267 PH 281 277-5030
FAX 281 277-4191 HRACHOVYN@EARTHLINK.NET
N J HRACHOVY,OWNER

HRC ENERGY HOLDINGS (LA),INC SEE
HALCON RESOURCES CORPORATION

HRC ENERGY LOUISIANA,LLC SEE
HALCON RESOURCES CORPORATION

HRC ENERGY RESOURCES (LAFOURCHE),INC SEE
HALCON RESOURCES CORPORATION

HRC ENERGY RESOURCES (WV),INC SEE
HALCON RESOURCES CORPORATION

HRUBETZ OIL COMPANY
5956 SHERRY LN STE 534
DALLAS,TX 75225-8016 PH 214 378-3633
FAX 214 378-3631
ALBERT HRUBETZ,PRES
MARY THOMPSON,ADMIN ASST

HS RESOURCES,INC SEE
QUESTAR EXPLORATION AND PRODUCTION CO

HSH ROYALTY CORP
PO BOX 1245

ANN ARBOR,MI 48106
PH 734 663-7046 HSHROYALTY@GMAIL.COM
DEBORAH FREDERICKS,PRES
GEORGE OWENS,REG AGENT PH 918 587-0021

HSSG LP SEE
HUNT OIL COMPANY

HUB CITY INDUSTRIES INC
4700 NE EVANGELINE THRUWAY
LAFAYETTE,LA 70520 PH 337 886-3232
FAX 337 886-7443
WWW.HUBCITYINDUSTRIES.COM
ROBERT L BUTLER,ACIDIZING MGR
JOHN M EGLE,PRES
CHAD A TOUCHET,VP ENGRG
GLENN P DAUTERIVE,MKTG MGR
DEAN A BUTLER,VP
RHONDA A BUTLER,EXEC ADMIN ASST
DIANE P BARTLETT,HR MGR,CONTROLLER
RODNEY P DARTEZ,REG TECH MGR
MICHAEL R KEYS,SLS REPR
DONALD I FOLEY JR,OPERS MGR
ABNER J POIENCOT JR,CEMENTING SUPVSR/SA
SHAWN G BERNARD,DIV LAB MGR

HUBBARD DEV CO,SEE
BRECK OPERATING CORP

HUBBELL LIGHTING,INC
MFG OF EXTREME MARINE LIGHTING
2000 ELECTRIC WAY
CHRISTIANSBURG,VA 24073-2500
PH 540 382-6111
WEBMASTER@HUBBELL-LTG.COM
JOE ENGLE

HUBLEY JAMES G,C.P.L.
PO BOX 7014
TYLER,TX 75711-7014 PH 903 561-0384

HUDDLESTON & COMPANY INC
1221 MCKINNEY STE 3700
HOUSTON,TX 77010 PH 713 209-1100
FAX 713 209-1104 FAX 713 752-0828
WWW.HUDDLESTONCO.COM
B P HUDDLESTON,PE,CHRMN
PETER D HUDDLESTON,PE,PRES
JOHN P KRAWTZ,PE,SR VP
GREGORY S MITSCHKE,PE,SR VP OPERS
WM PAUL HUDDLESTON,VP
FLORA M HUDDLESTON,SECY/TREAS
KATHY B HUDDLESTON,PE,PETR ENGR
KAREN R DIXON,ENGR
JEFF MCCLELLAN,IT
WILL HUDDLESTON,ANALYST

HUDDLESTON LAND SERVICES,INC
PO BOX 52105
SHREVEPORT,LA 71135-2105
PH 318 797-1009 FAX 318 797-1031
JHUDDLESTON@SHREVE.NET
GERALD HUDDLESTON,OWNER

HUDSON CHARLIE & ASSOCIATES INCORPORATED
OIL & GAS LEASING
14520 WUNDERLICH STE 160
HOUSTON,TX 77069 PH 281 580-8536
FAX 281 580-8538

HUDSON ENGINEERING CONSULTANTS
207 RENEE AVE
LAFAYETTE,LA 70503-3331 PH 318 233-4178
W M DUB HUDSON,PE,PRES
COYDEAN HUDSON,SECY

HUDSON JOHN PETROLEUM GEOLOGIST,INC
PO BOX 283,410 LEXINGTON
FORT SMITH,AR 72902
PH 479 783-5574 CEFOSE1@ARCOXMAIL.COM
JOHN G HUDSON

HUFFORD ENERGY LAND SERVICES SEE
ENERGY LAND SERVICES

HUGGS GAS MARKETING,INC
333 TEXAS ST STE 840
SHREVEPORT,LA 71101-3678 PH 318 221-4499
GERALD E HUGGS JR,PRES

HUGGS INCORPORATED
333 TEXAS ST STE 840
SHREVEPORT,LA 71101-3678 PH 318 221-4499
FAX 318 222-3216
G E HUGGS JR,PRES

HUGGS INTRASTATE GAS PIPELINE COMPANY
333 TEXAS ST STE 840
SHREVEPORT,LA 71101-3678 PH 318 221-4499
FAX 318 222-3216
GERALD E HUGGS JR,PRES

HUGHES BYRON OIL EXPL & PROF LAND SVCS
PO BOX 1485
JACKSON,MS 39215-1485 PH 662 402-6876
PH 662 545-1394 FAX 601 924-1274
WWW.BHUGHESOIL.COM
BYRON HUGHES,OWNER
BYRONHUGHES@LIVE.COM

HUGHES DAN A,COMPANY,LP
PO BOX 669,208 E HOUSTON ST 78102
BEEVILLE,TX 78104-0669
PH 361 358-3752 FAX 361 358-0598
DAN A HUGHES,CEO
DAN A HUGHES JR,PRES
KATHLEEN KARCHER,VP ACCT
HANK KREMERS,COO/VP LAND
KIRKBY TOWNSEND,CFO
JOHN HUMSTON,GEOL MGR
LEONEL SAAVEDRA,EXPL MGR
WADE CHAPMAN,OPERS MGR
RALPH SANDOVAL,PROD ADMIN
JOHN BOND,OFC MGR
HOUSTON,TX OFFICE - 1001 FANNIN STE 4775
FIRST CITY TOWER,77002 PH 713 759-1769
JOHN BOND,OFC MGR

HUGHES DANIEL C A PROFESSIONAL LAW CORP
126 HEYMANN BLVD
LAFAYETTE,LA 70503 PH 337 237-6566
FAX 337 237-6567 WWW.HUGHESAPLC.COM
DANIEL C HUGHES,ATTY
DAN@HUGHESAPLC.COM
MELINDA RAMSON,PARALEGAL

HUGHES EASTERN CORPORATION
605 NORTHPARK DR STE A
RIDGELAND,MS 39157-4843 PH 601 898-0051
FAX 601 898-0233
EMIL H PAWLIK,PRES
TERRY HARGIS,ENGR
ALBERT S GRAY,COMPTROLLER
VALERIE SELMAN,LAND

HUGHES H O,OIL PROD
611 WOODBINE LN
HATTIESBURG,MS 39402-2050 PH 601 261-3302

HUGHES MARK J & ASSOC
910 CRAIG DR
HENDERSON,KY 42420-2766 PH 270 869-0067

PH 270 860 9886 FAX 270 831-1955
COLLEDGE@INSIGHTBB.COM
MARK J HUGHES

HUGHES SOUTH CORPORATION
PO BOX 720369
BYRAM,MS 39272-0369 PH 601 420-9892
FAX 601 420-9893
DUDLEY J HUGHES,PRES

HUGHES WILLIAM M OIL & GAS & INVESTMENTS
P O BOX 130955
TYLER,TX 75713-0955
PH 903 939-9888 PH 903 521-7822
BADBILLHUGHES@GMAIL.COM

HUGHETT ENGINEERING,INC
PO BOX 600163
DALLAS,TX 75360 PH 214 802-0266
JOHN P HUGHETT,PE
JOHNHUGHETT@HUGHETTENGINEERING.COM

HUGHEY W R,OPERATING CO,INC
PO BOX 907
WHITEHOUSE,TX 75791-0907 PH 214 595-1224
W R HUGHEY,CHRMN OF BD
FRANK HUGHEY,PRES
J L GULLEY JR,VP
CYNTHIA HAISTEN,SECY

HUGUS INVESTMENT CO INC
PO BOX 7310
TYLER,TX 75711-7310
PH 903 561-5495 FAX 903 581-7965
BILLS@HUGUS.NET

HUGUS MARY ELLEN,OIL OPR
PO BOX 7310
TYLER,TX 75711 PH 903 561-5495
FAX 903 581-7965 BILLS@HUGAS.NET

HULL JOHN T,CPL
6251 VAN BUREN ST
DAPHNE,AL 36526-7157 PH 334 621-9758
FAX 334 621-9610

HULSEY OIL COMPANY,INC
4424 LARCHMONT ST
DALLAS,TX 75205-1621 PH 214 521-4256
ALAN A HULSEY,PRES

HUMPHREY HUGH,REAL ESTATE
5301 GEN MEYER AVE
NEW ORLEANS,LA 70114 PH 504 392-3203

HUMPHREY OIL & GAS INC
5433 WHITES BOTTOM RD
KETTLE,KY 42752-8623 PH 270 433-7612
FAX 270 433-5620 HUMPHREYOIL@HOTMAIL.COM
ALAN HUMPHREY,PRES

HUMPHREY OIL CORPORATION
3004 FAIRMOUNT ST
DALLAS,TX 75201-1251 PH 214 528-9620
FAX 214 528-9621
CHARLES B HUMPHREY,PRES
SHEILA B IRONS,VP

HUMPHREY OIL INTERESTS L.P.
C/O HUMPHREY OIL CORP GENERAL PARTNER
3004 FAIRMOUNT ST
DALLAS,TX 75201-1251 PH 214 528-9620
FAX 214 528-9621
CHARLES B HUMPHREY,PRES
SHEILA IRONS,VP

HUNT ARENA CORPORATION SEE
HUNT OIL COMPANY

HUNT CHIEFTAIN DEVELOPMENT LP
SEE HUNT OIL COMPANY

HUNT CONSOLIDATED INC SEE
HUNT OIL COMPANY

HUNT EQUITIES INC
SEE HUNT OIL COMPANY

HUNT GEORGE D,OIL PROD
PO BOX 22787
JACKSON,MS 39225-2787
PH 601 948-7400 FAX 601 948-7412
CHARLES G GATES,OWNER

HUNT GRAHAM,PH D,CONSULTING GEOL
4082 ELMWOOD AVE
LOUISVILLE,KY 40207-2174 PH 502 895-6341

HUNT GROWTH CAPITAL LP
SEE HUNT OIL COMPANY

HUNT HASSIE EXPLORATION CO SEE
HHE COMPANY

HUNT INTERNATIONAL RESOURCES SEE
HUNT OIL COMPANY

HUNT INVESTMENT COMPANY LP
SEE HUNT OIL COMPANY

HUNT MAX TANK TRUCK SERVICE AND
PORTABLE OIL TREATING
RR 1 BOX 2400
DALE,IL 62817-9005 PH 618 773-4212

HUNT MEXICO INC SEE
HUNT OIL COMPANY

HUNT OIL COMPANY
1900 N AKARD ST
DALLAS,TX 75201-2300
PH 214 978-8000 FAX 214 978-8888
WWW.HUNTOIL.COM
RAY L HUNT,CHRMN/CEO
PRES-HUNT CONSOLIDATED,INC
STEVE SUELLENTROP,PRES
HUNTER L HUNT,PRES/CEO-HUNT CONSOLIDATED
ENERGY
THOMAS E MEURER,SR VP
DONALD F ROBILLARD,SR VP/CFO
DENNIS GRINDINGER,EXEC VP
CHRISTOPHER W KLEINERT,PRES/CEO-HUNT
CONSOLIDATED INVESTMENTS
KEVIN CAMPBELL,SR VP/CIO
DAVID CHAPMAN,VP-KURDISTAN OPERS
BILL REX,VP LAND
THOMAS J CWIKLA,EXEC VP-NORTH AMERICA
PAUL HOFFMAN,SR VP HUMAN RESOURCES
JEANNE L PHILLIPS,SR VP-CORP AFFAIRS &
INTL RELS
PAUL HABENICHT,EXEC VP-NORTH AMERICA
DAN RAY,SR VP MKTG
DONNA GERMAN,VP/TREAS/CHF RISK OFCR
STEVE KUYKENDALL,VP PURCHASING
PAUL LICATA,SR VP-ENVIRO,HEALTH,& SAFETY
JESS NUNNELEE,VP NORTH AMERICAN PROD
POYNOR,TX FAIRWAY PROD DIST OFFICE -
PO BOX 138,11333 FM 315,75782
PH 903 876-2227 FAX 903 876-2188
JAMEY HYDE,LEAD FRMN
MIDLAND,TX PRODUCTION DISTRICT OFFICE -
200 N LORAINE,STE 1310
79701 PH 432 684-8093 FAX 432 684-0655

HUNT OIL COMPANY OF LOUISIANA INC SEE
HUNT OIL COMPANY

HUNT OIL COMPANY OF NEVADA SEE
HUNT OIL COMPANY

HUNT OIL COMPANY OF PERU LLC SEE
HUNT OIL COMPANY

HUNT OIL TOOL CO
PO BOX 51171,1030 E ST MARY BLVD BLDG 3
LAFAYETTE,LA 70505 PH 337 322-6663
JAMES H HUNT HUNT@HUNTOILTOOL.COM

HUNT OIL USA INC SEE
HUNT OIL COMPANY

HUNT OVERSEAS OIL COMPANY SEE
HUNT OIL COMPANY SEE

HUNT PETROLEUM AEC INC SEE
XTO OFFSHORE INC

HUNT PETROLEUM CORPORATION SEE
XH LLC

HUNT POWER CANADA SEE
HUNT OIL COMPANY

HUNT PRIVATE EQUITY GROUP SEE
SEE HUNT OIL COMPANY

HUNT SECURITIES CORP
SEE HUNT OIL COMPANY

HUNT VALLEY RESOURCES INC
522 EAST EIGHTH ST
TRAVERSE CITY,MI 49686 PH 231 499-9687
CONTACT@HUNTAVALLEYRESOURCES.COM
BEN VALLEY
CORPORATE OFFICE - 1135 TERMINAL WAY
STE 209 RENO,NV 98502
WWW.HUNTVALLEYRESOURCES.COM

HUNT VENTURES SEE
HUNT OIL COMPANY

HUNTER DEWAYNE J,PETROLEUM ENGINEER
8137 RIVER RD
WAGGAMAN,LA 70094-2321 PH 504 431-9246
FAX 504 431-8812 PH 504 782-8725
DHUNTER403@AOL.COM
DEWAYNE J HUNTER,PRES
MAGGIE HUNTER,SECY

HUNTER ENERGY CORPORATION
PO BOX 1689
RUSTON,LA 71273-1689 PH 318 255-2400
FAX 318 251-1211
WWW.HUNTERENERGYCORP.COM
STEPHEN O SMITH,PRES
STEVE@HUNTERENERGYCORP.COM
S HUNTER SMITH,VP
HUNTER@HUNTERENERGYCORP.COM

HUNTER EXPLORATION COMPANY,INC
PO BOX 51405
LAFAYETTE,LA 70505-1405
PH 337 232-1700 FAX 337 234-0403
DAVID STURLESE,PRES,GEOL

HUNTER JOE A,PETR LAND SERVICE
PO BOX 669
BURNET,TX 78611-0669
PH 979 820-0334 FAX 512 756-8058

HUNTER LAND SERVICES,LLC
PO BOX 669
BURNET,TX 78611-0669 PH 979 820-0334
FAX 512 756-8058
JOE A HUNTER,OWNER

HUNTLEY & HUNTLEY INC
4314 OLD WILLIAM PENN HWY #100
MONROEVILLE,PA 15146-1455 PH 412 380-2355
FAX 412 380-4003 KMANGINI@HUNTLEYINC.COM

HURD ENTERPRISES LTD
7373 BROADWAY STE 200
SAN ANTONIO,TX 78209-3265 PH 210 829-5255
FAX 210 829-5061 WWW.HURDENTERPRISES.COM
JOHN R HURD,CHRMN
EUGENE E GARCIA,PRES
JOHN R HURD JR,PRES
JOHN HAGY,LAND MGR
HARRY A BALLING,CHF GEOL
JAMES C KUSTER,CONTROLLER
DEBBIE DORSETT,GEOL ENGR

HURON LAND SERVICES,LLC
1 STEWART PLAZA
DUNBAR,WV 25064 PH 304 546-8365
ARNOLD L SCHULBERG,LDMN
ASCHULBERG@SCHULBERGLAW.COM

HURRIKAIN ENERGY LLC
PO BOX 1433
PEARSALL,TX 78061-1433 PH 830 334-7330
JOHN G KAIN,MGR

HUSKY OIL CO SEE
MARATHON OIL CO

HUSKY OIL OPERATIONS LTD
PO BOX 6525,STATION D 707-8 AVE SW
CALGARY,ALTA,CAN T2P 3G7 PH 403 298-6111
FAX 403 298-7464
JCS LAU,CEO

HUTCHISON OIL & GAS CORP
700 N PEARL ST STE 2150
DALLAS,TX 75201 PH 214 220-9010
FAX 214 220-9012
CHUTCHISON@HUTCHISONOIL.COM
WILLIAM L HUTCHISON,PRES
CHARLES D HUTCHISON,VP

HW OPERATING,LLC
INDEPENDENT OIL AND GAS EXPL AND PROD CO
PO BOX 5332,900 8TH ST STE 419
WICHITA FALLS,TX 76307 PH 940 500-4026
JOEL HAWKINS,PRES
MARK SUTTON,VP LAND/ACQS
DREW CARNES,VP PROD/OPERS
JERRY GILBERT,CONS GEOL
LEAH WALKER,ACCT

HYCALOG SEE
NOV REEDHYCALOG

HYDRAULIC SYSTEMS INC
27601 COMMERCE OAKS DR
THE WOODLANDS,TX 77385 PH 832 791-5000
WWW.HSI-POWER.COM SALES@HSI-
POWER.COM

HYDRAULIC WELL CONTROL SEE
BOOTS & COOTS SERVICES

HYDREX CORP
PO BOX 310542,144 LANDA ST STE 157
NEW BRAUNFELS,TX 78131 PH 830 626-3479
MARK S WOODWARD,PRES/CEO
MARKWOODWARD@HYDREXCORP.COM

HYDREX OPERATING,INC
PO BOX 310542,144 LANDA ST STE 157
NEW BRAUNFELS,TX 78131 PH 830 626-3479
MARK S WOODWARD,PRES/CEO

HYDRIL COMPANY LP SEE
TENARIS GLOBAL SERVICES

HYDRIL PRESSURE CONTROL
3300 N SAM HOUSTON PKWY E
HOUSTON,TX 77032-3411 PH 281 449-2000

FAX 281 985-3480 FAX 281 985-3262 (O&RF)
ANCHORAGE,AK OFFICE - 7900 KING ST 99518
PH 907 522-2550 FAX 907 522-1995
BAKERSFIELD,CA OFFICE - 4708 NEW HORIZON
BLVD 93313 FAX 661 420-8740
MIKE EDWARDS PH 661 609-2981
FELIPE TORRES PH 661 302-7287
BAKERSFIELD,CA OFFICE - 3237 PATTON WAY
93308 PH 661 588-9332 FAX 661 588-2550
LAFAYETTE,LA OFFICE - 1249 EVANGELINE
THRUWAY 70518 PH 337 837-6654
FAX 337 837-8988
HUMBLE,TX OFFICE - 18000 EASTEX FRWY
77396 PH 281 985-8800 FAX 281 985-8600
HUMBLE,TX (VETCOGRAY) OFFICE - 12221 N
HOUSTON ROSSLYN 77086 PH 281 691-2392
NISKU,ALBERTA,CANADA OFFICE - 1110 5TH ST
T9E 8B6 PH 780 955-1930 FAX 780 955-1940

HYDRO-SEARCH,INC SEE
H S I GEOTRANS,INC

HYDROCARBON CAPITAL PARTNERS LLC SEE
LEOR EXPLORATION,LLC

HYDROCARBON HORIZONS INC
600 LEOPARD ST STE 1724
CORPUS CHRISTI,TX 78473-0044
PH 361 887-6655 FAX 361 887-6341
BRIAN S CALHOUN,PRES

HYDROCARBON INVESTMENTS INC
7235 N GREEN RIVER RD
EVANSVILLE,IN 47725 PH 812 867-8011
FAX 812 867-8012
HYDROCARBONINVESTMENTS@HOTMAIL.COM
CRAIG KENDALL,PRES

HYDROCARBON TECHNOLOGY ENGINEERING,INC
PO BOX 7347
GRAND RAPIDS,MI 49510-7347
PH 616 452-3279 FAX 616 452-3290
WWW.HTENGINEERING.COM
DCOOPER@HTENGINEERING.COM
D M COOPER,PRES

HYDROCARBON WELL SERVICES INC
PO BOX 995,2934 OLD WESTON RD
BUCKHANNON,WV 26201 PH 304 472-9600
HYDROCARBON@HYDROCARBONWELL.COM

HYDROSTATIC OILFIELD TESTING,INC
PO BOX 2,1605 COMMERCE ST
MAGNOLIA,AR 71754-0002
PH 870 234-7638 FAX 870 234-6843
BILLY PHARR,PRES
RANDY PHARR,VP
TOM WARE,PACKER SPEC
JOHNNY OTWELL,FISHING TOOL SUPVSR
JASON MCWILLIAMS,FISHING TOOL SUPVSR
JOHN ABLE,SHREVEPORT BRANCH MGR
BARRON LAMBERT,TOOL SPEC
JASON HAMILTON,TOOL SPEC
JIMMY PRATT,TOOL SPEC
JOHN ABLE IV,DIST SLS
MIKE VAUGHAN,AREA SLS

HYLAND ABSTRACTING,LLC
PO BOX 243
SLAUGHTER,LA 70777 PH 225 937-3445
WWW.HYLANDABSTRACTING.COM
PATIA@HYLANDABSTRACTING.COM
HYPATIA LACOUR,RL,OWNER

HYQUEST ENERGY INC
PO BOX 52567
MIDLAND,TX 79710 PH 432 686-0307
JAMES R DAMMANN,PRES

IBERIA PARISH ASSESSOR'S OFFICE
121 W PERSHING ST STE 100
NEW IBERIA,LA 70560 PH 337 369-4415
FAX 337 369-4406 WWW.IBERIAASSESSOR.ORG
RICKEY J HUVAL,SR,CLA-ASSESSOR
IBERIAASSESSOR@BELLSOUTH.NET
MARNELL FREMIN,CHF DEPUTY
MARNELL.FREMIN@IBERIAASSESSOR.ORG
ELAINE LANNIE,PERSONAL PROPERTY
ELAINE.LANNIE@IBERIAASSESSOR.ORG
PATTY ROMERO,PERSONAL PROPERTY
PATTY.ROMERO@IBERIAASSESSOR.ORG

IBERIA PETROLEUM CO
ONE GREENWAY PLZ STE 700
HOUSTON,TX 77046 PH 713 627-8946
W DOUGLAS ANKENMAN JR,PRIN
E PHILIP CANNON,PRIN

IBEX PARTNERSHIP,SEE
BRECK OPERATING CORP

IDC ENERGY CORPORATION
1801 PATTERSON ST
HOUSTON,TX 77007 PH 713 869-0077
FAX 713 869-0078

IGNITION SYSTEMS & CONTROLS,LP
2525 N LONGVIEW ST
KILGORE,TX 75662 PH 903 983-3844
FAX 903 984-7041
JOEL TURNER,BRANCH MGR
CURTIS S LOUGH,INSIDE PARTS SALES
SAM GATES,SVC TECH
EDWARD CAMAILLE,FIELD TECH
JERRY GIDDENS,TECH SALES
ROD WILSON,TECH SLS

IHRDC (INTERNATIONAL HUMAN RES DEV CORP)
535 BOYLSTON ST
BOSTON,MA 02116-3720 PH 617 536-0202
DAVID A T DONOHUE,PRES

IHS
INFO SVCS TO OIL & GAS IND/WELL & PROD
DATA TO ECONOMIC & CONSLT PROD & SERVIC-
ES
- DENVER CORPORATE OFFICE -
15 INVERNESS WAY EAST
ENGLEWOOD,CO 80112-5776
PH 303 736-3000 800 OIL-DATA
FAX 303 736-3150 SALES.ENERGY@IHS.COM
WWW.IHS.COM/ENERGY
- SERVICES:WORLDWIDE WELL & PROD DATA -
SCOTT KEY,PRES & CEO
JERRE STEAD,EXEC CHRMN
RICHARD WALKER,EXEC VP GLOBAL FIN
BRIAN SWEENEY,SR VP GLOBAL SLS
DANIEL YERGIN,VICE CHRMN
STEPHANIE BUSCEMI,SR VP/CMO
JONATHAN GEAR,SR VP INDUSTRIALS
STEPHEN GREEN,EXEC VP LEGAL & CORP SECY
ANURAG GUPTA,EXEC VP STRATEGY,PROD & OPER
TODD HYATT,SR VP,CHF FIN & IT OFCR
SEAN MENKE,EXEC VP RESOURCES
JANE OKUN BOMBA,SR VP/CHF SUSTAINABILITY
IR & COMMUNICATIONS OFC
JEFF SISSON,SR VP & CHF HR OFCR

HOUSTON,TX SALES OFFICE - 5333 WESTHEIMER
STE 100,77056 PH 713 840-8282
PH 800 756-5333 FAX 713 599-9100
- SALES/TECHNICAL SERVICES -
MARK ROSE,EXEC SR VP,AMERICAS
SLAVO PASTOR,SVP ENERGY TECH
JIM WORTHAM,SR DIR DATA LOGIC SERVICES
KELLY CULLIGAN,VP SLS
CARL GARRISO,VP GLOBAL MKTG
DALLAS,TX SALES OFFICE - 17177 PRESTON RD
STE 200,75248 PH 972 783-8002
PH 800 468-3381 FAX 972 783-0058
- SALES/TECHNICAL SERVICES -
JEFF KAY,VP AMERICAS SLS OPERS
OKLAHOMA CITY,OK SALES OFFICE - 4045 NW
EXPY STE 300,73115 PH 405 232-2722
PH 800 341-4677 FAX 405 231-2502
- SALES/TECHNICAL SERVICES -
CHUCK DUNN,VP N REGION SLS MGR
LARRY GRIFFIN,DIR N REG SLS
MIDLAND,TX SALES OFFICE -
10 DESTA DR #620E,79705
PH 432 682-2343 FAX 432 683-5817
- SALES/TECHNICAL SERVICES -
EDUARDO MARTINEZ,GLOBAL ACCT MGR
CALGARY,ALBERTA,CANADA OFFICE -
STAMPEDE STATION STE 200
1331 MACLEOD TRL SE,T2G 0K3
PH 403 770-4646 FAX 403 770-4647
STU PRITCHARD,SR DIR SLS
BRUCE SKETCHLEY,VP ENERGY TECH SLS
RUSS SAGERT,VP CANADA OPERS

IHS ENERGY SEE
IHS

IHS HEROLD
AN IHS COMPANY
200 CONNECTICUT AVE STE 3A
NORWALK,CT 06854
PH 203 847-3344 FAX 203 847-5566
WWW.HEROLD.COM
HOUSTON,TX OFFICE - 5333 WESTHEIMER RD
STE 100,77056 PH 713 840-8282
FAX 713 499-4381

ILIOS RESOURCES,INC
9467 ELLERBE RD
SHREVEPORT,LA 71106-7444
PH 318 219-2464 FAX 318 219-2466
INQUIRY@ILIOSRESOURCES.COM
WWW.ILIORESOURCES.COM
LAURA M FITZGERALD,CPL,PRES

ILLINOIS ENERGY LLC
3703 N ELSTON AVE
CHICAGO,IL 60618
PH 773 772-6771 FAX 773 772-6779
SAUL AZAR,MGR
WESTRIDGE5653@YAHOO.COM

ILLINOIS STATE GEOLOGICAL SURVEY
615 E PEABODY DR
CHAMPAIGN,IL 61820-6964 PH 217 244-2414
FAX 217 333-0802 WWW.ISGS.UIUC.EDU

IMPACT EXPLORATION
3939 BEE CAVE RD STE C-100
AUSTIN,TX 78746 PH 512 370-1955
ROSS W HINTON,PRTNR,GEOL
ROSSWHINTON@GMAIL.COM
JAMES E HOUSTON,PRTNR,GEOPHY

JIM.HOUSTON@IMPACTEXPLORATION.COM

IMPERIAL OIL & GAS CO
PO BOX 51426
LAFAYETTE,LA 70505-1426 PH 337 234-5107
ROBERT C PETTIT,PRES
MICHEL E MIKE PETTIT,VP,GEOL

IMPERIAL OIL COMPANY
22499 IMPERIAL VALLEY DR
HOUSTON,TX 77073-1173 PH 281 209-1150
FAX 281 209-1154
GSWEBB@IMPERIAL-OIL-COMPANY.COM
ELLIS RUDY,PRES
GEORGE S WEBB,VP
SUZANNE WHITE,SECY

IMPERIAL SNUBBING SERVICES SEE
SUPERIOR ENERGY SERVICES COMPANY

IN OIL CO,THE
PO BOX 17835
SUGAR LAND,TX 77496-7835
PH 713 977-7200 FAX 281 277-4877
CLEMENT CHANG,PRES

INDEPENDENT EXPLORATION & PRODUCTION
GROUP,LLC
PO BOX 2840
RIDGELAND,MS 39158 PH 601 927-9499
JACKSON,MS OFFICE - 1501 LAKELAND DR
STE 301 39216
MAC MCGEHEE
MAC.MCGEHEE@STRONGROCKENERGY.COM
NEIL BARNES
NEIL.BARNES@IEPMGROUP.COM

INDIAN EXPLORATION,INC
PO BOX 51371
LAFAYETTE,LA 70505-1371
PH 337 237-2609 FAX 337 237-6727
GUY F OWENS,PRES,GEOL
BRIAN K VESEY,CEO,GEOL
HARDY ANDRUS,FLD SUPT
LARRY L SWAN,LAND MGR

INDRILLERS L.L.C.
PO BOX 509,1315 N MISSION RD
MOUNT PLEASANT,MI 48804-0509
PH 517 772-5955 FAX 517 772-3558
JAMES BIGARD,VP
STEVEN BIGARD,CONTRACT MGR
RICK HUGGARD,DRLG SUPT

INERT GAS,INC,NITROGEN SERVICES
2690 APPELT DR
HOUSTON,TX 77015 PH 281 457-9700
FAX 281 457-3611
ALLAN C KNAPP,PRES

INGRAM CACTUS COMPANY SEE
CAMERON

INLAND ENERGY COMPANY
974 E FORTIFICATION ST
JACKSON,MS 39202-2423
PH 601 969-1160 FAX 601 969-1162
DAVID MILLER,CHRMN,CEO
BRYANT G MILLER,VP
DAVID W MILLER,SECY/TREAS

INLAND OCEAN INC
PO BOX 6949,1815 E LAWNDALE
SAN ANTONIO,TX 78209-0949 PH 210 828-2625
FAX 210 828-2629 INLANDO@SBCGLOBAL.NET
HANS R F HELLAND,PRES

INLAND OIL AND GAS
RR 1 BOX 1618
CHIRENO,TX 75937-9744 PH 936 362-2573
INLANDOIL@QZIP.NET
JOE HIBBARD,PRES
WENDY TYLICH,PROD MGR

INLAND ROYALTY COMPANY
PO BOX 225,514 OAK AVENUE
SULPHUR SPRINGS,TX 75483-0225
PH 903 885-9606 FAX 903 885-8812
JEFF R MASSEY,PRES MASSEYJR@VERIZON.NET

INNOVA EXPLORATION,INC
PO BOX 129
TRAVERSE CITY,MI 49685-0129
PH 231 929-3985 FAX 231 947-1815
RON BUDROS,PRES,CERT GEOL
WWW.INNOVA-EXPLORATION.COM

INNOVATIVE BUSINESS SOLUTIONS,INC SEE
TOBIN INTERNATIONAL,LTD

INNOVATIVE ENERGY SERVICES
5250 FM 2855
KATY,TX 77493 PH 281 392-5199
PH 281 392-5199 FAX 281 371-0905
WWW.INNOVATIVEENERGYSERVICES.COM
RICK ADAMS,PRES
WILLIAM CLAYTON,VP
QUITMAN,TX FIELD OFFICE - 2465 FM 2088
75783 PH 903 967-3674 FAX 903 967-3675
RANDY GIBBS,WORKOVER RIG SUPVSR
PH 903 219-1120
CLEBURNE,TX FIELD OFC - 2475 E RENFRO ST
BURLESON,TX 76028 PH 817 295-1131
FAX 817 295-1131
MELVIN POWELL,SWAB RIG SUPVSR
PH 817 480-3339

INPLEX CUSTOM EXTRUDERS LLC
1663 S MT PROSPECT ROAD
DES PLAINES,IL 60018 PH 847 827-7049
ROBERT ANDERSON

INTEGRAL RESOURCES,INC
1010 LAMAR STE 1650
HOUSTON,TX 77002
PH 713 650-8058 FAX 713 650-8057
TIM MAPES,VP EXPLOR
TIM.MAPES@INTEGRAL-RESOURCES.COM

INTEGRATED ENERGY INCORPORATED
5 KERBY LN
MENDHAM,NJ 07945-2901 PH 713 650-8414
DONNIE JONES,GEO CONSLT

INTEGRATED GEOPHYSICS CORP
50 BRIAR HOLLOW LN STE 400W
HOUSTON,TX 77027 PH 713 680-9996
FAX 713 682-6928 WWW.IGCWORLD.COM
CORINE PRIETO,PRES

INTEGRATED SEISMIC SOLUTIONS,INC
2015 CROCKER ST
HOUSTON,TX 77006-1303 PH 713 650-9824
FAX 713 650-3699 ISSHOU.COM
OTTO.WELPER@ISSHOU.COM
OTTO J WELPER,PRES

INTERCOASTAL ENERGY,INC
PO BOX 55562
HOUSTON,TX 77255 PH 713 465-6421
BENJAMIN L HINDS,PRES

INTERIOR FUELS COMPANY
170 E VAN HORN RD

FAIRBANKS,AK 99701 PH 907 456-1312
FAX 907 456-1659

INTERMOOR INC
101 YOUNGSWOOD RD
MORGAN CITY,LA 70380-2276 PH 985 385-3083
PH 800 451-8106 FAX 985 631-2015
INFO@INTERMOOR.COM
WWW.INTERMOOR.COM
CHUCK MINTON,PRES
LARRY PUCKETT,VP
HARRY WILSON,VP,BUS DEV
THOMAS FULTON,VP/PRIN ENGR
ANTHONY PALMATURE,OPERS
RONNIE CRAIG,OPERS
DANIEL BERGERON,PUR MGR
SHARON BOX,PUR ASST
IRA MORRISON,HSE MGR
SHIRLEY GIROIR,ADMIN MGR
LORI BERGERON,ACCT
TONYA LACOSTE,BILLING
SCOTT THOMAS,FIN CONT
TERRY WILLIAMS,ACCT MGR
WILLARD WILSON,MARINE DEPT
DEWEY FLEETWOOD,MARINE SPECIALIST
IKE BURKE,MARINE SPECIALIST
VIRGIL MADDEN,MARINE SPECIALIST
CHARLES FUSSELL,MARINE SPECIALIST
JOSEPH HEBERT,JR,MARINE SPECIALIST
KENNY MAGGARD,SLS
KATHY LEGNON,SLS
DEBBIE PERCLE,SECY
HENRY DAIGLE JR,YARD SUPVSR
ALLEN EISENMAN,ASST YARD MGR
TIM HAMIL,OPER
MICKEY NAQUIN,ACCT
CARRIE ADAMS,OPER SECY
JEFF PUCKETT,MARINE SPEC
ROBERT BLANCO,SALES
JAMIE ARMSTRONG,STAFF ENGR
BENJAMIN BOONE,ENGR
KELLE CARTER,SR SECY
DAVID COBB,SR ENGR
KAREN HORWOOD,STAFF ENGR
PATRICK KILGORE,SR MARINE ENGR
ARMANDO LEDESMA,SR DESIGNER
MICHAEL LEDESMA,SR DESIGNER
REGAN MILLER,ENGR
MARK NOLET,LEAD ENGR
JOHN RIGGS,SR PROJ MGR
TODD VESELIS,SR MARINE SPEC
GORDON WILDE,PRIN ENGR
JOSEPH ADKINS,SLS MGR
LISA LUNA,RECPT

INTERNATIONAL DEVELOPMENT CORP
PO BOX 381
RIDGE,MD 20680 PH 301 872-5423
C D RAINEY,PRES
CDRAINEY@NETZERO.NET
MICHAEL RAU,VP
MARISA R RAU,SECY

INTERNATIONAL LOGGING,INC SEE
WEATHERFORD

INTERNATIONAL PETROLEUM & EXPLORATION
OPERATING CORPORATION - SEE INTERNATIONAL
PETROLEUM & EXPLORATION

INTERNATIONAL PETROLEUM & EXPLORATION
ROYALTY CORPORATION SEE INTERNATIONAL
PETROLEUM & EXPLORATION

INTERNATIONAL SERVICE CO
333 4TH AVE
INDIALANTIC,FL 32903-4213
PH 321 724-1443 FAX 321 724-1443
DENNIS SAMUELS,PRES
KATHERINE SWANBERG,MNGNG DIR
ROBERT COHEN,COORD DIR

INTERNATIONAL SNUBBING SERVICES,LLC SEE
SUPERIOR ENERGY SERVICES

INTERNATIONAL WELL TESTERS,INC
PO BOX 53875
LAFAYETTE,LA 70505-3875 PH 337 233-7649
PH 800 238-7649 FAX 337 332-4080
WWW.IWT.NET
BREAUX BRIDGE,LA FACILITY
1803-E MILLS HWY,70517
PH 337 332-4519 PH 800 238-7649
BEEVILLE,TX FACILITY
3880 HWY 59 W,78102 PH 361 358-1999
NICK GILBERT,OPERS MGR
PH 337 278-2535 NICK@IWT.NET
JOANN CORMIER,OFC MGR
PH 337 233-7649 JOANNC@IWT.NET
MALCOM LEGER,SLS MGR
PH 337 654-6633 MALCOMML@IWT.NET
RYAN PRIAT,ENVIRO/SAFETY DIR (LANDMARK
SAFETY) PH 337 406-0069 RPRIVAT@COX.NET

INTERSTATE EXPLORATIONS,LLC
OIL & GAS EXPLORATION & PRODUCTION
1331 LAMAR ST STE 1370
HOUSTON,TX 77010 PH 713 308-4900
DAN WILKS,PRES/CEO
FARRIS WILKS,COO
ROBERT DAWSON,SR VP EXPL
RDAWSON@IE-LLC.NET
GARY SCHENK,VP LAND GSCHENK@IE-LLC.NET
STEPHEN CARROLL,EXPL MGR
SCARROLL@IE-LLC.NET

INTERSTATE GAS MARKETING INC
825 CALIFORNIA AVE
BELLEVUE,PA 15202 PH 412 761-6904
FAX 570 383-9304
MICHAEL MELNICK,PRES
PAUL G RUDDY,VP,SLS,MKTG
JOHN PISARCIK,VP,TRANS & EXCHANGE
BILL GREGG,VP,GAS PROCUREMENT

INTERSTATE ROYALTIES SEE
DAVIS BROS,LLC

INTERTEK CALEB BRETT
2 RIVERWAY FL 5TH
HOUSTON,TX 77056-2062 PH 713 407-3500
FAX 713 407-3594 WWW.INTERTEK-CB.COM
JAY GUTIERREZ,PRES
LEO GUTIERREZ,REG FIN OFCR
KIM BO ROUSSEL,EXEC VP,CB USA OPERS
JERRY DIFEDE,VP/FLORIDA,CARIBBEAN &
VENEZUELA OPERS
JORGE CLAUDIO,VP/LATIN AMER
GRAHAM LEES,VP,QUALITY & COMPLIANCE
RICK HUNTLEY,VP,HUMAN RES
TOM DRING,VP,INFO TECHNOLOGY AMERICAS
MARK DORNAK,CONTROLLER
CHRIS DESLATTE,PURCH MGR

NEIL CHAPMAN,LAB BUS DEV MGR AMERICAS
JOHNNIE WILSON,INSPEC SLS/COORD MGR
JOHN QUERRY,INTL COORD MGR
MARK DUNCAN,ACCT COORD MGR AMERICAS
KERRY WALTER,MKTG SVC MGR
DEBBIE PHELPS,MKTG BUS DEV
JOHNNIE WILSON,SR MGR CONTRACTUAL
CONFORMANCE AMERICAS
RAYMOND LLOYD,CONTRACT ADMINS AMERICAS
BRENT MACKIN,VP/LABS AMERICAS
BALTIMORE,MD OFFICE - 2402 PETROLIA AVE
21226 PH 410 354-3010 FAX 320 998-0957
CBWPHILLY@INTERTEK.COM
WALTER MARSH,BRANCH MGR
BOSTON,MA OFFICE - 230 CRESCENT AVE
CHELSEA,MA 02150 PH 617 884-8993
FAX 617 884-5412
RON MARTIN,AREA MGR
BROWNSVILLE,TX OFFICE - 9400 OLD STATE
HWY 48,78521 PH 956 838-5065
PH 956 838-2866 FAX 832 201-7837
BROWNSVILLE@INTERTEK.COM
ENRIQUE PERALAS,BRANCH MGR
HOUSTON,TX OFFICE - 16640C JACINTO PORT
BLVD,77015 PH 281 452-1011
FAX 281 452-6894
CBWCHANNELVIEW@INTERTEK.COM
MIKE RICE,BRANCH MGR
ROMEOVILLE,IL OFFICE - 725 OAKRIDGE DR
60446 PH 708 458-2261 FAX 708 458-3368
JEFF KAYLOR,AREA MGR
VERN KITZMILLER,BRANCH MGR
CINCINNATI,OH OFFICE - PO BOX 389209
45238,4760 RIVER RD,45233
PH 513 941-8888 FAX 513 941-8012
MAGDALENA MICKI OVERBERG,BRANCH MGR
CORPUS CHRISTI,TX OFFICE - 134 HEINSOHN
RD,STE A,78406 PH 361 289-7474
FAX 361 289-7477
CORPUSCHRISTIOPS@INTERTEK.COM
JEFF BYRANT,BRANCH MGR
FREEPORT,TX OFFICE - 214 N GULF BLVD
77541 PH 979 233-5288 FAX 979 233-9552
DISPATCH-FREEPORT@ITSCB.COM
JOHNNIE WILSON III,OPERS MGR/ASST
GONZALES,LA OFFICE - 2632 RUBY AVE
70737 PH 225 647-4819 FAX 225 647-1904
CBWGONZALES@INTERTEK.COM
KIM BO ROUSSEL,EXEC VP
GRETNA,LA OFFICE - 1145 4TH ST,70053-5908
PH 504 362-9898 FAX 504 362-2521
CBWGRETA@INTERTEK.COM
GERARD LANDECHE,BRANCH MGR
KAPOLEI,HI OFFICE - 91-110 HANUA ST #204
PH 808 682-2532 808 682-0703
FAX 808 682-0723 CBWHAWAII@INTERTEK.COM
FRANKLIN YOGI,OPERS MGR/ASST
PASADENA,TX OFFICE - 3741 RED BLUFF RD
STE 105 PH 713 534-0020 FAX 713 456-1190
CBWHOUOPS@INTERTEK.COM
KEVIN MCFADDEN,VP/WEST GULF COAST
DEER PARK,TX OFFICE - 1114 SEACO AVE
77536 PH 713 844-3200 FAX 713 844-3330
CBWDEERPARK@INTERTEK.COM
WAYNE KRIEL,SR VP,TECH SVCS
JACKSONVILLE,FL OFFICE - 5401 EVERGREEN

AVE,32208 PH 904 353-1220 904 353-7457
FAX 904 353-1230
GORDON JENKINS,BRANCH MGR
SULPHUR,LA OFFICE - 2717 MAPLEWOOD DR
70663 PH 337 625-7060 FAX 337 625-4330
CBWLAKECHARLES@ITSCB.COM
MORGAN FISHER,OPERS MGR
SIGNAL HILL,CA OFFICE - 1941 FREEMAN AVE
STE A,90755 PH 562 494-4999
FAX 562 494-4498
CBWLOSANGELES@INTERTEK.COM
MARK S THORESON,BRANCH MGR
LOUISVILLE,KY OFFICE - PO BOX 22211,40252
1000 WASHBURN AVE,40222
PH 502 425-6430 FAX 502 429-5892
CBWLOUISVILLE@INTERTEK.COM
JIM FIGANIAK,BRANCH MGR
WEST MEMPHIS,AR OFFICE - 207 N OK ST
72301 PH 870 702-7097 FAX 870 702-7847
DAVID LUNCEFORD,BRANCH MGR
CHICKASAW,AL OFFICE - 505 N CRAFT HWY
36611 PH 251 457-8751 FAX 251 457-0382
CBWMOBILE@INTERTEK.COM
BYRON PITTMAN,BRANCH MGR
NEW HAVEN,CT OFFICE - 10 STILES ST,06512
PH 203 467-3471 FAX 203 467-8083
ITSCBNH@INTERTEK.COM
HOWARD SCHOLL,BRANCH MGR
ST ROSE,LA OFFICE - 149 PINTAIL RD,70087
PH 504 602-2000 FAX 504 602-2020
CBWNEWORLEANS@INTERTEK.COM
BILLY MCINNIS,BRANCH MGR
CARTERET,NJ OFFICE - 1000 PORT CARTERET
DR,07008 PH 732 969-5200
FAX 732 969-5291 NYHARBOROPS@INTERTEK.COM
MATT CORR,VP/EAST COAST
PRESTON SMITH,BRANCH MGR
NEWPORT NEWS,VA OFFICE - 11872 CANON BLVD
STE E,23606 PH 757 873-0133
FAX 757 873-1459
ALLISON.MOFFAT@INTERTEK.COM
WALTER ROWE,BRANCH MGR
CANTON,IL OFFICE - 250 N 6TH,61520
PH 309 647-1629 FAX 309 647-1761
DON DOERR,BRANCH MGR
ESSINGTON,PA OFFICE - 327 ERICKSON AVE
19029 PH 610 521-1725 610 521-1728
FAX 610 521-1445 CBWPHILLY@INTERTEK.COM
MATT CORR,VP/EAST COAST
MARK STEWART,BRANCH MGR
MIDLAND,PA OFFICE - 1406 MIDLAND AVE
15059 PH 724 643-9381 FAX 724 643-9387
ANDREW T LONGSHORE,BRANCH MGR
NEDERLAND,TX OFFICE - 2780 HWY 69 N
77627 PH 409 727-3664 FAX 409 727-7457
CBWNEDERLAND@INTERTEK.COM
DARON KEEL,BRANCH MGR
FORT LAUDERDALE,FL OFFICE - 2608 S
FEDERAL HWY,33316 PH 954 462-4945
FAX 954 462-4946 ITSCBPOEV@ITSCB.COM
RANDY FELDBRUEGGE,BRANCH MGR
SOUTH PORTLAND,ME OFFICE - 78 PLEASANT
AVE,04106 PH 207 799-5569
FAX 207 799-0136 ITSCBPORT@INTERTEK.COM
PORTLAND,OR OFFICE - 5880 NW ST HELENS RD
BLDG #6,97210 PH 503 222-3004

FAX 503 222-3054
  CBWPORTLANDOR@INTERTEK.COM
  SCOTT WINNER,BRANCH MGR
ST LOUIS,MO OFFICE - 1211 BELGROVE,63137
  PH 314 869-7878 FAX 314 869-1574
    CHERYL.WHITE@INTERTEK.COM
  KENNETH LANCY,BRANCH MGR
BENICIA,CA OFFICE - 6050 EGRET CT,94510
  PH 707 746-0556 FAX 707 745-1123
    ITSCBSF@INTERTEK.COM
  PAUL KELLETT,VP/WEST COAST
  EDWARD BAIS,BRANCH MGR
JACKSONVILLE,FL OFFICE - 5401 EVERGREEN
  AVE,32208 PH 904 353-1220
  FAX 904 353-1230
    DON SPROUSE,AREA REPR
BELLINGHAM,WA OFFICE - 801 W ORCHARD DR
  STE #5,98225 PH 360 671-0919
  FAX 360 733-4121
    CBWBELLINGHAM@INTERTEK.COM
  WILLIAM JOE HEMPHILL,BRANCH MGR
TAMPA,FL OFFICE - 4951A E ADAMO DR
  STE 130,33605 PH 813 248-5154
  FAX 813 247-6762 CBWTAMPA@INTERTEK.COM
  RONALD DICKET,BRANCH MGR
TEXAS CITY,TX OFFICE - 101 20TH ST S
  77590 PH 409 948-4481 FAX 409 945-0486
    CBWTXCITY@INTERTEK.COM
  JAY BREWER,BRANCH MGR
HOLLAND,OH OFFICE - 1020 S HOLLAND
  SYLVANIA RD,43528 PH 419 866-4004
  FAX 419 866-4003
    ROBERT F MCBATH,BRANCH MGR
VALDEZ,AK OFFICE - PO BOX 1389
  354 FAIRBANKS,99686
  PH 907 835-4331 FAX 907 835-2093
    CBWVALDEZ@INTERTEK.COM
  CLARK MASTERS,BRANCH MGR

INTERVENTION ENERGY LLC
  PO BOX 1028
  MINOT,ND 58702-1028 PH 917 592-3166
    JOHN ZIMMERMAN
    JOHN@INTERVENTIONENERGY.COM

INTRASEARCH INC,GEOL
  10465 PARK MEADOWS DR STE 201
  LONE TREE,CO 80124-5321
  PH 303 759-5050 FAX 303 759-0400
    WWW.MAPMART.COM
    INFO@INTRASEARCH.COM
    MICHAEL PLATT,PRES

INTREPID DRILLING LLC
  320 SECOND ST
  COLUMBIA,MS 39429-2954 PH 601 731-1010
  FAX 601 731-2119 WWW.INTREPIDDRILLING.COM

INVESTORS ENERGY,LLC
  2530 SCOTTSVILLE RD,STE 12
  BOWLING GREEN,KY 42104 PH 270 843-0660
    ENERGY@INVESTORSENEGYLLC.COM
    THOMAS W SPROUSE

INVESTORS FINANCIAL SERVICES,INC
  PO BOX 41106
  HOUSTON,TX 77241-1106 PH 713 759-0823
    JOHN BYARS,CPA,PRES

IOGA WEST VIRGINIA
  IND OIL & GAS ASSOC OF WEST VIRGINIA,INC
  300 SUMMERS ST STE 820

CHARLESTON,WV 25301
PH 304 344-9867 FAX 304 344-5836
  CBURD@IOGAWV.COM
  CHARLIE BURD,EXEC DIR

IRI INTERNATIONAL CORPORATION SEE
  NATIONAL OILWELL VARCO

IRISH OIL & GAS CO,OIL OPR
  PO BOX 42429
  HOUSTON,TX 77242-2429 PH 713 782-3831
  FAX 713 782-6439 LFY@OILGASCONSULT.COM
    LEIGHTON F YOUNG,JR,PRES & GEOL

IRONCROSS,INC
  PO DRAWER 1349
  JENA,LA 71342-1349
  PH 318 992-6518 IRONCROSSINC@YAHOO.COM
    EARL W PEAVY,PRES
    MARGARET A PEAVY,SECY/TREAS
    SHEILA K CHANDLER,TECH ADMIN SVCS

IRONITE PRODUCTS CO,INC
  2001 BRADY AVE
  EAST SAINT LOUIS,IL 62207-1858
  PH 314 725-7900 FAX 636 532-1842
    WWW.IRONITESPONGE.COM
    RICHARD FOX,PRES
    JUNE WEIBLE,MKTG MGR

IRONROCK WEBB ENERGY GROUP LLC
  LANDMEN/OIL & GAS INTERESTS
  101 E COMMERCE ST
  BRENHAM,TX 77833
  PH 979 836-2104 FAX 979 836-3524
  PH 512 913-5635 WWW.IRONGROUP.COM
    KIRK E WEBB,PRES,LDMN
  UVALDE,TEXAS OFFICE - 1941 W FM 2369
  78802 PH 830 278-7157 FAX 830 278-7159

IRONWOOD OIL & GAS LLC SEE CL&F RESOURCES

IROQUOIS PIPELINE OPERATING CO
  ONE CORPORATE DR STE 600
  SHELTON,CT 06484-6211
  PH 203 925-7200 FAX 203 925-7013
    BRIAN WOLF,MGR,ENGRG SERVICES
    PAUL R AMATO,DIR/FIELD SRVS/RIGHT-OF-WAY

ISMAK PETROLEUM CO,INC
  5885 N CROSSVIEW RD
  SEVEN HILLS,OH 44131-1919 PH 216 267-0212
    DR I J SUNEJA,PRES

ITS
  7908 N SAM HOUSTON PKWY W STE 500
  HOUSTON,TX 77064-3513 PH 713 961-8000
  FAX 713 621-0111
    C R BUD HIPP,PRES

J & B ENTERPRISES
  342 PARSONS GRN
  SHREVEPORT,LA 71106-8379
  PH 318 798-2380 FAX 318 797-9846
    JRIZER@BELLSOUTH.NET
    JAMES A RIZER,PRES
    BEV RIZER,SECY/TREAS

J & B ENTERPRISES SEE
  HUCKABAY JOHN

J & C DRILLING COMPANY INC
  PO BOX 216,115 E PURISIMA
  REFUGIO,TX 78377 PH 361 526-2376
    BILL B WALES,PRES
    J STEVEN WALES,VP,SECY

J & D TRUCKING LLC
  PO BOX 21112

BEAUMONT,TX 77720 PH 409 221-7994
FAX 409 422-4179
  JOEY LEMAIRE JOEYLEMAIRE359@YAHOO.COM
  DAVID SANDERS

J & J EXCAVATING & MATERIALS
  4236 NORTH US HWY 83
  CRYSTAL CITY,TX 78839 PH 830 374-5262
  FAX 830 374-5261 JANDJ@MECWB.COM
  JJEXCAVATING.COM

J & J PETROLEUM LAND SERVICES LLC
  910 PIERREMONT RD STE 410
  SHREVEPORT,LA 71106-2056 PH 318 861-8434
  FAX 318 861-8412
    JAMES M MONK,MNGNG PRTNR
    JESSICA B MONK,MNGNG PRTNR
    GEORGIA S MONK,LDMN

J AND L OIL & GAS CORP
  3152 E MAIN RD
  DUNKIRK,NY 14048 PH 716 673-9116
    LOUIS J NALBONE,PRES
    JOHN J NALBONE JR,VP

J C INTERNATIONAL LTD
  2200 HANCOCK ST
  GRETNA,LA 70053-3606 PH 504 362-0826
  FAX 504 366-7921
    WWW.JCINTERNATIONALLTD.COM
    JC@JCINTERNATIONALLTD.COM
    J M BONILLA,PRES
    MRS J M BONILLA,SECY/TREAS

J C PETROLEUM,INC
  2112 JUSTICE ST
  MONROE,LA 71201 PH 318 325-7788
  FAX 318 398-0069
    JOHN C CHRIS STRICKLER JR,CPL
    CSTRICKLER@JCPETROLEUM.COM

J L C ENTERPRISES,INC
  615 UPPER N BROADWAY STE 1935
  CORPUS CHRISTI,TX 78401-0779
  PH 361 887-2991 FAX 361 883-4790
    JAMES L CLAUGHTON,PRES
    CLAUSOIE@SBCGLOBAL.NET

J L H CORPORATION SEE
  HENSON EXPLORATION LP

J L M PARTNERSHIP
  PO BOX 2445
  CORPUS CHRISTI,TX 78403-2445
  PH 361 853-5453

J M K PETROLEUM CORPORATION
  1017 LONG PRAIRIE RD STE 201
  FLOWER MOUND,TX 75022
  PH 972 539-2767 FAX 972 539-2768
    GREGGAHART@HOTMAIL.COM

J P MORGAN CHASE BANK
  OIL,GAS & MINERAL MANAGEMENT GROUP
  2200 ROSS AVE FL 7
  DALLAS,TX 75201 PH 214 965-3258
  FAX 214 965-3558
    BERT HAYES-DAVIS,ORGANIZATION HEAD
  DALLAS,TX OFFICE - 2200 ROSS AVE FL 7
  75201 PH 214 965-3257 FAX 214 965-3558
    SHERI ANDERSON
    H L TOMPKINS
    FRANK MEDRANO
  FORT WORTH OFFICE - 420 THROCKMORTON ST
  FL 2,76102 PH 817 884-4443
  FAX 817 884-5458

SUSAN BARRY
JASON BECK
MELODY MARTINEZ
PHILIP METTHAM

J. B. DRILLING COMPANY INC
PO BOX 6634
FORT SMITH,AR 72906-6634 PH 918 436-7771
FAX 918 436-2619
B R COOPER,PRES
E D COOPER,VP

J.D. DRILLING COMPANY
PO BOX 369
RACINE,OH 45771-0369 PH 740 949-2512
FAX 740 949-2018
JAMES E DIDDLE,PRES

J.D. FIELDS & CO,INC
1330 GREENGATE DR STE 120
COVINGTON,LA 70433
PH 985 234-4567 FAX 985 234-4572
BRIAN MCHALE
BMCHALE@JDFIELDS.COM

J.D. GAS & OIL,INC
6995 SWEETHEART DR
ZANESVILLE,OH 43701-8607
PH 740 796-3305 FAX 740 796-3305
JOHN R DOSCH,PRES
TERRY L DUNN,PROD SUPT
PATRICK J TAYLOR,ENGR

J.P. OIL COMPANY,INC
PO BOX 52584
LAFAYETTE,LA 70505-2584 PH 318 234-1170
FAX 318 234-9891
J P VAN WAY,CHRMN
CHRIS VAN WAY,PRES,CEO
FRANK WALKER,CFO
TAMMY SCRANTZ,ACCT SUPVSR
LEROY GOETZMANN,LDMN
GARY HERNANDEZ,WORKOVER SUPT
DONALD ROMERO,PROD SUPT
WALLACE FONTENOT,FIELD SUPT
LYLE ZERINGUE,ENV MGR
BOB BROWN,RESERVOIR ENGR
BOYD GETZ,GEOL
HANK DAVID,PROD ENGR
MORTIN RICHARD,MAINT SUPT

J.S. PERSON,INC
PO BOX 1131,411 N FREDONIA
LONGVIEW,TX 75606-1131 PH 903 758-2631
FAX 903 753-3066
J S PERSON,PRES

J&J TECHNICAL SERVICES,LLC
JET PUMPS & PROD SYSTEMS FOR O&G INDUSTRY
5220 HOLLYWOOD AVE
SHREVEPORT,LA 71109 PH 318 636-6844
FAX 318 636-6904 WWW.J-JCOMPANIES.COM

J&S OIL & GAS LLC
24900 PITKIN RD STE 200
SPRING,TX 77386 PH 281 453-8200
RONNIE MONTGOMERY II

J-O'B OPERATING CO
PO BOX 5928,400 TEXAS ST STE 800
SHREVEPORT,LA 71135-5928
PH 318 222-8400 FAX 318 222-8484
MICHAEL R MCCRARY,PRES
ROGER M BARNES,VP OPERS

J-W ENERGY COMPANY
15505 WRIGHT BROTHERS DR
ADDISON,TX 75001
PH 972 233-8191 FAX 972 991-0704
HOWARD G WESTERMAN JR,CHRMN/CEO
G GENE GRADICK,PRES
RICHARD T CLEMENT,EXEC VP
PAUL D WESTERMAN,COO
C D MCDANIELS,VICE CHRMN,EXEC VP
DON G BIZZELL,VP J-W ENERGY CO/PRES J-W
POWER CO
DANNY T HENDRIX,VP J-W ENERGY CO/PRES J-W
MEASUREMENT CO
GENE C DALEY,VP J-W ENERGY CO/PRES J-W
OPERATING CO
PAUL N STEPHENSON,VP J-W ENERGY CO/PRES
J-W MANUFACTURING CO
LARRY H CARPENTER,VP J-W ENERGY CO/PRES
J-W GATHERING CO,J-W PIPELINE CO,Q-WEST
ENERGY CO
JAMES SKIP HERALD,VP J-W ENERGY CO/PRES
J-W WIRELINE CO
LINDON H LENERS,VP FIN
JOHN A DANIELS,BUS DEV MGR
PH 972 233-8191 JDANIELS@JWENERGY.COM
JOHN MAHAN,NEW VENTURES MGR
PH 972 233-8191 JMAHAN@JWENERGY.COM

J-W GATHERING COMPANY SEE
J-W MIDSTREAM COMPANY

J-W MANUFACTURING COMPANY
GATOR VALVE HEADQUARTERS
115 THRUWAY PARK RD
BROUSSARD,LA 70518
PH 337 837-8228 FAX 337 837-8229
GATOR@JWOPERATING.COM
HOUMA,LA SLS OFFICE- 280 EQUITY BLVD
BLDG C 70360 PH 985 868-8215
PH 985 991-8450 FAX 985 868-8218
MANUFACTURING@JWOPERATING.COM
KILGORE,TX MFG FCLT- 1708 COX DR 75663
PH 903 984-6332 FAX 903 986-3858
LONGVIEW,TX MFG FCLT- 2315 STATE HWY 322
75603 PH 800 436-7808 PH 903 643-3413
FAX 903 643-3586
SHERMAN,TX MFG FCLT- 1701 TEXOMA DR 75090
PH 903 892-0561 FAX 866 441-8175
BRISTOW,OK MFG FCLT- 23630 S 369TH W AVE
74010 PH 800 331-7267 PH 918 367-5523
FAX 918 367-6154
CASPER,WY MFG FCLT- 222 N COLE CREEK RD
82609 PH 800 442-2465 PH 307 234-1672
FAX 307 234-0009

J-W MEASUREMENT COMPANY
15505 WRIGHT BROTHERS DR
ADDISON,TX 75001
PH 972 233-8191 FAX 972 991-0704
MEASUREMENT@JWENERGY.COM
COTULLA,TX DIST OFFICE- 380 W FM 468
78014 PH 830 483-4636
GODLEY,TX FLD/SLS OFC- 313 W RAILROAD ST
76044 PH 817 309-2404 FAX 817 309-2407
TYLER,TX FLD/SLS OFC-3401 N NE LOOP 323
75708 PH 903 510-8000 FAX 903 510-8008
VICTORIA,TX FLD/SLS OFC-4603 E JUAN LINN
ST 77901 PH 361 576-2613 FAX 361 576-3922
HOUSTON,TX SLS OFC-515 N SAM HOUSTON PKWY

STE 640 77060 PH 281 445-7179
FAX 281 445-9570
MIDLAND,TX SLS OFC-2052 COMMERCE RD 79703
PH 432 685-9700
OZONA,TX SLS OFFICE- 516 9TH ST 76943
PH 325 392-9356 FAX 325 392-9956
ELK CITY,OK DIST OFC-110 MEADOW RIDGE DR
73644 PH 580 303-7116 FAX 877 751-6132
COALGATE,OK FLD OFFICE- 903 S BROADWAY
74538 PH 580 927-2254 FAX 580 927-2304
MOUNDS,OK FLD/SLS OFFICE- 20612 S HWY 75
74047 PH 918 827-5770 FAX 918 827-5773
TULSA,OK SLS OFC-9726 E 42ND ST STE 229
74146 PH 972 233-8191
SHREVEPORT,LA DIST OFFICE- 669 AERO DR
71107 PH 888 226-9110 PH 318 226-9110
FAX 318 425-2517
BROUSSARD,LA FLD/SLS OFFICE- 214 THRU WAY
70518 PH 800 264-3785 FAX 337 837-5513
CARLSBAD,NM FLD OFC-3611 NATIONAL PARKS
HWY 88220 PH 575 234-9011
FAX 575 234-9036
FARMINGTON,NM SLS OFC- 1201 TROY KING RD
87401 PH 888 661-2932 PH 505 324-8880
FAX 505 324-8881
CENTENNIAL,CO DIST OFC-7074 S REVERE PKWY
80112 PH 800 333-4990 PH 303 422-4990
FAX 303 422-0178
LIBERAL,KS SLS OFC- 1480 GENERAL WELCH
BLVD 67901 PH 620 626-5728
FAX 866 626-4822
CANONSBURG,PA DIST OFC- 586 PLUM RUN RD
15317 PH 724 749-5200 PH 903 235-7634
SEWICKLEY,PA DIST OFC- 2200 GEORGETOWN DR
STE 301 15143 PH 724 749-4745
PH 903 235-7634
MONTOURSVILLE,PA SLS OFC-4885 LYCOMING
MALL DR 17754 PH 570 368-8567
FAX 570 971-8015
CASPER,WY DIST OFFICE-222 N COLE CREEK RD
82609 PH 800 442-2465 PH 307 234-1672
FAX 307 234-0009
ROCK SPRINGS,WY FLD/SLS OFC-
7530 FOOTHILLS BLVD 82901 PH 800 524-4342
PH 307 382-2474 FAX 307 382-2489
WILLISTON,ND SLS OFFICE- #10 74TH ST E
58801 PH 800 225-7268 PH 701 572-0061
FAX 701 572-3084
QUITMAN,AR DIST OFFICE- 40 DAMASCUS RD
72131 PH 501 589-2348

J-W MIDSTREAM COMPANY
15505 WRIGHT BROTHERS DR
ADDISON,TX 75001 PH 972 233-8191
FAX 972 991-0704 GATHERING@JWENERGY.COM
ROANOKE,TX DIST OFFICE - 11350 CLEVELAND
GIBBS STE 107 76262 PH 682 237-6164
FRIERSON,LA DIST OFFICE - 2601 STONEWALL
FRIERSON RD 71027 PH 800 274-0033
PH 318 925-8088 FAX 318 925-8058

J-W OPERATING COMPANY
15505 WRIGHT BROTHERS DR
ADDISON,TX 75001
PH 972 233-8191 FAX 972 991-0704
EXPLORATION@JWENERGY.COM
LONGVIEW,TX DIST OFFICE- 122 DOVEL RD
75607 PH 800 436-7808 PH 903 643-3413

FAX 903 643-3586

ALVARADO,TX FLD OFFICE- 714 CR 207 76009
PH 817 783-3570 FAX 817 783-3516

ARP,TX FLD OFFICE- 11956 CR 2222 75750
PH 903 566-8651

JUSTIN,TX FLD OFFICE- 316 E 5TH ST 76247
PH 940 648-2842 FAX 940 648-2855

SHREVEPORT,LA DIST OFFICE- 7607 FERN AVE
STE 403 71105 PH 524-5300
FAX 318 524-5399

HAUGHTON,LA FLD OFFICE- 3920 HWY 527
71037 PH 318 987-8003 FAX 318 987-3373

FRIERSON,LA FLD OFFICE -
2601 STONEWALL-FRIERSON RD 71027
PH 800 274-0033 PH 318 925-8088
FAX 318 925-8058

CENTENNIAL,CO DIST OFFICE- 7074 S REVERE
PKWY 80112 PH 800 333-4990
PH 303 422-4990 FAX 303 422-0178

SEWICKLEY,PA DIST OFFICE- 2200 GEORGETOWN
DR STE 301 PH 724 749-4745

J-W POWER COMPANY SEE
J-W OPERATING COMPANY

J-W WIRELINE COMPANY
15505 WRIGHT BROTHERS DR
ADDISON,TX 75001
PH 972 233-8191 FAX 972 991-0704
WIRELINE@JWOPERATING.COM

FLINT,TX REG OFFICE-19081 STATE HWY 155 S
75762 PH 903 534-0671 FAX 903 566-0050

EDINBURG,TX DIST OFFICE-4501 N HWY 281
78539 PH 956 287-0389

GODLEY,TX DIST OFFICE-8609 RIVER HILLS RD
76044 PH 682 459-5054

LAREDO,TX DIST OFFICE- 6086D WARD AVE
78043 PH 956 287-0398

MARSHALL,TX DIST OFFICE- 6365 US HWY 59 S
75672 PH 903 935-9200 FAX 903 935-9215

MONAHANS,TX DIST OFFICE- 1600 W 15TH ST
79756 PH 432 943-4448 PH 432 943-4431
FAX 432 943-4205

VICTORIA,TX DIST OFC-4607 E JUAN LINN ST
77901 PH 361 579-4540 PH 361 212-6103
FAX 361 576-3922

HOUSTON,TX SLS OFC-515 N SAM HOUSTON PKWY
E STE 640 77060 PH 281 445-7179
PH 281 468-8953 FAX 281 445-9570

OKLAHOMA CITY,OK REG OFC-5208 W RENO
STE 288 73127 PH 405 495-4499
FAX 405 495-4492

WOODWARD,OK DIST OFC-ROUTE 1 BOX 259
73801 PH 580 254-2755 PH 580 254-3842
FAX 580 254-2898

MCALESTER,OK DIST OFC-1899 E ELECTRIC AVE
74501 PH 918 429-1290 FAX 918 429-1299

TULSA,OK SLS OFFICE- 6538 S 110 EAST AVE
74133 PH 918 671-5210

HAUGHTON,LA REG OFFICE- 3000 HWY 80 E
71037 PH 318 390-6680 FAX 318 390-7240

CENTENNIAL,CO REG OFC-7074 S REVERE PKWY
80112 PH 800 333-4990 PH 303 422-4990
FAX 303 422-0178

BRIGHTON,CO DIST OFC-1760 CR 27 BLDG A/B
80603 PH 303 637-9751 FAX 303 637-9754

STERLING,CO DIST OFFICE-14279 HWY 14
80751 PH 970 522-0292 FAX 970 522-0291

HOBBS,NM DIST OFFICE- 5014 CARLSBAD HWY
88240 PH 575 393-9200

SEARCY,AR DIST OFFICE- 1000 QUEENS WAY
72143 PH 501 278-5193 FAX 501 278-5198

BROCKWAY,PA DIST OFC-250 INDUSTRIAL PARK
15824 PH 814 268-1056 PH 724 599-6255
FAX 814 268-1059

SEWICKLEY,PA SLS OFC-2200 GEORGETOWN DR
STE 301 15143 PH 724 749-4745

ROOSEVELT,UT DIST OFFICE- 2010 W 1760 S
84066 PH 435 725-0136 FAX 435 725-0138

WESTON,WV DIST OFFICE-376 HOPE STATION RD
26452 PH 304 269-0633 FAX 304 269-0635

ROCK SPRINGS,WY DIST OFC- 80 RELIANCE RD
82901 PH 307 382-3364 FAX 307 382-3154

JABSCO OIL,LLC
4100 JOE MALLISHAM PKWY
TUSCALOOSA,AL 35401-9327
PH 205 349-1117 FAX 205 349-1105
JOHN LANG,EXPL MGR
RANDY ALLEN,SR LDMN
DEBORAH CLARDY,OFC MGR,PROD SUPVSR
ADAM LANG,GEOL

JACK CO,THE
PO BOX 697,JACK DR
INDIANA,PA 15701-0697
PH 724 463-5159 FAX 724 463-5129

JACKSOCO OIL COMPANY INC
PO BOX 737
POINT CLEAR,AL 36564 PH 251 990-3406
T K JACKSON III,PRES
KAREN H DIARD,ASST SECY/BOOKKEEPER

JACKSON & BLAND,INC
1525 BINGLE RD
HOUSTON,TX 77055-3226
PH 713 467-4202 FAX 713 467-5020
RONALD C JACKSON,PRES
MICHAEL R BLAND,VP

JACKSON & HUNGER,INC
PO BOX 1200
KATY,TX 77492-1200 PH 281 392-2294
ROBERT BOBBY JACKSON,PRES
GRACIE LEMASTER

JACKSON HINDS LIBRARY SYSTEM
300 N STATE ST
JACKSON,MS 39201-1705 PH 601 968-5811
FAX 601 968-5806

JACKSON JACKY H,GEOL
PO BOX 468
WEST COLUMBIA,TX 77486 PH 409 345-6556
JACKY H JACKSON,PRES 2-J ENTERPRISES INC

JACKSON JIM BOB,IND GEOL
8912 FM 2354
BAYTOWN,TX 77523-9235
PH 281 383-2102 JHKRANCH@WT.NET

JACO TROY INC
PO BOX 1476
SHERMAN,TX 75091 PH 903 868-2703
FAX 903 893-0697
TROY JACO,PRES

JACOBI-JOHNSON ENERGY INC SEE
EXCO RESOURCES,INC

JACOBS & WEAVER
101 TUPELO ST
WINNFIELD,LA 71483-2575 PH 318 628-4618
D D JACOBS

JACOBS D D,PRODUCTION CO
101 TUPELO ST
WINNFIELD,LA 71483-2575 PH 318 628-4618
A T WILLIAMS,PROD SUPT
W W SHIVERS,OFC MGR

JACOBS DRILLING COMPANY
101 TUPELO ST
WINNFIELD,LA 71483-2575 PH 318 628-4618
D D JACOBS

JACOBS MANUEL & KAIN
500 SAINT LOUIS ST STE 200
NEW ORLEANS,LA 70130-2118 PH 504 523-1444
800-426-1444 FAX 504 524-1655

JACOBS ROBERT R,PETR GEOL
PO BOX 12024
JACKSON,MS 39236-2024 PH 601 362-4846

JACOBS ROYALTY & MINERALS CO
PO BOX 12202
DALLAS,TX 75225-0202 PH 214 750-7507
J MICHAEL JACOBS,OWNER

JADA INC
PO BOX 808
EUNICE,LA 70535-0808 PH 318 457-3215

JAECON CORP
PO BOX 741053,2600 S GESSNER STE 312
HOUSTON,TX 77274-1053 PH 713 977-4982
FAX 713 977-4983
ROBERT ARONSTEIN,PRES
LEWIS F JUDSON,SR VP
CAROL KAMIN,OFC MGR

JAG OPERATING,LLC
416 TRAVIS ST STE 910
SHREVEPORT,LA 71101
PH 318 424-4986 FAX 318 227-0736

JAIME SYLVESTER R,LAW OFFICES OF
15300 WESTHEIMER RD #105
HOUSTON,TX 77082-1451
PH 281 597-9495 FAX 281 597-9621

JAMAJO INDUSTRIES
2124 FAIRFIELD AVE
SHREVEPORT,LA 71104 PH 318 221-1657
FAX 318 221-1894
JAMES M JONES,PRES
CARL W JONES,SECY/TREAS
J A MONTGOMERY,OFC MGR

JAMAR ENERGY CO
PO BOX 51134,BLDG 7 HEYMANN BLVD
LAFAYETTE,LA 70505-1134 PH 337 232-4088
FAX 337 234-5320
JACK P MARTIN,PRES

JAMES DRILLING COMPANY,INC
PO BOX 1393,HWY 167 N
WINNFIELD,LA 71483-1393 PH 318 628-2182
FAX 318 628-3092
LEROY W JAMES,PRES
LARICA J FAIR,CONTROLLER,PERSONNEL MGR
ROGER VERRETT,SHOP FRMN
CLEM DUFFIE,DRILLER
LANCE JAMES,DRILLER
JOHN ALLEN FLOYD,FIELD SUPT
JODY JAMES,TOOLPUSHER

JAMES DRILLING EXPLORATION & PROD CO,INC
PO BOX 1393
WINNFIELD,LA 71483-1393 PH 318 628-7373
318 628-2182 FAX 318 628-3092
LEROY W JAMES,PRES

LARICA J FAIR,OFC MGR
JODY E JAMES,DRLG SUPT
ROGER VERRET,SHOP FRMN
ALLEN JOHN FLOYD,DOZER OPER

JAMES KNOBLOCH PETROLEUM CONSULTANTS INC
2337A STATE ROUTE 821
MARIETTA,OH 45750-5362
PH 740 373-9522 FAX 740 373-2750
TIMOTHY S KNOBLOCH,PRES
TKNOBLOCH@JKPCINC.COM

JAMES SERVICES,LLC
PO BOX 1249
RUSTON,LA 71273-1249
PH 318 255-3059 FAX 318 251-0008
ROBERT E JAMES,MGR

JAMIN ENERGY,INC
PO BOX 429
BELLVILLE,TX 77418-0429 PH 979 865-9924
FAX 979 865-9322
BAYSHOREEXPL@SBCGLOBAL.NET
JAMIN SWANTNER,PRES
JANE R SWANTNER,SECY/TREAS

JANDAR EXPLORATION LC
6775 OLD JACKSONVILLE HWY STE 1
TYLER,TX 75703
PH 903 705-0625 FAX 888 843-8082
INFO@JANDAREXPLORATION.COM
RONNIE SWINK,PRES
TODD SWINK,VP

JANIC DIRECTIONAL SURVEY INC
PO BOX 91830
LAFAYETTE,LA 70509-1830
PH 337 234-9183 FAX 337 234-0092
WWW.JANICSURVEY.COM
NICKY GUIDRY,PRES
JIM W WEBB,CEO
MELINDA RICHARD,OFC MGR
WILL GUIDRY,SLS

JANNAH HUNT OIL COMPANY SEE
HUNT OIL COMPANY

JAPAN OIL GAS AND METALS NATIONAL
CORPORATION
ONE RIVERWAY STE 450
HOUSTON,TX 77056-1945 PH 713 622-0204
FAX 713 622-1330

JAPEX (U.S.) CORP
5051 WESTHEIMER RD STE 425
HOUSTON,TX 77056-5833 PH 713 334-9800
FAX 713 334-9850 WWW.JAPEX.CO.JP
MITSURU KAMON,PRES KAMON@JAPEX.COM

JARECKI VALVES
VALVES UP TO 24 ,2 & 3 WAY VALVES
PRESSURE CLASS UP TO 4500 & TEMP TO 1800F
6910 W RIDGE RD
FAIRVIEW,PA 16415-2029 PH 814 474-2666
FAX 814 474-3645 JARECKI@VELOCITY.NET
JARECKIVALVES.COM
FRANK E JARECKI,PRES,OWNER
FRANK E JARECKI JR,VP
SANDRA JARECKI,SECY

JARRATT WILLIAM E,OIL PROD
623 DUMBARTON DR
SHREVEPORT,LA 71106-6811 PH 318 865-9372

JARVIS DRILLING,INC,OIL PRODUCERS
4600 N PLEASANT VALLEY RD
HENDERSON,KY 42420-8813 PH 270 827-5149

MIKE UTLEY,FLD MGR
ALBANY,KY OFFICE - RTE 4,BOX 501,42602
DAVID TEAL,FRMN
BOWLING GREEN,KY OFFICE - 320 NEW PORTER
PIKE,42103-9138 PH 270 781-7505
T S BALLANCE,PRES
RIVERS FORD,GEN MGR
RAY CALVERT,SUPT

JASPER OIL PRODUCERS INC
118 W MAIN ST
MOUNT STERLING,IL 62353-1224
PH 217 773-3909 FAX 217 773-3900
JASPEROIL@FRONTIER.COM
GARY L SHIELDS,PRES
PATRICK SHIELDS,VP
OREN MILES,LDMN
TRINA TANGEROSE,ADMIN ASST
TOD D DOSS,GEOL
ARI KOGUT,RESIDENT GEOL
CHARLES R WILES,GEOL

JATCO INC,ENVIRONMENTAL EQUIP
244 NW 111TH ST
OKLAHOMA CITY,OK 73114-6602
PH 405 755-4100 FAX 405 755-4101

JATH OIL COMPANY SEE
MACK OIL CO

JAY MANAGEMENT COMPANY,LLC
2425 W LOOP S STE 810
HOUSTON,TX 77027
PH 713 621-5946 FAX 713 621-3988
EDY FRANCIS,CFO

JAY PETROLEUM INC SEE
CHESAPEAKE ENERGY CORPRATION

JAY PETROLEUM,LLC
2425 W LOOP S STE 810
HOUSTON,TX 77027 PH 713 621-5946
FAX 713 621-3988
EDY FRANCIS,CFO

JAY-BEE OIL & GAS INC
BY ITS AGENT DMRB SERVICES,LLC
1720 ROUTE 22 EAST
UNION,NJ 07083-6112
PH 908 686-1493 FAX 908 688-4380
JAYBEEOIL.COM INFO@JAYBEEOIL.COM
RANDY J BRODA
CAIRO,WV FIELD OFFICE - RT 1 BOX 5
26337 PH 304 628-3111 PH 304 628-3107

JAY-DEE OPERATING COMPANY
1006 KARNAK DR
CORPUS CHRISTI,TX 78412-3804
PH 361 993-5300
JOE D SHROPSHIRE,OWNER
S M SHROPSHIRE,ENGR
F J GRASSBAUGH,SR ACCT
K MULVEY,OFC MGR

JCR LAND & TITLE
309 LA RUE FRANCE STE 203
LAFAYETTE,LA 70508 PH 337 233-3429
FAX 337 233-4594

JEAN-BATISTE ENERGY RESOURCES,LLC
PO BOX 81083
LAFAYETTE,LA 70598 PH 337 254-6986
STINGERSERVICESLLC@GMAIL.COM
DONALD D DAYE,COO

JEANERETTE LUMBER & SHINGLE/MINERALS,LLC
228 ST CHARLES AVE STE 1424

NEW ORLEANS,LA 70130 PH 504 568-1922
FAX 504 568-9438
DOWNMANS@DOWNMANSASSOC.COM
LANE M KINCANNON,PRES/CEO
MICHELLE KITTO,EXEC ADMIN ASST
DEBRA ORR-MOONEY,ACCT MGR
SUE SHELLEY,LAND TECH
TIMMY AUCOIN,LAND MGR

JEEMS BAYOU PRODUCTION CORPORATION
P O BOX 639
OIL CITY,LA 71061-0639 PH 318 995-7179
SHREVEPORT,LA LAND DEPT OFFICE -
201 ENERGY SQ,212 TEXAS ST,71101
PH 318 227-2219

JEFFBOAT LLC
1030 EAST MARKET ST
JEFFERSONVILLE,IN 47130-4332
PH 812 288-0200
JERRY R LINZEY,SR VP,MFG
BARKER PRICE,VP BUS DEV

JEFFERSON CORPORATION
PO BOX 36430
GROSSE POINTE,MI 48236-0430
PH 313 885-0930 FAX 313 885-0630
JAMES H BEDSWORTH,PRES

JEFFREYS RODNEY W,OIL PROPERTIES
16 AUTUMN PARK DR
JACKSON,MS 39206 PH 601 366-8180

JEFFREYS W KEVIN,CERT PROF LDMN
PO BOX 5344
BRANDON,MS 39047-5344 PH 601 214-6700

JEFFREYS,E GEOFFREY,GEOL ENGR
PETROLEUM CONSULTANT
505 N INGLESIDE ST
FAIRHOPE,AL 36532
PH 251 621-1850 EGJEFFREYS@AOL.COM

JEM ASSOCIATES
PO BOX 202
YOUNGSVILLE,PA 16371-0202
PH 814 726-9576 FAX 814 723-0987
JOHN E MCCOOL,PRES

JENCO OIL CO
407 HUTSON DR
CORSICANA,TX 75110-1388 PH 903 874-1071
TED JENNINGS,OWNER

JENKINS BORDEN,PETR GEOL
PO BOX 2996
CORPUS CHRISTI,TX 78403-2996
PH 361 887-8331

JENKINS STEVEN B
919 MILAM STE 1910
HOUSTON,TX 77002-5811
PH 713 652-5887 FAX 713 951-0620

JENKINS TAMARA C
919 MILAM STE 1910
HOUSTON,TX 77002-5811
PH 713 652-5887 FAX 713 951-0620

JENNINGS RICHARD A
PO BOX 3759
MIDLAND,TX 79702 PH 432 683-3272
PH 432 683-3272 FAX 432 683-3244

JERNIGAN OIL COMPANY,INC
109 DR MARTIN LUTHER KING JR DR N
AHOSKIE,NC 27910 PH 252 332-2131
FAX 252 332-7611 INFO@JERNIGANOIL.COM
STEPHEN A JERNIGAN,PRES

MARCIA BUTLER,SECY
VANESSA ETHERIDGE,TREAS
SHIRLEY WEBBER
AL HUNTER,CONTROLLER
WINFALL,NC OFFICE - 121 WINFALL BLVD
27985 PH 252 426-5745 FAX 252 426-5746

JERON OIL & GAS INC
230 W MAIN ST
DENISON,TX 75020-3025 PH 903 463-6104
FAX 903 463-7794
RONALD G CASTLEBERRY,PRES
JAMES FERRELL,VP
GREG RIEPL,GEOL
SONYA SOOTER,ADMIN ASST,OFC MGR

JESS ENERGY COMPANY
PO BOX 1360
TYLER,TX 75710-1360 PH 903 596-9813
FAX 903 596-9814
S D SMITH,PRES

JESSUP HARPER DEAN,LLC
6860 N DALLAS PKWY STE 200
PLANO,TX 75024 PH 972 851-1000
FAX 817 490-0320 WWW.JHDPETRO.COM
GREG JESSUP,CEO GLJESSUP@JHDPETRO.COM
DAVID K HARPER,CFO DKHARPER@JHDPETRO.COM
JENNIFER CALLAHAN,VP OPERS/BUS DEV MGR
JCALLAHAN@JHDPETRO.COM
STANLEY D CARROLL,JD,LANDMAN
SDCARROLL@JHDPETRO.NET

JESSUP RANDLE V,LAW OFFICES OF
18802 KINGSLAND BLVD
HOUSTON,TX 77094 PH 281 578-6800
RVJESSUP@JESSUPLAW.COM
WWW.JESSUPLAW.COM
RANDLE V JESSUP,ATTORNEY-AT-LAW

JET OIL PRODUCERS INC
PO BOX 930
COLDSPRING,TX 77331-0930 PH 713 528-2551
T R STALDER,PRES

JET PRODUCTION CO,INC
PO BOX 1859
KILGORE,TX 75663-1859 PH 214 984-0567
C N SCHWAB,PRES

JET STREAM INVESTMENTS,LTD
PO BOX 1797
WASKOM,TX 75692-1797 PH 903 687-2980
FAX 903 687-3359
W L RUDD III,PRES

JINKINS RON OIL PROD
7 SUN CT
NATCHEZ,MS 39120-5121 PH 601 446-8818

JL RESOURCES,LLC
8610 N NEW BRAUNFELS STE 400
SAN ANTONIO,TX 78217
PH 210 832-0525 FAX 210 832-0530
JUSTIN W LITTLE,PRES/CEO
SCOTT MCCARTHY,COO
BRIAN ARRIAGA,CFO
CHRIS CANTRELL,VP RESERVOIR/PROD
SPENCER HINES,VP LAND
STEVE HALE,VP GEOSCIENCE
TIM MCGOVERN,VP EXPL
JARRAD WOLFE,VP DRLG
TERESA KEETON,ADMIN/REG
MARK GETZEN,CONTROLLER
ERICA POST,ASST CONTROLLER

TANNER BOWERSOX,EXPL GEOL
TERRY WHATLEY,LDMN

JLA RESOURCES CO
3600 OLD BULLARD RD STE 200
TYLER,TX 75701-8658
PH 903 561-5558 FAX 903 561-4722
STAN EDWARDS,PRES
RYAN EDWARDS,VP

JN EXPL & PROD LTD PRTNR SEE
SEE ENERGY CONSULTANTS,LLC

JN OIL & GAS,INC SEE
ENERGY CONSULTANTS,LLC

JOE MARIE OIL CO
PO BOX 844
WIMBERLY,TX 78676-0844 PH 409 542-5581
BILLIE M BISETT,PRTNR
DON BISETT,PRTNR
KENNARD BISETT,LAND MGR

JOHN ZINK HAMWORTHY COMBUSTION
11920 E APACHE ST
TULSA,OK 74116 PH 918 234-1800
PH 800 421-9242 INFO@JOHNZINK.COM
WWW.JOHNZINKHAMWORTHY.COM

JOHNS JOHN N,JR
PO BOX 921,1213 W 2ND ST
CROWLEY,LA 70526-0921 PH 318 783-3394
FAX 318 783-7607 PH 800 467-8222
JOHN N JOHN (1979)
JOHN N JOHN,JR (1983)
JOHN N JOHN,III
JOSPEH A JOHN
WILLIAM M JOHN
CHRISTOPHER C JOHN

JOHNSON & LINDLEY INC
PO BOX 27727
HOUSTON,TX 77227-7727 PH 713 627-1101
STEVEN J LINDLEY,PRES

JOHNSON CHARLES G,CHUCK,GEOL
11434 WHISPER GREEN ST
SAN ANTONIO,TX 78230-3508 PH 713 464-6305

JOHNSON HARRY V,OIL & GAS PROPERTIES
8017 JEFFERSON HWY STE A4
BATON ROUGE,LA 70809-1681 PH 225 926-2478
FAX 225 927-9982
HARRY V JOHNSON,PRES

JOHNSON JOAN BLAFFER
2933 DEL MONTE DR
HOUSTON,TX 77019
PH 713 942-2322

JOHNSON KENNETH R,GEOL
4718 HALLMARK DR APT 453
HOUSTON,TX 77056-3914 PH 713 782-4824
FAX 713 334-8693

JOHNSON LARRY L,OIL PROPERTIES
P O BOX 12004
JACKSON,MS 39236-2004 PH 601 352-0020

JOHNSON MINERALS CO
624 TRAVIS ST STE 200
SHREVEPORT,LA 71101-3014 PH 318 221-4201
JAMES C JOHNSON III,MNGNG PRTNR
JOHN B JOHNSON,PRTNR
HENRY B JOHNSON JR,PRTNR
SHIRLEY A ADAMS,OFC MGR
CINDY WALKER,SECY

JOHNSON RESOURCES,LLC
PO BOX 10459

CORPUS CHRISTI,TX 78460-0459
PH 361 242-2385 FAX 361 242-1240
OMAR VILLARREAL,PRES/CO-OWNER

JOHNSON WILLIAM A & ASSOC,PETROLEUM GEOL
PO BOX 3576
PALESTINE,TX 75802-3576
PH 903 389-3135 FAX 903 389-3142
CAPTAINWILLIEJ@YAHOO.COM

JOHNSTON & OWEN,OIL PRODUCERS
PO BOX 6170
TYLER,TX 75711-6170 PH 903 597-3585
R N JOHNSTON,PRTNR

JOHNSTON BETTY T MARITAL TRUST
2424 WILCREST STE 105
HOUSTON,TX 77042 PH 281 340-9200
FAX 281 340-9201

JOHNSTON JERRY T,ATTY
115 BUILDERS SQUARE DR
BRANDON,MS 39047 PH 601 825-2265

JOHNSTON L N
1919 WEST 3RD AVE
CORSICANA,TX 75110-4262 PH 214 874-3004

JOHNSTON ROBERT L AND ASSOCIATES
PROVIDES PROFESSIONAL LAND SVCS
10248 CARDIFF DR
KEITHVILLE,LA 71047
PH 318 925-0000 BOBSRULE99@EARTHLINK.NET
ROBERT L JOHNSTON

JOMAC PROPERTIES
330 MARSHALL ST STE 930
SHREVEPORT,LA 71101-3018 PH 318 424-2031
PHIL ISRAEL,GEN MGR
HOBSON C MCGEHEE JR,JACKSON,MS,PRTNR
DONALD B MCGEHEE,MIAMI,FL,PRTNR
B BRYAN JONES III,YAZOO CITY,MS,PRTNR
WILLIAM C MCGEHEE,DENVER,CO,PRTNR

JONES & MITCHELL EXPLORATION COMPANY
1106 CASTLE HILL TRAIL
KINGWOOD,TX 77339-3053 PH 281 359-7777
STERLING B JONES,CEO
JAMES L MITCHELL,PRES

JONES & ZWIENER,INC
34011 DOBBIN HUFSMITH RD
MAGNOLIA,TX 77354
PH 832 934-2002 FAX 832 934-2005
WILLIAM F ZWIENER,PRES
BZWIENER@JONESANDZWIENER.COM
DOUGLAS G JONES,VP
DOUG@JONESANDZWIENER.COM

JONES AND NIX PLLC,ATTORNEYS
PO BOX 55601,814 N PRESIDENT ST
JACKSON,MS 39296-5601 PH 601 948-6800
FAX 601 948-7100 JONES-NIX@ATT.NET
W ROGER JONES,JR,PARTNER
ROGERJONES@ATT.NET
JAMES JIM M NIX,PRTNR JIMNIX@ATT.NET

JONES BROTHERS INTERESTS
2124 FAIRFIELD AVE
SHREVEPORT,LA 71104 PH 318 221-1657
FAX 318 221-1894
JAMES M JONES,OWNER
CARL W JONES,OWNER
J A MONTGOMERY,OFC MGR
MARY STUART,SECY

JONES CARL W
2124 FAIRFIELD AVE

SHREVEPORT,LA 71104 PH 318 221-1657
FAX 318 221-1894
J A MONTGOMERY,OFC MGR
MARY STUART,SECY

JONES DOUGLAS G
34011 DOBBIN HUFSMITH RD
MAGNOLIA,TX 77354 PH 832 934-2002
FAX 832 934-2005
DOUG@JONESANDZWIENER.COM

JONES EDWIN M,OIL CO
115 E TRAVIS ST STE 404
SAN ANTONIO,TX 78205-1662 PH 210 226-8385
FAX 210 226-8126 EMJONESOIL.COM

JONES HOWARD M,OIL PROD,LEASE BROKER
PO BOX 258
SAINT JOSEPH,LA 71366-0258
PH 318 766-3902

JONES JAMES M
PO BOX 1320
SHREVEPORT,LA 71164-1320 PH 318 221-1657
FAX 318 221-1894
J A MONTGOMERY,OFC MGR
MARY STUART,SECY

JONES JAY F,INC
2622 S 46TH ST
FORT SMITH,AR 72903-3529
PH 479 494-0644 FAX 479 494-1932
JAY F JONES,PRES
JAYJONES1@COX.NET

JONES MARIETTA HODGES,RPL
ABSTRACT - EAST TEXAS & NW LOUISIANA
2230 WOODSPRINGS RD
LOGANSPORT,LA 71049-2455 PH 318 858-3430
PH 318 422-5546
MARIETTAJONES1967@GMAIL.COM

JONES OBRIEN INC SEE
J-O'B OPERATING CO

JONES OIL COMPANY INC
PO BOX 2031,14 MORAN ROAD
NATCHEZ,MS 39121-2031
PH 601 442-1671 FAX 601 442-8738
WILLIAM T JONES JR,PRES

JONES OPERATING CO INC
2124 FAIRFIELD AVE
SHREVEPORT,LA 71104 PH 318 221-1657
JAMES MARSHALL JONES,PRES
J MARSHALL JONES JR,VP
ANN MONTGOMERY,SECY/TREAS

JONES RICHARD K,IND GEOL
300 N SIERRA VISTA DR
TUCSON,AZ 85719 PH 318 984-6952

JONES W ROGER,JR,ATTY AT LAW
PO BOX 55601,814 N PRESIDENT ST
JACKSON,MS 39296-5601 PH 601 948-6800
FAX 601 948-7100 JONES-NIX@ATT.NET
ROGER JONES ROGERJONES@ATT.NET
JIM NIX JIMNIX@ATT.NET

JONES WILLIAM T,JR
PO BOX 2031,14 MORAN ROAD
NATCHEZ,MS 39121-2031
PH 601 442-1671 FAX 601 442-8738
WTJ@DOZERLLC.COM
KATHY JONES,SECY

JORDAN DEVELOPMENT COMPANY,LLC
1503 GARFIELD RD N
TRAVERSE CITY,MI 49686-5111

PH 231 935-4220 FAX 231 935-4450
ROBERT M BOEVE,OWNER

JORDAN EXPLORATION COMPANY,LLC
1503 GARFIELD RD N
TRAVERSE CITY,MI 49686-5111
PH 231 935-4220 FAX 231 935-4450
ROBERT M BOEVE,OWNER
WAYNE A STERENBERG,OWNER

JORDAN KAISER & SESSIONS,LLC
CONS CIVIL ENGRS
PO BOX 1267,279 LOWER WOODVILLE RD
NATCHEZ,MS 39121-1267
PH 601 442-3628 FAX 601 442-5511
WWW.JKSLLC.COM LMARLING@JKSLLC.COM
C HAYDEN KAISER III,PRTNR
DOUGLAS M WIMBERLY,PRTNR
MALCOLM G BARLOW,PLS
LUTHER L MARLING,PLS

JORDAN MARGARET K
28 MACKENZIE CT
NEWNAN,GA 30263 PH 205 239-9063

JORDAN OIL & GAS,INC
6305 S CLIFF DR
FORT SMITH,AR 72903 PH 479 484-5059
FAX 479 484-5168
MIKE JORDAN,OWNER

JORIAH OIL & GAS INC
PO BOX 1095,7610 N US HWY 87
MELVIN,TX 76858
PH 325 456-1969 FAX 325 286-4564
JTINS284@MSN.COM

JOS ENERGY CORP
8584 KATY FWY STE 417
HOUSTON,TX 77024 PH 713 365-9783
JOHN O SMITH,PRES

JOSEY LENOIR M INC
4202 YOAKUM BLVD
HOUSTON,TX 77006-5418
PH 713 526-3844 FAX 713 526-4507
LENOIR M JOSEY,PRES
PHILIP PAVLICH,MGR PROD
BEN HOOPER,MGR GEOL
LENOIR M JOSEY III,MGR OPERS

JOSH FIELDS & ASSOCIATES
PO BOX 411
OKEMOS,MI 48805-0411
PH 517 337-4480 FAX 517 337-4879
JOSH@JOSHFIELDSLEGAL.COM
JOSH FIELDS,MNGNG ATTY

JOSLIN BOWDON ENERGY SERVICES
21518 WEST WALLIS DR
PORTER,TX 77365 PH 281 778-3387
INFO@JOSLINBOWDON.COM
ROBERT BOBBY BOWDON

JOURNEY OPERATING LLC
PO BOX 18018,14090 SW FWY STE 300
SUGAR LAND,TX 77496 PH 281 340-2072
FAX 281 340-2073

JOYCE J G PETR GEOL
2121 SAGE RD STE 170
HOUSTON,TX 77056-4305 PH 713 961-7778
JOYCEOIL@AOL.COM

JOYCE OIL & GAS,INC
2121 SAGE RD STE 170
HOUSTON,TX 77056-4305 PH 713 961-7778
FAX 713 961-7781

J G JOYCE,PRES
L T JOYCE,VP

JUMONVILLE OIL COMPANY (JUMOCO)
3636 S SHERWOOD FOREST BLVD STE 111
BATON ROUGE,LA 70816-2262 PH 225 293-1704
DAN JUMONVILLE,PRES

JUNCTION CITY OIL COMPANY
PO BOX 1184
PETAL,MS 39465-1184
PH 601 583-9991 FAX 601 583-9881
GEORGE E GILLESPIE JR,VP

JUNCTION CITY OPERATING,LLC SEE
FIELD MANAGEMENT,LLC

JURA-SEARCH INC
GULF COAST PROSPECT GENERATION & EXPL
PO BOX 320426,546 KEYWAY DR STE C
FLOWOOD,MS 39232
PH 601 932-0002 FAX 601 932-0820
LAWRENCE R BARIA,PRES
BEARLEAR@BELLSOUTH.NET

JURASIN OIL & GAS INC
9700 RICHMOND AVE STE 124
HOUSTON,TX 77042-4821 PH 832 242-6000
FAX 713 917-0493
JOHN M JURASIN,PRES,CEO
ADMIN@JURASINOILGAS.COM
WWW.JURASINOILGAS.COM

JURIK EXPLORATION CO
124 ROSA AVE
METAIRIE,LA 70005 PH 504 837-7185
OCEAN SPRINGS,MS OFFICE - 2836 EAGLE PINE
DR 39564 PH 228 875-7895
PAUL JURIK,GEOL JUREXCO.P@GMAIL.COM

JUSTISS MEARS OIL CO INC SEE
JUSTISS OIL CO,INC

JUSTISS OIL CO INC
PO BOX 2990,1120 E OAK ST
JENA,LA 71342-2990 PH 318 992-4111
FAX 318 992-7201 WWW.JUSTISSOIL.COM
JUSTISS@JUSTISSOIL.COM
J F JUSTISS JR,CHMN BD/CFO
J F JUSTISS III,PRES
W B MCCARTNEY,EXEC VP
CRAIG BREITHAUPT,CFO
WAYNE PRITCHARD,DRLG MGR
JERRY PEAVY,PROD MGR
TODD WEBB,PERSONNEL MGR

JW ENERGY RESOURCES SEE
CHOCTAW NATURAL GAS,LLC

JX NIPPON OIL EXPLORATION (U.S.A.) LTD
1 RIVERWAY STE 1600
HOUSTON,TX 77056
PH 713 260-7400 FAX 713 978-7800
RYOSUKE HOJO,PRES
YUICHI MORITA,CFO
YASUNAKI IIDA,GM/ADMIN
STEVEN R FLY,VP LAND & INS
FRANK DAVIS III,LAND MGR
DANIEL B NEWMAN,MGR/EXPL
CRYSTAL BRIGHAM,ASSOC MGR/ADMIN
CURTIS R O'NEAL,ACCT MGR

K & J OIL,INC
2305 HWY 6 SOUTH STE E
HOUSTON,TX 77077
PH 281 413-8118 FAX 281 597-8319
KEN MILLER,PRES

KEN@TRANSPORTSPECIALISTSINC.COM
J MILLER,VP

K & R OPERATING COMPANY
PO BOX 3268
PIKEVILLE,KY 41502-3268 PH 606 432-1456
FAX 606 433-0703
BOB ROBERTS,OWNER

K B S ENERGY,LLC
32 SHORELAKE DR
KINGWOOD,TX 77339-3601
PH 281 360-8072
MICHAEL M HINZE,PRES
ANDREA J HINZE,CFO

K C I COMPRESSION COMPANY,LP
4444 BRITTMOORE RD
HOUSTON,TX 77041-8004 PH 281 890-5155
FAX 281 890-2266
JIM SWENKE,SR VP,SALES/MKTG
BRYAN STEWART,MGR,OPERS/MAINTENANCE
MARSON STANFILL,SLS
TERRY CONNORS,SLS
TIM TIMMERMAN,SLS
JESS FOSTER,MKTG

K F G PETROLEUM CORPORATION
118 LOWER WOODVILLE RD STE 2
NATCHEZ,MS 39120-4448 PH 601 446-5219
FAX 601 446-9907 KFGPETRO@BELLSOUTH.NET
G STEPHEN GUIDO,PRES
ROBERT A KADANE,VP

K L H,INC
PO BOX 44203
SHREVEPORT,LA 71134-4203 PH 318 572-8810
FAX 318 227-2602 CELTOIL@YAYOO.COM
JIM M LOVE,PRES

K PETROLEUM INC
905 CREEKSIDE PLZ
GAHANNA,OH 43230 PH 614 532-5420
FAX 614 532-5424
JAM KHORRAMI,PRES

K-D OPERATIONS
6516 SUNRISE
N RICHLAND HILLS,TX 76182
PH 817 829-2648 FAX 817 416-4616
DEWAYNE BROCK,OWNER
KATHY BROCK,OWNER

K-EXPLORATION CO
PO BOX 681
MANDEVILLE,LA 70470-0681 PH 985 626-7843
FAX 800 738-7143 ROB@KEXPLORATION.COM
ROBERT A SCHROEDER,PRES

K-J COMPANY,INC,REGULATORY CONSULTANTS
PO BOX 53572
LAFAYETTE,LA 70505 PH 337 235-6543
FAX 337 237-3571 K-JCOMPANY.COM
KJCO@K-JCOMPANY.COM
JO BETH TAYLOR,PRES
MONA VIENNE
FRED DEDON,PE
SANDRA NIELSON

K-MAC VACUUM TRUCK SERVICE,INC
PO BOX 797
FRIENDSWOOD,TX 77549-0797
PH 281 482-9554 FAX 281 482-0918
W SMITH,PRES
DWIGHT PUGH,SLS
HECTOR F SOTO,SLS

LUPE GUTIERREZ,DISPATCH

K-N OPERATING CORP SEE
KACHINA OIL & GAS,INC

KABCO OIL & GAS CO
3400 W MARSHALL AVE STE 324
LONGVIEW,TX 75604-5048 PH 903 759-2908
WILLIAM A BROWN,PRES
MARY CORBET,OFC MGR

KADANE CORPORATION
4809 COLE AVE STE 100,LB 114
DALLAS,TX 75205-3552 PH 214 219-7800
LOU KADANE,PRES,CEO
MICHAEL L GUSTAFSON,VP
JOHN CLIFTON,CONTROLLER

KAIN PETROLEUM LLC
PO BOX 1433
PEARSALL,TX 78061-1433 PH 830 466-5492
JOHN G KAIN,MGR

KAISER HERMAN,GEOL,OIL PRODUCER SEE
KAISER-FRANCIS OIL CO

KALER ENERGY CORP
70 NE LOOP 410 STE 810
SAN ANTONIO,TX 78215
PH 210 824-1361 EXT 206 FAX 210 824-1419
JOHN A KALER II,PRES
MARK BROWN,GEOL
MRBROWN@KALERENERGY.COM

KALOS CORPORATION
305 S BROADWAY AVE STE 403
TYLER,TX 75702-7306 PH 903 592-7986
LARRY G WRIGHT,PRES
JANE WRIGHT,OFC MGR

KALYN/SIEBERT TRAILERS
PO BOX 1078
GATESVILLE,TX 76528-0758 PH 254 865-7235
FAX 254 865-7234 800 525-9689

KAPADIA & ASSOCIATES INTERNATIONAL,INC
906 AUTUMN OAKS DR
HOUSTON,TX 77079-3603 PH 713 468-8445
FAX 713 468-8445
KAPADIAINTL@EARTHLINK.NET
BIPIN R KAPADIA,PRES

KARR CHARLES,P.A.,LAW OFFICES OF
7415 WESTMINISTER PL
FORT SMITH,AR 72903-4250 PH 479 782-4028
FAX 479 782-6410
CHARLES KARR

KASH OIL & GAS,INC
PO BOX 51847
LAFAYETTE,LA 70505-1847
PH 337 237-0304 FAX 337 237-0308
RONALD J HOOVER,ENGR
RICHARD J JONES,ENGR

KATTY INDUSTRIES OF ODESSA LTD SEE
COMPRESSOR RENEWAL SERVICES LTD

KATY PIPELINE AND PRODUCTION CORP
PO BOX 468
LUFKIN,TX 75904 PH
FAX 936 632-8338
MELVIN R TODD,PRES

KATZ OIL COMPANY
PO BOX 18167
SAN ANTONIO,TX 78218-0167 PH 210 240-9317
CAROL K GARDNER,PRES
M B GARDNER JR,VP,SECY/TREAS

KAVOURAS THOMAS,OPERATOR,PRODUCER
209A S 2ND ST STE 211
APOLLO,PA 15613-1108
PH 724 478-1532 FAX 724 478-3160
OFFICE@GASANDOILCOMPANY.COM
ANDRON KAVOURAS,WELL SVCS MGR

KAYA SYSTEMS LLC
109 FALLING SHOALS DR
ATHENS,GA 30605-5740 PH 706 534-2284
INFO@KAYASYSTEMS.COM

KBR
PO BOX 3,601 JEFFERSON AVE
HOUSTON,TX 77001-0003
PH 713 753-2000 FAX 713 753-7836
WILLIAM P 'BILL' UTT,PRES,CEO
SUE CARTER,SR VP,CFO
ANDREW D FARLEY,SR VP,GEN COUNSEL
KLAUDIA J BRACE,SR VP,ADMIN
MARK S WILLIAMS,GROUP PRES GOV & DEF
INFRASTRUCTURE AND MINERALS,POWER & IND
JOHN L ROSE,GROUP PRES,HYDROCARBONS
TOM MUMFORD,SR VP,COMM
DENNIS CALTON,EXEC VP,OPERS
DAVID ZIMMERMAN,PRES,SVCS
JOHN QUINN,PRES,DOWNSTREAM
MITCH DAUZAT,PRES,GAS MONETIZATION
ANDREW PRINGLE,PRES,INTL GOV & DEFENSE
COLIN ELLIOTT,PRES,INFRASTRUCTURE & MINS
ROY OELKING,PRES,OIL & GAS
TOM VAUGHN,PRES,POWER & IND
TIMOTHY B CHALLAND,PRES,TECH
ARLINGTON,VA OFFICE- 2451 CRYSTAL DR
22202 PH 703 526-7500
AUBURN,ME OFFICE- 127 FIRST FLIGHT DR
KITTYHAWK INDUSTRIAL PARK 04210
BIRMINGHAM,AL BE&K OFFICE-
2000 INTERNATIONAL PARK DR 35243
PH 205 972-6000
DALLAS, TX OFFICE- 1444 OAK LAWN STE 100
75207 PH 214 752-8300
DEER PARK, TX OFFICE- 1707 CENTER ST
77536-3509 PH 713 753-3600
NEWARK,DE OFFICE- 242 CHAPMAN RD 19702
GREENVILLE,SC OFFICE- 201 E MCBEE AVE
STE 400 29601
HOUSTON,TX BE&K OFFICE-
14701 ST. MARY'S LN STE 500 77079
PH 832 486-4500
RALEIGH,NC OFFICE- 2450 PERIMETER PARK DR
#100 27560
EDMONTON,ALBERTA,CANADA OFFICE- 3300 76TH
T6P 1J4 PH 780 468-1341
EDMONTON,ALBERTA OFFICE- 1259 91ST ST SW
T6X 1E9 PH 780 468-1341
NEW LISKEARD,ONTARIO KBR WABI OFFICE-
PO BOX 2522 HWY 11 N P0J 1P0
PH 705 647-5897
EDIFICIO SANTOS MONTERREY,N.L.,MEXICO-
AVENIDA MADERO 1955 PTE, DESP 400
PH 52 818 348 9855
- SOUTH AFRICA -
JOHANNESBURG,SOUTH AFRICA OFFICE- UNIT 8
KBR HOUSE, FOURWAYS OFFICE PARK,CNR OF
FOURWAYS BLVD & ROOS AVENUE
PH 27 11 361 0300
SECUNDA,MPUMALANGA,SOUTH AFRICA OFFICE-

KIEWIET OFFICE PARK,BLOCK D, 2302
PH 27 17 634-4454
- AUSTRALIA -
ADELAIDE,AUSTRALIA OFFICE- 186 GREENHILL
PARKSIDE SA 5063 PH 61 8 8301 1234
ANTHONY BOWMAN,STATE GEN MGR
BRISBANE,AUSTRALIA OFFICE- LEVEL 11
199 GREY ST, SOUTH BANK QUEENSLAND 4101
PH 61 7 3721 6555
JAMES WRIGHT,STATE GEN MGR
CANBERRA,AUSTRALIA OFFICE- LEVEL 4
11 LANCASTER PLACE,MAJURA PARK,AUSTRALIAN
CAPITAL TERRITORY, 2609 PH 61 2 6102 2600
RAY REDMAN,STATE GEN MGR
GOLD COAST,AUSTRALIA OFFICE- 10/60 NERANG
NERANG OLD 4211 PH 61 7 5502 4660
MELBOURNE,AUSTRALIA OFFICE- LEVEL 3
441 ST KILDA RD, MELBOURNE VIC 3004
PH 61 3 9828 5333
SAM COWELL,STATE GEN MGR
PERTH,AUSTRALIA OFFICE- 100 ST GEORGES
TERRACE, WESTERN AUSTRALIA, 6000
PH 61 8 6444 3000
BRUCE FRANKLIN, STATE GEN MGR
SYDNEY,AUSTRALIA OFFICE-LEVEL 13,201 KENT
NEW SOUTH WALES, 2000 PH 61 2 8284 2000
PERRY COHN, STATE GEN MGR
- AZERBAIJAN -
BAKU,AZERBAIJAN OFFICE- OFFICE ISW
NATAVAN BLDG 5 TBILISI AVE BLOCK 1003
AZ1065 PH 994 12 496 90 00

- KELLOGG CHINA, INC. -

BEIJING,CHINA OFFICE- UNIT D FLOOR 7
TOWER A OF GATEWAY PLAZA NO 18
XIANGUANGLI,DANGSANHUAN BEILU CHAO YANG
DISTRICT PH 86 10 8486 2640
FAX 86 10 8486 2639
- INDIA -
HARYANA,INDIA OFFICE- 1ST FLOOR TOWER A
TECHNOPOLIS,GOLF COURSE RD,SECTOR 54
GURGAON 122 002 PH 91 12 4455 7630
FAX 91 12 4455 7620
JASPAN SINGH,DIRECTOR
- INDONESIA -
JAKARTA,INDONESIA OFFICE- LNDMRK BLDG
TOWER B 12TH FLOOR, JL SUDIRMAN KAV 1
12910 PH 62 21 3006 1000
FAX 62 21 3000 2040
- KAZAKHSTAN -
ATYRAU,KAZAKHSTAN OFFICE-7 AZATTYK AVE
ATYRAU OBLAST 060002
- SINGAPORE -
SINGAPORE OFFICE- 79 ANSON RD #20-01
079906 PH 65 6210 7000 FAX 65 6210 7020
KCS ENERGY INC
SEE PETROHAWK ENERGY CORP
KCS RESOURCES,INC
SUBSIDIARY OF KCS ENERGY,INC
1360 POST OAK BLVD STE 150
HOUSTON,TX 77056 PH 908 632-1770
WWW.KCSENERGY.COM
JAMES W CHRISTMAS,CHRMN,CEO
HOUSTON,TX OPER OFFICE - 5555 SAN FELIPE
STE 1200,77056 PH 713 877-8006

FAX 713 877-1372
WILLIAM N HAHNE,PRES
CLIFF FOSS,VP EXPL
WES VANNATTA,VP OPER & ENGRG
PAUL C BRAUN,LAND
DAVID CHANDLER,CONTROLLER
TULSA,OK MID-CONT DIVISION OFFICE -
PO BOX 707130,74170-7130
7130 S LEWIS AVE,STE 700,74136
PH 918 488-8283 FAX 918 488-8182
D BRAD MAGILL,VP EXPL
DAVID R RICK DEFFENBAUGH,VP LAND
H WELDON HOLCOMBE,VP MC OPER & ENGRG
KEARY JON A SEE
BENCHMARK LAND SERVICE,LLC
KEARY KENT,LDMN,CPL
PO BOX 12943
JACKSON,MS 39236-2943 PH 601 898-1803
KEATLEY VICKIE
3320 HINTON RD
ATHENS,WV 24712 PH 304 384-7254
FAX 304 384-9468
KEBERT PETROLEUM LLC
2999 DELAWARE AVE
MCCOMB,MS 39648 PH 601 684-7188
DEAN KEBERT,MNGNG MEMBER
HIDKEBERT@YAHOO.COM
KEC ACQUISITION CORP SEE
AMERICAN EXPLORATION CO
KEEGAN ED A (OVERSEAS EXPLORATION)
PO BOX 451,207 MEADOWDALE DR
ROCKWALL,TX 75087-0451 PH 972 771-0000
FAX 972 771-0055
KEELING LEE AND ASSOCIATES INC
15 E 5TH ST STE 3500
TULSA,OK 74103 PH 918 587-5521
FAX 918 587-2881 WWW.LKAENGINEERS.COM
CONTACT@LKAENGINEERS.COM
GORDON L ROMINE,PRES/PETR ENGR
JOHN R WHEELER,VP/GEOL
PHILLIP W GRICE,SECY/TREAS,SR EVAL ENGR
W DAVID WOODRUFF,SR EVAL ENGR
LEE A KEELING,PRES/EX OFFICIO
KENNETH RENBERG,VP/EX OFFICIO
KEETON HAROLD W,C.P.L.
· 100 VALERIA CT
BELLE CHASSE,LA 70037 PH 504 340-6356
FAX 504 340-6356
KEITH DAISY-TRUST
PO BOX 238
DALLAS,TX 75221-0238 PH 214 528-0086
PH 214 528-4478 FAX 214 528-2361
THOMAS MAX NYGAARD,TRUSTEE
KEITH WALTER AND DAISY TRUST
PO BOX 238
DALLAS,TX 75221-0238 PH 214 528-4478
FAX 214 528-2361
THOMAS MAX NYGAARD,TRUSTEE
KEITO GAS,INC
PO BOX 256
RENO,OH 45773 PH 740 630-5974
TODD HEFTER,CEO
KEITH NORTH,VP FLD OPERS
KELCAS WELL SERVICES LTD
PO BOX 21345
OWENSBORO,KY 42304 PH 270 683-1322

FAX 270 683-1613
KELCO OIL FIELD GROUP,A DIV OF CP KELCO
10920 W SAM HOUSTON PKWY N #800
HOUSTON,TX 77064-5756 PH 713 895-7575
JAMES SEHEULT,DIR SALES & TECH AMERICAS
JAMES SCHKADE,DIR AMERICAS SALES
KELJOR GROUP,LLC
20734 LA COTE CIR
SPRING,TX 77388
PH 713 301-7070 WWW.KELJOR.COM
PATRICK DONAIS,EXPL CONSLT PAT@KELJOR.COM
KELL EAST,INC
PO BOX 1285,2330 E CALUMET ST
CENTRALIA,IL 62801-9119 PH 618 533-0700
DANIEL N KOLLER
KELLEY & ABIDE COMPANY,INC
4401 EUPHROSINE ST
NEW ORLEANS,LA 70125-1349 PH 504 822-2700
FAX 504 822-2761
A J ABIDE,CEO
GREG ABIDE,PRES
RICHARD ABIDE,VP
KELLEY BROTHERS CONTRACTORS,INC
PO BOX 1079
WAYNESBORO,MS 39367-0312
PH 601 735-2541 FAX 601 735-2809
JERRY KELLEY,PRES
MARK KELLEY,MGR
KELLEY ENVIRONMENTAL ENGINEERING,INC
5403 ENCHANTED MIST DR
HUMBLE,TX 77346 PH 281 446-4427
FAX 281 446-7573
J ROGER KELLEY,PRES
KELLEY OIL & GAS CORPORATION SEE
CONTOUR ENERGY CO
KELLOGG BROWN & ROOT,INC SEE
KBR
KELLY GREG A,INC
PO BOX 7987
TYLER,TX 75711-7987 PH 903 595-5299
GREG A KELLY,PRES
KELLY RICHARD
203 STORY LN
CORSICANA,TX 75109-9475
PH 903 654-2873 FAX 903 874-1838
WELLSWEEP3711@SBCGLOBAL.NET
KELTON CO,LLC
PO BOX 230,220 W GARDEN STE 605
PENSACOLA,FL 32591-0230 PH 904 434-6830
FAX 904 434-6842
TOM SYLTE,PRES TWSYLTE@BELLSOUTH.NET
KEMKALKEN RESOURCES LLC
PO BOX 516
TYLER,TX 75710 PH 903 571-9830
FAX 903 852-6698
CHRISTOPHER W WALKER,PH.D.,CPL,MGR
CHRISTOPHER.WALKER@SUDDENLINKMAIL.COM
KEMP GEOPHYSICAL CORPORATION SEE
3D GEOPHYSICAL,INC (END OF ALPHA)
KEMPER VALVE & FITTING CORP
12343 CUTTEN RD
HOUSTON,TX 77066 PH 281 781-2730
PH 800 231-2724 WWW.KEMPERVALVE.COM
JOE KEMPER,PRES
PERRY TRAHAN,NATL SLS MGR
P.TRAHAN@KEMPERVALVE.COM

KEN PETROLEUM CORPORATION
OIL & GAS/OPR & PROD
8080 N CENTRAL EXPY STE 1000
DALLAS,TX 75206-1804 PH 214 891-8410
FAX 214 891-8414
KENNETH C ENGLISH,PRES
PAUL LECOCKE,VP,CONTROLLER
EDNA,TX FIELD OFFICE - PO BOX 817,77957
PH 361 782-5206
LU EGG,OFC MGR

KENLEY RAYMOND A,OIL PROD
6206 CHEVY CHASE
HOUSTON,TX 77057-3516 PH 713 782-3504

KENNE EXPLORATION,INC
2207 REDCLIFF
MISSOURI CITY,TX 77489
PH 281 499-5799 GASNOIL@COMCAST.NET
STEPHEN KENNE

KENNEDY LAND SERVICES,INC
PO BOX 110145
CARROLLTON,TX 75011 PH 972 416-4325
PATRICK KENNEDY
PJKENNEDY@KENNDEDYLANDSERVICES.COM

KENRELL PETROLEUM RESOURCES,INC
PO BOX 517
BELLAIRE,TX 77402-0517 PH 713 664-4115
RANDY CALHOUN,PRES

KENT GARRY D,OIL & GAS,INC
RR 1 BOX 121
LOVELAKE,TX 75851-9717 PH 409 636-7289
LARRY KENT,CONS GEOL
TIM REED,CONS DRLG ENGR

KENT PRODUCTION,LLC
PO BOX 131524
HOUSTON,TX 77219-1524 PH 713 658-1142
FAX 713 658-0739
ROBERT W KENT,PRES RWKENTOG@AOL.COM

KENTUCKY OIL & GAS ASSOCIATION
306 W MAIN ST STE 404
FRANKFORT,KY 40601 PH 502 226-1955
FAX 502 226-3626 WWW.KYOILGAS.ORG
ANDREW MCNEILL,EXEC DIR
ASTRUD MASTERSON,ASSOC DIR

KENTUCKY OIL GATHERING CORP
CRUDE OIL PURCHASER/TRANSPORTER IN
KY,TN & VA
PO BOX 430
FRAZEYSBURG,OH 43822
PH 800 846-6642 FAX 740 828-3660
BRIAN R JONARD,PRES
CARL ROSS,STATE MGR/KY
IDA LEWIS,DIV ORDERS

KERN RIVER GAS TRANSMISSION COMPANY
PO BOX 71400
SALT LAKE CITY,UT 84171-0400
PH 801 583-8800 FAX 801 584-7752
B E O'NEIL,PRES,INTERSTATE NATURAL GAS
PIPELINE GROUP
C WADLINGTON JR,SR VP,GEN MGR
R L SLUDER,DIR,OPERS
K R HOHENSHELT,MGR,ENV SVCS
K T MORGAN,MGR,RIGHT-OF-WAY
B JENSEN,MGR,ADMIN
G L ROBERTS,MGR,OCCUP & PIPELINE SAFETY
P D DEAN,MGR,GAS CONTROL

KERNS PETROLEUM,INC
3611 PAESANOS PKWY STE 202
SAN ANTONIO,TX 78231-1257 PH 210 829-7881
FAX 210 829-7883 WWW.KERNSPETRO.COM
ELIZABETH CANTRELL,PRES

KERR ED SEE
ARMSTRONG OIL & GAS,INC

KERR JAIN & ASSOC,SEE
VENEX CORP

KERR-MCGEE CORPORATION SEE
ANADARKO PETROLEUM CORPORATION

KERR-MCGEE OIL & GAS CORPORATION SEE
ANADARKO PETROLEUM CORPORATION

KERR-MCGEE OIL & GAS ONSHORE LLC SEE
ANADARKO PETROLEUM CORPORATION

KERRCO LTD
808 TRAVIS ST STE 2200
HOUSTON,TX 77002 PH 713 229-9899
J ROBINSON KERR,MNGNG PRTNR

KESLAR,CHARLES Z AGENCY,INC
PO BOX 126,3335 RT 31 WEST
DONEGAL,PA 15628
PH 724 552-9000 FAX 724 593-7756
WWW.GASANDOILLEASES.COM
C ZANE KESLAR,PRES
CZK@GASANDOILLEASES.COM

KESTERSON DONALD C,INC
P O BOX 2036
PARKERSBURG,WV 26102-2036 PH 304 295-5511

KESTREL ENERGY INC SEE
SAMSON RESOURCES COMPANY

KET INTEREST,LLC
7500 SAN FELIPE STE 475
HOUSTON,TX 77063 PH 713 706-3090
KEN TRAHAN,PRES
KTRAHAN@WOODSTONERESOURCES.COM

KEY ENERGY PRESSURE PUMPING SERVICES
PO BOX 3120
MIDLAND,TX 79702-3120 PH 432 620-0307
FAX 432 571-7570 WWW.AMENERGY.COM
JOHN CARNETT,VP
BOB MATHEWS,US SALES MGR
BMATHEWS@AMENERGY.COM
BOB WIESMAN,SAFETY & LOSS CONTROL
CHAD GARNER,ENGR
DUSTY WEATHERLY,ENGR
MARK ACKLIN,SLS
MIKE BOWLING,SLS
CRAIG HERTAL,TECH SVCS LAB MGR
MATT SIMMONS,CONTROLLER
TERRY WELSCH,PURCHASING MGR
MIDLAND,TX DIST OFFICE - PO BOX 3120
79702-3120,2401 E I-20 ACCESS RD 79701
PH 432 570-4899 FAX 432 687-2542
JOE LUMAN,DIST MGR
CURTIS HUFF,STIM OP SUPVSR
HUGO SEGURA,CEMENT OP SUPVSR
BOBBY TUBBS,DIST ENGR
DENNIE MARTIN,ENGR
JESSIE ALEJANDRO,FLD SLS
TOMMY TIMS,FLD SLS
CHARLIE HAMMOND,FACILITY MGR
FAIRVIEW,OK DIST OFFICE - RR 1,BOX 62
73737,1 1/2 MILES N OF FAIRVIEW,OK ON
HWY 60,PH 580 227-9170
FAX 580 227-2814

RON CALAWAY,DIST MGR
TONY MENDAL,OPERS SUPVSR
JAMES SEGARS,DIST ENGR
JOE MELTON,FLD SLS
RANDY MENDAL,FLD SLS
OKLAHOMA CITY,OK SALES OFFICE -
1000 W WILSHIRE STE 224,73116
PH 405 843-8200 FAX 405 843-8436
JIM OWENS,SLS
GARY FOLMNSBEE,SLS
FARMINGTON,NM DIST OFFICE - PO BOX 302
87499,708 S TUCKER,87401
PH 505 325-4192 FAX 505 564-3524
MIKE MCNEESE,DIST MGR
ROWZ MARTINEZ,OPERS SUPVSR
CLIFF ANDERSON,SLS
MIKE BROWN,TECH SLS
HOUSTON,TX SALES OFFICE - 3100 TIMMONS
STE 300,77027 PH 713 869-6020
FAX 713 599-0913
JAY MASON,SLS
DALLAS,TX OFFICE - 15851 N DALLAS PKY
STE 600,ADDISON,TX 75001
PH 972 561-8784 FAX 972 561-8783
JIM RUCKER,SLS
P J EDSALL,SLS
CHICO,TX DISTRICT OFFICE - PO BOX 67
705 WEATHERFORD,76431
PH 940 644-5977 FAX 940 644-5997
HARRY LITTLETON,DIST MGR
STEVE HOUSTON,STIM OP SUP
JEFF WILKINSON,REG ENGR
DANNY RUSSELL,SLS
STEVE SCHAEFER,DIST ENGR
JIMMY LOVEN,CEMENT OP SUP

KEY ENERGY SERVICE INC
WORKOVER & COMPLETION CO
321 RENAULD DR
LAFAYETTE,LA 70507 PH 337 266-4900
FAX 337 267-3482 WWW.KEYENERGY.COM
LYNN TRAHAN
CHRIS NED

KEY EXPLORATION COMPANY
AND KEY OPERATING COMPANY
PO BOX 52963
LAFAYETTE,LA 70505-2963
PH 337 233-9445 FAX 337 237-5056
BILL GUIDRY,PRES BGUIDRY@KEYOPERATING.COM

KEY OIL COMPANY
22 GARTON PLZ
WESTON,WV 26452-2129 PH 304 269-7102
FAX 304 269-7134
JAN CHAPMAN,PRES
KAREN COOK,CORP SECY
KERRI MALFREGEOT,ADMIN ASST
GREG KELLEY,OPERS MGR

KEY PRODUCTION COMPANY,INC SEE
CIMAREX ENERGY CO

KGA OIL COMPANY INC
PO BOX 308
HIGH ISLAND,TX 77623-0308 PH 409 286-5511
FAX 409 286-5512
FRANK E HATCHER,CONTRACT OPER

KIAMICHI OIL COMPANY,LLC
PO BOX 12844
JACKSON,MS 39236-2844 PH 601 953-2853

RUFFIAN56S@AOL.COM
JACK STRIPLING,LDMN

KIATTA HOWARD W
815 WALKER ST STE 1502
HOUSTON,TX 77002-5384 PH 713 951-9090
HOWARD W KIATTA,PRES,GEOL

KIDD DRILLING,INC
DRILLING & COMPLETION CONTRACTOR
328 N HART ST
PRINCETON,IN 47670-1537 PH 812 386-6320
FRANCIS P KIDD,OWNER
RUTH KIDD,OWNER

KIDD HUBERT E,BROKERAGE & LEASES
1428 E RICHARDS ST
TYLER,TX 75702-6253 PH 903 597-8307
FAX 903 597-8308
HUBERT E KIDD,PETR LDMN
LEE KIDD

KIDD INDUSTRIES INC,OIL PRODUCER
328 N HART ST
PRINCETON,IN 47670-1537 PH 812 386-6320
FRANCIS P KIDD,OWNER
RUTH KIDD,OWNER

KIDD L LEE,BROKERAGE & LEASES
1428 E RICHARDS ST
TYLER,TX 75702-6253 PH 903 597-8307
FAX 903 597-8308
L LEE KIDD,PETR LDMN

KILBARGER INVESTMENTS
PO BOX 946,GALLAGHER AVE
LOGAN,OH 43138-0946 PH 740 385-6019
FAX 740 385-7254
EDW F KILBARGER,PRES
JAMES E KILBARGER,VP
TONY KILBARGER,VP

KILBURN LAW FIRM
5300 MEMORIAL DR STE 550
HOUSTON,TX 77007
PH 713 974-1333 FAX 713 974-5333
KERRY A KILBURN,MGR
KKILBURN@KILBURNLAW.COM

KILLGORE THOMAS M,INC
815 RIVER OAKS DR
COVINGTON,LA 70433-5062
PH 985 893-8652 FAX 985 893-8652
THOMAS M KILLGORE,OWNER
THOMAS M KILLGORE,JR,MGR
E HUMMEL KILLGORE

KILLIAN OIL CO
PO BOX 561359
CHARLOTTE,NC 28256-1359 PH 704 596-0873
DON KILLIAN,OWNER

KILMARNOCK OIL CO,INC
319 W 7TH AVE
CORSICANA,TX 75110-6447 PH 903 874-4725
CLIFFORD L BROWN III,PRES
ORANGEFIELD,TX OFFICE - PO BOX 292
77639 PH 409 735-4001
CLAY DARDEAU,FLD SUPT

KILPATRICK CAMPBELL,IND PETR LAND AGT
2710 SUNSET BLVD
HOUSTON,TX 77005-2442 PH 713 871-0943

KILRUSH PETROLEUM,INC
815 WALKER ST #1045
HOUSTON,TX 77002-5721
PH 713 222-1020 FAX 713 222-1023

JACK REIDY,PRES

KIMMEL CONSTRUCTION CO INC
PO BOX 310
SHELOCTA,PA 15774-0310 PH 724 354-2977
FAX 724 354-2021
GERALD L KIMMEL,PRES

KIMRAY INC
OIL & GAS EQUIP & CONTROLS
52 NW 42ND ST
OKLAHOMA CITY,OK 73118-8590
PH 405 525-6601 FAX 405 525-7520
WWW.KIMRAY.COM INFO@KIMRAY.COM
JIM CAMERON,VP SALES
BAKERSFIELD,CA (SALES & SVC) OFFICE -
3680 STANDARD ST 93309-5227
PH 661 323-7773 FAX 661 323-7774
JESS RING JRING@KIMRAY.COM
HOUMA,LA (SALES & SVC) OFFICE -
166 THOMPSON RD STE 2 70363-7317
PH 985 876-6700 985 860-1043
FAX 985 876-5545
DOUG BOUDREAUX DBOUDREAUX@KIMRAY.COM
LAFAYETTE,LA (SALES & SVC) OFFICE -
209 HULCO,SCOTT,LA 70583-5333
PH 337 261-2462 337 298-3691
FAX 337 261-2404
LARRY SAVOIE LSAVOIE@KIMRAY.COM
SHREVEPORT,LA (SALES & SVC) OFFICE -
1100 HAWN DR 71107 PH 318 424-2468
PH 318 349-2554 FAX 318 424-2494
WILLIAM MOORE WMOORE@KIMRAY.COM
KALKASKA,MI (TREND SVCS) OFFICE -
PO BOX 458,311 MAPLE ST 49646
PH 231 258-9951 FAX 231 258-9751
WWW.TRENDSERVICES.NET
SUPPORT@TRENDSERVICES.NET
MIKE BABCOCK
LAUREL,MS (SALES & SVC) OFFICE -
5445 HWY 11 N STE A 39437
PH 601 649-8898 601 340-1637
FAX 601 649-8894
KEITH JONES KJONES@KIMRAY.COM
FARMINGTON,NM-SOUTHERN CO-UTAH & ARIZONA
(OIL & GAS EQUIP) OFFICE - 4910 E MAIN ST
87402 PH 505 325-2629 FAX 505 327-5459
WWW.OGEQUIP.COM
INFORMATION@OGEQUIP.COM
DREW DEGNER
BOWMAN,ND (DOUBLE EE SERVICE INC)
OFFICE - 413 6TH ST NE 58623
PH 701 523-4767 FAX 701 523-4784
WWW.DOUBLEEE.COM
CARLA ADKISSON CARLA@DOUBLEEE.COM
WESTHOPE,ND & MONTANA (DOUBLE EE SVC,INC)
OFFICE - PO BOX 3,CORNER OF 1ST & 1ST W
58793 PH 701 245-6651 FAX 701 245-6652
WWW.DOUBLEEE.COM
MARK ELLIOTT
WILLISTON,ND & MONTANA (DOUBLE EE SERVICE
INC) OFFICE - PO BOX 2417,2210 4TH AVE W
58802-2417 PH 701 572-2332
PH 800 932-8803 FAX 701 572-8387
WWW.DOUBLEEE.COM R2D2@DOUBLEEE.COM
RUSS EVITT
OKLAHOMA CITY,OK & KS (SALES & SVC)
OFFICE - 8 NORTHWEST 42ND ST 73118

PH 405 525-6604 FAX 405 525-5630
WEB:YOU ARE HERE INFO@KIMRAY.COM
JIM WELLS
CORPUS CHRISTI,TX SOUTH & EAST TX
(SALES & SVC) OFFICE - 721 HIGH STARR DR
78408-2512 PH 361 884-5770
PH 361 244-0713 FAX 361 884-5771
MARK DRAGOO MDRAGOO@KIMRAY.COM
CONROE,TX SOUTH & E TX (SALES & SVC)
OFFICE - 11133 I-45 SOUTH STE A
77304-4892 PH 936 441-2468
PH 936 441-2468 FAX 936 441-5778
RICHARD HARTLEY RHARTLEY@KIMRAY.COM
KILGORE,TX SOUTH & EAST TX (SALES &
SVC) OFFICE - 208 N HWY 42 75662-5020
PH 903 988-2468 903 714-6991
FAX 903 988-2021
RALPH MESSER RMESSER@KIMRAY.COM
ODESSA,TX SOUTH,EAST & WEST TX
(CONTROL EQUIPMENT,INC) OFFICE -
PO BOX 1152,2311 E 2ND ST 79760
PH 432 332-1438 FAX 432 332-7205
WWW.CEITEXAS.COM
STACY THATCHER THATCHER@CEITEXAS.COM
CLEBURNE,TX (CONTROL EQUIPMENT,INC)
OFFICE - 1655 S MAIN 76033
PH 817 202-0842 FAX 817 202-8996
WWW.CEITEXAS.COM
MICHAEL ATCHLEY MATCHLEY@CEITEXAS.COM
PAMPA,TX SOUTH & EAST TX (CONTROL EQUIP-
MENT,INC) OFFICE - PO BOX 1836
1301 N PRICE RD 79065
PH 806 669-7444 FAX 806 669-7445
WWW.CEITEXAS.COM
HAL WEST
WICHITA FALLS,TX SOUTH & EAST TX
(CONTROL EQUIPMENT,INC) OFFICE -
4511 JACKSBORO HWY 76302
PH 940 767-5841 FAX 940 767-4301
WWW.CEITEXAS.COM
SCOTT MCNEELY
VERNAL,UT (OIL & GAS EQUIP) OFFICE -
847 SOUTH 1500 EAST 84078
PH 435 789-3556 FAX 435 789-7009
WWW.OGEQUIP.COM
CARMAN DAVID CDAVID@OGEQUIP.COM
FORT MORGAN,CO (ROCKY MTN OILFIELD
WAREHOUSE) OFFICE - 5098 E BURLINGTON
80701 PH 970 768-7799 FAX 970 867-5778
JACK HORTON JACKH@RMOW.COM
CASPER,WY NORTHERN CO (RKY MTN OILFIELD
WAREHOUSE) OFFICE - 414 S ELM 82601
PH 307 266-2260 FAX 307 266-2261
RKYMTN1@RMOW.COM
FLIP COOPER
ROCK SPRINGS,WY-NORTHERN CO (RKY MTN
OILFIELD WAREHOUSE) OFFICE - 2901
KILLPECKER DR 82901 PH 307 382-2076
FAX 307 382-2083
KEVIN WRIGHT KEVINW@RMOW.COM

KINCHELOE JESSE M,CONSULTING GEOL
100 LANDON LN
CAMPBELLSVILLE,KY 42718-1649
PH 270 789-2886 FAX 270 465-8402

KINDEE OIL & GAS LOUISIANA,LLC
800 WILCREST STE 214

HOUSTON,TX 77042
PH 713 334-2830 FAX 713 334-1830
STEPHEN GRAVES,MNGNG DIR
GEORGE PLACKE,PE

KINDEE OIL & GAS TEXAS,LLC
800 WILCREST STE 214
HOUSTON,TX 77042
PH 713 334-2830 FAX 713 334-1830
STEPHEN GRAVES,MNGNG DIR
GEORGE PLACKE,PE

KINDER MORGAN
500 DALLAS ST STE 1000
HOUSTON,TX 77002 PH 713 369-9000
WWW.KINDERMORGAN.COM

- CO2 MARKETING -
DOUG MCMURREY (KINDER MORGAN CO2 CO)
PH 713 369-9159
BILL STOKES (KINDER MORGAN TREATING)
PH 713 369-8515
- NATURAL GAS PIPELINE MARKETING -
JAMES BRETT,CENTRAL REGION (NGPL,MEP,
KM LOUISIANA) PH 630 725-3040
NORMAN HOLMES,EAST REGION PH 205 325-7401
WILL BROWN,WEST REGION (TRANSCOLORADO,
CIG,RUBY,WIC,WYCO & YOUNG GAS STORAGE)
PH 719 520-4250
GREG RUBEN,WEST REGION (EPNG/MOJAVE)
PH 719 520-4870
RENE JAGOT,MIDSTREAM PH 713 369-9242
- PRODUCT PIPELINES MARKETING -
KAREN KABIN (COCHIN & CYPRESS)
PH 713 369-9268
JEFF KABIN (TRANSMIX) PH 713 369-8567
JIM KEHLET (PACIFIC OPERATIONS)
PH 714 560-4773
KEVIN MOSS (PLANTATION PIPELINE)
PH 713 369-8015
JIM LELIO (CENTRAL FLORIDA PIPELINE &
KINDER MORGAN SE TERMINALS
PH 713 369-8733
PETE DITO (PRODUCTS PIPELINES TARIFFS)
PH 714 560-4780
DEE PANZA (KINDER MORGAN TERMINALS)
PH 713 369-8758

- KINDER MORGAN - CANADA -
CALGARY,ALBERTA,CANADA OFFICE - 300 5TH
AVE SW STE,2700 T2P 5J2 PH 403 514-6400
PH 800 535-7219 FAX 403 514-6401
EXTERNALRELATIONS@KINDERMORGAN.COM
ANDREW GALARNYK,DIR EXTERNAL RELS
ANDY_GALARNYK@KINDERMORGAN.COM
PH 403 514-6536
LEXA HOBENSHIELD,MGR EXTERNAL RELS
LEXA_HOBENSHIELD@KINDERMORGAN.COM
PH 604 268-3013
- TRANS MOUNTAIN SYSTEM OFFICES -
SHERWOOD PARK,AB,CAN OFFICE -
780 449-5900 FAX 780 449-5901
EDSON,AB,CAN OFFICE - PH 780 723-4425
FAX 780 723-4953
JASPER,AB,CAN OFFICE - PH 780 852-4225
FAX 780 852-5660
BLUE RIVER,BC,CAN - PH 250 673-8321
FAX 250 673-8286

KAMLOOPS,BC,CAN OFFICE - PH 250 371-4000
FAX 250 371-4001
HOPE,BC,CAN OFFICE - PH 604 869-5993
FAX 604 869-2721
BURNABY,BC,CAN OFFICE - PH 604 268-3000
FAX 604 268-3001
BELLINGHAM,WA OFFICE - PH 360 398-1541
FAX 360 398-7432
- EXPRESS & PLATTE SYSTEMS OFFICES -
HARDISTY,AB,CAN OFFICE - PH 780 888-2239
FAX 780 888-2537
REGINA,SK,CAN (COCHIN) OFFICE -
PH 306 949-0555 FAX 306 543-1855
- CROSSING & CONSTRUCTION APPROVALS -
TRANS MOUNTAIN (BC),JET FUEL (VANCOVER,
BC) & PUGET SOUND SYSTEMS (WASHINGTON ST)
PH 604 268-3000 OR 866 268-3001
TRANS MOUNTAIN,EXPRESS,COCHIN SYSTEMS
(ALBERTA) PH 780 449-5900 OR 800 535-7219
EXPRESS & PLATTE SYSTEMS (UNITED STATES)
PH 307 237-5590 OR 800 700-8666
- TERMINALS (CANADA) -
BILL HENDERSON,VP-TERMINALS
PH 403 514-6638 FAX 403 514-6657
CHRIS LLIFFE,DIR BUS DEV
PH 403 514-6479 FAX 403 514-6657
MARK WRIGHT,DIR ENGRG PH 403 514-6498
FAX 403 514-6657
KEVIN JONES,REG VP (VANCOUVER WHARVES)
PH 604 904-7221 FAX 604 982-7113
TIM AYLING,MGR SLS & MKTG (VANCOUVER
WHARVES) PH 604 904-7206 FAX 604 982-7113

KING ENERGY RESOURCES
PO BOX 291963
KERRVILLE,TX 78029 PH 830 285-3063
FAX 830 896-5493
STEPHEN KING,MNGNG PRTNR
SWKING242@WINDSTREAM.NET

KING F B
PO BOX 216
HOMER,LA 71040-0216 PH 318 927-2582

KING JAMES E
PO BOX 5473
SHREVEPORT,LA 71135-5473 PH 318 393-3251

KING R A & SONS,LTD
2020 CLARINDA AVE
WICHITA FALLS,TX 76308 PH 940 766-0084

KING RANCH MINERALS,INC
THREE RIVERWAY STE 1600
HOUSTON,TX 77056-1967
PH 832 681-5700 FAX 832 681-5749
WILLIAM R BILLY MURPHY JR,VP/GEN MGR

KING ROBERT E & BEVERLY L
401 MARKET ST STE 400
SHREVEPORT,LA 71101 PH 318 221-1803

KINGSMILL RIESS,LLC
201 SAINT CHARLES AVE STE 3300
NEW ORLEANS,LA 70170-3400
PH 504 581-3300 FAX 504 581-3310
MARGUERITE K KINGSMILL,PRTNR
MICHAEL R C RIESS,PRTNR

KINLEY CORPORATION
3295 MAPLE AVE
ALLEGANY,NY 14706
PH 716 372-4534 FAX 716 372-0820
JAMES H KINLEY,CHRMN

JAMES L KINLEY,PRES

KINLEY SERVICES,AN EXPRO GROUP CO
10815 HUFFMEISTER RD
HOUSTON,TX 77065 PH 281 977-2600
FAX 281 977-0045 WWW.EXPROGROUP.COM
RODNEY KORCZYNSKI,KINLEY PRODUCT MGR
JOE PALASH,POWER TOOLS MGR
RANDALL DAVID,CALIPER-OPERS SUPVSR

KINNEBREW ENERGY GROUP,LTD
PO BOX 601
SHREVEPORT,LA 71162-0601 PH 318 868-7380
FAX 318 865-7386
GRACE M KINNEBREW,PRES

KINSEY INTERESTS INC
401 EDWARDS ST STE 1805
SHREVEPORT,LA 71101-3172
PH 318 222-7173 FAX 318 673-1417
GLENN V KINSEY,PRES
CHRISTOPHER M KINSEY,CEO
J CHRIS COLVIN,CFO
MALISSA F BLACKBURN,LDMN
LANDGIRL@KINSEYINC.COM
LAWRENCE RUSSO,GEN COUNSEL
LLOYD BROWN,CIO

KINZUA ENERGY DEVELOPMENT CO (KEDCO)
170 FAUBEL ST
SARASOTA,FL 34242
PH 941 349-6000 FAX 941 866-2610
TJGEORGE1@EARTHLINK.NET
THOMAS J GEORGE,PRES

KIRBY INLAND MARINE,INC
BARGE TRANSPORTATION COMPANY
PO BOX 1537
HOUSTON,TX 77251-1537 PH 713 435-1000

KIRK WILLIAM L,JR
REGISTERED LAND PROFESSIONAL
4313 SPRING ROW
NORTHPORT,AL 35473 PH 205 657-0377

KIRKWOOD R L
PO BOX 47531
SAN ANTONIO,TX 78265-7531 PH 361 224-0114

KITTRELL SCOTT R
121 S BROADWAY AVE STE 708
TYLER,TX 75702-7281
PH 903 593-4592 FAX 903 597-1513

KITTY HAWK ENERGY,LLC
PO BOX 52026,1602 PINHOOK RD #200
LAFAYETTE,LA 70505-2026
PH 337 232-7572 FAX 337 233-3743
WWW.KITTYHAWKENERGY.COM
GUY C ELLISON JR,MNGNG MEMBER
ENERGYGUY@KITTYHAWKENERGY.COM
DAN BLOOMER,EXPL MGR
DBLOOMER@KITTYHAWKENERGY.COM
GREG W ELLISON,GEN MGR
GREG@KITTYHAWKENERGY.COM
GUY C ELLISON,GEOL
GEOGUY@KITTYHAWKENERGY.COM
RONALD GROST,GEOL
RGROST@KITTYHAWKENERGY.COM
MATTHEW BROUSSARD,GEOL
M.BROUSSARD@KITTYHAWKENERGY.COM
JAN CAVALIER,GEOL
JAN@KITTYHAWKENERGY.COM

KLABZUBA OIL AND GAS
100 LEXINGTON ST STE 50

FORT WORTH,TX 76102
PH 817 336-5757 FAX 817 336-5927
ROBERT W PARK,CEO
JOHN R BROWN,CFO
DENVER,CO OFFICE - 700 17TH ST STE 1300
80202 PH 303 299-9097 FAX 303 299-9087
STEVE FRAZIER,PRES

KLAM A FRANK,LAND SERVICES
8309 CEDARBRAKE DR
HOUSTON,TX 77055-4823 PH 713 461-0968
FAX 713 467-0158 KLAMLAND@SWBELL.NET
A FRANK KLAM,CPL

KLEIN MICHAEL L OIL PROD
600 N MARIENFELD ST STE 906
MIDLAND,TX 79701-3363 PH 432 684-8442

KLENTOS EXPLORATION,INC
PO BOX 51555,OCS 126 HEYMANN BLVD
LAFAYETTE,LA 70505-1555 PH 337 232-6377
FAX 337 235-6355
PETE J KLENTOS,GEOL

KLINESMITH LAUDEMAN & TALBOT,INC
PO BOX 6738
METAIRIE,LA 70009-6738 PH 504 833-8900
FAX 504 833-8980

KLONDIKE OIL AND GAS,LP
7720 OLD CANTON RD STE C-2
MADISON,MS 39110 PH 601 856-8883
JAMES O STEPHENS JIM@KLONDIKEOIL.COM

KLOTZMAN M S EXPLORATION CO
PO BOX 3723
VICTORIA,TX 77903-3723 PH 361 573-2416
MARK S KLOTZMAN,PRES
MELVIN KLOTZMAN,ENGR
MARTY RECHTERMAN,PROD SUPVSR
DAVID RUGGS,FIELD SUPT
ROBIN RUSSELL,ACCT

KLOTZMAN MELVIN,PETR CONS,INC
PO BOX 3723,603 MESQUITE LN
VICTORIA,TX 77903-3723 PH 361 573-2416
FAX 361 573-3902

KNABE,TOM
1708 CR 341
MUENSTER,TX 76252-4708 PH 940 759-2884

KNEESE LAND MANAGEMENT COMPANY LTD
PO BOX 62
JUNCTION,TX 76849-0062
PH 325 446-8737 FAX 325 446-4293
CURTKLM@VERIZON.NET

KNIERIM CO,INC
PO BOX 265
CASEY,IL 62420-0265 PH 217 932-2222
FAX 217 932-6059
JIM KNIERIM,PRES

KNIGHT OIL TOOLS
PO BOX 2116
ALICE,TX 78333-2116
PH 361 888-8507 FAX 361 884-0440

KNIGHT RESOURCES,LLC
24 WATERWAY AVE
THE WOODLANDS,TX 77382 PH 281 882-8566
FAX 281 882-8560
WWW.KNIGHTRESOURCESLLC.COM
F P PACO MCLAUGHLIN,SR VP
FMCLAUGHLIN@KNIGHTRESOURCESLLC.COM
BRANDON MATHEINE,VP ENGRG
CLIFF CROWE,VP EXPL

SKIP ST ROMAIN,VP BUS DEV
JIM BIBBY,DIR OF LAND

KNOLL GROVER,LDMN,ROYALTY,LEASES,OIL PROP
527 N MAIN ST
CLARENDON,AR 72029-2017
PH 870 747-5491 FAX 870 747-5491
WWW.DUCKALL.COM GROVER@DUCKALL.COM

KNOX INSURANCE GROUP,LLC SEE
BANCORPSOUTH INSURANCE SERVICE

KNUPKE JAMES A,GEOL
601 GRANT PL
CORPUS CHRISTI,TX 78411-2311
PH 361 852-5955 PH 361 739-2250
JIMKNUPKE@GRANDECOM.NET

KOCH EXPLORATION COMPANY,LLC
950 17TH ST STE 1900
DENVER,CO 80202
PH 303 325-2569 FAX 303 325-2599

KOCH HEAT TRANSFER COMPANY
12602 FM 529
HOUSTON,TX 77041
PH 713 466-3535 FAX 713 466-3701
WWW.KOCHHEATTRANSFER.COM

KOCH OIL CO,DIV OF KOCH INDUSTRIES SEE
KOCH PETROLEUM GROUP,LP

KOCH PETROLEUM GROUP,LP SEE
FLINT HILLS RESOURCES,LP

KOCH SPECIALTY PLANT SERVICES
12221 E SAM HOUSTON PKWY N
HOUSTON,TX 77044-5094 PH 713 427-7700
PH 800 765-9177 WWW.KOCHSERVICES.COM

KOCH-GLITSCH,LP
4111 E 37TH N
WICHITA,KS 67220 PH 316 828-5110
FAX 316 828-5263
- MASS TRANSFER & KOCH SPEC PLANT SVC -
HOUSTON,TX OFFICE - 12221 E SAM HOUSTON
PKWY N,77044 PH 713 427-7700
WWW.KOCH-GLITSCH.COM

KOCH-OTTO YORK
6611 KILLOUGH ST
HOUSTON,TX 77086-3817 PH 800 736-7036
FAX 281 445-7032 WWW.KOCH-OTTOYORK.COM

KONGSBERG SIMRAD,INC
5373 W SAM HOUSTON PKWY N
HOUSTON,TX 77040-6625
PH 760 471-2223 FAX 760 471-1121
WWW.KSISM.COM
CHUCK TUCKER,CHF ENGR
JERRY REED,OPERS MGR
JIM ALLAN,SLS MGR

KONTIO DAVID R,GEOL CONSULTANT
1330 LEESON DR
BOWLING GREEN,KY 42103-1526
PH 270 782-3403

KOONTZ W E,LLC
6609 FALCON RIDGE DR
MCKINNEY,TX 75071-7770 PH 972 984-1811
FAX 972 984-1812 QUICKCO@SBCGLOBAL.NET
ALAN D QUICK,MGR
WANDA K QUICK,MGR

KORBUT WELLSITE INTERNATIONAL LTD
13566 SAN MARTIN LN
HOUSTON,TX 77083 PH 713 896-0369
ROY KORBUT,PRES
LUPE KORBUT,SECY/TREAS

KOREA NATIONAL OIL CORP
5555 SAN FELIPE ST STE 1175
HOUSTON,TX 77056-2722 PH 281 493-1798
FAX 281 493-1774
SANG-GEUN,HAN,GEN MGR

KORNFERRY INTERNATIONAL
700 LOUISIANA ST STE 3900
HOUSTON,TX 77002-2722 PH 713 651-1834
FAX 713 651-0848
BRUCE W PETERSON,SR CLIENT PRTNR

KOSAREK CHARLIE,CONS GEOL & PETR ENGR
208 WEST EVERGREEN ST
BOERNE,TX 78006-2508 PH 830 816-5443
PH 210 413-6652 FAX 830 816-5443

KOSCO ENERGY L.L.C.
PO BOX 2104
TRAVERSE CITY,MI 49685-2104
PH 231 947-4546 FAX 231 947-0171
ALAN J KOSTRZEWA,MGR/MEMBER

KOSO AMERICA,INC
REXA/KOSO HAMMEL DAHL
MFG/REXA ELECTRAULIC ACTUATORS & DRIVES &
KOSO HAMMEL DAHL CONTROL VALVES
4 MANLEY ST
WEST BRIDGEWATER,MA 02379-1017
PH 508 584-1199 FAX 508-584-2525
SALES@REXA.COM WWW.KOSOAMERICA.COM
BOB SASS,INSIDE SLS MGR BSASS@REXA.COM

KOSTRZEWA DANIEL J,IND PROD
PO BOX 2408,716 CHEROKEE
TRAVERSE CITY,MI 49685-2408
PH 231 941-5654 FAX 231 941-8495
DJKOST@AOL.COM

KPMG,LLP
909 POYDRAS ST STE 2900
NEW ORLEANS,LA 70112-4029
PH 504 523-5000 FAX 504 529-1518

KRAFFT, THOMAS D
5406 CROSSWATER DR
COLLEGE STATION,TX 77845-4387
PH 601 856-6676 601 260-0118
THOMASKRAFFT@BELLSOUTH.NET

KRAKER & MARTIN ENERGY
2431 E 61ST ST STE 425
TULSA,OK 74136 PH 918 492-6500
FAX 918 492-6540
STEVE C KRAKER,MNGNG PRTNR

KRESCENT ENERGY COMPANY,LLC
5005 RIVERWAY DR STE 550
HOUSTON,TX 77056-2142 PH 713 993-0000
FAX 713 993-0011
ROBERT BURTON,FOUNDER-COO
BBURTON@KRESCENTENERGY.COM
CHRIS BURKARD,PRES,CEO
JIM MEYERHOFF,EXPL MGR,SR GEOPHY
AMY ROZZELL,OFC MGR

KRITI TE ENERGY,INC
11767 KATY FWY STE 930
HOUSTON,TX 77079
PH 713 655-7070 FAX 713 655-7106
ALAN M CRAWFORD,PRES
LYNN WRIGHT,VP FIN

KRONFELD LYDIA B TRUST SEE
PLYMOUTH RESOURCES INC

KRUEGER RUDY WAREHOUSE
PO BOX 19177,155 COL JOHN PITCHFORD PKY

NATCHEZ,MS 39120-9177 PH 601 445-5921
FAX 601 445-0167
CHRISTIAN KRUEGER,SALES

KRUGLIAK WILKINS GRIFFITHS & DOUGHERTY
CO,LPA
4775 MUNSON ST NW
CANTON,OH 44718 PH 330 497-0700
FAX 330 497-4020 WWW.KWGD.COM
WILLIAM G WILLIAMS,ATTY
BWILLIAMS@KWGD.COM

KTM ENERGY COMPANY
2424 EDENBORN AVE STE 610
METAIRIE,LA 70001-6473
PH 504 831-4912 FAX 504 872-0194
WWW.KTMENERGY.COM
INFO@KTMENERGY.COM
KYLE T MARKS,PRES

KUNKEL K RESOURCES
PO BOX 2336
AUSTIN,TX 78768-2336 PH 512 447-4226
KIM KUNKEL

KUTNER LAND COMPANY LLC
3011 WHITTLE WAY
MIDLAND,TX 79707-5272 PH 817 236-3734
FAX 817 236-3734

KV CORPORATION
PO BOX 51747
LAFAYETTE,LA 70505-1747 PH 337 278-8016
KAY VOORHIES RAYMOND
KAYRAYMOND@COX.NET

KYLE EMILY LAND SERVICES INC
2610 DEATON ST
LAKE CHARLES,LA 70601
PH 337 526-6341 EKLS.INC@GMAIL.COM

L & A CONTRACTING COMPANY
PO BOX 16749
HATTIESBURG,MS 39404-6749 PH 601 264-2100
FAX 601 264-3922

L & A ENERGY,INC
6202 STRATMOR CT
SPRING,TX 77389-4981
PH 281 367-9212 FAX 281 367-6232
SCOTT ABEL,VP
TOM LOGAN,PRES

L & B OIL COMPANY
3405 DEL MONTE
HOUSTON,TX 77019-3115
PH 713 874-0033 FAX 713 874-0037
F R LAUSEN

L & F DRILLING COMPANY,INC
600 LEOPARD ST STE 1520
CORPUS CHRISTI,TX 78473-1601
PH 361 882-7404 FAX 361 882-7076
JIMMIE B MYERS,PRES
RUTH B HANS,CONSLT

L & G OIL COMPANY
DBA JENNY LEWIS RAPPEPORT
PO BOX 2067
LONGVIEW,TX 75606-2067 PH 972 758-8261

L & M OIL CO SEE
CHOLLA PETROLEUM INC

L A B PETROLEUM INC
13423 BLANCO RD,#142
SAN ANTONIO,TX 78216-2187 PH 512 492-5611
LAURENT BAILLARGEON,PRES

L A G CONSULTANTS,PRODUCTION,CONSTRUCTION
P O BOX 7041,BPS
BAYTOWN,TX 77520-7041 PH 281 428-7273
LEONARD GREEN,CONSLT

L C SMITH PRODUCTION INC
WORKOVER RIGS,EQ SALES
PO BOX 1552
CONROE,TX 77305-1552
PH 936 756-6666 FAX 936 539-6992
PH 936 672-4494 979 595-8225
L C SMITH,OWNER

L MECOM ENERGY LLC
PO BOX 460
CHAPPELL HILL,TX 77426 PH 979 277-0615
PH 979 836-7382 FAX 979 277-9320
INFO@LMECOM.COM

L O & L CORP
14427 BROOKHOLLOW #224
SAN ANTONIO,TX 78232-3826
PH 210 495-1600 FAX 210 495-1606
LOLCORP@SBCGLOBAL.NET
JOHN STRICKLAND,OWNER

L S E ENERGY COMPANY
PO BOX 1645
COVINGTON,LA 70434-1645 PH 504 892-0634
J STEPHEN LEE,PRTNR
JAMES C SEVERSON,PRTNR
KEVIN J SEVERSON,PRTNR

L'HERISSON L E DOC ,CPL,AND ASSOCIATES
LAND SERVICES/BROKERAGE
PO BOX 4284
BATON ROUGE,LA 70821-4284 PH 225 343-5713
L E DOC L'HERISSON,CPL

LA CAMPANA,INC
PO BOX 2916
PORT ARANSAS,TX 78373-2916
PH 713 851-9688
M SUSANNE BELL,PRES
ROBERT E BELL,VP RBELL75961@AOL.COM

LAAHNZ CORPORATION,THE
1101 W 34TH ST
AUSTIN,TX 78705-1907 PH 512 918-3042
B C CHIMENE,TREAS

LABOKAY NATURAL RESOURCES
PO BOX 421047
HOUSTON,TX 77242-1047
PH 713 783-1884 FAX 713 783-1183
PAREE S PREJEAN,BUS MGR
PPREJEAN@LABOKAY.COM

LACE OPERATING
PO BOX 921
KILGORE,TX 75663-0921 PH 903 984-3443
HAL FRANKLIN,OWNER
CHARLA ROLPH,AGENT

LACY & BYRD INC SEE
BYRD OPERATING CO

LAFAYETTE EXPLORATION & DEVELOPMENT CO
PO BOX 53561,124 KIMBALL DR
LAFAYETTE,LA 70505-3561
PH 337 984-9211 FAX 337 984-9218
CHARLES J SMITH,PRES
WILLIAM C WELP,EXPL COORD

LAFAYETTE GEOLOGICAL RESEARCH CTR LLC
201 HEYMANN BLVD STE 33
LAFAYETTE,LA 70503 PH 337 233-8197
FAX 337 233-8177

ORDERS@LAFAYETTEGRC.COM
NANCY BROWN,MGR
NANCY@LAFAYETTEGRC.COM

LAFAYETTE LAND SERVICES,LLC
PO BOX 53961,1126 COOLIDGE BLVD STE 211
LAFAYETTE,LA 70505
PH 337 233-8500 FAX 337 233-8584
KARL BOURQUE,LDMN KARLB@LAFLAND.COM
EUGENE LOZES,LDMN
LAUREN BROACH,LDMN
ROBERT GUIDRY,LDMN

LAFAYETTE PALEO LABS,INC
PO BOX 82097,111 PINE PK
LAFAYETTE,LA 70598-2097
PH 337 264-1782 FAX 337 264-1794
WWW.LAFAYETTEPALEO.COM
TOM SHUNICK,PRES
BSPALEO@COX-INTERNET.COM
BARBARA K ALEXANDER,SECY/TREAS
BALEXANDER@COX-INTERNET.COM

LAFITTE EXPLORATION,INC
5611 E MORGAN AVE
EVANSVILLE,IN 47715-2317 PH 812 474-4257
FAX 812 474-4258
RONALD L MITCHELL,PRES
KIRK L MITCHELL,VP,SECY

LAFORET KIM M,INDEPENDENT
3110 WHITE OAKS DR
LANSING,MI 48906-9014 PH 517 321-8768

LAGCOE SEE
LOUISIANA GULF COAST OIL EXPOSITION

LAGONDA OIL COMPANY
146 IVY LN
VENETIA,PA 15367 PH 724 731-0128
JOHN M BEST,PRES
DONALD D SAXTON JR,VP

LAIRD MACK ESTATE
2901 N HENDERSON AVE
DALLAS,TX 75206 PH 214 763-1081

LAKE C W & ASSOCIATES,LTD
PO BOX 1863
KENEDY,TX 78119 PH 830 583-9855
CARROL W LAKE,PRES
CARROL.LAKE@CWLAKE.COM
CHRISTOPHER W LAKE,VP
CHRIS.LAKE@CWLAKE.COM

LAKE OIL COMPANY
1720 RIKISHA LN
BEAUMONT,TX 77706-2631 PH 409 899-5448
1 ROTARY
WANDA L PAULER,PRES

LAKE RONEL OIL COMPANY
PO BOX 179,115 E ELM ST
TYLER,TX 75710-0179 PH 903 597-6381
PEYTON M LAKE,CHRMN,CEO
JAMES J MAZZU,PRES
WILLIAM S BLOMDAHL,VP LAND
DAVID YOUNGER,VP,PROD/ENG
JANET K BOWERS,CORP SECY

LAKESHORE PETROLEUM CORPORATION
PO BOX 53385,230 HEYMANN BLVD
LAFAYETTE,LA 70505-3385 PH 337 235-0590
FAX 337 235-7062 HISECO@HISECOMPANIES.COM
WWW.HISECOMPANIES.COM
BILL R HISE,OPERS
RICHARD W HISE,EXPL & PROD

ANNE W HISE,LAND

LAKEWOOD PETROLEUM
PO BOX 1760
TRAVERSE CITY,MI 49685-1760
PH 231 941-4546
J MICHAEL QUIRK,PRES
MICHAEL W FLYNN,LAND MGR

LAM CAMARILLO & MOORE
2000 SMITH ST
HOUSTON,TX 77002-8652 PH 713 651-9433
FAX 713 651-9852

LAMARKITA,INC
PO BOX 921
KILGORE,TX 75663-0921
PH 903 984-3443 FAX 903 983-2526
PANCHO CORDELL,PRES

LAMB SERVICES,INC
OILFIELD EQUIPMENT SALES
PO BOX 81429
LAFAYETTE,LA 70598-1429
PH 337 560-0230 FAX 337 560-0231
SALES@LAMBSERVICES.COM
WWW.LAMBSERVICES.COM
EDWARD LAMB,PRES
STACEY REAUX,VP
JOHN BIBAEFF JR,VP/ENG MGR
CHARLIE JOUBERT,CREDIT/CONTRACTS MGR
ROY SALAS,CONTROLLER

LAMBERT DONNIE W,OIL & GAS PROPERTIES
PO BOX 5098,103 MILLCREEK CORNERS STE A
BRANDON,MS 39047-5098 PH 601 919-3600
FAX 601 919-3999 DLAMBERT@PETROPROLLC.COM
DONNIE W LAMBERT,OWNER
CHERRY R LAMBERT,ADMIN SECY

LAMBERT E M,BUDDY,OIL & GAS LEASES
100 WELLS ST
LAFAYETTE,LA 70506-6076 PH 318 981-2197

LAMCO OIL,LLC
PO BOX 510, 410 COOKE ST
NOCONA,TX 76255 PH 940 825-3126
PAUL W LAMAR
KYLE W LAMAR

LAMMONS ENERGY CORP
304 STONEHEDGE DR
GREENVILLE,SC 29615-3746 PH 803 297-4298
THOMAS L LAMMONS,PRES,EXPL MGR
RICHARD L BURDINE,GEOL
CHRIS WYATT,PROD MGR

LAMOCO,INC
PO BOX 5098
BRANDON,MS 39047-5098
PH 601 919-3600 800 880-0680
FAX 601 919-3999 DLAMBERT@PETROPROLLC.COM
DONNIE W LAMBERT,PRES

LAMPERT EXPLORATION CORP,OIL,GAS EXPL
5646 MILTON ST STE 413
DALLAS,TX 75256 PH 214 369-6463
LEON M LAMPERT,PRES

LAMSON OIL CORPORATION
P O BOX 52109
LAFAYETTE,LA 70505-2109 PH 318 237-8506
GARY LAMSON,PRES
ROBERT ELWELL,GEOL
SUSAN K MCDOWELL,SECY

LAMSON PETROLEUM CORPORATION
PO BOX 53106

LAFAYETTE,LA 70505-3106 PH 318 233 8020
FAX 318 234-7376
ALFRED LAMSON
GARY LAMSON
CURTIS J MARSE,ACCT
ELAINE POOKIE CURRY,SECY

LANAUX WALTER T,IND OIL & GAS PROD
404 NOTRE DAME ST PH 2
NEW ORLEANS,LA 70130-7906 PH 504 523-1189
FAX 504 523-3412 WLANAUX@BELLSOUTH.NET

LANCER RESOURCES COMPANY
6034 W COURTYARD DR STE 205
AUSTIN,TX 78730-5003 PH 512 481-1775
FAX 512 481-1980 LANCERCO@TEXAS.NET
ROD C ROBERTS,PRES

LAND AND NATURAL RESOURCE DEVELOPMENT INC
3600 WATERMELON RD
204 ENERGY CENTER
NORTHPORT,AL 35473 PH 205 248-6701
FAX 205 248-6704 LANDINC@LAND-INC.NET
STEVEN T WOLF

LAND COOPER B
791 SPRINGWOOD RD
HOT SPRINGS,AR 71913-9214
PH 501 767-9107
PH 501 538-4836 COOPERLAND1@AOL.COM

LAND DEPARTMENT INC,THE
3730 KIRBY DR STE 1000
HOUSTON,TX 77098 PH 713 974-5263
FAX 713 974-2053 WWW.LANDDEPT.COM
LANDDEPT@LANDDEPT.COM
MICHAEL H MANN,PRES,CPL
MICHAELHMANN@LANDDEPT.COM

LAND J P ASSOCIATES,INC
4909 E PERSHING AVE
SCOTTSDALE,AZ 85254 PH 713 271-1567
J P LAND,PRES

LAND RESOURCES INC
PO BOX 51721
LAFAYETTE,LA 70505-1721 PH 337 234-7339
FAX 337 234-6265
JOHN MELANCON,PRES

LAND SERVICES INC
2400 NORTHERN VISIONS DR
TRAVERSE CITY,MI 49684-7034
PH 231 947-9400 FAX 231 947-9405
WWW.LANDSERVICESINC.COM
JOSEPH M HOLT,PRES
JHOLT@LANDSERVICESINC.COM

LANDER OPERATING AND PRODUCTION CO SEE
J&J PETROLEUM LAND SERVICES LLC

LANDHOOK,INC
PO BOX 845,HWY 35 SOUTH
FOREST,MS 39074 PH 601 527-1639
EDDIE DEARMAN,PRES
EDDIE.DEARMAN@LANDHOOK.COM
DIANE WIGGINS,SECY OF TREAS

LANDMARK RESOURCES,INC
CROSS INDEX SVCS/EXPL,PROF,OPERS,PRODUCER
1616 S VOSS RD STE 150
HOUSTON,TX 77057-2630
PH 713 243-8550 FAX 713 243-8551
JEFFREY R WOOD,PRES
JEFF@LANDMARKRESOURCES.COM
BECKY PITTS,OFC MGR
BECKY@LANDMARKRESOURCES.COM

HEATHER BAIN,CONTROLLER
HEATHER@LANDMARKRESOURCES.COM
ELIZABETH WOOD,ADMIN ASST
ELIZABETH@LANDMARKRESOURCES.COM
JOHN AIVANO,GEOL
JOHN@LANDMARKRESOURCES.COM
ROBERT GLENN,PE
ROBERT@LANDMARKRESOURCES.COM

LANDOWNERS INTEREST INC
PO BOX 1060
BREAUX BRIDGE,LA 70517-1060
PH 337 332-5987
DANIEL J REDMOND,PRES

LANDPOINT SURVEYS,INC
PO BOX 1600,611 ELDORADO RD
MAGNOLIA,AR 71753-1600 PH 870 234-6384
FAX 870 234-6455 WWW.LANDPOINT.NET
JAMES LATSON SOUTER,OWNER

LANDPRO CORP
21755 I45 N BLDG 7
SPRING,TX 77388-3621
PH 281 363-4213 FAX 281 292-9737
WWW.LANDPRO.COM SALES@LANDPRO.COM
LUIGI S BALLATORI,PRES

LANDRUM CHARLES C & ASSOCIATES
7245 FLOOD REEF
PENSACOLA,FL 32507 PH 850 492-7414
FAX 850 492-7423
CHARLES C LANDRUM,LDMN,OWNER
RHONDA D WOODSON,LAND ADMIN

LANDRY CYRIL J,III
PO BOX 66769
BATON ROUGE,LA 70896-6769
PH 225 343-1311 FAX 225 343-2841
JLANDRY@CYPRESSLA.COM

LANDSOLUTIONS,INC
PO BOX 53073,714 E KALISTE SALOOM RD
STE C-1, 70508
LAFAYETTE,LA 70505-3073
PH 337 232-8340 INFO@LANDSOLUTIONS.US
WWW.LANDSOLUTIONS.US
RANDY W BREAUX,CPL

LANDTEMP,INC
3730 KIRBY DR STE 1000
HOUSTON,TX 77098
PH 713 974-5263 WWW.LANDTEMP.COM
MELINDA BARTON,VP
MBARTON@LANDTEMP.COM
SUSANA GUEVARA TORRES,OFC MGR
SGTORRES@LANDTEMP.COM

LANDTRAC LAND SERVICES
12540 STATE HWY 155 N
TYLER,TX 75708 PH 903 245-8212
JOE NIVISON
J.NIVISION@LANDTRACLANDSERVICES.COM

LANDWORKS,INC
GIS SOFTWARE DEV/MAPPING SVCS FOR LEASES
WELLS,RIGHTS OF WAY & PIPELINES
2600 S GESSNER RD STE 420
HOUSTON,TX 77063-3214 PH 713 334-3030
FAX 713 334-3828 WWW.LANDWORKS.COM
JERRY K BRAMWELL,PRES,CEO
JBRAMWELL@LANDWORKS.COM
EDWARD O PERRY,MGR,BUS DEV
JULIE M HILL,MGR,PRODUCT DEV

LANE DEVELOPMENT COMPANY
PO BOX 202
YOUNGSVILLE,PA 16371-0202
PH 814 726-9576 FAX 814 723-0987
JOHN E MCCOOL,PRES

LANG CARL D,GEOL
PO BOX 6534
SAN ANTONIO,TX 78209-0534 PH 210 828-2215

LANGHAM PEPPER & ASSOCIATES,INC
5701 WOODWAY DR STE 222
HOUSTON,TX 77057-2245 PH 713 961-4205
R JOHN PEPPER,PRES
JPEPPER@PETROLEUM-ENGINEER.COM
R S STEVE LANGHAM,VP

LANGLEY J C,OIL PROD
PO BOX 204
SMACKOVER,AR 71762-0204 PH 870 725-2176

LANGLOIS PETROLEUM CORP
9495 MEADOW LN
OSCAR,LA 70762-6228 PH 225 638-3242
CHARLES A LANGLOIS,PRES
LORRAINE P LANGLOIS,SECY/TREAS
CARL J LEONARD,AGENT

LANGSTON DRILLING CO,INC
P O BOX 746
SHREVEPORT,LA 71162-0746 PH 318-227-8777
JIMMY LANGSTON,PRES
A W LANGSTON,VP
PEGGY CLINE,SECY/TREAS

LANIER BUSINESS PRODUCTS
6620 RIVERSODE DR #103
METAIRIE,LA 70003-7107 PH 504 733-0455

LANKFORD DRILLING COMPANY,INC
800 S JACKSON ST
MCLEANSBORO,IL 62859-1571 PH 618 643-4092
KENNETH LANKFORD,PRES

LANOCO,LLC
PO BOX 6566
TYLER,TX 75711-6566 PH 903 581-1112
FAX 903 561-7758
DREW LANDES,PRES
JIM ARNOLD,VP
LARRY DIXON,VP

LANTANA RESOURCES,INC
57 PULLIAM DR
PLEASANTON,TX 78064-1530 PH 830 569-5541
FAX 830 281-8120
DAVID A SMITH,PRES
D MIKE SMITH,VP

LAPCO OIL & GAS COMPANY
5315-D FM 1960 RD W #164
HOUSTON,TX 77069-4403 PH 281 556-5434

LAPEROUSE ABSTRACT CO
126 HACKER ST
NEW IBERIA,LA 70560-4524 PH 337 369-9500
KEITH E LAPEROUSE

LAPEYRE AND LAPEYRE,LLP
400 MAGAZINE STE 304
NEW ORLEANS,LA 70130
PH 504 524-5152 FAX 504 524-3321
F HENRI LAPEYRE,JR
LAPEYRE@ATT.NET
ETIENNE C LAPEYRE

LAPIS OPERATING INC
2323 S VOSS RD #525
HOUSTON,TX 77057 PH 713 532-2200

FAX 713 532-2214
W B MCCARTER JR,PRES

LARD OIL COMPANY
914 FLORIDA AVE SW
DENHAM SPRINGS,LA 70726
PH 800 738-7738 FAX 225 664-3217
WWW.LARDOIL.COM INFO@LARDOIL.COM
PLAQUEMINE,LA OFFICE - 57975 JOFFRION ST
70764 PH 225 687-3610
GUEYDAN,LA OFFICE - 701 FIRST ST 70542
PH 337 536-6738
NEW IBERIA,LA OFFICE - 1052 JANE ST 70563
PH 337 365-8584
LAUREL,MS OFFICE - 1253 HILLCREST 39440
PH 800 748-9934
PEARL,MS OFFICE - 982 N BIERDEMAN RD
39208 PH 601 936-8922
PURVIS,MS OFFICE - 343 HWY 589 39475
PH 601 794-6444

LAREDO ENERGY OPERATING,LLC
840 W SAM HOUSTON PKWY STE 400
HOUSTON,TX 77024
PH 713 600-6000 FAX 713 600-6001
WWW.LAREDOENERGY.COM
GLENN D HART,PRES/CEO
P RICHARD GESSINGER,VP/CFO
KEN CRAVENS,VP LAND
ROBERT SWANSON,VP FINANCE/ACCTG
JERRY HOLDITCH,VP EXPL
SCOTT STEVENSON,VP ACQS
STEVE JAQUES,VP INFO SYS
JEFF SHYER,VP OPERS
MICHAEL HART,DIR CORP FIN
PAUL THOMPSON,SR GEOL
JOHN HENNESSY,GEOPHY
DOUG KAISER,PROD MGR
LORI WALTERS,MGR RESERVOIR ENGRG
RONNIE RODRIGUEZ,GAS MKTG/REV

LARIAT PETROLEUM INC SEE
NEWFIELD EXPLORATION MID-CONTINENT INC

LARIO OIL & GAS COMPANY
301 S MARKET ST
WICHITA,KS 67202-3861
PH 316 265-5611 FAX 316 265-5610
M W O'SHAUGHNESSY,CHMN/PRES/CEO
D E LOGER,SR EXEC VP/CFO
E D STINSON,SR VP LAND & LEGAL
NANCY WESTEMAN,EXEC ASST
D W MUNRO,OPERS MGR
JAY SCHWEIKERT,OPERS ENGR
PAULA SULLIVAN,DIST LDMN
JOHN HASTINGS,DIV GEOL
BOB BAYER,GEOL
PAULS VALLEY,OK OFFICE- PO BOX 1052
73075 PH 405 238-5609
L PARKS,AREA PROD SUPT
B BLAKEY,ASST PROD FRMN
MURDOCK,KS OFFICE- PO BOX 84,67111
PH 620 297-3222
ALVIN BRADLEY SANDER,SOUTH KS DIST SUPT
GARDEN CITY,KS OFFICE- PO BOX 1093
67846 PH 620 277-2149
LARRY KARLIN,W KANSAS DISTRICT SUPT
ODESSA,TX (WEST TEXAS/NEW MEXICO AREA) -
OFFICE - 5013 ANDREWS HWY,79762
PH 432 362-0429

M E WILLADSON,AREA PROD SUPT
DENVER,CO OFFICE- PO BOX 29,80201-0029
1675 LARIMER ST,80202 PH 303 595-8030
M W O'SHAUGHNESSY,CHMN/PRES/CEO
REED WEILY,SR VP & MGR FOREIGN INV
ADAM STRUNK,SR ENGR
RYAN P O'SHAUGHNESSY,EXEC VP
G D VOGT,DIV ENGR
J V WARE,DIV GEOL
DAVID THORPE,DIV LDMN

LARRON ENERGY CORP
1070 DUNDEE AVE STE C
EAST DUNDEE,IL 60118 PH 847 836-2000
L BUETTNER,PRES

LARSON ENERGY LLC
E & P,ACQUISITION,LAND CONSULTANTS
PO BOX 498
ROANOKE,TX 76262 PH 972 571-8198
FAX 817 490-0320 WWW.LARSONENERGY.COM
GLJESSUP@JHDPETRO.COM

LARSON JAMES T DRILLING COMPANY
4 AVERILL ST
WARREN,PA 16365-3102 PH 814 728-9427
JAMES T LARSON,PRES

LARUE & LARUE
5521 BROWN RD
OCEAN SPRINGS,MS 39564
PH 228 875-5383
I P LARUE JR,PRTNR
FRED LARUE,PRTNR

LARUE AND ASSOCIATES
6205 ROBINSON STILL RD
VANCLEAVE,MS 39565-8204
PH 228 875-8350 FAX 228 875-8350
WILLIAM T LARUE,CPL,PRTNR

LAS ANIMAS MINERALS LIMITED
4925 GREENVILLE AVE STE 714
DALLAS,TX 75206-4084 PH 214 808-9300
BOND W BEAMS,MNGNG GEN PRTNR
BBEAMS@CHARTER.NET

LASER EXPLORATION INC
PO BOX 8604
DEERFIELD BEACH,FL 33441-8604
PH 305 427-0610
CHARLES LASER,PRES
SUSAN LASER,EXEC VP
GLENDA LYNN LASER,VP

LASER MARKETING COMPANY
1010 MASTERS WAY
HUMBLE,TX 77339 PH 713 229-6011
FAX 713 229-5603
F BOYD CHERRY,VP,SUPPLY & TRANS
CHRIS M FISCHER,VP,MKTG
DAVID H CAVAZOS,MKTG MGR
JOHN H SWATEK,MKTG MGR
JOHNNY H TRAMEL,SR GAS SUPPLY REPR
GAYE SEAY,GAS SUPPLY REPR
RICHARD PINION,TRANS COORD

LASSER INC
2312 E LOOP 820 STE A
FORT WORTH,TX 76112 PH 800 489-3282
FAX 817 446-9705 WWW.LASSERDATA.COM
LPD-SALES@LASSER.COM
JOHN A VANCE,CEO
RICHIE WORTHINGTON,PRES

LASSWELL G F CO INC,SUPPLIERS-FLUE
AND DRILL CASING BRUSHES
PO BOX 262373,7126 KIRBYVILLE
HOUSTON,TX 77207-2373 PH 713 644-4313
PH 800 666-4313 FAX 713 644-0130
JEANNE FRYAR,PRES

LATHROP RICHARD D,PETR GEOL
27134 HARMONY HLS
SAN ANTONIO,TX 78260-5518 PH 830 980-7078
RDLATHROP@YAHOO.COM

LATIGO PETROLEUM,INC
700 MILAM ST STE 3100
HOUSTON,TX 77002-2764 PH 713 579-6000
FAX 918 582-3115 WWW.LATIGOPETRO.COM
MIKE EVANS,DIV EXPL & PROD MGR
ROBERT SPAHR,DIV LAND & ADMIN MGR
JIM LOLLAR,SR OPERS ENGR
MIDLAND,TX OFFICE - PO BOX 10340,79702
JERRY A COOPER,EXEC VP/WESTERN REG
RICHARD L WRIGHT,DIV OPERS MGR
GARY J HOOSE,DIV EXPL MGR
TERRENCE TERRY GRANT,LAND MGR
MARK KELLY,DIST PETR ENGR
HOUSTON,TX OFFICE - PO BOX 2504
77252-2504 PH 713 297-5000
FAX 713 297-5100
PAUL G VAN WAGENEN,CHRMN,PRES,CEO
JOHN O MCCOY JR,VP,CHF ADMIN OFCR
J D MCGREGOR,SR VP,SALES
DAVID R BEATHARD,SR VP,ENGRG
STEPHEN R BRUNNER,EXEC VP,OPERS
JAMES P ULM II,SR VP,CFO
THOMAS E HART,VP,CHF ACCT OFCR
LEAH SMITH,VP,ACQ

LATIMER D GAIL ENTERPRISES,INC
PO BOX 849
SNYDER,TX 79550-0849 PH 325 574-0106
D GAIL LATIMER,CHRMN OF BD

LATIMER SAM W III,INDEPENDENT
5155 WAYNELAND DR UNIT K4
JACKSON,MS 39211 PH 601 956-0696

LATSHAW DRILLING & EXPLORATION COMPANY
PO BOX 691017
TULSA,OK 74169-1017 PH 918 355-4380
FAX 918 355-4392
TRENT B LATSHAW,PRES

LAUREL OPERATING COMPANY,INC SEE
UNION PACIFIC RESOURCES COMPANY

LAURENT OIL & GAS
11 SLEEPY OAKS CIR
HOUSTON,TX 77024-5427 PH 713 464-0299
PH 713 515-0675
WWW.GULFCOASTCONSULTINGGEOLOGIST.COM
SCOTT LAURENT,PRES
S.LAURENT@SBCGLOBAL.NET

LAURENT ROLAND W & ASSOC
1016 MYRTLE PL
LAFAYETTE,LA 70506-3330 PH 318 233-3507
ROLAND LAURENT,PRES

LAVENDER JUNE HERNDON
PO BOX 3505
MCALLEN,TX 78502-3505
PH 956 687-9521 FAX 956 687-8664
JUNE HERNDON LAVENDER,IND PETR LDMN

LAVERTY ASSOCIATES,INC,LEASE ACQ,MINERALS
R/O/W ACQ

PO BOX 394,64 W LUDINGTON DR
FARWELL,MI 48622-0394 PH 888 255-9702
JOHN W LAVERTY,PRES,OWNER,R/O/W ACQ LDMN
JWLAVERTY@EARTHLINK.NET
NORA JANE LAVERTY,SECY/TREAS
PATRICK W LAVERTY,LDMN,R/O/W ACQ
MICHAEL T LAVERTY,LDMN,R/O/W ACQ

LAWBAR PETROLEUM,INC
221 E 9TH ST STE 401 SAN JACINTO BLDG
AUSTIN,TX 78701-2512 PH 512 472-2189
FAX 512 472-2180

LAWCO EXPLORATION,INC
PO BOX 425
BENTONVILLE,AR 72712-0425
PH 479 273-2670 WWW.LAWCOENERGY.COM
JAMES R LAWSON,PRES
AARON LAWSON,VP
RICHALLE NEY,CFO
JACK TARKINGTON,ENGR
VALORIE B LAWSON,OFC MGR
STEVE MILLIGAN,GEOPHY
PHILLIP SHELBY,GEOL
LYNETTE DAVIS,EXEC ASST
MARCIA THOMAS,GEO TECH
RACHEL NUTT,ACCT MGR
GAYLENE WURTZBACHER,LAND MGR
CHARLES WOHLFORD,ENGR

LAWFORD ENERGY,INC
PO BOX 690022
HOUSTON,TX 77269-0022
PH 281 416-4091
PHERL BROSSMAN,PRES
PHERLBROSSMAN@HOTMAIL.COM

LAWRENCE OIL COMPANY
PO BOX 251,801 W 9TH ST
MOUNT CARMEL,IL 62863-0251
PH 618 262-4138
LAWRENCE SADLEK JR,PRES
BARBARA SADLEK,SECY
MELISSA PRAY,OFC MGR

LAWSON & CO,FILTERS
539 PETERS RD
HARVEY,LA 70058
PH 504 366-8742 FAX 504 366-4377

LAWSON ENGINEERING,INC SEE
OAKLAND AGENCY ACCOUNT

LAWSON JAMES R,OIL & GAS PRODUCER
PO BOX 425
BENTONVILLE,AR 72712-0425 PH 479 273-2670

LAWTON WILLIAM B CO,L.L.C.
641 W PRIEN LAKE RD
LAKE CHARLES,LA 70601
PH 337 480-3799 FAX 337 480-2527
WILLIAM B LAWTON,PRES
WILL DROST,VP

LAY BEN R,INDEPENDENT
PO BOX 1391
SHREVEPORT,LA 71164 PH 318 222-4477

LAYNE TEXAS
5931 BRITTMORE RD
HOUSTON,TX 77041 PH 713 466-5001
WWW.LAYNECHRISTENSEN.COM
1037@LAYNECHRISTENSEN.COM

LAYTON ENERGY CORPORATION
2100 WEST LOOP SOUTH STE 1601
HOUSTON,TX 77027-3515

PH 713 590-2820 FAX 713 590-2827
WWW.LAYTONENERGY.COM
DANIEL LAYTON,PRES
J CLARKE LEGLER,EXEC VP,CFO

LB OIL COMPANY
PO BOX 19195
NATCHEZ,MS 39122 PH 601 442-0424
PH 601 870-5007 FAX 601 442-0365
BROCK VINES,PRES
MATTHEW VINES,VP LAND
HALEY VINES,SECY/TREAS

LCVEGAS CORP
10455 N CENTRAL EXPWY
STE 109,BOX 256
DALLAS,TX 75231 PH 469 232-3375
FAX 469 232-3376

LEADER EXPLORATION,INC
11872 WORTHINGTON RD
PATASKALA,OH 43062-9770 PH 740 927-9173
AMY L BURKE ABURKE@EE.NET

LEADS RESOURCES,LLC
2006 AMBASSADOR CAFFERY PKWY
LAFAYETTE,LA 70506-2810
PH 337 981-1657 FAX 337 981-1653
WLANDRYUWE@AOL.COM
MIKE ELLIS,PRES
WAYNE LANDRY,VP
DEBBIE LEMOINE,SECY
DONNA MARQUETTE,SECY

LEAR INDUSTRIES,LLC
PIPELINE ENGINEERING & DESIGN
903 BARONRIDGE DR
SEABROOK,TX 77573
PH 281 326-3530
LAWRENCE E REARICK,CEO,PRES
LANCE JAMESON,VP FIN

LEASEARCH ASSOCIATES,INC
PO BOX 916
MAGNOLIA,TX 77353
PH 832 934-2665 FAX 832 934-2669
WWW.LEASEARCHASSOCIATES.COM
LEASEARCH@REAGAN.COM
MARIE ELMORE LEE,CPL
MAGNOLIA,TX OFFICE - 20555 FM 1488 RD
STE 2D 77355

LEASES & MINERALS
102 ALPHA DR
LAFAYETTE,LA 70506-3922
PH 337 984-6302 ELSTONGUNN@COX.NET
GEORGE W HARRIS,III

LEBEN OIL CORPORATION SEE
KAISER-FRANCIS OIL COMPANY

LEBEOUF BROTHERS TOWING,LLC
PO BOX 9036
HOUMA,LA 70361 PH 985 594-6691
FAX 985 594-5253
DISPATCH@LEBEOUFTOWING.COM
CECIL NEAL,VP OPERS
MARK BOURGEOIS,EXEC VP
RUSTY LEBEOUF,TRAFFIC COORD (DISPATCH)
TOMMY HENRY,TRAFFIC COORD (DISPATCH)
ZACH TAYLOR,BUS DEV

LEBLANC ARTHUR C,JR,CPL,IND LDMN
PO BOX 53877,200 HEYMANN BLVD BLDG 15
LAFAYETTE,LA 70505-3877 PH 337 233-9099
FAX 337 237-4912 WWW.ACLALAND.COM

ARTLEBLANC@ACLALAND.COM

LEBLANC J BURTON
OIL GAS TECH
535 WOODLEIGH DR
BATON ROUGE,LA 70810-5327 PH 225 572-5453
BURTLEB@COX.NET WWW.OILGASTECH.COM

LEE HITE & WISDA LTD
5005 WOODWAY DR STE 375
HOUSTON,TX 77056-1780
PH 713 629-5150 FAX 713 629-5799
JAMES H LEE
GEORGE C HITE
MICHAEL R WISDA
ROBERT J BAKER
SHARON CLOER

LEE J S,PETROLEUM,INC
PO BOX 1645
COVINGTON,LA 70434-1645 PH 504 892-0634
J STEPHEN LEE,PRES

LEEDE EDWARD H
6400 S FIDDLERS GREEN CIR STE 2100
GREENWOOD VILLAGE,CO 80111-4962
PH 303 721-8000 FAX 303 290-8211

LEEDE OPERATING COMPANY,LLC
6400 S FIDDLERS GREEN CIR STE 2100
GREENWOOD VILLAGE,CO 80111-4938
PH 303 721-8000 FAX 303 290-8211
WWW.LEEDECO.COM
EDWARD H LEEDE,MGR
MARGARET ANNE LEEDE,MGR
KEVIN LEEDE,MGR
MICHAEL H LEEDE,MGR
JOHN G LEEDE,EXPL MGR
RUSTY BRUSENHAN,LAND MGR
INES SOLIS,ACCT MGR

LEFRAK ENERGY
1301 MCKINNEY STE 3150
HOUSTON,TX 77010
PH 713 600-6350 FAX 713 600-6354
JON PRUET,LAND MGR
JPRUET@LEFRAKENERGY.COM

LEGACY ENERGY CORPORATION
8017 JEFFERSON HWY STE C-4
BATON ROUGE,LA 70809-1681 PH 225 927-2482
ROGER L HEBERT,PRES

LEGACY ENERGY,INC - A TEXAS CORP
PO BOX 1360
TYLER,TX 75710-1360
PH 903 596-9813 FAX 903 596-9814
STEVEN D SMITH,PRES

LEGACY OPERATING COMPANY
8017 JEFFERSON HWY,STE C-4
BATON ROUGE,LA 70809-1721 PH 225 927-2482
ROGER L HEBERT,PRES

LEGACY RESOURCES CO,LP
OIL & GAS EXPL & PROD
1423 W CAUSEWAY APPROACH
MANDEVILLE,LA 70471-3045 PH 985 674-4443
FAX 985 674-1114
WWW.LEGACYRESOURCESCO.COM
MARK F SMITH,PRES
CARL SOUTHERN,VP,LAND & BUS DEV
BERNIE KELLER,VP,OPERS

LEGENDS EXPLORATON LP
5851 SAN FELIPE ST STE 760
HOUSTON,TX 77057-8015

PH 713 781-6974 FAX 713 781-6980
J DENNY BARTELL,PRES
JDBARTELL@LEGENDSEXPL.COM
LARRY D BARTELL,VP
LDBARTELL@LEGENDSEXPL.COM
MARK BRONSTON,VP EXPL
JOHN J AMORUSO,CPG,VP
LIZ POWELL,GEOL
JAMES BARTELL,NEW VENTURES
L JEWEL DUPAS,ADMIN MGR
LDUPAS@LEGENDSEXPL.COM
CORALEE HOWSE,ACCT MGR
CHOWSE@LEGENDSEXPL.COM

LEGER PRODUCTION COMPANY,INC
P O BOX 310
HAMSHIRE,TX 77622-0310 PH 409 296-9611
ALLEN R LEGER,PRES

LEGGETTE BRASHEARS & GRAHAM INC
INVESTIGATION & REMEDIATION/ENV,CIVIL ENG
4 RESEARCH DR STE 301
SHELTON,CT 06484-6242 PH 203 944-5000
WWW.LBGWEB.COM INFO@LBGHQ.COM
JOHN NASO JR,PRES
WILLIAM BECKMAN,SR VP
J KEVIN POWERS,SR VP
FRANK GETCHELL,SR VP
W JOHN SEIFERT,SR VP
ROBERT GOOD JR,SR VP
TIMOTHY KENYON,SR VP
THOMAS CUSACK,SR VP
DAVID TERRY,SR VP
MATTHEW PERAMAKI,SR VP
MICHAEL MANOLAKAS,SR VP
JAMES BEACH,SR VP
KIMBERLY BLOMKER,SR VP
JOHN BENVEGNA,VP
FARMINGTON,CT OFFICE - 6 EXECUTIVE DR
STE 109,06032 PH 860 678-0404
TAMPA,FL OFFICE - 10014 N DALE MABRY HWY
STE 205,33618 PH 813 968-5882
N KANSAS CITY,MO OFFICE - 405 E 19TH AVE
STE A2,64116 PH 816 421-7766
SIOUX FALLS,SD OFFICE - 140 E HINKS LN
STE 126,57104 PH 605 334-6000
WETMORE,MI OFFICE - E9573 MAPLE RIDGE CT
49895 PH 906 387-1966
WHITE PLAINS,NY OFFICE - 110 CORPORATE
PARK DR STE 112,10604 PH 914 694-5711
UPPER SADDLE RIVER,NJ OFFICE-
600 E CRESENT RD STE 200,07458
PH 201 818-0700
MADISON,WI OFFICE - 6409 ODANA RD,STE C
53719 PH 608 441-5544
FREEPORT,IL OFFICE - 773 W LINCOLN BLVD
STE 102,61032 PH 815 297-8888
W CHESTER,PA OFFICE-901 S BOLMAR ST STE B
19380 PH 610 430-7764
ST PAUL,MN OFFICE - 8 PINE TREE DR
STE 250,55112 PH 651 490-1405
AUSTIN,TX OFFICE - 1101 S CAPITAL OF
TEXAS HWY STE B-220,78746 PH 512 327-9640
HOUSTON,TX OFFICE - 11111 KATY FWY
STE 850,77079 PH 713 468-8600
COLUMBUS,OH OFFICE - 104 MILL ST,STE I
43230 PH 614 416-9100
ADDISON,TX OFFICE - 15305 N DALLAS PKWY

STE 300,75001 PH 972 715-2049
SAN ANTONIO,TX OFFICE -12702 TOEPPERWEIN
STE 212,78233 PH 210 590-1331
HOUSTON,TX OFFICE - 650 N SAM HOUSTON
PKWY E STE 313,77060 PH 281 913-1938
BURLINGTON,ND OFFICE - 511 VALLEY AVE
58722 PH 701 839-8001
HANCOCK,MI OFFICE - 200 MICHIGAN ST
49930 PH 906 370-6028
DULUTH,MN OFFICE - 302 W SUPERIOR STE 70
LONSDALE BLDG,55802 PH 218 336-2280
AUSTIN,TX OFFICE - 13740 RESEARCH BLVD
STE Q2,78750 PH 512 219-9991
ORLANDO,FL OFFICE - 1425 CHATFIELD PLACE
32814,PH 407 228-2829

LEHNERTZ-FAULKNER,INC
3300 S BROADWAY AVE,STE 103
TYLER,TX 75701 PH 903 592-3311
FAX 903 592-1339
BRUCE C FAULKNER,PRES
LYNN JONES,OFC MGR

LEMARCO OPERATING,INC
800 BERING STE 150
HOUSTON,TX 77057 PH 713 782-5847
FAX 713 782-9967
JOSEPH R FRAZIER,PE
GILBERT X HERNANDEZ,GEOL
GREGG B MARTINEZ,GEOPHY

LEMARIE LOUIS E,GEOL
2 YOSEMITE DR
NEW ORLEANS,LA 70131 PH 504 393-8659
FAX 504 393-8659 LEMARIE6@COX.NET

LEMM CORP
PO BOX 3075
CORDOVA,TN 38088-3075 PH 901 624-1325

LEMOINE D J ENTERPRISE,INC
2006 AMBASSADOR CAFFERY PKWY
LAFAYETTE,LA 70506-2810 PH 337 983-0344
FAX 337 981-1653 DJLEMOINE@AOL.COM

LEMON CREEK OIL & GAS,LTD
PO BOX 192199
DALLAS,TX 75219-2199
PH 214 443-0553 FAX 214 528-8060
EDWARD J HUTLAS,MNGNG MEMBER

LEMONS MARC D,IND PETR LDMN
8207 ROBERT E LEE DR
TYLER,TX 75703-4862
PH 903 520-7311 903 561-6484
MLEMONS@PRODIGY.NET

LEONARD GARY,PETR LDMN,CPL
400 TRAVIS ST STE 809
SHREVEPORT,LA 71101-3111 PH 318 222-9555
FAX 318 227-9762

LEROY 2000,LLC
PO BOX 192199
DALLAS,TX 75219-2199
PH 214 443-0553 FAX 214 528-8060
EDWARD J HUTLAS,MNGNG MEMBER

LERRO ASSOCIATES
OIL & GAS INTEREST DEVELOPMENT
PO BOX 27888
FRESNO,CA 95729-7888 PH 559 799-4179
FAX 559 326-7721 TRANSPORTGAS.COM
PAUL W LERRO,OWNER

LESCO CONSULTING INC
2211 CHERRYTREE RIDGE LANE

HOUSTON,TX 77062 PH 832 654-1750
FAX 281 488-3733
WALTON C HUFF,PRES
WCHUFF1@SBCGLOBAL.NET

LESSER PAUL,GEOL
9660 HILLCROFT ST STE 200 B
HOUSTON,TX 77096 PH 713 772-4340
FAX 713 334-3623 PAULLESSER@EARTHLINK.NET

LETCO OIL & GAS INC
10985 HWY 36 N
BRENHAM,TX 77833 PH 979 451-1706
ROSS L MARTELLA III,PRES

LEVINE DEVELOPMENT CO INC,OIL PROD
1169 HAYNESVILLE RD
REYNOLDS STA,KY 42368 PH 270 276-5671
SYD H LEVINE,PRES

LEWIS H C OIL COMPANY
P O BOX 649,HWY 52 N
WELCH,WV 24801-0649 PH 304 436-2148
H C LEWIS JR,PRES
H C LEWIS III,VP
DEBRA L LAWSON,SECY

LEWIS H GUINN,III,OIL OPR
PO BOX 12663
PENSACOLA,FL 32591
PH 850 512 8428 PH 850 549-3823
H GUINN LEWIS,III
CHUCK GUINN LEWIS
CG.LEWIS@ME.COM

LEWIS OIL CORPORATION
PO BOX 12663
PENSACOLA,FL 32591
PH 850 512-8428 PH 850 549 3823
H GUINN LEWIS III,PRES
CHUCK GUINN LEWIS,VP CG.LEWIS@ME.COM
SCOTT C BRADY,SECY

LEWIS OIL PROPERTIES LTD
PO BOX 12663
PENSACOLA,FL 32591
PH 850 512-8428 PH 850 549-3823
H GUINN LEWIS,MNGNG GEN PRTNR
JACK W LEWIS,GEN PRTNR
CHUCK GUINN LEWIS,GEN PRTNR
CG.LEWIS@ME.COM
SCOTT C BRADY,SECY

LG&E NATURAL GATHERING & PROCESSING SEE
CONOCO,INC

LIBERDA ROLAND D,PETR GEOL
PO BOX 52241,OCS 133 S AUDUBON BLVD
LAFAYETTE,LA 70505-2241 PH 337 235-5288
GINGER BLANCHET,OFC MGR

LIBERTY HEAD PETROLEUM,INC
7551 CALLAGHAN RD STE 360
SAN ANTONIO,TX 78229 PH 210 341-6681
R W JONES JR,PRES

LIBERTY OIL & GAS CORP
P O BOX 542
OLNEY,IL 62450-0542 PH 618 393-2124

LIGHT WALTER SCOTT
PO BOX 6598
SAN ANTONIO,TX 78209 PH 210 828-6203
FAX 210 828-6204 LIGHTNINGOIL@AOL.COM

LIGHTHOUSE EXPLORATION LP
600 LEOPARD ST STE 1022
CORPUS CHRISTI,TX 78401 PH 361 693-4001
GREG@LIGHTHOUSEEXPLORATION.COM

GREGORY W GARBE,PE,PRES
BOWEN W WATERS,PE,VP
RETT FISHER,PG,GEOPHY MGR

LIGHTNING ELIMINATION SYSTEMS (LES)
OIL FIELD LIGHTNING & SURGE SUPPRESSION
17574 HARD HAT DR STE 5
COVINGTON,LA 70435 PH 504 915-1914
FAX 985 643-9268 WWW.NOLIGHTNING.COM
ROBERT MORRIS,PRES
TERRY CHARRIER,ENGR
BENJAMIN HEARST,SLS CONSLT
BHEARST@NOLIGHTNING.COM

LIGHTNING OIL COMPANY
PO BOX 6598
SAN ANTONIO,TX 78209-0598 PH 210 828-6203
FAX 210 828-6204 LIGHTNINGOIL@AOL.COM
WALTER SCOTT LIGHT,PRES

LINCOLN PETROLEUM RESOURCES CORP SEE
PREMIER ENERGY LLC

LIND GEOPHYSICAL CO
PO BOX 1523
CONROE,TX 77305-1523 PH 936 264-1300
FAX 936 264-1307
L W LIND,OWNER

LINDBERG SALES INC
2019 WHITE OAK LN
HIGHLAND,IN 46322-3543 PH 708 758-1500
FAX 708 758-1550
HIGHLAND,IN OFFICE - 2019 WHITE OAK LN
46322
SCOTT C LINDBERG

LINDENMUTH & ASSOCIATES,INC
510 HEARN ST STE 200
AUSTIN,TX 78703-4516 PH 512 322-9779
PH 512 322-9810 FAX 512 499-0829
GLINDENMUTH@LLBCOMPANY.COM
GERALD S LINDENMUTH,PRTNR
JUSTIN LYNCH,PRTNR
PAUL BULLER,PRTNR
TIM KIRBY,PRTNR
GORDON DEEN,PRTNR

LINDER ENERGY COMPANY
1800 CAROL SUE AVE STE 6
GRETNA,LA 70056-4114 PH 504 392-2004

LINDER OIL COMPANY,A PARTNERSHIP
106 PARK PL STE 200
COVINGTON,LA 70433-6102 PH 985 898-2503
FAX 985 898-2509

LINDON EXPLORATION CO
7 SWITCHBUD PL C192 STE 307
THE WOODLANDS,TX 77380-3707
PH 281 367-9091
WWW.LINDONEXPLORATION.COM
THOMAS R WITTICK,PRES
TOM-WITTICK@SBCGLOBAL.NET
MARTHA WITTICK,VP FIN

LINDSEY RESOURCES,LLC N.L.L.
333 WILDER PLACE
SHREVEPORT,LA 71104-4527 PH 318 861-3288

LINK ENERGY LIMITED PARTNERSHIP SEE
PLAINS MARKETING,LP

LINN ENERGY,LLC
600 TRAVIS ST STE 5100
HOUSTON,TX 77002 PH 281 840-4000
MARK ELLIS,PRES & CEO
KOLJA ROCKOV,EXEC VP & CFO

DAVID ROTTINO,SR VP & CAO
ARDEN WALKER,SR VP & COO
TOM EMMONS,VP HR & EHS
MARK CAHILL,VP MKTG
CLAY JEANSONNE,VP INVESTOR RELATIONS
JAMIN MCNEIL,VP MID-CONT SHALLOW OPERS &
CALIFORNIA
BORGER,TX OFFICE - PH 806 274-6331
BREA,CA OFFICE - PH 714 257-1600
CISNE,IL OFFICE - PH 618 673-2781
COAHOMA,TX OFFICE - PH 432 270-3673
ELK CITY,OK OFFICE - PH 580 243-1050
FAIRFAX,OK OFFICE - PH 918 642-1285
HOMER,LA OFFICE - PH 318 353-6606
HOMINY,OK OFFICE - PH 918 885-6060
KINGFISHER,OK OFFICE - PH 405 375-6065
LEWISTON,MI OFFICE - PH 989 786-7592
LOCO HILLS,NM(GRAYBURG) OFFICE -
PH 575 677-2162
ODESSA,TX OFFICE - PH 432 366-1557
OKLAHOMA CITY,OK OFFICE - 14000 QUAIL
SPRINGS PKWY STE 5000,73134
PH 405 241-2200
MARK OWEN,VP MID-CONT DEEP OPERS
PAUL DARGEN,DIR SUPPLY CHAIN
RATLIFF CITY,OK OFFICE - PH 580 856-2165
SHIDLER,OK OFFICE - PH 918 793-2001
SYRACUSE,KS OFFICE - PH 620 384-5620
TRAVERSE CITY,MI OFFICE - PH 231 941-7302
TROUP,TX OFFICE - PH 903 842-3590
TULSA,OK OFFICE - PH 918 879-4200
ULYSSES,KS OFFICE - PH 620 356-1237
WHEELER,TX OFFICE - PH 806 826-0030

LINN OPERATING INC SEE
LINN ENERGY,LLC

LION OIL TRADING & TRANSPORTATION,LLC
PO BOX 7005,1001 SCHOOL ST
EL DORADO,AR 71731-7005 PH 870 864-1246
FAX 870 864-1341
DEWAYNE CARMICHAEL,VP CRUDE SUPPLY
DEWAYNE.CARMICHAEL@LIONOIL.COM
CHRIS LEACH,CRUDE OIL REPR
CHRIS.LEACH@LIONOIL.COM PH 870 814-8079
MERRY STANLEY,DIR-MIDLAND CRUDE OPERS
MERRY.STANLEY@LIONOIL.COM PH 432 684-
4210
BRENTWOOD,TN OFFICE - 7002 COMMERCE WAY
37027 PH 615 771-6701
MARK SMITH,EXEC VP PH 615 224-1118
SCOTT MCCRARY,VP CRUDE TRADING
PH 615 224-0812

LIPARI MARK W,PETR LAND SRVS
PO BOX 82285
LAFAYETTE,LA 70598 PH 337 706-8650
PH 337 344-8059
MLIPARI@PENTERRASERVICES.COM

LISKOW & LEWIS
A PROFESSIONAL LAW CORPORATION
PO BOX 52008,822 HARDING ST
LAFAYETTE,LA 70505-2008
PH 337 232-7424 FAX 337 267-2399
WWW.LISKOW.COM FIRM@LISKOW.COM
LAWRENCE P SIMON JR,ATTY
GEORGE H ROBINSON JR,ATTY
JOSEPH C GIGLIO JR,ATTY
JAMES N MANSFIELD III,ATTY

BILLY J DOMINGUE,ATTY
JOSEPH P HEBERT,ATTY
RICHARD W REVELS JR,ATTY
MARK A LOWE,ATTY
GEORGE ARCENEAUX III,ATTY
MATT JONES,ATTY
JAMIE D RHYMES,ATTY
SHAWN C RHYMES,ATTY
BRIAN W CAPELL,ATTY
NICK S WISE,ATTY
APRIL ROLEN-OGDEN,ATTY
PENNY L MALBREW,ATTY
JEFF D LIEBERMAN,ATTY
HUNTER A CHAUVIN,ATTY
BRITTAN J BUSH,ATTY
JULIE S CHAUVIN,ATTY
WILLIAM E KELLNER,ATTY
NEW ORLEANS,LA OFFICE - 701 POYDRAS ST
STE 5000,ONE SHELL SQ,70139-5099
PH 504 581-7979 FAX 504 556-4108,4109
GENE A LAFITTE,ATTY
JOHN M WILSON,ATTY
JOE B NORMAN,ATTY
JONATHAN A HUNTER,ATTY
CHERYL M KORNICK,ATTY
DANA M DOUGLAS,ATTY
KELLY BRECHTEL BECKER,ATTY
JOSEPH I GIARRUSSO III,ATTY
JAMES E LAPEZE,ATTY
COLLETTE R GORDON,ATTY
KATHY M DETERMAN,ATTY
MARK L MCNAMARA,ATTY
HOUSTON,TX OFFICE - FIRST CITY TOWER
1001 FANNIN ST STE 1800,77002
PH 713 651-2900 FAX 713 651-2908
MARILYN MALONEY,ATTY
WILLIAM W PUGH,ATTY
ROBERT THERIOT,ATTY
JANA L GRAUBERGER,ATTY
MICHAEL GOLEMI,ATTY
EVERARD A MARSEGLIA JR,ATTY
ANDREW WOOLEY,ATTY

LITTLE LOU OPERATING CO INC
PO BOX 1255
PORTLAND,TX 78374-1183
PH 361 888-6200 FAX 361 888-6205
LOUIS E LITTLE,PRES

LITTLE TRIBE OIL CO LTD,PETR INVESTMENTS
AND DRILLING PROSPECTS
PO BOX 131928
TYLER,TX 75713-1928
PH 903 839-2800 FAX 903 839-2115
JOHN H ZOLLER,MNGNG & GEN PRTNR
MICHAEL E ZOLLER,LIMITED PRTNR
PAULA J ZOLLER SINGLETARY,LIMITED PRTNR
REBECCA D ZOLLER CANAL,LIMITED PRTNR
MARY K ZOLLER MEADE,LIMITED PRTNR
TERESA C ZOLLER MEADE,LIMITED PRTNR
MELISSA A ZOLLER SYMES,LIMITED PRTNR
JENNIFER A ZOLLER STEPHENSON,LIMIT PRTNR

LIVELY EXPLORATION CO
2450 FONDREN STE 260
HOUSTON,TX 77063 PH 713 840-1905
FAX 713 621-0059
H B LIVELY,CHRMN OF BD,PRES
JUDY WATSON,VP

DOROTHY K WIND,SECY/TREAS

LIZAK GEOLOGY & ENGINEERING,INC
1805 EVANS ST STE 1
NORTHAMPTON,PA 18067 PH 610 262-9120
JOHN B LIZAK,PRES
WILLIS L PUGH,STAFF GEOL
MARION GORDON,CHF DRAFTSMAN
STEVE CATTANI,ENGR
EVANSVILLE,IN OFFICE - P O BOX 4733
1006 DIAMOND AVE STE 3 47724-0733
PH 812 425-2490

LLD INTERESTS,INC
8918 TESORO DR STE 505
SAN ANTONIO,TX 78217-6220 PH 210 828-4610
P R MAYO JR,PRES

LLECO HOLDINGS,INC SEE
LOUISIANA LAND & EXPLORATION COMPANY,THE

LLOG EXPLORATION COMPANY,LLC
1001 OSCHNER BLVD STE 200
COVINGTON,LA 70433 PH 985 801-4300
FAX 985 801-4796 WWW.LLOG.COM
SCOTT GUTTERMAN,PRES & CEO
TIM LINDSEY,SR VP PROD/OPERS
JAY COLE,VP DW EXPL
BRUCE COOLEY,VP FAC
RICK FOWLER,VP DW PROJ
MALLOY FRENCH,VP SHELF & ONSHORE EXPL
JAMES BASSI,CAO
PHILIP LEJEUNE,CFO
RANDY PICK,MNGNG DIR A&D
HOUSTON,TX OFFICE - CITY CENTRE THREE
842 W SAM HOUSTON STE 600,79024
PH 281 752-1100 FAX 281 596-0219
JOHN DOUGHTIE,VP EXPL
MIKE ALTOBELLI,VP LAND
SCOTT SPENCE,LAND MGR-GOM SHELF
MIKE BREEN,LAND MGR-ONSHORE

LLOYD W BALDWIN,IND OIL PRODUCER
PO BOX 1847,1818 CAPITAL TOWERS
JACKSON,MS 39215-1847 PH 601 948-5838
FAX 601 948-5840

LLOYDS REGISTER OF TECHNICAL SERVICES,INC
1401 ENCLAVE PKWY STE 200
HOUSTON,TX 77077-2053 PH 281 675-3100
FAX 281 675-3143
D C WALKER,CONTRACTS MGR

LMP PETROLEUM INC
615 N UPPER BROADWAY STE 1770
CORPUS CHRISTI,TX 78401-0773
PH 361 883-0923 FAX 361 883-7102
GEOLOGY@LMPEXPLORATION.COM
WWW.LMPEXPLORATION.COM
MICHAEL S PEDROTTI,PRES
MICHAEL E LUCENTE,VP,EXPL GEOL
LOUIS R LAMBIOTTE,GEOL

LOCIN OIL CORPORATION
25231 GROGAN'S MILL RD STE 500
THE WOODLANDS,TX 77380-3105
PH 281 362-8600 FAX 281 419-6626
MICHAEL J NICOL,PRES

LOCKHEED MARTIN CORP
MFG SUBSEA SYSTEMS,ENGRG SERVICE
100 E 17TH ST
RIVIERA BEACH,FL 33404-5664
PH 561 842-5261 FAX 561 842-5303
JAMES L WEITZEL,VP

THOMAS DE GROOT,ENGRG MGR
PAUL D RUSHFELDT,DEPUTY/SPEC PROGRAMS MGR

LOCKLIN ALLEN C,INDEPENDENT EXPL GEOL
PO BOX 6337,1100 HEINES DR
TYLER,TX 75711-6337 PH 903 592-1308
FAX 903 597-4035

LODI DRILLING & SERVICE COMPANY
PO BOX 155
LODI,TX 75564-0155 PH 903 753-7251
FAX 903 753-7942
LODI,TX OFFICE - P O BOX 155,75564
PH 903 665-2507 FAX 903 665-3162
DE BERRY,TX OFFICE - P O BOX 390,75639
PH 903 766-3488
J C (SONNY) MCKNIGHT,GEN MGR

LOFLIN JOHN N,OIL & GAS PROPERTIES
162 COTTONWOOD
UVALDE,TX 78801-6811 PH 830 591-9193

LOFTIN GRADY A,GEOPHY
23238 GENERAL GARDNER LN
ZACHARY,LA 70791-6122 PH 225 654-0760

LOFTIS OIL PRODUCERS
157 COUNTY RD 2300E
GREENUP,IL 62428 PH 217 932-2312
ELDON LOFTIS,OWNER

LOG LIBRARY INC
P O BOX 4095,2621 STRINGTOWN RD
EVANSVILLE,IN 47724-0095 PH 812 425-4321
BOB SKEELS,PRES

LOGAN SHEETS EXPLORATION CO,INC SEE
SHEETS EXPLORATION CO,INC

LOGO INC.
1301 MCKINNEY STE 3150
HOUSTON,TX 77010 PH 713 600-6350
FAX 713 600-6354
JON PRUET,LAND MGR

LOGTECH WIRELINE SERVICES,INC SEE
WEDGE DIA-LOG,INC

LOMA OIL COMPANY
8700 CROWNHILL BLVD STE 404
SAN ANTONIO,TX 78209-1128 PH 210 824-6633
FAX 210 824-3553
WALTER J BUZZINI,III,PRES
WALTER J BUZZINI,IV,MGR

LOMAK PETROLEUM INC SEE
RANGE RESOURCES CORPORATION

LOMOCO INC
PO BOX 6007
TYLER,TX 75711-6007 PH 903 592-3667
DONALD P WARREN,PRES
DWARREN@LOMOCOINC.COM

LONE CYPRESS ENGINEERING,INC
13702 GAINESWAY DR
CYPRESS,TX 77429-5125
PH 713 553-6984 FAX 281 370-0684
GLENN SLIVA,PRES

LONE STAR PRODUCTION COMPANY
800 BERING DR STE 440
HOUSTON,TX 77057
PH 713 784-7474 FAX 713 784-7407
T GRANT JOHNSON,PRES
DAVID J DALLY,GEOL
BLAKE P PATTERSON,GEOL
ELI R HUFFMAN,LDMN

LONG & SONS,INC
3751 ELSON ST SE

MAGNOLIA,OH 44643 PH 330 866-3558

DANNY LONG,PRES

LONG G J & ASSOC INC

41 MAIN ST

FARMINGTON,CT 06032-2229 PH 713 461 9931

G J LONG,CHRMN

LONG GEORGE L,GEOL

18314 EDWARDS OAKS

SAN ANTONIO,TX 78259 PH 210 822-0300

LONG ISLAND ENVIRONMENTAL ASSESSMENT,INC

FULL SVC ENVIRONMENTAL CONSULTING FIRM

225 ATLANTIC AVE

PATCHOGUE,NY 11772-3241 PH 631 447-6400

PH 888 EAR-6789 FAX 631 447-6497

WWW.ENVIRO-ASMNT.COM

HOFMANN@ENVIRO-ASMNT.COM

DAVID VIGLIOTTA,PRES

JOHN HOFMANN,ENVIRONMENTAL MGR

LONG JOHN M,LC

823 BIG SKY BND

SAN ANTONIO,TX 78216 PH 210 276-0318

JOHN M LONG,PETR GEOL

JOHNLONGGEOLOGIST@GMAIL.COM

LONG KEITH A,PETR CONSULTANT

PO BOX 820

COVINGTON,LA 70434-0820

PH 985 892-5582 FAX 985 892-5598

OILMANLA@AOL.COM

LONG PETROLEUM,LLC

PO BOX 1813,400 TEXAS ST STE 800

SHREVEPORT,LA 71166-1813

PH 318 221-3516 FAX 318 221-6304

DENMAN M LONG,CHRMN

SCOTT S LOWE,CFO

KEVIN O LONG,PRES

KEVIN@LONGPETRO.COM

DAVID G BENSCOTER,VP,EXPL

LONG RESOURCES,INC

18314 EDWARDS OAKS

SAN ANTONIO,TX 78209

PH 210 822-0300

LONG RIDGE FARM ENERGY

RT 1 BOX 263B

HARRISVILLE,WV 26362-9751

PH 304 643-2791 FAX 304 643-2791

WWBART@HOTMAIL.COM

LONGFELLOW ENERGY LP

16803 DALLAS PKWY

ADDISON,TX 75001

PH 972 590-9900 FAX 972 590-9900

WWW.LONGFELLOWENERGY.COM

LONGHORN INC - CONSULTING INC

200 WATERVIEW DR

POTTSBORO,TX 75076 PH 903 786-2676

FAX 903 786-2696

MIKE CLARK,PRES

LONGLEAF ENERGY GROUP,INC

PO BOX 809

BREWTON,AL 36427-0809

PH 251 867-5413 FAX 251 867-5427

THOMAS E MCMILLAN,JR,PRES

TMCMILLAN@LONGLEAFENERGY.COM

ROGER M CHAPMAN,GEOL

RCHAPMAN@LEIGHPLACE.COM

PAULA PETTIS,LDMN

PPETTIS@LONGLEAFENERGY.COM

LONQUIST & COMPANY,LLC SEE

LONQUIST FIELD SERVICE

LONQUIST FIELD SERVICE

3345 BEE CAVE RD STE 201

AUSTIN,TX 78746 PH 866 777-3869

PH 512 732-9812 FAX 512 732-9816

WWW.LONQUISTFIELDSERVICE.COM

RICHARD R LONQUIST,PE/PRES

PH 512 699-1527 RICHARD@LONQUIST.COM

DON E CHARBULA,PE/VP

PH 512 732-9812 DON@LONQUIST.COM

ERIC T BUSCH,VP

PH 832 216-0785 ERIC@LONQUIST.COM

JOHN W WICKENS,VP

PH 512 732-9812 JOHN@LONQUIST.COM

SCOTT C SHIFFLETT,SR PETR ENGR

PH 325 280-3308 SCOTT@LONQUIST.COM

LISA B HUNTER,SR PETR ENGR

PH 512 732-9812 LISA@LONQUIST.COM

CORWIN Y AMES,PETRO ENGR

PH 512 732-9812 CORWIN@LONQUIST.COM

G TYSON MCCLEAD,PETR ENGR

PH 512 732-9812 TYSON@LONQUIST.COM

CHRISTOPHER B WEYAND,STAFF ENGR

PH 512 732-9812

CHRIS.WEYAND@LONQUIST.COM

DAWN SMYTH,VP ADMIN

PH 512 732-9812 DAWN@LONGQUIST.COM

CONNIE ASTRACHAN,STAFF ENGR

PH 512 732-9812 CONNIE@LONQUIST.COM

NATHANIEL L BYARS,STAFF ENGR

PH 512 732-9812 NATHANIEL@LONQUIST.COM

STEPHANIE L HOWARD,GIS ANALYST

PH 512 732-9812 STEPHANIE@LONQUIST.COM

RAQUEL FOTI,SR TECH ANALYST

PH 512 732-9812 RAQUEL@LONQUIST.COM

MARCIA GOSSETT,ACCT MGR

PH 512 732-9812 MARCIA@LONQUIST.COM

CHERYL DUNN,STAFF ACCT

PH 512 732-9812 CHERYL@LONQUIST.COM

TRICIA HENRY,MGR OF HR & OFC OPERS

PH 512 732-9812 TRICIA@LONQUIST.COM

LORI SCOTT,FIN ASST

PH 512 732-9812 LORI@LONQUIST.COM

TESSA BLACKMAN,FIN ASST

PH 512 732-9812 TESSA@LONQUIST.COM

MARIA RIVAS,ADMIN ASST

PH 512 732-9812 MARIA@LONQUIST.COM

ZAK SOLOMON,TECH ANALYST

PH 512 732-9812 ZAK@LONQUIST.COM

TREY SIMONS,IT ASST

PH 512 732-9812 TREY@LONQUIST.COM

ROBERT S CREWS,PETR ENGR

PH 713 559-9955 ROB@LONQUIST.COM

R COLEMAN HALE,PETR ENGR

PH 713 559-9950 COLEMAN@LONQUIST.COM

PETER W JORDAN,PH.D.,SR SCIENTIST

PH 713 559-9957 PETER@LONQUIST.COM

STEPHEN L PATTEE,SR PROJ MGR

PH 281 773-0728 STEVE@LONQUIST.COM

TADD J BUSCH,PROJ MGR

PH 701 306-8580 TADD@LONQUIST.COM

BEN H BERGMAN,SR STAFF ENGR

PH 713 559-9950 BEN@LONQUIST.COM

MITCH SORBY,STAFF ENGR

PH 701 367-4723 MITCH@LONQUIST.COM

JOHN E PIEHL,SR PROJ ENGR

PH 713 559-9950 JOHN.PIEHL@LONQUIST.COM

CHRIS OLFERS,PROJ TECH

PH 713 559-9950 CHRIS@LONQUIST.COM

SUSAN BROUSE,ADMIN ASST

PH 713 559-9950 SUSAN@LONQUIST.COM

HOUSTON,TX OFFICE - 1001 MCKINNEY STE 420

77002 PH 713 559-9950 FAX 713 559-9959

LOOMIS INTERNATIONAL,INC

HYDROSTATIC PIPE TESTING,HELIUM LEAK

DETECTION,TORQUE TURN/MONITORING SERV-

ICES

TONG SVCS & RACK TESTING OF TUBULARS

PO BOX 6408,100 N RICHEY ST

PASADENA,TX 77506-0408 PH 713 477-7146

PH 800 847-5624 FAX 713 920-2463

WWW.LOOMISINTL.COM

SALES@LOOMISINTL.COM

LARRY C JOHNSON,PRES/CEO

KIRK REYNOLDS,DIR BUS DEV

KENT PADGETT,CUST SVC MGR

- REGIONAL OFFICES -

NEW IBERIA,LA OFFICE - PO BOX 13440

70562-3440,6603 OLD SPANISH

TRAIL E,70560 PH 337 365-7341

FAX 337 364-2332 NEWIBERIA@LOOMISINTL.COM

HOUMA,LA OFFICE - PO BOX 1143,70360-1320

305 MOFFETT RD,70360 PH 985 853-0019

FAX 985 853-0690 HOUMA@LOOMISINTL.COM

JOE PUGH,DIST MGR

EL CAMPO,TX OFFICE - PO BOX 1308,77437-

1308, 2670 HWY 71 N PH 979 543-3351

FAX 979 643-3352 ELCAMPO@LOOMISINTL.COM

ALICE,TX OFFICE - PO BOX 2028,78332-2028

901 GOLIAD ST PH 361 664-6501

FAX 361 664-6526 ALICE@LOOMISINTL.COM

RON MALLET,DIST MGR

BROOKHAVEN,MS OFFICE - PO BOX 4656

39603-6656 1585 W INDUSTRIAL PK RD 39601

PH 601 823-1920 FAX 601 823-1922

BROOKHAVEN@LOOMISINTL.COM

PETE TATUM,DIST MGR

BRYAN,TX OFFICE - PO BOX 1341

1830 ROUGHNECK DR 77806 PH 979 778-1450

FAX 979 778-1750 BRYAN@LOOMISINTL.COM

ALBERT BRIDGE,DIST MGR

LOOMIS RAYMOND C JR,ATTORNEY AT LAW/LDMN

3531 HUNTWICK LANE

SAN ANTONIO,TX 78230 PH 281 374-2102

RAYMONDLOOMIS.WEBS.COM

LORD CORPORATION

111 LORD DR

CARY,NC 27511 PH 877 275-5673

WWW.LORD.COM/OILANDGAS

OILANDGAS@LORD.COM

LOST CIRCULATION SPECIALISTS,INC

PO BOX 2127,14011 PARK DR STE 103

TOMBALL,TX 77377 PH 281 252-4243

FAX 281 255-9570 WWW.MAGMAFIBER.COM

WWW.LOSTCIRCULATION.COM

STEVE MONTGOMERY,PRES

GUNAR MONTGOMERY,STAFF ENGR

RANDI MONTGOMERY,OFC MGR

LOTHROP ED

2121 QUEENS RD E

CHARLOTTE,NC 28207-2729 PH 972 935-2868

LOUIS DREYFUS NATURAL GAS CORP SEE
 DOMINION OKLAHOMA TEXAS EXPLORATION & PRODUCTION,INC (DOTEPI)
LOUIS GILBERT & ASSOCIATES INC
 PETROLEUM CONSULTANTS
 3636 N CAUSEWAY BLVD STE 204
 METAIRIE,LA 70002-7215 PH 504 834-8112
 FAX 504 834-1736
  LOUIS GILBERT,GEOL LOUIS@LOUISGILBERT.COM
  DOFFIE ROSS,GEOL DOFFIE@LOUISGILBERT.COM
  JOE SMITH,CONSLT JOE@LOUISGILBERT.COM
LOUISE DRILLING CO INC
 BOX 467
 LOUISE,TX 77455-0467 PH 409 648-2364
 HERBERT ROADES,PRES
LOUISIANA CUTLER OIL & GAS CORPORATION
 309 LA RUE FRANCE APT 201
 LAFAYETTE,LA 70508-3137 PH 337 264-9074
 FAX 337 264-9499
  ANITA B BERARD,SECY
  CATHY D LABRY,ADMIN
  CHAD J COURVILLE,LAND MGR
LOUISIANA DELTA OIL COMPANY,LLC
 1927 LOHMANS CROSSING STE 204
 LAKEWAY,TX 78734
 PH 512 428-6224 FAX 512 428-6524
  WWW.LADELTAOIL.COM
  PHIL B BRYANT,JR,PRES
   PBBRYANT@LADELTAOIL.COM
  ETHAN A MILLER,CFO
  EUGENE A CARTER,DIR OF DEV
  MICHELLE E GOODWIN,ACCT & REGULATORY
LOUISIANA ENERGY CONSULTANTS,INC
 PO BOX 7746
 SHREVEPORT,LA 71137
 PH 318 227-0181 FAX 318 425-5245
  ROBERT J MOFFATT JR,PRES/GEOL
LOUISIANA ENVIRONMENTAL TECHNICAL SVCS
 PO BOX 3774
 BAY SAINT LOUIS,MS 39521-3774
 PH 318 325-7344 FAX 318 361-3900
  LETS@BAYOU.COM
  AMY KRAMER,PRTNR
  DENIS BROWN,PRTNR
LOUISIANA GAS DEVELOPMENT CORPORATION
 416 TRAVIS ST STE 200
 SHREVEPORT,LA 71101
 PH 318 227-9299 FAX 318 227-9298
  JOHN ILES,LAND/LEGAL
  GENE MILLER,GEOL/GEOPHY
LOUISIANA GENERAL OIL COMPANY
 74360 RIVER RD
 COVINGTON,LA 70435-2214 PH 985 898-2503
LOUISIANA GULF COAST OIL EXPOSITION
  (LAGCOE)
 PO BOX 53427
 LAFAYETTE,LA 70505-3427 PH 337 235-4055
 FAX 337 237-1030 WWW.LAGCOE.COM
  ANGELA CRING,EXEC DIR INFO@LAGCOE.COM
LOUISIANA LAND MANAGEMENT INC
 P O BOX 52408,1116 COOLIDGE BLDG HC2
 LAFAYETTE,LA 70505-2408 PH 318 232-0651
  EDWARD J DAUTERIVE,PRES
LOUISIANA LAND OFFSHORE EXPLORATION CO
 SEE LOUISIANA LAND & EXPLORATION COMPANY

LOUISIANA NATURAL GAS EXPLORATION &
 PRODUCTION COMPANY
 6811 THEALL RD STE B
 HOUSTON,TX 77066-1120 PH 713 462-5581
 FAX 713 462-0327
  TIM EDWARDS,PRES
LOUISIANA NATURAL GAS GATHERING
 COMPANY,INC
 6811 THEALL RD STE B
 HOUSTON,TX 77066-1120 PH 713 462-5581
 FAX 713 462-0327
  TIM EDWARDS,PRES
LOUISIANA OFFICE OF MINERAL RESOURCES
  LOUISIANA STATE MINERAL AND ENERGY BOARD
 PO BOX 2827,617 N 3RD ST 8TH FL
 BATON ROUGE,LA 70821-2827 PH 225 342-4615
 FAX 225 342-4527 OMR@DNR.STATE.LA.US
  WWW.DNR.LOUISIANA.GOV/MINERAL
  STACEY TALLEY,DEPUTY ASST SECY/OFC OF
   MINERAL RESOURCES
  VICTOR M VAUGHN,GEOL ADMINS/OFC OF
   MINERAL RESOURCES & EXEC OFCR TO THE
   STATE MINERAL AND ENERGY BD
  FREDERICK D HECK,DIR-PETROLEUM LANDS DIV
   OFC OF MINERAL RESOURCES
  RACHEL NEWMAN,DIR-MINERAL INCOME DIV
   OFFICE OF MINERAL RESOURCES
LOUISIANA OIL & GAS ABSTRACTING SERV INC
 2315 CARONDELET ST
 NEW ORLEANS,LA 70130-5811 PH 504 522-6599
  BILL T MCFARLAND,PRES
LOUISIANA OIL & GAS ASSOCIATION
 PO BOX 4069
 BATON ROUGE,LA 70821-4069
 PH 800 443-1433 WWW.LOGA.LA
  DON BRIGGS,PRES
  GIFFORD BRIGGS,VP
  CECE RICHTER,EXEC ASST CECE@LOGA.LA
  BEN BROUSSARD,MKTG DIR
LOUISIANA ONSHORE EXPLORATION,LLC
 1003 HUGH WALLIS RD STE A-1
 LAFAYETTE,LA 70508-2528
 PH 337 769-1598 FAX 337 234-2197
  ELLIS GUILBEAU,GEOL
   ERGUILBEAU@LUSFIBER.NET
  DAVID BIEBER,GEOL
   DBIEBER@LUSFIBER.NET
  SHELLEY L THOMAS,OFC MGR
LOUISIANA STATE LAND OFFICE
 PO BOX 44124,1201 N 3RD ST STE G-150
 BATON ROUGE,LA 70804 PH 225 342-4575
 FAX 225 342-5458
  CHARLES ST ROMAIN,ADMIN
LOUISIANA STATE UNIVERSITY,PETR ENGRG
 RESEARCH & TECH TRANSFER LAB
 3516 PATRICK TAYLOR HALL
 BATON ROUGE,LA 70803-6417 PH 225 578-8458
 FAX 225 578-8433 WWW.PETE.LSU.EDU
  JOHN ROGERS SMITH,FACULTY ADVISOR
   JSMITH5@LSU.EDU
  JEANETTE WOODEN,OFC MGR
LOUISIANA TANK,INC
 PO BOX 1863
 LAKE CHARLES,LA 70602-1863
 PH 337 436-1000 FAX 337 436-9602
  S M JORDAN,PRES

  KEVIN DUFRENE,SECY
LOUISIANA TAX COMMISSION
 PO BOX 66788,5420 CORPORATE BLVD STE 107
 BATON ROUGE,LA 70896-6788
 PH 225 925-7830 FAX 225 925-7827
LOUISIANA VALVE SOURCE INC
 101 METALS DRIVE
 YOUNGSVILLE,LA 70592
 PH 337 856-9100 WWW.LAVALVE.COM
  KIRT HEBERT KIRT@LAVALVE.COM
LOUISIANA WELL SERVICE COMPANY,INC
 PO BOX 952,280 HIGHLAND BLVD
 NATCHEZ,MS 39121-0952 PH 601 442-6648
 FAX 601 442-3961 BELLEX@BELLSOUTH.NET
  ALTON J OGDEN,JR,PRES
  JEFF L BURKHALTER,VP
LOUTEX PRODUCTION COMPANY
 18149 HWY 80 EAST
 WASKOM,TX 75692 PH 903 687-4350
 FAX 903 687-4494
LOVE CLYDE E,OIL OPR
 PO BOX 44203
 SHREVEPORT,LA 71134-4203 PH 318 572-8810
LOVELESS GEOLOGICAL SERVICES
 PO BOX 238
 MONROE CITY,IN 47557-0238 PH 812 743-2735
  ERNEST LOVELESS JR,CONS GEOL
   PH 812 743-5257
  BRADLEY E LOVELESS,CONS GEOL
   PH 812 268-0804
   BRAD@LOVELESSGEOLOGICAL.COM
LOVETT FRANK PETROLEUM GEOLOGIST
 PO BOX 69
 ALVORD,TX 76225-0069 PH 940 644-5393
LOVITT R CAMERON JR,CPL
 PO BOX 16161
 HATTIESBURG,MS 39404-6161 PH 601 261-9798
 FAX 601 261-0884 CAMERONLOVITTCPL@AOL.COM
LOW LAND CONSTRUCTION CO,INC
 946 LEFORT BYPASS RD
 THIBODAUX,LA 70301-8502 PH 985 446-1314
 FAX 985 446-3456
  DAVID J ROBICHAUX,JR,PRES
  DAVID C ROBICHAUX,VP
  HENRY LERAY,SUPT
  DIONNE M ROBICHAUX,SECY
LOWERY OIL COMPANY,OIL PROD
 200 N JEFFERSON STE 620
 EL DORADO,AR 71730 PH 870 862-0121
  JOHN LOWERY JR,PRES
LOWRANCE INC
 401 CR 332
 EASTLAND,TX 76448 PH 254 629-3984
LOWRY COMPANY
 PO BOX 84
 COVE,AR 71937
 PH 479 629-5915 FAX 870 387-8265
  DAVID LOWRY,PRES ROLLAND@GMAIL.COM
  SONJA LOWRY,VP
LR ENERGY,INC
 8150 N CENTRAL EXPY STE 1605
 DALLAS,TX 75201
 PH 214 691-5800 FAX 214 691-5866
  JOHN G BURKE,COO
LUFKIN AUTOMATION
 811 WILLOW OAK DR

MISSOURI CITY,TX 77489 PH 281 495-1100
FAX 281 495-6333 WWW.LUFKIN.COM
RON HOLSEY,GEN MGR
ANDY CORDOVA,GEN SLS MGR
ACORDOVA@LUFKIN.COM
JOHN PIKE,INTL SALES MGR

LUFKIN INDUSTRIES INC
PO BOX 849
LUFKIN,TX 75902-0849 PH 936 634-2211
FAX 936 633-3563
KILGORE,TX OFFICE - PO BOX 871,I-20 &
ST 42,75662-0871 PH 903 984-3875
FAX 903 984-2449
ODESSA,TX OFFICE - PO BOX 1632,E HWY 80,
79760 PH 432 563-0363 FAX 432 561-8203
OKLAHOMA CITY,OK OFFICE - PO BOX 95205
73143,2300 S PROSPECT,PH 405 677-0567
FAX 405 677-7045
BAKERSFIELD,CA OFFICE -
2500 PARKER LN,93308 PH 661 327-3563
FAX 661 327-0690
CASPER,WY OFFICE - 610 N
WAREHOUSE RD,82601 PH 307 234-5346
FAX 307 472-0723
HOUSTON,TX DOMESTIC AND INTERNATIONAL
SALES OFFICE - 9821 KATY FWY STE 900,
77024 PH 713 468-7804 FAX 713 468-6880

LUGENBUHL WHEATON PECK RANKIN & HUBBARD
601 POYDRAS ST STE 2775
NEW ORLEANS,LA 70130 PH 504 568-1990
FAX 504 310-9195 WWW.LAWLA.COM
RODGER WHEATON,ATTY
SRWHEATON@LAWLA.COM
STEWART PECK,ATTY
SPECK@LAWLA.COM

LUITJEN CRAIG & MARK,TRUST
C/O CRAIG M LUITJEN
9280 DIETZ ELKHORN RD
BOERNE,TX 78015-4900 PH 210 313-9963

LUITJEN JOY G & D M
C/O CRAIG M LUITJEN
9280 DIETZ ELKHORN RD
BOERNE,TX 78015-4900 PH 210 313-9963

LUKER ENERGY
PO BOX 331654
CORPUS CHRISTI,TX 78463
PH 361 882-6951 FAX 361 882-6966
STEVE LUKER,MNGNG PRTNR
STEVE.LUKER1@GMAIL.COM

LUNDSTROM CONSULTING SERVICE
2521 YUPON ST
HOUSTON,TX 77006-2533 PH 713 528-7142
FAX 713 781-0039
VIRGINIA M MORGAN,SECY

LYLE CASHION COMPANY
PO BOX 4099
BRANDON,MS 39047-4099 PH 601 992-5010
M L CASHION,JR

LYLE ENGINEERING COMPANY
5702 SPANISH OAK DR
HOUSTON,TX 77066-2338 PH 281 580-7546
KENNETH R LYLE,PRES
DAVID RAWLS,ENGR
LLOYD BROUSSARD
BILL BLACKBURN

LYMAC,LLC
PO BOX 1013
MADISON,MS 39130 PH 601 969-1831
FAX 601 853-0923 WWW.LYMACLLC.COM
BOB MCELROY,PRES-LAND

LYNX ENERGY COMPANY,INC SEE
LYNX OPERATING CO,INC

LYNX INFORMATION SYSTEMS,INC
GEOPHYSICAL CONTRACTOR
16420 PARK TEN PL STE 150
HOUSTON,TX 77084-5097 PH 281 599-7226
FAX 281 599-7790 WWW.LYNX-INFO.COM
LYNX@LYNX-INFO.COM
KEVIN ERFURDT,PROD MGR
NEREIDA RUIZ,OFC MGR
GIL HERNANDEZ,OPERS MGR
WILL THOMPSON,SLS MGR
S GONZALEZ,GIS ANALYST
J DANIEL,GIS ANALYST

LYNX OPERATING CO,INC
2100 ROSS AVE STE 860 LB 52
DALLAS,TX 75201-6717
PH 214 969-5555 FAX 214 954-0713
ROBERT S CRAINE,PRES
MIDLAND,TX OFFICE - 600 N MARIENFELD
STE 918,79701-4317 PH 432 687-0084
FAX 432 687-4955
EDWARD (ED) PITTINGER,SR VP/COO
WILL CRAINE,VP BUS DEV

LYONS & LYONS INC,EXPLOR GEOL & GEOPHY
PO BOX 14148
TULSA,OK 74159-1148 PH 918 587-2497
FAX 918 592-4456
TREVOR M LYONS,CHRMN OF BD
PHILIP W STONECIPHER,CONTROLLER

LYONS P M,CONS GEOL
513 CHIPPENHAM DR
BATON ROUGE,LA 70808-5610
PH 318 234-1495

M & B OPERATING CO INC
601 BAILEY
FORT WORTH,TX 76107 PH 817 698-0414
FAX 817 698-0425
RICHARD D MOTE,PRES
CAROLE B MOTE,VP
BOB HAMMAN,FLD SUPT
CHUCK TAYLOR,ACCT
GLENN PARRY,ENGR

M & D INDUSTRIES OF LOUISIANA,INC
PO BOX 82007
LAFAYETTE,LA 70598-2007 PH 800 772-6833
FAX 337 981-2131 WWW.ULTRASEALINC.COM
DON BURTS,VP
ROBERT COPELAND,OPERS MGR
DONNIE BURTS,SLS
CHARLES JUSTUS,SLS

M & L ROYALTY CO
PO BOX 66802
HOUSTON,TX 77006-6802 PH 713 526-8919
FAX 713 526-9108
PATRICIA B ROWE,OWNER
G M MAC ROWE,III,PRES

M & M PRODUCTION
1201 BROOKWOOD DR
EL DORADO,AR 71730 PH 870 814-7627
MIKE MEEKS,PROD

M G N OIL & GAS CORP SEE
KACHINA OIL & GAS,INC

M H C CORP,DRILLING
P O BOX 7405
TYLER,TX 75711-7405 PH 903 595-1341
PH 903 595-4323

M IV OPS,INC
9310 BROADWAY ST BLDG 2-204
SAN ANTONIO,TX 78217-5906
PH 210 930-5220 FAX 210 930-5235
ALFRED J BACON,PRES PH 210 602-2442

M J SYSTEMS
NORTH AMERICAN LIBRARY OF WELL LOGS
RASTER IMAGE WELL LOGS,LOGSLEUTH SOFTWARE
5085 OAKLAND ST
DENVER,CO 80239-2723 PH 303 371-1960
PH 800 310-6451 WWW.MJLOGS.COM
BILL.BROCK@MJLOGS.COM
CALGARY ALTA,CAN OFFICE - 2410 10TH
AVE SW,T3C 0K6 PH 800 310-6451

M J Z PETROLEUM CORPORATION
PO BOX 275
THORNDALE,TX 76577-0275
PH 713 724-0984 MJZPETROLEUM@YAHOO.COM

M K M & ASSOCIATES,INC
PETROLEUM LAND SERVICES
PO BOX 52928
LAFAYETTE,LA 70505-2928 PH 337 989-7200
FAX 337 989-7279 WWW.MERLINOIL.COM
MARK K MILLER,PRES
MELISSA MCGILL,OFC MGR
HOUMA,LA OFFICE - 310 LAFAYETTE ST
70360 PH 504 873-7332

M P H PRODUCTION COMPANY
PO BOX 2955
VICTORIA,TX 77902 PH 361 572-3051
ROBERT E DAVIS,PRES
RDAVIS@UPLANDENERGY.COM

M S C CORPORATION
2323 S VOSS STE 215
HOUSTON,TX 77057
PH 713 783-5080 FAX 713 783-5258
BRUCE M MCINTYRE,PRES

M.S.D. OIL & GAS,MINERAL & LEASE ACQ SEE
DEASON MARK S

M-I L.L.C. SEE
M-I SWACO

M-I SWACO
- HEADQUARTERS -
PO BOX 42842,5950 N COURSE DR
HOUSTON,TX 77242-2842
PH 713 739-0222 QUESTIONS@MISWACO.COM
WWW.MISWACO.COM
- US REGION -
HOUSTON,TX DIST OFFICE - 7151 OFFICE CITY
DR,#101,77087 PH 713 640-3200
FAX 713 649-6901
HOUSTON,TX OFFICE - NORTHWOODS INDUSTRIAL
PARK-WEST 12243 A FM 529,77041
PH 713 983-1700 FAX 713 983-1720
LAFAYETTE,LA OFFICE - 1819 PINHOOK,#205
70508 PH 337 233-1714 FAX 337 233-1769
LAFAYETTE (MAURICE) LA OFFICE -
139 W ETIENNE,70555 PH 337 893-3335
FAX 337 898-9194
NEW ORLEANS,LA OFFICE - 1615 POYDRAS ST

#830,70112 PH 504 524-4516
LAKE CHARLES,LA WAREHOUSE -
  HIGHWAY 397,70601 PH 337 436-7503
  FAX 337 436-8377
BERWICK,LA WAREHOUSE -
  3809 BELLVIEW FRONT ST,70342
  PH 985 385-2660 FAX 985 385-2807
PORT ALLEN,LA WAREHOUSE -
  7271 HIGHWAY 190,W SISTER DR,70767
  PH 225 334-9364 FAX 225 334-9926
ABBEVILLE,LA INTRACOASTAL CITY WAREHOUSE-
  OFF HIGHWAY 333,70510
  PH 337 893-5852 FAX 337 893-2109
CAMERON,LA WAREHOUSE -
  END OF CARTER RD,70631
  PH 337 775-5311 FAX 337 775-5369
FOREST HILL,LA MCNARY WAREHOUSE -
  PO BOX 218,71430 PH 318 748-4718
  FAX 318 748-4706
HARVEY,LA OFFICE - 4300 PETERS RD,70059
  PH 504 368-1414 FAX 504 368-8664
VENICE,LA WAREHOUSE - #9 MCDERMOTT,70091
  PH 504 534-7422 FAX 504 534-9420
GOLDEN MEADOW,LA PORT FOURCHON WAREHOUSE-
  499 A J ESTAY #2,70357
  PH 985 396-2851 FAX 985 396-2237
DULAC,LA HOUMA/DULAC WAREHOUSE -
  9202 GRAND CAILOU RD,70353
  PH 504 563-4413 FAX 504 563-4370
GRAND ISLE,LA WAREHOUSE -
  WALNUT AT BAYOU REGAUD,70358
  PH 504 787-3486 FAX 504 787-2314
THEODORE,AL WAREHOUSE - 7625 DAUPHIN
  ISLAND PKWY,36582 PH 334 433-6170
  FAX 334 433-5435
CORPUS CHRISTI,TX OFFICE -
  711 N CARANCAHUA,#1200,78401
  PH 361 886-3400 FAX 361 886-3425
PORT O'CONNOR,TX OFFICE -
  HWY 185 ON WATER ST,77982
  PH 512 983-2278
SCOTT,LA OFFICE - 6315 CAMERON ST,70583
  PH 337 234-6395 FAX 337 235-5166
BEEVILLE,TX WAREHOUSE - 207 REYES RD
  78102 PH 361 358-0181 FAX 361 358-0712
EDINBURG,TX WAREHOUSE -
  617 W UNIVERSITY,78539
  PH 956 383-1679 FAX 956 380-6771
HEBBRONVILLE,TX WAREHOUSE -
  815 E GALBARITH,78361
  PH 361 527-3264 FAX 361 527-4645
MIDLAND,TX OFFICE - 508 W WALL,#750
  79701 PH 432 683-2065 FAX 432 683-1434
PECOS,TX LIQUID MUD PLANT -
  2120 SCATON,79772 PH 432 447-6576
HOUSTON,TX NORTH COURSE OFFICE -
  5950 NORTH COURSE DR,77072
  PH 281 988-1836 FAX 832 351-4322
TYLER,TX OFFICE - 6401 FM 2767,75708
  PH 903 533-0340 FAX 903 533-0363
DALLAS,TX SALES OFFICE - 8150 NORTH
  CENTRAL EXPWY,#675,75206 PH 214 691-1396
  FAX 214 368-2139
GALVESTON,TX PLANT -
  4105 PORT INDUSTRIAL,77553
  PH 409 763-2249 FAX 409 763-5647

AMELIA,LA PLANT -
  2150 HWY 662 N,70340
  PH 985 631-2779 FAX 985 631-9740
DENVER,CO OFFICE - 410 17TH ST,STE 800
  80202 PH 303 623-0911 FAX 303 572-7044
RIFLE,CO OFFICE - 125 W 4TH ST,#206
  81650 PH 970 625-8326 FAX 970 625-3904
CASPER,WY OFFICE - 152 N DURBIN,STE 210
  84601 PH 307 472-0809 FAX 307 472-3052
ROCK SPRINGS,WY OFFICE - 350 SIGNAL DR
  82901 PH 307 472-7257
RIVERTON,WY OFFICE - 877 NORTH 8TH WEST
  #2,82501 PH 307 856-6063 FAX 307 856-1852
RIVERTON,WY WAREHOUSE - 302 EAST PARK
  82501 PH 307 856-9626 FAX 307 857-2548
BIG PINEY,WY WAREHOUSE - 22 ALSADE DR
  83113 PH 307 276-3051 FAX 307 276-3040
GRANGER,WY WAREHOUSE -
  COUNTY RD 219,#3625,82934
  PH 307 875-5753 FAX 307 875-6240
WAMSUTTER,WY WAREHOUSE -
  401 GLEASON,82336 PH 307 328-1700
  FAX 307 324-6333
RANGELY,CO WAREHOUSE - 750 COUNTY RD
  81648 PH 970 675-2244 FAX 970 675-2245
BAIROIL,WY WAREHOUSE -
  1111 PURPLE SAGE,82322
  PH 307 324-5563 FAX 307 324-5563
EVANSTON,WY WAREHOUSE - 101 MEADOW LN
  82930 PH 307 789-0908 FAX 307 789-3413
VENTURA,CA DISTRICT OFFICE -
  1000 S HILL RD,#220,93003
  PH 805 644-8445 FAX 805 644-8868
BAKERSFIELD,CA OFFICE - 6301 SEVEN SEAS
  AVE,93308 PH 661 589-6370
  FAX 661 589-6112
BAKERSFIELD,CA OFFICE - 7803 SHOFNER LN
  93308 PH 661 587-7787 FAX 661 587-6278
OXNARD,CA WAREHOUSE -
  725 PACIFIC AVE,93030
  PH 805 487-6391 FAX 805 483-0757
OKLAHOMA CITY,OK OFFICE -
  14000 QUAIL SPRINGS PKWY,#5100,73134
  PH 405 752-6900 FAX 405 752-6960
CHICKASHA,OK OFFICE - 110 S RESEARCH RD
  73018 PH 405 224-4170 FAX 405 224-1429
ANTLERS,OK WAREHOUSE - PO BOX 790,74523
  PH 580 298-5569 FAX 580 298-5560
ELK CITY,OK WAREHOUSE - PO BOX 609,73648
  PH 580 225-2482 FAX 580 225-2484
ARDMORE,OK WAREHOUSE - PO BOX 1647,73402
  PH 580 223-1822 FAX 580 226-5409
CYRIL,OK WAREHOUSE - HWY 277 S,73029
  PH 405 464-3552
WILLISTON,ND OFFICE - 410 22ND ST W,58801
  PH 701 572-7731 FAX 701 572-7419
LIBERAL,KS WAREHOUSE - PO BOX 1959,67905
  PH 316 624-0122 FAX 316 624-0163
ANCHORAGE,AK DISTRICT OFC-721 W 1ST AVE
  99501 PH 907 274-5564 FAX 907 279-6729
PURDHOE BAY,AK/NORTH SLOPE OFFICE-
  PO BOX 3400082,99734 PH 907 659-2694
  FAX 907 659-2292
NIKISKI,AK WAREHOUSE/STOCKPOINT-
  PO BOX 6974,99635 PH 907 776-8680
  FAX 907 776-5698

- CANADA REGION -
- M-I DRILLING FLUIDS,CANADA -
CALGARY,AB,CAN OFFICE -
  700 - SECOND ST SW,5TH FLOOR,T2P 2W2
  PH 403 290-5300 FAX 403 290-5323
SPRUCE GROVE,AB,CAN OFFICE -
  39 ALBERTA AVE,T7X 3B3
  PH 780 962-8221 FAX 780 962-4691
DARTMOUTH,NOVA SCOTIA OFFICE -
  55 MOSHER DR,B3B 1E5
  PH 902 463-8015 FAX 902 468-5103
NISKU,ALBERTA OFFICE - 1406 8TH ST
  T9E 7M1 PH 780 955-3388 FAX 780 955-2064
ST JOHN'S,NEWFOUNDLAND,CAN OFFICE -
  410 LOGY BAY RD,A1A 5C6
  PH 709 754-9001 FAX 709 754-9099
- SOUTH AMERICA BUSINESS UNIT -
CARACAS,VENEZUELA (M-I SWACO) OFFICE -
  TORRE HUMBOLDT,PISO 19 OFICINA 19-01
  AV RIO CAURA,PRADOS,DEL ESTE,1080
  PH 0 58-212-9074969 FAX 0 58-212-9074926
BOGOTA,COLUMBIA (M-I SWACO) OFFICE -
  CARRERA 9A NO. 99-07 OFICINA
  301 TORRE 1,SANTA FE DE BOGOTA
  PH 0 57-1-6 51 34 34
  FAX 0 57-1-2 96 09 28
CARACAS,VENEZUELA OFFICE - AV RIO CAURA
  TORRE HUMBOLDT,PISO 20
  20-10,PRADOS DEL ESTE,1080-A
  PH 0 058-212-9074926
CIUDAD OJEDA,VENEZUELA (M-I SWACO) OFC -
  AVENIDA INTERCOMUNAL LAS MOROCHAS
  CALPON DOWELL-BARRIO LA LIBERTAD
  CIUDAD OJEDA,EDO.ZULIA
  PH 0 58-265-6311017 FAX 0 58-265-6315541
MATURIN,VENEZUELA OFC - AVENIDA BOLIVAR
  C/C BOLIVAR,CENTRO COMERCIAL VICTORIA
  PISO. 1,OFICINAS 1 Y 2,MATURIN
  ESTADO MONAGAS
  PH 0 58 291-6421011 FAX 0 58 291-3000157
QUITO,ECUADOR (M-I SWACO) OFFICE -
  IRLANDA E10-16 Y REPUBLICA DEL SALVADOR
  EDIFICIO TORRE XXI,PISO W1,QUITO
  PH 0 593 2 2255104 FAX 0 593-2-2261701
TRINIDAD & TOBAGO (M-I TRINIDAD LIMITED)
  OFFICE - 403 PACIFIC AVE
  POINT LISAS INDUSTRIAL ESTATE,POINT LISAS
  PH 0 (868)679-8200 FAX 0 (868)679-8320
PORT OF SPAIN,TRINIDAD & TOBAGO
  (M-I TRINIDAD LIMITED) OFFICE -
  ABERCROMBY CT,ABERCROMBY ST
  PH 0 868 624-5302 FAX 0 868 624-3254
- SOUTH AMERICA / MEXICO & CENTRAL AMER-
VILLAHERMOSA MCA,MEXICO OFFICE -
  CARRETERA CARDENAS-VILLAHERMOSA,KM 146
  RANCHERIA PLATANO Y CACAO,4TA SECCION
  MUNICIPIO CENTRO,VILLAHERMOSA,TABASCO
  PH 0 52-993-3101590 FAX 0 52-993-3101591
CIUDAD DEL CARMEN,MEXICO OFFICE -
  AVENIDA CENTRAL SUR 5
  PUERTO INDUSTRIAL PESQUERO LAGUNA
  AZUL,CIUDAD DEL CARMEN,MEXICO
  PH 0 52 993 310 1590
  FAX 0 52 993 310 1591
VERACRUZ,MEXICO OFFICE -
  AVE FRAMBOLLANES LOTE 8 MAZANA 5

ENTRE CIRUELAS Y AV. ACASIAS,VERACRUZ
PH 0 52 229 920 82 07
BRAZIL OFFICE - 19 DE FEVEREIOR,N 30-4
ANDAR-BOTAFOGO,RIO DE JANEIRO
PH 0 55-21-30945700
BUENOS AIRES,ARGENTINA OFFICE -
JANEIRO (MI SWACO BUENOS AIRES)
SUIPACHA 238 1 PISO,CAPITAL FEDERAL
CP 1008 PH 0 54-11-50323007
FAX 0 54-11-50323048
SANTA CRUZ,BOLIVIA OFFICE - KM 3-1/2
CARRETERA A COCHABAMBA
PH 0 5913-3531580 FAX 0 5913-3525376
AMAZONICA,PERU OFFICE - SANTA CRUZ
PH 0 51 1 065 267839
PH (011)(56-61)23-1880
TALARA,PERU OFFICE - PH 0 51 073 382253
FAX 0 51 073 384159
LIMA,PERU OFFICE - R RIERA NAVARRETE 765
SAN ISIDRO PH 0 51 1 442 4143
FAX 0 51 1 442 4141
  - EASTERN HEMISPHERE BUSINESS UNIT-
WESTHILLS,ABERDEENSHIRE,UK OFFICE -
(M-I DRILLING FLUIDS UK LTD) ENDEAVOUR DR
ARNHALL BUSINESS PK,AB32 6UG SCOTLAND,UK
PH 44-1224-742200 FAX 44-1224-742288
  - EASTERN HEMISPHERE NORTH/CASPIAN REG -
AZERBAIJAN OFFICE - 201 MURTUZA
MUKHTAROV ST,FLOORS 4,5,6
BAKU,AZERBAIJAN 1065
PH (994-12)497 4213
FAX (994-12)497 2221
LOKBATAN,UTYAZHELITEL,AZERBAIJAN PLANT -
(AZERI MI DRILLING FLUIDS LTD)
PH (994-12)932602
PH/FAX (994-12)933784
ALMATY,KAZAKHSTAN,OFC - (M-I DF,INTL,BV)
132 DOSTYK AVE OFFICE 13,FL 8,050051
REPUBLIC OF KAZAKHSTAN
PH 7 (3272)59 00 54(55,56,57)
FAX (7-3272)590058
TENGIZ,KAZAKHSTAN OFFICE - (TCO LLP)
KARATON-1,ATYRAU OBLAST 060107
PH 7(312)3024715/4717
FAX (7-312)3024577
AKTAU,KAZAKHSTAN OFC - (M-I DRILLING
FLUIDS INTL,B.V.) 2ND MCR,HOTEL AKTAU
SUITE 200-206,AKTAU 130001
MANGISTAU REGION,KAZAKHSTAN
PH 7 (3292) 50 87 73;50 58 98
FAX 7(3292) 52-47-52
AKTOBE,KAZAKHSTAN OFFICE -
(M-I DRILLING FLUIDS,INT,B.V.)
12 MICRODISTRICT,BLOCK 21B
PH 7(3132)23-75-92/93/94
FAX 7 (3132) 548020
ATYRAU,KAZAKHSTAN OFC - (M-I DF,INTL,BV)
48 AZATTYK AVENUE
PREMIER ATYRAU BUSINESS CENTER,OFF.702
FL 7,ATYRAU,060005,KAZAKHSTAN
PH (7-3122)970123;97 01 24;58 61
FAX (7-3122) 586112
ASHGABAT,TURKMENISTAN OFFICE -
(M-I SWACO UK LTD) 1,YUNUS EMRE ST
MCR.MIR-2/1, EMPERIAL INTERNATIONAL
BUSINESS CENTER,BLOCK A ,9TH FL,744017

PH (993) 12445306 FAX (993) 12454861
BALKANABAT,TURKMENISTAN OFFICE -
(M-I SWACO UK,LTD) BLOCK 145
PH (993) 22243143 FAX (993) 22243143
  - EASTERN HEMISPHERE NORTH/EUROPE REG -
FRANCE BRANCH OFFICE - (MI-DRILLING
FLUIDS INTL B.V.) AVENUE JOLIOTT CURIE
BP 205-LONS,64146 BILLERE
PH (33) 559923551/559923565
FAX (33) 559923556
GERMANY OFFICE - (M-I SWACO DEUTSCHLAND
GMBH) GRAFFTRING 5-7,29227 CELLE
PH (49-5141) 98410 FAX (49-5141) 84064
ITALY OFFICE - (M-I ITALIANA,S.P.A.)
VIALE FAMAGOSTA,75,20142 MILANO
PH (39-02) 847451 FAX (39-02) 84745250
NETHERLANDS OFC- (M-I DRILLING FLUIDS BV)
PANNEKEETWEG 17,1704 PL HEERHUGOWAARD
PH (31-72)5763120 FAX (31-72)5763131
ROMANIA OFC - (M-I PETROGAS SERVICES
ROMANIA SRL) CALEA VICTORIEI,155,BLOC D1
TRONSON 8,ETAJ 4,SECTOR 1
BUCHAREST 010073,ROMANIA
PH (4-021)3131328 FAX (4-021)3131378
AUSTRIA OFC - (M-I SWACO HANDELS GMBH)
ERZHERZOG-WILHELM-RING 1-3/TOP 4
BADEN,2500 PH (43-2252) 89711
FAX (43-2252) 42796
  -EASTERN HEMISPHERE RUSSIA & UKRAINE-
MOSCOW,RUSSIA OFC - (M-I SWACO)
4TH FLOOR,BUSINESS CENTER
AKADEMICHESKY ,PROSPECT 60-LETYA
OKTYABRYA,9,BUILD 2,MOSCOW,117312
PH 7(495)4118090 FAX 7(495)4118091
NIZHNEVARTOVSK,RUSSIA OFC- (M-I DRILLING
FLUIDS UK,LTD) - KUZOVATKINA ST
15,OFFICE 16,NIZHNEVARTOVSK,628600
PH (7-3466)410198 FAX (7-3466)410219
NOYABRSK,RUSSIA OFC -(M-I DRILLING
FLUIDS LTD) 49 LENINA ST
(SCHLUMBERGER OFC) NOYABRSK,629840
PH (8-3496)352026,X129
FAX (8-3496) 354286
SAKHALIN,RUSSIA OFC- (M-I SWACO SAKHALIN)
16 KARI MARKS ST,4TH FLR,OFFICE 409-410
693000 YUZHNO-SAKHALINSK
PH 7(4242) 462958 FAX 7(4242) 462960
TOMSK,RUSSIA OFFICE - (M-I SWACO)
OFFICE #404,PR-T FRUNZE,117A,634021
PH 7(3822) 26 38 72
FAX 7(3822) 26 38 72
  - EASTERN HEMISPHERE NORTH SEA REG -
STAVANGER,NORWAY OFC - (M-I NORGE AS)
GAMLE FORUSVEI 43,N-4033 FORUS
PH (47-51)577300 FAX (47-51)576503
BERGEN,NORWAY OFFICE - KOKSTADDALEN 18
5257 KOKSTAD,BERGEN 5000
PH (47-55)529800/30/35 FAX (47-55)529840
TORVASTAD,NORWAY - (KARMOY FACTORY)
STORESUNDVEIEN 390,4260 TORVASTAD
PH (47-52)856380 FAX (47-52)856381
DIRECT LINE: (47-52) 856382
TURKMENISTAN,DENMARK OFFICE -
TRAFIKHAVNSKAJ 7,1 SAL (POB 1095)
PH 45 75 13 00 55 FAX 45 75 13 46 77
COPENHAGEN,DENMARK OFC- (M-I DENMARK APS)

ARNOLD NIELSENS BOULEVARD 68A 1.TH
DK-2650 HVIDOVRE PH (45-33) 116544
FAX (45-33) 116520
ABERDEEN HOLBURN HOUSE,UK OFFICE -
(M-I DRILLING FLUIDS UK LTD) HOLBURN
HOUSE,475-485 UNION ST,ABERDEEN,AB11 6DB
PH (44-1224)336336 FAX (44-1224)336350
ABERDEEN,SCOTLAND PLANT,UK -
(M-I DRILLING FLUIDS U.K. LTD)
GREENBANK CRESCENT,EAST TULLOS,AB12 3BG
PH (44-1224)891418/874403
FAX (44-1224) 897149
ABERDEEN,SCOTLAND POCRA QUAY,UK OFC -
(M-I DRILLING FLUIDS UK,LTD)
POCRA QUAY,FOOTDEE AB11 5DQ
PH (44-1224)584336
FAX (44-1224)576119
GREAT YARMOUTH PLANT,UK -
PH (44-1493)332958 FAX (44-1493)332728
DUBAI- (M-I SWACO EHS) EXECUTIVE
BULD NO.3,INSIDE OILFIELDS SUPPLY CENTER
JEBEL ALI FREE ZONE,PO BOX 213379
PH 971-4-883 1922 FAX 971-4-883 19 39
  - EASTERN HEMISPHERE SO/ASIA PACIFIC REG-
BANGKOK,THAILAND REGIONAL OFFICE -
(M-I SWACO (THAILAND) LTD)
11TH FLOOR RASA TWR,555 PHAHOLYOTHIN RD
KWANG CHATUCHAK,KHET CHATUCHAK
PH (66-2)9370058 FAX (66-2)9371022
BANGLADESH OFFICE - (M-I SWACO)
APARTMENT 104 (LAKE SIDE),GULSHAN #2
DHAKA 1212 PH (88-02)885-1135
FAX (88-02)885-1135
BATAM,INDONESIA BATAM PLANT -
JALAN TOKA,BATU AMPAR,PULAU BATAM 29432
PH (62-778)412022 FAX (62-778)412021
JAKARTA,INDONESIA OFFICE -
(P T M-I INDONESIA) BELTWAY OFFICE PARK
BLDG A,3RD FLR,JALAN LET.JEND.TB.
SIMATUPANG NO.41,12550
PH (62-21)780-6578/4922
FAX (62-21)780-6608/780-6901
KALIJAPAT,INDONESIA WAREHOUSE -
KALIJAPAT V,JALAN KETEL UAP,ANCOL BARU
TANJUNG PRIOK,JAKARTA
PH (62-21)43907962 FAX (62-21)43907961
MIPC CIKARANG,INDONESIA OFFICE -
(PT M-I PRODUCTION CHEMICALS INDONESIA)
CIKARANG INDUSTRIAL ESTATE-JABABEKA
JI.JABABEKA XVII E,BLOK U KAVLING NO. 27A
CIKARANG,BEKASI 17530,JAWA BARAT
PH (62-21)8900305 FAX (62-21)8900289
PERTH,AUSTRALIA OFFICE - (M-I AUSTRALIA
PTY LTD) - 11TH FLR 251 ADELAIDE TERRACE
PERTH,WESTERN AUSTRALIA 6000
PH (61-8)94402900 FAX (61-8)93251897
DAMPIER AUSTRALIA OFC - (M-I AUSTRALIA
PTY LTD) MOFF RD,WESTERN AUSTRALIA 6714
PH (61-8)91856166 FAX (61-8)91856199
NEW ZEALAND OFFICE- (M-I NEW ZEALAND LTD)
88-92 PARAITE ROAD,BELL BLOCK
NEW PLYMOUTH,NEW ZEALAND
PH (64-6)7550037 FAX (64-6)7553300
BEIJING,CHINA OFC - (M-I SWACO (TIANJIN)
ENGINEERING CO LTD) TOWERCREST PLAZA
RM 906/908,NO.3 MAIZIDIAN XI LU

CHAO YANG DISTRICT,100016
PH (86-10)84583396 FAX (86-10)84583315
SHEKOU,CHINA OFC - (CHINA NANHAI-MAGCOBAR
MUD CORP LTD) TIMES PLAZA BLDG,STE 3208
TAI ZI ROAD 1,SHEKOU,SHENZHEN
PEOPLE'S REPUBLIC OF CHINA
PH (86-755)26817755 FAX (86-755)26817756
TIANJIN,CHINA OFC (M-I SWACO (TIANJIN)
ENGINEERING CO LTD) BLOCK A3
NEW SKYLINE BLDG,NO.12 NANHAI RD,2ND AVE
TEDA,TIANJIN,30047,PEOPLE'S REP OF CHINA
PH (86-22)6628 2290
FAX (86-22)6628 2296
BALIKPAPAN,INDONESIA OFC - (PT M-I
INDONESIA) JI M.T. HARYONO NO.129
RT. 84 RING RD,KELURAHAN GUNUNG.BAHAGIA
BALIKPAPAN SELATAN,76114
PH(62-542)874338 FAX (62-542)874339
KEMAMAN,MALAYSIA OFFICE - A29 & 31,GROUND
FLR,ADMINISTRATION BLDG A,KEMAMAN SUPPLY
BASE,24007 KEMAMAN,TERENGGANU
PH (60-9)8631386 FAX (60-9)8631376
KUALA LUMPUR,MALAYSIA OFC - (M-I DRILLING
FLUIDS (M) SDN BHD) SUITE 13.2,WEST WING
ROHAS PERKASA,NO.8,JALAN PERAK,50450
PH (60-3)21617655 FAX (60-3)21617485
LABUAN,MALAYSIA WAREHOUSE NO.1 -
ASIAN SUPPLY BASE,RANCA-RANCA INDUSTRIAL
ESTATE,PO BOX 82087,87030 FT LABUAN,SABAH
PH (60-8)7413015 FAX (60-8)7413016
PHILIPPINES OFFICE- (M-I DRILLING FLUIDS)
C/O CSA OILFIELD SUPPLIES CO,INC
UNIT 7-B,PDCP BANK CENTRE BLDG
CORNER OF LEVISTE ST & RUFINO ST
SALCEDO VILLAGE,MAKATI CITY
PH (632)8922528 FAX (632)8922554
SINGAPORE OFC - (M-I DRILLING FLUIDS
(SINGAPORE) PTE.LTD) BLDG 400,JETTY LINK
LOYANG CRESCENT,508988
PH (65)63830500 FAX (65)63830996
BANGKOK,THAILAND OFC - (M-I SWACO
THAILAND LTD) 11TH FLR RASA TWR
555 PHAHOLYOTHIN RD,KWANG CATUCHAK
KHET CATUCHAK,10900
PH (662)9370055 FAX (662)9370059
SONGKHIA,THAILAND OFC - (M-I SWACO
SONGKHLA) 287 MOO 5 TAMBOON SATINGMOR
SINGHANAKORN COUNTRY,90100
PH (667)433 2803/5 FAX (667)433 2802
VIETNAM OFFICE - (M-I DRILLING FLUIDS
VIETNAM J/V CO) 99 LE LOI ST,VUNG TAU
PH (84-64)832670/839066
FAX (84-64)839855
- EASTERN HEMISPHERE MIDDLE EAST REG-
DUBAI OFFICE - (M-I SWACO) EXECUTIVE BLDG
NO.3,INSIDE OILFIELDS SUPPLY CENTER
JEBEL ALI FREE ZONE,PO BOX 213379
PH 971-4-883 19 22 FAX 971-4-883 19 39
ABU DHABI OFFICE - (M-I OVERSEAS)
AL KHAILY BLDG,6TH FLR,APP NO.602/603
PO BOX 4076,ABU DHABI
UNITED ARAB EMIRATES
PH 971-2-645 66 77 FAX 971-2-645 66 97
DUBAI UAE OFFICE - (M-I SWACO)
PO BOX 17120,ROUND ABOUT 11
JEBEL ALI FREE ZONE

PH 971-4-883 06 44 FAX 971-4-883 71 97
DUBAI,UAE OFFICE- (M-I GULF SERVICES LLC)
B-25,INSIDE OILFIELDS SUPPLY CENTER
PO BOX 2851,JEBEL ALI FREE ZONE
PH 971-4-883 70 42 FAX 971-4-883 71 39
DUBAI,UAE OFFICE - (SWACO ARABIA LDC)
B-56 OILFIELD SUPPLY CENTER COMPLEX
JEBEL AIL FREE ZONE,PO BOX 7623
PH 971-4-883 7247 FAX 971-4-883 7140
INDIA OFFICE - (M-I OVERSEAS LTD)
302,PRIME CORPORATE PARK
230/231 SAHAR RD,NEXT TO ITC MARATHA
SHERATON HOTEL,ANDHERI (EAST)
PH 91-22-30838000 FAX 91-22-30838038
KUWAIT OFFICE - (KUWAIT DRILLING FLUIDS &
OIL SERVICES) S.A.K.-SHUAIBA INDUSTRIAL
AREA,SOUTH GATE,PO BOX 4544,SAFAT-13046
PH 965-326 2434/326 2455/326
FAX 965-326 2269
OMAN,DUBAI,UAE OFC - (C/O MI GULF
SERVICES LLC) B-25,INSIDE OILFIELDS
SUPPLY CENTRE,PO BOX 2851
JEBEL ALI FREE ZONE
PH (968)602621 FAX (968)602084
SIND,PAKISTAN OFC - (M-I OVERSEAS LTD
(PAKISTAN BRANCH) #501,SYEDNA TAHER
SAIFUDDIN BLDG,BEAUMONT RD,CIVIL LINES
KARACHI-75530 PH 92-21-111 10 20 30
FAX 92-21-568 48 06
QATAR OFFICE - (M-I QATAR WLL)
HBK TOWER,1ST FLR,OFFICE NO.12
MUSHERIEB ST,PO BOX 22767
PH 974-436 9791 FAX 974-436 9793
SAUDI ARABIA OFC - (ARABIAN MINERALS &
CHEMICALS CO LTD) DAMMAM FIRST INDUSTRIAL
AREA,DAMMAM PH 966-3-8472187
FAX 966-3-8473472
MUSCAT,OMAN OFC - (OHI OPES LLC-LOCAL
AGT) MUD INDUSTRIES LLC,PO BOX 889,PC 113
PH (968)2447 8655 FAX (968)2448 2136
YEMEN OFFICE - (M-I SWACO YEMEN)
VILLA NO.3 DAMASCUS ST,HADDA
PO BOX 16093,SANA'A
PH 967-1-417 544 FAX 967-1-412 056
- EASTERN HEMISPHERE NORTH AFRICA REG-
EGYPT OFFICE - (MIOL EGYPT BRANCH)
4 EL SAHA EL SHABIA ST,PO BOX 61,11431
MAADI,CAIRO,EGYPT
PH (20-2)3588463/3588416/3597776
FAX (20-2)3585944
ALEGRIA OFFICE - ALGIERS-53
RUE ABRI AREZKI,ALEGRIA,HASSI MESSAOUD
Z-I ROUTE D'El BORMA BP
PH ALGIERS 213-21-601615/6000116
MOROCCO OFFICE - COMABAR,33 AVENUE TAREK
IBN ZIAD,RABAT,10 000
PH (212-37)767685/6 FAX (212-37)763875
TUNISIA OFFICE - BW NAFTAFLUIDS TUNISIA
GREEN CENTER,BLOC D,D3.1 & D2.1
RUE DU LAC DE CONSTANCE
LES BERGES DU LAC,1053 TUNIS
PH (216-71)962143 FAX (216-71)962447
CAPE TOWN,SOUTH AFRICA OFC -
(M-I OVERSEAS LIMITED) 101 NEWPORT HOUSE
CNR EBENEZER & PRESTWICHS RD
GREEN POINT 80515

PH (27-21)4199135 FAX (27-21)4199149
CABINDA,ANGLOA OFC - (MIOL-WEST AFRICA)
MALONGO TERMINAL,USA PH (1-925)8421111
EXT 3092 FAX (244-222)692600 EXT 3503
LUANDA,ANGOLA OFC - (MIOL-ANGOLA)
LARGO LUTHER KING,135
PH (244-222)332537 FAX (244-222)371275
SOYO BASE,ANGOLA OFC - PH 871 761890288
FAX 871 761890279
DOUALA,CAMEROON BRANCH OFFICE -
(M-I OVERSEAS LTD) BASE UIC,WOURI
B.P. 5420 PH (237)3406102
FAX (237)3406102
CONGO OFFICE - (MIOL CONGO-WEST AFRICA
COUNTRY) BP 1102,POINTE-NOIRE
PH (242)941926 FAX (242)942744
EQUATORIAL GUINEA OFC - (M-I EQUATORIAL
GUINEA,SL) AVENIDA DE LA INDEPENDENCIA 43
MALABO PH (240)091036/094532
FAX (240)091035
GABON OFFICE - (M-I GABON SA)
BATIMENT TOTAL,EX-DEX,B.P. 633
PORT GENTIL PH (241)565217/565430
FAX (241)550588
IVORY COAST OFFICE - (M-I OVERSEAS LTD)
ZONE INDUSTRIELLE DE VRIDI
RUE L28 METALLURGIE,18 B.P. 17
ABIDJAN 18,COTE D'IVOIRE
PH (225)21217855 FAX (225)21217856
LAGOS,NIGERIA OFC - (M-I NIGERIA LTD)
THE OCTOGON,6TH FLR
13A A.J.MARINHO DR,VICTORIA ISLAND ANNEXE
PH (234-1)2618517/2618518/2623583
FAX (234-1)2615247
PORT HARCOURT,NIGERIA OFFICE -
2 RECLAMATION RD,PORT HARCOURT
RIVERS STATE,NIGERIA
PH (234-84)233142 FAX (234-84)232439
WARRI,NIGERIA OFC - OLD NPA YARD
WARRI,DELTA STATE
PH (234-53)251824 FAX (234-53)253241

MACDIARMID A N COMPANY
PO BOX 12468
SAN ANTONIO,TX 78212-0468
PH 210 735-8400
JOHN MACDIARMID,ENGR

MACDONALD DEVELOPMENT COMPANY
770 SOUTH POST OAK LN,STE 630
HOUSTON,TX 77056-1913 PH 713 961-9395

MACDONALD R D,JR,ESTATE,OIL PROP
770 SO POST OAK LN,STE 630
HOUSTON,TX 77056-1913 PH 713 961-9395
W S ARENDALE,JR,CO-EXEC

MACFARLANE COMPANY-USA LLC
116 N WASHINGTON AVE
EL DORADO,AR 71730-5607 PH 870 863-6060
FAX 870 863-6062

MACHIN & ASSOC,INC,OIL OPR,ENGR
PO BOX 2999,507 MAGRILL ST,75601
LONGVIEW,TX 75606-2999
PH 903 753-2694 FAX 903 753-4957
THOMAS J MACHIN,PRES
ARTY MACHIN,VP
PEGGY MCMILLAN,SECY/TREAS

MACHIN PETROLEUM TITLE SERVICE,LLC
2219 FIRESTONE CIRCLE

TYLER,TX 75703 PH 214 707-1215
JEFF MACHIN,PRES JEFFMACHIN@YAHOO.COM

MACK ENERGY CO,OIL & GAS PRODUCTION
PO BOX 400,1202 N 10TH ST
DUNCAN,OK 73534-0400 PH 580 252-5580
T H MCCASLAND,III,PRES
RANDY W SMITH,VP,PROD
CHRIS K FOWLER,VP,EXPL
TIMOTHY L HANSON,SR GEOL
DANNY M BRYANT,PROD SUPT
RICHARD L FAULKNER,WATERFLOOD ENGR
GIL L MESSERSMITH,LAND MGR
ROGER D FAULKENBERRY,SR LDMN
NOBLE W MEANS,TREAS
JOHN R BRAUGHT,SECY
LAFAYETTE,LA OFFICE - 5000 AMBASSADOR
CAFFERY PKWY,BLDG 15A,70508
PH 337 988-9256
CHRIS FOWLER,VP EXPL
RANDY SMITH,VP PROD
TIM LEDET,DIST LANDMAN
JOHN HOLLIER,GEOL/GEOPHY
CECILE JOHNSON,REGULATORY
CLAIRE HOLLIER CHOLLIER@MACKENERGY.COM

MACK GROUP,LLC,THE
ASBESTOS ABATEMENT/DEMOLITION CONTRACTOR
1500 KINGS HWY N STE 209
CHERRY HILL,NJ 08034
PH 973 759-5000 INFO@MACKGRP.COM
STEVE KING

MACK OIL CORPORATION
7721 OUTER DR S
TRAVERSE CITY,MI 49685 PH 231 946-5349
JOHN W MACK,PRES
MICHAEL J MACK,VP OPERS
ROBERT L MACK,VP LAND

MACK,PRESTON
4411 SARONG DR
HOUSTON,TX 77096-4426 PH 713 721-6408

MACKENCO INC
7917 STATION ST
COLUMBUS,OH 43235 PH 614 436-1229
KENNER MCCONNELL III,PRES

MACKINAW TWO LLC
PO BOX 1405
BOCA GRANDE,FL 33921 PH 318 393-4434
FAX 941 964-1112
PALMER LONG,PRES

MACOMBER DONALD,JR,PALEONTOLOGIST
125 CHARLESTON PARK
METAIRIE,LA 70005-3967 PH 504 885-3930

MADISON ENERGY ADVISORS,INC SEE
OIL & GAS JOURNAL EXCHANGE

MAGEE ROBERT L
8055 FM 359 S #667
FULSHEAR,TX 77441 PH 281 808-6565
RLMAGEE@MAGEEOGP.COM

MAGGERT ENERGY CORPORATION
PO BOX 9066
THE WOODLANDS,TX 77387-9066
PH 281 364-8057
KENT W MAGGERT,PRES

MAGNOLIA ENERGY SERVICES,LLC
PO BOX 53602,714 E KALISTE SALOOM RD D-2
LAFAYETTE,LA 70505-3602
PH 337 269-1799 FAX 337 269-1794

WILLIAM J DAIGLE,MGR
BILL@MAGNOLIAENERGY.NET

MAGNOLIA INVESTMENTS,INC
PO BOX 53606
LAFAYETTE,LA 70505-3606
PH 337 235-8983 COFFEYGLENN@BELLSOUTH.NET
GLENN H COFFEY,PRES

MAGNOLIA PETROLEUM COMPANY,LLC
3811 TURTLE CREEK BLVD STE 1900
DALLAS,TX 75219 PH 214 521-4900
FAX 214 521-4989 INFO@BURNETTPETRO.COM
KYLE R BURNETT,PRES
DEBBE CHABOT,OFC MGR

MAGNOLIA PRODUCTION
OIL & GAS OPERATOR/PRODUCTION/RECORDS
PO BOX 420,9038 TEXAS HWY 77 E
ATLANTA,TX 75551 PH 903 796-1855
LORLAN4@WB4ME.COM
LANE EASON

MAGNOLIA TORQUE & TESTING
208 EASY ST
LAFAYETTE,LA 70506-3014
PH 318 233-1790 FAX 318 233-6365
RAY ABSHIRE,PRES

MAGNUM ENGINEERING CO
500 N SHORELINE BLVD STE 322
CORPUS CHRISTI,TX 78401-0313
PH 361 882-3858 FAX 361 884-9355

MAGNUM HUNTER RESOURCES,INC SEE
CIMAREX ENERGY CO

MAGNUM OIL,LLC
2007 LEXINGTON AVE
OWENSBORO,KY 42301-4688 PH 270 684-4002
AVERY E SMITH,MEMBER,GEN MGR
CARL L HENRY JR,MEMBER,PROD MGR

MAGNUM PETROLEUM INC
PO BOX 54712
OKLAHOMA CITY,OK 73154-1712
PH 405 417-2033

MAGNUM PRODUCING,LP
500 N SHORELINE BLVD STE 322
CORPUS CHRISTI,TX 78401-0313
PH 361 882-3858 FAX 361 884-9355
HOUSTON,TX OFFICE - 7600 W TIDWELL,#505
77040 PH 713 462-2388 FAX 713 462-2599

MAGUIRE OIL COMPANY
5950 BERKSHIRE LN STE 1500
DALLAS,TX 75225
PH 214 741-5137 FAX 214 658-8005
CARY M MAGUIRE,PRES,CEO
BLAINEY MAGUIRE HESS,SR VP & COO
V D FLOURNOY,VP LAND

MAJCHSZAK FRANK L,CONS PETR GEOL
3179 PALOMAR AVE
COLUMBUS,OH 43231-3107 PH 614 895-2675

MAJOR CONTROLS INC
MFG OF LIQUID LEVEL CONTROL
3034 S MADISON AVE
TULSA,OK 74114-5231 PH 918 445-7401
FAX 918 445-7443
GLENN A WRIGHT,PRES
LARRY E HILL,VP,GEN MGR
TRACEY WRIGHT,MKTG MGR,SALES
FRED OCKERMAN,ENGR COORDINATOR

MALATEX INC
5904 CLEVELAND PL

METAIRIE,LA 70003 PH 504 455-5400
FAX 504 455-5449
MILTON J BERNOS,JR

MALLARD DRILLING CORPORATION
PO BOX 1527,5918 FAIRFIELD AVE
SHREVEPORT,LA 71165-1527
PH 318 869-2074 FAX 318 869-2074
THOMAS G CARMODY,JR,DIR
ANTHONY P CARMODY,DIR

MALLARD PRODUCTION COMPANY
PO BOX 52287,705 W PINHOOK RD
LAFAYETTE,LA 70505-2287
PH 337 237-2923 FAX 337 232-7929
DAVID ALWELL,PRES
RICHARD CHALMERS,EXEC VP

MALONE OIL & GAS EXPLORATION,INC
610 MARSHALL ST,STE 722
SHREVEPORT,LA 71101-5601 PH 318 425-3464
MAX T MALONE,PRES,GEOL

MALONE PETROLEUM CONSULTING
12651 BRIAR FOREST DR STE 165
HOUSTON,TX 77077-2376 PH 281 531-1500
ROBERT P MALONE,AUDIT CONSULTANT

MALONEY LAND SERVICES LLC
PO BOX 82235
LAFAYETTE,LA 70598-2235
PH 337 278-1222 FAX 337 706-8655
JIM MALONEY,MNGNG MEMBER
JIMATMALONEYLAND.COM

MANAGEMENT CONSULTANTS
169 E TERRACE
LAKEWOOD,NY 14750 PH 716 763-5445
DAVID G REYNOLDS,PRES

MANAGEMENT RECRUITERS OF NEW ORLEANS,INC
3527 RIDGELAKE DR
METAIRIE,LA 70002-3614 PH 504 831-7333

MANAK J F,PC
ATTORNEY FOR JFM ENERGY CO
2047 COUNTY RD 351
HONDO,TX 78861 PH 830 426-8820
JOE MANAK JFMANAK@GMAIL.COM

MANDALAY OIL & GAS,LLC
4084 HWY 311
HOUMA,LA 70360-8132 PH 337 232-7669
FAX 337 232-7689 WWW.MANDALAYENERGY.COM
DSPRINGER@MANDALAYENERGY.COM
DEBBIE K BUSHNELL-SPRINGER,PRES
LEN SPRINGER,LDMN
FLORA SPRINGER,EXEC ASST
FLORA@MANDLAYENERGY.COM

MANESS PETROLEUM CORPORATION
PO BOX 313,1425 SOUTH MISSION RD
MOUNT PLEASANT,MI 48804-0313
PH 989 773-5475 FAX 989 775-5053
DAVID MANESS
DAVE@MANESSPETR.COM
TIM MANESS
TIM@MANESSPETR.COM

MANETEK INC
MANUFACTURING TECHNOLOGY
105 BURGESS ST
BROUSSARD,LA 70518 PH 337 837-2921
FAX 337 837-2963
F L LEBLANC,CMFGE,P.E.,PRES
DAN BARRON,FRMN
KEITH LEBLANC,PURCHASING

MANLEY DONALD C INDEPENDENT LANDMAN
766 OAKDALE DR
AUSTIN,TX 78745 PH 512 992-0097
MANLEYDON@YAHOO.COM

MANTI RESOURCES,INC
MANTI OPERATING COMPANY
4900 WOODWAY STE 1100
HOUSTON,TX 77056 PH 361 888-7708
FAX 361 888-4418
LEE BARBERITO,PRES
CHRIS DOUGLAS,EXPL MGR
TIM P BOYLE,LAND MGR
BARRY CLARK,GEN MGR

MANTLE OIL & GAS LLC
900 W PARKWOOD AVE
FRIENDSWOOD,TX 77546 PH 281 317-8222
CHRIS BARDEN,MGR CHRIS@MANTLELLC.COM

MANZIEL INTERESTS OIL OPR & PROD
PO BOX 6005,110 W 8TH ST
TYLER,TX 75711-6005 PH 903 592-4315
FAX 903 592-6655
MRS DOROTHY N MANZIEL,OWNER
NOLAN MANZIEL
N PAUL MANZIEL

MAP DRILLING CO
4801 N TURNBULL DR
METAIRIE,LA 70002-1448 PH 985 727-7303
FAX 985 727-7304 DARCY@MAPDRILLING.COM
R L PRICHARD,PRES
RAYDENE S PRICHARD,EXEC V P

MAP PRODUCTION CO,INC
68 INVERNESS DR E STE 102
ENGLEWOOD,CO 80112-5108 PH 303 799-6060
SCOTT HUDSON

MAPCO OIL & GAS CO,SEE
CNG PRODUCING CO

MAPCO PETROLEUM INC
P O BOX 2930
MEMPHIS,TN 38101-2930 PH 901 774-3100
R G ALEXANDER,VP REFINING
L J EDWARDS,WHOLESALE SLS MGR

MAPES,TIM
1010 LAMAR ST STE 1650
HOUSTON,TX 77002
PH 713 650-8058 FAX 713 650-8057
TIM.MAPES@INTEGRAL-RESOURCES.COM

MAPP OILFIELD SERVICES,INC
PO BOX 3777,941 HWY 550 NW
BROOKHAVEN,MS 39601-7777
PH 601 835-2013 WWW.MAPPOILFIELD.COM
STACEY E SAUCIER,PRES

MAR LOW CORPORATION
PO BOX 51673,120 OIL CTR BLDG 12 STE 103
LAFAYETTE,LA 70505-1673
PH 337 234-9446 FAX 337 234-9494
MICHAEL T LOWRY,PRES
LYNDA N WIRT,OFC MGR

MARABLE ALLEN C,PET LAND SERVICES
PO BOX 926
RURAL RETREAT,VA 24368 PH 903 312-1904
PH 903 592-8604

MARAN OIL COMPANY OIL PROD
10100 REUNION PL STE 635
SAN ANTONIO,TX 78216 PH 210 377-0669
ROBERT A ANDERSON

MARANTO JAMES T
416 TRAVIS ST STE 1400
SHREVEPORT,LA 71101-3112 PH 318 222-0761

MARATHON ENERGY
868 39TH ST
BROOKLYN,NY 11232 PH 718 435-2200
FAX 718 435-3096 WWW.MECNY.COM
JERRY DRENIS,CO-FOUNDER/PRES
BOBBY BEYS,CO-FOUNDER/EXEC VP
CHRISOULA VLACHOU-DRENIS,GEN MGR
MICHAEL STOLPER,GEN COUNSEL
JEFF GRYGIER,CFO
JIMMY MOUTAFIS,VP SLS
SHAHJEHAN SAJID,VP SLS
GUS SFAKIANOS,VP MECH SVCS
RACHEL E BAIER,DIR PRICING & MKTG DEV
CHRIS SKULIKIDIS,DIR FIN
ANTHONY RENNER,FLEET OPERS MGR
PENNY GUIDA,OPERS DIR
JOANNA ANASTASIADIS,CONTROLLER
SCOTT BURNS,MKTG & BUS DEV DIR

MARATHON OIL
5555 SAN FELIPE ST
HOUSTON,TX 77056 PH 888 522-8871
WWW.MARATHONOIL.COM
LEE M TILLMAN,PRES/CEO
SYLVIA J KERRIGAN,EXEC VP/GEN COUNSEL &
SECY
JOHN R (JR) SULT,EXEC VP/CFO
MORRIS R CLARK,VP/TREAS
DEANNA L JONES,VP-HR AND ADMIN SVCS
CATHY KRAJICEK,VP-HEALTH,ENVIRO,SFTY &
SECURITY
T M (MITCH) LITTLE,VP-INTL & OFFSHORE
EXPL/PROD OPERS
BRUCE A MCCULLOUGH,VP/CIO
LANCE W ROBERTSON,VP-N AMERICA PROD OPERS
MICHAEL J STOVER,VP-OPERS SVCS
PATRICK J WAGNER,VP-CORP DEV
GARY E WILSON,VP-CONTROLLER & CAO
TULSA,OK OFFICE - PO BOX 21158 74121-1158

MARATHON PETROLEUM CORPORATION
REFINING,MARKETING & TRANSPORTATION
539 S MAIN ST
FINDLAY,OH 45840 PH 419 421-2121
WWW.MARATHONPETROLEUM.CM

MARCO LAND & PETROLEUM,INC
2811 KEEGO RD
BREWTON,AL 36426-8058 PH 334 867-5457
FAX 334 867-5458
COSBY H MARTIN JR,PRES,DRLG OPERS

MARCONI EXPLORATION,INC
5521 BRIAR DR STE 150
HOUSTON,TX 77056-1107 PH 713 627-9223
FAX 801 739-4583 MARCONIEXP@AOL.COM
STEVEN H VOSS,PRES PH 713 252-2000

MARDEN PETROLEUM EXPLORATION CO
PO BOX 941
MARIETTA,OH 45750-0941 PH 740 373-9446
FAX 740 373-7074
RANDALL A MASON,PRES
J J ARNALL,PROD,OPERS SUPVSR

MAREX,INC
PETR EXPLOR,DEV & OILFIELD MGMNT
13819 THREADALL PARK DR
HOUSTON,TX 77077 PH 281 556-0097

FAX 281 556-1209 RBERTAGNE@COMCAST.NET
ROBERT G BERTAGNE,PRES

MARIETTA MACK
127 COURT ST
MARIETTA,OH 45750-3312 PH 740 373-7200
FAX 740 373-1674
PAUL BEE,SERVICE MGR

MARINE KATHY L ATTORNEY AT LAW,PC
PO BOX 337
CARROLLTON,AL 35447 PH 205 367-8207
FAX 205 367-8416 KMARINE@KMARINELAW.COM

MARINE OPERATORS INC,BARGE RENTALS
PO BOX 51694
LAFAYETTE,LA 70505-1694
PH 337 232-9248 FAX 337 232-9043
WWW.MOPBARGES.COM BARGES@MOP-
BARGES.COM
STEVEN H ORTTE,PRES

MARINE PROPERTIES LLC
3030 LAUSAT ST
METAIRIE,LA 70001-5924 PH 504 831-7779
FAX 504 831-8315 MSHALETT@MINDSPRING.COM
MONTE C SHALETT,PRES

MARINER ENERGY,INC
2000 W SAM HOUSTON PKWY S STE 2000
HOUSTON,TX 77042-3622
PH 713 954-5500 FAX 713 954-5555
WWW.MARINER-ENERGY.COM
SCOTT D JOSEY,CHRMN,CEO,PRES
DALTON F POLASEK,COO
TERESA G BUSHMAN,SR VP,GEN COUNSEL & SECY
JUDD A HANSEN,SR VP,SHELF/OHSHORE
CORY L LOEGERING,VP,DEEPWATER OPERS
JESUS G MELENDREZ,SR VP,CCO,CFO,TREAS
MIKE C VAN DEN BOLD,SR VP,CEO

MARION OPERATING CORP
PO BOX 453
MARION,OH 43301-0453 PH 740 386-6328
FAX 740 386-6831
DICK HART,OWNER
ROSALIE COFFEY,OFC MGR

MARITECH RESOURCES,INC
24955 INTERSTATE 45 NORTH
THE WOODLANDS,TX 77380
PH 281 364-4343 FAX 281 364-4310
WWW.MARITECHRESOURCES.COM
VAN GOFF,VP

MARITIME EQUIPMENT,INC
WINCH & EQUIPMENT RENTALS & SALES
200 ARDOYNE DR
HOUMA,LA 70360-7949 PH 504 631-3454
FAX 504 631-2015
MICHAEL BORDELON,PRES
SHIRLEY GIROIR,ACCT

MARITIMES & NORTHEAST PIPELINE SEE
DUKE ENERGY GAS TRANSMISSION

MARK PRODUCT & SERVICE CO, INC
4587 S FM 908
ROCKDALE,TX 76567
PH 936 525-0915 LANDMLS@WILDBLUE.NET
ROBERT MARK BRUSCATO,PRES
CONNIE COLLARD-BRUSCATO,LDMN

MARK PRODUCTS SEE
SERCEL INC

MARK V PETROLEUM COMPANY
PO BOX 9106

(800) 375-1838
WWW.ARMSTRONGOIL.COM

If your company is not listed in our directory, we would like to list it in the next edition of our directory - absolutely FREE. To be listed, we need it in writing. Please fill out the form below or visit our website and fill out the listing form there. If you wish to use the form below, just mail it or fax it to us at (800) 375-1838.

Company Name _____

Physical Address _____

Mailing address if different _____

Phone # _____ Fax # _____

Email address _____

Key personnel and their titles:

_____

_____

_____

_____

If you need to list additional offices, please include on letterhead

To Order Call (800) 375-1838 or
www.armstrongoil.com

Nationwide Office Directory
Full 8 1/2" x 11" book size
Entire Nation
over 16,000 companies listed

$ 225 (no discount available)

Nationwide Mini Directory (Briefcase)
Small Size 5 1/4" x 8 1/4"
Same complete nationwide information
over 16,000 companies listed

$ 140 w / discount*

Texas Directory
Includes
Texas and S.E. New Mexico

$ 80 w / discount*

Louisana / Gulf Coast Directory
Includes the following states:
Gulf coast of Texas, Louisana
Arkansas, Mississippi,
Alabama, Georgia, Florida
N.E. states

$80 w / discount*

Rocky Mountain / Central U.S. Directory
Includes the following states:
West Texas and Panhandle of Texas
Oklahoma, New Mexico
Colorado, Alaska and all
Western U.S. states

$80 w / discount*

* discount applies when invoice is paid within 30 days after receipt of order.

MONROE,LA 71211-9106 PH 318 323-9664
FAX 318 323-4078
FRANK SPOONER,PRES
MARY F SPOONER,SECY

MARKET HUB PARTNERS SEE
DUKE ENERGY GAS TRANSMISSION

MARKS EXPLORER LLC
601 POYDRAS ST STE 2345
NEW ORLEANS,LA 70130 PH 504 828-2564
FAX 504 828-2566 MARKSEXPLORER.COM
EVERARD W MARKS III
KYLE T MARKS,LAND MGR
DARNELL DEE ABADLE,ACCT MGR
JULES B SACHS,MASTER GEOL
BRITTA MARKS,MGR
GRETCHEN HAMMERSTROM,ASST

MARLIN ENERGY LLC
3861 AMBASSADOR CAFFERY PKWY STE 600
LAFAYETTE,LA 70503-5270
PH 337 769-0032 FAX 337 769-4342
RICHARD G ZEPERNICK,PRES/CEO
CLINT P CREDEUR,VP EXPL & PROD
EUGENE MINVIELLE III,CFO & TREAS
MIKE LIPARI,LAND MGR
MIKE.LIPARI@MARLINENERGY.NET

MARLIN EXPLORATION,LLC
PO BOX 1367,401 EDWARDS ST STE 1200
SHREVEPORT,LA 71164-1367
PH 318 222-8406 FAX 318 222-6061
MEI@MARLINEXPLORATION.COM
JON Q-PETERSEN,PRES
AUTIE T ORJIAS,VP/LAND MGR
CODY LENERT,CHF GEOL
DEAN GILES,SECY/TREAS

MARMATON OIL COMPANY
PO BOX 580405
HOUSTON,TX 77258-0405 PH 281 335-4100
FAX 281 335-4111 WWW.MARMATONOIL.COM
HOUSTON,TX OFFICE - 1100 NASA PARKWAY
STE 108 77058
NICK W GOODRICH,PRES
NWGOODRICH@MARMATONOIL.COM
PATRICIA HENDERSON,SECY/TREAS
PAHENDERSON@MARMATONOIL.COM

MAROPCO,INC
7600 W TIDWELL RD STE 800
HOUSTON,TX 77040-6718
PH 713 690-4321 FAX 713 690-3054
E PIERCE MARSHALL,PRES
EYYONNE SCURLOCK,SECY TO THE PRES

MARPCO INC
P O BOX 426,SCOTT RD
SCOTT,LA 70583-0426 PH 318 232-2448
M A MARTIN,OWNER

MARQUEE CORPORATION
950 ECHO LANE STE 355
HOUSTON,TX 77024
PH 713 222-7706 FAX 713 222-8611
MARK KOBELAN,PRES
GARY ROEDER,VP

MARR OIL & GAS,LTD
325 N SAINT PAUL ST STE 2500
DALLAS,TX 75201-3814 PH 214 748-9614
RAY H MARR,PRES
DOUGLAS W BONNER,EXEC VP

MARSAT
2015 EVANS RD STE 100
SAN ANTONIO,TX 78258-7428 PH 210 494-9192
FAX 210 494-5301
FRANK J SITTERLE,PRES

MARSH TRANSPORT,INC
P O BOX 70
BALDWIN,LA 70514-0070 PH 318 923-7341
GLENN FAUCHEUX,PRES

MARSH USA INC
701 POYDRAS ST STE 4125
NEW ORLEANS,LA 70139-7702 PH 504 522-8541
FAX 504 524-5854 WWW.MARSH.COM
ROBERT M MONSTED JR,MNGNG DIR
OUIDA S TURNER,SR VP
DAVID B GORNEY,MNGNG DIR
MICHAEL N BROWN,MNGNG DIR
DANELLE HEATHMAN,VP

MARSHALL DWIGHT,OP
1608 SAUNDERS AVE
CARMI,IL 62821-2300 PH 618 384-8360

MARSHALL JACK W,IND GEOL
PO BOX 10828
EL DORADO,AR 71730 PH 870 234-2261

MARSHLAND PETROLEUM COMPANY
3220 HUNTINGDON PL
HOUSTON,TX 77019-5926 PH 713 521-9603
FAX 713 521-2835

MARTENS FIELD SERVICES,INC
PO BOX 1357
KAILUA KONA,HI 96745 PH 214 893-9185
SALLY MARTENS

MARTEX OPERATING,LLC
209 N NEW HAMPSHIRE ST
COVINGTON,LA 70433 PH 985 819-0010
BOB BAILEY RBAILEY@MARTEXLLC.COM
JEFF MARTIN JGM@MARTEXLLC.COM

MARTIN ANDREW SEA SERVICE,INC,DRLG CONTR
202 DEMANDRE ST
BELLE CHASSE,LA 70037 PH 504 522-5746

MARTIN FUELS COMPANY,INC
PO BOX 630811
NACOGDOCHES,TX 75963-0811
PH 936 560-6477 FAX 936 569-8128
RICHARD M FOSHEE,PRES
CARLA JO FOSHEE,SECY/TREAS

MARTIN H J EXPLORATION INC
6400 S LOCUST WAY
CENTENNIAL,CO 80111 PH 303 721-0843
HENRY J MARTIN,PRES

MARTIN HARRY L,OIL OPR
2929 BUFFALO SPEEDWAY STE 214,LAMAR TWR
HOUSTON,TX 77098-1712 PH 713 965-0622

MARTIN JACK P,IND GEOL
PO BOX 51134,BLDG 7 HEYMANN BLVD
LAFAYETTE,LA 70505-1134 PH 337 232-4088
FAX 337 234-5320

MARTIN JAMES B,OIL & GAS LEASE BROKER
1407 N RUSTON AVE
EVANSVILLE,IN 47711-4975 PH 812 479-6290

MARTIN JOSEPH A,CPL
PO BOX 51512
LAFAYETTE,LA 70505-1512 PH 337 233-7118
JOSEPH4850@MSN.COM

MARTIN L A & ASSOCIATES
INTERNATIONAL PETR CONSULTANTS

9422 SINFONIA DR
HOUSTON,TX 77040-2594 PH 713 466-8502
FAX 713 466-8903 WWW.LAMARTIN-PE.COM
LAMARBEST@AOL.COM
L A MARTIN,PRES

MARTIN OIL COUNTRY TUBULAR,INC
PO BOX 426
SCOTT,LA 70583-0426 PH 337 233-7036
FAX 337 264-1412 MOCT@COX-INTERNET.COM
D F MARTIN,PRES
J A MARTIN,SECY/TREAS

MARTIN PRODUCTION COMPANY
400 TRAVIS ST STE 1504 BECK BLDG
SHREVEPORT,LA 71101-3113
PH 318 425-5464 FAX 318 425-5246
ROBB MARTIN,PRES
DILLON B CANNON,OPERS ENGR

MARTIN R E OIL COMPANY
2400 AUGUSTA DR STE 355
HOUSTON,TX 77057-5032
PH 713 977-4400 FAX 713 977 4450
RONALD E MARTIN,PRES

MARTIN RONALD L CO,THE
2929 BUFFALO SPEEDWAY STE 214,LAMAR TWR
HOUSTON,TX 77098-1712 PH 713 965-0622

MARTIN STOWERS
PO BOX 360
WEST HAMLIN,WV 25571-0360
PH 304 824-7495 FAX 304 824-5440
J ALLEN MARTIN,PRTNR

MARTIN,BODE,WERNER & MANN PC
5100 WESTHEIMER STE 100
HOUSTON,TX 77056 PH 713 968-9215
JOHN BODE
KEITH B WERNER

MARTINEAU PETROLEUM,INC
4625 GREENVILLE AVE STE 205
DALLAS,TX 75206-5044 PH 214 361-0855
DAVID T MARTINEAU,PRES
JOHN DRAKE,GEO MGR

MARTZ WELL SERVICE
5101 ROCKY RILL AVE NE
CANTON,OH 44705-3269 PH 216 493-0303
GARY MARTZ,OWNER

MARWELL PETROLEUM LP
1770 ST JAMES PL STE 406
HOUSTON,TX 77056-3424 PH 713 781-1105
GRANT FAULCONER,PRES

MASON A GEORGE JR,PSC SEE
MASON GEORGE LAW FIRM,PSC

MASON CHARLES,ATTY
4605 POST OAK PLACE STE 250
HOUSTON,TX 77027 PH 713 236-8303
FAX 713 247-0407 CM@JHYI.COM

MASON DON & SON,LLC
PO BOX 45
NORPHLET,AR 71759-0045 PH 870 546-3455

MASON ENERGY CORPORATION
2139 SHEFFIELD DR
JACKSON,MS 39211 PH 601 982-2443
FAX 601 354-4627
DICK B MASON III,PRES

MASON EXPLORATION CO
503 TIMBER TERRACE RD
HOUSTON,TX 77024-5627
PH 713 686-7094 FAX 713 686-7095

GUNSTONWEST@SBCGLOBAL.NET
ROBERT C MASON,PRES

MASON GEORGE LAW FIRM,PSC
COALBED METHANE,OIL,GAS & COAL LAW
3070 LAKECREST CIR STE 400 PMB 278
LEXINGTON,KY 40513 PH 859 224-0789
PH 859 327-4740 FAX 859 296-2998
WWW.GEORGEMASONLF.COM
GEORGE@GEORGEMASONLF.COM

MASON RICHARD H,GEOL,
3737 CALION RD
EL DORADO,AR 71730-2738 PH 501 862-5155

MASOODI MINI VENTURES INC
PO BOX 2136
BUFFALO,NY 14240-2136 PH 716 480-4351
FAX 716 876-3261
GHULAM S MASOODI,MD,PRES

MASSCO INC
230 THRUWAY PK
BROUSSARD,LA 70518 PH 337 837-9209
FAX 337 837-9200 SALES@MASSCO-INC.COM
MARK KERBY
HOUMA,LA OFFICE - PO DRAWER 1230
70361,100 N LACARPE CIR
PH 985 868-7395 FAX 985 851-3474
JOHN MCMEEL

MASSEY & MASSEY OIL & GAS SEE
MASSEY,W T

MASSEY JEFF R & ASSOCIATES
PO BOX 225,514 OAK AVENUE
SULPHUR SPRINGS,TX 75483-0225
PH 903 885-9606 FAX 903 885-8812
JEFF R MASSEY,OWNER MASSEYJR@VERIZON.NET

MASTER WELL WORKS,INC
PO BOX 8
EVANGELINE,LA 70537-0008
PH 318 824-2099 FAX 337 824-9577
WIL FRUGE,PRES

MATAGORDA PIPELINE PARTNERSHIP SEE
AMERICAN EXPLORATION CO

MATAGORDA PRODUCTION COMPANY
675 BERING STE 650
HOUSTON,TX 77057-2128 PH 713 334-1238
HERSHAL C FERGUSON,JR

MATCO OIL COMPANY
PO BOX 93
SARATOGA,TX 77585-0093 PH 409 274-5311
B H TOMLINSON,PRES
T B TOMLINSON,VP

MATHEWS DON L
PO BOX 921
KILGORE,TX 75663-0921 PH 903 984-3443
CHARLA ROLPH,AGENT

MATHEWS HOOPER W,JR
P O BOX 1009
ATMORE,AL 36504-1009 PH 205 368-3197

MATHY MIKE,INDEPENDENT EXPLORATION GEOL
1922 FAR NIENTE
SAN ANTONIO,TX 78258-4516
PH 210 408-2772 FAX 210 408-2772
MIKEMATHY@SATX.RR.COM

MATRIX GAS CORPORATION
5725 COMMONWEALTH BLVD
SUGAR LAND,TX 77479-3999 PH 281 265-1212
FAX 281 265-1778
VICTOR T LINCK,PRES

FRED C BRYLA,VP
KAREN S LINCK,VP
LARRY W LATHROP,VP
BRUCE C CONWAY,DIR

MATRIX PETROLEUM,LLC
1401 ENCLAVE PKWY STE 400
HOUSTON,TX 77077 PH 281 597-7022
FAX 281 597-8880
JOSEPH A REEVES JR,CHRMN & CEO
J DREW REEVES,VP LAND & LEGAL
JEFFERY T ROBINSON,VP ADMIN-TECHNOLOGY
THOMAS J TOUREK,EXPL DIR

MATTYE CARTER FAMILY TRUST
98 SAN JACINTO BLVD FSR-1 #2705
AUSTIN,TX 78701 PH 713 826-7718
JOHN B BECKWORTH,TRUSTEE
JBBECKWORTH@BECKWORTHINTERSTS.COM

MAVERICK EXPLORATION & PRODUCTION,INC
3301 VETERANS DR STE 107
TRAVERSE CITY,MI 49684-4564
PH 231 929-3923 FAX 231 929-3914
MAVERICKEANDP@AOL.COM
DWIGHT GOOKIN,PRES
TAMMI LUMLEY,ACCT MGR
RITA GOOKIN,PROD TECH
STEVE DETWILER,OPERS MGR
ALAN BLAIR,LEGAL & LAND MGR

MAVERICK LAND SERVICES,INC
203 N WELLINGTON ST
MARSHALL,TX 75670 PH 903 934-8400
ROBERT E ASHMORE,PRES
BASHMORE@MAVERICKLANDSERVICES.COM

MAXIMA ENERGY CORPORATION
PO BOX 531,300 FM RD 1252 E
KILGORE,TX 75663-0531 PH 903 983-2641
FAX 903 984-4538 MAXIMA@ESAWIRELESS.COM
BILL MAXWELL,PRES
RODNEY WILLIAMS,FLD SUPVSR

MAXIMUS OPERATING LTD
PO BOX 1706
LONGVIEW,TX 75606-1706 PH 903 753-0941
FAX 903 753-2644
JAMES R WRIGHT,PRES
ERIC JOSEPH,VP
STEVE BODENHEIMER,VP

MAXUS ENERGY CORPORATION
114 ARNOLD ST STE 4
HOUSTON,TX 77007 PH 281 681-7262
GARARDO CORTES,EXPL/PROD MGR
BRENT BARKER,LDMN BBARKER1955@AOL.COM

MAXUS EXPLORATION COMPANY SEE
MIDGARD ENERGY COMPANY

MAXWELL ENERGY INC
PO BOX 849
BROOKHAVEN,MS 39602-0849
PH 601 833-1323 FAX 601 833-1247
D W MAXWELL,PRES DWMAXWELL@BELLSOUTH.NET

MAY GEORGE N & ASSOC,CONS,PALEO
PO BOX 51858,201 HEYMANN BLVD
LAFAYETTE,LA 70505-1858 PH 337 234 3379
FAX 337 234-3389
WILLIAM S GRUBB,CONS PALEONTOLOGIST,OWNER
DELVIE M HEMPHILL,SECY,OFC MGR

MAY GEORGE W,OIL LEASE BROKER,OIL PROPS
4527 EASTWOOD RD
JACKSON,MS 39211-6116 PH 601 366-1804

MAY JOE A,OIL & GAS LEASES & RYLTS
4527 EASTWOOD RD
JACKSON,MS 39211-6116 PH 601 354-4899

MAY,MUROV AND NIERMAN
PO BOX 3985
SHREVEPORT,LA 71133 PH 318 861-6974
RON NIERMAN,MGR
OVERTON,TX OFFICE - PO BOX 430
75684 PH 903 834-3661
RICHARD M MAY,MGR

MAYEAUX J A
P O BOX 10104,1136 FIRST NATL BK BLDG
JACKSON,MS 39286-0104 PH 601 352-7781

MAYFAIR PROPERTIES,LLC
900 E LAKEVIEW DR
MCALLEN,TX 78501
PH 956 994-9009 FAX 956 686-5494
JAMES W COLLINS,PRES
KENNETH D CREWS,IN-HOUSE ATTY/OIL & GAS

MAYFIELD SWD LLC
2204 ARROWWOOD CT
MCKINNEY,TX 75070 PH 972 571-6648
FAX 972 529-9524

MAYFIELD WALTER G
PRESIDENT OF GOLDSTON OIL CORPORATION
PO BOX 570365
HOUSTON,TX 77257-0365 PH 713 355-3408
FAX 713 355-4248
RODNEY E HENCKEL,EXEC VP
DON W PISKLAK,TREAS
GREG COLBURN,DRLG,PROD MGR
KENT JOHNSTON,LDMN,MGR

MAYHALL FONDREN BLAIZE (ATTORNEYS)
5800 ONE PERKINS PL DR STE 2-B
BATON ROUGE,LA 70808
PH 225 810-4998 FAX 225 810-4999
WWW.MFBFIRM.COM
KIM G MAYHALL
CHARLES G BLAIZE,JR CBLAIZE@MFBFIRM.COM
JAMIE S MANUEL
SCOTT R PATTON
ANDREA M TETTLETON
MARGARET G PATTON
SPENCER R SCHOONENBERG

MAYNE & MERTZ,INC
PO BOX 183
MIDLAND,TX 79702-0183
PH 432 683-1600
W TAYLOR MAYNE,PRES
D'ANN BIRKHEAD,ACCTG
HOUSTON,TX OFFICE - 24 GREENWAY PLZ
STE 546,WESLAYAN TWR,77046
PH 713 963-0031 FAX 713 963-0034
CARTER CLINE,LAND ADV
MICHAEL C PUZIO,PTNR/GEOL
HOWARD MAYNE,LAND MGR
SAN ANGELO,TX OFFICE - 427 W CONCHO
76903 PH 325 658-8299 FAX 325 653-7958
LEN P MERTZ,VP & CFO

MAYO OIL COMPANY
8918 TESORO DR STE 505
SAN ANTONIO,TX 78217-6220 PH 210 828-4610
PAUL R MAYO JR,OWNER

MAYO PAUL R,JR
8918 TESORO DR STE 505
SAN ANTONIO,TX 78217-6220 PH 210 828-4610

MAZE EXPLORATION INC SEE
AMERICAN EXPLORATION CO
MB&G OIL FABRICATION
PO BOX 120399,2611 HWY 271
TYLER,TX 75712-0399 PH 903 593-0400
MBGOILFIELDFABRICATION@YAHOO.COM
LARRY MOORE
MCALESTER FUEL COMPANY,THE
PO BOX 541053
HOUSTON,TX 77254-1053
PH 713 524-9960 FAX 713 522-9239
WWW.MCALESTERFUEL.COM
WALTER H WALNE III,ASST CORP SECY,
GEN COUNSEL
E G WALLACE JR,EXPL MGR & CHRMN
D CHRIS BARDEN,MGR,OPERS
JOSEPH COX,CONTROLLER
CHRISTOPHER BARDEN,PETR ENG
JOSIE FRIDLEY,OFC MGR,SECY/TREAS
JOSIE@MCALESTERFUEL.COM
WESLEY FRANKLIN,CHF GEOL CONSLT
BILL RIENITS,CHF GEOPHY CONSLT
MCBAY COMPANY
8548 FM 2022 NORTH
GRAPELAND,TX 75844
PH 936 544-5224 FAX 936 544-9329
MCBRIDE J L ENTERPRISES
P O BOX 2316
KILGORE,TX 75663 PH 903 984-8377
JERREL L MCBRIDE,EQUIP SLS MGR
DEBRA G MCBRIDE,PROD,OFC MGR
DAVID A MCBRIDE,DRLG SUPT
MCBRIDE L R,ENGINEERING,INC SEE
L.R. MCBRIDE,INC
MCCABE L RICHARD & COMPANY
PO BOX 3091 GLENSTONE STATION
SPRINGFIELD,MO 65808-3091 PH 417 865-4442
R L MC CABE,PRES,CEO
L FELDMANN,VP
M MCCABE,VP
G FELDMANN,MNGNG DIR
A FELDMANN,ASST DIR
MCCALL PIPE SUPPLY INC
RR 1 BOX 40
FAIRMOUNT CITY,PA 16224-9601
PH 814 275-2505 FAX 814 275-2505
CARL E MCCALL,OWNER
MCCALLON EARL R
D/B/A PETROLEUM LAND CONSULTING
108 BLACK OAK LN
MADISONVILLE,LA 70447-9362
PH 985 845-8760 EMCCALLON@YAHOO.COM
MCCANN J J,WATER WELL DRLG & SERVICE
910 SHORT LN
LAKE CHARLES,LA 70601-7063
PH 318 439-4279
MCCANN LAND SERVICES
PO BOX 820308
HOUSTON,TX 77282 PH 281 493-9462
MCCARTER JOHN H,JR,GEOL
2012 UNIVERSITY AVE
MONROE,LA 71203-3434 PH 318 343-2090
MCCARTY WARD,INC
PO BOX 788
LIBERTY,TX 77575
PH 936 336-7313 FAX 936 336-1010

WMCCARTY@TXUCOM.NET
CURTIS HUDNALL,PRES
JOHN HUDNALL,VP
MCCAUGHEY OIL CORPORATION
PO BOX 6990
TYLER,TX 75711-6990 PH 903 592-0578
FAX 903 561-4254
KEVIN HALBERT,PRES
CHARLOTTE HALBERT,VP
LINDA B DORSEY,SECY/TREAS
MCCAULEY O BULLOCK JR,INC
8655 JEFFERSON HWY 9 STONES THROW
BATON ROUGE,LA 70809 PH 225 603-4884
FAX 225 922-9309
MCCLAIN FORREST M,IND OIL OPR & GEOL
6689 HOBBS LANDING DR E
DUBLIN,OH 43017-6020 PH 713 896-9937
FAX 713 896-7537
MCCLELLAN DAN R,GEOL
PO BOX 1086
BENTON,LA 71006-1086 PH 318 425-7074
MCCLELLAN T R GEOL
PO BOX 1086
BENTON,LA 71006-1086 PH 318 326-4563
MCCLOSKEY,RAY
OIL LEASES
3771 PURDUE ST
HOUSTON,TX 77005-1127 PH 713 817-5650
RAY.MCCLOSKEY@COMCAST.NET
RAY MCCLOSKEY,CPL OWNER
MCCLURE ALAN C,ASSOCIATES,INC
2929 BRIARPARK DR STE 220
HOUSTON,TX 77042-3717 PH 713 789-1840
FAX 713 789-1347 WWW.ACMA-INC.COM
INFO@ACMA-INC.COM
SCOTT C MCCLURE,PRES
DEITMAR DETER,ASSOC
DARREL HARVEY,SR STAFF NAVAL ARCHITECT
MCCLYMOND,LTD SEE
PETROLEUM EXPLORATION CO,LTD
MCCOMBS ENERGY
5599 SAN FELIPE ST STE 1200
HOUSTON,TX 77056-2728 PH 713 621-0033
FAX 713 621-1670 WWW.MCCOMBSENERGY.COM
BILL FORNEY,JR,PRES
RICKY HAIKIN,VP,FIN
LARRY WYONT,VP,OPERS
PHILLIP FORNEY,VP,GEOL
CHARLES FORNEY,VP,LAND
BILLY FORNEY III,VP
JOHNNY FORNEY,VP
MCCOMMONS OIL COMPANY
1700 COMMERCE ST STE 1200
DALLAS,TX 75201-5354 PH 214 742-9183
FAX 214 742-9186
BRUCE MCCOMMONS,PRES
JAMES W MCCOMMONS,VP
NANCY SQUYRES,OFC MGR
DAVID WEATHERFORD,FLD OPERS
MCCONNELL & SCULLY INC,OIL WELL SERVICING
146 W MAIN ST
HOMER,MI 49245 PH 517 568-4104
PH 517 568-4106(SHOP) FAX 517 568-7120
PH 517 568-3838(PUMP SHOP)
WWW.MCCONNELLSCULLY.COM
MCCONNELLANDSCULLYINC@GMAIL.COM

RON MCCONNELL,CEO
RONNIE MCCONNELL JR,PRES
KEVIN SMITH,VP OPERS
ELAINE M SEITZ,SECY/TREAS,OFC MGR
MCCOOK COMPANY
3600 OLD BULLARD RD STE 200
TYLER,TX 75701 PH 903 509-2511
PETER MCCOOK,PETR LDMN
MCCORD EXPLORATION CO SEE
MCCORD PRODUCTION LTD
MCCORD PRODUCTION LTD
55 WAUGH DR STE 515
HOUSTON,TX 77007 PH 713 651-1414
FAX 713 651-0077
CHARLES T MCCORD,III,OWNER
CMCCORD@MCCORDPROD.COM
DONNA K RAINS,ADMIN MGR
DRAINS@MCCORDPROD.COM
MCCOY M R
PO BOX 4333
SHREVEPORT,LA 71134-0333 PH 318 221-5568
MCCOY REAGAN S
100 W HOUSTON STE 1500
SAN ANTONIO,TX 78205-1424
PH 210 224-4455 FAX 210 224-6430
MCCREA PETROLEUM CONSULTANTS LLC
19012 ADRIAN WAY
LAKE TRAVIS,TX 78645-9664
PH 512 217-3699
CLIFF MCCREA
MCCREVEY JOHN A,CONSULTING GEOL
2 CARLOTTA COURT
HOUSTON,TX 77074-7817 PH 713 777-8303
MCCUBBIN OIL COMPANY
1100 WINCHESTER CIR
KILGORE,TX 75662-3450 PH 903 984-0504
REX MCCUBBIN,OWNER
CHARLA R WISDOM,AGENT
MCCULLOUGH WELL SERVICE
1309 WILLOW LN
PENNSBORO,WV 26415 PH 304 659-3230
FAX 304 659-2805
B F MCCULLOUGH,OWNER
MCCULLOUGH/WESTERN ATLAS INTERNATIONAL
SEE ATLAS WIRELINE SERVICES DIV OF
WESTERN ATLAS INTERNATIONAL,INC
MCCUTCHIN RONALD LEE
PO BOX 670307,10711 PRESTON RD STE 200
DALLAS,TX 75367-0307 PH 214 750-7799
FAX 214 750-7790
MCDAVID JOHN SANFORD,ATTORNEY AT LAW
OIL/GAS TITLE OPINIONS,BOARD WORK &
RELATED REAL ESTATE MATTERS
PO BOX 23059,2000 AMSOUTH PLAZA
JACKSON,MS 39225-3059 PH 601 360-9014
FAX 601 355-6136 WWW.YOUNGWILLIAMS.COM
JMCDAVID@YOUNGWILLIAMS.COM
MCDAVID NOBLIN & WEST PLLC
248 E CAPITOL ST STE 840
JACKSON,MS 39201-2505
PH 601 948-3305 FAX 601 354-4789
MNW@MNWLAW.COM
JOHN L MCDAVID
WILLIAM C NOBLIN,JR
WILLIAM ERIC WEST

MCDONALD BOTTOM HOLE PRESSURE SPECIAL,INC
RENTALS,REPAIRS,CALIB,SLS,INTERPRETATIONS
AND REPORTING (RESERVOIR DATA)
1969 GRAND CAILLOU RD
HOUMA,LA 70363
PH 985 873-0120 FAX 985 873-0844
WWW.MCDONALDGAUGES.COM
KENNETH D MCDONALD,PRES
KEN@MCDONALDGAUGES.COM

MCDONALD RESOURCES
600 ALLEN CAMP RD
JEFFERSON,TX 75657 PH 903 672-5297
CHARLIE MCDONALD,OWNER

MCDONALD ROLAND E TRUST
4849 GREENVILLE AVE STE 1350
DALLAS,TX 75206-4124 PH 214 369-7608
FAX 214 369-4242
CLYDE S MCCALL JR,TRUSTEE
MAE C PLASCH PESEK,VP/TECH SVCS

MCDONOUGH MARINE SERVICE
17500 MARKET ST
CHANNELVIEW,TX 77530-3800 PH 281 452-5887
FAX 281 452-9682 WWW.MCDONOUGHMARINE.COM
RON WHITE,VP,PROJ CARGO
JOHN STEVENSON,SALES MGR/TX
DAVID RIGGINS,SALES

MCDONOUGH N E & CO
6715 HOLLYTREE CIR
TYLER,TX 75703-0925
PH 903 509-4141 FAX 903 509-4142
N E MCDONOUGH,CEO,PRES

MCDOWELL ROBERT E,PETR ENGR,IND PROD
PO BOX 5897,3556 YOUREE DR
SHREVEPORT,LA 71135-5897 PH 318 869-2088

MCDOWELL SAFETY & HEALTH SERVICES
PO BOX 190, 808 UTILITY RD
SANGER,TX 76266-0190 PH 940 458-0203
KEN ROGUS KROGUS@MCDOWELLSAFETY.COM

MCELWAINE & ASSOCIATES,INC
CONSULTANTS,GEOL,MINING,ENVIRONMENTAL
4300 LOCHRIDGE RD
NORTH LITTLE ROCK,AR 72216-7456
PH 501 372-3362

MCEVER OIL COMPANY
8198 FM 2064
TROUP,TX 75789 PH 903 842-3013
FAX 903 842-3014
CARL MCEVER,PRES

MCEVOY WILLIS SEE
CAMERON

MCFARLAND BILL T,OIL & GAS PROPERTIES,INC
24619 POTTER RD
OPP,AL 36467-6013 PH 334 493-0420

MCFARLAND-TRITAN,LLC
921 SEACO CT
DEER PARK,TX 77536 PH 713 864-3366
FAX 713 864-3252 SALES@MCFARLANDPUMP.COM
DAN SHAW,PRES
CHRIS ENGEL,SLS

MCGEE DRILLING
PO BOX 4052
LIBERTY,TX 77575-4052 PH 409 336-7181
PH 409 336-8302
JERRY MCGEE,DRLG SUPT

MCGEHEE H C,OIL PROD
4034 EASTWOOD DR

JACKSON,MS 39211-6443 PH 601 354-1084

MCGINTY-DURHAM,INC
PO BOX 7979
ALEXANDRIA,LA 71306-0979 PH 318 445-0054
FAX 318 445-0804
JMCGINTY@MCGINTYDURHAM.COM
JOE K MCGINTY JR,PRES

MCGOLDRICK BRUCE M
8808 MCGOLDRICK DR
SHREVEPORT,LA 71129-5014 PH 318 687-6490

MCGOLDRICK OIL CO
8808 MCGOLDRICK DR
SHREVEPORT,LA 71129-5014 PH 318 687-6490
FAX 318 687-3710
BRUCE M MCGOLDRICK,OWNER

MCGOWAN WORKING PARTNERS,INC
PO BOX 55809,1837 CRANE RIDGE DR
JACKSON,MS 39296-5809
PH 601 982-3444 FAX 601 982-1879
SIBLEY,MS SHOP - PH 601 446-5380
WATERPROOF,LA HOLLY RIDGE SHOP -
PH 318 749-3481
VIDALIA,LA FAIRVIEW SHOP -
ROANOKE,LA SHOP - PH 337 753-2385
EUNICE,LA BAYOU MALLET SHOP -
PH 337 457-2770
EUNICE,LA TEPETATE SHOP -
GIST,TX FIELD SHOP - PH 409 745-1830
ANAHUAC,TX FIELD SHOP -
VICTORIA,TX HEYSER FIELD -
PH 361 897-1918
LAPLACE,LA BONNET CARRE SHOP -
PH 985 652-2825
DERIDER,LA DEQUINCY SHOP -
PH 337 786-8011
BELLE CHASE,LA STELLA SHOP -
THOMPSON,TX N THOMPSON SHOP -
PH 281 343-0541
DERIDDER,LA HURRICANE CREEK SHOP -
PH 337 725-6282
PIERCE,TX N WITHERS FIELD OFFICE -
PH 979 543-1936
COTTON LAKE FIELD - CHAMBERS CO,TX
N SHANNON FIELD - ORANGE COUNTY,TX
THOMPSON FIELD - FORT BEND COUNTY,TX
KINDER,LA FIELD OFFICE - PH 337 738-3016
OPELOUSAS FIELD - ST LANDRY PARISH,LA
SAVOY FIELD - ST LANDRY PARISH,LA
CHOUPIQUE FIELD - CALCASIEU PARISH,LA
SINGER FIELD - BEAUREGARD PARISH,LA
COLORADO FIELD - JIM HOGG COUNTY,TX
LUNDELL FIELD - DUVAL COUNTY,TX
SEVEN SISTERS FIELD - DUVAL COUNTY,TX
HARTBURG,NW FIELD - NEWTON COUNTY,TX
WEST LASALLE FIELD - JACKSON COUNTY,TX
MAGNET WITHERS FIELD,ETTA FIELD & LANE
CITY FIELD - WHARTON COUNTY,TX
WALKMAN FIELD - BRAZORIA COUNTY,TX
LOCKRIDGE FIELD - BRAZORIA COUNTY,TX
JACKSON PASTURE FIELD - CHAMBERS CO,TX
LARTO LAKE FIELD - CATAHOULA PARISH,LA
LONG SLOUGH FIELD - LASALLE PARISH,LA
SANDY BAYOU FIELD - LASALLE PARISH,LA
SALINE LAKE FIELD - CATAHOULA & LASALLE
PARISHES,LA
VACUUM FIELD - LEA COUNTY,NM

COTTONWOOD,SOUTH FIELD - LIBERTY
COUNTY,TX
PERKINS FIELD - CALCASIEU PARISH,LA
LAKE ST JOHN FIELD - CONCORDIA &
TENSAS PARISHES,LA
KOONTZ FIELD - VICTORIA COUNTY,TX
LUCILLE FIELD - LIVE OAK,TX
ALLIMAR FIELD - LIVE OAK COUNTY,TX
SHULER FIELD,UNION CO,AR
FLAT BRANCH FIELD - GREENE CO,MS
LIVINGSTON FIELD - POLK CO,TX
WEST EUCUTTA FIELD - WAYNE CO,MS
EAST MAGNET WITHERS FLD - WHARTON CO,TX
WEST MAGNET WITHERS FLD - WHARTON CO,TX
LOLITA FIELD - JACKSON CO,TX
ELTON FIELD - JEFFERSON DAVIS PARISH,LA
EAST RICHIE FIELD - ACADIA PARISH,LA
PLYMOUTH FIELD - SAN PATRICIO COUNTY,TX
SAXET FIELD - NUECES COUNTY,TX

MCGOWEN & FOWLER,PLLC
2602 MCKINNEY AVE STE 305
DALLAS,TX 75204 PH 214 265-1335
FAX 214 265-7727 WWW.MCGOWENFOWLER.COM
JAMES MCGOWEN JIM@MCGOWENFOWLER.COM
HOUSTON,TX OFFICE - 8584 KATY FWY STE 335
77024 PH 713 722-7500 FAX 713 722-9675

MCGREGOR OIL & GAS,INC
1733 WOODSTEAD CT STE 200
THE WOODLANDS,TX 77380-3401
PH 281 363-0099
JAY W MCGREGOR,EXPL MGR

MCGREGOR OIL COMPANY
PO BOX 5909,901 PIERREMONT RD
SHREVEPORT,LA 71135-5909 PH 318 865-0133
FAX 318 865-1305
JAMES H MCGREGOR,PRTNR
JAY MCGREGOR,PRTNR,GEOL

MCGUIRE T W & ASSOCIATES,INC,PETR ENGRS
PO BOX 1763,416 TRAVIS ST STE 1400
SHREVEPORT,LA 71166-1763 PH 318 222-0761
FAX 318 222-0799
JAMES T MARANTO,PRES
ROBERT T MARANTO,PETR ENGR & VP

MCINTYRE BRUCE M & CO
2323 S VOSS STE 215
HOUSTON,TX 77057 PH 713 783-5080
FAX 713 783-5258
BRUCE M MCINTYRE,PRES

MCKAY EQUIPMENT,LLC
633 PAPWORTH AVE
METAIRIE,LA 70005-3112
PH 504 828-1068 FAX 504 828-1422
MCQUIP.COM
MARK MCKAY,OWNER
LARRY HAMM,SLS MGR LARRY@MCQUIP.COM

MCKIM & CREED,INC
SURVEY AND ENGINEERING
9960 W SAM HOUSTON PKWY S STE 200
HOUSTON,TX 77099
PH 713 659-0021 PH 281 741-1460
JAY CANINE,VP

MCKINNEY DRILLING COMPANY
1265 BLAIRS BRIDGE RD
LITHIA SPRINGS,GA 30122
PH 404 948-9521 FAX 404 948-9553
WWW.MCKINNEYDRILLING.COM

SAMMY ODUM,DIST MGR
ED MUNN,DIST MGR

MCKINNEY OIL PRODUCER
PO BOX 14
LOUISVILLE,IL 62858-0014 PH 618 665-3374
RONALD MCKINNEY,PRES

MCKINNON LAND SERVICES LLC
412 TURTLE CREEK DR
SHREVEPORT,LA 71115 PH 318 470-9370
PATRICK MCKINNON
PATMCKINNON@COMCAST.NET

MCKNIGHT PEYTON,OIL OPR & PROD
814 KINGSWOOD DR
TYLER,TX 75703-3540
PH 903 509-1500 FAX 903 533-9391
PEYTON MCKNIGHT,OWNER
MABLE SULLIVAN,OFC MGR

MCKOWN C I & SON,INC
PO BOX 711
NEWTON,WV 25266-0711 PH 304 565-7318
FAX 304 565-3804

MCLARTY OIL PROPERTIES,INC
102 N COLLEGE AVE STE 304
TYLER,TX 75702-7213
PH 903 597-1302 FAX 903 597-1310
SPMCOIL@AOL.COM
S P PAT MCLARTY,LDMN

MCLEOD CURTIS R,OIL & GAS,PETR LDMN,CPL
400 TRAVIS ST STE 809
SHREVEPORT,LA 71101-3111 PH 318 227-9508
FAX 318 227-9762

MCLEOD GEORGE L,INC
14825 ST MARYS LN STE 115
HOUSTON,TX 77079-2989 PH 713 464-8900
FAX 713 464-8902

MCLEOD RICHARD
PETR GEOL OIL & GAS PROSPECTS,
DETAIL FIELD STUDIES
3610 CAPE FOREST DR
KINGWOOD,TX 77345-1321 PH 281 913-2136
FAX 281 913-2129 RRMCLEODGEOL@AOL.COM

MCMAHAN THOMAS V
P O BOX 1517
HOUSTON,TX 77251-1517 PH 713 977-8194
FAX 713 781-3863 TOM@TOMMCMAHAN.COM

MCMORAN OIL & GAS LLC SEE
MCMORAN EXPLORATION CO

MCMURREY EXPLORATION & PRODUCTION CO LLC
PO BOX 925217
HOUSTON,TX 77292 PH 281 293-0811
JAMES M MCMURREY,CO-OWNER
CHARLES D MCMURREY SR,CO-OWNER

MCMURREY R J,PRODUCTION CO
PO BOX 6890
TYLER,TX 75711-6890 PH 903 597-7081
BETTY MCMURREY,OFC MGR

MCMURRY-MACCO LIFT SYSTEMS SEE
WEATHERFORD

MCNAMES & PATTERSON
P O BOX 12781
JACKSON,MS 39236-2781 PH 601 981-9533
P M MCNAMES,PRTNR
GARY K PATTERSON,PRTNR

MCNEELY JOHN B,IND GEOL,OIL OPERATOR
808 TRAVIS STE 1424
HOUSTON,TX 77002-5726 PH 713 651-1200

JOHNB.MCNEELY@SBCGLOBAL.NET

MCQUEEN & MCQUEEN
ENERGY ADVISORY & MGMNT FIRM
2110 PINE RIVER DR
KINGWOOD,TX 77339-2343 PH 281 358-2463
FAX 281 358-2463 JEMC@KINGWOODCABLE.COM
JERELD E MCQUEEN

MCRAE EXPLORATION & PRODUCTION,INC
7904 N SAM HOUSTON PKWY W STE 310
HOUSTON,TX 77064-3454 PH 281 664-2700
FAX 281 664-2707
CODY A MCRAE,PRES
MICHAEL G NALL,VP,TREAS
F J MESTAYER,VP EXPL

MCROBERTS FRANCINE L
225 SUNSET DR
BROWNSVILLE,TX 78520-7313 PH 956 542-7346

MCTEE CLIFFORD R,GEOL
PO BOX 356
TILDEN,TX 78072-0356 PH

MD TOTCO
1200 CYPRESS CREEK RD
CEDAR PARK,TX 78613
PH 512 340-5000 FAX 512 340-5219
MDTOTCOCUSTOMERSERVI@NOV.COM
GREG MARTIN,VP
ALLEN THOMAS,GENERAL MGR,CEDAR PARK
MIKE SMITH,ORDER FULLFILL & FLD ENGRG
- MD TOTCO - HOUSTON -
HOUSTON,TX OFFICE - 12950 W LITTLE YORK
RD BLDG A,77041 PH 713 937-5700
FAX 713 937-5730
CLIFF PRICE,SR DIR GLOBAL OPERS
BOBBY STINNETT,SR DIR DRLG OPTIMIZATION
STEVE WALSH,DIR OF GLOBAL SLS
STEVE THOMPSON,DIR,NEW BUS DEV
JEFF DUGAN,DIR OF OPERS,BLACKSTAR
KEITH FOLKS,COORD
- MD TOTCO - GULF COAST REGION -
HOUSTON,TX OFFICE - 8535 JACKRABBIT RD
STE N,77095 PH 832 575-2000
FAC 832 575-2090
ANDREW RITZELL,MGR,GULF COAST REG
CRAIG BICE,MGR,SOUTH TEXAS DIST
JASON NIGHTENGALE,MGR,CENT TEXAS DIST
BEN FRAZAR,MGR,RIG UP GROUP
NEW ORLEANS,LA OFFICE - 1515 POYDRAS ST
STE 850,70112 PH 504 636-3664
FAX 504 636-3670
SHELBY EDWARDS,MGR,EASTERN REG
CHRIS DEGEORGE,MGR,NORTHEAST DIST
CHRIS WESTPHAL,MGR,OKLAHOMA DIST
CONWAY,AR OFFICE - 320 GRIFFITH ST STE 1
72034 PH 501 328-2122 FAX 501 328-2036
BROUSSARD,LA OFFICE - 1027 N CRUSE AVE
70518 PH 337 837-4725 FAX 337 837-4612
LAUREL,MS OFFICE - HWY 84 EAST,VICTORY RD
39440 PH 337 837-4725
ELK CITY,OK OFFICE - 1022 S MERRITT RD
73644 PH 580 225-8980 FAX 580 225-8982
MCALESTER,OK OFFICE - 1216 GEORGE NIGH
EXPY STE A,74501 PH 918 423-6206
FAX 918 429-0938
YUKON,OK OFFICE - 919 17TH ST,73099
PH 405 350-7408 FAX 405 354-6749
DUBOIS,PA OFFICE - 602 W DUBOIS AVE #9

15801 PH 814 502-9200 OR 800 445-9051
SHREVEPORT,LA OFFICE - 5100 INTERSTATE CR
STE B,71109 PH 318 635-9700
FAX 318 635-9755
ALICE, TX OFFICE - 2351 ENERGY AVE,78332
PH 361 668-8288 FAX 361 664-2875
BUFFALO,TX OFFICE - 1789 HWY 79 S,75831
PH 903 322-6610 FAX 903 322-6612
FORT WORTH,TX OFFICE - 2354 GREAT SW PKWY
76106 PH 817 625-8000 FAX 817 625-7811
TYLER,TX OFFICE - 4912 HIGH TECH DR,75703
PH 903 534-3677 FAX 903 534-0845
HOUSTON,TX (WAGNER INSTRUMENTATION) OFC -
8020 EL RIO,77054 PH 713 741-9470
FAX 713 741-9473
WILLIAM ALLISON,DIST MGR
STAFFORD,TX (BLACKSTAR EM) OFFICE -
10404 MULA RD,77477 PH 281 568-1336
FAX 281 568-1405
JEFF DUGAN,DIR OF OPERS
- MC TOTCO - WESTERN REGION -
ODESSA,TX OFFICE - 822 W SECOND ST,79763
PH 432 337-5311 FAX 432 332-3966
MIKE HORTON,MGR,WESTERN REG
ARMANDO OCHOA,MGR,ROCKY MTN DIST
DANIEL HERNANDEZ,MGR,WEST TEXAS/PACIFIC
COAST DIST
ANCHORAGE,AK (QUADCO,INC - DISTRIB) OFC -
6116 NIELSON WAY,99518 PH 907 563-8999
FAX 907 563-8985
BAKERSFIELD,CA OFFICE - 3559 LANDCO DR
STE B,93308 PH 661 633-9241 OR 9247
FAX 661 633-2047
RIFLE,CO OFFICE - 702A BUCKHORN DR,81650
PH 970 625-4390 FAX 970 625-4391
AZTEC,NM OFFICE - 30 CR 3351,87410
PH 970 625-4390 FAX 970 625-4391
HOBBS,NEW OFFICE - 1926 W BENDER,88240
PH 505 393-7166 FAX 505 393-3993
WILLISTON,ND OFFICE -
PO BOX 1142,101 W 22ND ST,58801
PH 701 770-0629 FAX 701 774-7398
VERNAL,UT OFFICE - 4971 S 4625 E,84078
PH 435 790-7756 FAX 435 789-6568
ROCK SPRINGS,WY OFFICE -
PO BOX 1633,6451 FOOTHILL BLVD, BLDG B
82902-1633 PH 307 362-2402
FAX 307 362-2698
- CANADA -
LEDUC,ALBERTA,CAN OFFICE - 6621-45TH ST
T9E7E3 PH 780 986-6063 FAX 780 986-6845
RANDY BAUDIN,MGR,CANADIAN REGION
JASON LEHMAN,STORE MGR
GRANDE PRAIRIE,ALBERTA,CAN - 11453-97 AVE
T8V5R8 PH 780 539-6281 FAX 780 539-6250
CALGARY,ALBERTA,CAN OFFICE -
2935 - 19 ST,NE,T2E7A2
PH 403 569-2050 FAX 403 569-2079
LISE MARTIN,STORE MGR LISE.MARTIN@NOV.COM
- MEXICO -
VILLAHERMOSA,TABASCO,MEXICO OFFICE -
PARQUE INDUSTRIAL DEIT CARRET
VHSA-CARDENAS R/A ANACLETO CANABAL 1RA
SECCION PH 52 993 310-3100
JOSE PEREZ,AREA MGR
- SINGAPORE -

SINGAPORE OFFICE -
 C/O NATIONAL OILWELL VARCO PTE LTD
 29,TUAS BAY DR 637429 PH 65 6594-1000
 FAX 65 6795-2291
  BILL JAENSCH,REG MGR
  WILANIN NENG BUAH,SLS ENGR
 - CHINA -
BEIJING CHINA OFFICE -
 C/O NATIONAL OILWELL VARCO INTL INC
 AIR CHINA PLAZA STE 1603-1606
 NO.36 XIAOYUN RD,CHAOYANG DIST,100027
 PH (+86-10) 8447-5109
 FAX (+86-10) 8447-5110 OR 8447-5898
  JOE LEOW,REG SLS MGR
  SAM LI,AREA MGR
 - MIDDLE EAST-AFRICA -
 - UNITED ARAB EMIRATES -
DUBAI OFFICE - JEBEL ALI FREE ZONE
 (SOUTH) DUBAI U.A.E.
 PO BOX 61490,PLOT S 50601
 PH 971 4 811-0100 FAX 971 4 811-0285
  RAFFOUL RAFFOUL,REGIONAL MGR
  JIHAD SALIBA,INSIDE SLS
  DALE SLOUGH,SLS ACCT MGR
 - SAUDI ARABIA (VETCO) -
AL KHOBAR 31952,KSA OFFICE -
 VETCO SAUDI ARABIA
 PO BOX 31849
 PH 966-3-882-6300 FAX 966-3-822-9595
  SALES.VETCO@VARCO.COM.SA
 - ALGERIA -
OUARGLA,ALGERIA OFFICE -
 C/O NATIONAL OILWELL VARCO
 BP 52,HASSI-MESSAOUD 30500
 PH 213-0-29-73-12-54
 FAX 213-0-29-73-12-69
  NADIR BENZINA,SLS & SVC,AFRICA
 - VENEZUELA -
  TUBOSCOPE BRANDT DE VENEZUELA
ZONA INDUSTRIAL MARACAIBO,ESTADO ZULIA,
 AV 53 140-315
 PH 58 261 7349 619,7349 701,7358 824
 FAX 58 261 7349 624
  JORGE RINCON,REG MGR
ZONA INDUSTRIAL,MATURIN,VENEZUELA OFFICE
 VARCO DE VENEZUELA-EAST
 PARCELA NO.6,MANZANA NO.8,GALPON
 INDUSTRIAL NO.3 PH 58 291 6516 489
 PH 58 291 6516 866 FAX 58 291 6516 083
  LEONARDO MOJICA,OPERS MGR
CIUDAD OJEDA,ESTADO ZULIA,VENEZUELA OFC -
 TUBOSCOPE BRANDT DE VENEZUELA
 SECTOR LAS MOROCHAS,CALLE AMPARO #130
 DESTRAS DE MCDONALD
 PH/FAX 58 265 631 6028
  NESTOR URDANETA
 - ARGENTINA -
PROVINCIA DE NEUQUEN,ARGENTINA OFFICE
 TUBOSCOPE VETCO ARGENTINA S.A.
 PARQUE INDUSTRIAL ESTE LOTE 3
 SECCION E NEUQUEN PH 54 299 44 13207
 PH 54 299 44 13185
  ALEJANDRO ARAUJO,AREA MGR
 - BRAZIL -
 AV.AMARAL PEIXOTO, KM 164,5
 IMBOASSICA-MACAE/RJ CEP 27925-290

PH 55 22 2773 0600 FAX 55 22 2773 0606
 RENATO SANT'ANA,DIST MGR
 - SCOTLAND -
PORTLETHEN,ABERDEEN,SCOTLAND OFFICE -
 BADENTOY CRESCENT,BADENTOY PARK,AB12 4YD
 PH 44 1224 343 701 FAX 44 1224 343 643
  DEREK FORSYTH,REG MGR
  ALLEN MCINTOSH,AREA MGR NORTH SEA/NORWAY
  STUART DEMPSTER,INSIDE SLS
  DAVID SUTHERLAND,PROJ ENGR
  BRYAN SCHEWE,REG SVC MGR
 - RUSSIA -
MOSCOW 101000 RUSSIA OFFICE -
 ULANSKY LAND 5,3RD FL
 PH 7 495 775 2540 FAX 7 495 981 3470
  MAXIM SEDOV,AREA MGR
 - INDIA -
NATIONAL OILWELL VARCO PTE LTD
 (INSTRUMENTATION MD TOTCO)
MUMBAI INDIA OFFICE -
 B WING,1ST FL,AKRUTI TRADE CENTRE,RD #7
 MIDC,MAROL,ANDHERI EAST 400093
 PH 91 22 6140 3200 FAX 91 22 6140 3290
  GEORGE GABRIEL,COUNTRY MGR
  K S NAGENDRA,ADMIN MGR
  ANAND NARAYANASWAMY,SVC MGR
  CHETAN KENY,SLS ENGR

MDC OIL COMPANY
 2 PINE BRIAR CIR
 HOUSTON,TX 77056-1113 PH 713 840-7030
 GMANDDD@SBCGLOBAL.NET
  GORDON G MARCUM II,PRES
  LARRY S MARCUM,VP

MDU RESOURCES GROUP,INC
  ELECTRIC/NAT GAS DISTRIB,UTILITY SVCS
  PIPELINE/MIDSTREAM,OIL/NAT GAS PROD
  CONSTRUCTION MATERIALS & SERVICES
 PO BOX 5650
 BISMARCK,ND 58506-5650 PH 701 530-1000

MEADOR ENTERPRISES INC
 6852 CR 296E
 KILGORE,TX 75662 PH 903 643-2304
  KIT MEADOR,PRES
  DIANA MEADOR,SECY/TREAS

MEAGHER ENERGY ADVISORS
 PO BOX 4782,6040 GREENWOOD PLAZA BLVD
 GREENWOOD VILLAGE, CO 80111
 PH 303 721-6354 FAX 303 721-0216
 WWW.MEAGHERADVISORS.COM
  MATTHEW E MEAGHER,PRES
  MMEAGHER@MEAGHERADVISORS.COM
  CHRIS MCCARTHY,PE,EXEC VP
  CMCCARTHY@MEAGHERADVISORS.COM
  DAVID BICKERSTAFF,CONSLT GEOL
  DBICKERSTAFF@MEAGHERADVISORS.COM
  NICK ASHER,VP BUS DEV
  NASHER@MEAGHERADVISORS.COM
  JANICE HAWKINS,LDMN
  JHAWKINS@MEAGHERADVISORS.COM
  AARON HUGEN,RESERVOIR & FACILITIES ENGR
  AHUGEN@MEAGHERADVISORS.COM
 TULSA OK OFFICE - 1731 E 71ST 74136-5108
 PH 918 481-5900 FAX 918 481-5901
  TERI L WILLIAMS,COO
  TWILLIAMS@MEAGHERADVISORS.COM
  MATT WILLIAMS,BUS DEV

  MWILLIAMS@MEAGHERADVISORS.COM
  JACQUE L SEMPLE,PROJ MGR
  JSEMPLE@MEAGHERADVISORS.COM
  BUCK WALSH,RESERVOIR ENGR
  BWALSH@MEAGHERADVISORS.COM
  BRANDI DANIELS,ENGNR TECH
  BDANIELS@MEAGHERADVISORS.COM
  JEAN HALL,CPL,SR LDMN
  JHALL@MEAGHERADVISORS.COM
  PAUL MCNABB,SR ENGRG ANALYST
  PMCNABB@MEAGHERADVISORS.COM

MEARS A W DOWNING,JR
 712 MAIN ST STE 2200
 HOUSTON,TX 77002-3290 PH 713 546-2527
 FAX 713 546-2507
  DOWNINGM@MOSBACHERENERGY.COM

MEAUX ROBERT J GEOL
 2919 ROYAL CIRCLE DR
 KINGWOOD,TX 77339-2557 PH 281 358-8487

MECKEL L D AND COMPANY,GEOL
 1120 RACE ST
 DENVER,CO 80206-2809 PH 713 523-8862
 FAX 713 523-8944

MECOM JOHN W COMPANY,THE
 P O BOX 2566
 HOUSTON,TX 77252-2566 PH 713 993-0225
  JOHN W MECOM,JR,CHRMN OF BD,CHF EXEC OFCR
  JOHN P O'ROURKE,TREAS/SECY

MEDALLION OIL COMPANY
 PO BOX 1101,1407 FANNIN ST
 HOUSTON,TX 77251-1101 PH 713 654-0144
 FAX 713 654-1524 WWW.MEDGRP.COM
  ROBERT J PILEGGE,CEO
  JERELD E MCQUEEN,PRES JEMC@MEDGRP.COM

MEDCO ENERGI US,LLC
 PO BOX 52506
 LAFAYETTE,LA 70505-2506
 PH 337 237-1822 FAX 337 237-1823
 LAFAYETTE,LA OFFICE - 201 RUE IBERVILLE
 STE 700, 70508
  MARTIN BECH,PRES
  MARTIN.BECH@US.MEDCOENERGI.COM
  ALLISON BOURGEOIS,CONTROLLER/MGR FIN
  ALLISON.BOURGEOIS@US.MEDCOENERGI.COM
  TERRY SUAREZ,LAND/LEGAL
  TERRY.SUAREZ@US.MEDCOENERGI.COM
  AMY FELL,PROD ACCT/REG COORD
  AMY.FELL@US.MEDCOENERGI.COM
  TED RUSSELL,PROD/OPERS & DRLG ENGR
  TED.RUSSELL@US.MEDCOENERGI.COM
  EARL BRUNET,OPERS MGR
  EARL.BRUNETL@US.MEDCOENERGI.COM

MEEKER & COMPANY INC
 OIL PRODUCERS
 PO BOX 470155
 FORT WORTH,TX 76147-0155 PH 817 738-5487
  L H MEEKER,PRES

MEEKS RONALD L,ATTY,C.P.L.
 PO BOX 3340
 CONROE,TX 77305-3340
 PH 713 516-8466 RLMMEEKS@GMAIL.COM

MELANCON JOHN A,CPL
 PO BOX 51721
 LAFAYETTE,LA 70505-1721
 PH 337 394-3324

MELANCON JOHN A,JR,OIL & GAS PROPERTIES
 PO BOX 52741
 LAFAYETTE,LA 70505-2741 PH 318 234-7339
 FAX 318 234-6265
  JOHN A MELANCON JR,CPL,OWNER

MELDER JACK O,P.E.
 10927 BRITTWAY
 HOUSTON,TX 77043 PH 281 589-6284
 FAX 281 589-6525

MELLON CREEK OPERATING CO
 ONE O'CONNOR PLAZA STE 1100
 VICTORIA,TX 77901-6549 PH 361 578-6271
 FAX 361 576-6890
  HUBERT BOWERS,ENGR

MELTON DOUGLAS C,JR,CONSULTANT
 14 RANNOCH DR
 BELLA VISTA,AR 72715-5603 PH 479 646-4669
  DOUG MELTON,OWNER

MELTON J ALLEN,PETROLEUM GEOL
 401 BRIARGATE WALK CIR
 LAFAYETTE,LA 70503 PH 337 237-5923
 FAX 337 235-6355

MENG OPERATING & EXPLORATION CO
 205 S BROADWAY ST
 NATCHEZ,MS 39120-3445 PH 601 442-6101
  LESTER MENG,JR,PRES

MERIDIAN ABSTRACT & TITLE,INC
  FULL SVC PETR ABSTRACTING,MORTGAGE TITLE
  REPORTS & MINERAL SEARCHES
 PO BOX 400,6009 MARSH RD
 HASLETT,MI 48840-0400 PH 517 339-4411
 PH 800 945-6645 FAX 517 339-4485
  RICHARD B PATTERSON,OWNER
  GAIL A GREEN,MGR
   GREENG@MERIDIANLANDGROUP.COM
  JEANETTE BUNN,SECY

MERIDIAN ENERGY CORPORATION
  LAND,EXPL & GAS STORAGE CONSUL SVCS
 PO BOX 610,6009 MARSH RD
 HASLETT,MI 48840-0610
 PH 517 339-8444
  RICHARD B PATTERSON,RPL/PRES (AAPL)(MAPL)
  JAMES R PATTERSON,CPL/LAND MGR (AAPL)
  (MAPL)

MERIDIAN LAND GROUP
 PO BOX 610,6009 MARSH RD
 HASLETT,MI 48840 PH 517 339-8444
  RICHARD B PATTERSON,PRES/RPL (MAPL)(AAPL)
  JAMES R PATTERSON,CPL/LAND MGR (MAPL)
  (AAPL)
  ADELE THOMPSON,LDMN (MAPL)
  TERRI SOHN,LAND ADMIN
  JENNA LOLLI,LAND ADMIN
  BOBBIE BLACK,LAND ADMIN

MERIDIAN OIL INC SEE
 BURLINGTON RESOURCES OIL AND GAS COMPANY

MERIDIAN PIPE & EQUIPMENT COMPANY INC
 417 W 18TH STE 102
 EDMOND,OK 73013
 PH 405 471-6645 FAX 405 471-6657
  DON PUMPHREY,VP,SLS PH 405 691-7058
 WICHITA,KS OFFICE - 727 N WACO STE 400
 67203-3900 PH 316 263-3201
 FAX 316 268-0718
  KELLY BREWSTER,CONTROLLER

MERIDIAN PRODUCTION SERVICES,LLC
 PO BOX 610,6009 MARSH RD
 HASLETT,MI 48840 PH 517 339-8444
  RICHARD B PATTERSON,MEMBER (AAPL)(MAPL)
  JENNA LOLLI,ADMIN ASST (AAPL) (MAPL)

MERIT ENERGY COMPANY LLC
 13727 NOEL RD STE 1200
 DALLAS,TX 75240 PH 972 701-8377
 FAX 972 960-1252 WWW.MERITENERGY.COM
  INFO@MERITENERGY.COM
  JASON LINDMARK,VP BUS DEV
   JASON.LINDMARK@MERITENERGY.COM
  MEGAN CUDDIHY,VP INVEST RELS
  MELANIE LANE,VP HUMAN RESOURCES

MERIT ENERGY SERVICES LLC SEE
 PENTERRA SERVICES,LLC

MERIT OILFIELD SERVICES,INC
 PO BOX 1858
 BUNA,TX 77612-1858 PH 409 994-5857
 FAX 409 994-5081
  ANDY WHITEHEAD,PRES
  AUSTIN WHITEHEAD,VP

MERKEL OIL
 151 REBECCA RD
 SUNNYVALE,TX 75182 PH 972 226-7033
  MERK13@YAHOO.COM

MERLIN EXPLORATION INC SEE
 ZORTH INC

MERLIN OIL & GAS,INC
 PO BOX 52928
 91 SETTLER'S TRACE BLVD,BLDG 4
 LAFAYETTE,LA 70508 PH 337 989-7200
 FAX 337 989-7279 WWW.MERLINOIL.COM
  MARK MILLER MARKMILLER@MERLINGAS.COM
   MARK.MILLER@MKMVENTUREGROUP.COM

MERLIN RESOURCES INC
 3002 COUNTRY CLUB RD
 LAKE CHARLES,LA 70605-5920
 PH 337 477-9952 FAX 337 477-9953
  MERLINMJV@SUDDENLINK.NET
  MERLIN J VERRET,PRES

MERLON INTERNATIONAL,INC
 5151 SAN FELIPE ST STE 2050
 HOUSTON,TX 77056-3727
 PH 713 365-9936 FAX 713 365-9987
  WWW.MERLONPET.COM
  JOHN R BARNWELL,PE,VP OPERS

MERMIS ENGINEERING INC,CONS PETR ENGRG
 21615 FRONTIERSMAN CT
 HOCKLEY,TX 77447 PH 281 290-8924
  DELVEN MERMIS,PE

MERRICO ACQUISITION SEE
 AMERICAN EXPLORATION CO

MERRIGAN KEVIN
 17 ROSE DR
 FORT LAUDERDALE,FL 33316
 PH 954 522-3344
  KEVIN MERRIGAN,PRES

MERRILL LYNCH BUSINESS FINANCIAL SERVICES
 1221 MCKINNEY STE 3900
 HOUSTON,TX 77010-2024
 PH 713 658-1218 FAX 281 528-4767
  BOBBY MOORE

MERRITT ENGINEERING,INC
 650 POYDRAS ST STE 2660
 NEW ORLEANS,LA 70130 PH 504 566-9802

 DAVID M METTZ,PETR ENGR

MERTZ ENERGY
 2211 NORFOLK ST STE 614
 HOUSTON,TX 77098 PH 281 205-8140
  CONTACT@MERTZENERGY.COM

MESA
  MFG OF MAGNESIUM,CAST IRON & SPEC
  ANODES
  ENGINEERING SOLUTIONS,TURNKEY CONSTR
  SVCS
 PO BOX 52608,4445 S 74TH E AVE
 TULSA,OK 74152-0608 PH 888 800-6372
 FAX 918 627-2676 WWW.MESAPRODUCTS.COM
  JOHN R COLE,VP-BUS DEV
   COLEJ@MESAPRODUCTS.COM
 HOUSTON,TX GULF COAST REG/MATERAL SLS
  OFFICE - PO BOX 671608,77267
  PH 281 445-8700 FAX 281 445-8880
 TALLAHASSEE,FL SOUTHEAST REG/MATERAL SLS
  CONSTRUCTION & TECH SVCS OFFICE -
  PO BOX 14325,32317 PH 850 893-9366
  FAX 850 893-9434

MESA OPERATING CO SEE
 PIONEER NATURAL RESOURCES COMPANY

MESA PRODUCTS,INC SEE
 MESA

MESOTEX ENERGY INC
 2205 CAPRI COURT
 PEARLAND,TX 77581 PH 713 542-8342
 FAX 281 741-3871 MESOTEX@USA.NET
  JOHN R LEWIS,PRES,GEOL

MESQUITE DEVELOPMENT CORP
 208 PRINZ ST
 SAN ANTONIO,TX 78213-1920
 PH 210 344-6588
  JOHN HERNDEN,PRES

MESSERS COMPANY,INC,THE
 7924 SUMMER NIGHT LN
 RICHMOND,TX 77469-4655
 PH 832 620-5167 HFMESSER@ATT.NET
  HENRY F MESSER,PRES

MESTENA OPERATING,LLC
 500 N SHORELINE BLVD STE 700
 CORPUS CHRISTI,TX 78401
 PH 361 884-2191 FAX 361 884-4730
  GEORGE E TANNER,PRES
  BRYAN CHAMBLESS,PROD MGR

METANO ENERGY III, LP
 7330 SAN PEDRO AVE STE 620
 SAN ANTONIO,TX 78216-6261
 PH 210 798-1414 FAX 210 798-1424
  ROBERT OLIVER,PRES
  JOHN BISSELL,EXEC VP
  MARK PARRISH,VP LAND
  ROGER ESPINOSA,EXPL

METERSMART,LP SEE
 HUNT OIL COMPANY

METRON GAS MEASUREMENT COMPANY SEE
 J-W MEASUREMENT COMPANY

METROPOLITAN WATER COMPANY,LP
 PO DRAWER 1146
 BRENHAM,TX 77834-1146
 PH 979 836-0122 FAX 979 836-0164
  WWW.METWATER.COM WSC@METWATER.COM
  W SCOTT CARLSON,PRES
  BETTY J CARLSON,VP/TREAS

SUSAN CARLSON,VP/SECY
THOMAS PUSATERI,LDMN
MELISSA WALKER,ADMIN ASST

MEWBOURNE OIL COMPANY
PO BOX 7698,3620 OLD BULLARD RD
TYLER,TX 75711-7698
PH 903 561-2900 FAX 903 561-1515
CURTIS W MEWBOURNE,CEO
KEN S WAITS,PRES,COO
ROE BUCKLEY,CHMN OF BD,CFO
MONTY WHETSTONE,VP OPER
BRUCE INSALACO,VP EXPL
MIDLAND,TX DIST OFFICE - 500 W TEXAS AVE
STE 1020,79701 PH 432 682-3715
FAX 432 685-4170
LARRY CUNNINGHAM,DIST MGR
HOBBS,NM DIST OFFICE - 701 S CECIL ST
88241 PH 575 393-5905
ROBIN TERRELL,DIST MGR
PERRYTON,TX DIST OFFICE - 601 E LOOP 143
79070 PH 806 435-6881 FAX 806 435-6885
BRENT THURMAN,DIST MGR
OKLAHOMA CITY,OK DIST OFFICE - ONE
LEADERSHIP SQ,211 N ROBINSON STE 2000
73102 PH 405 235-6374 FAX 405 232-8006
TONY PHILLIPS,DIST MGR
WOODWARD,OK DIST OFFICE - 6535 ST HWY 15
73802,PH 580 256-3101 FAX 580 256-3560
RONNIE HOWELL,DIST MGR
AMARILLO,TX DIST OFFICE - 1616 S KENTUCKY
STE C-160,79102 PH 806 352-7520
FAX 806 352-3259
CODY OWENS,DIST MGR

MH KOOMEY INC
8909 JACKRABBIT ROAD
HOUSTON,TX 77095 PH 281 855-3200
FAX 281 855-0319
DAVID W ELLIS,PRES
CATHLEEN HARVILL,CONTROLLER
GLYNN HOLLIER,SLAES/MKTG MGR
BOB COWAN,INTL SALES MGR
ROBERT DEAN,DOMESTIC SALES REP
BROUSSARD,LA BRANCH OFFICE - 105-A BALBOA
70518 PH 318 837-9832 FAX 318 837-2119
GEORGE LELEUX,REG MGR
KOOMEY CONTROL SYSTEMS OF CANADA,LTD -
607 22ND AVE,NISKU,ALBERTA,CANADA T0C-2G0
PH 780 955-2400 FAX 780 955-3470
VANDA LANGEDAHL,JENS SEHESTED

MHR LAND SERVICES,LLC
400 TRAVIS ST STE 1401
SHREVEPORT,LA 71101 PH 318 221-3433
FAX 318 221-3432 WWW.MHRLAND.COM
MELVIN HOWARD REAGAN,OWNER/OPER
HREAGAN@MHRLAND.COM
GARETH L JONES,OPERS MGR
GJONES@MHRLAND.COM
CHRISSY S SMITH,OFC MGR
CSMITH@MHRLAND.COM

MHW INC
PO BOX 742484
DALLAS,TX 75374-2484 PH 972 437-6777
FAX 972 235-5899
W P MASSEY,CHRMN,PRES,CONS
PH 972 661-8769
GLENN R MASSEY,VP

11917 QUEENSBURY,HOUSTON,TX 77024
FRED P MASSEY,SECY/TREAS
50 RIVERCREST,HOUSTON,TX 77042
6917 HELSEM WAY,DALLAS,TX 75230

MIAMI CORPORATION
228 ST CHARLES AVE STE 802
NEW ORLEANS,LA 70130
PH 504 581-3850 FAX 504 581-3855
GORDON L WOGAN,SR VP
LAFAYETTE,LA OFFICE - 309 LA RUE FRANCE
STE 201,70508 PH 337 264-1695
FAX 337 264-9499
CHAD J COURVILLE

MICHAEL JAMES F,IND GEOL
PO BOX 12108
JACKSON,MS 39236-2108 PH 601 981-3338

MICHAEL JAMES T,GEOL
477 FOX BAY DR
BRANDON,MS 39047-8679 PH 601 898-8271

MICHAEL PETROLEUM CORPORATION SEE
LAREDO ENERGY

MICHI CORP
1700 POST OAK BLVD STE 600,2 BLVD PL
HOUSTON,TX 77056
PH 713 266-1200 FAX 713 266-0395
MIKE BLOOM,PRES

MICHIGAN DEPT OF NATURAL RESOURCES
OFFICE OF MINERALS MANAGEMENT
PO BOX 30452
LANSING,MI 48909-7952 PH 517 284-5844
FAX 517 284-5890 WWW.MICHIGAN.GOV/DNR
MARK SWEATMAN,MGR
ANDREA TURNER,ASST TO MGR
KAREN MAIDLOW,MIN PUR APPLICATIONS
PETER ROSE,O&G OFFSET DRAIN/UNDERGROUND
GAS STORAGE/GEOLOGY
JULIE MANSON,O&G LEASE MGMT UNIT MGR
RICK HICKS,LSE RELEASES
JENNIFER HUHN,ASSGN/EXT/DIR LSE
CAROL SIIRA-STEVENS,DEPT TECH/O&G LSE MGT
KIM VENNE,LSE AUCTION/NOMINATIONS
CYNTHIA WATSON,LSE COMPLIANCE (NONREV)
TRACIE BONNER,REV VERIFY UNIT MGR
JULIE CHRYSLER,AUDITS/PPC AGREEMENTS
DANA DUMONT,DIV ORDER/SHUT-IN
CHRIS MCMILLAN,ROYALTY/RENT PMTS/PPC SCH
KRIS THELEN,UNIT AGEEMENTS/POOLINGS

MICHIGAN PETROLEUM GEOLOGISTS,INC
PO BOX 358,1178-28 MILE RD
LITCHFIELD,MI 49252-0358 PH 517 542-3940
M W CASEY JONES,PRES,GEOL
INALEE M JONES,SECY/TREAS

MICHIWEST ENERGY INC
OIL & GAS EXPLORATION COMPANY
1425 S MISSION RD
MOUNT PLEASANT,MI 48858-4665
PH 989 772-2107 FAX 989 772-0451
MICHIWEST@AOL.COM
WILLIAM J STRICKLER,PRES
WILLIAM D STRICKLER,VP

MICRO OPERATING,INC
385 HOLLY TRAIL E
HOLLY LAKE RANCH,TX 75765-7531
PH 903 530-6888 PH 903 613-0275
JR7425@LIVE.COM
JOHN WATSON,PRES

JOHN WATSON II,VP

MICRO-SMART SYSTEMS,INC
5355 ANDERSON RD
HOUSTON,TX 77053-2137 PH 713 433-2277
FAX 713 433-2443 INFO@MICRO-SMART.COM
OTIS ANDERSON,VP,ENGRG

MICRO-STRAT INC
BIOSTRATIGRAPHY SEQUENCE STRATIGRAPHY
5755 BONHOMME RD STE 406
HOUSTON,TX 77036-2013
PH 713 977-2120 FAX 713 977-7684
WALTER W WORNARDT,PH D,PRES

MICRO-TES,INC
12500 NETWORK BLVD STE 201
SAN ANTONIO,TX 78249-3308 PH 210 558-4674

MICRON EAGLE HYDRAULICS
1291 N POST OAK RD ST 170
HOUSTON,TX 77055 PH 713 812-0720
HENRY NAGEL HENRY@MICRONEAGLE.COM

MID AMERICAN INVESTMENT CORP SEE
AMERICAN EXPLORATION CO

MID SOUTH LAND SERVICES
PO BOX 766
MONTROSE,AL 36559-0766 PH 251 929-1860
ROBERT MIKE NEWSOME,PRES/PRTNR
FAIRHOPE,AL OFFICE - 107 MOCKINGBIRD LN
36532

MID-CENTRAL LAND SERVICES,INC
PO BOX 5588
EVANSVILLE,IN 47716-5588
PH 812 476-9393 FAX 812 476-9950
DPERDUE@MIDCENTRALLAND.COM
WWW.MIDCENTRAL.COM
DALE E PERDUE,MNGNG PRTNR
NATHAN E PERDUE,OPERS DIR
NPERDUE@MIDCENTRALLAND.COM
MARY PERDUE,GENERAL COUNSEL
MPERDUE@MIDCENTRALLAND.COM

MID-CON ENERGY CORPORATION
2431 E 61ST ST STE 850
TULSA,OK 74136 PH 918 743-7575
FAX 918 743-8859
WWW.MIDCONENERGYPARTNERS.COM
CHARLES R OLMSTEAD,EXEC CHRMN
ROLMSTEAD@MIDCON-ENERGY.COM
JEFFREY R OLMSTEAD,CEO
JOLMSTEAD@MIDCON-ENERGY.COM
MICHAEL D PETERSON,CFO
MPETERSON@MIDCON-ENERGY.COM
NATHAN P PEKAR,GEN COUNSEL
NPEKAR@MIDCON-ENERGY.COM
RHONDA STACY,VP LAND
RSTACY@MIDCON-ENERGY.COM
LARRY MORPHEW,VP OPERS PH 918 223-5196
LMORPHEW@RDTPROPERTIES.COM
CHAD B ROLLER,VP EXPLOITATION
CROLLER@MIDCON-ENERGY.COM
DALLAS,TX OFFICE - 2501 N HARWOOD
STE 2410 75201 PH 972 479-5980
FAX 469 206-6823
DRUMRIGHT,OK FIELD OFFICE - RT 1 BOX 180
74030 PH 918 352-3783 FAX 918 352-3861

MID-CONTINENT OIL & GAS ASSOCIATION
(MISSISSIPPI-ALABAMA DIV) SEE US OIL &
GAS ASSOCIATION (ALABAMA/MISSISSIPPI DIV)

MID-EAST OIL COMPANY
PO BOX 1378,255 AIRPORT RD
INDIANA,PA 15701-5378 PH 724 349-6690
FAX 724 349-6711
MARK A THOMPSON,PRES
BRADLEY A BROTHERS,CONTROLLER

MID-SOUTH CONTROL LINE
PO BOX 699,5216 TARAVELLA RD
MARRERO,LA 70073-0699
PH 504 348-0867 FAX 504 347-8733

MID-STATE ENERGY INC
758 N. 4TH AVE
LAUREL,MS 39440 PH 601 649-1668
GEORGE A VINCENT,JR,PRES

MIDAMERICA RESOURCES,INC SEE
SEABOARD OIL COMPANY

MIDCO EXPLORATION,INC
PO BOX 1278
WESTMONT,IL 60559-3878
PH 630 655-2198 FAX 630 665-2260
MIDCOEXPLORATION@GMAIL.COM
KENT H WELTMER,PRES
EARL T JOYCE JR,OFC MGR

MIDCOAST ENERGY RESOURCES,INC SEE
ENBRIDGE ENERGY COMPANY,INC

MIDGARD ENERGY COMPANY SEE
CRESCENDO RESOURCES,LP

MIDLAND CORP,OIL PROD
611 WOODBINE LN
HATTIESBURG,MS 39402-2050 PH 601 261-3302
MARY M HUGHES,PRES
H O HUGHES,VP,SECY

MIDLAND MARINE CORP
P O BOX 19458
HOUSTON,TX 77224-9458 PH 713 290-8200
FAX 713 290-8740
DENNIS L KIRWIN
GEORGE E FORCE,JR
GREAT NECK,NY OFFICE - 60 CUTTER MILL RD
STE 312,11021 PH 516 504-4595

MIDLAND PIPE CORP
PO BOX 8470
METAIRIE,LA 70011-8470 PH 504 837-5766
FAX 504 831-3746

MIDLAND RESOURCES INC
PO BOX 245
GREENBRIER,AR 72058-0245 PH 501 679-2432
RUSS BENTON

MIDLAND RESOURCES OPERATING COMPANY,INC
SEE VISTA RESOURCES,INC

MIDNITE ENERGY INC,A PROF ENERGY LAND CO
PO BOX 53373,304 AUDUBON BLVD
LAFAYETTE,LA 70505-3373 PH 337 232-0336
FAX 337 232-5035 KIPLAST@COX-INTERNET.COM
KIP A LASTRAPES,CPL,PRES

MIDROC OPERATING COMPANY
PO BOX 191407
DALLAS,TX 75219-8407
PH 214 906-4231 DLCLARK1@AIRMAIL.NET
DONALD L CLARK,PRES

MIDWAY DRILLING CO
7927 SUMMER NIGHT LN
ROSENBERG,TX 77469-4556 PH 281 936-1134
HENRY F MESSNER,PRES-OWNER-DIR
HFMESSER@ATT.NET
SALLY S MESSER,VP-SECY/TREAS-DIR

MIDWEST RESOURCES,INC
PO BOX 76
ELM GROVE,WI 53122-0076 PH 262 786-6338
STEVEN L BAPTIE

MIDWEST SOIL REMEDIATION,INC
PO BOX 437
INGLESIDE,IL 60041 PH 847 306-3757
WWW.MIDWESTSOIL.COM
MIKE FETHERLING
MIKE.FETHERLING@MIDWESTSOIL.COM

MIKA MEYERS BECKETT & JONES PLC
900 MONROE AVE NW
GRAND RAPIDS,MI 49503-2474
PH 616 632-8000 FAX 616 632-8002
MVANALLSBURG@MMBJLAW.COM
MARK A VAN ALLSBURG,OIL & GAS ATTY

MILAGRO EXPLORATION
1301 MCKINNEY STE 500
HOUSTON,TX 77010 PH 713 750-1600
FAX 713 750-1601
WWW.MILAGROEXPLORATION.COM
MARSHALL MUNSELL,EXEC VP-BUS DEV & LAND
GARY MABIE,PRES & COO

MILER LYNN A,CERT PROF LDMN,INVESTMENTS
2202 N GLENWOOD DR
STILLWATER,OK 74075-2811 PH 405 377-8284
KAREN MILER,SECY

MILES OREN F.C.P.L.
1013 W MAIN ST
OLNEY,IL 62450-1101 PH 618 928-0734

MILES PETROLEUM CORPORATION
1013 W MAIN ST
OLNEY,IL 62450-1101 PH 812 899-3982
OREN F MILES,PRES

MILESTONE ENERGY LLC
333 TEXAS ST,STE 516
SHREVEPORT,LA 71101
PH 318 212-0470 FAX 318 212-0469
JOE A LOTT,MNGNG PRTNR
THOMAS A GILES,LDMN

MILJOCO CORPORATION
200 ELIZABETH ST
MT CLEMENS,MI 48043-1643 PH 888 888-1498
WWW.MILJOCO.COM INFO@MILJOCO.COM
MICHAEL MROZ MMROZ@MILJOCO.COM

MILLENNIUM EXPLORATION COMPANY,LLC
400 N LOOP 1604 E STE 202
SAN ANTONIO,TX 78232 PH 210 579-0734
FAX 210 764-5927
WWW.MILLENNIUMEXPLORATION.COM
RICHARD MONROY,PRES/CEO
RICHARD@MILLENNIUMEXPLORATION.COM

MILLER & SMITH GAS MARKETING,INC
545 N UPPER BROADWAY STE 400
CORPUS CHRISTI,TX 78401
PH 361 883-7700 FAX 361 883-7701
J MARK MILLER,PRES
S KYLE SMITH,VP KYLE@MILLERSMITHGAS.COM

MILLER BRYANT G,OIL PROPERTIES
1837 PEACHTREE ST
JACKSON,MS 39202-1132
PH 601 360-2850 FAX 601 360-1487

MILLER DAVID,OIL PROP
974 E FORTIFICATION ST
JACKSON,MS 39202-2423
PH 601 969-1160 FAX 601 969-1162

DAVID W MILLER,GEOL & LAND
BRYANT G MILLER,LAND

MILLER ENERGY
277 S ROSE ST STE 3300
KALAMAZOO,MI 49007-4722
PH 269 324-3390 FAX 269 324-3584
MICHAEL J MILLER,PRES
JAMES R CARL,CFO

MILLER ENERGY INC
952 ECHO LANE STE 331
HOUSTON,TX 77024
PH 713 953-0191 FAX 713 953-0528
RICHARD WILKERSON,PRES
JAMES K SHOWS,CONTROLLER
DONNA AZCUY,EXEC ASST

MILLER JAMES VAL ,IND PETR LDMN
430 1ST ST
JENNINGS,LA 70546-5432 PH 318 824-4564

MILLER JEFFREY D,CPL
PO BOX 12242
JACKSON,MS 39236-2242 PH 601 594-5617

MILLER JOHN G,CERTIFIED PROF LDMN
PO BOX 51242,106 REPRESENTATIVE ROW STE B
LAFAYETTE,LA 70505-1242 PH 337 233-4156
FAX 337 233-9917 JOHN@OILANDSERVICES.COM

MILLER LAND PROFESSIONALS,LLC
974 E FORTIFICATION ST
JACKSON,MS 39202-2423
PH 601 969-1160 FAX 601 969-1162
WWW.MILLERLANDPROFESSIONALS.COM
DAVID W MILLER,PRES DAVWMIL@AOL.COM
THOMAS E MALEY,LAND SUPVSR
DAVID M CARTER,LAND SUPVSR

MILLER M M & SONS,LTD
PO BOX 611
ALICE,TX 78333-0611 PH 361 256-3817
JAMES W MILLER,PRTNR,MGR

MILLER OIL & GAS OPERATIONS,INC
5027 HASTINGWOOD DR
HOUSTON,TX 77084 PH 713 622-8100
FAX 713 961-2958
WILLIAM JAMES MILLER,PRES,CHMN OF BOARD

MILLER R A ENERGY,INC
PO BOX 2050
KILGORE,TX 75663-2050 PH 903 983-3055
FAX 903 983-1931
RAMILLER@CABLELYNX.COM
RAY A MILLER,PRES

MILLER RANDY V,PETROLEUM GEOL
7 ROBIN RUN DR
THE WOODLANDS,TX 77381 PH 832 656-9631
PH 281 292-4336 RVMIL@HOTMAIL.COM

MILLER W C,OPERATING COMPANY
8700 CROWNHILL BLVD STE 702
SAN ANTONIO,TX 78209-1132 PH 210 824-5736
FAX 210 824-5736
W C BILL MILLER,PRES

MILLICO ENERGY INC SEE
TRIDENT OFFSHORE PETROLEUM

MILLS BENNETT ESTATE
611 LEE SHORE LN
HOUSTON,TX 77079 PH 281 558-2788
FAX 713 461-8310
RAY VAN EATON,GEN SUPT
DAVID VASUT,TREAS

MILLS MICHAEL W
102 INGLENOOK CIR
LAFAYETTE,LA 70508-6434
PH 337 264-1931
MICHAEL W MILLS,PRES

MILLS PETROLEUM OIL & GAS
9610 TJ DR
AMARILLO,TX 79119-3874 PH 806 359-5988
G MILLS,OWNER,PRES
AMY MILLS,VP
ASHLEY MILLS,VP
DAVID MILLS,CUSTODIAN

MILLS ROBERT M,OIL & GAS INVESTMENTS
PO BOX 5745
SHREVEPORT,LA 71135-5745 PH 318 798-3070
ROBERT M MILLS,PRES
VASSAR WHERRITT MILLS,VP

MILPARK DRILLING FLUIDS SEE
BAKER HUGHES INTEQ

MINARD RUN OIL COMPANY
PO BOX 18,609 SOUTH AVE
BRADFORD,PA 16701-0018 PH 814 362-3531
FAX 814 368-4834 FAX 814 362-6765
WWW.MINARDRUNOIL.COM
INFO@MINARDRUNOIL.COM
FREDERICK W FESENMYER,PRES/CEO
DARWIN A NOWAK,VP/CFO
W E JOHN BULMER,SR VP
JAMES J MACFARLANE,VP OPERS
LENNY J MCKEIRNAN,VP ADMIN
MARCIA STEWART,LSE MGR

MINCHEN & MINCHEN
1753 NORTH BLVD
HOUSTON,TX 77098-5413
PH 713 528-6967 FAX 713 528-6979
MEYER A MINCHEN,OWNER

MINCHEN MEYER A
1753 NORTH BLVD
HOUSTON,TX 77098-5413
PH 713 528-6967 FAX 713 528-6979

MINER R C OIL,INC
209 LOUISIANA AVE
CORPUS CHRISTI,TX 78404-1703
PH 361 884-1500 FAX 413 410-3009
1099EXPRESS.COM

MINERAL INVESTMENT CORPORATION
3000 WILCREST DR STE 115
HOUSTON,TX 77042-3365 PH 713 977-0313
DAVID B LAWRENCE,JR,PRES

MINERAL MANAGEMENT INFORMATION SYSTEMS
INC
PO BOX 52161
LAFAYETTE,LA 70505-2161 PH 337 232-9468
TIMOTHY MAHONEY,PRES

MINERAL RESEARCH & CONSULTING,INC SEE
KME TITLES & RESEARCH INC

MINERAL SERVICES,INC
PO BOX 244
SAINT JACOB,IL 62281-0244 PH 618 644-2414
FAX 618 644-2415 MINSERV@HOMETEL.COM
KAREN S SCHULTZE,PRES

MINERAL VALUATION & CAPITAL,INC
NORTHEAST OFFICE
1805 EVANS ST
NORTHAMPTON,PA 18067-1531
PH 610 262-9120 FAX 610 262-4212

JOHN B LIZAK,PRES
GARY SCHMITZ,ENERGY MINERALS GROUP
WES COSGRIFF,CAPITAL SOURCING MGR
EVANSVILLE,IN OFFICE - PO BOX 4733
47724-0733,1006 DIAMOND AVE STE 3
PH 812 425-2490 FAX 812 425-2491

MINERAL VENTURES,INC
PO BOX 277
FARMERVILLE,LA 71241
PH 318 368-0651 FAX 318 368-0652
MINERALVENTURES@OECCWILDBLUE.COM
LISA LAMBERT,PRES

MINERAL WELLS B&PT,INC
PO BOX 1588,3833 FM ROAD 1821
MINERAL WELLS,TX 76068-1588
PH 940 325-4406 FAX 940 325-2979
JOHNNY WHARTON,PRES

MINTER LARRY S,INDEPENDENT
PO BOX 53756,820 E SAINT MARY BLVD
LAFAYETTE,LA 70505-3756 PH 337 233-5570
FAX 337 233-5577 LSMINTER@BELLSOUTH.NET

MIOCENE OIL & GAS INC
PO BOX 52121
LAFAYETTE,LA 70505-2121 PH 337 232-2866
FAX 337 233-4527 PAYZONE@MSN.COM
MARVIN A MUNCHRATH,PRES
DWIGHT A MUNCHRATH,VP EXPL
LAURIE PFEFFER,OFC MGR

MIRACLE EXPLORATION CO,INC
2806 LASALLE ST
MONROE,LA 71201 PH 318 325-9728
JOHN P NORRIS,JR,PRES
WILLIAM F LANE,SECY/TREAS

MIRAMAR PETROLEUM INC
802 N CARANCAHUA #1220 TEXAS COMMERCE PLZ
CORPUS CHRISTI,TX 78470-0001
PH 361 884-2927
JOHN L CLANTON,PRES

MISSALA INC,OIL & GAS EXPLORATION
15116 HWY 12 E
CALEDONIA,MS 39740 PH 601 765-4238
FAX 601 765-4128
CHET MEAUX,PRES

MISSION LAND SERVICES,INC
PO BOX 357
GOLIAD,TX 77963 PH 361 645-2119
PH 361 676-0579
WWW.MISSIONLANDSERVICES.COM
DALTON THIGPEN
DALTON@DALTONTHIGPEN.COM

MISSISSIPPI BUREAU OF GEOLOGY SEE
MISSISSIPPI OFFICE OF GEOLOGY

MISSISSIPPI CHEMICAL CORP
PO BOX 388
YAZOO CITY,MS 39194-0388 PH 662 746-4131
FAX 662 746-9158 WWW.MISSCHEM.COM
CHARLES O DUNN,PRES,CEO
C E MCCRAW,SR VP,OPERS
WILLIAM L SMITH,VP,GEN COUNSEL
WILSON HARVEY,DIR OF PURCHASING/CONTRACTS

MISSISSIPPI GEOLOGICAL SOCIETY
PO BOX 422
JACKSON,MS 39205-0422 PH 601 354-6328

MISSISSIPPI OFFICE OF GEOLOGY
PO BOX 2279
JACKSON,MS 39225-2279 PH 601 961-5500

FAX 601 961-5521 WWW.DEQ.STATE.MS.US
- OFFICE OF GEOLOGY -
MICHAEL B E BOGRAD,DIR
MICHAEL_BOGRAD@DEQ.STATE.MS.US
BRENDA COOK,SECY
- SURFACE GEOLOGY -
DAVID T DOCKERY,III,DIV DIR
TYLER BERRY,GEOL
JAMES STARNES,GEOL
DANIEL MORSE,GIS SPECIALIST
- ENVIRONMENTAL GEOLOGY -
JOHN C MARBLE,DIV DIR
ANDREW NEWCOMB,GIT
ROBERT ERVIN,SR ENVIRO ANALYST
MICHAEL PIPPINS,SR ENVIRO ANALYST
ARCHIE MCKENZIE,SR ENVIRO ANALYST
JONATHAN MCKINNON,SR ENVIRO ANALYST
TREY MAGEE,SR ENVIRO ANALYST
- GEOSPATIAL RESOURCES -
STEPHEN D CHAMPLIN,DIV DIR
JOHN KING,GIT
PETER HUTCHINS,SR SYSTEMS ADMIN
BARBARA YASSIN,GIS SPECIALIST
- MINING & RECLAMATION -
JAMES MATHENY,DIV DIR
BRANDON CUMMINS,GIT
THOMAS RAY,ENVIRO SCI
RON PORTER,ENVIRO SCI
SANDY SAIK,SECY
LONNIE BARRIER,ENVIRO ENGR
ANDREW HITCHCOCK,ENVIRO ENGR TECH

MISSISSIPPI X RAY SERVICE,INC
P O BOX 127,456 MAIN ST
WESSON,MS 39191-0127 PH 601 643-2278
H KEITH RUSSELL,PRES
SHARRON RUSSELL,VP
W L SMITH,GEN MGR

MITCH-WELL ENERGY INC
13255 UNION RD
WATERFORD,PA 16441-8143 PH 814 796-3576
FAX 814 796-3576

MITCHELL ENERGY & DEVELOPMENT CORP SEE
DEVON ENERGY CORPORATION

MITCHELL ENERGY COMPANY,LP SEE
DEVON ENERGY CORPORATION

MITCHELL GEO N DRLG CO,INC
PO BOX 550,1239 COUNTY RD 1500N
CARMI,IL 62821-0550 PH 618 382-2343
PH 382-5032 FAX 618 384-2435
WWW.MITCHELL-DRILLING.COM
NRGY@MITCHELL-DRILLING.COM
GEO N MITCHELL,CEO
CHRIS A MITCHELL,PRES,GEOL
CARL JULIAN,VP,DRLG SUPT
RON WOOTEN,VP,CPA

MITCHELL GEO N PRODUCTION CO
PO BOX 254,1239 COUNTY RD 1500N
CARMI,IL 62821-0254 PH 618 382-2343
FAX 618 384-2435
WWW.MITCHELL-DRILLING.COM
NRGY@MITCHELL-DRILLING.COM
GEO N MITCHELL,OWNER
CHRIS A MITCHELL,CERTIFIED GEOL
RON WOOTEN,CPA,OFC MGR
RON MURDACH,PROD SUPT
CARL JULIAN,DRLG SUPT

MITCHELL MARK A SR
PO BOX 53808
LAFAYETTE,LA 70505-3808
PH 337 504-2145 FAX 337 504-2146
MARK A MITCHELL SR,CPL
MMITCHELL@COX-INTERNET.COM
YVONNE B MITCHELL,LDMN

MITSUI E&P USA LLC
9 GREENWAY PLAZA STE 1250
HOUSTON,TX 77046 PH 713 960-0023
FAX 713 960-0247
RANDALL D JONES,CPL,LAND MGR & ACQS
R.JONES@MITSUI-EP.COM

MIXON BROS DRILLING,INC
PO BOX 2432
MONROE,LA 71207-2432 PH 318-396-1784
DONNIE MIXON,PRES

MKM & ASSOCIATES INC
91 SETTLERS TRACE BLVD BLDG 4
LAFAYETTE,LA 70508 PH 337 989-7200
MARK K MILLER,PRES

MLC OPERATING,LP
PO BOX 5692,600 N MARIENFELD STE 301
MIDLAND,TX 79704 PH 432 687-3334
MIKE MOUNT,PRES/COO/HOUSTON
DOUG TORR,VP OPERS/MIDLAND
HOUSTON,TX OFFICE - 3555 TIMMONS LN
STE 1115,77027 PH 713 255-6200
FAX 713 651-3180

MOBIL EXPLORATION & PRODUCING U S INC SEE
EXXON MOBIL CORPORATION

MOCO INC
603 NORTHPARK DR STE 100
RIDGELAND,MS 39157-5232 PH 601 957-3550
FAX 601 956-8964
MICHAEL L BLACKWELL,PRES
DON NOBLITT,VP

MOFFATT ROBERT J,JR,GEOL
PO BOX 7746
SHREVEPORT,LA 71137 PH 318 227-0181

MOFFITT & ASSOCIATES,INC
PETROLEUM LAND CONSULTANTS
PO BOX 2786
CORPUS CHRISTI,TX 78403-2786
PH 361 884-9273 FAX 361 888-5100
WILLIAM P MOFFITT WPMOFFITT@AOL.COM
MICHELLE M MOFFITT M4MOFFITT@AOL.COM

MOHR ENGINEERING SEE
STRESS ENGINEERING SERVICES INC

MOMENTUM OIL & GAS,LLC
20445 STATE HIGHWAY 249 STE 300
HOUSTON,TX 77070 PH 832 698-5600
RUSTY SHEPHERD,CEO
LOREN LONG,PRES
BRUCE MATSUTSUYU,VP EXPL & DEV
COLBY WILLIFORD,VP LAND
CWILLIFORD@MOMENTUMOG.COM

MONARCH ENERGY,LLC
7110 WALDEN DR
TYLER,TX 75703-0915 PH 903 581-4181
FAX 903 581-2028
DONN R BYRNE,PRES

MONCRIEF OIL
MONTEX DRILLING COMPANY
950 COMMERCE MONCRIEF BLDG
FORT WORTH,TX 76102-5418

PH 817 336-7232 FAX 817 336-3164
W A MONCRIEF,JR
C B MONCRIEF
T O MONCRIEF
JAY SMITH,GAS CONTRACTS
CASPER,WY OFFICE - PO BOX 2573,82602
DAVE KAMBER

MONITOR DRILLING,LTD
401 WESTCHESTER
CORPUS CHRISTI,TX 78408 PH 713 857-7093
S J MORRISON,PRES
DAVID WITHERS,V P

MONJU PAUL & ASSOCIATES,INC
A FULL SERVICE LAND CORP
PO BOX 51151,OCS BLDG 6 HEYMANN OIL CTR
LAFAYETTE,LA 70505-1151
PH 337 235-9837 FAX 337 235-9725
PAUL A MONJU JR,PRES
PMONJU@YAHOO.COM

MONROE GARY A & ASSOCIATES PETROLEUM
LAND SERVICES INC
2409 S 51ST CT
FORT SMITH,AR 72903 PH 479 785-2613
FAX 479 478-8877 WWW.GARYAMONROE.COM
GARY A MONROE,PRES
CONWAY,AR OFFICE - 950 HOGAN LN 72034
PH 501 505-8282
GARY JEREMIAH,MGR
ELMIRA,NY OFFICE - 206 W WATER ST
14901-2913 PH 607 846-3681
BRIAN WELCH,MGR
CANTON,OH OFFICE - 4125 HILLS & DALES RD
NW STE 300/400A PH 330 493-0302
DEAN STALLINGS,MGR
EDMOND,OK OFFICE - 937 NW 164TH ST STE 2
PH 405 471-6040 BHAVIN NAIK,MGR
TULSA,OK OFFICE - 7335 S LEWIS AVE
STE 204 74136
JOEL JOHNSON,MGR

MONSANTO OIL COMPANY SEE
BHP PETROLEUM (AMERICAS) INC

MONSEN PEDER OIL OPR
515 HOUSTON AVE
HOUSTON,TX 77007-7706 PH 713 227-3003

MONTCALM R T,GEOL
OIL,GAS,LIGNITE & MINERALS EXPL
PO BOX 865
MANSFIELD,LA 71052-0865 PH 318 872-2728
FAX 318 872-0688 RRM@SHREVE.NET

MONTECRISTO PETROLEUM COMPANY,INC
PO BOX 130865
HOUSTON,TX 77219-0865 PH 713 526-2266
FAX 713 526-6199

MONTEREY,INC
524 CAMINO LOS ALTOS
SANTA FE,NM 87501-8305 PH 505 982-0075
FAX 505 982-0636
JOHN ROY MELTON,PRES

MONTERO EXPLORATION CO
PO BOX 52223,108 PRYTANIA DR
LAFAYETTE,LA 70505-2223
PH 337 216-9355 FAX 337 216-9355
DUDLEY MONTERO,PETR GEOL/GEOPHY
DUDLEYMONTERO@COX.NET

MONTEX EXPLORATION COMPANY
245 COMMERCE GREEN BLVD STE 280

SUGAR LAND,TX 77478-3684 PH 281 313-5944
FAX 281 313-9036
GLENN J RYAN,PRES
MICHAEL W MURPHREE,VP

MONTGOMERY ENERGY RESOURCES,INC
PO BOX 234
MONTGOMERY,TX 77356 PH 832 482-9343
FAX 936 597-5405 PH 713 899-9709
MARY CHEATHAM
MARY@MONTGOMERYENERGYRESOURCES.COM

MONTGOMERY EXPLORATION CO,LTD
2701 STATE ST
DALLAS,TX 75204-2634 PH 214 742-1160
FAX 214 220-0195
DON D MONTGOMERY JR,GEN PRTNR

MONTOUR PRODUCTION COMPANY
4040 BROADWAY ST STE 105
SAN ANTONIO,TX 78209-6300 PH 361 826-1444
JOE PARKER,PRTNR
JOHN PARKER,PRTNR
GEORGE PARKER JR,PRTNR

MOODY EVELYN,WILIE
2499 FM 217
VALLEY MILLS,TX 76689-3136
PH 713 789-5999 FAX 713 789-5999

MOODY WILLIAM C,JR, & ASSOCIATES,LLC
121 KINGSTON DR
SLIDELL,LA 70458-1737 PH 504 649-4343
FAX 504 649-4400
WALTER L KNOWLES,GEOSCIENTIST

MOON & HINES LLC
PO BOX 3216
RIDGELAND,MS 39158-3216 PH 601 572-8300
FAX 601 572-8310 WWW.MHTONLINE.COM
E R HINES JR,GEOL
SCOTT HINES,LAND MGR
SHINES@MHTONLINE.COM
TODD HINES,GEOL THINES@MHTONLINE.COM

MOON L H FAMILY LTD
3216 RICE BLVD
HOUSTON,TX 77005-2932 PH 903 561-1568

MOON-HINES-TIGRETT OPERATING CO,INC
PO BOX 3216,599 NORTHPARK DR
RIDGELAND,MS 39158-3216 PH 601 572-8300
FAX 601 572-8310 WWW.MHTONLINE.COM
GREG MUELLER,ENGR
GMUELLER@MHTONLINE.COM
SCOTT HINES,PRES SHINES@MHTONLINE.COM
TODD HINES,VP THINES@MHTONLINE.COM
KIM LYLE,ACCT KLYLE@MHTONLINE.COM

MOORE CANDACE
2436 CR 411
NACOGDOCHES,TX 75961 PH 936 560-4743

MOORE DRILLING
19001 COSHOCTON RD
MOUNT VERNON,OH 43050-9229
PH 740 392-0898
ROBERT E MOORE,OWNER
MICHAEL A MOORE,OWNER

MOORE J W
PO BOX 225
MOORINGSPORT,LA 71060-0225
PH 318 996-7569

MOORE MCCORMACK ENERGY INC,SEE
C X Y ENERGY INC

MOORE PRODUCTION
6458 DICK ELLIOTT RD
BRYAN,TX 77808-7720 PH 409 589-2512
PH 409 820-1337

MOORE RONALD L,P.C.
COUNSELORS/ATTORNEYS AT LAW
5900 FAIRDALE LN
HOUSTON,TX 77057-6307
PH 713 266-4433 FAX 713 266-8282
RONALD L MOORE,OIL/GAS/MINERAL LAW

MOORE TOM E,IND OIL OPER
PO BOX 2156
MIDLAND,TX 79702-2156 PH 432 682-8697
FAX 432 682-0530
TOM E MOORE

MOORE WELL SERVICES,INC
PO BOX 1399
STOW,OH 44224-1399
PH 216 650-4443 FAX 216 650-0105
ROBERT L MOORE,PRES
JEFFREY D MOORE,VP,CONSTR,PIPELINE OPR
KEITH R MOORE,VP,DRLG,RIG OPERS

MOORES PUMP & SUPPLY,INC
119 CASON RD
BROUSSARD,LA 70518-3204 PH 337 839-8964
PH 800 960-7867 FAX 318 837-4752
DON CARLIN,CEO
PAT BERNARD,PRES
JOSEPH GUILLORY,VP,OPERS
STEPHEN SMITH,GEN MGR
LENORA TUTTLE,CAO
GERALD LANDRY,MGR FABRICATION
JOHNNY MERCER,MGR SANDBLASTING
KENNY VINCENT,MGR,ROD PUMP/CRANE
JOE MILAZZO,MGR,PACKER
ENNIS RICHARD,MGR,MAINTENANCE/RENTAL
SCOTTY ROY,ASST MGR,MAINTENANCE/RENTAL
GREG DOMINGUE,MGR,MACHINE SHOP
GREG ARSEMENT,ASST MGR,MACHINE SHOP
LAUREL,MS OFFICE - 915 E MAIN ST
SANDERSVILLE,MS 39477 PH 601 425-5166
FAX 601 425-1942
RON DICKERSON,MGR

MORAN CORPORATION THE,OIL PROD
3843 N BRAESWOOD
HOUSTON,TX 77025 PH 713 526-4171
C W SUNDAY,PRES

MORAN JACK,DRILLING COMPANY
24840 DEAL RD
GAMBIER,OH 43022-9744 PH 740 668-4681
JACK MORAN,OWNER

MORAN RESOURCES COMPANY
2803 SACKETT ST
HOUSTON,TX 77098-1125
PH 713 759-1555 FAX 713 759-0123
PATRICK J MORAN,PRES
ANN CURRENS,VP

MORANSCO ENERGY CORPORATION
OIL AND GAS DRILLING & OPERATING
PO BOX 241
SHREVEPORT,LA 71162
PH 318 221-5001 FAX 318 221-5003

MORGAN ENTERPRISES,INC
950 ECHO LANE STE 355
HOUSTON,TX 77024 PH 713 222-7706
MARK KOBELAN,PRES

MOROCO,INC
14061 WILLOW GLEN CT STE 139
PORT CHARLOTTE,FL 33953-5666
PH 941 255-9724
RONALD E MORRIS,PRES

MORRIS PIPELINE COMPANY
3417 MILAM STE H
HOUSTON,TX 77002-9531
PH 713 526-1260 FAX 713 521-3364
DMDUNWOODY@YAHOO.COM
DAVID M DUNWOODY,PRES

MORRISON JIMMIE D,CONS GEOL
407 WEAVER'S WAY
BOSSIER CITY,LA 71111-5920
PH 318 742-2441

MORROW CLIFF,LEASE BROKER
296 EAGLE BEND WAY
SHREVEPORT,LA 71115-2990 PH 318 783-5724

MORROW OIL & GAS CO
PO BOX 721060
BYRAM,MS 39272
PH 601 878-2108 FAX 601 878-2106
JOAN V MORROW,PRES
MARY ELLEN JONES,OFC MGR

MORROW OPERATING CO,INC
PO BOX 6718
JACKSON,MS 39282-6718
PH 601 878-2108 FAX 601 878-2106
JOAN V MORROW,PRES

MORSE ROBERT
211 HILL COUNTRY LN
SAN ANTONIO,TX 78232-2905 PH 512 869-3300

MORTIMER PRODUCTION COMPANY
1020 NE LOOP 410 STE 555
SAN ANTONIO,TX 78209 PH 210 821-6168
FAX 210 828-8738
GLENN G MORTIMER III,PRES
LEON N WALTHALL III,VP

MORTON MAX F,IND PETR LDMN
145 E 13TH
CASPER,WY 82601 PH 307 234-6496
NOTAXMAX@VCN.COM

MOSBACHER ENERGY COMPANY
712 MAIN ST STE 2200
HOUSTON,TX 77002-3290
PH 713 546-2500 FAX 713 546-2611
ROBERT MOSBACHER JR,CHRMN OF BD
A W DOWNING MEARS JR,PRES/CEO
STEPHEN R SIEGFRIED,EXEC VP/OPERS
GERALD BENDELE,VP,CFO
P WAYNE SNOW,VP,GEOL OPERS
JASON HANLON,VP,LAND/LEGAL

MOSCHEL & COMPANY LEASES & ROYALTIES
P O BOX 2814
MCALLEN,TX 78502-2814 PH 512 682-2294

MOSELEY RESOURCES,LLC
59 SWEDE SPRINGS
BOERNE,TX 78006-6170
PH 281 787-4412
SAMUEL G MOSELEY,OWNER
SANDSMOSELEY@GMAIL.COM

MOSSER H J,OIL PROPERTIES
PO BOX 145
ALICE,TX 78332 PH 361 664-6261
H J MOSSER JR,OWNER

MOUNGER WILLIAM D,IND OIL OPR
4450 OLD CANTON RD STE 203
JACKSON,MS 39211-5991 PH 601 354-2479

MOUNT THOMAS M
3105 KENTUCKY AVE
KENNER,LA 70065-4632 PH 504 443-1471

MOUNTAIN V OIL & GAS,INC
PO BOX 470
BRIDGEPORT,WV 26330-0470
PH 304 842-6320
STEVE SHAVER,PRES SMSHAVER@EARTHLINK.NET
MIKE SHAVER,VP
BOB LOWTHIR,PROD COORD
DON HENRY,PROD COORD
RICK THOMAS,LAND MGR

MOUNTAINEER PETROLEUM LAND SERVICES INC
448 CHURCH ST S
RIPLEY,WV 25271-1614 PH 304 372-5189
RALPH L PARSONS,OWNER,PRES

MOUTON STEPHEN INC
209 LAUREL ST
LAFAYETTE,LA 70501-6245 PH 318 234-7364
FAX 318 237-0641
PAUL ELLIOT STEPHEN MOUTON,PRES,LDMN
REAL ESTATE BROKER,OIL LAND LEASE &
PROPERTY MANAGEMENT/APPRAISALS
TOOL & EQUIPMENT BROKER
IMPORT EXPORT BROKER

MPS PRODUCTION COMPANY
5405 ENCINAS ROJAS ST
AUSTIN,TX 78746-2209 PH 713 799-1090
JAMES SUD,PRES,TREAS
MRS JOEANN MARPHIS,OFC MGR,SECY

MQUEST INTERNATIONAL INC
6603 AMPTON DR
SPRING,TX 77379-7601 PH 281 468-1151
THOMAS E MOON,PRES

MS ENERGY SERVICES
3335 POLLOK DR
CONROE,TX 77303 PH 936 442-2500
PH 936 442-2200,800 769-5988
FAX 936 442-2599
INFO@MSENERGYSERVICES.COM
ALLEN NEEL,PRES & CEO
PAUL CULBRETH,VP & COO
RON WHITTIER,CFO
DAVID STUART,GEN MGR
- REGIONAL OFFICES -
HOUSTON,TX OFFICE-1030 REGIONAL PARK DR
77060 PH 281 951-4346 FAX 281 951-4342
DALLAS,TX OFFICE-307 W 7TH ST STE 1800
FT. WORTH,TX 76102 PH 817 870-4847
FAX 817 870-4829
FORT WORTH,TX OFC-7821 WILL ROGERS BLVD
76140 PH 817 568-1038
CORPUS CHRISTI,TX OFFICE-PO BOX 4357
1579 N LEXINGTON 78469 PH 817 568-1038
PH 800 880-7468 FAX 361 289-7320
ODESSA,TX OFFICE-1620 S MARLIN DR 79763
PH 800 769-5988 FAX 936 422-2599
LAFAYETTE,LA OFC-PO BOX 630,301 MARCON DR
70518 PH 337 267-7468 PH 800 259-2867
FAX 337 267-9409
WASHINGTON,PA OFFICE-1215 HENDERSON AVE
15301 PH 724 222-9650 FAX 724 222-9656
DENVER,CO OFC-1600 BROADWAY ST STE 2400

80202 PH 303 542-1957 FAX 303 542-1958
GRAND JUNCTION,CO OFFICE-742 W WHITE AVE
81501 PH 970 257-1911 PH 970 257-1946
FAX 970 257-1947
BAKER,MT OFFICE-PO BOX 1115,22 S 4TH ST W
59313 PH 403 778-3983 PH 877 844-9850
FAX 406 778-3982 FAX 970 257-1947

MUCHER JOE,ESTATE
PO BOX 6694
SAN ANTONIO,TX 78209
PH 210 226-1226 FAX 210 226-5790
JOE MUCHER,OWNER
STEPHEN H BLOUNT,PRES
SUZANNE TURNER,OFC MGR

MUDLOGGING SYSTEMS,INC
574 NORTHGATE DR #2
GRAND JUNCTION,CO 81505
PH 970 243-3044 FAX 970 243-1272
WWW.MUDLOGSYS.COM WFOSTER@MUD-
LOGSYS.COM
ANDY KELLEY,PRES
WADE FOSTER,VP,MKTG

MUENSTER DRILLING COMPANY INC
415 CR 350,PO BOX 53
MUENSTER,TX 76252-0053 PH 940 759-4949
DOYLE HESS,OWNER

MUGG JOHN D,JR
3607 RUSTLING OAKS
SAN ANTONIO,TX 78259-3629 PH 210 496-5381

MULLEN EXPLORATION,INC
PO BOX 929,416 HARDY LN
BROOKHAVEN,MS 39602-0929 PH 601 833-2809
FAX 601 833-3609
LOUIS MULLEN,PRES

MULLER F J,LEASE BROKER
P O DRAWER 1270,203 N AVE K
CROWLEY,LA 70527-1270 PH 318 783-4944
F J MULLER,OWNER,IND OPR
JAY LEJEUNE,BOOKKEEPER
GAIL MULLER ADAMS,C P A

MULTI-SHOT DIRECTIONAL SERVICES SEE
MS ENERGY SERVICES

MULTICOMM SCIENCES INTERNATIONAL,INC
266 W MAIN ST
DENVILLE,NJ 07834-1233 PH 973 627-7400
FAX 973 625-1002
V NEXON,JR,PRES
S CRIMMINS,SECY

MUNICIPAL ENERGY RESOURCES CORPORATION
THREE RIVERWAY STE 1900
HOUSTON,TX 77056 PH 713 888-0133
ROBERT D MURPHY JR,PRES
ROBERT.MURPHY@MUNIENERGY.COM

MUNOCO COMPANY L.C.
200 N JEFFERSON AVE STE 308
EL DORADO,AR 71730-5853 PH 870 863-7118
FAX 870 863-6528
ROBERT C NOLAN,MNGNG MEMBER
ERNEST K KAVANAUGH,GEOL
W T WATSON,JR,LDMN

MURCHISON OIL & GAS INC
7250 DALLAS PKWY STE 1400 LEGACY TOWER 1
PLANO,TX 75024-4920
PH 972 931-0700 FAX 972 931-0701
J D MURCHISON,CEO
R TAZEWELL SPEER,PRES

MICHAEL S DAUGHERTY,COO
SHANNON HALL,CFO
MARK INGRAM,CONTROLLER
JACK RANKIN,VP OPERS
BRETT AUSTIN,VP LAND
CARLA TRACY,LDMN
CINDY COTTRELL,REGULATORY
DENA DENOOYER STROH,GC
MIDLAND,TX OFFICE - 300 N MARIENFELD
STE 300,79701 PH 432 686-2063
FAX 432 686-2043
TOM DICKEY,DIV MGR

MURCO OIL & GAS,LLC
400 TRAVIS ST STE 1910
SHREVEPORT,LA 71101-3188 PH 318 221-7373
FAX 318 227-3060
THOMAS H MURPHY
ALAN W MURPHY

MURFIN DRILLING COMPANY,INC
250 N WATER ST STE 300
WICHITA,KS 67202-1299
PH 316 267-3241 FAX 316 267-6004
WWW.MURFININC.COM
DAVID L MURFIN,PRES
DAVID DOYEL,EXEC VP
ROBERT D YOUNG,TREAS/CFO
LEON RODAK,VP PROD/PROD MGR
BLAINE F MILLER,DRLG MGR
SCOTT ROBINSON,GEOL MGR
MICHAEL A PISCIOTTE,LAND MGR
MICHEL RUNNION,GEOL
BO BEINS,GEOL
FRANCIS HITSCHMANN,PROD ENGR
KEN DEAN,PROD GEOL
ROBERT KRAMER,PROD ENGR
TOM MELLAND,PROD ENGR
RON SCHRAEDER,PROD ENGR
NICK AHLERICH,PROD ENGR
ALISSA TEVIS,EQUIP MGR
RICHARD W GREEN,CONTROLLER
BONNIE SCHROEDER,ACCTG MGR
CAROL WARHURST,HUMAN RESOURCES
JAMES R DANIELS,CONSLT
D'ANN DRENNAN,ASST TO PRES
SHAUNA GUNZELMAN,GEOL ADMIN
DEBBIE (MANN) SHAHAN,ASST TO CFO
ELIZABETH CLARK,DRLG ASST
MARGO GROVER,PROD ASST
RUSSELL,KS FIELD OFFICE - PO BOX 288
67665-0288 PH 785 483-5371
FAX 785 483-4459
STAN FROETSCHNER,PROD SUPT
PH 785 483-1197
CRAIG HUTCHISON,PROD FRMN
PH 785 623-0123
MARK ROBBEN,PROD FRMN PH 785 735-4621
COLBY,KS DRLG & TRUCKING OFFICE -
PO BOX 661,67707-0661 PH 785 462-7541
BERNIE MEYER,DRLG SUPT PH 785 443-1016
MARTIN RUDA,TRUCK SUPT PH 785 443-1176
ERNIE COLSON,TRUCK PUSHER PH 785 443-0492
PAMELA THOMPSON,ASST
- TOOLPUSHERS -
RIG#2 ARTURO CABEZAS-PH 785 443-0495
RIG#3 KLINT BO FARR-PH 785 470-7203
RIG#4 KELLY WILSON-PH 785 769-6103

RIG#7 KELLY WILSON-PH 785 769-6103
RIG#8 TRAVIS MARTIN-PH 785 694-3669
RIG#14 GREG UNRUH-PH 785 443-0181
RIG#16 ANDREW DINKEL-PH 785 443-2377
RIG#20 GREG CONDREN-PH 785 443-3048
RIG#21 JUAN TINOCO-PH 785 443-0127
RIG#22 SAMMY FABELA-PH 785 443-1630
RIG#24 TONY MARTIN-PH 785 769-4144
RIG#25 RAYMOND BLAND-PH 785 443-2331
COLBY,KS PROD & MAINT FIELD OFFICE -
PO BOX 661,67701 PH 785 462-6781
FAX 785 462-7592
BUCK SALAS,PROD FRMN PH 785 567-7138
NATHAN WITT,PROD FRMN PH 785 269-7649
GLEN WAHRMAN,PROD FRMN PH 785 269-7261
TROY GONZALES,PROD FRMN PH 785 269-7626
JOHN TURNER,PROD ASST
BEN SIMMINGER,PROD FRMN-PH 785 269-7508
HILL CITY,KS PROD OFFICE-2598 280TH AVE
PO BOX 130,67642 PH 785 421-2103
FAX 785 421-2843
JOHN GERSTNER,PROD SUPT - PH 785 567-8104
WADE KING,PROD FRMN - PH 785 567-3004
HILL CITY,KS WELL SVC/ROUSTABOUT OFC
7 INDUSTRIAL PARK DR LOT 3,PO BOX 130
67642 PH 785 421-2101 FAX 785 421-2038
JESSE SPARGO,SUPT - PH 785 567-8142
THERON BRUNING,FRMN - PH 785 567-8142
LEE REIN,FRMN - PH 785 567-6430
PAUL (PD) WILLIAMS,FRMN-PH 785 623-1364
GARDEN CITY,KS FIELD OFFICE
3490 W JONES,67846 PH 620 277-0562
FAX 620 277-0573
JAMES ESQUIVEL,PROD FRMN PH 620 272-4913
LOGAN,KS FIELD OFFICE - PO BOX 277
67646 PH 785 689-7567 FAX 785 689-7569
RIC HOCKMAN,PROD PH 785 567-8036

MURPHY EXPLORATION & PRODUCTION CO
9805 KATY FRWY STE G-200
HOUSTON,TX 77024 PH 281 675-9000
WWW.MURPHYOILCORP.COM
ROGER W JENKINS,PRES
EUGENE T COLEMAN,EXEC VP-OFFSHORE &
INTL OPERS
MICHAEL MCFADYEN,EXEC VP-NORTH AMERICAN
ONSHORE OPERS
RON MANZ,EXEC VP-EXPL & BUS DEV

MURPHY F W
CONTROL SYSTEMS & SERVICES DIV
105 RANDON DYER RD
ROSENBERG,TX 77471 PH 281 633-4500
FAX 281 633-4588
JACK MALEY,VP OPERS-OIL & GAS

MURPHY OIL COMPANY
1691 LYNN DR
LANCASTER,OH 43130-2014 PH 740 681-3420
JOHN R MURPHY,OWNER

MURPHY OIL COMPANY,LTD
PO BOX 2721,STATION M
CALGARY,ALBERTA,CAN T2P 3Y3
CALGARY,AB OFFICE - 4000,520-3 AVE SW
CENTENNIAL PLACE-E TOWER PH 403 294-8000

MURPHY OIL CORPORATION
PO BOX 7000,200 PEACH ST
EL DORADO,AR 71731-7000 PH 870 862-6411
WWW.MURPHYOILCORP.COM

ROGER W JENKINS,PRES & CEO
WALTER K COMPTON,EXEC VP & GEN COUNSEL
JOHN W ECKART,EXEC VP & CFO
KEITH CALDWELL,SR VP & CONTROLLER
KELLI M HAMMOCK,SR VP-ADMIN
K TODD MONTGOMERY,SR VP-CORP PLNG & SVCS
TED BOTNER,VP/LAW & CORP SECY
TIM BUTLER,VP-TAX
JOHN W DUMAS,VP-CORP INSURANCE
JOHN GARDNER,VP & TREAS
BARRY JEFFERY,VP-INVESTOR RELS
   PH 870 864-6501
ALLAN J MISNER,VP-INTERNAL AUDIT
KATIE SANDIFER,COMMUNITY RELS
   PH 870 864-6565

MURRAY & ASSOCIATES
PO BOX 425
AVINGER,TX 75630-0425 PH 903 562-1007
   WILLIAM D MURRAY,JR

MURRAY ENERGY RESOURCES LLC
727 W HEIGHTS HOLLOW LANE
HOUSTON,TX 77007 PH 713 775-3470
   JEFFERY MURRAY MJRM2@HOTMAIL.COM

MURRAY W D,PETR LDMN
1510 LYNNVIEW DR
HOUSTON,TX 77055-3428 PH 713 468-8609

MURRAY WM D,JR,IND PETR LDMN
1510 LYNNVIEW DR
HOUSTON,TX 77055-3428 PH 713 468-8609

MURVIN OIL COMPANY
PO BOX 297
OLNEY,IL 62450-0297 PH 618 393-2124
FAX 618 395-3116 WWW.MURVINOIL.COM
   MURVIN@MURVINOIL.COM
   GREGG C GIBSON,PRES
   ANTHONY C GIBSON,VP

MUSLOW IRWIN I
315 CORINNE CIR
SHREVEPORT,LA 71106-6003 PH 318 868-5195

MUSLOW OIL AND GAS,INC
333 TEXAS ST STE 2222
SHREVEPORT,LA 71101-5303 PH 318 221-8694
FAX 318 227-2106
   ERIC C WEISS,PRES

MUSSELMAN JAMIE B,OIL OPR SEE
MUSSELMAN OILFIELD SERVICES LLC

MUSSELMAN JOHN A
727 S CHILTON
TYLER,TX 75701-1708 PH 903 597-4279
FAX 903 597-4282
   JMUSSELMAN@SUDDENLINK.NET

MUSSELMAN OILFIELD SERVICES LLC
10632 N IH 35
SAN ANTONIO,TX 78233 PH 210 654-8336
FAX 210 654-1725
   J B MUSSELMAN JR,PRES

MUSTANG DRILLING INC
PO BOX 1810
HENDERSON,TX 75653-1810 PH 903 657-0566
FAX 903 657-5682
   ANDY MILLS,PRES
   AMILLS@MUSTANGDRILLING.COM

MUSTANG EXPLORATION CO INC
PO BOX 467
LOUISE,TX 77455-0467 PH 713 648-2641

MUSTANG RESOURCES CORP SEE
BLUE DOLPHIN ENERGY COMPANY

MWD SERVICES,LLC
PO BOX 750
YOUNGSVILLE,LA 70592-0750
PH 337 856-5965 FAX 337 856-9091
   WWW.MWDSI.COM
   CLYDE J CORMIER,PRES
   GORDON OGDEN,CFO
   RICKY FAUL,VP/SYSTEM SUPPORT
   JAMES MARKS,VP/LA SLS
   JAMIE TOUCHETT,VP US SLS
   JAMES GLYNN,OPERS MGR

MYERS A J PRODUCTION
PO BOX 751
JACKSBORO,TX 76458-0751 PH 940 567-1517
FAX 940 567-2031
   A J MYERS,PRES
   MYERSROUSTABOUT@YAHOO.COM

MYERS GAS
PO BOX 65
KENNERDELL,PA 16374 PH 814 385-6473
   CHARLES E MYERS,OWNER

MYERS JIMMIE B,OIL OPR
600 LEOPARD ST STE 1520
CORPUS CHRISTI,TX 78473-1601
PH 361 882-7404 FAX 361 882-7076
   RUTH B HANS,AGENT

N & M RESOURCES, LLC
SEE PHILLIPS WM N, CPL

NAA,LP SEE
PLYMOUTH RESOURCES INC

NABORS ABANDONRITE SEE
NABORS INDUSTRIES LTD

NABORS ALASKA DRILLING INC SEE
NABORS INDUSTRIES LTD
2525 C STREET # 200

NABORS CANADA DRILLING SEE
NABORS INDUSTRIES LTD

NABORS COMPLETION & PRODUCTION SERVICES
515 W GREENS RD STE 1170
HOUSTON,TX 77067-4599
PH 800 299-1388 PH 888 622-6777
PH 281 874-0035
   - EXECUTIVE -
   LARRY HEIDT,PRES PH 281 775-8193
   STEVE JOHNSON,EXEC VP PROD
   RONNIE WITHERSPOON,EXEC VP COMPLETION
   ABIGAIL HUNTER,EXEC ADMIN ASST
   JENNIFER STEFFLER,EXEC ASST
   - OPERATIONS -
   MICHAEL SEYMAN,VP NORTHERN DIVISON
   RICK JACQUIER,VP SOUTHERN DIVISION
   - BUSINESS DEVELOPMENT INITIATIVES -
   FRED BELJARS,VP BUS DEV
   MICHAEL STUCKART,BUS SUPT ANALYST
   LANCE LEIBOLE,DIR FACILITIES & ASSET MGMT
   DAMIAN ROCKETT,PROJ MGR
   TYLER HOFFMAN,BUS ANALYST
   DUANE MCCOY,FLEET MGR PH 281 380-9391
   DIANE HALLMARK,ANALYST PH 281 775-2468
   DANNA STOKES,ANALYST PH 281 775-5151
   - SALES -
   JIM DOUGHERTY,VP SALES
   MARK MCINTYRE,REG SR SALES MGR
   KRISTIN BROWN,ADMIN ASST

DAVID BURLEIGH,SLS ACCT MGR
CHRIS MELBER,SLS ACCT MGR
BRADLY KAUFMAN,ENGINEER
LANCE CASEY,SLS ACCT MGR
CHRIS MELBER,SLS ACCT MGR
JULIAN ZAMUDIO,SLS ACCT MGR
CHIP CLINKSCALES,SLS ACCT MGR SAN ANTONIO
ERNEST ORTIZ,ENGINEER PH 281 775-8440
   - ENGINEERING -
TOBY KING,ENGRG MGR
   - COILED TUBING -
MIKE BAILEY,MGR
ALBERT GARCIA,SUPVSR PH 337 467-9537
   - FLUIDS SERVICES -
ROBBY NELSON,SR DIR
   - MAINTENANCE -
JOHN HALLMARK,SR DIR
PATRISE SCOTT,CLERK PH 281 775-2412
CHANCE DOBBS,OPER SUPT COOR
GARY BROWN,SR MGR
PARAGON BULIDING - 450 GEARS RD STE 790
HOUSTON,TX 77067
   - PLUG & ABANDONMENT -
JACK RENSHAW,DIR SPECIAL SVCS
MONTY MCCARVER,OPERS MGR
JUSTIN MCWHORTER,OPERS SUPT
JUSTIN CRIDER,MGR
   - BIDS & CONTRACTS -
RICH MURRAY,VP CONTRACTS
MATT HALL,ANALYST PH 281 775-8420
MARIO VILLARREAL,ANALYST PH 281 775-8466
CHRIS HENGST,ANALYST PH 281 775-8434
MAYRA DAVIDSON,ADMIN PH 281 775-8138
SHERRY SPILLER,ADMIN PH 281 775-8489
   - CREDIT -
GEORGE MCNINCH,COLLECTIONS MGR
DAVID OROSZ,SR CREDIT REP PH 281 775-5135
ROSA TENNYSON,CREDIT ANALYST
CARMEN MAXIE,OFC ASST PH 281 775-2402
DAVID STEEL JOHNSON,CREDIT COOR
   - FINANCE & ACCOUNTING DEPT -
ANDY STEPHENS,VP FINANCE
TRAVIS BRIDGES,SR MGR FINANCE
DAWN CLAGG,DIR ACCTG
LOURDES FERNAN,A/R MGR
XUAN NGUYEN,ACCTG SUPVSR
GIZELLE WILLIAMS,MGR FIXED ASSETS
LEE KNAPE,CONTROLLER
STEVE SIMMONS,SR MGR FINANCE
ASHLEY GUMINO,SR MGR PERFORM REPORTING
CHARLIE DAVIS,BUDGET/FORECAST MGR
TYLER STRAUSS,ACCT
KIM POWELL,ANALYST
ANGELA MURPHY,SR ASST
MARQUISA SINGLETON,SR ASST
ANH NGO,ADMIN ASST
FATIME FAMPER,SR ACCT
DOUG NGUYEN,ASSET SUPVSR
NATE FOSTER,FIN REPORTING MGR
CHER SCOTT,SR ACCT
   - HUMAN RESOURCES -
FRANK LABRENZ,DIR EMPLOYEE RELS
JOHN MULDER,SR HR MGR/PAYROLL HRIS
TARA ELDERS,PAYROLL MGR
DEBBIE BONNETTE,EMPLOYMENT MGR
SUZANNE D'AMBROSIO,ADMIN

SUSAN HALL,HR ANALYST
ANGELA GUERVARA,RECRUITER
CAROLINA MOSCOSO,ADMIN ASST
KATHY FONTE,ADMIN
LORI CANSLER-OJEDA,ADMIN
WILMA SOUTHERN,ADMIN ASST
- RIG SERVICES -
TRIP ELLISON,SR DIR RIG SERVICES
CLEON SHELTON,SR PROJ MGR
NITA MARKS,ADMIN
JONATHAN ETHRIDGE,PROJ MGR
SAN ANGELO,TX MANUFACTURING COMPLEX -
PO BOX 60890,1214 GAS PLANT RD 76904
PH 325 651-2200 FAX 325 651-2240
NEAL GRIGG,EQUIP MGR
ERNIE LACROIX,DIR
ROBERT BRADDOCK,ELECTRICAL TECH
JAMES BEHRINGER,HEAD MECHANIC
- SAFETY -
JOHN SROCK,SR DIR HSE
LES TEAGUE,SR MGR
MIKE KRUPP,HSE COOR
WHITNEY DILLON,SR ROAD SFTY MGR
MARY STAREWICH,ANALYST
- COMPLIANCE & TRAINING -
JIM KULIS,SR DIR
MONICA WOLF,TRAINING ADMIN
BILL MIDOCK,TRAINING SUPVSR
ABEL MOLINA,SFTY/TRNG SPECIALIST
CONRAD ACOSTA,SFTY/TRNG SPECIALIST
JOHN DUPREE,SFTY/TRNG SPECIALIST
-D.O.T. DEPT -
MARK WUTHRICH,D.O.T. COMPLIANCE MGR
TERESA AST,SR ASST
CHRISTI FIGUEROA,SUPERVISOR
VERN BRADFORD,SFTY/TRNG SPECIALIST
MIKE ROBERTS,SFTY/TRNG SPECIALIST
- STIMULATION -
STAN WILLIS,SR DIR
- CENTRAL REGION -
COLUMBIA,MS REG OFFICE - 336 SINGELY RD
39429 PH 601 444-4577 FAX 601 444-4579
GARY JONES,REG DIR
GARY J JONES,MGR
PATRICK ANDREWS,MGR
GEORGE DARR,MGR
LARRY SPEIGHTS,SLS REP
SHELTON BOLEWARE,MGR STIMULATION
DANIEL CARPENTER,CLERK
LISA JOHNSON,REG CONTROLLER
- ARK-LA-TEX REGION -
LONGVIEW,TX REG OFC-406 AMBASSADOR ROW
75604 PH 903 753-3036 FAX 903 753-7991
CHARLES GREENWOOD,DIST MGR
JAY LYNN JONES,OPERS SUPT
LISA JOHNSON,REG CONTROLLER
TERRI SIPES,OFC ASST
CATHY FEAZELL,ADMIN ASST
KARLA FARREL,ASST
G.T. NEHLS,PROJ MGR
- SAFETY -
WAYNE HOWARD,SAFETY MGR
BUD TURNER,SFTY/TRNG SPECIALIST
BRANDON DAVIDSON,SFTY/TRNG SPECIALIST
MICHAEL NICKENS,SFTY/TRNG SPECIALIST
- PLUG & ABANDONMENT PROJECT -

JACK RENSHAW,SR OPERS MGR
MONTY MCCARVER,OPERS MGR
JUSTIN MCWHORTER,OPERS SUPT
BRECKENRIDGE,TX OFFICE - 2343 HWY 183 N
76424 PH 888 274-6430 PH 254 559-7511
FAX 254 559-8957
DOUG KIRK,AREA MGR
BRYAN,TX OFFICE - 8388 WEST SH 21 77807
PH 979 779-3582 FAX 979 822-3450
JIM SUTHERLAND,AREA MGR
EDDIE EMBRA,OPERS SUPT
DORA SEELYE,OFC ASST-NFS
CRESSON,TX OFFICE - 12890 CLEBURNE HWY
76035 PH 817 396-4315 FAX 817 396-4319
CHUCK DODSON,OPERS MGR
STEVE MCENTIRE,AREA MGR
RANDY WEST,EQUIP SUPT
MARCIA GLOVER,ADMIN ASST
STEPHANIE MCCOY,OFC ASST
MELANIE HOOPER,OFC ASST
CONNIE LAMBS,OFC ASST
JIM EMORY,OFC ASST
MICHAEL WANDEL,CLERK
BRENDA LEWELLEN,OFC ADMIN
ZERNE LANCE,OFC ASST
DINA WESTBROOK,OFC ASST
CRESSON,TX OFFICE - 12890 CLEBURNE HWY
76035 PH 800 899-3941 PH 871 396-4870
FAX 281 775-8222
MARK FOLEY,EMPLOYMENT COOR
ANGELA SEASTRUNK,CLERK
- SALES -
JOSEPH LEGENZA,REG SLS MGR
JOHN PRESTON,SLS REP
WALTER PAPPY CLOWER,SLS REP
DECATUR,TX OFFICE - 2273 N WHY 287 76234
PH 940 626-3735 FAX 940 626-3737
GEORGE MUMMA,AREA MGR
JOHN RICH SHARAR,OPERS SUPT
DEWAYNE ALLEY,DISPATCHER
GLADYS WATHEN,DISPATCHER
JOSHUA FOLEY,DISPATCHER
LA GRANGE,TX OFFICE -416 AIRPORT RD 78945
LONGVIEW,TX OFFICE - 404 AMBASSADOR ROW
75604 PH 800 594-2100 PH 903 753-7915
FAX 903 757-2857
JOHN CRIDER,AREA MGR RIGS
RUSSELL MCCULLOUGH,OPERS SUPT
LINDA WARD,CLERK
DENISE HUX,CLERK
RANDY HARRELL,DISPATCHER
NACOGDOCHES,TX OFC-3415 NW STALLINGS DR
75964 PH 936 462-9436 FAX 936 462-9613
ROSEVELT JOLLY,TRUCK SUPVSR
TOLAR DISPATCH PH 254 834-3493
ALICE,TX OFC-PO BOX 1878,438 FLOURNOY RD
78333 PH 800 225-4146 PH 361 668-1562
CARLOS HINOJOSA,AREA MGR
GERRY GUZMAN,OPERS SUPT
MELISSA BOSTON,OFC ADMIN
DOLORES GAZA,CLERK
FILBERTO GONZALEZ,OPERS TECH
ASHERTON OFC-PO BOX 659,11981 S HWY 83
78827 PH 830 468-3401 FAX 830 468-3301
JOHN BERLANGA,AREA MGR
JAMES CHANDLER,OPERS SUPT

KEITH PERKINS,DISPATCHER
EL CAMPO,TX YARD-1408 E JACKSON 77437
PH 979 543-2757 FAX 979 543-7436
JEFF HANDY,AREA MGR
DON TAYLOR,OPERS SUPT
RACHEL MARTINEZ,CLERK
KENEDY,TX OFFICE - 620 S CR 153 78119
PH 830 583-0337 FAX 830 583-9751
JIM REEVES,AREA MGR
TAMMY DAVIS,OPERS SUPT
PAULINE MARTINEZ,CLERK
CHERYL GUTHRIE,CLERK
MARY SHAWN,DISPATCHER
RHONDA SNOW,DISPATCHER
MISSION,TX OFC-PO BOX 1378,8320 W MILE 7
78572 PH 800 225-4148 PH 956 581-1646
FAX 956 581-5231
ARNOLD DAVILA,OPERS MGR
MISSY ARTEAGA,OFC ADMIN
VANESSA GARCIA,CLERK
JOE VILLARREAL,DISPATCHER
ABRAHAM GARCIA,DISPATCHER
PLEASANTON,TX OFFICE - 586 CR 429 78064
PH 210 918-9800 FAX 210 918-9892
RON PRICHARD,DIST CONTROLLER
RUSSELL FLOYD,MGR CEMENTING
- SAFETY -
CHRISTOPHER LOVE,MGR SAFETY
VICTORIA,TX OFFICE - PO BOX 3345
6204 US HWY 59 N 77903 PH 800 371-4149
PH 361 576-9081 FAX 361 576-6452
JEFF HANDY,AREA MGR
DON TAYLOR,OPERS SUPT
ZAPATA,TX OFFICE -PO BOX 160,779 FM 496 W
78076 PH 800 477-2251 PH 956 765-6948
FAX 956 765-6109
- WEST TEXAS REGION -
MIDLAND,TX OFFICE - PO BOX 51670
3300 N A ST BLDG 2 STE 200 79710
PH 432 683-5000 FAX 432 683-3697
JAMEY BAUERLEIN,REG DIR
HAZEL FLORES,SR OPERS MGR
BENNY BALDWIN,SR OPERS MGR
BILLY RUMBAUGH,OPERS MGR
GENARO MARIN,OPERS MGR
ANDREWS,TX OFFICE - PO BOX 1977
701 NW MUSTANG DR 79714 PH 432 523-4420
FAX 432 524-2936
BRUCE MUNOZ,AREA MGR
BIG LAKE,TX OFFICE - 100 US HWY 67 W
76932 PH 325 884-2536 FAX 325 884-2211
RAY WOODALL,AREA MGR
DAVID PARKER,OPERS SUPT RIGS
CLAUDIO SOSA,OPERS SUPT
BIG SPRING,TX OFFICE - 2900 HWY 87 N
79720 PH 432 263-8444 FAX 432 263-8446
PHILLIP SMITH,OPERS SUPT
KIM IRWIN,HR/AP
CARLSBAD,NM OFC-PO BOX 9,3006 E GREENE ST
88221 PH 575 885-3372 FAX 575 885-3396
FREEMAN YOUNG,AREA MGR
OSCAR AGUILERA,OPERS SUPT
CRANE,TX OFFICE - PO BOX 1117,917 SE CR
79731 PH 432 558-3491 PH 432 558-2615
FAX 432 558-2402
TERRY CARRELL,AREA MGR

DEAN DEARING,OPERS SUPT
DENVER CITY,TX OFFICE - PO BOX 1358
2450 STATE HWY 214 79323 PH 806 592-2111
FAX 806 592-8282
PABLO PORTILLO,AREA MGR
ARMANDO ONTIVEROS,OPERS SUPT
DENVER CITY,TX OFFICE - PO BOX 1390
1161 HWY 83 79323 PH 806 592-9128
FAX 806 592-9139
REYMUNDO ZUBIA,FISHING TOOL AREA MGR
CRAIG FLETCHER,OPERS SUPT
ALEX SMITH,SR SLS REP
NANCY TERREL,OFC ADMIN
EUNICE,NM SATELLITE YARD - PO BOX 1311
2400 AVE O 88231 PH 888 343-6911
PH 575 394-2557 FAX 575 394-3526
FORT STOCKTON,TX OFFICE - PO DRAWER N
5000 FM 1053 N 79735 PH 432 336-5472
FAX 432 336-7400
SCOTT MANN,AREA MGR
HOBBS,NM OFFICE - PO BOX 2545
5208 LOVINGTON HWY 88241 PH 575 392-6591
FAX 575 392-3100
RONNIE MUNOZ,AREA MGR
SERGIO MARTINEZ,OPERS SUPT
MARGARET COBARRUBIO,OFC ADMIN
HOBBS,NM FISHING TOOLS OFC - PO BOX 1228
3311 W CR 88241 PH 575 397-3144
FAX 575 397-3150
EPI ESPARZA,OPERS SUPT
HOBBS,NM TRUCKS OFFICE - PO BOX 5208
3221 W CR 88240 PH 575 392-2577
FAX 575 392-9577
BENNY BALDWIN,OPERS MGR
FREEMAN YOUNG,AREA MGR
LEROY MORALES,OPERS SUPT
IRAAN,TX OFFICE -PO BOX 576,498 N HWY 349
79706 PH 432 836-4332 FAX 432 836-4330
TROY SPARKS,AREA MGR
MIDLAND,TX OFFICE - PO BOX 52140
3506 N CR 1148 79710 PH 432 617-4560
FAX 432 617-4563
MIDLAND,TX OFFICE - 8001 W INDUSTRIAL AVE
79706 PH 432 561-5822 FAX 432 561-5823
DAVID WINKLES,SUPT
DONNIE BLANKENSHIP,MGR
JULIA WILLIAMS,DOCUMENTATION ADMIN
BRUCE GREER,MGR STIMULATION
JULIO CASTILLO,MGR CEMENTING
MIDLAND,TX DOWNHOLE OFFICE-3000 S CR 1255
79706 PH 432 561-8044 FAX 432 561-8131
MONAHANS,TX OFFICE - PO BOX 1190
110 INDUSTRIAL 79756 PH 432 943-2227
FAX 432 943-2318
ODESSA,TX FISHING SVCS OFC-3400 MANKINS
79764 PH 432 617-8364 FAX 432 362-0800
REYMUNDO ZUBIA,FISHING TOOL AREA MGR
BARRY PARKS,EMPLOYMENT COOR
OZONA,TX OFFICE - PO BOX O,561 HWY 163 N
76943 PH 325 392-2313 FAX 325 392-2962
CODY HOOVER,AREA MGR
SAN ANGELO,TX OFFICE - PO BOX 61395
1214 GAS PLANT RD 76906 PH 800 211-4418
PH 325 651-9241 FAX 325 651-2260
JESSE HERNANDEZ,AREA MGR
JOSE PATO PALACIO,OPERS SUPT

SAN ANGELO,TX FISHING TOOL OFFICE -
PO BOX 61395,6501 US HWY 277 S 76906
PH 325 651-9241 FAX 325 651-9247
KENNETH MILLER, OPERS SUPT
SNYDER,TX OFFICE - 2857 US HWY 180 W
PH 325 573-2621 FAX 325 573-2864
NORINE BERNAL,AREA MGR
RAMON VALADEZ,OPERS SUPT
SONORA,TX OFC-PO BOX 726,1810 S HWY 277
76950 PH 325 387-3819 FAX 325 387-3717
JAIME SANTOS,AREA MGR
- MID CONTINENT REGION -
EL RENO,OK OFFICE - 4301 US 66 E 73036
PH 405 262-6262 FAX 405 262-4694
JUSTIN THOMPSON,OPERS SUPT
MARCOS GUZMAN,OPERS SUPT
ELK CITY,OK OFFICE - 3408 S HWY 6 73644
PH 580 225-7415 FAX 580 225-0244
ROBERT TAYLOR,AREA MGR
RICK MCMANAMAN,OPERS SUPT
ELK CITY,OK OFFICE - 100 PANEL RD 73644
PH 580 243-4000 FAX 580 243-4908
BRIAN MERZ,AREA MGR
CLIFFORD CAMPBELL,OPERS SUPT
GUYMON,OK OFC-PO BOX 2010,214 NE 24TH ST
73942 PH 580 338-7777 FAX 580 338-2670
BRENT MCCARTER,AREA MGR
MARLOW,OK OFFICE - 809 E HWY 29 73055
PH 580 658-1465 FAX 580 658-2384
KENNETH HOWELL,DIST MGR
PERRYTON,TX OFFICE - PO BOX 1266
800 E LOOP 143 79070 PH 806 435-5494
FAX 806 435-6339
JUSTIN LEUTWYLER,AREA MGR
CARLOS SEGURA,OPERS SUPT
RICHARD KIDWELL,FISHING TOOLS SVCS MGR
SWEETWATER,OK OFFICE - PO BOX 157,HWY 152
73666 PH 580 534-2210 FAX 580 534-2211
GARY GREGORY,AREA MGR
WOODWARD,OK OFFICE - PO BOX 547
4413 OKLAHOMA AVE 73802 PH 580 256-3353
FAX 580 256-8466
BRENT MCCARTER,AREA MGR
SALOMON GARCIA,OPERS SUPT
- ROCKY MOUNTAIN REGION -
BILLINGS,MT OFFICE - 2048 OVERLAND AVE
STE 101 59102 PH 406 245-1515
FAX 406 248-1774
TONY LEE,DIR
GREG BURBACH,SR OPERS MGR
BRAD HJELM,SLS MGR
TODD WREN,REG HSE MGR
MARK KITZENBERG,REG CONTROLLER
BAKER,MT OFFICE - PO BOX 1158
912 E MONTANA AVE HWY 12 59313
PH 406 778-2527 FAX 406 778-2758
JARROD DYEKMAN,AREA MGR
BELFIELD,ND OFFICE - PO BOX 1000
935 HWY 10 E 58622 PH 701 575-4333
FAX 701 575-8511
GLENN HANSON,AREA MGR
ED SHYPKOWSKI,OPERS SUPT
BOB MATTHEWS,HSE MGR
BELFIELD,ND OFC-PO BOX 1000,956 1ST AVE
58622 PH 701 575-4776 FAX 701 575-4084
DENVER,CO OFFICE - 475 17TH ST STE 1100

80202 PH 303 295-6800 PH 303 308-6560
RHETT COY,REG DIR
ROBERT SHARPE,TECH MGR
ERIC GOODLIN,MGR SAFETY
JAMES LLOYD,SR SLS MGR
FAIRFIELD,ND OFFICE - 12790 20TH ST SW
58627 PH 701 575-2106 FAX 701 575-2129
FORT LUPTON,CO OFFICE - 12670 WCR 25 1/2
PH 970 785-6575 FAX 970 785-6205
TRAVIS FRY,MGR DOWNHOLE SURVEYING
GLENDIVE,MT OFFICE - 135 HWY 16 UNIT C
59330 PH 406 377-2535 FAX 406 377-2539
GLENDIVE,MT SHOP - 2900 N ANDERSON 59330
PH 406 377-5004 FAX 406 377-3129
PLENTYWOOD,MT OFC-PO BOX 421,114 HWY 5 E
59254 PH 406 895-2253 FAX 406 895-2463
ROCK SPRINGS,WY OFFICE - 22A TRI STATE RD
82901 PH 307 362-3376 FAX 307 362-3376
NICK HEGEL,OPERS SUPT
CHRISTOPHER LEE,MGR STIMULATION
GARY WALL,MGR ELECTRONICS ENGINEERING
DON HARDINGER,MGR CEMENTING
THOMAS FREULER,MGR COOR SFTY
ROOSEVELT,UT OFFICE - PO BOX 1515
2240 W HWY 40 84066 PH 435 722-3451
FAX 435 722-9181
RAY MORLAN,AREA MGR
ROOSEVELT,UT OIL TOOL OFFICE - PO BOX 667
2602 W 2000 S 84066 PH 435 725-5344
FAX 435 725-5345
LEE SLAUGH,BRANCH MGR
SIDNEY,MT OFFICE - PO BOX 1507
12295 CR 349R 59270 PH 406 482-1647
FAX 406 482-7932
SCOTT WILCOX,AREA MGR
VERNAL,UT OFC-PO BOX 1094,4368 E 4700 S
84078 PH 435 781-0266 FAX 435 781-0270
BRYAN COOK,MGR STIMULATION
WILLISTON,ND OFFICE - PO BOX 4275
1015 58TH ST W 58801 PH 701 572-4583
FAX 701 572-9254
KEN IVEY,AREA MGR
WILLISTON,ND OFFICE - 5485 HWY 2 & 85
58801 PH 701 572-2042 FAX 701 572-2044
JOHN BROWN,DIST MGR
TROY MINCH,MGR/OPERS SUPPORT
- WESTERN REGION -
BAKERSFIELD,CA OFFICE - 1954 JAMES RD
93308 PH 661 392-7668 FAX 661 392-7674
DAVE WERNER,VP GEN MGR
GARY INGRAM,DIST EQUIP MGR
DARRYL CRISSMAN,OPERS SUPT
DARRELL LONG,OPERS SUPT
BAKERSFIELD,CA ACCTG CENTER -
3651 PEGASUS DR STE 101 93308
PH 661 391-3800 FAX 661 391-3806
ALAN POUNDS,DIR BUS DEV
PATRICIA HUNTER,PROCESS ANALYST
JAMES THOMAS JR,MGR ADMIN & REG AFFAIRS
LISA COSTON,CONTROLLER
MICHAEL HUFNAGEL,SR ACCT
LARRY KIRKS,PURCHASING SUPVSR
BAKERSFIELD,CA HR OFC-3701 PEGASUS DR
STE 102 93308 PH 661 615-5973
BAKERSFIELD,CA ADMIN OFC - 7515 ROSEDALE
HWY 93308 PH 800 299-2910 PH 661 589-3970

JOE DEFORD,SR OPERS MGR
LONNY HATRIDGE,DIST EQUIP SUPT
ROBERT RODRIGUEZ,MGR SFTY/TRNG
BAKERSFIELD,CA OPERS OFFICE -
7515 ROSEDALE HWY 93308 PH 800 299-2910
PH 661 589-3970 FAX 661 589-5276
GEORGE LUSK,AREA MGR
JEFF ROWLAND,AREA MGR
TROY AUGE,AREA MGR
GREG PHILLIPS,OPERS SUPT
DAVE BAILEY,OPERS SUPT
RICK ROGERS,OPERS SUPT
GREG OSENBAUGH,OPERS SUPT
DAVE FEASTER,OPERS SUPT
SANTA MARIA,CA OFFICE-665 W BETTERAVIA RD
93454 PH 800 299-2921 PH 805 928-4353
FAX 805 928-7976
RON HAIRE,AREA MGR
RICHARD WINDES,OPERS SUPT
BAKERSFIELD,CA SPECIAL SVCS OFFICE -
1025 EARTHMOVER COURT 93314
PH 661 588-6140 FAX 661 588-6146
GREG TREMAIN,OPERS MGR
TIM KOPPI,AREA MGR
DUANE SIMPSON,AREA MGR
JERRY FERNANDEZ,AREA MGR
BRUCE FOSTER,OPERS SUPT
ROBERT GEORGATOS,OPERS SUPT
JOHN CULBERTSON,OPERS SUPT
BRANDON WRIGHT,OPERS SUPT
MICHAEL SMITH,OPERS SUPT
JEFFREY THOMPSON,OPERS SUPT
MIKE HUGHEY,BRANCH MGR
PHIL PAGE,SR TOOL SPECIALIST
VENTURA,CA OFFICE - 2567 N VENTURA AVE
BLDG A 93001 PH 805 648-2731
FAX 805 648-7939
RON HAIRE,AREA MGR
JUAN LANDRON,OPERS SUPT
RANCHO DOMINGUEZ,CA OFFICE - PO BOX 2290
19431 S SANTA FE AVE 90801
PH 800 299-2919 PH 310 639-7074
FAX 310 637-7082
JOHNNY SANCHEZ,SR OPERS MGR
GARY KAUFMAN,SR SFTY/TRNG SPECIALIST
DENNIS WANG,AREA MGR
VINCENT GARCIA,OPERS SUPT
JAMES MCCUSKER,OPERS SUPT
RANCHO DOMINGUEZ,CA OFFICE - PO BOX 2290
19431 S SANTA FE AVE 90221
PH 800 299-2919 FAX 310 637-7082
WILLIAM BUTERBAUGH,OPERS SUPT
- SOUTHERN APPALACHIA REGION -
BRIDGEPORT,WV OFFICE - PO BOX 4160
735 GENESIS BLVD 26330 PH 304 842-9560
FAX 304 842-9563
GEORGE BURGE,REG DIR
SCOTT SIAS,DIST MGR
CASEY ROUSH,MGR
CAROL BARTLETT,HR MGR
BRETT MORRIS,HSE MGR
DEREK DIERINGER,SFTY MGR
CASEY LONG,REG MAINTENANCE MGR
BUCHANNON,WV OFFICE - 82 ELKINS RD 26201
PH 304 472-2644 FAX 304 472-6855
CALVIN DRUMMOND,WIRELINE MGR

VERNON CASTO,WIRELINE MGR
LARRY ARMSTRONG,WIRELINE MGR
MARK LEWIS,WIRELINE MGR
COTTONDALE,AL OFFICE - 13645 HWY 11 N
PH 205 556-4542 FAX 205 556-4545
DONALD TUCKER,MGR CEMENTING
CARLOS COOPER,MGR STIMULATION
JANE LEW,WV OFFICE - PO BOX 749
528 INDUSTRIAL PARK RD 26378
PH 304 884-6591 FAX 304 884-6593
BRYAN WALTON,OPERS SUPT
JANE LEW,WV COMPLETION OFFICE -
1650 HACKERS CREEK RD 26378
PH 304 884-6684 FAX 304 884-6687
CURTISS MARTIN,DIST MGR
ANTHONY DEAN,STIMULATION SUPVSR
DUSTY CONRAD,MGR CEMENTING
NORTON,VA OFFICE - 580 HAWTHORN DR 24273
PH 276 679-5861 FAX 276 679-5863
MONTE MCREYNOLDS,DIST MGR
- NORTHERN APPALACHIA REGION -
INDIANA,PA OFFICE - 1380 RT 286 E STE 121
15701 PH 724 465-8904 FAX 724 465-8907
MIKE BENNER,DIR/OPERS MGR
JEFFREY MLAKER,MKTG MGR
DEBORAH RORABAUGH,REG MATERIALS MGR
JEFF BLANZY,REG MAINTENANCE MGR
MATT BLAUCH,DIR PROD DEV
SEAN REEGER,DIST TECH MGR
JOE CIESLINSKI,LAB MGR
DOUG SATTERFIELD,REG HSE MGR
KYLE BRUNO,HSE COOR
BLACKLICK,PA OFFICE - PO BOX 458
8300 RT 119 N 15716 PH 724 248-1001
FAX 724 248-1005 FAX 724 248-7351
RONALD GRIFFITH,MGR CEMENTING
WALTER BENNETT,MGR STIMULATION
SEAN REEGER,REG TECH MGR
CAMRIDGE,OH OFFICE - PO BOX 1583
110 GLENN HWY 43725 PH 740 432-3000
FAX 740 432-7000
GAYLORD,MI OFFICE - PO BOX 1950
614 EXPRESSWAY CRT 49734 PH 989 705-8301
MIKE BROWN,OPERS MGR
ROBERTA BUCHANAN,OFC MGR
OWEGO,NY OFFICE - 200 W AVE 13827
PH 607 687-8030 FAX 607 687-8032
STEVE APIGO,SUPT
DANNY BROWN,MGR CEMENTING
SHELOCTA,PA OFFICE - 228 LAWTON RD 15774
PH 724 354-3194 FAX 724 354-3179
ERIC LINGENFELTER,MGR BLACKLICK DOWNHOLE

NABORS DRILLING USA,LP
515 W GREENS RD STE 1000
HOUSTON,TX 77067-4531
PH 281 874-0035 FAX 281 775-8414
JOE HUDSON,PRES,CEO
ERNIE NELSON,VP CONTRACTS
- SOUTHERN DIVISION -
JIMMY STROUD,SR VP & GEN MGR/OPERS
TERRY HARPER,MGR MKTG
BOB WILDER,EXEC SLS/MKTG
PLEASANTON,TX (SOUTH TEXAS) OFFICE -
3840 E HWY 44,78332
PH 361 668-1674 FAX 361 668-6127
KEITH DUNN,DIST MGR

MATTHEW SPEER,MGR MARKETING
TYLER,TX (EAST TEXAS) OFFICE -
12031 STATE HWY 155,75708
PH 903 579-0719 FAX 903 877-9120
JOSEPH HUDSON,DIST MGR
TREVOR BRINKLEY,MGR MKTG
NEW IBERIA,LA (GULF COAST & OFFSHORE OFC)
4400 W ADMIRAL DOYLE DR,70560
PH 337 359-3300
DREW DAVIS,SR VP,HOUSTON OFC
HAP GIROUARD,DIST MGR
GEORGE COURVILLE,MKTG MGR
ODESSA,TX (WEST TEXAS) OFFICE -
2500 W OREGON,79764-1798
PH 432 363-8180 FAX 432 550-0863
JAMES NASH,DIST MGR
- NORTHERN DIVISION -
JOEY HUSBAND,SR VP & GEN MGR
TERRY BOYD,VP OPERS
STEVE HULSE,CORP VP MKTG
BRENT WULF,VP MKTG
DENVER,CO OFFICE - 475 17TH ST STE 850
80202 PH 303 308-8181 FAX 303 308-8102
JAMES LEISER,MKTG MGR
BAKERSFIELD,CA OFFICE - 3919 ROSEDALE HWY
93308 PH 661 635-1440 FAX 661 322-4619
RON CLEVELAND,DIST MGR
WILLISTON,ND OFFICE - HWY 2 & 85 NORTH
58801 PH 701 572-6704 FAX 701 572-0758
SCOTT REID,DIST MGR
CASPER,WY OFFICE - 6500 W ZERO RD 82604
PH 307 472-4097 FAX 307 473-2206
LEE HUTCHINSON,DIST MGR
OKLAHOMA CITY,OK (MID-CONTINENT) OFFICE -
10100 NW 10TH ST 73127
PH 405 324-8081 FAX 405 324-8845
ROB HILL,DIST MGR
JOE RAUSCH,MKTG MGR
CLEARFIELD,PA (NORTHEAST) OFFICE -
143 CRESSWOOD DR 16830
PH 814 768-4643 FAX 814 768-4650
JEFF COX,DIST MGR
JASON HUDSON,MKTG MGR
- YARDS -
HOUSTON,TX (BREEN YARD) - 8400 BREEN RD
77064 PH 713 849-9391 FAX 713 849-4682
CROSBY,TX (CROSBY YARD) - 2100 CROSBY
DAYTON RD 77532 PH 281 462-1730
FAX 281 462-2190
OKLAHOMA CITY,OK (ROCKWELL YARD) -
5500 S ROCKWELL ST 73079
PH 405 745-3457 FAX 405 745-6713

NABORS INDUSTRIES LTD
PO BOX HM3349,MINTFLOWER PLACE
8 PAR-LA-VILLE RD
HAMILTON,BERMUDA HM08 PH 441 292-1510
FAX 441 292-1334 WWW.NABORS.COM
EUGENE M ISENBERG,CHRMN,CEO
ANTHONY G PETRELLO,DEPUTY CHRMN,PRES,COO
MARTY J WHITMAN,LEAD DIR
JACK WEXLER,DIR EMERITUS
HOUSTON,TX OFC-515 W GREENS RD STE 1200
77067 PH 281 874-0035 FAX 281 872-5205

- NABORS DRILLING USA, LP -

HOUSTON,TX OFC-515 W GREENS RD STE 1000
77067 PH 281 874-0035 FAX 281 775-8147

- NABORS ALASKA DRILLING,INC -

ANCHORAGE,AK OFFICE-2525 C ST STE 200
99503 PH 907 263-6000 FAX 907 563-3734

- NABORS DRILLING (CANADA) -

CALGARY,ALBERTA,CAN OFFICE-500 4TH AVE SW
STE 2800 T2P2V6 PH 403 263-6777
FAX 403 269-7352
NISKU,ALBERTA,CAN OFFICE-902 20TH AVE
BOX 1006 T9E8A8 PH 780 955-2381
FAX 780 955-2188

- NABORS INTERNATIONAL,INC -

HOUSTON,TX OFFICE-515 W GREENS RD STE 900
77067 PH 281 874-0035 FAX 281 775-8144

- NABORS PRODUCTION SERVICES -

SYLVAN LAKE,ALBERTA,CAN OFC-33 SCHENK
INDUSTRIAL RD T4S2J9 PH 403 887-7400
PH 800 999-1536 FAX 403 887-3050
BROOKS,ALBERTA,CAN OFC-PO BOX 429 T1R1B4
PH 403 362-6600 PH 888 987-4628
PH 403 362-6641 FAX 403 362-3832
LEDUC,ALBERTA,CAN OFC-7009 45TH ST T9E7H1
PH 780 986-0036 FAX 780 986-0048
DRAYTON VALLEY,AB,CAN OFC-PO BOX 6509
8120 50TH AVE T7A1R9 PH 780 542-4689
PH 800 662-7182 FAX 780 542-7856
CLAIRMONT,ALBERTA,CAN OFC-8601 99 ST
T0H0W0 PH 780 567-2705 PH 888 893-3764
FAX 780 567-5275
SLAVE LAKE,ALBERTA,CAN OFC-PO BOX 248
1500 15TH AVE NE T0G2A2 PH 780 849-2727
PH 877 849-0499 FAX 780 849-2780
CHARLIE LAKE,B.C.,CAN OFC-PO BOX 749
13395 TOMPKINS FRONTAGE RD MILE 54 ALASKA
HWY V0C1H0 PH 250 785-2307
PH 800 386-1824 FAX 250 785-0321
LLOYDMINSTER,ALBERTA,CAN OFC-1812 50 AVE
BAY 7 T9V2W7 PH 780 875-4484
FAX 780 875-4855

- NABORS SWABTECH -

SYLVAN LAKE,ALBERTA,CAN OFC-33 SCHENK
INDUSTRIAL RD T4S2J9 PH 403 887-7400
PH 888 310-7922 FAX 403 887-3050

- NABORS ABANDONRITE -

CALGARY,ALBERTA,CAN OFC-500 4TH AVE SW
STE 2800 T2P2V6 PH 403 237-8000
FAX 403 237-8001

- NABORS WELL SERVICES -

HOUSTON,TX OFC-515 W GREENS RD STE 1170
77067 PH 281 874-0035 PH 800 299-1388
PH 888 622-6777

- NABORS OFFSHORE CORPORATION -

HOUSTON,TX OFFICE-515 W GREENS RD STE 500
77067 PH 281 874-0406 FAX 281 775-8462
HARVEY,LA OFFICE-3640 PETERS RD 70058
PH 504 362-8033 FAX 504 365-3200
HOUMA,LA (INLAND SVCS DIV) OFFICE-
PO BOX 466,410 PALM AVE 70361
PH 985 868-1874 PH 800 862-2493
FAX 985 876-7908

- PEAK ENERGY SERVICES -

HOUSTON,TX OFFICE-515 W GREENS RD STE 600
77067 PH 281 872-7325 PH 888 622-6777
FAX 281 775-4963
EL RENO,OK OFFICE-201 E JENSEN 73036
PH 405 262-7879 PH 800 303-9581
FAX 405 262-7873
POCOLA,OK OFFICE-1803 N GRAY ST 74902
PH 918 436-7434 FAX 918 436-7515
ALICE,TX OFFICE-3880 E HWY 44 78332
PH 361 668-9953 PH 888 550-9608
FAX 361 668-9624
BRIDGEPORT,TX OFFICE-1854 W HWY 380
76426 PH 940 683-8094 PH 866 456-9525
FAX 940 683-4109
BRYAN,TX OFFICE-2900 CLARKS LN 77808
PH 979 778-1901 PH 888 744-6683
FAX 979 778-8720
HOUSTON,TX OFFICE-18300 BEAUMONT HWY
77049 PH 281 456-8439 FAX 281 456-0038
KILGORE,TX OFFICE-694 FM 1252 E 75662
PH 903 988-1144 FAX 866 872-9992
FAX 903 988-2288
PALESTINE,TX OFFICE-9182 S US HWY 79
75801 PH 903 538-2121 PH 800 225-9633
FAX 903 538-2285
ROCK SPRINGS,WY OFFICE-1101 NORTH ST
82943 PH 307 362-9773 PH 877 744-6683
FAX 307 362-4814

- PEAK OILFIELD SERVICES -

ANCHORAGE,AK OFFICE-2525 C ST STE 201
99503 PH 907 263-7000 FAX 907 263-7041
PEAK@PEAKALASKA.COM
PRUDHOE BAY,AK OFFICE-POUCH 340005
99734 PH 907 659-2033
NIKISKI,AK (COOK INLET) OFFICE-
PO BOX 7159 99635 PH 907 776-4030
VALDEZ,AK OFFICE-PO BOX 3209 99686
PH 907 835-4043
PALMER,AK (PRECISION POWER,LLC) OFFICE-
-A DIVISION OF PEAK OILFIELD SERVICES-
200 E COMMERCIAL DR 99645
PH 907 746-7797 FAX 907 746-7772
PRECISIONPOWER@PREPOWER.NET

- RYAN ENERGY TECHNOLOGIES (USA) -

HOUSTON,TX OFFICE-19510 OIL CENTER BLVD
77073 PH 281 443-1414 PH 800 682-0291
FAX 281 443-1476 RYAN.INFO@NABORS.COM
DENVER,CO (SALES) OFFICE-475 17TH ST

STE 850 80202 PH 303 308-8101
LFAYETTE,LA (GULF REG) OFFICE-108 BANKS
AVE 70506 PH 337 264-1035
FAX 337 264-1565
CASPER,WY (ROCKIES REG) OFC-1820 PYRITE
RD 82604 PH 307 234-9753 PH 800 503-5069
FAX 307 234-0795

- RYAN ENERGY TECHNOLOGIES (CANADA) -

CALGARY,ALBERTA,CAN OFFICE-500 4TH AVE SW
STE 2800 T2P2V6 PH 403 269-5981
FAX 403 263-2031
CALGARY,ALBERTA,CAN (TECH CENTRE) OFC-
61 AVE SE STE 2719 T2C4X3 PH 403 236-2157
FAX 403 263-2158
LEDUC,ALBERTA,CAN (MOTOR) OFFICE-
7009 45TH ST T9E7H1 PH 780 980-1425
FAX 780 980-1449

- CANRIG DRILLING TECHNOLOGIES -

MAGNOLIA,TX OFFICE-14703 FM 1488 77354
PH 281 259-8887 FAX 832 934-1920
INFO@CANRIG.COM WWW.CANRIG.COM
HOUSTON,TX OFFICE-12707 NORTH FRWY STE
STE 500 77060 PH 281 774-5600
FAX 281 774-5650
CALGARY,ALBERTA,CAN OFC-7475 51ST ST SE
T2C4L6 PH 403 237-6400 FAX 403 269-3090

NABORS INTERNATIONAL,INC SEE
NABORS INDUSTRIES LTD
NABORS OFFSHORE CORPORATION SEE
NABORS INDUSTRIES LTD
NABORS PRODUCTION SERVICES SEE
NABORS INDUSTRIES LTD
NABORS SWABTECH SEE
NABORS INDUSTRIES LTD
NACCI BRUCE OIL & GAS INTERESTS
PO BOX 270
CORPUS CHRISTI,TX 78403-0270
PH 361 887-7162 FAX 361 887-9262
NAI/LATTER & BLUM,INC
COMMERCIAL REAL ESTATE SVCS,WORLDWIDE
430 NOTRE DAME ST
NEW ORLEANS,LA 70130-3610
PH 504 569-9312 FAX 504 569-9336
WWW.LATTERBLUM.COM
INFO@LATTERBLUM.COM
PATRICK J EGAN,EXEC VP
PEGAN@LATTERBLUM.COM
NAIL BAY ROYALTIES,LLC
PO BOX 671099
DALLAS,TX 75367 PH 214 707-7535
FAX 214 572-2699 WWW.TRUNKBAY.NET
BENNY DUNCAN,MGR
BDUNCAN@TRUNKBAY.NET
NALCO/EXXON ENERGY CHEMICALS,LP SEE
ONDEO NALCO ENERGY SERVICES,LP
NALLY GAS PROPERTIES INC
PO BOX 5354
FORT SMITH,AR 72913-5354 PH 479 478-6236
CAROLYN NALLY,OWNER
KARLYN1942@SBCGLOBAL.NET
GRANT NALLY,ENGR
ERIC NALLY,LDMN

NAMIBIA HUNT OIL COMPANY SEE
HUNT OIL COMPANY
NANCE BILLY JAY
PO BOX 1252
SHREVEPORT,LA 71163-1252 PH 318 221-5030
NANTIM ENERGY,INC
PO BOX 80752,1101 S HUGH WALLIS RD #101
LAFAYETTE,LA 70598-0598
PH 337 234-6549 FAX 337 232-7797
JAMES F (JIM) HARDWICK,GEOL
NANTUCKET RESOURCES GROUP,LC
PO BOX 540244
HOUSTON,TX 77254-0244
PH 713 526-6021 PH 432 685-3296
FAX 713 526-6164
WWW.NANTUCKET-RESOURCES.COM
NAREMORE DAN,IND LDMN
208 PRESTON AVE
SHREVEPORT,LA 71105-3308 PH 318 861-7326
NARRAMORE PATRICIA TRUST
PO BOX 2020
TYLER,TX 75710-2020
PH 903 535-4266 FAX 903 535-4247
JOEY.HAND@REGIONS.COM
REGIONS BANK,TRUSTEE
JOSEPH E HAND JR,SR VP
NASH LINDA BAKER
125 BALDMAR RD
HENDERSONVILLE,NC 28791-9004
PH 828 696-2773 FAX 828 696-2773
NATCHEZ EXPLORATION,LLC
416 MAIN ST
NATCHEZ,MS 39120 PH 601 442-7400
FAX 601 442-7400
JOHN E MCCULLOUGH,PRES
NATCO (NATIONAL TANK CO) SEE CAMERON
NATIONAL ENERGY GROUP,INC SEE
NEG OPERATING LLC
NATIONAL ENERGY LLC
9302 CHARTER PINE ST
HOUSTON,TX 77070-2053
PH 281 413-4015 FAX 281 257-9466
MYRON KORPAN
NATIONAL FIDUCIARY SERVICES,NA
1717 SAINT JAMES PL STE 500
HOUSTON,TX 77056-3474
PH 713 850-0571 FAX 713 850-7516
DON G ROBINSON,VP
NATIONAL FIELD SERVICE CORP
162 ORANGE AVE
SUFFERN,NY 10901-6006 PH 914 368-1600
FAX 914 368-1989
DICK AVAZIAN,PRES
BOB HAYWARD,VP
MARGARET FORMAN,SECY/TREAS
NATIONAL K WORKS,INC
1717 BRITTMOORE RD
HOUSTON,TX 77043-2710 PH 713 467-4795
PIERO WOLK,PRES
DAVID JEKIELEK,PROJ ENGR
NATIONAL OILWELL VARCO
7909 PARKWOOD CIRCLE DR
HOUSTON,TX 77036 PH 713 375-3700
WWW.NOV.COM
CLAY C WILLIAMS,PRESIDENT & CHAIRMAN
SCOTT DUFF,VP,CORPORATE CONTROLLER &

CHIEF ACCOUNTING OFFICER
TOM MCGEE,VP CORPORATE DEVELOPMENT
DAVID REID,CHIEF MARKETING OFFICER
ALEX PHILIPS,CIO
BILL CRABBE,CHIEF HEALTH,SAFETY, &
ENVIRONMENT OFFICER
HEGE KVERNELAND,CORPORATE VP & CHIEF
TECHNOLOGY
LOREN B SINGLETARY,VP INVESTOR & INDUSTRY
CRAIG WEINSTOCK,SR VP & GENERAL COUNSEL
TOBY ZYROLL,PRESIDENT, NOV AMERON
ROBIN MACMILLAN,SR VP BUS DEV
GUIDO VAN DEN BOS,VP GLOBAL ACCOUNTS

- COMPLETION & PRODUCTION SOLUTIONS -

HOUSTON,TX OFFICE - 7909 PARKWOOD CIRCLE
DR 77036 PH 713 375-3700
GARRET SOBCZAK,GLOBAL TECHNICAL SALES &
MARKETING MANAGER-XL SYSTEMS

WELLBORE TECHNOLOGIES -

HOUSTON,TX OFFICE - 7909 PARKWOOD CIRCLE
DR 77036 PH 713 375-3700
MIKE MATTA,SEGMENT PRESIDENT
JACK COLBORN,CHIEF SALES OFFICER
BRETT CHANDLER,PRESIDENT-GRANT PRIDECO
ISAAC JOSEPH,PRESIDENT-TUBOSCOPE
MARK LAPEYROUSE,PRES-WELLSITE SERVICES
STEVEN BARTON,PRES-DYNAMIC DRLG SOLUTIONS
TED CHRISTIANSEN,PRESIDENT-INTELLISERV
KOSAY EL-RAYES,PRES-DRLG & INTERVENTION

- RIG SYSTEMS -

HOUSTON,TX OFFICE - 1000 RICHMOND AVE
77042 PH 713 346-7500
JOE ROVIG,PRES-RIG SYSTEMS & AFTERMARKET
KEVIN CHAPMAN,CHIEF SALES & PRODUCTION
OFFICER
BOB NICHOLSON,PRESIDENT-RIG SYSTEMS
AFTERMARKET
BILLY GILL,VP-SERVICE & REPAIR-EUROPE &
NORTH AND SOUTH AMERICA
DAVID MCLEAN,VP SERVICE & REPAIR-MIDDLE E
NORTH AFRICA, FSU, & ASIA
JAN MELSTVEIT,PRESIDENT-RIG SYSTEMS
OFFSHORE
MIKE LOUCAIDES,VP-RIG SYSTEMS SALES
OFFSHORE
WILLIAM KENT,VP-RIG SYSTEMS PROJECT SALES
JASON MAJOR,VP-SALES,RIG SYSTEMS,ASIA
PACIFIC & MIDDLE EAST
ANSTEIN HAGEN,VP-SALES,RIG SYSTEMS,EUROPE
AFRICA, & RUSSIA
SCOTT LIVINGSTON,PRESIDENT-RIG SYSTEMS
LAND
GRAHAM DAY,VP-SALES RIG SYSTEMS LAND
JEFF HUNTER,VP-REGIONAL SALES,RIG SYSTEMS
LAND, USA
MAJED HAMDAN,VP-REGIONAL SALES,RIG SYSTEM
LAND,MIDDLE EAST, AFRICA, & CIS
DOUGLAS KIDD,DIR BUSINESS DEVELOPMENT,RIG
SYSTEMS LAND,ASIA
RANDY SCATES,VP & GENERAL MANAGER,MOBILE

RIGS
NATIONAL OILWELL VARCO RIG SYSTEMS
10000 RICHMOND AVE
HOUSTON,TX 77042 PH 713 346-7500
JOE ROVIG,PRES-RIG SYSTEMS & AFTERMARKET
KEVIN CHAPMAN,CHF SLS & PRODUCTS OFCR
BOB NICHOLSON,PRES-RIG SYSTEMS
AFTERMARKET
BILLY GILL,VP SVC & REPAIR - EUROPE,
NORTH & SOUTH AMERICA
DAVID MCLEAN,VP SVC & REPAIR - MIDDLE E,
N AFRICA,FSU & ASIA
JAN MELSTVEIT,PRES-RIG SYSTEMS OFFSHORE
MIKE LOUCAIDES,VP-RIG SYSTEMS SLS
OFFSHORE
WILLIAM KENT,VP-RIG SYSTEMS PROJ SLS
JASON MAJOR,VP-SLS,RIG SYSTEMS - ASIA
PACIFIC & MIDDLE EAST
ANSTEIN HAGEN,VP-SLS,RIG SYSTEMS -
EUROPE,AFRICA & RUSSIA
SCOTT LIVINGSTON,PRES-RIG SYSTEMS LAND
GRAHAM DEY,VP-SLS,RIG SYSTEMS LAND
JEFF HUNTER,VP-REG SLS,RIG SYSTEMS LAND
USA
MAJED HAMDAN,VP-REG SLS,RIG SYS LAND,ME,
AFRICA & CIS
DOUGLAS KIDD,DIR BUS DEV,RIG SYS LAND,
ASIA
RANDY SCATES,VP & GEN MGR-MOBILE RIGS
NATIONAL PETROGRAPHIC SERVICE,INC
PALEONTOLOGISTS,PALYNOLOGIST,GEOLOGISTS,
GEOSCIENTISTS & GEOCHEMISTRY
5933 BELLAIRE BLVD STE 108
HOUSTON,TX 77081-5548 PH 713 661-1884
FAX 713 661-0625 NPSINC@FLASH.NET
WWW.NATIONALPETROGRAPHIC.COM
JOHN ARAIZA,PRES
NATIONAL PIPELINE MAPPING SYSTEM
WWW.NPMS.RSPA.DOT.GOV
NATIONAL PROPANE GAS ASSOCIATION
WWW.PROPANEGAS.COM
NATIONAL REGULATORY RESEARCH INSTITUTE
WWW.NRRI.OHIO-STATE.EDU
NATIONAL RENEWABLE ENERGY LABORATORY
WWW.NREL.GOV
NATIONAL SCALE TECHNOLOGY
160 W PARK LOOP NW
HUNTSVILLE,AL 35806 PH 800 264-9990
WEBMASTER@NATIONAL-SCALE.COM
NATIVE AMERICAN MARKETING,LLC
11490 WESTHEIMER RD STE 200
HOUSTON,TX 77077 PH 832 767-5695
FAX 866 704-5692
WWW.NATIVEAMERICANMARKETING.COM
LARRY LEBARRE,PRES
BRICE DILLE,CFO
BILL CURRY,COO - CARMEN,OK
DAMON SHERRELL,OPERS - CARMEN,OK
NATURAL ENERGY UTILITY CORPORATION
2560 HOODS CREEK PIKE
ASHLAND,KY 41102-2261 PH 606 324-3920
FAX 606 325-2991 HJFNEUC@AOL.COM
H JAY FREEMAN,PRES,CEO
NATURAL GAS & OIL ENGINEERING,PETR ENGR
P O BOX 78133
SHREVEPORT,LA 71107-5412 PH 318 227-2212

NATURAL GAS & OIL INC
PO BOX 326,116 25TH ST NE
FAYETTE,AL 35555-0326 PH 205 932-8935
FAX 205 932-3083
BILL W NEWTON,PRES

NATURAL GAS & OIL PROPERTY MANAGEMENT
P O BOX 78133
SHREVEPORT,LA 71137-8133 PH 318 221-0605
KENNETH W FRAZIER,PRES
LOYCE P PORTERFIELD,VP

NATURAL GAS ANADARKO COMPANY
PO BOX 809,1800 S MAIN
PERRYTON,TX 79070-0809 PH 806 435-6818
L KIRK COURSON,PRES
CRISTI MOGG,SEC/TREAS

NATURAL GAS MEASUREMENT INC
4410 DILLION LN STE 4
CORPUS CHRISTI,TX 78415
PH 361 884-8637 FAX 361 884-8702

NATURAL GAS RESOURCE CORPORATION
PO BOX 55768
HOUSTON,TX 77255-5768 PH 713 652-9626
BRUCE H HOUFF,PRES,GEOL

NATURAL GAS SUPPLY ASSOCIATION
WWW.NGSA.ORG

NATURAL OIL & GAS CORP
1410 W WARREN RD
BRADFORD,PA 16701-4113
PH 814 362-6890 FAX 814 362-6120
JOHN H REETZ,JR,PRES
JOE PAPALIA,SR DRLG SUPVSR
NEIL WALLACE,FLD SUPVSR
JANAE ANDERSON,VP TECH/MKTG

NATURAL RESOURCES INVESTMENT COMPANY
PO BOX 2840
RIDGELAND,MS 39158 PH 601 573-6852
CORNELIUS W NEIL BARNES,PRES

NATURAL RESOURCES REVENUE, OFFICE OF
U.S. DEPT OF THE INTERIOR
1849 C ST NW MAIL STOP 4211
WASHINGTON,DC 20240 PH 202 513-0600
WWW.ONRR.GOV
ANITA GONZALES-EVANS,CONGRESSIONAL
LIAISON PH 202 513-0607
ANITA.GONZALES-EVANS@ONRR.GOV
DENVER,CO OFFICE - PO BOX 25165
80225 PH 303 231-3162
DALLAS,TX OFFICE - 4050 ALPHA RD STE 420
FARMERS BRANCH,TX 75244 PH 214 640-9030
HOUSTON,TX OFFICE - 15109 HEATHROW FOREST
PKWY STE 200 77032 PH 281 987-6800
FARMINGTON,NM OFFICE - 6251 COLLEGE BLVD
STE B 87402 PH 505 564-7640
PH 800 238-2839
OKLAHOMA CITY,OK OFFICE - 4013 NW EXPY
STE 230 73116 PH 800 354-7015
PH 405 879-6000 (AUDIT & COMPLIANCE)
PH 405 879-6050 (STATE & INDIAN OUTREACH)
TULSA,OK OFFICE - 7615 E 63RD PL STE 105
74133 PH 918 610-6500

NAUMANN ROY L,GEOL
PO BOX 52406
LAFAYETTE,LA 70505-2406 PH 337 233-0363
FAX 337 232-1707

NAVIGATOR ENERGY SERVICES,LLC
2626 COLE AVE STE 850

DALLAS,TX 75204 PH 214 880-6000
JOHN O'SHEA,CEO
BERNIE THOMAS,CO-FOUNDER & VP
RANDY MARGO,SR VP-ENGRG & OPERS
MATT VINING,CO-FOUNDER & CCO
TYLER ANDERSON,BUS DEV REPR
MORGAN KUBALA,LAND & CONTRACTS COORD
BIG SPRING,TX OFFICE - 2000 S BIRDWELL LN
79720

NAVUS RESOURCES CORPORATION
PO BOX 671065
DALLAS,TX 75367-1065 PH 214 750-8308
FAX 214 750-0644

NCA ENERGY SERVICES,LLC SEE
CRESCENT ENERGY SERVICES,LLC

NDP RESOURCES LLC
PO BOX 477
HARROGATE,TN 37752-0477 PH 423 489-4150
NOAH J PATTON,MGR

NEARBURG PRODUCING COMPANY
PO BOX 823085
DALLAS,TX 75382-3085
PH 214 739-1778 FAX 214 739-4819
CHARLES E NEARBURG,PRES
DUANE A DAVIS,CFO & COO
MICHAEL C GRIFFIN,CTO
EMILY SHARP,CONTROLLER
MIDLAND,TX OFFICE - 3300 N A BLDG 2
STE 120,79705-5421 PH 432 686-8235
FAX 432 686-7806
BILL ELTON,SR GEOL
TIM GREEN,GAS MKTG MGR
RANDY HOWARD,LAND MGR/PERMIAN
TIMOTHY SPEER,SR ENGR

NECHES OIL & GAS COMPANY,INC
PO BOX 921
KILGORE,TX 75663-0921 PH 903 984-3443
MARK T NICHOLS,PRES
CHARLA ROLPH,AGENT

NEESE EXPLORATION COMPANY
GRAVITY & MAGNETIC DATA & PROCESSING
2116 THOMPSON RD STE H-1
RICHMOND,TX 77469-5428
PH 281 342-2884
ROBERT NEESE,PRES
B.NEESE@GRAVITYSERVICES.COM

NEESE INSTRUMENT COMPANY
GRAVITY METER LEASING & SALES
2116 THOMPSON RD STE H-1
RICHMOND,TX 77469-5428
PH 281 342-2884 WWW.GRAVITYSERVICES.COM
ROBERT NEESE,PRES
B.NEESE@GRAVITYSERVICES.COM
DENNIS ROHAN,MGR

NEFF HAROLD & ASSOCIATES
100 INDEPENDENCE PLACE STE 307
TYLER,TX 75703 PH 903 592-8211

NEGEM CHRIS H,ATTORNEY AT LAW
8620 N NEW BRAUNFELS AVE STE 105
SAN ANTONIO,TX 78217-6361 PH 210 226-1200
FAX 210 798-2654 WWW.NEGEMLAWFIRM.COM
CHRIS@NEGEMLAWFIRM.COM

NEINAST RUSSELL & ASSOCIATES SEE
RMN OIL & GAS LLC

NELSON ENERGY,INC
401 EDWARDS ST STE 1500

SHREVEPORT,LA 71101-3140
PH 318 226-0700 FAX 318 221-6919
RICHARD B NELSON,PRES
JOSEPH T SEPULVADO,CFO/VP
DANNY MORELAND,VP
SUSAN KRAMER DIGILORMO,LAND MGR

NELSON PIPE & SUPPLY INC
PO BOX 42
CARMI,IL 62821-0042
PH 618 265-3193 FAX 618 265-3303
ROBERT J NELSON PH 618 384-0212
ANTHONY L NELSON PH 618 384-0215

NEOZOIC GEOPHYSICAL SURVEY,LTD
31 RUSH HAVEN DR
THE WOODLANDS,TX 77381-3227
PH 281 419-0446 FAX 281 419-0417
LEWIS A MANSON,PRES
FRANK SEELY,OPERS

NESBITT INTERESTS
2815 LONG LAKE DR
SHREVEPORT,LA 71106-8423
PH 318 221-7196 FAX 318 221-7217
G G NESBITT III,MNGNG PRTNR

NET STROKE COMPANY
ECHOMETER SERVICE
4162 E MT GILEAD LN
DUNDAS,IL 62425-2423 PH 618 754-3413
PH 618 838-3413
JAMES R ERBACHER,PRES
BETTY D ERBACHER,SECY,OFC MGR

NETHERLAND SEWELL & ASSOCIATES,INC
ENGRG & GEOL CONSULTANTS TO OIL & GAS
IND
1601 ELM ST STE 4500 THANKSGIVING TWR
DALLAS,TX 75201-4754 PH 214 969-5401
FAX 214 969-5411 WWW.NETHERLANDSEWELL.COM
CLIFFORD H SCOTT REES III,CHRMN
G LANCE BINDER,EXEC VP
P SCOTT FROST,SR VP,CFO
DAN PAUL SMITH,SR VP
THOMAS J TELLA II,SR VP
ROBERT C BARG,SR VP
JOHN G HATTNER,SR VP
JOSEPH J SPELLMAN,SR VP
DANIEL T WALKER,SR VP,GEOL
HOUSTON,TX OFFICE - 1221 LAMAR STE 1200
77010-3072 PH 713 654-4950
FAX 713 654-4951
DANNY D SIMMONS,PRES
J CARTER HENSON JR,SR VP
MIKE K NORTON,VP,GEOL

NETTLECOMBE OIL COMPANY,INC
1010 LAMAR STE 800
HOUSTON,TX 77002
PH 713 652-4040 FAX 713 652-9090
PAUL HABERMAS,PRES

NEUHAUS V F PROPERTIES INC
SEE V F NEUHAUS PROPERTIES INC

NEUMIN PRODUCTION COMPANY
PO BOX 769
POINT COMFORT,TX 77978-0769
PH 361 987-8900 FAX 361 987-2283
TONY CHEN,ASST VP
WESLEY LIN,DIR
LARRY KARL,CONTRACTS MGR
T K TOMLINSON,ENGR CONS

JOHN FOESTER,GEOL CONSLT
JIM GILSTRAP,LAND CONSLT

NEVANEN ENERGY,INC
PO BOX 1231
NATCHEZ,MS 39121-1257 PH 601 446-8090
DOUGLAS L BROWN,PRES,PETR GEOL

NEVIS ENERGY SERVICES,INC SEE
PHOENIX TECHNOLOGY SERVICES USA INC

NEW & HUGHES DRILLING CO INC SEE
NEW,DAVID DRILLING CO INC

NEW CENTURY EXPLORATION,INC
8500 CYPRESSWOOD DR STE 104
SPRING,TX 77379
PH 281 664-7000 WWW.NEWCENTURYEXP.COM
PHIL MARTIN PHILMARTIN@NEWCENTURYEXP.COM

NEW MEXICO NATURAL GAS
3314 ROOSEVELT DR
ARLINGTON,TX 76016 PH 817 821-7482
FAX 817 548-8419
LARRY KELLY,CEO

NEW YORK LIFE OIL & GAS PRODUCTION
PARTNERSHIPS SEE AMERICAN EXPLORATION CO

NEWCASTLE RESOURCES,LLC
PO BOX 9425,1540 RICE RD STE 300
TYLER,TX 75711-7668
PH 903 581-9602 FAX 903 596-9019
WWW.NEWCASTLERESOURCES.COM
DAVID W KRAFVE,MEMBER
DAVIDKRAFVE@NEWCASTLERESOURCES.COM
BILL JAMISON,MEMBER

NEWFIELD EXPLORATION COMPANY
4 WATERWAY SQUARE PL STE 100
THE WOODLANDS,TX 77380-2764
PH 281 210-5100 FAX 281 210-5101
WWW.NEWFIELD.COM
LEE K BOOTHBY,CHRMN/PRES & CEO
GARY D PACKER,EXEC VP & COO
LARRY S MASSARO,EXEC VP & CFO
GEORGE T DUNN,SR VP DEVELOPMENT
W ALLEN DONALDSON,VP EXPLORATION
STEPHEN C CAMPBELL,VP INVESTOR RELS
GEORGE FAIRCHILD JR,CAO & ASST SECY
JOSEPH B JOHNSON,VP DRILLING
VALERIE A MITCHELL,VP CORP DEV
THOMAS M SMOUSE,VP ADMIN & HR
JAMES T ZERNELL,VP PROD
CHRIS J MALAN,VP LAND
JOHN D MARZIOTTI,GEN COUNSEL & SECY
SUSAN G RIGGS,TREASURER
DAVID A DUBIEL,CORP LAND MGR
DENVER,CO (ROCKY MTNS) OFFICE - 1001 17TH
ST STE 2000,80202 PH 303 893-0102
FAX 303 893-0103
MATTHEW R VEZZA,VP ROCKY MTNS
CRAIG BLANCETT,LAND MGR ROCKY MTNS
BILL MITCHELL,LAND MGR WILLISTON BASIN
HOUSTON,TX OFFICE -363 SAM HOUSTON PKWY E
STE 100, 77060 PH 281 847-6000
FAX 281 405-4242
JOHN H JASEK,VP ONSHORE GULF COAST
GARY M WALKER,LAND MGR ONGC
TULSA,OK OFFICE -ONE WILLIAMS CENTER
STE 1900, 74172 PH 918 582-2690
FAX 918 582-2757
CLAY M GASPAR,VP MIDCONTINENT
STEVE R BOUDREAU,LAND MGR MIDCONTINENT

NEWFIELD PAUL,III,LDMN
3016 45TH ST
METAIRIE,LA 70001-4243 PH 504 835-3882

NEWGULF PETROLEUM LLC
1250 NE LOOP 410 STE 425
SAN ANTONIO,TX 78209 PH 210 826-9844
FAX 210 826-9676 MGAINEY@MPGSA.COM

NEWMAN LAND SERVICES,INC
6201 LOST CREEK DR
CORPUS CHRISTI,TX 78413 PH 361 510-5116
JOHN W NEWMAN,OWNER,PETR LDMN
JOHN@NOLEASE-NOGREASE.COM

NEWPARK DRILLING FLUIDS
21920 MERCHANTS WAY
KATY,TX 77449 PH 281 754-8600
PH 800 444-0682 FAX 281 754-8660
JIM SAMPEY,CEO
BRUCE SMITH,PRES
STEVE DANIEL,SR VP
PERRY BENNETT,EXEC VP
MARK HULSE,VP,SALES & MKTG
DAN KINSHELLA,VP,GULF COAST OPERS
TONY FREITAS,VP,FIN & ADMIN
MACK SMITHEY,DIR,PROD MGMNT
DAVID KONKIN,GULF COAST REG MGR
NEW ORLEANS,LA OFFICE - 1340 POYDRAS ST
STE 1750,70112 PH 504 523-8446
FAX 504 523-3309
JOE JOHNSON,PRES,NEWPARK PERFORMANCE SVC
BOB VAUGHN,S LA BUS UNIT MGR
TOM ROLLINSON,SALES MGR
MIDLAND,TX OFFICE - PO BOX 11245,79702
PH 432 697-8661 800 592-4627
FAX 432 697-8439
JOE HENDERSON,VP,PERMIAN BASIN BUS UNIT
LAFAYETTE,LA OFFICE - 207 TOWN CENTER PKY
1ST FL,70506 PH 318 988-5711
PH 800 726-6123 FAX 318 988-3908
MIKE REID,NEWPARK PERFORMANCE SVCS,INC
DENVER,CO OFFICE - 410 17TH ST STE 1375,
80202 PH 303 623-2205 FAX 303 595-9717
DON VALENTI,ROCKY MTN BUS UNIT MGR
SPANISH LAKE,LA OFFICE - 101 AIRPORT BLVD
NEW IBERIA,LA 70560 PH 318 364-9313
PH 800 493-9448 FAX 800 325-9478
KIM TILLERY,OPERS MGR,W LA DIST
CORPUS CHRISTI,TX OFFICE - 615 UPPER N
BROADWAY,STE 1420,78477 PH 361 883-9181
FAX 361 883-9174
FRANK BINNS,S TX DIST MGR
SAN ANTONIO,TX OFFICE - 8620 N NEW
BRAUNFELS STE 534,78217
PH/FAX 210 820-3717
TERRY GILL,ACCT REPR
OKLAHOMA CITY,OK MID-CONTINENT OFFICE -
5560 NW 72ND ST,73132 PH 405 721-0207
PH 800 256-4864 FAX 405 721-0174
DOUG FRANTZ,MID-CONTINENT BUS UNIT MGR
DALLAS,TX OFFICE - 5000 LBJ FWY STE 700,
75244 PH 972 387-5220 888 387-5220
FAX 972 387-5298
BILL GRISHAM,EXEC SALES MGR
TYLER,TX OFFICE - 1901 RICKETY LN STE 214
75703 PH 903 939-8086 FAX 903 939-8508
CHARLES CURTIS,AUSTIN CHALK BUS UNIT MGR
CALGARY,CAN OFFICE - STE 300,635-6TH AVE

SW,CALGARY,ALTA,CAN T2P 0T5
PH 403 266-7383 FAX 403 263-1760
BOB OUTHWAITE,PRES,NEWPARK CANADA,INC
DARRYL ARNDT,VP OPERS
ROSS KOVACS,VP SLS
PATRICK MURPHY,VP-CANADA
BILL REBER,VP BUS DEV
MIKE FERSTER,ACCT MGR
TRENT ULMER,ACCT MGR

NEWPARK MATS & INTEGRATED SERVICES
2900 HIGHWAY 93
CARENCRO,LA 70520 PH 337 981-5058
PH 877 628-7623 WWW.NEWPARKMATS.COM
SAMMY COOPER,PRES
MICHAEL SPARKS,DIR,INTL SLS & SVCS
CARRIE MARKETTE,CONTROLLER
STEVE PIERSON,VP SLS
CHRIS RABALGIS,EHS SLS MGR
LAFAYETTE,LA OFFICE-207 TOWN CENTER PKWY
2ND FLOOR,70506 PH 337 984-4445
FAX 337 984-6176
SCOTT,LA OPERATIONS DIVISION -
110 EMERALD DR,LAFAYETTE,LA 70506
PH 337 233-7357 FAX 337 233-7789
MARK PHILLIPS,SITE MGR
SCHRIEVER,LA OPERATIONS DIVISION -
349 HWY 20,70395
PH 985 447-2909 FAX 985 446-1374
JOEY BONVILLAIN,LA REG MGR
BEAUMONT,TX OPERATIONS DIVISION -
16341 W HWY 90,77713
PH 409 752-5800 FAX 409 752-5731
TERRY ALWELL,SITE MGR
BAY CITY,TX OPERATIONS DIVISION -
1561 HWY 35 SOUTH, 77414
PH 979 245-3894 FAX 979 244-9458
JON JOINES,TX REG MGR

NEWPARK RESOURCES,INC
NEWPARK DRILLING FLUIDS
NEWPARK MATS & INTEGRATED SERVICES
EXCALIBAR MINERALS
2700 RESEARCH FOREST DR STE 100
THE WOODLANDS,TX 77381 PH 281 362-6800

NEWPORT OIL CORPORATION
PO BOX 3307
SEMINOLE,FL 33772 PH 727 446-4200
FAX 727 446-7755
JOHN E BRUYNELL,PRES
JEBRUYNELL@CS.COM

NEWPORT OPERATORS,L.L.C.
PO BOX 721,148 E MAIN ST STE B
NEW ROADS,LA 70760-0721 PH 225 638-3060
FAX 225 638-3093
STEVE W WHEELER,PRES
DEBORAH M WHEELER,OFC MGR

NEWSOME MIKE
LANDMAN/BROKER/LAND SERVICES
MID SOUTH LAND SERVICES
PO BOX 766
MONTROSE,AL 36559-0766 PH 251 929-1860

NEWTON DON W,OIL PRODUCER
13114 HWY 45
LOUISVILLE,IL 62858-2927
PH 618 665-3638

NEXUS DRILLING CORPORATION
PO BOX 903

JANE LEW,WV 26378-0903 PH 304 884-7832
FAX 304 884-6978
ROBERT E PAYNE,PRES

NFR ENERGY LLC SEE SABINE OIL & GAS LLC

NGO DEVELOPMENT CORPORATION
PO BOX 517,1500 GRANVILLE RD
NEWARK,OH 43058-0517 PH 800 255-6815
FAX 740 344-2054 WWW.THEENERGYCOOP.COM
DANIEL S MCVEY,VP,COO/GAS OPERS
GREG MASON,E & P MGR

NICHOLS ENTERPRISES,INC
5731 HWY 71 NORTH
EL CAMPO,TX 77437-9705 PH 979 543-4833
FAX 979 543-3507 PJNICHOLS@AFO.NET
PAT NICHOLS,PRES

NICO RESOURCES,LLC
EXPLORATION/PRODUCTION
1490 W CANAL CT STE 3000
LITTLETON,CO 80120-5648
PH 303 730-7373 FAX 303 794-9261
BROOK J PHIFER,PRES
CODY PHIFER,ACQS MGR

NICOR DRILLING COMPANY SEE
ADCOR DRILLING INC

NIELSON ENTERPRISES INC SEE
TEX-OK ENERGY,LIMITED PARTNERSHIP

NIERMAN & BRAUNIG LLC
PO BOX 36852
SHREVEPORT,LA 71133-6852 PH 318 861-6974
RON NIERMAN,MGR
BILL BRAUNIG,MGR

NINA RESOURCES,LP
11111 KATY FWY STE 600
HOUSTON,TX 77079-2116 PH 713 463-6700
FAX 713 463-6722
JOSEPH G WILLIAMS

NINIAN OIL CO SEE
AMERICAN EXPLORATION CO

NINIAN OIL FINANCE CORP SEE
AMERICAN EXPLORATION CO

NITRO-LIFT TECHNOLOGIES,LLC
2801 SE EVANGELINE TRWY
LAFAYETTE,LA 70508-2204 PH 337 704-9500
FAX 337 704-9095 WWW.NITROLIFT.COM
VERNON DANIELS,COO
DANNY DANIELS,CTO
EDWARD R RUSTY LAMB,CEO
EM ROOSEVELT,GEN MGR
CHASE DANIELS,OPERS MGR
MILL CREEK,OK (OPERS HDQRS-RAVIA) - 8980
HWY 1 SOUTH,74856 PH 580 371-3700
PH 580 266-6600 FAX 580 371-3722
PH 580 266-6600 (AFTER HRS)

NIVLA OIL CORPORATION
PO BOX 521,102 N COLLEGE AVE STE 513
TYLER,TX 75710-0521 PH 903 597-9061
BEN E SUTTON,PRES

NIXON LOG SERVICE
WELL LOGS,REPRODUCTION SUPPLIES
PO BOX 407
CORPUS CHRISTI,TX 78403-0407
PH 361 882-2551 FAX 361 882-2556
LETTY BETANCOURTH,LOG MGR
ROSE MARTINEZ,GEN MGR/OWNER

NL HYCALOG SEE
HYCALOG

NOBLE CHARLES O
BOX 1428,NOBLE BLDG
LAKE CHARLES,LA 70601 PH 318 433-9725

NOBLE DRILLING CORPORATION
13135 DAIRY ASHFORD RD STE 800
SUGAR LAND,TX 77478-3686 PH 281 276-6100
FAX 281 276-6656 WWW.NOBLECORP.COM
DAVID W WILLIAMS,CEO
TOM MITCHELL,SR VP,CFO
JULIE J ROBERTSON,VP,ADMIN/CORP SECY
TOMMY TRAVIS,VP,DIV MGR GOM

NOBLE ENERGY,INC
1001 NOBLE ENERGY WAY
HOUSTON,TX 77070 PH 281 872-3100
FAX 281 872-3111 INFO@NOBLEENERGYINC.COM
DAVID STOVER,PRES,COO
BOB BEMIS,VP EH & S
CHARLES J RIMER,VP OPERS SVCS
DENVER,CO OFFICE - 1625 BROADWAY STE 2200
80202 PH 303 389-3600
CRAIG S KOINZAN,BUS DEV MGR
ARDMORE,OK OFFICE - P O BOX 909 73402
PH 800 220-5824 PH 580 223-4110
ROYALTYRELATIONS@NOBLEENERGYINC.COM

NOBLE ROYALTIES,INC
15601 N DALLAS PKWY STE 900
ADDISON,TX 75001-6098
PH 972 720-1888 FAX 972 720-1899
WWW.NOBLEROYALTIES.COM
A SCOTT NOBLE,PRES,CEO
J D DOUG BRADLEY,SR VP,LAND
LAMAR LLOYD,ENGRG DIR
BRUCE MORRIS,BUS DEV DIR
JOSH PRIER,BUS DEV DIR

NOBLES ALLEN & ASSOCIATES INC
PROFESSIONAL LAND SURVEYORS
312 GOVERNMENT AVE #1
NICEVILLE,FL 32578-1809 PH 850 634-4221
FAX 850 654-4254
DOUGLAS A VANDEN HEUVEL,PLS

NOLIN ANDREW C,JR AND ASSOCAITES
1411 UPPER WETUMPKA RD
MONTGOMERY,AL 36107-1219 PH 205 264-9788
FAX 205 264-9983

NOMAD ENERGY
2800 POST OAK BLVD FL 61
HOUSTON,TX 77056-6131 PH 832 437-4026
FAX 832 437-4036
WAYNE BRUNT,OPERS MGR/SR ACCT REPR
WAYNE.BRUNT@NOMADENERGY.COM
PH 281 660-3352

NOMECO OIL & GAS CO SEE
CMS OIL AND GAS COMPANY

NORCEN EXPLORER,INC SEE
UNION PACIFIC RESOURCES

NORDAN TRUST,THE
112 E PECAN ST STE 500
SAN ANTONIO,TX 78205-1516
PH 210 222-1271 FAX 210 222-1402

NORM SOLUTIONS LLC
INFO WEBSITE - OIL & GAS NATURALLY
OCCURING RADIOACTIVE MATERIAL
2501 CENTENNIAL DR STE 116
ARLINGTON,TX 76011 PH 817 917-0987
WWW.NORMSOLUTIONS.COM
WADE HALL WADE@NORMSOLUTIONS.COM

NORMAL LIQUID TRANSPORTS
890 KINSFATHER RD
NOCONA,TX 76255 PH 940 872-0032
FAX 940 825-5117

NORMAN W D,JR,OIL PROPERTIES
PO BOX 52228
NEW ORLEANS,LA 70152 PH 504 525-0815
PH 504 450-0413 FAX 504 680-6048
WDNORMAN@AOL.COM

NORMAN WYATT T,III,LANDMAN
1330 AIRLINE RD
CORPUS CHRISTI,TX 78412-3910
PH 361 883-8712 WTNORMAN@THE-I.NET

NORTEX CORPORATION
3009 POST OAK BLVD STE 1212
HOUSTON,TX 77056 PH 713 658-1142
FAX 713 658-0739 WWW.NORTEXCORP.COM
ROBERT W KENT,EXEC VP,LAND,ACQ

NORTH AMERICAN CONTROLS CORP
CONTROL SYSTEMS
11680 BEAMER RD STE D
HOUSTON,TX 77089 PH 281 481-3073
FAX 281 481-3074 WWW.NACCINC.COM
MARTHA G SAUCEDO,PRES
JOEL SAUCEDO,VP
DAN SAUCEDO,PE PRINCIPAL SYSTEMS ENGR
DSAUCEDO@NACCINC.COM

NORTH AMERICAN RESERVE CORP
16800 IMPERIAL VALLEY DR STE 382
HOUSTON,TX 77060 PH 281 405-9100
BBOSS422@AOL.COM WWW.NARCORP.COM
BRENT BOSSART

NORTH AMERICAN RESOURCES CORPORATION
PO BOX 27945
HOUSTON,TX 77227-7945 PH 713 626-5357
FAX 713 552-1731
G W DUNEGAN,CHRMN OF BD
W K ROBBINS JR,PRES
G HERBST,VP,SECY/TREAS
J SOTO,MGR,LAND DEPT

NORTH CAMBRIA FUEL CO
175 MCKNIGHT RD
BLAIRSVILLE,PA 15717-7961
PH 724 459-3714

NORTH CENTRAL OIL CORPORATION SEE
POGO PRODUCING COMPANY

NORTH COAST ENERGY EASTERN,INC SEE
EXCO RESOURCES

NORTH COAST ENERGY,INC SEE
EXCO RESOURCES,INC

NORTH EASTERN OHIO OIL & GAS EXPLOR,INC
4665 BEIDLER RD
WILLOUGHBY,OH 44094-4645 PH 440 269-1100
FAX 440 269-1026
MARTIN M KAUFMAN
ARNOLD KAUFMAN

NORTH LOUISIANA LAND ASSOCIATES,INC
416 TRAVIS ST STE 1200
SHREVEPORT,LA 71101-5504
PH 318 222-7464 FAX 318 222-7466
LACY H WILLIAMS,MGR
CURRIE SMITH,LDMN
KEM HARGROVE,LDMN
DAVE GIDDINGS,DIV ORDER ANALYIST

NORTHEAST ENERGY DEVELOPMENT LLC
PO BOX 249

MILLPORT,NY 14864 PH 607 739-2825
VINCENT C STALIS BUCKMNT@INFOBLVD.NET

NORTHERN BORDER PIPELINE
717 TEXAS ST STE 2400
HOUSTON,TX 77002 PH 832 320-5000
- MEASUREMENT -
AMBERLY WESTER PH 832 320-5256
FAX 832 320-6256
- IMBALANCES -
AARON BARBER PH 832 320-5426
ADAM WILLBORN PH 832 320-5250
FAX 832 320-6213
- CONTRACT/CAPACITY RELEASE ADMIN -
ALAN CARR PH 832 320-5226
MARGARET MAHLE PH 832 320-5673
LETICIA GARZA-BROWN PH 832 320-5416
FAX 832 320-5760
- OTHER CUSTOMER SERVICE INQUIRIES -
JOSEPH POLLARD PH 832 320-5257
FAX 832 320-6257
- COMMERCIAL CONTACTS -
- MARKETING
BILL FONDA PH 402 492-7430
FAX 402 492-7488
- REGULATORY -
JOAN COLLINS PH 832 320-5651
FAX 832 320-6651
- GOVERNMENT RELATIONS -
BETH JENSEN PH 402 492-3400
FAX 402 492-7491
- PUBLIC RELATIONS -
DAVID DODSON PH 832 320-5667
FAX 832 320-5555
- CORPORATE OFFICIALS -
PRESIDENT,TRANSCANADA NORTHERN BORDER
INC
DEAN FERGUSON PH 832 320-5503
FAX 832 320-6503
ASSOC GEN COUNSEL,NORTHERN BORDER P/L
TRANSCANADA NORTHERN BORDER,INC
EVA NEUFELD PH 832 320-5626
FAX 832 320-6626

NORTHERN GEOPHYSICAL OF AMERICA SEE
3-D GEOPHYSICAL,INC (END OF ALPHA)

NORTHERN NATURAL GAS COMPANY
1111 S 103RD ST
OMAHA,NE 68124-1091 PH 402 398-7000
MARK HEWETT,PRES

NORTHLAND-NORWARD ENERGY SERVICES SEE
WEATHERFORD INTERNATIONAL LTD

NORTHRIDGE ENERGY COMPANY
PO BOX 6905
MIRAMAR BEACH,FL 32550-1006
PH 850 622-0435 FAX 888 632-5013
NORTHRIDGEENERGY@EARTHLINK.NET
THOMAS A MOORE,PRES

NORTHSTAR ENERGY LLC
880 MUNSON AVE STE C
TRAVERSE CITY,MI 49686
PH 231 941-0073 FAX 231 933-0757
MARK WILSON,PRES
JOHN COATES,SR VP
JOHN C HUNTER,DIR ENGRG & PROD
REBECCA ABBOTT,DIR OF LAND

NORTHSTAR EXPLORATION COMPANY
PO BOX 5A,910 HARDING ST 70503

LAFAYETTE,LA 70505-6001 PH 337 233-0830
FAX 337 233-9772
CALVIN BARNHILL,PRES
JACKIE BARNHILL,OFC MGR

NORTHSTAR GAS COMPANY,INC
PO BOX 440789
HOUSTON,TX 77244
PH 281 493-5532 FAX 281 497-4795
HARRY F DEAN,PRES
KENNETH M MCKINNEY,EXEC VP,FIN
CASEY ZACHARY,OPERS MGR

NORTHSTAR OFFSHORE GROUP,LLC
11 GREENWAY PLAZA STE 2800
HOUSTON,TX 77046
PH 713 626-9696 FAX 713 626-3444
WWW.NSTAROFFSHORE.COM
S GLYNN ROBERTS,PRES
GAYLON E FREEMAN,EXEC VP
WARD MALOY,VP ENGRG
BRIAN H MACMILLAN,SR VP LAND
JAMES P ULM II,CFO
ROGER B SOUDERS,VP LAND
MICHAEL RAUCH,VP/TREAS

NORTHSTAR TRAINING
PO BOX 51420
LAFAYETTE,LA 70505-1420
PH 337 269-1662 FAX 337 269-4056
WWW.NORTHSTARTRAININGINC.COM
OFFICE@NORTHSTARTRAININGINC.COM
CALVIN BARNHILL,PRES

NORTHWEST CRUDE CORPORATION SEE
EIGHTY EIGHT OIL LLC

NORTHWEST HYDRAULICS INC SEE
VARI-JAK WELL PUMPING UNITS

NORTHWEST PIPELINE CORPORATION
PO BOX 58900,295 CHIPETA WAY
SALT LAKE CITY,UT 84158-0900
PH 801 583-8800 FAX 801 584-7752
PHIL WRIGHT,PRES,WGP
RANDY BARNARD,SR VP,TECH SVCS & OPERS
A G BRIDGES,VP,COMMERCIAL OPERS
BRUCE REEMSNYDER,SR COUNSEL
LARRY HJALMARSON,VP,TECH SVCS,OPERS &
ENGRG SVCS
P DEAN,DIR,SLC TECH SVCS-GP
BARRY ORGILL,DIR,OPERS & GP
E R BREWER,DIR MKTG SVCS
L M GERTSCH,DIR,RATES & REGULATORY

NORTHWIND EXPLORATION
AND NORTHWIND EXPLORATION,INC
5300 MEMORIAL DR STE 490
HOUSTON,TX 77007 PH 713 864-9292
FAX 713 864-9244
BRIAN SMYTH,PRTNR,GEOL
JESSE FOWLER,PRTNR,GEOL

NORTHWOOD ENERGY CORPORATION
941 CHATHAM LN STE 100
COLUMBUS,OH 43221-2471 PH 614 457-1024
FAX 614 457-7295
RALPH W TALMAGE,PRES

NORTON OIL COMPANY INC
PO BOX 65090
SHREVEPORT,LA 71136-5090 PH 318 795-0905
FAX 318 798-2036
M L NORTON,PRES,TREAS
RICHARD W NORTON,III,VP,SECY

NORWOOD MINERAL MANAGEMENT,INC
PO BOX 55587
JACKSON,MS 39296-5587 PH 601 982-4077
CAROLINE VAUGHAN GOODMAN,PRES

NOV BRANDT SEE
NOV FLUIDCONTROL

NOV FLUIDCONTROL
4310 N SAM HOUSTON PKWY E
HOUSTON,TX 77032 PH 713 482-0500
WWW.NOV.COM
LAFAYETTE,LA OFFICE - 221 RUE DE JEAN
STE 301 70508 PH 337 237-5300
FAX 337 237-9696
FRANK GAUTHIER,SLS MGR
PAXTON LATIOLAIS,INSIDE SLS REPR
BRYAN SUIRE,VP SOUTHERN US
KANSAS HERNANDEZ,SOUTHERN US DIR OF WASTE
MGMNT SLS
JENNINGS,LA OFFICE - 4178 TRAILER TOWN RD
70546 PH 800 359-5951 FAX 337 774-2347
DON GAUTHIER,REG VP EASTERN US
RICKY MONCEAUX,OPERS MGR
NEW ORLEANS,LA OFFICE - 1515 POYDRAS ST
STE 1850 70112-3785 PH 504 636-3672
FAX 504 636-3670
FARON CHATAGNIER,SLS/SOLIDS CONTROL
CORPUS CHRISTI,TX OFFICE - 426 FLATO RD
78405 PH 361 289-7794 FAX 361 289-9058
DAVE BAILEY,SLS REPR
ODESSA,TX OFFICE - 4710 ANDREWS HWY 79762
PH 432 550-6802 FAX 432 550-3190
KEVIN CONKLIN,DIST MGR
OKLAHOMA CITY,OK OFFICE - 5500 N WESTERN
AVE STE 200 73118 PH 800 725-4986
FAX 405 354-6749
GREGG WOLF,CAPITAL SLS FLD SLSMN
BAKERSFIELD,CA OFFICE - 7300 DOWNING AVE
93308 PH 661 588-8503 FAX 661 855-8506
MIKE PENSINGER,OPERS MGR
DICKINSON,ND OFFICE - 4695 2ND ST SW
58601 PH 701 227-8608 FAX 701 227-8612
DAVE BARTH,FLD SVC MGR
DENVER,CO OFFICE - 216 16TH ST STE 915
80202 PH 303 592-9250
MIKE RICHARDS,TECH & CAPITAL SLS MGR-
RKY MTNS

NOV REEDHYCALOG
500 CONROE PARK WEST DR
CONROE,TX 77303 PH 936 444-4000
FAX 936 444-4700 WWW.REEDHYCALOG.COM
JEREMY THIGPEN,PRES

NOVA DIRECTIONAL,INC
PO BOX 1862
CYPRESS,TX 77410 PH 281 246-1149
FAX 281 246-1149 WWW.NOVADIRECTIONAL.COM
EDWARD CHICLAMONTE
EDC@NOVADIRCTIONAL.COM
MIKE KRAJNIK

NOW DEVELOPMENT CO,INC
416 E MULBERRY ST
TYLER,TX 75702-7432 PH 903 597-3305
NOEL D ISCHY,PRES
KYLE F ISCHY,VP

NOWCAM SERVICES SEE
CAMCO COILED TUBING SERVICES

NOWSCO WELL SERVICE INC SEE
BJ SERVICES COMPANY,USA

NQL ENERGY SERVICES
1507-4TH ST
NISKU,ALBERTA,CAN T9E 7M9
PH 780 955-8828 800 700-7942
FAX 780 955-3309 WWW.NQL.COM
BAKER,MT OFFICE - PO BOX 1277, 59313
PH 406 853-2738
BILL MUDD,SLS REP
BAKERSFIELD,CA OFFICE - 7005 DOWNING ST
93308 PH 661 327-0226 FAX 661 588-2953
JOSH ALLEN,DIST MGR
DENVER,CO OFFICE - 1630 WELTON ST,
STE 300,80202 PH 303 925-0399
MIKE SCHARDT,SLS REP
GRAND JUNCTION,CO OFFICE -
694 MIRANDA DR 81505
PH 970 640-1095 FAX 970 314-7199
GREG HESS
INTERLOCHEN,MI OFFICE - 2610 GONDER RD,
46943, PH 231 357-3377 FAX 231 275-7398
GLEN WRIGHT,SLS REP
OKLAHOMA CITY,OK OFFICE - 3900 S HARMON
73179 PH 405 688-5000 FAX 405 688-5001
RICK MCELHANEY,DIST MGR
DALE RODGERS,REG MGR
CASPER,WY OFFICE - 2262 N 6 MI RD,82604
PH 307 237-9163 FAX 307 237-9166
DOUG HUDSON,REG MGR
STAFFORD,TX OFFICE - 10404 MULA RD
77477, PH 281 568-1336 FAX 281 568-1405
TOM SIMMONS,REG MGR
JEFF DUGAN,EM-MWD SLS MGR
VERNAL, UT OFFICE - PH 435 828-8130
SCOTT REVERT,SLS REP
ODESSA,TX OFFICE - 2124 MAURICE RD
79763, PH 432 580-5346 FAX 432 580-5481
J C LEONARD,DIST MGR
MORGANTOWN,WV OFFICE - 2000 MORGANTOWN
INDUSTRIAL,26501
PH 304 482-6706 FAX 304 594-3088
ZACH COLLINS
WILLIS,TX OFFICE - 9730 SHEPARD HILL RD
77318 PH 936 344-7700 FAX 936 344-7709
KELLY SMITH,SLS REP
YOUNGSVILLE, LA OFFICE - 103 GUERNSEY LN
70592 PH 337 856-5300 FAX 337 856-5585
PRESTON DOMINGUE
SCOTT KERSTETTER
CALGARY, ALBERTA OFFICE - #3 700,435-4TH
AVE S.W., T2P 3A8
PH 403 266-5861 FAX 403 266-2225
ESTEVAN,SASKATCHEWAN OFFICE - BOX 671
KENSINGTON DR N, S4A 2A6
PH 306 634-8828 FAX 306 634-7747
CORY BJORNDAL,DIST MGR
GRANDE PRAIRIE, ALBERTA OFFICE -
11233-91 AVE, T8V 5Z3 PH 780 532-8115
866 782-5752 FAX 780 402-6944
ROD LONG,DIST MGR
NISKU, ALBERTA OFFICE - 1507-4TH ST
T9E 7M9, PH 780 955-8828 FAX 780 955-3309
SANDY DEWAAL,REG MGR
DOUG EDWARDS,VP,MFG
ANACO, ESTADO ANZOATEGUI OFFICE -

CALLE PRINCIPAL, SECTOR EL OCHO
PH 58-282-425-5478 FAX 58-282-425-5055
JULIO LUGO,OPERS MGR
MIGUEL AMORUSO,SLS REP
BARINAS, ESTADO BARINA OFFICE -
CARRETERA VIEJA VIA EL TORENO, AL LADO
CLUB PH 58-273-5330808 FAX 58-273-5331284
JORGE NAVA,OPERS MGR
CIUDAD OJEDA, ESTADO ZULIA OFFICE -
AV. INTERCOMMUNAL SECTOR TAMARE
PH 58-265-631-0511 FAX 58-265-631-4491
JOE WOOD,REG MGR
ERIDOLFO NAVA,OPERS MGR
ANACO, ESTADO ANZOATEGUI OFFICE -
AV. FRANCISCO DE MIRANDA, #24
PH 58-282-4256648 FAX 58-282-4256648
LEONEL VARGAS,OPERS MGR
SANTA CRUZ, BOLIVIA OFFICE -
CASILLA POSTAL NO. 2075 PH 5913-352 4107
FAX 591-3-355 7555
PABLO VILLAGRA,MGR
AKERSLOOT, THE NETHERLANDS OFFICE -
NQL ENERGY SRVCS, BOEKEL 38, 1921 CE
PH +31(0)72-535 35 35
FAX +31(0)72-532 0268
GUY FILION,REG MGR
STEPHAN GEGUSS,BIT SLS
DUBAI, UNITED ARAB EMIRATES OFFICE -
PO BOX 37621 PH 9714-347-7719
FAX 9714-347-7723
SCOTT GRAMLICH,DIST MGR

NRN LAND SERVICES,LLC
201 LAURENCE DR PMB 103
HEATH,TX 75032 PH 972 998-9199
BARBARA L NERREN,LAND MGR
LANDMAN@NERREN.NET

NUEVO ENERGY COMPANY SEE
PLAINS EXPLORATION & PRODUCTION CO

NULL W M OPERATIONS,INC
7010 ADCOTE DR
CORPUS CHRISTI,TX 78413-5312
PH 361 980-1580
HARRIET NULL,OWNER
GARLAND DERRINGER,CPA,COMPTROLLER

NUMA
646 THOMPSON RD
THOMPSON,CT 06277-2214
PH 800 356-NUMA FAX 860 923-2617
WWW.NUMAHAMMERS.COM NUMA@NUMA-
HAMMERS.COM
RALPH H LEONARD,PRES

NYE ENGINEERING INC,ENGR PETR
400 FENCE POST RD
FRIENDSWOOD,TX 77546-4639 PH 281 482-4244
FAX 281 482-1989

NYLIFE RESOURCES,INC SEE
AMERICAN EXPLORATION CO

O C S,INC SEE
OPERATORS & CONSULTING SERVICES,INC

O.G.P. OPERATING,INC
8140 WALNUT HILL LN STE 610
DALLAS,TX 75231-4332 PH 214 696-2393
FAX 214 361-9121 WWW.OGPENERGY.COM
C MITCHELL JOHNSTON,PRES
DAVID G BURNS,VP

O-TEX PUMPING,LLC
306 W WALL ST STE 700
MIDLAND,TX 79701 PH 432 685-9901
FAX 432 685-1219 WWW.OTEXPUMPING.COM
BRENT BARBOUR,PRES/CEO
BRENTB@OTEXPUMPING.COM
MIDLAND,TX FIELD OFFICE - PO BOX 51005
79710,2611 E I-20,79706
PH 432 686-8559 FAX 432 686-8511
RON GUNDY,DIST MGR
RONG@OTEXPUMPING.COM
ELCO ARMENDARIZ,OPERS MGR
ELCOA@OTEXPUMPING.COM
JESSE ULATE,TX REG MGR
JESSEU@OTEXPUMPING.COM
PAMPA,TX OFFICE - 1865 W MCCULLOUGH,79065
PH 806 665-0552 FAX 806 665-0596
JOE COTTA,DIST MGR JOEC@OTEXPUMPING.COM
HOUSTON,TX (SLS) OFFICE - 1095 EVERGREEN
CIR STE 200 THE WOODLANDS,TX 77380
PH 281 210-0020 FAX 432 685-1219
KEVIN SWIKERT
KEVIN.SWIKERT@OTEXPUMPING.COM
DUNCAN,OK (ADMIN) OFFICE - 7303 N HWY 81
73533 PH 580 251-9919 FAX 580 255-4777
DOUG RATHER,COO
DOUGR@OTEXPUMPING.COM
OKLAHOMA CITY,OK (SLS) OFFICE - 211 N
ROBINSON AVE STE 1900,LEADERSHIP SQUARE
N TOWER 73102 PH 405 600-7451
FAX 405 600-9312
DOUG CALDWELL,CORP SLS MGR
DOUGC@OTEXPUMPING.COM
DAVIS,OK OFFICE - 37044 E CR 1690
WYNNEWOOD,OK 73098 PH 405 665-1957
FAX 405 665-1982
BRIAN GREER,DIST MGR
BRIANG@OTEXPUMPING.COM
FAIRVIEW,OK OFFICE - 601 INDUSTRIAL BLVD
73737,PH 580 227-2727 FAX 580 227-3606
LARRY CARPENTER,DIST MGR
LARRYC@OTEXPUMPING.COM
MALVERN,OH OFFICE - 7200 SYCAMORE RD
44644 PH 330 863-0664 FAX 330 863-0614
RICK CONLEY,DIST MGR
RICKC@OTEXPUMPING.COM
MUNCY VALLEY,PA OFFICE - SR 220 BOX 4787
17758 PH 570 946-4480 FAX 570 946-4483
RON BAKER,DIST MGR RONB@OTEXPUMPING.COM
BUTLER,PA OFFICE - 2916 OLD ROUTE 422 E
FENELTON,PA 16034 PH 724 256-9280
FAX 724 256-9281
RON BAKER,DIST MGR RONB@OTEXPUMPING.COM
DUNCAN,OKLAHOMA TRAIN FACLTY - 5045 N HWY
81,73533 PH 580 251-9503 FAX 580 251-9885
RONNIE COLE,HR RONNIEC@OTEXPUMPING.COM
BOB WALDEN,OK REG MGR
BOBW@OTEXPUMPING.COM
DUNCAN,OKLAHOMA LAB - 1110 MARTIN LUTHER
K,73533 PH 580 786-4403 FAX 580 786-4404
DEBORAH BLANTON
DEBORAH.BLANTON@OTEXPUMPING.COM
LARRY CARPENTER LARRYC@OTEXPUMPING.COM

O'BENCO,INC
PO BOX 6149,425 ASHLEY RIDGE BLVD STE 300
SHREVEPORT,LA 71136-6149

PH 318 865-8568 FAX 318 869-3335
WWW.OBRIENENERGYCO.COM
WILLIAM J O'BRIEN III,CHRMN/CEO
WILLIAM J O'BRIEN IV,SR VP/EXPL & PROD
MIKE AMEEN,SR VP/COO
GARY LOVE,SR VP/GEN COUNSEL/SECY
JASON WARREN,SR VP/CAO
ALAN BRITTAIN,VP EXPL
STEVE HARRIS,VP OPERS & PROD
GEORGE MEARS,VP LAND

O'BRIEN ENERGY COMPANY
PO BOX 6149,425 ASHLEY RIDGE BLVD STE 300
SHREVEPORT,LA 71136-6149
PH 318 865-8568 FAX 318 869-3335
WWW.OBRIENENERGYCO.COM
WILLIAM J O'BRIEN III,CHRMN/CEO
WILLIAM J O'BRIEN IV,SR VP/EXPL & PROD
MIKE AMEEN,SR VP/COO
GARY LOVE,SR VP/GEN COUNSEL/SECY
JASON WARREN,SR VP/CAO
ALAN BRITTAIN,VP EXPL
STEVE HARRIS,VP OPERS & PROD
GEORGE MEARS,VP LAND

O'BRIEN ENERGY RESOURCES CORPORATION
18 CONGRESS ST STE 207
PORTSMOUTH,NH 03801-4016
PH 603 427-2099 FAX 603 427-2499
JOHN FORMA,PRES
PATRICIA O'BRIEN,SECY/TREAS

O'BRIEN PAUL F JR,FAMILY,LLC
PO BOX 6655
SHREVEPORT,LA 71136-6655
PH 318 869-3293 FAX 318 869-8925
ERNEST OBERING O'BRIEN,GEOL
PATSY DESSELLE,REV/JIB
ALDEN OBERING O'BRIEN
ALDEN O'BRIEN HAASS
PAUL F O'BRIEN III,ENGR
MIKE MUSE,CPA
GINGER SWANSON,CAP/SECY

O'CONNOR D K,LEASES,ROYALTIES,WELL DEALS
138 LORMAN LN
MADISON,MS 39110-7112 PH 601 366-9409

O'CONNOR ENTERPRISES,INC
5634 SANFORD RD
HOUSTON,TX 77096-6142 PH 713 665-6661
KEVIN C O'CONNOR,PRES,IND LDMN

O'DONNELL CONSULTING ENGINEERS,INC
ENGRG DESIGN/ANALYSIS,MECHANICAL TROUBLE-
SHOOTING,FATIGUE & FAILURE ANALYSIS
2940 S PARK RD
PITTSBURGH,PA 15102-1686
PH 412 835-5007 FAX 412 835-5017

O'HERN JIM AND ASSOCIATES
PO BOX 1903,1322 N B ST
FORT SMITH,AR 72902-1903
PH 479 783-7242 FAX 479 783-7537
WWW.JIMOHERN.NET SEMAJRIS@LIVE.COM
JIM O'HERN,CPL/ATTY AT LAW
PAULA WITYAK,ADMIN ASST

O'LEARY'S OIL & GAS INC
2210 NE DANIELS ST
ARCADIA,FL 34266-5710 PH 863 990-7927
FAX 863 494-7871
JIM O'LEARY,PRES
JAY WIGFALL,PUMPER,ABILENE,TX

O'NEAL MARK A & ASSOCIATES,INC
PO BOX 66573,522 EUROPE ST
BATON ROUGE,LA 70896-6573
PH 225 389-1100 MARK@MARKAONEAL.COM
MARK A O'NEAL,CPL,PRES

O'NEAL PATRICIA J LLC
675 N HENDERSON ST
FORT WORTH,TX 76107-1479
PH 817 625-8246 FAX 817 626-7269

OAKLAND AGENCY ACCOUNT
PO BOX 5605
SHREVEPORT,LA 71135-5605 PH 318 222-8400

OAKLAND CORP,SEE
J-O'B OPERATING CO

OAKROCK EXPLORATION CO
7 MISTFLOWER PL
THE WOODLANDS,TX 77381 PH 210 387-5255
BARBARA F BOWDEN,PRES

OASIS PETROLEUM LLC
1001 FANNIN STE 202
HOUSTON,TX 77002-6712 PH 713 574-1770
FAX 713 751-1801 713 751-0188
TOMMY NUSZ,PRES & CEO
TAYLOR REID,VP & COO
ROBIN HESKETH,VP OPERS ENGRG
RHESKETH@OASISPETR.COM
CASH SMITHWICK,VP ENGRG
CSMITHWICK@OASISPETR.COM
BRETT NEWTON,VP RESERVOIR ENGRG
BEVERLY HOFFMAN,PROD & REGULATORY ANALYST
BHOFFMAN@OASISPETR.COM
BOB CANDITO,VP GEOL
BCANDITO@OASISPETR.COM
GEORGE STOVALL,VP GEOPHY
GSTOVALL@OASISPETR.COM
DEAN GILBERT,VP DEV GEOL
DGILBERT@OASISPETR.COM
KENT BEERS,VP LAND KBEERS@OASISPETR.COM
TOM F HAWKINS,LD MGR/MKTG MGR
THAWKINS@OASISPETR.COM
MARK TAYLOR METZ,SR LDMN
MMETZ@OASISPETR.COM
KELLY DOMNIQUE,MGR LD ADMIN
KDOMNIQUE@OASISPETR.COM

OBIE INC
9 CAMDEN PL
CORPUS CHRISTI,TX 78412
PH 361 992-2725
JOSEPH A OBRIEN,PRES

OBO INC
PO BOX 22577
HIALEAH,FL 33002-2577
PH 305 821-8300 FAX 305 826-9782
LOWELLII@OBO.NET

OBRIEN JOSEPH A
9 CAMDEN PL
CORPUS CHRISTI,TX 78412
PH 361 992-2725

OBRIEN R E
5925 LINE AVE STE 8
SHREVEPORT,LA 71106-2049 PH 318 868-6748

OCCIDENTAL OIL & GAS CORPORATION
10889 WILSHIRE BLVD
LOS ANGELES,CA 90024-4201
PH 310 208-8800
WILLIAM E ALBRECHT,PRES OCCIDENTAL

OIL & GAS USA
SANDY LOWE,PRES OCCIDENTAL OIL & GAS -
INTL PROD & ENGRG
ANITA POWERS,EXEC VP/WORLDWIDE EXPL
OCCIDENTAL OIL & GAS CORP
ROY PINECI,VP & CONTROLLER,OCCIDENTAL
PETROLEUM CORP
RICHARD S KLINE,VP,COMMUNICATIONS &
PUBLIC AFFAIRS,OCCIDENTAL PETROLEUM CORP
ROGER TUCKER,VP WORLDWIDE ENGINEERING
DARIN MOSS,VP,HUMAN RESOURCES
MICHAEL PRESTON,VP,GEN COUNSEL
WESLEY SCOTT,VP,HEALTH,ENVIRO & SAFETY
SECURITY,OCCIDENTAL OIL & GAS
KEVIN O'DONNELL,VP/WORLDWIDE DRLG

OCCIDENTAL PERMIAN LTD
5 GREENWAY PLAZA STE 110
HOUSTON,TX 77046 PH 713 366-5249
FAX 713 366-5200 MARK_HODGE@OXY.COM
MARK E HODGE,SR LDMN ADVSR

OCCIDENTAL PETROLEUM CORP,EXEC OFCS
10889 WILSHIRE BLVD
LOS ANGELES,CA 90024-4201 PH 310 208-8800
DR RAY I IRANI,CHRMN,PRES,CEO
STEPHEN I CHAZEN,SR EXEC VP,CFO
DONALD P DEBRIER,EXEC VP,GEN COUNSEL SECY

OCEAN ENERGY INC SEE
DEVON ENERGY CORPORATION

OCEAN ENERGY RESOURCES,INC SEE
DEVON ENERGY CORPORATION

OCEAN OIL INTERNATIONAL CORP
NAVAL ARCH & MARINE ENGR,EXPERT WITNESS
PO BOX 47188
ST PETERSBURG,FL 33743 PH 727 347-2556
FAX 727 343-9717 WWW.SITERRIFIC.COM/PAZOS
OCEANOILPAZOS@BELLSOUTH.NET
NEW ORLEANS,LA OFFICE - 3501 HOLIDAY DR
STE 314,70114 PH 504 367-4072
FAX 504 367-3790
HECTOR V PAZOS,PE,PRES
HECTORPAZOS75597@AOL.COM

OCHEEKAWA INTERESTS
CONTRACTOR CONSULTANT FOR GEOLOGICAL
AND ENVIRONMENTAL SERVICES USA
102 TARPON ST
LAFAYETTE,LA 70508-5039 PH 318 232-6640
JAMES A BAIRD,CONS GEOL,GULF COAST PROV
JAMES_BAIRD@BELLSOUTH.NET

OCONEE LIMITED PARTNERSHIP
2828 ROUTH ST STE 500
DALLAS,TX 75201 PH 214 661-3185
FAX 214 661-3187
PETER R VIG,MGR PVIG@ROUNDROCKCAPITAL.COM

OCONNELL JOHN,OIL & GAS,LAND & LEGAL
7 SHADOW LN
METAIRIE,LA 70005 PH 504 835-5617

ODEGARD ENERGY INC
952 ECHO LN STE 390
HOUSTON,TX 77024 PH 713 881-9030
FAX 713 881-9078
MICHAEL A ODEGARD,PRES
MAODEGARD@ACEXPLORATION.COM

ODEN & ASSOCIATES,LLC
OIL & GAS EXPLORATION
PO BOX 1806,416 TRAVIS ST STE 400
SHREVEPORT,LA 71166-1806

PH 318 222-2400 FAX 318 226-0840
ODENASSOC@BELLSOUTH.NET
STUART L ODEN,GEOL
ALAN SCHLICHTEMIER,GEOL
ROLAND FRAUTSCHI
LISA CROW

ODFJELL TANKERS (USA) INC
12211 PORT RD
SEABROOK,TX 77586-1624 PH 713 844-2200
FAX 713 844-2211

ODUM OIL & GAS CO
4705 OSAGE DR
BOULDER,CO 80303-3904 PH 303 499-7626
FAX 303 499-7623
JOHNNIE D ODUM,PRES
DEBORAH E ODUM,VP

OFFICE OF SURFACE MINING RECLAMATION &
ENFORCEMENT (OSM) WWW.OSMRE.GOV

OFFSHORE LOGISTICS INC SEE
BRISTOW U.S.,LLC

OFFSHORE PARAGON PETROLEUM,INC
10333 RICHMOND AVE STE 730
HOUSTON,TX 77042-4474 PH 713 960-0815
FAX 713 621-2779 WIN44NER@SBCGLOBAL.NET
WILLIAM F HOWELL,PRES

OFFSHORE SANITATION & EQUIP RENTAL,SEE
OSERS,INC

OFRIEL EDWARD W,LEASES
1213 BAJAT RD
CARENCRO,LA 70520-5521 PH 318 234-0774

OGDEN ALTON J,JR
PO BOX 952,280 HIGHLAND BLVD
NATCHEZ,MS 39121-0952 PH 601 442-6648
FAX 601 442-3961 BELLEX@BELLSOUTH.NET

OGDEN JERRY P,PETR ENGR
PO BOX 101,14 HEATHER DR
NATCHEZ,MS 39121-0101
PH 601 446-8105 FAX 601 446-8844
JERRY P OGDEN,OWNER/PE/GEOL
OIL & GAS EXPL

OGDEN RESOURCES CORP
3740 COPPERFIELD DR STE 103
BRYAN,TX 77802-5933
PH 409 696-2767 FAX 409 696-3264
STEPHEN E OGDEN,PRES
ROBERT N KOELBL,VP
MICHAEL CROCKER,FLD SUPVSR

OGERD CORP
PO BOX 42367
HOUSTON,TX 78242 PH 713 783-8660
FAX 713 952-2440
DAVIS X SUN,PRES

OGIA INSURANCE AGENCY
PO BOX 146
GROVE CITY,OH 43123 PH 614 875-6442
PH 1-800-334-5488
MARK FRESHWATER,PRES
LINDA CUSTER,VP

OGINFO.COM LLC
PO BOX 23014,101 N SHORELINE BLVD STE 420
CORPUS CHRISTI,TX 78403-2645
PH 361 904-0071 FAX 361 904-0105
WWW.OGINFO.COM
CHAD FEERICK,PRES CHAD@OGINFO.COM

OGM,INC
333 BLACKLATCH LN

CAMP HILL,PA 17011
PH 717 439-2897 WWW.OILGASMINERALS.COM
JIM LINDHOME JLINDHOME@GMAIL.COM

OGS LABORATORY,INC SEE NEWPARK RESOURCES

OGS PIPELINE,LLC
907 RR 620 SOUTH STE 201
AUSTIN,TX 78734 PH 512 610-5100
FAX 512 610-5108
JOHN GILLIES,PRES
JGILLIES@OGSPIPELINE.COM
TIM VAN ACKEREN,EXEC VP
TVANACKEREN@OGSPIPELINE.COM
ROY BREHM JR,VP RBREHM@OGSPIPELINE.COM

OGTRADES,LLC
SPECIALIZES IN OIL & GAS AUCTIONS
4516 LOVERS LN STE 199
DALLAS,TX 75225 PH 817 366-1015
WWW.OGTRADES.COM
JOHN WHELAN JPMWHELAN@OGTRADES.COM

OHARE JOHN P
2232 SOUTH PINEY PT #112
HOUSTON,TX 77063-1428
PH 713 975-7224 JANDGOHARE@GMAIL.COM

OHEIM COMPANY THE
7718 BENT TREE DR
AMARILLO,TX 79121-1930 PH 806 356-6655
FAX 806 356-6656
DONALD H OHEIM,PETR ENGR

OHIO ENERGY ASSETS,INC
PO BOX 377
LAURELVILLE,OH 43135-0377 PH 740 332-9511
FAX 740 332-6296
NANCY MELVILLE,PRES

OHIO GAS COMPANY
PO BOX 528,200 W HIGH ST
BRYAN,OH 43506 PH 419 636-1117
FAX 419 636-2134
ROBERT S EYRE,VP,GAS SUPPLY

OHIO INDEPENDENT LOGGING SERVICES INC
PO BOX 179,210 SECOND ST
SAINT MARYS,WV 26170-0179 PH 304 684-7686
LOREN E BAGLEY,PRES

OHIO KENTUCKY OIL CORPORATION
510 SPRING ST STE B
MOUNT STERLING,KY 40353 PH 859 276-3500
FAX 859 276-0699 OILSTRIKE@MW.TWCBC.COM
OHIOKENTUCKYOIL.COM
CAROL CAMPBELL,PRES
JOHNNIE Y SPAULDING,VP

OHIO OIL AND GAS ASSOCIATION (OOGA)
PO BOX 535,1718 COLUMBUS RD SW
GRANVILLE,OH 43023-0535 PH 740 587-0444
FAX 740 587-0446 WWW.OOGA.ORG
BILL BENNETT,PRES
THOMAS E STEWART,EXEC VP
STEWART@OOGA.ORG
JERRY JAMES,VP
JOEL RUDICIL,TREAS

OHIO PRODUCTION CORP
PO BOX 377
LAURELVILLE,OH 43135-0377
PH 740 332-9511 FAX 740 332-6296
NANCY MELVILLE,PRES

OIL & GAS ASSET CLEARINGHOUSE,INC,THE
PO BOX 671787
500 N SAM HOUSTON PKWY W STE 150

HOUSTON,TX 77067 PH 281 873-4600
FAX 281 873-0055 WWW.OGCLEARINGHOUSE.COM
KENNETH R OLIVE JR,PRES/CEO
RONALD K BARNES,EXEC VP/COO
WILLIAM KEITH GIBBS,VP LAND
CHASE MORRIS,VP BUS DEV-N TEX/LA
JOHN R KLEE,VP BUS DEV-RKY MTN REG
ROBERT L DAWSON,VP BUS DEV-MID CONT REG
KEVIN R TOWNSEND,VP BUS DEV
DENNA K ARIAS,BUS DEV MGR

OIL & GAS ENVIRONMENTAL SERV CO,INC,THE
(ENSERCO,INC)
P O BOX 5370
VIENNA,WV 26105 PH 304 295-3333
FAX 304 295-8600
WALTER H ALLEN,PRES
C W WILSON,VP
JOHN SIMONS,FIELD SUPT

OIL & GAS OPERATORS,INC,PETR ENGINEER
105 RIDGEMONT DR
ALVIN,TX 77511 PH 281 331-3008
OGO@SBCGLOBAL.NET
NORMAN P FAIST,PRES

OIL AIR HYDRAULICS,INC SEE
PARKER HANNIFIN CORP

OIL AND GAS PROPERTIES
PO BOX 56651,3220 AUDLEY ST
HOUSTON,TX 77256 PH 713 806-0674
ROBERT J HOLLEY,JR
ROBERTJHOLLEYJR@AOL.COM

OIL AND GAS PROPERTY MANAGEMENT,INC
101 N RIVERIDGE DR
LAFAYETTE,LA 70508-7815 PH 318 856-8501
FAX 318 856-8634 RPVERRET@BELLSOUTH.NET
ROBERT P VERRET,JR,PRES

OIL AND GAS RESERVES INC
4600 OCEAN DR STE 304
CORPUS CHRISTI,TX 78412
PH 361 883-7033
H T HOP NOLEN,OWNER
DAVID W NOLEN,PRES

OIL CENTER RESEARCH LLC
PO BOX 91510,616 W PONT DES MOUTON
LAFAYETTE,LA 70509-1510
PH 337 232-2496 FAX 337 234-5825
WWW.OILCENTER.COM
ESALES@OILCENTER.COM

OIL CITY SUPPLY CO
PO BOX 670
OIL CITY,LA 71061-0670
PH 318 995-6631 FAX 318 995-6630
TOMMY PAUL,MGR
ED ROBBINS,OUTSIDE SLS

OIL COUNTRY MANUFACTURING
300 W STANLEY AVE
VENTURA,CA 93001-1350 PH 805 643-1200
FAX 805 643-6832
ED PATTERSON,GEN MGR
BAKERSFIELD,CA SALES OFFICE -
3515 STANDARD ST,93308 PH 661 322-5966
FAX 661 322-9531
GREG KEETEN,DIST MGR
ODESSA,TX SALES OFFICE - 6103 ANDREWS
HIGHWAY,79762

OIL COUNTRY PIPE & SUPPLY
PO BOX 921

KILGORE,TX 75663-0921
PH 903 984-3443 FAX 903 983-2526
RANDALL BROOKS,PRES

OIL COUNTRY TUBULAR CORP
PO BOX 51123
LAFAYETTE,LA 70505-1123 PH 337 233-2102
FAX 337 269-9335 JC@OILCOUNTRYTUBULAR.COM
J C GALLET,PRES
BRANDON GALLET,SALES
PAULETTE FONTENOT,OFC MGR

OIL FIELD RENTAL SERVICE CO SEE
ENTERRA OIL FIELD RENTAL

OIL GAS & MINERAL MANAGEMENT,INC
910 TRAVIS ST STE 1910
HOUSTON,TX 77002-5809 PH 713 652-5055
FAX 713 951-0620
STEVEN B JENKINS,PRES

OIL GAS MANAGEMENT INC
1224 ADMIRAL BLVD
KANSAS CITY,MO 64106-1523
PH 816 421-2272 FAX 816 421-2272
FRED CARLSON,PRES
AMANDA SANDER,SECY

OIL INDUSTRIES LIBRARY,INC SEE
COASTAL BEND GEOLOGICAL LIBRARY,INC

OIL LAND SERVICES,INC
PO BOX 51242,106 REPRESENTATIVE ROW STE B
LAFAYETTE,LA 70505-1242 PH 337 233-4156
FAX 337 233-9917 JOHN@OILLANDSERVICES.COM
JOHN G MILLER,CPL,PRES
VIRGINIA H MILLER,SECY/TREAS

OIL LEASE OPERATING CO
PO BOX 930
COLDSPRING,TX 77331-0930 PH 713 528-3206
TED R STALDER,PRES

OIL MOP,LLC
131 KEATING DR
BELLE CHASSE,LA 70037
PH 800 645-6671
SHAW THOMPSON,PRES
JOSEPH CHRISTIANA,VP SALES & MKTG
ED TURNER,OPERS MGR

OIL NUT BAY ROYALTIES,LP
PO BOX 671099
DALLAS,TX 75367 PH 214 707-7535
FAX 214 572-2699 WWW.TRUNKBAY.NET
BENNY DUNCAN,MGR
BDUNCAN@TRUNKBAY.NET

OIL PRODUCERS ASSOCIATION,INC
PO BOX 639
SPRINGFIELD,IL 62705-0639
PH 217 544-4844 FAX 217 546-8969
CHRISTIAN H HOMEIER,PRES
RENEE C HOMEIER,SECY/TREAS

OIL PRODUCERS,INC
PO BOX 336
WEST FRANKFORT,IL 62896-0336
PH 618 932-2111 FAX 618 932-3115
SAMUEL H POLLACK,PRES
SAMCAT336@YAHOO.COM

OIL STOP,INC SEE
SUPERIOR ENERGY SERVICES

OIL WELL BUYERS CORPORATION
5433 WESTHEIMER STE 604
HOUSTON,TX 77056-5392 PH 713 960-9541
FAX 713 960-9542

GENE A SMITHERMAN,PRES,PETR ENGR

OIL WELL LOGGING CO,INC,(OWLCO)
MUD LOGGING,COMPUTERIZED
3970 HWY 43 N
BRANDON,MS 39047 PH 601 829-0800
ELLISVILLE,MS OFFICE - PO BOX 756,39437
PH 601 477-8315
A B NICHOLS,PRES

OIL WELL PRODUCTION INC
PO BOX 160
DAISETTA,TX 77533-0160 PH 713 536-6710
DOUGLAS,DOUG,LANDRY,CO-OWNER

OILCO EXPLORATION INCORPORATED
5773 WOODWAY DR STE 444
HOUSTON,TX 77057 PH 713 783-9160
JAMES L STROOPE JR,PRES

OILFIELD WATER LOGISTICS
8214 WESTCHESTER DR STE 850
DALLAS,TX 75225 PH 214 292-2011
TY O'RAND
TORAND@OILFIELDWATERLOGISTICS.COM

OILTIZER INC
210 PARK AVE STE 1110
OKLAHOMA CITY,OK 73102
PH 800 255-7215 FAX 877 453-2262
HELP@OILTIZERONLINE.COM
WWW.OILTIZER.COM

OKLAHOMA BAPTIST UNIVERSITY
C/O BAPTIST FOUNDATION OF TEXAS
1601 ELM ST STE 1700
DALLAS,TX 75201 PH 214 978-3333
WWW.BFTX.ORG
WILLIAM T FRANCIS,OIL & GAS MGR
WILL.FRANCIS@BFTX.ORG PH 214 978-3333

OKLAHOMA BASIC ECONOMY CORP,DRLG CONTR
SEE PONTOTOC PRODUCTION COMPANY INC

OKLAHOMA OIL COMPANY
WHOLLY OWNED SUB OF INTER-AMERICAN CORP
3419 WESTMINSTER AVE
DALLAS,TX 75205 PH 214 696-6700
FAX 214 696-6957 OOIL@IACX.COM
WHEELER M SEARS,PRES
M SCOTT SEARS,VP

OLD PINE ENERGY CORP
PO BOX 30281
AUSTIN,TX 78755-3281
PH 512 458-3322 FAX 512 732-9880
JOSEPH G DALY,PRES

OLD RIVER EXPLORATION,INC
PO BOX 668,117 GLOUCESTER RD
NATCHEZ,MS 39121-0668 PH 601 445-4348
601 446-8366
JOSEPH J RING III,PRES

OLDS JERRY C
PO BOX 556,625 HIGH ST
WORTHINGTON,OH 43085-0556 PH 614 888-2770
JERRY C OLDS,PROD

OLEBROOK
DIRECTIONAL DRILLING SERVICES
PO BOX 2437
CLEBURNE,TX 76033 PH 817 556-3800
FAX 817 556-3804 SALES@OLEBROOK.US
JAMIE JONES,PRES
PAUL GREERN,SLS

OLEUM OPERATING COMPANY,LC
PO BOX 1263

LONGVIEW,TX 75606-1263
PH 903 758-9896 FAX 903 758-9876
OLEUMOPERATING.AOL.COM
MICHAEL SNELL,MNGNG MEMBER
ANDREW SNELL,VP OPERS

OLIVER LONNIE G,CONS GEOL
4926 IVORY MEADOWS LN
HOUSTON,TX 77084-3991 PH 713 461-3875

OLIVER VIRGIL,PETROLEUM LANDMAN
8700 S 31ST TER
FORT SMITH,AR 72908-8744
PH 501 646-7287 FAX 479 646-7287
PH 479 285-0579

OLIVER W COURTNEY JR,OIL OPR
498 WOODLAND DR
ZWOLLE,LA 71486-4911 PH 318 645-4001
GOVCO@BELLSOUTH.NET

OLIVER WILLIAM B,GEOL
PO BOX 52114
LAFAYETTE,LA 70505-2114 PH 318 237-7788
FAX 318 237-4334

OLIVIER NICHOLAS D,IND OIL OPER,OWNER
125 NEWBURY TERRACE
SAN ANTONIO,TX 78209
PH 504 913-1373 PFOLIVIER@AOL.COM

OMA SYSTEMS
2859 KULP RD
EDEN,NY 14057-9411 PH 716 992-4333
FAX 716 646-6615
RAYMOND DOBAJ,MGR

OMAN HUNT OIL COMPANY SEE
HUNT OIL COMPANY

OMEARA INC
650 POYDRAS ST STE 2235
NEW ORLEANS,LA 70130-6101 PH 504 522-0288
FAX 504 522-0289 INFO@OMEARAINC.COM
M P OMEARA JR,OWNER

OMEGA ENERGY CORPORATION
2623 LOGANRITA AVE
ARCADIA,CA 91006-5028 PH 812 962-5746
FAX 626 226-5885 WWW.OMEGA-ENERGY.COM
PRINCETON,IN OFFICE - 4600 S 175 E 47670
JAKE BARBEE,PRES
NELLIE WILLIAMS,CONTROLLER
ARCHIE WALLS,FLD OPERS

OMNI LABORATORIES INC
CORPORATE OFFICE
8845 FALLBROOK DR
HOUSTON,TX 77064-4856 PH 832 237-4000
FAX 832 237-4700 WWW.OMNILABS.COM
CHRIS BECHTEL,PRES
NEW ORLEANS,LA OFFICE - 717 GIROD ST
70130 PH 504 523-7211 FAX 504 523-4311
LAFAYETTE,LA OFFICE - 2020 PINHOOK RD
STE 501,70508 PH 337 234-3400
FAX 337 234-3471
CORPUS CHRISTI,TX OFFICE - 2209 N PADRE
ISLAND STE W,78468 PH 361 884-0683
FAX 361 884-8283
JACKSON,MS OFFICE - 125 FAIRMONT PLZ
39208 PH 601 939-3200 FAX 601 939-3597
BAKERSFIELD,CA OFFICE - 6000 SCHIRRA CT
BLDG A,93313 PH/FAX 661 396-8696
PORT OF SPAIN,TRINIDAD OFFICE -
PH 868 662-5412
RIO DE JANEIRO,BRAZIL OFFICE -

PH 5521 2201-4773
MARACAIBO,VENEZUELA OFFICE -
PH 58261 749-5316

OMNI OIL CORP
1013 W MAIN ST
OLNEY,IL 62450-1101 PH 618 928-0734
OREN F MILES,PRES
OREN F MILES II,VP LAND

OMNI PETROLEUM SERVICES INC SEE
OMNI LABORATORIES INC

ON-MARK CORPORATION
205 BROADMOOR ST
MONROE,LA 71203-4125
PH 318 537-1103
LLOYDEHARGROVE@YAHOO.COM
LLOYD E HARGROVE,PRES

ONAGER ENERGY COMPANY
3306 CANDLEKNOLL DR
SPRING,TX 77388-5818
PH 281 440-9965 FAX 281 440-9964
DUDLEY S TOELKE DUD@FLASH.NET

ONE CYPRESS ENERGY
10100 REUNION PL STE 350
SAN ANTONIO,TX 78216 PH 210 340-5900
WWW.ONECYPRESSENERGY.COM
SCOTT PHIPPS,SR VP/TREAS & FIN
CHAD SMITH,SR VP TERMINAL OPERS
JOHN SUMMERS,SR VP MKTG
STACY TANEY,ROYALTY & DIV INTEREST
DOUG PINKSTON,DIR TRUCKING OPERS
JOE GARCIA,DIR TERMINAL OPERS

ONE HUNDRED ONE ENERGY CORP SEE
101 ENERGY CORP (END OF ALPHA)

ONE NATION ENERGY SOLUTIONS,LLC
4404 BLOSSOM ST
HOUSTON,TX 77007-5535
PH 713 861-0600 FAX 713 861-0608
WWW.ONENATIONENERGY.COM
TERRY PIERCE,PRES
TPIERCE@ONENATIONENERGY.COM
TIM BALASKI,VP

ONEBANE LAW FIRM
A PROFESSIONAL CORP
PO BOX 3507,1200 CAMELLIA BLVD STE 300
LAFAYETTE,LA 70502-3507 PH 337 237-2660
FAX 337 266-1232 INFO@ONEBANE.COM
WWW.ONEBANE.COM

ONEILL EXPLORATION COMPANY
4007 MCCULLOUGH #455
SAN ANTONIO,TX 78212-9623 PH 210 289-6488
FAX 210 828-2075 ONEXCO@SWBELL.NET
WWW.PETROLEUMLANDSERVICES.COM
MICHAEL P O'NEILL,PRES

ONSITE SERVICES SEE
SUPERIOR ENERGY SERVICES

OPAL RESOURCES LLC
7600 W TIDWELL STE 500
HOUSTON,TX 77040 PH 713 647-7300
FAX 713 461 0103 WWW.OPALRESOURCES.COM
INFO@OPALRESOURCES.COM
RICK LESTER,CEO
GERALD LONG,SR VP OPERATIONS
LES MCCORMICK,VP LAND & BUS DEV
LES.MCCORMICK@OPALRESOURCES.COM
RICK CASTAGNO,MRG RESERVOIR ENGRG
JOHN ALLRED,ENGRG MGR

DAN CREIGHTON,CHF GEOSCIENTIST

OPERATORS & CONSULTING SERVICES,INC
OILFIELD CONSULTING SERVICES
3861 AMBASSADOR CAFFERY PKWY STE 250
LAFAYETTE,LA 70503-5267 PH 337 234-0100
FAX 337 234-0193
W J ARTIGUE,PRES
W C ROBERTSON,PROD MGR
J O RICHARD,SECY/TREAS
C E DUPUIS,RISK MGR
J C WINKLE,ADMIN MGR
F W BROUSSARD,OPERS MGR
C E SELF,PROD SUPT
C R DROST,PROD SUPT
D W CORMIER,PROD FRMN
R L GUILLORY,PROD FRMN
K R JOHNSON,SAFETY DIR
C E STOUT,TRAINING SUPVSR
E P GUIDRY,JR,DRLG MGR
J BLACKWELL,CONS COORD
J T DADE,CONST MGR
P J ANDRUS,CONST COORD
B N JOHNSON,CONST ENGR
G S CRANE,BUS DEV MGR
TONY PESSON,MECH FRMN
M BORQUE,REFRIGERATION FRMN
E FRUGE,JR,SHORE BASE MGR
T OPIELA,SHORE BASE SUPVSR
P W ARTIGUE,ELECTRONIC DEPT MGR
T REASONEL,ACCT MGR
F L DEARE,REG COMPLIANCE COORD
M L LEGROS,ADMIN ASST
E C BROUSSARD,PROD ASST
T G DUPLECHIN,ADMIN ASST
M PROVENCHER,ACCNTG ASST
M D SMITH,ACCNTG ASST
K BROUSSARD,ACCNTG ASST
K A FUSILIER,ACCNTG ASST
V L MENARD,RECPT/SECY
R HALE,MECH SVCS SUPT

OPHIR RESOURCES,INC
106 PARSONAGE LN
LAFAYETTE,LA 70503-5932 PH 337 981-5302
FAX 337 988-3076
DWAYNE K VAUGHN,PRES

OPTIMEDA ENTERPRISES
6610 SHADOWCREST
HOUSTON,TX 77074-6820 PH 713 777-6395
DR LLOYD R WALKER,OWNER

ORAVETZ ENERGY COMPANY
705 BECKY DR
TYLER,TX 75703 PH 903 534-1975
J ASHTON ORAVETZ III,PRES

ORBIT ENERGY,INC
400 E KALISTE SALOOM RD
LAFAYETTE,LA 70508-8508
PH 337 291-2720 FAX 337 291-2722
MATT G CHIASSON,PRES
MATT@ORBITENERGY.COM
TIMOTHY J BENNETT,EXPL MGR
TIM@ORBITENERGY.COM
BRUCE N CHIASSON,VP,LAND
BRUCE@ORBITENERGY.COM
COURTNEY K CLINE,CONTROLLER
COURTNEY@ORBITENERGY.COM
EVELYN J COOPER,OFC MGR

ECOOPER@ORBITENERGY.COM

ORBIT GAS TRANSMISSION,INC
600 BARRETT BLVD
HENDERSON,KY 42420-4955 PH 270 827-2093
FAX 270 826-3763 WWW.ORBITGAS.COM
JAMES F MARTIN,PRES
JANE BERRONG,SECY

ORION ENERGY CORPORATION SEE
AMBRIT ENERGY CORP

ORION PETRO CORPORATION
PO BOX 609,125 N 11TH
MOUNT VERNON,IL 62864-0013
PH 618 244-2370 FAX 618 244-2371
WAYNE L KREHBIEL,PRES

ORLEANS EXPLORATION CO INC,OIL OPR & EXPL
PO BOX 325
FRANKLIN,LA 70538-0325 PH 337 828-1955
FAX 337 828-4319 JPE3@COX.NET
JAMES P EVANS,III,PRES

ORTHWEIN PETROLEUM INCORPORATED
PO BOX 14180
OKLAHOMA CITY,OK 73113-0180
PH 405 478-7663 FAX 405 478-2661
RICHARD J ORTHWEIN,PRES

ORTMAN DRILLING INC
241 N 300 W
KOKOMO,IN 46901-3984 PH 765 459-4125
FAX 765 459-8750
RICK ORTMAN,PRES

ORVILLE E & MERCEDES TUNSTILL
MINERAL TRUST
PO BOX 50119
AUSTIN,TX 78763 PH 512 791-4551
JEANIE TUNSTILL COWDEN,TRUSTEE

ORX RESOURCES,INC
400 POYDRAS ST STE 1100
NEW ORLEANS,LA 70130-3264
PH 504 581-1806 FAX 504 581-9492
CAROLA@ORX.COM
J LUIS BANOS,JR,CEO
JAMES E ORTH,PRES,COO
A E BUZZ JEHLE,VP,CFO

ORYX ENERGY COMPANY SEE
KERR-MCGEE CORP

OSAGE ENERGY CORPORATION
PO BOX 53963
LAFAYETTE,LA 70505-3963 PH 337 232-9485
JACK W LARIMER,PRES
RUTH T LARIMER,LDMN

OSBORN HEIRS COMPANY
PO BOX 17968,1250 NE LOOP 410 #1100
SAN ANTONIO,TX 78217-0968 PH 210 826-0700
FAX 210 826-7559 DONW@OSBORNHEIRS.COM
MIKE STEVENSON,PRES
PAT GARCIA,CFO
DON WADSWORTH,VP LAND & EXPL
NANCY FITZSIMON,VP,ACQS
JOHN LONG,GEOL MGR

OSBORN W B OIL & GAS OPERATIONS
PO BOX 8C
SAN ANTONIO,TX 78217-8199 PH 210 826-8654
FAX 210 826-7318 BILLYO@WBOSBORN.COM
W B OSBORN,III,PRES
P K ROBERTS,GEOL
REX BOURLAND,LAND MGR
C CURTIS CRUMINE,ENGR,MGR OF BUS DEV

GARY PALMER,OPERS MGR

OSO ROYALTY COMPANY SEE
SASSER ROYALTIES

OSTRANDER C E, P.E.
CONSLTNG PETR ENGR
121 VINE DR
BRANDON,MS 39047 PH 601 291-0492
FAX 601 992-9167
CHARLESOSTRANDER@BELLSOUTH.NET

OSWALD INTERNATIONAL CONSULTING,INC
13939 BRETAGNE DR
HOUSTON,TX 77015-3001 PH 713 455-0751
LOUIS A OSWALD,JR,PRES,GEOPHY

OSYKA CORPORATION
PO BOX 420368
HOUSTON,TX 77242-0368
PH 281 293-0296 FAX 281 293-0497
BBRDTG@OSYKA.COM WWW.OSYKA.COM
MICHAEL F HARNESS,CHRMN,PRES & CEO
TYRONE G BYRD,EXEC VP & CFO
GEORGE J EDWARDS,EXEC VP,BUS DEV

OTIS ENGINEERING CORP SEE
HALLIBURTON ENERGY SERVICES

OTIS INSTRUMENTS,INC
301 S TEXAS AVE
BRYAN,TX 77803 PH 979 776-7700
FAX 979 776-7719 WWW.OTISINSTRUMENTS.COM
OTIS@OTISINSTRUMENTS.COM

OTTINGER HEBERT,LLC
ATTORNEYS AT LAW
PO BOX 52606,1313 W PINHOOK RD
LAFAYETTE,LA 70505-2606
PH 337 232-2606 FAX 337 232-9867
WWW.OTTINGERHEBERT.COM
PATRICK S OTTINGER
LARRY C HEBERT
MARK D SIKES
PAUL J HEBERT
K WADE TRAHAN
STUART M SIMONEAUD
TAMMY P PRATT
DAVID K MCCRORY
VALERIE V GUIDRY
CHRISTIAN COX PREJEAN
WILLIAM H L KAUFMAN
BENJAMIN D JONES
TALBOTT P OTTINGER
G QUINN SALMON
MICHAEL C WYNNE

OTTS,MOORE AND JORDAN,ATTYS
PO BOX 467
BREWTON,AL 36427-0467 PH 205 867-7724
FAX 205 867-2624
LEE M OTTS,PRTNR
JOHN THADDEUS MOORE,PRTNR
JAMES DAVID JORDAN,PRTNR

OVERLY OPERATING COMPANY,OIL PROD
114 GATEWOOD
SAN ANTONIO,TX 78209
PH 210 826-3822 FAX 210 826-7255
F A OVERLY,OWNER

OVERTON ENERGY,LLC
4265 SAN FELIPE STE 1040
HOUSTON,TX 77027-2929 PH 713 580-7250
WWW.OVERTONENERGY.COM
CARTER OVERTON

OWENS HARRY J
PO BOX 524
LONGVIEW,TX 75606-0524 PH 903 753-4522
FAX 903 753-9717

OWENS INDUSTRIAL DEV AND MKT CO
7959 SOUTHMEADOW DR
HOUSTON,TX 77071
PH 713 686-8664 FAX 713 484-5511
CHRIS OWENS,DIR
JO OWENS,VP
JU OWENS,EXEC VP
CHRS OWENS II,ADMIN VP

OWENS ROBERT M,GEOL
1307 HEATHWOOD DR
HOUSTON,TX 77077-3011 PH 281 493-4525

OWENSBY & KRITIKOS INC
PO BOX 1217,671 WHITNEY AVE BLDG B
GRETNA,LA 70054-1217 PH 504 368-3122
FAX 504 362-4546
T A KRITIKOS,CHRMN
JOHN W OWENSBY,V CHRMN
BOB LEDET,PRES
DANNY VORENKAMP,OPERS MGR
SCOTT BARBIER,ASST GEN MGR
VAL GUILBEAU,E/C COORD
SAM SPEER,SALES CONS
CHARLES DONEWAR,SALES
MARK STEIN,SUPVSR NDT
KATHERINE KAY,SAFETY ENGR
TOM BAXTER,SUPVSR ENGRG
LAFAYETTE,LA OFFICE - 111 LAFFERTY DR
BROUSSARD,LA 70518 PH 318 837-9721
FAX 318 837-1316
STEVE ERCOLI,MGR
MIKE CROCHET,SALES,MKTG
ROY RICHARD,SUPVSR NDT

OWL PETROLEUM COMPANY,EXPL & PROD
12438 SHEPHERDS RIDGE DR
HOUSTON,TX 77077-2920 PH 281 497-7994
JO ANN WILSON,PRES

OXBOW EXPLORATION COMPANY
PO BOX 5344
BRANDON,MS 39047-5344 PH 601 214-6700
W KEVIN JEFFREYS,PRES

OXFORD OIL COMPANY,THE
PO BOX 910,4900 BOGGS ROAD
ZANESVILLE,OH 43702-0910 PH 740 452-4503
JOHN W STRAKER JR,PRES
GRAHAM ROBB,VP,PROD
ROBERT MACLEAN,SR LDMN
JACK GREENE,SR PETR ENGR

OXLEY PETROLEUM CO SEE
CHESAPEAKE ENERGY CORPORATION

OXO ENERGY LLC
PO BOX 196128
DALLAS,TX 75219 PH 318 222-0304
FAX 318 868-9091
JAMES LATHAM,MGR

OXY PETROLEUM INC
SEE OCCIDENTAL PETROLEUM CORPORATION

OXY RESOURCES CALIFORNIA LLC SEE
VINTAGE PRODUCTION CALIFORNIA LLC

OXY USA INC SEE
OCCIDENTAL OIL & GAS CORP

OZ GAS CORPORATION
8765 SPRING CYPRESS RD L-109

SPRING,TX 77379-3194
PH 281 370-5300 FAX 281 444-5497
ROBERT R DITTO,CHRMN
SUSAN HAMM,VP,OPERS

OZARK OIL & GAS INC
109 N 6TH ST
FORT SMITH,AR 72901-2103 PH 501 783-2792
FAX 501 783-0028
ROBIN W CLEGG,PRES
BENNIE B WESTPHAL,CHF EXEC OFCR

P & L ENERGY,LLC
1032 HANOVER CT
KINGSPORT,TN 37660-5839 PH 423 288-3259
FAX 423 288-0230
ALLAN R POOLE II,MNGNG MEMBER
JAMES P LONG,MNGNG MEMBER

P & S PERFORATORS,INC
PO BOX 3215
VICTORIA,TX 77903-3215 PH 361 578-4372
FAX 361 578-4360

P & W INDUSTRIES,LLC (PIPE,SCRAP METAL
PROC,INVESTMENT RECOVERY)
PO BOX 1550,68668 HWY 59
MANDEVILLE,LA 70470-1550 PH 985 892-2461
FAX 985 892-2618 WWW.PANDWINDUSTRIES.COM
LH@PANDWINDUSTRIES.COM
HARRY A WARNER,CEO
GLENN P WARNER,PRES
LUCY HOLSTON,VP,ADMIN
DAVIS GARDNER,EXEC VP
WILDA SHARP,SLS REPR
HERMAN FARRINGTON,SLS REPR

P J PETROLAND,LLP
1317 BOB WHITE LN
KATY,TX 77493-2131
PH 281 639-5566 PJPOOL@PJPETROLAND.NET
PORTER J POOL,CPL
JOANNE POOL,LDMN

P M EXPLORATION INC
4411 SARONG DR
HOUSTON,TX 77096-4426 PH 713 228-4111

P.O.&G OPERATING LLC
5847 SAN FELIPE ST STE 3200
HOUSTON,TX 77057-3187 PH 713 244-0779
FAX 713 244-0650
STEVEN A PFEIFER,PRES
CHRISTOPHER A MOORE,VP/OPERS

P.O.C. OPERATING COMPANY
24 GRAND CANYON DR
NEW ORLEANS,LA 70131
PH 504 393-7382 FAX 504 835-8751
JAMES M WESSEL,PRES

PACHUTA CORP
35 N WYNDEN
HOUSTON,TX 77056 PH 713 626-7972

PACIFIC ENERGY RESOURCES,INC
5851 SAN FELIPE STE 455
HOUSTON,TX 77057
PH 713 529-9394 FAX 713 529-9184
STAFFORD E ANDREWS,PRES

PACIFIC ENTERPRISES ABC CORPORATION SEE
SEMPRA ENERGY PRODUCTION CO

PACIFIC ENTERPRISES OIL COMPANY (USA) SEE
HUNT OIL COMPANY

PACIFIC PROCESS SYSTEMS,INC
WELL TESTING,EQUIPMENT & FIELD SERVICES

11811 NORTH FWY STE 480
HOUSTON,TX 77060 PH 281 999-0558
    JERRY WISE,PRES JERRY@PPS-EQUIPMENT.COM
    ALAN GEORGE,SECY/TREAS
BAKERSFIELD,CA OFFICE - 5055 CALIFORNIA
    AVE STE 220 93309 PH 661 321-9681
VENTURA,CA OFFICE - 2280 N VENTURA AVE
    93001 PH 805 643-8183
COMPTON (LOS ANGELES) CA OFFICE - 2232 E
    GLADWICK ST 90220 PH 310 631-8844
ALVARDO,TX OFFICE - 4701 S I-35 WEST
    76009 PH 817 783-3331
WASHINGTON,PA OFFICE - 841 LYNN PORTAL RD
    15301 PH 724 229-3978

PALA-INTERSTATE,INC
    PO BOX 15949,16347 OLD HAMMOND HWY
    BATON ROUGE,LA 70895-5949
    PH 225 272-5194 FAX 225 272-5239
        INFO@PALAGROUP.COM
        SCOTT BARRENGER,PRES

PALEO CONTROL INC
    PO BOX 41751
    HOUSTON,TX 77241 PH 713 849-0044
        WWW.PALEOCONTROL.COM
        INFO@PALEOCONTROL.COM
        LOYD TUTTLE,PRES,OWNER
        ROBERT D LISKA,PALEO GEOL
        JAMES H THORPE,PALEO GEOL

PALEO DATA
    6619 FLEUR DE LIS DR
    NEW ORLEANS,LA 70124-1429
    PH 504 488-3711 FAX 504 488-6292
        WWW.PALEODATA.COM INFO@PALEODATA.COM
        ARTHUR S WATERMAN,PRES
        NORMAN S VALLETTE,EXEC VP

PALM OPERATING,LLC
    6751 N FEDERAL HWY STE 200
    BOCA RATON,FL 33487 PH 561 391-1100
    FAX 561 391-2801
        DONALD C SIDER,CEO DSIDER@SIDERLAW.COM
    STROUD,OK OFFICE PH 918 968-0574
        MIKE SHIELDS,FLD SUPVSR

PALM PRODUCTION COMPANY
    21 CLANSMOOR CT
    SUGAR LAND,TX 77479-2518 PH 281 980-4083
    FAX 281 980-7951
        STUART G SHARROCK,PRES
            SHARROCK.STUART@GMAIL.COM

PALMER ENERGY COMPANY INC
    241 N SUPERIOR ST
    TOLEDO,OH 43604
    PH 419 539-9180 FAX 419 539-9185
        MARK R FRYE,PRES

PALMER JOHN T,OIL & GAS PRODUCER
    401 EDWARDS ST STE 1400
    SHREVEPORT,LA 71101 PH 318 222-0517
    FAX 318 424-3256 WWW.PALMERPETRO.COM
    JPALMER@PALMERPETRO.COM

PALMER PETROLEUM
    PO BOX 324
    FISHERS,IN 46038-0324 PH 616 781-8672
    W C PALMER,OWNER

PALMER PETROLEUM INC
    401 EDWARDS ST STE 1400
    SHREVEPORT,LA 71101-3143
    PH 318 222-0517 FAX 318 424-3256

WWW.PALMERPETRO.COM
PPI@PALMERPETRO.COM
JOHN T PALMER,CHRMN OF BD
WILLIAM R DOWNS,PRES
RICHARD W PALMER,VP
LAURA SPEIR,CONTROLLER
GEORGE WHITTINGTON,LDMN
RONNIE MADOLE,OPERS MGR
JOHN PALMER,EXPL MGR
GREG ZERRAHN,SR GEOL
MIKE ROBERTS,GEOPHY

PALMETTO RESOURCES INC SEE
    PALM PRODUCTION CO

PALOMA RESOURCES,LLC
    1021 MAIN ST FL 10
    HOUSTON,TX 77002-6517 PH 713 650-8500
        CHARLES T MCCORD III,PRTNR
        JOHN V WHITING,PRTNR
        CHRIS N O'SULLIVAN,PRTNR

PALOMINO ENERGY LP
    PO BOX 700826
    SAN ANTONIO,TX 78270-0826 PH 210 316-2320
    FAX 210 497-2615
        H L BLOMQUIST III,G.P.

PAN ENERGY CO,INC
    7301 MILESTRIP RD
    ORCHARD PARK,NY 14127-1410
    PH 716 662-5439 FAX 716 662-2518
        GIORGIO PANNELLA,PRES

PAN MUTUAL ROYALTIES INC SEE
    HERITAGE ROYALTIES,INC

PAN-OK PRODUCTION CO,INC
    119 RIDGEWAY DR STE B3
    LAFAYETTE,LA 70503-3431 PH 337 989-8119
    FAX 337 989-2773
        KURT CARLETON,PRES

PANENERGY FIELD SERVICES,INC SEE
    DUKE ENERGY FIELD SERVICES,INC

PANENERGY NATURAL GAS CORPORATION SEE
    DUKE ENERGY NATURAL GAS CORPORATION

PANGAEA LAND SERVICES
    1901 LONG PRAIRIE RD STE 200
    FLOWER MOUND,TX 75022 PH 214 503-9932
        INFO@PANGAEALAND.COM
        JOHN PETROPOULOS

PANHANDLE EASTERN CORPORATION SEE
    PANENERGY FIELD SERVICES,INC

PANHANDLE PRODUCERS & ROYALTY OWNERS ASSN
    3131 BELL ST STE 209
    AMARILLO,TX 79106-5030
    PH 806 352-5637 FAX 806 359-1274
        PPROA@PPROA.ORG WWW.PPROA.ORG
        - OFFICERS -
        DOUG FISK,PRES - VALPOINT ENERGY,LLC
        PAUL A CLARK,PAST PRES-PAC PRODUCTION CO
        GREG GRAHAM,VP - KISMET PROPERTIES,INC
        STACEY LADD,VP - WBD OIL & GAS INC
        DOUG SAUNDERS,SECY - TAYLOR/HERRING CO
        JEFFERY A MCCARN,TREAS-BROWN & FORTUNATO
        - EXECUTIVE COMMITTEE -
        DON CAMERON - CISCO ENERGY LLC
        WILLIAM M SMITH - WM SMITH ENERGY LLC
        GENE GALLEGOS - UNIT TEXAS DRILLING LLC
        THOMAS G LADD - LADDEX,LTD
        TODD LOVETT - MEWBOURNE OIL CO
        PRESTON BOYD - VALERO ENERGY

JERROD IMEL-TOP O'TEXAS OILFIELD SERV,LTD
ETHAN D HOUSE - ENERGYNET.COM
W JEFF CHESNUT - CORLENA OIL COMPANY
        - STAFF -
        H WAYNE HUGHES,EXEC VP
        SHERRI ELKINS,OFC MGR

PANTALEO A J & ASSOC,INC
    134 NICKERSON PKWY
    LAFAYETTE,LA 70501-6510 PH 318 232-4478
        A J PANTALEO,PRES
        E S PANTALEO,SECY/TREAS

PANTHER OIL CO
    600 S TYLER LB 12081
    AMARILLO,TX 79101 PH 806 374-2052
        TOM J WHITTENBURG,PRES

PANTHER PIPELINE LLC
    16000 STUEBNER AIRLINE STE 420
    SPRING,TX 77375 PH 832 552-3600
        WWW.PANTHERPIPELINE.COM
        DENNIS NOVOSAD,SR VP-BUS DEV
            DENNIS.NOVOSAD@PANTHERCOMPANIES.COM

PAPCO,INC
    PO BOX 627
    WARREN,PA 16265-0627 PH 409 296-2213
    FAX 409 296-2253
        JON A PETERSEN,PRES
        DARRYL E PIERCE,PE,SECY
        DANIEL PIERCE,VP/GULF COAST

PAR CO DRILLING INC
    PO BOX 873,144 PROVIDENCE RD
    NATCHEZ,MS 39121-0873 PH 601 442-6421
    FAX 601 442-0421
        DEBORAH PARKS,PRES,SECY/TREAS

PAR MINERALS CORP
    509 MARKET ST STE 300
    SHREVEPORT,LA 71101-3251
    PH 318 221-6156 FAX 318 221-6188
        WINDELL PHILLIPS,PRES
        DARRELL GARRETT,VP LAND
        CARRIE COLLINS,LAND
        RICHARD PHILLIPS,GEOL
        MATT WHITEHEAD,EXPL MGR
        BOB SHARP,GEOL
        JIM RIZER,PROD ENGR
        KAREN DALE,ACCT
        SONYA BAKER,PROD REV ACCT MGR
            SBAKER@PARMINERALS.COM
        SHEILA DAVIS,ACCT
        MICHELLE WALDROP,ACCT

PARAGON OIL CO,INC
    PO BOX 885
    MOUNT VERNON,IL 62864-0018
    PH 618 244-5541

PARDEE MINERALS LLC
    3350 HIGHWAY 6 #427
    SUGAR LAND,TX 77478-4524
    PH 281 494-8098 FAX 281 494-8099
        WILLIAM D JAMES,SR VP
            BILL.JAMES@PARDEE.COM

PARHAM JAMES W (OIL & GAS OPERATOR)
    PO BOX 803
    MAGNOLIA,AR 71754-0803
    PH 870 234-4008 FAX 870 234-7202

PARHAM V S,LEASES,ROYALTIES & PROD
    P O BOX 803,MCALESTER BLDG
    MAGNOLIA,AR 71753

PH 870 234-4008 FAX 870 234-7202

PARKER & PARSLEY PETROLEUM CO SEE
   PIONEER NATURAL RESOURCES COMPANY

PARKER DRILLING COMPANY
   5 GREENWAY PLAZA STE 100
   HOUSTON,TX 77046 PH 281 406-2000
   FAX 281 406-2001 WWW.PARKERDRILLING.COM
      ROBERT L PARKER JR,CHRMN
      DAVID C MANNON,PRES & CEO
      W KIRK BRASSFIELD,SR VP & CFO
      RICHARD BAJENSKI,DIR,INVESTOR RELS
      ROSE MALTBY,PUB RELS MGR
      DAVID MCCANN,DIR,BUS DEV
   NEW IBERIA,LA OFFICE - 1110 UNIFAB RD
      70560 PH 800 264-7678 FAX 337 364-3152
      TOBY BEGNAUD,US SLS MGR PH 337 373-6249
      KENT GERDSEN,US SLS MGR PH 337 373-6393
   ANCHORAGE,AK OFFICE - 1420 E TUDOR RD
      99507 PH 907 339-4010
      BOBI AKERS,SR ADMIN ASST

      - INTERNATIONAL -
   THE NETHERLANDS OFFICE -
   2266 KA LEIDSCHENDAM,VLIETWEG 17V

      - CIS/EURASIA/AFRICA/MIDDLE EAST -
   ALMATY,KAZAKHSTAN,CIS OFFICE - 32A MANAS
      ST,SAT BUSINESS CENTER,OFC 402,050008
      ANDRE KOZYREV,BUS DEV MGR

   BOGOTA,COLUMBIA OFFICE - CALLE 100
      NO.19-54,OFICINA 904 PH +57-1-635-2800
      JUAN J CAMACHO,REG CONTRACTS MGR
   SINGAPORE OFFICE - 152 BEACH RD,#18-07/08
      GATEWAY EAST,189721 PH +65-6751-5050
      ORLANDO ALFONSO,BUS DEV MGR

PARKER HANNIFIN CORP
   6035 PARKLAND BLVD
   CLEVELAND,OH 44124 PH 216 896-3000
   FAX 216 896-4000 WWW.PARKER.COM
   HOUSTON,TX OFFICE - 15102 SOMMERMEYER ST
      77041 PH 713 937-8900 FAX 713 937-0438

PARKER TOOL INC
      OIL & GAS FISHING TOOL RENTAL
   PO BOX 1468
   GRAHAM,TX 76450 PH 940 521-0915
   FAX 940 549-8770
      JAMES PARKER,PRES
      GARY EGELHOFF,VP/OWNER
         GARYEGELHOFF@HOTMAIL.COM

PARKER USA DRILLING COMPANY
   1110 UNIFAB RD
   NEW IBERIA,LA 70560-9641 PH 337 364-3122

PARKS A J,GEOL
   152 VIDOR LN
   SHREVEPORT,LA 71105-3561 PH 318 221-1911

PARMAC LLC
   PO BOX 1149,12TH & OAK
   COFFEYVILLE,KS 67337-0917 PH 620 251-5000
   FAX 620 251-0225 WWW.PARMACBRAKE.COM
      DERRICK MORRIS,PRES
         DMORRIS@PARMACBRAKE.COM
      STEVE BRASCHLER,CHF ENGR
      GREG DOTY,INQUIRIES & ORDERS
   OKLAHOMA CITY,OK OFFICE - PH 405 634-1417
   ODESSA,TX OFFICE - PH 432 332-6433

HOUSTON,TX OFFICE - PH 713 956-7400

PARRISH W F,JR,OIL & GAS OPERATIONS
   10 W MAIN STE 211
   ARDMORE,OK 73401-6515
   PH 580 223-2988 FAX 580 223-2988
      W F PARRISH JR,OPER
      DANNY SIKES,FIELD SUPR

PARTEN OPERATING INC
   211 HIGHLAND CROSS DR STE 100
   HOUSTON,TX 77073-1700 PH 281 874-2101
   FAX 281 874-2107
      JOHN R PARTEN,PRES

PASADENA OIL & GAS CORP
   PO BOX 148
   TRAVERSE CITY,MI 49685-0148
   PH 231 929-1500 FAX 231 929-1502
      THEODORE H STEGMAN,PRES
      BRAD L GELBAUGH,SECY/TREAS

PATE GEORGE S
   P O BOX 2977
   MONROE,LA 71207-2977 PH 318 655-9005

PATRICK ENERGY GROUP
   6660 S SHERIDAN RD STE 250
   TULSA,OK 74133 PH 918 477-7755
   FAX 918 491-6680
      MARK PATRICK,PRES
   JACKSON,MI OFFICE - PO BOX 747,49204-0747
      PH 517 787-6633 FAX 517 787-6630
      U E PATRICK,CHRMN

PATRICK OPERATING COMPANY
   PO BOX 66802,2110 LEXINGTON
   HOUSTON,TX 77266 PH 713 526-8919
   FAX 713 526-9108 GMR3@PEOPLEPC.COM
      G M ROWE III,PRES

PATRICK PETROLEUM LLC SEE
   PATRICK ENERGY GROUP

PATRICK PRODUCTION COMPANY
   PO BOX 66802
   HOUSTON,TX 77006-6802 PH 713 526-8919
   FAX 713 526-9108
      G M ROWE JR,PRES
      G M ROWE III,VP

PATRIOT EXPLORATION LLC
   15 VALLEY DR STE 19
   GREENWICH,CT 06831-5205 PH 713 800-5700
   FAX 713 800-5710
      JACK BAYLESS,VP
         JBAYLESS@PATRIOTEXPLORATION.COM

PATTCO INC,SEE
   GREAT EASTERN ENERGY & DEVELOPMENT CORP

PATTEN PRODUCING CO
   PO BOX 10
   MILLERSBURG,OH 44654-0010 PH 330 674-3046
   FAX 330 674-3248
      KIMBERLY MATHIE,PRES

PATTERSON ENERGY INC
   PO BOX 635
   MADISONVILLE,LA 70447-0635
   PH 985 892 9227 FAX 985 892-5628
      EARL W PAT PATTERSON,PRES
         PH 985 373-4192

PATTERSON REAL ESTATE AGENCY,INC
   6712 W MAIN ST
   HOUMA,LA 70360 PH 504 868-5230

PATTERSON TUBULAR SERVICES
   2828 TECHNOLOGY FOREST BLVD

THE WOODLANDS,TX 77381-3907
   PH 281 452-5443 FAX 832 295-4555
   PH 800 452-5443
CHANNELVIEW,TX OFFICE - PO BOX 117
   539 S SHELDON RD, 77530 PH 281 452-5443
   PH 800 452-5443 FAX 281 452-3293
MORGAN CITY,LA OFFICE - PO BOX 939
   7056 S RAILROAD AVE 70381 PH 985 384-3166
   PH 800 352-5913 FAX 985 384-8943

PATTERSON-UTI DRILLING COMPANY LLC
   PO BOX 1416,4510 LAMESA HWY
   SNYDER,TX 79550-1416 PH 325 574-6300
   FAX 325 574-6390 PATENERGY.COM
      CLOYCE A TALBOTT,CEO,PRES
      JOHN VOLLMER,III,CFO
   MIDLAND,TX OFFICE - 9915 INDUSTRIAL AVE
      79703 PH 432 561-9382 FAX 432 561-9388
   MIDLAND,TX OFFICE - 410 N LORAINE
      79701 PH 432 682-9401
   BRIDGEPORT,TX OFFICE - PO BOX 128
      76426 PH 940 683-5106
   SAN ANGELO,TX OFFICE - 4105 S CHADBOURNE
      76903 PH 325 651-6603
   LEVELLAND,TX OFFICE - 1950 AVE S
      79336 PH 806 894-5478 FAX 806 894-5430
   TYLER,TX OFFICE - 11940 CONSTANTINE AVE
      75708 PH 903 877-3659
      RAY MULLICAN,AREA MGR
      DAVID MELTON,CONTRACT MGR
   CORPUS CHRISTI,TX OFFICE - PO BOX 9699
      78406 PH 361 299-0040
   HOUSTON,TX OFFICE - 654 N SAM HOUSTON PKY
      EAST,77060 PH 281 591-1381
   LA GRANGE,TX OFFICE - PO DRAWER 629
      78945-0629 PH 979 242-5143
   VICTORIA,TX OFFICE - 4906 E HOUSTON HWY
      77901 PH 361 576-6896
   OKLAHOMA CITY,OK OFFICE - 6000 SW 44TH ST
      73179-8002 PH 405 686-0006
      FAX 405 686-0150
   WOODWARD,OK OFFICE - PO BOX 1027
      73801 PH 580 256-5064
   DUNCAN,OK OFFICE - RT 4,BOX 50B
      73533 PH 580 470-9001
   DENVER,CO OFFICE - 1512 LARIMER ST
      #730 PH 303 542-1900 FAX 303 542-1903
   GILCREST,CO OFFICE - 19370 US HWY 85
      80623 PH 970 737-9061 FAX 970 737-9057
   VERNAL,UT OFFICE - 1120 E 1500 SOUTH
      84078 PH 435 789-7856
   WILLISTON,ND OFFICE - 14126-B HWY 2 WEST
      58802 PH 701 572-4060 FAX 701 572-4062
   HOBBS,NM OFFICE - PO BOX 1860,88241
      901 W MARLAND,88240 PH 575 397-3511
      FAX 575 397-3516
   AZTEC,NM OFFICE - 328 CR 350,87410
      PH 505 334-8361 FAX 505 334-8426
   CASPER,WY OFFICE - 5981 POISON SPIDER RD
      82644 PH 307 472-0181

PATTERSON, J A & ASSOCIATES
   3538 HIGHWAY 282
   VAN BUREN,AR 72956-8728 PH 479 782-0694
      JUANITA L PATTERSON,EXEC VP
         NPATTERSON42542@YAHOO.COM

PATTILLO BILL,PETR ENGR
   PO BOX 580552

HOUSTON,TX 77258-0552
PH 281 333-3749 FAX 281 333-3749

PATTON CAMILLE COCKE
1502 AUGUSTA STE 250
HOUSTON,TX 77057 PH 713 784-3755

PATTON GRIER P
1502 AUGUSTA STE 250
HOUSTON,TX 77057 PH 713 784-3755

PATTON OIL CO SEE
GREAT EASTERN ENERGY & DEVELOPMENT CORP

PAUL DOROTHEA BAKER
1507 LOMA VISTA ST
PASADENA,CA 91104
PH 626 791-5606

PAWNEE OIL & GAS,INC
PO BOX 831253
RICHARDSON,TX 75083-1253 PH 972 234-8801
FAX 972 234-8830
JAMES A HAYDEN II,PRES

PAWNEE OIL CORP
PO BOX 1425,435 W WASHINGTON ST
SPRINGFIELD,IL 62705-1425 PH 217 522-2407
FAX 217 522-8785
FRANK VALA,DIR,PRES
LESTER E COLLINS,CHRMN OF BD,VP
ROSALIE MCDERMOTT,SECY/TREAS
LINDA VALA,DIR
LINDA POTTER,DIR
STEWART LANG,GEOL
WILBUR LADSON,CENTRAL IL MGR

PAYNE JOHNSTON
801 FIRST PL
TYLER,TX 75702-5745
PH 903 592-4369 FAX 903 592-4360

PAYNE M J RESOURCES LP
100 E FERGUSON ST STE 801
TYLER,TX 75702-5745 PH 903 592-4369

PAYNE WILLIAM R BILL ,GEOL
PO BOX 1170
CORPUS CHRISTI,TX 78403-1170
PH 361 991-5310

PAYNE-JOHNSTON MANAGEMENT,INC
801 1ST PL
TYLER,TX 75702-5745
PH 903 592-4369 FAX 903 592-4360

PC LTD SEE
BRECK OPERATING CORP

PDC RECYCLING
3128 WALTON BLVD
ROCHESTER HILLS,MI 48309
PH 866 887-3270 CONTACT@PDCRECYCLING.COM
MATT SPENCER

PEABODY A L
1124 LOWER WOODVILLE RD
NATCHEZ,MS 39120 PH 601 445-5101

PEACOCK ELWIN M,INC
1108 RIVER GLYN DR
HOUSTON,TX 77063-1517 PH 713 827-1818
ELWIN M PEACOCK,PRES

PEACOCK OIL & GAS PROPERTIES,LTD
8585 PEACOCK WAY
SAN ANTONIO,TX 78217 PH 210 824-1471
FAX 210 824-7776 WWW.PEACOCKOILANDGAS.COM
JOE R PEACOCK
JOE R PEACOCK,JR
DEBORAH J HEWETT

PEAK ENERGY SERVICES
SEE NABORS INDUSTRIES LTD

PEAK ENERGY,LLC
3639 AMBASSADOR CAFFERY PKWY STE 201
LAFAYETTE,LA 70503-5200
PH 337 988-6050 FAX 337 988-1090
JAMES D COLLIER,PRES
EARL P CHAMPAGNE,VP
CHRIS FONTANA,GEOL
MARY J ONEBANE,OFC MGR
PAUL THARP,GEOPHY

PEAK OILFIELD SERVICES COMPANY SEE
NABORS INDUSTRIES LTD

PEAK USA ENERGY SERVICES,LTD
515 W GREENS RD STE 1170
HOUSTON,TX 77067-4541 PH 281 872-7325

PEARL BILL H PRODUCTION INC
11005 TIMBERGROVE LN
CORPUS CHRISTI,TX 78410-2517
PH 361 241-4033 FAX 361 241-4552
MARK PEARL,PRES
DIANE M PEARL,VP

PEARL EXPLORATION INC
1314 MADISON ST
ALICE,TX 78332-3744 PH 361 664-2605
ROBERT E PEARL,PRES
BILL H PEARL,VP

PEC
SAFELAND/SAFEGULF ACCREDITING ORG
233 GENERAL PATTON AVE
MANDEVILLE,LA 70471 PH 214 549-6925
ELIZABETH HALEY ELIZABETH@PECSAFETY.COM

PEC MINERALS LP
16400 DALLAS PKWY STE 400
DALLAS,TX 75248
PH 214 522-9131 FAX 972 934-2310
WWW.PROVIDENCE-ENERGY.COM
MICHAEL ALLEN,PRES
MALLEN@PROVIDENCE-ENERGY.COM
CLARK HELLIER,EXPL MGR
ANN HALLAM,LAND MGR PH 972 392-6124
AHALLAM@PROVIDENCE-ENERGY.COM
COLLIN MAY,LDMN-OK PH 972 392-6154
CMAY@PROVIDENCE-ENERGY.COM

PECORARO ROGER P,CPL
PO BOX 1564
MANDEVILLE,LA 70470-1564 PH 504 914-9511
FAX 985 727-9511 RPP01@BELLSOUTH.NET

PEDEN JOHN A,CPL
PO BOX 68,200 W MAIN STE B
VAN,TX 75790-0068 PH 903 963-7326
PH 903 963-8851 FAX 903 963-5097
JPCPL@AOL.COM
ANDY PEDEN,LDMN

PEDEN LAND & MINERALS
OIL & GAS LEASING,TITLES & CURATIVE
PO BOX 68,200 W MAIN
VAN,TX 75790
PH 903 963-7326 FAX 903 963-5097
JPCPL@AOL.COM
JOHN A PEDEN,CPL
ANDY PEDEN,LDMN
KEVIN REED,LDMN
DEBBIE CARTER,LDMN

PEDERNALES ENERGY,LLC
6363 WOODWAY DR STE 560

HOUSTON,TX 77057-1757
PH 713 782-1311 FAX 713 785-9415
N JOSEPH JOE BAILEY,OWNER
GEORGE GEE V KANE III,OWNER
MIKE LUNCEFORD,VP,OPERS & ENGRG
MLUNCEFORD@PEDERNALESENERGY.COM
CAROLYN HOWREN,OFC MGR
CHOWREN@PEDERNALESENERGY.COM
RICHARD SMITH,VP,GEOSCIENCE
CLAY BROLLIER,GEO-TECH

PEDERNALES PRODUCTION,LP
6363 WOODWAY DR STE 560
HOUSTON,TX 77057-1757
PH 713 782-1311 FAX 713 785-9415
N JOSEPH JOE BAILEY,OWNER
GEORGE GEE V KANE III,OWNER
MIKE LUNCEFORD,VP,OPERS & ENGRG
MLUNCEFORD@PEDERNALESENERGY.COM
RICHARD SMITH,VP,GEOSCIENCE
CLAY BROLLIER,GEO-TECH
CAROLYN HOWREN,OFC MGR
CHOWREN@PEDERNALESENERGY.COM

PEGASI OPERATING INC
PO BOX 2033
TYLER,TX 75710-2033
PH 903 595-4139 FAX 903 595-0344
WWW.PEGASIENERGY.COM
MIKE H NEUFELD,CEO
W L SUDDERTH,VP
BILLY DENMAN,LAND MGR
LORA BLACK,COMPTROLLER
JONATHAN WALDRON,CFO

PEGASUS CEMENTERS INC
PO BOX 17925,17 BITTERBLUE LN
SAN ANTONIO,TX 78217-7925
PH 210 824-5957 PEGASUSCEMENT@AOL.COM
TOM M GOUGER,III

PEL-TEX OIL COMPANY,LLC
520 POST OAK BLVD STE 475
HOUSTON,TX 77027
PH 713 439-1530 FAX 713 439-1023
EARL P BURKE JR,CHRMN/CEO
GLENN P BURKE,PRES
BRIAN D BURKE,VP

PELICAN ENERGY,LLC
PO BOX 9
OCEAN SPRINGS,MS 39566 PH 228 324-2245
W B DICKERSON JR,MGR WBDJR@BELLSOUTH.NET

PELICAN OIL & GAS,INC
2424 EDENBORN AVE STE 610
METAIRIE,LA 70001-6473
PH 504 523-4071
ROY E LASSUS JR,PRES
MARSHALL J VINET,VP
PETER U SCHLEGEL,V P

PELICAN PETROLEUM SERVICES LLC
P O BOX 52861
SHREVEPORT,LA 71135 PH 318 286-4740
GEORGE A THARPE,VP LAND
GTHARPE@PELICANPETRO.COM

PELICAN RESERVE PIPELINE CO
7412 SHADYVILLA LN
HOUSTON,TX 77055-5116 PH 713 680-3600

PELL ROBERT W & ASSOCIATES,INC
COMPLETE LAND SERVICES
5506 PAGEWOOD LN

HOUSTON,TX 77056-7231 PH 713 898-9632
ROBERT W PELL,PRES RWPELL@AOL.COM
JANET M PELL,BUS MGR

PELLEGRINI THOMAS L
1776 WOODSTEAD CT STE 105
THE WOODLANDS,TX 77380-3401
PH 281 367-7004

PELLERIN MILNOR CORP
PO BOX 400
KENNER,LA 70063-0400
PH 504 467-9591 FAX 504 468-3094
WWW.MILNOR.COM
MILNORINFO@MILNOR.COM

PELTO OIL COMPANY SEE
ENERGY DEVELOPMENT CORPORATION

PEMS PETROLEUM CONSULTANTS,INC
1364 CUTTER COVE
SLIDELL,LA 70458 PH 601 799-1466
PHIL HEBERT,PRES,CONSLT
SYBIL HEBERT,VP

PENCOR DIV OF CORE LABORATORIES LP
5820 HWY 90 E
BROUSSARD,LA 70518 PH 337 839-9060
PH 800 234-4205 FAX 337 839-9070
CHARLES.HURLEY@CORELAB.COM
WWW.CORELAB.COM
CHARLES HURLEY,GEN MGR
DWAYNE HYMEL,OPERS MGR
TED SANDOZ,FLD SVCS MGR
WILLIAM TODDY GUIDRY,TECH MGR

PENDRAGON PRODUCTION COMPANY
PO BOX 271668
HOUSTON,TX 77277-1668 PH 713 669-9810
PATRICK W ARTHUR,PRES
KELLY LEE,SECY

PENICK,MARTIN LAND SERVICES
MINERAL TITLE RESRCH,FORESTRY/LAND SVCS
PO BOX 631180
NACOGDOCHES,TX 75963-1180
PH 936 559-3504 MARTINPENICK@GMAIL.COM

PENKOTA WIRELINE SEE
PIONEER ENERGY SERVICES

PENN VIRGINIA OIL & GAS CORPORATION
840 GESSNER RD STE 800
HOUSTON,TX 77024
PH 724 743-6640 FAX 724 743-1101
WWW.PENNVIRGINIA.COM
H BAIRD WHITEHEAD,PRES
MICHAEL E STAMPER,VP,REG MGR

PENN VIRGINIA OIL & GAS,L.P.
840 GESSNER RD STE 800
HOUSTON,TX 77024-4147
PH 713 722-6500 FAX 713 722-6600
WWW.PENNVIRGINIA.COM
MIKE MOONEY,VP,GULF COAST
DIANE KERR,EXPL MGR
ED JOHNSON,VP LAND

PENN VIRGINIA RESOURCE PARTNERS,LP (PVR)
3 RADNOR CORP CTR STE 301
100 MATSONFORD RD
RADNOR,PA 19087-4545 PH 610 975-8200
FAX 610 975-8201 WWW.PVRESOURCE.COM
WILLIAM H SHEA JR,DIR & PRES & CEO OF
PVR'S GEN PRTNR
BRUCE D DAVIS JR,EXEC VP & GEN COUNSEL OF
PVR'S GEN PRTNR

ROBERT B WALLACE,EXEC VP & CFO OF PVR'S
GEN PRTNR
KEITH D HORTON,EXEC VP & COO OF PVR'S
GEN PRTNR (COAL)
MARK D CASADAY,EXEC VP & COO OF PVR'S
GEN PRTNR - MIDSTREAM (MARCELLUS & MID
CONT AREA)

PENNCO ENERGY,INC
PO BOX 1083,2237 S ACADIAN THRUWAY
BATON ROUGE,LA 70821-1083 PH 225 383-3412

PENNECO OIL COMPANY,INC
6608 RT 22
DELMONT,PA 15626 PH 724 468-8232
FAX 724 468-8230 WWW.PENNECO.COM
PENNECO@PENNECO.COM
TERRENCE S JACOBS,PRES

PENNINGTON INC
LEASING,RIGHT-OF-WAY,SEISMIC,TITLE
156 LAKEVIEW CIR
CROCKETT,TX 75835 PH 936 544-4126
PH 936 546-1088 FAX 936 545-2616
J RICHARD (RIC) PENNINGTON,PRES
RPEN75835@YAHOO.COM

PENNINGTON OIL COMPANY
PO BOX 1083,2237 S ACADIAN THRUWAY #601
BATON ROUGE,LA 70821-1083 PH 225 383-3412
FAX 225 381-0128
PENNINGTON@PENNINGTONOIL.COM

PENNSYLVANIA GENERAL ENERGY COMPANY,LLC
120 MARKET ST
WARREN,PA 16365 PH 814 723-3230
FAX 814 723-3502
THOMAS H HENRY,CHRMN
DOUGLAS E KUNTZ,PRES,CEO

PENNSYLVANIA TITLE AND ABSTRACT CO INC
PO BOX 148
EMPORIUM,PA 15834-0148 PH 814 486-3046
FAX 814 486-0464
DAVID J REED,PRES
DAVID WHEDDBIE,LDMN
GINI MCDERMOTT,LDMN
RICHARD LINDHOME,LEGAL COUNSEL

PENNTEX RESOURCES LP SEE
SNOWMASS ENERGY PARTNERS LTD

PENROC OIL CORPORATION
PO BOX 2769
HOBBS,NM 88241-2769 PH 505 397-3596
M Y MERCHANT,PRES
S WATSON,SECY/TREAS

PENSCO
411 WALL ST
LAFAYETTE,LA 70506-3029 PH 318 233-9914
FAX 318 233-9916
PETER A HOPPE JR,CIVIL ENGR
ALLEN L MARTIN,CIVIL ENGR,LAND SURV
AL REAUX,CIVIL ENGR,LAND SURV
PAT LANDRY,CIVIL ENGR
KEITH BERGERON,CIVIL ENGR
DAVID BOURQUE,CIVIL ENGR
MARK L SAVOY,CIVIL ENGR
MARTIN T POIRRIER,EIT
KEN FONTENOT,LAND SURV
JOHN MILLER,LAND SURV
RODNEY THERIOT,PARTY CHF
RICKY RICHARD,PARTY CHF
EMERY LEGER,PARTY CHF

MIKE BOURQUE,PARTY CHF
CHARLENE BLANCHARD,SECY

PENTA RESOURCES,INC.
PO BOX 51874, 233 LA RUE FRANCE
LAFAYETTE,LA 70505 PH 337 237-4842
PH 337 237-4842 FAX 337 237-4847
JIM DIEHL DIEHLLAND@AOL.COM

PENTAGON PETROLEUM,INC
842 MAIN ST
BATON ROUGE,LA 70802-5528 PH 225 343-2323
FAX 225 343-2341 LSHACK@PENTAGONOIL.COM
LARRY SCIACCHETANO,CHRMN

PENTERRA SERVICES,LLC
PETROLEUM LAND SERVICES
PO BOX 82285
LAFAYETTE,LA 70598 PH 337 706-8650
DAVID DAUTERIVE,PRTNR,LDMN
DDAUTERIVE@PENTERRASERVICES.COM
MARK W LIPARI,PRTNR,LDMN
MLIPARI@PENTERRASERVICES.COM

PEP DRILLING COMPANY
PO BOX 024,123 S 10TH ST
MOUNT VERNON,IL 62864-0017
PH 618 242-2205 FAX 618 242-0812
PURSIE E PIPES,OWNER

PEPPARD & ASSOCIATES SEE
GEOMAP COMPANY

PERCHERON
1904 N GRAND PKWY STE 200
HOUSTON,TX 77449 PH 832 300-6400
WWW.PERCHERONLLC.COM

PERCHERON ENERGY,LLC
PO BOX 840
SIMONTON,TX 77476
PH 281 346-2300 FAX 281 346-2319
PERCHERONLLC.COM
KATHY MILLER,PRES
JEFF TRLICEK,VP

PERKINS OIL & GAS,INC
PO BOX 547
PENNSBORO,WV 26415-0547
PH 304 659-3570 FAX 304 659-3575
CLAY M PERKINS

PERKINS STANLEY L,PETR GEOL,OIL,GAS PROD
PO BOX 781555
SAN ANTONIO,TX 78278 PH 210 415-5795
STANLEY L PERKINS SR,PETR GEOL
SPERKINSAG@HOTMAIL.COM
SAN ANTONIO,TX DISTRICT OFFICE - 1800 NE
LOOP 410 STE 305,78217 PH 210 828-3889
FAX 210 821-3795
STANLEY L PERKINS JR,PETR GEOL
STANPERKINS@SBCGLOBAL.NET
CREEDE,CO DISTRICT OFFICE - PO BOX 492
81130 PH 719 658-0320 FAX 719 658-0320

PERKINS SUPPLY
OILFIELD & INDUSTRIAL SUPPLIES
2966 NORTHWEST TURNPIKE
PENNSBORO,WV 26415-9603
PH 304 659-3570 FAX 304 659-3575
DERYL PERKINS,VP
GREG POWERS,STORE MGR

PERMIAN BASIN INTERNATIONAL OIL SHOW
5030 E UNIVERSITY BLVD STE A104
ODESSA,TX 79762-8145 PH 432 367-1112
FAX 432 367-1113 WWW.PBIOILSHOW.ORG

ANTHONY FRY,EXEC DIR
ANTHONYFRY@PBIOILSHOW.ORG

PERMIAN OPERATING LIMITED PARTNERSHIP SEE
SCURLOCK PERMIAN LLC

PERRET P C AND ASSOCIATES SEE
VANGUARD GEOSCIENCE LLC

PERRET PAUL C,CONSULTING GEOL
5800 BANCROFT DR
NEW ORLEANS,LA 70122
PH 504 583-9521
PAULPAROTSR@AOL.COM

PERRITT & VICKERS,INC
PO BOX 457,371 HWY 82 E
MAGNOLIA,AR 71753-0457 PH 870 234-6020
FAX 870 234-1831
SAMMY T CRABTREE,PRES
BILLY T VICKERS,VP

PERRY & PERRY INC SEE
LANDSMITH PETROLEUM RESOURCES,INC

PERRY D R JR,PETR ENGR
PO BOX 20584
HOUSTON,TX 77225-0584 PH 713 669-0715
D RAYMOND PERRY,JR,PETR ENGR

PERRY THOMAS M,JR,GEOL
120 S BROADWAY AVE STE 108
TYLER,TX 75702-7232 PH 903 597-9432

PERRYMAN OPERATING INC
100 E CORSICANA ST #202
ATHENS,TX 75751-2567 PH 214 675-5633
KRISTIN L PERRYMAN,MNGNG DIR
W C CHIP PERRYMAN III,MNGNG DIR

PERRYMAN WYNNE F,IND PETR LDMN
1415 S VOSS RD STE 110
HOUSTON,TX 77057 PH 713 623-0038
FAX 713 623-4525

PERSUN MARK D,ESQ
158 E MAIN ST
SOMERSET,PA 15501-2006 PH 814 445-4021
FAX 814 445-4944 WWW.MARKPERSUNLAW.COM
MARK D PERSUN,ATTY MDPERSUN@VERIZON.NET

PERU HUNT OIL DEVELOPMENT COMPANY SEE
HUNT OIL COMPANY

PESCADORES ENERGY SERVICES,LLC
PO BOX 131116
TYLER,TX 75713 PH 903 530-0959
FAX 281 254-7948 LAND.LEASES@YAHOO.COM
WWW.PESCADORESENERGYSERVICES.COM
RONALD THOMPSON,PRES
THOMAS THOMPSON,CEO
ANNE BARLOW,CFO
FRED NIXON,VP SUPPLY & LOGISTICS
BENNY MILLER,VP OPERS

PETCO LIMITED SEE
BRECK OPERATING CORP

PETCO PETROLEUM CORP
108 E OGDEN AVE
HINSDALE,IL 60521-3572 PH 630 654-2282
FAX 630 325-5170 WWW.PETCOPETROLEUM.COM
J D BERGMAN,PRES

PETCOM SEE
PETROLEUM CORP OF MISSISSIPPI

PETER PAUL PETROLEUM COMPANY
1221 MCKINNEY ST STE 3700
HOUSTON,TX 77010-2010 PH 713 209-1100
FAX 713 209-1104 WWW.PPP-CO.COM
B P HUDDLESTON,PE,CHRMN

PETER D HUDDLESTON,PE,PRES
FLORA M HUDDLESTON,SECY/TREAS
GLENDA DOLE,CPA,CFO
PETER CURRIE,SR VP
GREGORY S MITSCHKE,PE,SR VP OPERS
WM PAUL HUDDLESTON,VP
KELLY J HALL,SR LAND MGR
MELTON SMITH,OPERS MGR
GORDON D LOOMIS,CPL
RAY MECHE,IT
REBECCA TRISTAN,OPERS ASST
SANDRA CORNELIUS,LAND ASST
LESLIE LAFON,OPERS ASST
MARY MICAK,ACCT
MARCUS W DIOSDADO,ACCT
KIMBERLY GAIENNIE,ACCT
SAMANTHA RIGGS,ACCT
YVETTE M BRYANT,ACCT
DEBRA MORENO,ACCT
DARLA SMITH,ACCT
KRISTIN D AVALOS,ADMIN ASST

PETERS & ASSOC,INC
DBA/ BACHRACH & WOOD
2821 HARVARD AVE
METAIRIE,LA 70006 PH 504 454-0001
FAX 504 454-2257 WWW.BACHRACH-USA.COM
BACHRACH@BACHRACH-USA.COM
A C PETERS,CEO
JAMES BAILEY,PRES

PETRO ENERGY GROUP
OIL & GAS CONSULTANTS
PO BOX 691485
HOUSTON,TX 77269-1485 PH 281 890-1818
FAX 866 557-7471 WWW.PEG-US.COM
LISA BARFIELD LBARFIELD@PEG-US.COM

PETRO EVALUATION SERVICES,INC
3927 CLEVELAND RD
WOOSTER,OH 44691-1223
PH 330 264-4454 FAX 330 345-6617
JAY G HENTHORNE JR,PRES
STEVE FRANKS,SUPT OF OPERS

PETRO GUARDIAN
LIGHTNING,STATIC & ELECTRICAL PROTECTION
29089 KRENTEL RD
LACOMBE,LA 70445 PH 504 915-1914
BENJAMIN HEARST
BHEARST@PETROGUARDIAN.COM

PETRO LAND SERVICES,INC
169 VIDOR LN
SHREVEPORT,LA 71105 PH 318 861-0317
FAX 318 670-8512
GEORGE P MORAN,CPL,PRES,TREAS
GMORAN08@COMCAST.NET

PETRO PLEX OIL CO INC
6299 W LIBERTY LANE
HOMOSASSA,FL 34448 PH 352-804-1396
ARLEN JUMPER,PRES
LINDA MATTHEWS,PUMPER

PETRO ROYAL LLC
3388 WINTHROP CT
MOBILE,AL 36695 PH 251 605-1307
FAX 251 471-2875
J F KILBORN JR,LAND MGR

PETRO VEST,INC
14 GREENWAY PLZ UNIT 16P
HOUSTON,TX 77046-1424 PH 713 626-0303

FAX 713 626-0480
D L MCCLURE,PRES
DL.MCCLURE@PETROVEST.US
M T MCCLURE,VP
MIKE.MCCLURE@PETROVEST.US

PETRO-BEST RESOURCES LTD,OIL GAS EXPL DEV
PO BOX 1446
JACKSON,MS 39215-1446 PH 601 354-4200
HOBOY70@AOL.COM

PETRO-DRIVE INC,OILFIELD CONSTRUCTION
200 S BERNARD RD
BROUSSARD,LA 70518-7034 PH 318 837-1181
LOCATED 510 LAFLAMME,BROUSSARD,LA 70518
FAX 318 837-1181 318 837-9915
CHARLES R MILAM,PRES
BENNY MANUEL,GEN MGR
THOMAS W MAUTNER,VP,FIN
PAUL ADAMS,OPERS MGR
MACQUELINE THIBEAUX,EXEC SECY
JILL LOUVIERE,CONTROLLER
WANDA TRAHAN,OFC MGR
ED HEBERT,SALES
MIKE KENNEY,SALES
ROBERT HUTCHINSON,INSIDE SALES
JULIUS MILLER,SALES
HOUSTON,TX OFFICE - 908 TOWN & COUNTRY
BLVD STE 232,77024 PH 713 932-6671
FAX 713 932-6773
RANDY HARTLEY,HOUSTON AREA SALES
- OPERATIONS-BOCO -
GORDON ROMERO,GEN MGR
KEITH SIMON,SALES
MITCH REED,SALES

PETRO-DYNAMICS INC,SUB OF PETRO-DRIVE INC
PILE & HAMMER ANALYSIS,ENGRG,CONS,DESIGN
200 S BERNARD RD
BROUSSARD,LA 70518-7034 PH 318 837-1181
RONNIE ARCENEAUX,VP,OPERS

PETRO-EQUIPMENT,INC
WIRELINE TRUCKS & SUPPLIES
PO BOX 2309
BUCKHANNON,WV 26201-2309 PH 304 472-8753
FAX 304 472-0829
W P BURR,PRES

PETRO-GUARD CO,INC
2450 FONDREN RD STE 105
HOUSTON,TX 77063 PH 713 974-5550
DEWEY A STRINGER,III,PRES
MARK STRINGER,VP
WANDA KOVAR,COMPTROLLER

PETRO-HUNT,LLC
ROSEWOOD COURT
2101 CEDAR SPRINGS RD STE 600
DALLAS,TX 75201 PH 214 880-8400
FAX 214 880-7101 WWW.PETRO-HUNT.COM
BRUCE W HUNT,PRES
DOUGLAS H HUNT,VP ACQS & DIVESTITURES
TOM E NELSON,VP FIN
BOBBY DONOHUE,VP LAND
TOMMY MOFFETT,VP ENGRG
MARSHALL T HUNT,DIR CORP DEV
JAMES MASON,TREAS
DALE HOSTENSKE,EXPL MGR
LIZ LUTHANS,CRUDE OIL MARKETING
FRED HOSEY,GEN COUNSEL/OIL & GAS
RUBY STAR,CONTROLLER

WALTER P ROACH,VP HR
DAVID CLARK,SAFETY & ENVIRON DIR
CORPUS CHRISTI,TX PRODUCTION OFFICE -
710 BUFFALO ST STE 301,78401
PH 361 887-2111 FAX 361 887-1804
DARRELL KEENER,DIST CLERK
BISMARCK,ND LAND OFFICE - 400 E BROADWAY
STE 414,58501-4072
PH 701 258-1557 FAX 701 258-1562
JEFF HERMAN,DIST MGR
KILLDEER,ND GAS PLANT OFFICE - 813 123RD
AVE SW,58640 PH 701 863-6500
FAX 701 863-6999
RODNEY KROGH,PLANT MGR
KILLDEER,ND PRODUCTION OFFICE - 390 119TH
AVE SW 58640 PH 701 863-6622
FAX 701 863-6620
ELVIS ENTZEL,DIST MGR
MIKE ENDRUD,PROD MGR
BRANDON,MS GAS PLANT OFFICE -
- PURSUE ENERGY CORPORATION -
2173 SHELL OIL RD 39042
PH 601 845-2252 FAX 601 845-4218
SUMMERFIELD,LA PRODUCTION OFFICE -
5158 HWY 9,71079
PH 318 927-2067 FAX 318 927-3765
TULLOS,LA CENTRAL LA PROD OFFICE -
44 ETHYL ST 71479 PH 318 534-6313
FAX 318 534-6303
DENVER,CO EXPLORATION OFFICE -
600 17TH ST STE 2250S,80202
PH 303 382-1914 FAX 303 295-1059
STEPHEN L BRESSLER,SR GEOL

PETRO-LAND GROUP,INC
120 S COLLEGE
TYLER,TX 75702 PH 903 595-4293
FAX 903 593-8497 WWW.PETROLAND.COM
TERRY W FOWLER,PRES
PHILIP R NOBLES,VP

PETRO-LAND RESOURCES,INC
PO BOX 53712,300 RUE BEAUREGARD STE H
LAFAYETTE,LA 70505-3712
PH 337 265-3948 FAX 337 265-3905
WWW.PETROLAND-SOUTHERNFIELD.COM
PHILLIP W THOMAS,CPL,PRES
PHIL.THOMAS@PETRO-LAND.COM

PETRO-PRO,LLC
PO BOX 5098,103 MILLCREEK CORNERS STE A
BRANDON,MS 39047-5098 PH 601 919-3600
PH 800 880-0680 FAX 601 919-3999
DLAMBERT@PETROPROLLC.COM
DONNIE W LAMBERT,OWNER,MGR

PETRO-QUEST OIL & GAS,LP
PO BOX 294151
KERRVILLE,TX 78029-4151
PH 830 895-5755 FAX 830 895-1837
MARK HOFFMANN
MIKE STEPPE

PETRO-STEEL INC,SUB OF PETRO-DRIVE INC
PIPE,STEEL,TUBULAR
200 S BERNARD RD
BROUSSARD,LA 70518-7034 PH 318 837-1181
BONI SUIRE,VP
ELMER SAVOIE,OPERS MGR
ED HEBERT,INSIDE SLS

PETRO-VENTURES,INC
201 RUE IBERVILLE STE 500
LAFAYETTE,LA 70508-3295 PH 337 289-6676
FAX 337 289-6678
WALTER B SONNY COMEAUX III,PRES/CEO

PETROBRAS AMERICA,INC
10350 RICHMOND AVE STE 1400
HOUSTON,TX 77042
PH 713 808-2000 FAX 713 808-2017
HOUSTON,TX BRANCH OFFICE - 2101 CITY WEST
BLVD BLDG 3 STE 200,77042
PH 713 808-3000 FAX 713 808-2007
ALBERTO GUIMARAES,PRES
JOAO CARLOS FIGUEIRA,SR VP UPSTREAM
VALDISON MOREIRA,SR VP DOWNSTREAM
GUSTAVO BARBOSA,ACCT/FIN MGR
HEBER RESENDE,CORP SUPPORT MGR
SERGIO BARON,TRADING MGR
MICHAEL DITCHFIELD,PLNG/PERFORMANCE &
NEW BUS MGR
RUI FONSECA,HEALTH,SAFETY & ENVIRO MGR
JORGE LUIS BRAGA,PROCUREMENT MGR
PAULO DE TARSO GUIMARAES,EXPL MGR
CHERYL SAHA,LAND MGR
FARID SHECAIRA,DEV & PROD MGR
MAURICIO PESTANA,TECH SVRS MGR
CESAR PALAGI,WALKER RIDGE PROD ASSETS MGR
FERNANDO BARROS,DOWNSTREAM ENGRG &
CONSTRUCTION MGR
GIAMPAOLO DONATO,REFINING MGR

PETROCASA ENERGY
1901 LONG PRAIRIE RD STE 200
FLOWER MOUND,TX 75022 PH 214 503-9932
INFO@PETROCASA.COM
JOHN PETROPOULOS

PETROCHEM ENGINEERING SERVICES,INC
PO BOX 1340
MINDEN,LA 71058-1340 PH 318 221-1225
RALPH L HOCK,PRES
LARRY L HOCK,VP

PETROCHEM OPERATING CO
PO BOX 670
MINDEN,LA 71058-0670 PH 318 221-1225
LARRY L HOCK,PRES
F BRUCE HOCK,VP
PHYLLIS POWELL,LAND DEPT MGR
LISA HOCK,PROD & ACCT SECY

PETROCORP INCORPORATED SEE
UNIT PETROLEUM COMPANY

PETROFINA DELAWARE,INCORPORATED SEE
TOTALFINAELF E&P USA,INC

PETROHAWK ENERGY CORPORATION
1360 POST OAK BLVD STE 150
HOUSTON,TX 77056
PH 832 204-2700 FAX 832 204-2800
TULSA, OK OFFICE - 6100 S YALE AVE
STE 500, 74136
PH 918 488-8283 FAX 918 488-8182

PETROHILL RESOURCES,LLC
3343 LOCKE AVE STE 103
FORT WORTH,TX 76107-5702 PH 817 877-0341
FAX 817 877-0177
MICHAEL WALTRIP,MGR
MARGERY HANNA,MGR

PETROHOOD CORPORATION
PO BOX 1592

RUSTON,LA 71273-1592 PH 318 251-2720
FAX 318 251-2030 JOHN@HOODCOMPANIES.NET
JOHN M HOOD,PRES,CEO
SETH HOOD,VP,COO
MATT WOODARD,SECY,TREAS,CFO
RENE DAVIDSON,OFC MGR

PETROL ENERGY CORPORATION SEE
SCOTT ROYCE ARNOLD

PETROLEASE TEXAS
PO BOX 325
YANTIS,TX 75497-0325
PH 903 383-3239 PETROLEASE@GMAIL.COM
PHIL SARTIN,JR,CPL
KAY SARTIN,LDMN

PETROLERO,LLC
PO BOX 112843
CARROLLTON,TX 75011 PH 214 274-3039
FAX 214 739-4458 WWW.PETROLEROLLC.COM
ED GONZALES,PRES ED.G@PETROLEROLLC.COM

PETROLEUM ADVISORS INTL,INC
PO BOX 19945
HOUSTON,TX 77224-1945
PH 713 821-0062 FAX 713 821-0063
M C ZEID,PRES,CEO

PETROLEUM CLUB OF SHREVEPORT
416 TRAVIS ST STE 1500
SHREVEPORT,LA 71101-5506 PH 318 425-4251
FAX 318 425-1431
KORLIS CROOK,GEN MGR

PETROLEUM CORPORATION OF MISSISSIPPI
P O BOX 16893
JACKSON,MS 39236-6893 PH 601 981-7200
D PRESTON REEVES,PRES

PETROLEUM CORPORATION OF TEXAS,SEE
BRECK OPERATING CORP

PETROLEUM DEVELOPMENT COMPANY
401 S BOSTON AVE STE 1850
TULSA,OK 74103-4060
PH 918 583-7434 FAX 918 583-7451
WM DENNIS INGRAM,PRES
VIRGINIA INGRAM,SPEC PROJ
SHERI JONES,ACCT

PETROLEUM DISCOVERY SYSTEMS,INC
PO BOX 670386
DALLAS,TX 75367-0386 PH 972 484-3400
FAX 972 484-3420 JCHADSELL@SBCGLOBAL.NET
JAMES C HADSELL,PRES,CEO

PETROLEUM ENGINEERS INC
A SIERRA HAMILTON COMPANY
500 DOVER BLVD STE 310
LAFAYETTE,LA 70503 PH 337 984-2603
FAX 337 984-0854 WWW.SIERRA-HAMILTON.COM
AL BELLAIRE JR
MAHLON LEBLANC
HOUSTON,TX OFFICE - 777 POST OAK BLVD
STE 400,77056 PH 713 956-0956
JAMES STODDARD,CFO

PETROLEUM EXPLORATION INC
PO BOX 14145
JACKSON,MS 39236-4145 PH 601 940-5711
LOUNETTE WILLIAMS-MAXWELL,PRES

PETROLEUM FUNDING CORPORATION
1 VILLAGE GREEN CIR
CHARLOTTESVILLE,VA 22903-4619
PH 804 296-5158
THOMAS W GILLIAM JR,PRES

PETROLEUM INFORMATION/DWIGHTS LLC SEE
IHS

PETROLEUM INVESTMENTS INC
416 TRAVIS ST STE 612
SHREVEPORT,LA 71101-5502 PH 318 221-6143
FAX 318 221-6186 CVINC@BELLSOUTH.NET
CAMILLE C DESPOT,PRES
KATINA RIOS,OFC MGR

PETROLEUM LABS INC
333 E KALISTE SALOOM RD
LAFAYETTE,LA 70508-3240 PH 318 234-7414
JACK L VOINCHE,CHEM
HOUMA,LA OFFICE - PH 504 868-4820

PETROLEUM LAND ACQUISITIONS & MINERAL
TITLE SERVICES,LLC
2800 YOUREE DR STE 462
SHREVEPORT,LA 71104 PH 318 347-3457
HEIDI A LEE,OWNER HALEE62@GMAIL.COM

PETROLEUM LAND SERVICES
PO BOX 1263
GULFPORT,MS 39502
PH 251 610-1501 GCOOP@FRONTIERNET.NET
GREGORY COOPER

PETROLEUM LAND SERVICES LLC
A COMPLETE LAND SERVICE COMPANY
PO BOX 10506
CONWAY,AR 72034-0506 PH 479 461-6456
SHANNON L TAYLOR
SHANNON.TAYLOR@GMAIL.COM

PETROLEUM LANDMEN SERVICES
PO BOX 1152
FAYETTEVILLE,AR 72702-1152
PH 501 521-7008 FAX 501 521-4946
PAT GAZZOLA

PETROLEUM MATERIAL SERVICE
LOUISIANA OIL & GAS RESEARCH
PO BOX 5257
BATON ROUGE,LA 70821
PH 225 802-1211 FAX 225 753-4861
DARLENE TIGER TURPIN,CHRMN
TIGERTURPIN1@COX.NET
CLARE HANEY,PRES

PETROLEUM PIPE LINE & STORAGE CO
PO BOX 789
WILSON,WY 83014-0789 PH 214 597-6693
W F BRIDEWELL JR,SECY-TREAS

PETROLEUM PRODUCTION ENGINEERING
PO BOX 1401
FULTON,TX 78358 PH 361 205-4318
ALLEN ROSS,OWNER AROSSS60@GMAIL.COM

PETROLEUM PRODUCTION MANAGEMENT,INC SEE
GMX RESOURCES INC

PETROLEUM PROPERTIES CO,INC
BOX 737
FLORENCE,MS 39073-0737 PH 601 845-7349
FAX 601 845-6799
DAVID RINGER,PRES

PETROLEUM RESERVE CORPORATION,OIL PROD
1720 KENDARBREN DR
JAMISON,PA 18929
PH 215 918-0870
RICK STAEDTLER,PRES

PETROLEUM RESOURCE FIELD SERVICE CO
PO BOX 3002
LAREDO,TX 78044-3002 PH 956 725-5182
FAX 956 725-0113 PRFSC@ATT.NET

JESSE E HINES,CPL,SOLE PROPRIETOR

PETROLEUM RESOURCE MANAGEMENT COMPANY
AN OIL & GAS OPERATING COMPANY
733 HIGHGROVE PARK
HOUSTON,TX 77024-3698
PH 713 956-4148 FAX 713 957-8119
T R WEDDLE,PRES
GWYNNE DIEPHUIS,CORP SECY

PETROLEUM RESOURCES COMPANY,LLC
8148 CASTLE COVE RD
INDIANAPOLIS,IN 46256-4638
PH 317 409-4105
JOLINDA J ROBERTS,MGR

PETROLEUM RESOURCES MANAGEMENT CORP
3639 AMBASSADOR CAFFERY PKWY STE 201
LAFAYETTE,LA 70503-5200
PH 337 988-6050 FAX 337 988-1090
JAMES D COLLIER,PRES
EARL P CHAMPAGNE,VP
CHRIS FONTANA,GEOL
MARY J ONEBANE,OFC MGR
PAUL THARP,GEOPHY

PETROLEUM SERVICE PARTNERS,INC
FULL SVC GAS & OIL WELL OPER CO
1460 N OLD 119 HWY
INDIANA,PA 15701-7337
PH 724 349-1515 FAX 724 349-1542
CHARLES R BROWN,PRES

PETROLEUM TECHNOLOGIES INC
801 W 47TH ST STE 412
KANSAS CITY,MO 64112-1253
PH 816 531-6904 FAX 816 531-6905
ALAN J SEATON,PRES,EXPL MGR
CELINA SANCHEZ,CONTROLLER
RICK SINGLETON,WESTERN KS OPERS MGR
JERID HOEHN,EASTERN KS OPERS MGR

PETROLEUM UNLIMITED INC
3015 BAINBRIDGE CT
SUGAR LAND,TX 77478-4032 PH 281 242-6161
B J JOHNSON,PRES

PETROMAC HOLDINGS,LLC
1901 REGAL ROW
DALLAS,TX 75235 PH 214 912-4245
KYLE D MCAFEE KYLE@PETROMACHOLDINGS.COM

PETRON INDUSTRIES,INC
OPERATIONS/RENTAL/SERVICE
7701 W LITTLE YORK RD STE 800
HOUSTON,TX 77040-5493 PH 713 693-8700
FAX 713 464-4507 PETRON@PETRONWORLD.COM
WWW.PETRONWORLD.COM
JIM HORNUNG,REG SLS MGR
MARION H WINSETT,INSTRUMENTATION SLS
MARK PRUITT,SPEC PROJ DIR
HOUSTON,TX OPERATIONS OFFICE - 5921
THOMAS RD,77041 PH 713 937-7982
FAX 713 937-8845
JAMES LOZANO,OPERS MGR
LAFAYETTE,LA SALES & OPERS OFFICE - 5007
US HWY 90,BROUSSARD,LA 70518
PH 337 839-0058 FAX 337 839-0174
TIM VIATOR,SLS MGR
ALICE,TX OFFICE - 121A COMMERCE RD
78332 PH 361 668-0321 FAX 361 668-9039
DARRELL PRICHARD,SLS MGR

PETROPORT,INC (PTRO)
801 TRAVIS ST STE 2100

HOUSTON,TX 77002-5705 PH 713 568-4725
FAX 713 227-7626 WWW.BLUE-DOLPHIN.COM
IVAR SIEM,CHRMN,CEO,PRES
T SCOTT HOWARD,VP,TREAS,SECY

PETROQUEST ENERGY,LLC
PO BOX 51205,400 E KALISTE SALOOM #6000
LAFAYETTE,LA 70505-1205 PH 337 232-7028
FAX 337 232-0044 WWW.PETROQUEST.COM
CHARLES T GOODSON,CHRMN/CEO/PRES
ART M MIXON III,EXEC VP/OPERS & PROD
DANIEL G FOURNERAT SR,EXEC VP/
GEN COUNSEL/CAO/SECY
STEPHEN H GREEN,SR VP/EXPL
DALTON F SMITH III,SR VP/BUS DEV
W TODD ZEHNDER,COO
J BOND CLEMENT,EXEC VP/CFO/TREAS
ROBERT LEMAIRE,PROD SUPT
JOHN G STUART,SR OPERS MGR
ANGELLE PERRET,CONTROLLER
TERRY BROUSSARD,SR PROD ENGR
RENE' LEDET,RESERVOIR ENGR MGR
THOMAS MAKO,SR RESERVOIR ENGR
RICH DAVIS,PROD MGR/GULF COAST
THOMAS M BARRY,LAND MGR/GULF COAST REG
PETER GULOTTA JR,LAND MGR/OFFSHORE
BRYAN MARTINY,GEN MGR/LAND
NEVILLE CROWSON,S LA GEOSCIENCE MGR
PATRICK LANDRY,SR GEOL
NATASHA TRAHAN,GEOL
KEVIN JORDAN,SCOUT/GEO TECH
HOUSTON,TX OFFICE - 450 GEARS RD,STE 330
PARAGON ONE BLDG,77067 PH 713 784-8300
FAX 713 784-8327
MARK K STOVER,EXEC VP/CORP DEV
JAMES BLAIR,VP/BUS DEV
MARK H PARROT,SR GEOPHY
CELINE CAITHAMER,SR GEOL
TULSA,OK OFFICE - 1717 S BOULDER,STE 201
74119 PH 918 561-5627 FAX 918 582-2778
MARK CASTELL,MGR/OKLA ASSETS
TONY CERVI,LAND MGR/OKLA ASSETS
PH 918 344-2122
JIM VILBERT,SR GEOPHY/OKLA

PETROSOURCE,INC
PO BOX 5098,103 MILLCREEK CORNERS STE A
BRANDON,MS 39047-5098 PH 601 919-3600
FAX 601 919-3999 DLAMBERT@PETROPROLLC.COM
DONNIE W LAMBERT,OWNER,MGR

PETROSPECT OIL & GAS CORPORATION
1201 LOUISIANA ST STE 3350
HOUSTON,TX 77002-5686 PH 713 658-9167
FAX 713 658-0715
W E RUSS,PRES,GEOL

PETROTEX ENGINEER CO
11600 JONES RD STE 108
HOUSTON,TX 77070-5916 PH 281 517-0065
FAX 281 517-0660

PETROX,INC
10005 ELLSWORTH RD
STREETSBORO,OH 44241-1608 PH 330 757-3303
BENJAMIN W CART,PRES,OWNER
MARK G DEPEW,VP,OWNER

PETSEC ENERGY INC
301 E KALISTE SALOOM RD STE 300
LAFAYETTE,LA 70503 PH 337 989-1942
FAX 337 989-7271 WWW.PETSEC.COM.AU

ROSS KEOGH,PRES
HOUSTON,TX OFFICE - 1201 LOUISIANA
STE 520,77002 PH 713 457-5800
FAX 713 457-5838 WWW.PETSEC.COM
RON KRENZKE,VP

PETTIGREW & PETTIGREW LAND SERVICES
2441 HIGH TIMBERS STE 300
THE WOODLANDS,TX 77380 PH 281 465-0276
WWW.PANDPLANDSERVICE.COM
CATHALEEN D PETTIGREW
CATHALEEN@PANDPLANDSERVICE.COM
CHRIS PETTIGREW
CHRIS@PANDPLANDSERVICE.COM

PETTIT INTERNATIONAL
PO BOX 29237
SAN ANTONIO,TX 78229-0237 PH 210 325-4279
FAX 210 520-2013 BOBPETTIT@STIC.NET
ROBERT Y PETTIT,OWNER

PETTIT ROBERT C,INDEPENDENT OIL PRODUCER
PO BOX 51426
LAFAYETTE,LA 70505-1426 PH 337 234-5107
ROBERT C PETTIT,OWNER
MICHEL E MIKE PETTIT,GEOL

PETTY RAY GEOPHYSICAL,DIV GEOSOURCE INC
SEE HALLIBURTON GEOPHYSICAL SERVICES,INC

PEVETO & ASSOC INC
OIL & GAS LEASES,ROYALTIES
100 E FERGUSON ST STE 909
TYLER,TX 75702-5753 PH 903 592-3081
PH 903 520-4744 FAX 903 592-7996
RSPEVETO@SUDDENLINKMAIL.COM

PEX PETROLEUM CO
P O BOX 1227,207 S COMMERCE ST
NATCHEZ,MS 39121-1227 PH 601 442-3591
STEPHEN B FORMAN
PAUL H BYRNE,JR

PFIESTER SAM,OIL OPR
PO BOX 688
GEORGETOWN,TX 78627-0688 PH 512 818-0728

PFM,LLC
5959 WEST LOOP S STE 202
BELLAIRE,TX 77401-2403 PH 713 839-9010
WWW.PFMLAND.COM INFO@PFMLAND.COM
ROBERT D PORTMAN,CPL

PG&E GAS TRANSMISSION TECO,INC SEE
EL PASO PIPELINE GROUP

PG&E GAS TRANSMISSION,TEXAS CORP SEE
EL PASO PIPELINE GROUP

PG&E HYDROCARBONS COMPANY SEE
EL PASO PIPELINE GROUP

PG&E TEXAS ENERGY COMPANY SEE
EL PASO PIPELINE GROUP

PG&E TEXAS GAS STORAGE COMPANY SEE
EL PASO PIPELINE GROUP

PG&E TEXAS MANAGEMENT COMPANY SEE
EL PASO PIPELINE GROUP

PG&E TEXAS NATURAL GAS COMPANY SEE
EL PASO PIPELINE GROUP

PG&E TEXAS PIPELINE COMPANY SEE
EL PASO PIPELINE GROUP

PGP HOLDINGS 1,LLC
104 TOWN PARK DR
KENNESAW,GA 30144 PH 770 590-1000
PGPLAND@GASAUTHORITY.COM
A J FERRARO

PHARAOH & ASSOCIATES,INC
PO BOX 2127
HOUSTON,TX 77252-2127 PH 713 828-4157
FAX 713 520-7347
LOCATED 3 MILES E-290,GIDDINGS,TX
FARID PHARAON-PRES,OWNER

PHAROS CORPORATION SEE
HDR/PHAROS ONE COMPANY

PHELAN INVESTMENTS
1277 CALDER ST
BEAUMONT,TX 77701-1704 PH 409 832-0211
WWW.PHELANINVESTMENTS.COM
M A LAN PHELAN,II

PHELPS DUNBAR,LLP
COUNSELORS AT LAW
365 CANAL ST STE 2000
NEW ORLEANS,LA 70130-6534
PH 504 566-1311 FAX 504 568-9130
INFO@PHELPS.COM WWW.PHELPSDUNBAR.COM
GEORGE GILLY,PRTNR

PHELPS GEOSCIENCE LLC
19306 ALLVIEW LN
HOUSTON,TX 77094 PH 281 398-5208
JSFPHELPS@YAHOO.COM

PHIBRO ENERGY USA,INC SEE
BASIS PETROLEUM,INC

PHILCO (SUB OF WORKSTRINGS) SEE
SUPERIOR ENERGY SERVICES

PHILLIBER DIRECTIONAL DRILLING INC
PO BOX 926
YOUNGSVILLE,LA 70952
PH 337 837-2718 FAX 337 837-3195
ROBERT A PHILLIBER,PRES
BARRY PHILLIBER,SHOP MGR
GRANT VIATOR,MWD MGR

PHILLIPS CHEMICAL COMPANY SEE
PHILLIPS PETROLEUM COMPANY

PHILLIPS ENERGY,INC
330 MARSHALL ST STE 300
SHREVEPORT,LA 71101-3016
PH 318 222-1800 FAX 318 424-1257
FRED L PHILLIPS,PRES
COLLIN PHILLIPS,VP
TERESA DEAN,SEC/TREAS/COMPTROLLER
JILL CRAWFORD,LAND MGR

PHILLIPS FRED L,OIL PROD
330 MARSHALL ST STE 300
SHREVEPORT,LA 71101-3016 PH 318 222-1800
FAX 318 424-1257

PHILLIPS JACK E,OIL & GAS PRODUCER
8276 W FORD SPRINGS RD
BENTONVILLE,AR 72712-7526 PH 254 562-5116

PHILLIPS JACK L
PO BOX 1686,700 N MAIN ST STE B
GLADEWATER,TX 75647-1686 PH 903 845-2144
FAX 903 845-8226

PHILLIPS LAND ASSOCIATES,INC
PO BOX 101122
FORT WORTH,TX 76185-1122
PH 817 927-3370 FAX 817 920-1840
PHILLIPSLANDASSOC@GMAIL.COM
BRYCE P PHILLIPS,CPL

PHILLIPS LEE,JR,ESTATE,D/B/A SEE
PHILLIPS,LEE OIL COMPANY

PHILLIPS PETROLEUM COMPANY SEE
CONOCOPHILLIPS COMPANY

PHILLIPS PETROLEUM RESOURCES,LTD SEE
PHILLIPS PETROLEUM COMPANY

PHILLIPS PIPE LINE CO SEE
PHILLIPS PETROLEUM COMPANY

PHILLIPS WM N,CPL
PO BOX 1437
RIDGELAND,MS 39158
PH 601 982-3106 PH 601 953-2723
WM N PHILLIPS, MGR N & M RESOURCES LLC
NUTPHILLIPS@COMCAST.NET

PHILLIPS 66 COMPANY SEE
PHILLIPS PETROLEUM COMPANY

PHILMON OIL AND GAS
11 W MAIN ST
PARIS,AR 72855-3205
PH 501 963-3968 FAX 501 963-3968
DOYLE PHILMON,OWNER

PHOENIX DESIGN
PIPELINE DESIGN
3200 SW FWY STE 2130
HOUSTON,TX 77027 PH 713 208-2856
FAX 713 850-7780
J PAUL MATTESON,MGR

PHOENIX ENERGY INC
PO BOX 668,118 LOWER WOODVILLE RD STE 7
NATCHEZ,MS 39121-0668
PH 601 445-3200 FAX 601 446-8366
PHOENIXENERGYINC@BELLSOUTH.NET
JOSEPH J RING III,PRES

PHOENIX EXPLORATION COMPANY LP
333 CLAY ST STE 2000
HOUSTON,TX 77002 PH 713 756-2400
STEPHEN E HEITZMAN,PRES/CEO
JOHN HARRISON,CFO
JOHN A PARKER,SR VP,EXPL
KEITH O WESTMORELAND,SR VP,OPERS
TIMOTHY S DUNCAN,SR VP,BUS DEV
CARAN CROOKER,CONTROLLER
JAMES B GIBSON,MGR,LAND & BUS DEV
TONY VENDITTI,SR EXPL
DAVID KOSMITIS,SR EXPLORATIONIST
GERHART HUNTER,SR EXPLORATIONIST
MARK STEELE,SR EXPLORATIONIST
LAURA WILLIAMS,EXEC ASST
LWILLIAMS@PHOENIXEXPLORATION.COM

PHOENIX EXPLORATION,INC
3747 PEACHTREE RD NE UNIT 1708
ATLANTA,GA 30319
PH 601 366-1735 PH 601 946-2801
PATJMOORE2@ATT.NET

PHOENIX FUND,INC
8626 TESORO DR STE 801
SAN ANTONIO,TX 78217-6217 PH 210 828-4373
FAX 210 828-4088
CRANDELL ADDINGTON,PRES
WILLIAM R LOCKLEAR,SR PETR ENGR

PHOENIX GAS PIPELINE COMPANY
3200 SOUTHWEST FWY STE 2130
HOUSTON,TX 77027-7525
PH 713 208-2856 FAX 713 850-7780
GREGG BOURLAND,PRES
J PAUL MATTESON,VP

PHOENIX RESOURCE COMPANIES,INC,THE,SEE
APACHE CORPORATION

PHOENIX TECHNOLOGY SERVICES USA INC
1805 BRITTMOORE RD

HOUSTON,TX 77043 PH 713 337-0600
FAX 713 337-0599 WWW.PHXTECH.COM
EDWARD CHIARAMONTE,VP
MIKE KRAJNIK,OPERS MGR
PATT MAY,ACCT MGR
CASPER,WY OFFICE - 1076 N ROBERTSON RD
82604 PH 307 266-0164 FAX 307 472-5346
JIM CAMPBELL,OPERS MGR
TRAVERSE CITY,MI OFFICE - 327-A WELCH CT
49686 PH 231 995-0100 FAX 231 995-0120
PAUL CONTI,OPERS MGR
MARY ANN BLACK,SR DIRECTIONAL COORD

PIC OPERATING,LLC
3639 AMBASSADOR CAFFERY STE 201
LAFAYETTE,LA 70503-5200 PH 337 988-6050
FAX 337 988-1090
JAMES D COLLIER,PRES
EARL P CHAMPAGNE,VP OPERS
CHRIS FONTANA,GEOL
MARY J ONEBANE,OFC MGR
PAUL THARP,GEOPHY
HOUSTON,TX OFFICE - 5300 MEMORIAL DR
STE 610, 77007 PH 713 951-0096
FAX 713 951-0147
ED CHILDERS,VP DRLG

PICKER GERALD L,CONSULTING PETR GEOL
3888 STONEWATER DR
COLUMBUS,OH 43221-5931 PH 614 486-4991

PICKETT OILFIELD,LLC
PO BOX 5048
LIBERTY,TX 77575 PH 936 336-5154
FAX 936 336-3434 WWW.PICKETTOILFIELD.COM
ERNIE W PICKETT,OWNER
SALES@PICKETTOILFIELD.COM

PICKLE OIL & GAS CO INC
PO BOX 129
HANOVERTON,OH 44423-0129 PH 330 223-1074
FAX 330 223-1129
ALFRED S LEVINE,PRES

PIERPONT ENERGY TRUST
2803 GULF TO BAY BLVD STE 424
CLEARWATER,FL 33759
PH 813 287-9594 FAX 813 287-2904
ROBERT ROBINSON,TRUSTEE

PII NORTH AMERICA,INC
7105 BUSINESS PARK DR
HOUSTON,TX 77041-4040 PH 713 849-6300
FAX 713 937-0740 WWW.GEPOWER.COM/PII
CARY BOWMAN,SLS MGR
CARY.BOWMAN@OG.GE.COM

PILKO & ASSOCIATES
700 LOUISIANA STE 4500
HOUSTON,TX 77002 PH 281 875-3700
FAX 281 875-3900 WWW.PILKO.COM
INFO@PILKO.COM

PIN OAK OPERATING COMPANY,LLC
253 N COMMON ST
SHREVEPORT,LA 71101
PH 318 425-8080 FAX 318 425-4888
MAIL@PINOAKOPERATING.COM
JOHN H HYATT JR,MGR

PIN TORQUE
1907 VIDA SHAW RD
NEW IBERIA,LA 70563 PH 337 319-0201
MEREDITH ACKAL MEREDITH.ACKAL@GMAIL.COM

PINE MOUNTAIN OIL AND GAS,INC
A SUBSIDIARY OF RANGE RESOURCES INC
PO BOX 2136
ABINGDON,VA 24212-2136
PH 276 628-9001 FAX 276 628-7246
JERRY H GRANTHAM,VP
PHILIP S HORN,DIST LDMN

PINE TOP,INC
1932 AKRON PENINSULA RD
AKRON,OH 44313-4810 PH 216 929-2492
SAL CRANO,MNGNG PRTNR

PINEBELT ENERGY RESOURCES CORP
1292 BAGDAD CV
GULF BREEZE,FL 32563-3432 PH 850 932-2717
JWFUGATE@BELLSOUTH.NET
JAMES FUGATE,PRES
MIKE NEWSOME,VP

PINKSTON STEVEN D,CPL
PO BOX 954,121 S BROADWAY STE 528
TYLER,TX 75710-0954 PH 903 597-0551
FAX 903 597-2893 SPINK@SWBELL.NET

PINNACLE OPERATING COMPANY,INC
PO BOX 52074
SHREVEPORT,LA 71135
PH 318 868-1695 FAX 318 868-0615
STEPHEN R HERBEL,CEO
JERRY R WEBB,PRES

PINPOINT DRILLING & DIRECTIONAL SERVICES
24900 PITKIN RD STE 180
SPRING,TX 77386 PH 281 466-3580
FAX 281 466-3591 WWW.PINPOINTDRILL.COM
ROBERT J STAYTON,PRES

PIONEER DE COLUMBIA SEE
PIONEER ENERGY SERVICES

PIONEER DRILLING COMPANY SEE
PIONEER ENERGY SERVICES

PIONEER DRILLING SERVICES LTD SEE
PIONEER ENERGY SERVICES

PIONEER ENERGY SERVICES
1250 NE LOOP 410 STE 1000
SAN ANTONIO,TX 78209 PH 210 828-7689
FAX 210 828-8228 WWW.PIONEERES.COM
WM STACY LOCKE,PRES & CEO

- DRILLING SERVICES -

HOUSTON,TX (SALES) OFFICE - 16518
AVENPLACE RD TOMBALL,TX 77377
PH 855 736-1222 PH 281 251-1222
FAX 281 251-2715
JOEL POLLESCHULTZ,DIR TECHINAL SVCS
DENNIS G TEEL,MKTG REPR
DENVER,CO (SALES) OFFICE -1625 17TH ST
STE 306 80202 PH 720 468-1350
WYATT HALLIDAY,DIR OF SLS & MKTNG
SAN ANTONIO,TX OFFICE - 1250 NE LOOP 410
STE 1000 78209 PH 210 828-7689
FAX 210 828-8228
BRIAN L TUCKER,PRES
DONALD G LACOMBE,SR VP MKTG
J BLAINE DAVID,SR VP OPERS
CHRIS PRICE,VP ENGRG
RICH PLAGEMAN,VP HSE
CORPUS CHRISTI,TX (S TEXAS DIV) OFFICE -
PO BOX 2963 78403,334 FLATO RD 78405
PH 361 289-9241 FAX 361 289-9243

PAUL SNELLING,VP/DIV MGR
DENNIS TEEL,MKTG REPR
MIDLAND,TX (W TEXAS DIV) OFFICE - 4401 E
HWY 80 79706 PH 432 684-7360
FAX 432 684-4767
PAUL SNELLING,VP/DIV MGR
CHUCK CLINE,MKTG REPR
WILLISTON,ND (N DAKOTA DIV) OFFICE - PO
BOX 2507 58802,14195 HWY 2 WEST 58801
PH 701 774-2071 FAX 701 774-2075
SKIP LOCKEN,VP/DIV MGR
WYATT HALLIDAY,MKTG REPR
RICES LANDING,PA (APPALACHIA DIV) OFFICE-
1083 N 88 RD 15357 PH 724 592-6707
FAX 724 592-6549
SELDON 'GUS' MILLER,SUPT
JOEL POLLESCHULTZ,DIR TECHNICAL SVCS

- PIONEER DE COLUMBIA DRILLING SVCS -

BOGOTA,D.C. COLUMBIA OFFICE - CALLE 99
NO. 10-19,PISO 6 PH 57 1743 7880
FAX 57 1743 3864
JOSE PEPE PORTERO,GEN MGR
BIBIANA LEON,MKTG REPR

- WELL SERVICING -

EL CAMPO,TX DIVISION OFFICE - PO BOX 1208
2243 FM 1162 77437 PH 979 543-8802
FAX 979 543-8823
JOE FREEMAN,VP
RONNIE HENCERLING,DIST MGR
JR LEWIS,GULF COAST OPERS MGR
ALICE,TX DIVISION OFFICE - PO BOX 948
3198 HWY 44,78332 PH 361 664-4236
FAX 361 664-4517
JR GARCIA,DIST MGR
PALESTINE,TX DIVISION OFFICE -
PO BOX 1404,75802 15195 FM 645 75803
PH 903 538-0150 FAX 903 538-2251
STANLEY FIELDS SR,DIST MGR
KENNEDY,TX DIVISION OFFICE - PO BOX 127
424 HWY 239 78119 PH 830 583-0306
FAX 830 583-0370
JR GARCIA,DIST MGR
BRYAN,TX DIVISION OFFICE - PO BOX 3727
77805,2418 CLARKS LN 77808
PH 979 778-3448 FAX 979 778-3632
MIKE MILLER,DIV MGR
DANIEL HINDES,DIST MGR
LIBERTY,TX DIVISION OFFICE - PO BOX 10267
1751 MIZELL RD 77575 PH 936 334-1592
FAX 936 334-1522
CHIPPER SMITH,DIST MGR
GREENBRIER,AR DIVISION OFFICE -
34 PHILLIPS PLACE DR 72058
PH 501 581-0083 FAX 501 581-0088
TERRY GOWERS,DIST MGR
WILLISTON,ND DIVISION OFFICE -
PO BOX 908 58801,119 WELL ST E 58802
PH 701 572-1020 FAX 701 572-1024
TERRY LYNCH,DIST MGR
NEW IBERIA,LA DIVISION OFFICE -
4606 CURTIS LN 70560 PH 337 364-3989
PH 337 364-3988

MICHAEL MILLER,GEN MGR
LAUREL,MS DIVISION OFFICE -
2306 SUSIE B RUFFIN AVE 39440
PH 601 399-1648 FAX 601 399-1649
TONY WHITE,DIST MGR

- WIRELINE SERVICES -

- GULF COAST DIVISION -
HOUSTON,TX (SALES) OFFICE - 3730 KIRBY DR
STE 1200 77098 PH 713 397-4614
PH 832 260-8140 FAX 713 831-6812
KEITH PORTER,SLS
GEORGE TOMLINSON,SLS
BROUSSARD,LA (SALES) OFC- 1100 A SMEDE RD
70518 PH 337 364-9391 FAX 337 364-9393
CASEY DOMINGUE,DIV MGR
BRYAN,TX OFFICE - 4191 CHARLES AVE 77808
PH 979 778-0680
STEVE SHERMAN,DIV MGR
KENDAL BEASON,SLS
FORT WORTH,TX OFC - 307 W 7TH ST STE 1930
76102 PH 817 529-1995
JEFF BARTULLA,SLS
OKLAHOMA CITY,OK OFFICE-1535 SW 25TH ST
73129 PH 405 601-8755 FAX 405 601-7561
MONTE SCHMIDT,DIST MGR
GRAHAM,TX (OPEN HOLE) OFFICE -
PO BOX 1328,1708 US HWY 380 E
76450 PH 940 549-7914 FAX 940 549-1802
ALVIN CAULDER,DIV MGR
GRAHAM,TX (CASED HOLE) OFFICE -
PO BOX 1328,1708 US HWY 380 E
76450 PH 940 549-7912 FAX 940 549-7913
JOHNATHAN SOUTHERLAND,CASED HOLE FSM
CORPUS CHRISTI,TX OFFICE - 6741 IH 37
ACCESS RD 78409 PH 361 668-1612
RICHARD NATTRASS,DIST MGR
LAREDO,TX OFFICE - PO BOX 1638 78044
104 S AVIATOR RD 78043
PH 956 718-3100 FAX 956 718-3119
EDDIE SANCHEZ,DIST MGR
ROGELIO GONZALES,SLS
ROSHARON,TX OFFICE - 4010 CHANCE LANCE
77583 PH 281 431-2222 FAX 281 431-2239
TIM OGLE,DIST MGR
MIDLAND,TX OFFICE - 13010 HWY 191 79707
PH 432 563-2251 FAX 432 563-2260
FRANK MARQUEZ,DIST MGR
VICTORIA,TX OFFICE - 508 PROFIT DR 77901
PH 361 578-8851 FAX 361 574-1007
TERRY THEIDE,DIST MGR
LAFAYETTE,LA OFFICE - 102 MAGNATE DR
STE 101 70508 PH 337 232-9312
FAX 337 232-9358
KEVIN HEBERT,SLS
GLENN LACOBIE,SLS
BOSSIER CITY,LA OFFICE - 4425 VIKING LOOP
71111 PH 318 742-9114 FAX 318 742-4333
BRIAN HERREN,DIST MGR
HOUMA,LA OFFICE -2134 BAYOU BLUE RD 70364
PH 985 655-5463 FAX 985 655-5465
JIMMY PACHALL,DIST MGR

- NORTHERN ROCKIES DIVISION -
BILLINGS,MT OFFICE - 7069 NIEHENKE AVE

59101 PH 406 652-4400 FAX 406 256-3984
KEVIN HOWIE,DIV MGR
MARK FONDREN,SLS
CASPER,WY OFFICE - 1316 WILLER DR 82604
PH 307 472-6100 FAX 307 472-6107
KEVIN HOWIE,DIV MGR
MARK FONDREN,SLS
RON KIDDER,SLS

- SOUTHERN ROCKIES DIVISION -
DENVER,CO (SALES) OFFICE - 600 17TH ST
STE 2800 S 80202 PH 303 228-9490
WAYNE STOLTZ,SLS
FORT MORGAN,CO OFFICE - PO BOX 1277 12839
I-76 FRONTAGE RD 80701
PH 970 867-5171 FAX 970 867-5323
SCOTT DIZMANG,DIST MGR
JASON TURNER,DIST MGR

- MID-CONTINENT DIVISION -
HAYS,KS OFFICE - 1200 MAIN ST 67601
PH 785 625-3858
BRETT BECKER,SVC MGR
COLBY,KS OFFICE-2165 E HWY 24 67701
PH 785 443-3205
KEVIN LADRIGAN,DIST MGR
LIBERAL,KS OFFICE - 321A SOUTH CLAY ST
67901 PH 620 626-4466 FAX 620 626-4488
DAVID BURNS,DIST MGR

- PENKOTA WIRELINE SERVICES -

WILLISTON,ND OFC - 8508 DERRICK AVE 58801
PH 701 572-1087 FAX 701 572-6798
GARY FISHER,DIV MGR
DAVID KALIL,SLS
DICKINSON,ND OFFICE - 2564 SIMS ST 58601
PH 701 483-7613 FAX 701 483-7615
GARY FISHER,DIV MGR
DAVID KALIL,SLS

- COILED TUBING SERVICES -

CONVERSE,TX OFFICE - 13730 IH-10 E 78109
PH 210 278-5560
BILL BOUZIDEN,SR VP WIRELINE & COILED
TUBING SERVICES
RALPH TOWNSEND,VP WIRELINE SERVICES
ENRIQUE SANCHEZ,VP & BUS MGR
LARRY TIDWELL,VP WIRELINE SVCS SOUTH
GEORGE WEST,TX DIV OFFICE - PO BOX 989
3199 HWY 281 78022 PH 361 449-1405
FAX 361 449-1716
LUKE MENARD,DIST MGR
ARCADIA,LA DIV OFFICE - 198 NORTHGATE DR
71001 PH 318 263-8045 FAX 318 263-8048
PHILLIP ARMOND,DIST MGR
MAURICE,LA DIV OFFICE - 111 W ETIENNE RD
70555 PH 337 892-5900 FAX 337 832-5950
BILL BOUZIDEN,SR VP-COILED TUBING SVCS
LANCE KERN,DIST MGR
JONATHAN BRIGNAC,COILED TUBING SLS MGR
PIONEER ENERGY,LLC
PO BOX 285
SHREVEPORT,LA 71162-0285
PH 318 286-5400 PIONEERENERGY@AOL.COM

PIONEER EXPLORATION COMPANY
15603 KUYKENDAHL STE 200
HOUSTON,TX 77090-3655 PH 281 893-9400
FAX 281 893-7629
YOUNAS CHAUDHARY,PRES
JOHN R GILBERT,VP,LAND,MGR ACQS &
DIVESTMENTS
IJAZ REHMAN,FIN MGR
PIONEER FISHING AND RENTAL SERVICES SEE
PIONEER ENERGY SERVICES
PIONEER NATURAL RESOURCES COMPANY
5205 N O'CONNOR BLVD STE 200
IRVING,TX 75039-3746 PH 972 444-9001
FAX 972 969-3576 WWW.PXD.COM
SCOTT SHEFFIELD,CHRMN,CEO
TIM DOVE,PRES,COO
MARK BERG,EXEC VP-CORPORATE
CHRIS CHEATWOOD,EXEC VP-BUS DEV/
GEOSCIENCE
RICH DEALY,EXEC VP/CFO
BILL HANNES,EXEC VP-SOUTHERN WOLFCAMP
DANNY KELLUM,EXEC VP-PERMIAN OPERS
JOEY HALL,SR VP-SOUTH TEXAS OPERS
MIDLAND,TX OFFICE - PO BOX 3178
79702-3178 PH 432 683-4768
FAX 432 571-5063
PAUL MCDONALD,VP-PERMIAN ASSETS
DENVER,CO OFFICE - 1401 17TH ST STE 1200
80202 PH 303 298-8100 FAX 303 298-7800
TOM SHEFFIELD,VP-ROCKIES ASSETS
PIONEER OIL FIELD SERVICES,LLC
1290 STATE RD 67 N
VINCENNES,IN 47591
PH 812 882-0999 FAX 618 943-5523
WWW.PIONEEROILFIELDSERVICES.ORG
DONALD E JONES JR,PRES
MARK JONES,VP
BRENT JONES,VP OPERS
SONNY MCCULLEY,DRLG SUPT
BRADLEY E MCCULLEY,ASST DRLG SUPT
PIONEER PRODUCTION SERVICES SEE
PIONEER ENERGY SERVICES
PIONEER WELL SERVICES SEE
PIONEER ENERGY SERVICES
PIONEER WIRELINE SERVICES SEE
PIONEER ENERGY SERVICES
PIPELINE COMPANY,THE LLC
500 N SHORELINE BLVD STE 700
CORPUS CHRISTI,TX 78401
PH 361 884-2191 FAX 361 884-4730
GEORGE E TANNER,PRES
PIRA ENERGY GROUP
ENERGY CONSULTING - WORLDWIDE
3 PARK AVE 26TH FLR
NEW YORK,NY 10016-5902 PH 212 686-6808
FAX 212 686-6628 WWW.PIRA.COM
GARY N ROSS,CHF EXEC OFCR
MARK SCHWARTZ,PRES
GREGORY L SHUTTLESWORTH,MNGNG DIR
NATURAL GAS MKTG
ALLAN M STEWART,MNGNG DIR ELECTRICITY
PIRTLE BOBBIE SHERWOOD,OIL PROP SEE
BGSPE ENERGY,LTD
PIRTLE CHARLES R,ATTORNEY
12335 KINGSRIDE #345
HOUSTON,TX 77024-4116

PH 713 986-0419

PIRTLE ROBERT S,IND PROD
P O BOX 1310
TYLER,TX 75710-1310 PH 903 597-2655

PITTMAN WILLIAM G,CONS GEOL
10715 E TIMBERWAGON CIR
THE WOODLANDS,TX 77380 PH 281 367-9994

PITTS OIL COMPANY LLC
4600 GREENVILLE AVE STE 300
DALLAS,TX 75206-5038
PH 214 265-4300 POC_LLC@PITTSOIL.COM
WILLIAM A CUSTARD,CHRMN
W ALLEN CUSTARD III,PRES
DON APELAND,GEN COUNSEL
ALAN ASHLEY,VP GOVT AFFAIRS/ENV
TIM HAUSS,ENGR
GEORGE BANITCH,VP LAND
LYNDA HOFFMAN,DIV ORDER MGR
RON JOHNSON,CFO/EXEC VP
DAVID MARTINEAU,EXPL MGR
BOBBY L COLEMAN,EAST TX EXPL MGR
ADRON TEMPLE,WEST DIV SUPT
RONNIE MARKSBERRY,EAST DIV SUPT

PITZER CARROLL D,GEOL
13726 A LA ENTRADA ST
CORPUS CHRISTI,TX 78418-6059
PH 361 816-8569

PIZZITOLA RESOURCES,INC
4645 SWEETWATER BLVD STE 600
SUGAR LAND,TX 77479 PH 281 494-0007
FAX 281 494-0008 FJPIZZ3@AOL.COM
FRANK J PIZZITOLA III,PRES

PLACID OIL COMPANY
PO BOX 300,110 W 7TH ST
TULSA,OK 74102-0300 PH 918 561-2211
FAX 918 561-4663
DAVID R MARTIN,PRES,CEO
JAMES R NIEHAUS,EXEC VP
TOM L NOWELL,VP,CONTROLLER
BARRY E KELLOGG,VP,GAS MKTG,OPERS SVCS
AYLMER D MCREYNOLDS,VP,SAFETY ENV,HEALTH
KEP P DUCOTE,SR VP EXPL
HOUSTON,TX SOUTHERN REG OFFICE -
PO BOX 27570,5 GREENWAY PLZ
77227-7570 PH 713 840-4100
FAX 713 840-4179
ROBERT W BREWER,VP,SOUTHERN REG
MIDLAND,TX WESTERN REG OFFICE -
PO BOX 50250,6 DESTA DR,79705-0250
PH 432 685-5600 FAX 432 685-5754
DONALD E ROMINE,VP,WESTERN REG
OKLAHOMA CITY,OK MID-CONT REG OFFICE -
PO BOX 26100,14000 QUAIL SPRINGS PKY
73134-2600 PH 405 749-2000
FAX 405 749-2148
JOSEPH H CROSBY,VP,MID-CONT REG

PLACID REFINING COMPANY LLC
2901 WILCREST DR STE 250-CRUDE OIL DEPT
HOUSTON,TX 77042 PH 713 268-8840
FAX 713 268-8806 WWW.PLACIDREFINING.COM
DENNIS CERNOSEK,DIR OF CRUDE OIL &
REFINERY SUPPLY PH 713 268-8840
CHARLIE TEEPELL,MGR,CRUDE OIL & LPG SPLY
PH 713 268-8838

PLAINS EXPLORATION & PRODUCTION CO SEE
FREEPORT-MCMORAN OIL & GAS COMPANY

PLAINS MARKETING,LP
PO BOX 4648,333 CLAY STE 1600
HOUSTON,TX 77210-4648 PH 713 646-4100
FAX 713 646-4378 WWW.PLAINSMARKETING.COM
WWW.PAALP.COM
HARRY N PEFANIS,PRES
BRYAN JOYCE,DIR PH 713 646-4243
STEVE MCCLENATHAN,DIR PH 713 993-5151
ROBERT SANFORD,VP,LEASE SUPPLY
PH 713 646-4627
MARK GORMAN,VP,PAA PH 713 646-4655
SHARON CROWDER,MGR SCHEDULING
PH 713 646-4304
EDWIN WOOD,CRUDE OIL SCHEDULER
PH 713 646-4608
MARV SPINDLE,CRUDE OIL SCHEDULER
PH 713 646-4672
BETH SACHS,CRUDE OIL SCHEDULER
PH 713 646-4133
ALLEN POLACH,CRUDE OIL SCHEDULER
PH 713 646-4451
KEVIN TYLER,CRUDE OIL SCHEDULER
PH 713 646-4607
- SOUTHERN REGION -
JIM MENSAY,SR MKTG REPR PH 713 646-4276
PATRICIA A BANZHOF,SR MKTG REPR
PH 713 646-4298
MICHAEL (MICKEY) MILLER,SR MKTG REPR
PH 713 993-5152
- EASTERN REGION -
FERRIDAY,LA OFFICE - PO BOX 1199,71334
HWY 65-84 E,PH 601 442-3652
PH 318 757-3631 FAX 318 757-3852
LEE MARTIN,SR MKTG REPR
LAFAYETTE,LA OFFICE - 1604 W PINHOOK
STE 207,70508
PH 337 234-7122 FAX 337 234-5695
JERRY BRICE,SR MKTG REPR
JACKSON,MS OFFICE - 571 HIGHWAY 51
STE E,RIDGELAND,MS 39157
STEVENS HOLLISTER,SR MKTG REPR
ROBINSON,IL OFFICE - PO BOX 230
62454 PH 618 544-9558 FAX 618 544-3075
ROBERT E GARD,DIR
- WESTERN REGION -
MIDLAND,TX OFFICE - 10 DESTA DR STE 200 E
79705 PH 432 683-9622 FAX 432 683-0849
JEFF SAGE,SR MKTG REPR
MIKE WELLER,SR MKTG REPR
DOUG NOAH,SR MKTG REPR
MIKE BARTON,SR MKTG REPR
JEFF THOMAS,MKTG REPR
MARK THOMAS,DIR
ABILENE,TX OFFICE - PO BOX 330,79604-0330
PH 325 677-1331 FAX 325 677-1333
JOHN E ESTES,SR MKTG REPR
- NORTHERN REGION -
OKLAHOMA CITY,OK OFFICE - 9400 N
BROADWAY,#700,73114 PH 405 426-6580
FAX 405 475-5098
JAMES ROBERTS,REG DIR
KEN REASNOR,MKTG REPR
WICHITA,KS OFFICE - 7701 E KELLOGG DR
#555,67207
JOE HULLINGS,REG DIR
GEORGE STREEKER,SR MKTG REPR

DALLAS,TX OFFICE - 12700 HILLCREST
STE 158,75230 PH 972 991-7544
FAX 972 991-7547
KEITH D HALLORAN,DIR
DAVID A STELTER,SR MKTG REPR
MIKE WATSON,SR MKTG REPR
KILGORE,TX OFFICE - RR 1 BOX 216,HWY 42
ON FM 1252,75668 PH 903 983-1864
FAX 903 984-5950
KEVIN E WALKER,SR MKTG REPR
SHREVEPORT,LA OFFICE - PH 318 678-9400
FAX 318 678-9401
HARRY KING,SR MKTG REPR
JIM O'BANNON,SR MKTG REPR
SAN ANTONIO,TX OFFICE - 11550 I-10 W,#292
78230 PH 210 699-4055 FAX 210 699-4540
JACK BARTELS,SR MKTG REPR
- ROCKY MOUNTAIN REGION -
DENVER,CO OFFICE - 621 17TH ST STE 825
80293 PH 303 308-9157 FAX 303 308-9483
WALT A TEJAN,SR MKTG REPR
JIMMY GORDON,DIR
TIM GILL,MKTG REPR
JORDAN COLE,MKTG REPR
BAKERSFIELD,CA OFFICE - 6800 DISTRICT
BLVD,93313-2010 PH 661 836-6880
FAX 661 836-6850
TED MCCURDY,SR MKTG REPR
PH 713 993-5151

PLANNING & FORECASTING CONSULTANTS
PO BOX 820228
HOUSTON,TX 77282-0228 PH 281 497-2179
DALE W STEFFES,PRIN & FOUNDER
DALESTEFFES@COMCAST.NET

PLANTS AND GOODWIN,INC
1034 ROUTE 44
SHINGLEHOUSE,PA 16748-9326
PH 814 697-6330 FAX 814 697-7515
WWW.PLANTSGOODWIN.COM
PAUL R PLANTS,PRES
STEPHEN D PLANTS,VP,TREAS
TONYA L PECK,SECY
OFFICES@PLANTSGOODWIN.COM

PLAQUEMINES PARISH GOVERNMENT MINERAL OFC
8056 HWY 23 STE 309
BELLE CHASSE,LA 70037
PH 504 297-5677 FAX 504 297-5696
L V COOLEY IV,SPEC ASST PARISH ATTY
PH 985 445-3292 LV@PPGOV.NET
MARGARET A BONNEVAL,MINERAL LEASE ADMIN
PH 504 297-5677 MBONNEVAL@PPGOV.NET

PLAYA EXPLORATION,INC
PO BOX 789
BLANCO,TX 78606
PH 361 549-8565 PLAYAEXP@MSN.COM
RON MILLER,PRES,GEOL

PLAYA OIL & GAS LP
101 PARK AVE FL 48
NEW YORK,NY 10178-4799 PH 832 533-9655
GARY BEACH GMBEACH@PLAYAOIL.COM

PLEDGER PETROLEUM
606 WASHINGTON ST
NATCHEZ,MS 39120-3527 PH 601 442-9871
FAX 601 442-9871 PLEDGER1@EARTHLINK.NET
TIM G CHESTEEN,VP,EXPL & PROD

PLEDGER ROBERT E,CONS GEOL
1210 TRACE DR
HOUSTON,TX 77077 PH 832 512-0495
RPLEDGER@HOTMAIL.COM

PLOMIS-BRAUN SHARON
PO BOX 5872
SPRINGFIELD,VA 22150 PH 703 671-8933
FAX 703 493-9745 SHARONABRAUN@MSN.COM
SHARON PLOMIS-BRAUN, FED LAND LEASING,
LAND PATENT RESEARCH

PLS INC
1 RIVERWAY STE 2500
HOUSTON,TX 77056-1992 PH 713 650-1212
FAX 713 658-1922 WWW.PLSX.COM

PLS LOGISTICS
9140 HWY 6 N STE 1504
HOUSTON,TX 77095 PH 832 557-0829
ARJEY MORRIS ARJEYMORRIS_82@YAHOO.COM

PLUM CREEK TIMBERLANDS,LP
1 CONCORDS PKWY STE 755
ATLANTA,GA 30328 PH 770 829-6300
FAX 770 730-7272
MARLYN MINOR,NATURAL RESOURCE SPEC
MARLYN.MINOR@PLUMCREEK.COM
SEATTLE,WA OFFICE - 999 THIRD AVE,#430
98104 PH 206 467-3624 FAX 206 467-3786
RUSSELL HAGEN,GEN MGR ENERGY & NAT RES
RUSSELL.HAGEN@PLUMCREEK.COM

PLYMOUTH GAS MARKETING SEE
PLYMOUTH RESOURCES INC

PMI TEXAS,INC
PO BOX 580552
HOUSTON,TX 77258-0552
PH 281 333-3749 FAX 281 333-3749
BILL PATTILLO,PRES

PNP PETROLEUM,I L.P.
21260 GATHERING OAK STE 106
SAN ANTONIO,TX 78260 PH 210 494-9189
PHIL ZACCARIA,PRES
PNPPETROLEUM@YAHOO.COM

POCO OIL CO,OIL OPR
13103 HOLSTON HILLS DR
HOUSTON,TX 77069-2608 PH 281 440-9225
FAX 281 440-9229
ARTHUR L BEAR,PRES

PODOLSKY OIL CO
PO BOX 278,HWY 15 W
FAIRFIELD,IL 62837-0278 PH 618 842-2105
FAX 618 842-3092 PODOCO@MIDWEST.NET
BERNARD PODOLSKY,OWNER
MICHAEL D PODOLSKY,MGR,GEOL
BUD SHERADEN,PROD SUPT
MARGOT YOUNG,BOOKKEEPER
ALISHA LEWIS,ADMIN PROF
STEVEN GUSTISON,GEOL
THERESA BAKER,ADMIN PROF

POE DON PETROLEUM LAND SERVICES
1315 BREEZY BEND DR
KATY,TX 77494-6197 PH 713 468-1108
FAX 713 935-0108
DON POE,PRES,MGR,LAND SERVICES
J M POE,V P,MGR,TITLE RESEARCH
D G POE,GROUP MGR,DUE DILIGENCE

POGO PRODUCING COMPANY SEE
PLAINS EXPLORATION AND PRODUCTION CO

POLAR COMPLETIONS ENGINEERING SEE
WEATHERFORD INTERNATIONAL LTD

POLIS NYLE,LANDMAN
1210 GLOURIE DR
HOUSTON,TX 77055-6716 PH 713 225-6569

POLK ROSS B,CPL,ATTY
PO BOX 16598
HATTIESBURG,MS 39404-6598 PH 601 264-1885
FAX 601 296-0988

POLLACK PRODUCTION CO
PO BOX 336
WEST FRANKFORT,IL 62896-0336
PH 618 932-2111 FAX 618 932-3115
SAMUEL H POLLACK,OWNER
SAMCAT336@YAHOO.COM

POLLEYS G NAN
PO BOX 925
HOUSTON,TX 77001-0925 PH 281 804-1555

POLYMER DYNAMICS INC
11211 NEESHAW DR
HOUSTON,TX 77065 PH 281 894-6382
PH 888 765-9396 WWW.POLYDYN.COM
TRACEY MARQUART,OPERS MGR
TRACEY@POLYDYN.COM PH 702 985-8960

POLYMER SERVICES,LLC
1733 W ROAD
PLAINVILLE,KS 67663-7072 PH 800 625-3791
PH 785 434-2474 FAX 785 434-2476
WWW.POLYMERGEL.COM
RANDY PRATER,OWNER
RANDY@POLYMERGEL.COM
JEREMY MAKINGS,SALES ENGR
DONNA OCHS,OFC MGR

PONDER CHARLES M,DRLG CONS
417 CORONA DR
LAFAYETTE,LA 70503-4726 PH 318 984-9371

PONDER JACQUELINE L,CPL
P O BOX 785
YORKTOWN,TX 78164-0785 PH 713 436-1532
JAMES D PONDER,CPL

PONDEROSA OIL & GAS,LLC
5300 MEMORIAL DR STE 610
HOUSTON,TX 77007 PH 713 951-0096
BEN BARNES,MNGNG MEMBER
BEN@HAWKEYESTRATIGRAPHIC.COM

POOL CALIFORNIA ENERGY SERVICES,INC SEE
POOL WELL SERVICES CO

POOL COMPANY SALT WATER DISPOSALS SEE
NABORS WELL SERVICES

POOL COMPANY SEE
POOL WELL SERVICES CO

POOL COMPANY TEXAS LTD SEE
NABORS WELL SERVICES

POOL WELL SERVICES CO SEE
NABORS WELL SERVICES

POOL WYLMER C
PO BOX 4220
NEW ORLEANS,LA 70178-4220 PH 504 831-1500

POPEJOY RODNEY D,OIL LEASES
4949 GREENBRIAR DR STE C
CORPUS CHRISTI,TX 78413 PH 361 882-5868

PORT CITY PETROLEUM INC
PO BOX 5074
BEAUMONT,TX 77726-5074
PH 409 755-3180 FAX 409 751-0969
EDDIE ARNAUP,PRES

PORT NATURAL RESOURCES
PO BOX 2270
NATCHEZ,MS 39121-2270
PH 601 445-8659
M E RADZEWICZ,PRES/OWNER
CINDY HARRIS,ASST
KAY SMITH,ASST

PORTER JAMES W,IND
PO BOX 770
BLANCO,TX 78606-0770 PH 713 849-2996

PORTER SAMUEL G,GEOL
113 HEYMANN BLVD BLDG 6
LAFAYETTE,LA 70503-2398 PH 337 962-2760
SAMUELG_PORTER@YAHOO.COM

POST OAK PRODUCTION COMPANY
PO BOX 51847
LAFAYETTE,LA 70505
PH 337 237-0304 FAX 337 237-0308
RONALD J HOOVER,OWNER
RICHARD J JONES,OWNER

POTTER GARCIA MANAGEMENT GROUP
PO BOX 845
NATCHEZ,MS 39121-0845 PH 601 446-6090
WAYNE A POTTER,PRTNR
WAYNEPOTTER@BELLSOUTH.NET
SARA R GARCIA,PRTNR PH 601 807-4440
SARAREIDGARCIA@ATT.NET
MCKINNEY,TX OFFICE - 1740 WOODBRIDGE DR
75070

POTTER H A OIL AND GAS,LLC
10627 PIPING ROCK
HOUSTON,TX 77042 PH 713 781-7434
HOMER A POTTER III,MGR

POUNDS,J R INC
PO BOX 991
LAUREL,MS 39441-0991 PH 601 649-1743
FAX 601 649-2987
JIM POUNDS,PRES
TROY POUNDS,VP

POWDERHORN RESOURCES,LLC
105 FALCON PT
BOERNE,TX 78006 PH 713 542-0615
POWDERHORN@SKYWERX.COM
JOSEPH SCHUCHARDT,III

POWELL DAVID G
PO BOX 5513
LONGVIEW,TX 75608-5513 PH 903 234-1155
FAX 903 234-1160

POWELL GENE,INVESTMENTS,INC,OIL & GAS OPR
P O BOX 5513
LONGVIEW,TX 75608-5513 PH 903 297-7344
FAX 903 295-1950
KILGORE,TX OFFICE - PH 903 984-4356

POWELL J GORDON,CPL,PETROLEUM LDMN
1433 REGENCY OAKS DR E
MOBILE,AL 36609-2212
PH 251 343-6393 FAX 251 344-7288
JGP6337@AOL.COM
GORDON POWELL,PETR LDMN
LAURA A POWELL,ABSTRACTOR

POWELL ROBERT B,OIL PROPERTIES
103 BEAVER TAIL PT
HOUSTON,TX 77024-6233 PH 713 468-7401

POWER PRODUCTION COMPANY,INC
PO BOX 66802
HOUSTON,TX 77266-6802 PH 713 526-8919

FAX 713 526-9108
G M ROWE III,PRES

POWER RESERVES,INC
P O BOX 235
BRANCH,LA 70516 PH 318 334-7685
GARY FRUGE',PRES
JACKIE RICHARD,TREAS
MICHAEL FRUGE',SECY

POWERS MINERAL GROUP,INC
1208 W 39TH ST
AUSTIN,TX 78756-3922 PH 512 452-8084
PH 512 452-8084 FAX 512 452-8091
WWW.POWERSMINERALGROUP.COM
RAY B POWERS JR,PRES
RAYPOWERS@AUSTIN.RR.COM

PRAIRIE MINERALS LIMITED
4925 GREENVILLE AVE STE 714
DALLAS,TX 75206-4084 PH 214 369-2207
BOND W BEAMS,MNGNG GEN PRTNR
PH 214 808-9300 BBEAMS@CHARTER.NET

PRECISION DRILLING OILFIELD SERVICES CORP
10350 RICHMOND AVE STE 700
HOUSTON,TX 77042-4136 PH 713 435-6100
PH 800 553-7563 FAX 713 435-6180
KEVIN NEVEU,CEO
DAVID CROWLEY,PRES,US OPERS
DAVID W WEHLMANN,US EXEC VP,INVESTOR RELS
GRANT HUNTER,VP,US OPERS
RON HALE,US VP,SLS & MKTG
KENNETH HADDAD,US VP,BUS DEV
DALE LOVE,US VP,OPERS,SOUTHERN REG
RAY SMITH,US VP,OPERS,NORTHERN REG
TONY BARROWS,US VP,TECH SVCS
DONALD GUEDRY,US VP,FIN
JOEY HOPEWELL,US VP,TURNKEY SVCS
STEVE JAMES,VP HSE
BRADLEY DAVID,DIR,CAPITAL PROJ
BRAD LINDEMANN,DIR,HR
TAMARA GATLIN,US SR MGR,HR
JODY THOMPSON,MGR,BENEFITS
MIKE FLORES,RECRUITING MGR
JESSE CARTER,SR RECRUITER
MARK MORLOCK,ASSET MGR
ROBERT URBANOWSKI,MGR OF ENGRG
LARRY BURNETT,SR CONTRACTS/MKTG MGR
RICKY DOWELL,SR CONTRACTS/MKTG MGR
MARK H HULSE,SR CONTRACTS/MKTG MGR
TRAVIS FINDLEY,CONTRACTS/MKTG MGR
EVAN RUSSELL,MGR,OPERS
- ARK-LA-TX DIVISION -
SHREVEPORT,LA OFFICE - 333 TEXAS ST #925
71101 PH 318 213-1100 PH 800 959-3003
FAX 318 213-1155
DALE LOVE,US VP,OPERS
OSCAR BRADLEY,OPERS MGR
SAMANTHA BRADLEY,CONTROLLER,SOUTHERN REG
AMY CAMPBELL,HR MGR
JOHNNY DAY,DRLG SUPT
JEROME RUSSELL,DRLG SUPT
GLENN HUDSON,DRLG SUPT
BRITT LOTTINGER,HSE SUPVSR
- GULF COAST DIVISION -
EUNICE,LA OFFICE - 254 STANFORD RD
70535 PH 318 457-0500 PH 888 457-4089
FAX 337 457-0558
DALE LOVE,VP,OPERS,SOUTHERN REG

J D RICKS,OPERS MGR
ANDY ROUSSE,OPERS MGR
AMY CAMPBELL,HR MGR
JEREMY BERGERON,DRLG SUPT
LARRY DAIGLE,DRLG SUPT
KENNETH BERGERON,DRLG SUPT
RAYMOND HORTNESS,YARD SUPT
RYAN D'AUNOY,HSE MGR,SOUTHERN REG
MICHAEL WINJUM,SR HSE ADVSR
SCOTT WHITEHEAD,HSE ADVSR
- SOUTH TEXAS DIVISION -
ALICE OFFICE - 1907 E MAIN,78332-3710
PH 361 668-8364 PH 800 242-3280
FAX 361 668-0823
DALE LOVE,US VP,OPERS,SOUTHERN REG
DAVE WEBER JR,OPERS MGR
ELENA GIANNAREAS,HR MGR
DUMAS KUBALA,DRLG SUPT
DEAN MORAN,DRLG SUPT
SCOTT THORNBROUGH,DRLG SUPT
RICHARD LEAL,HSE ADVSR
DIONICIO ARREDONDO,HSE ADVSR
- MID-CONTINENT DIVISION -
WEATHERFORD,TX OFFICE - 113 S LINE
76086 PH 817 599-7012 FAX 817 599-0659
RAY SMITH,VP,OPERS
DAVE SCHMELZLE,OPERS MGR
JERRY HENDRY,DRLG SUPT
MIKE SKUCE,DRLG SUPT
JOHNNY ISON,DRLG SUPT
RHONDA ENGH,HR MGR
RYAN MORTON,HSE MGR,NORTHERN DIV
MIKE TRUITT,HSE ADVSR
CHUCK BULLARD,HSE ADVSR
MIKE MCFARLAND,HSE ADVSR
- ROCKY MOUNTAIN DIVISION -
CASPER,WY OFFICE - 2136 NOIL DR
82604 PH 307 266-0700 PH 866 522-0700
FAX 307 266-9864
RAY SMITH,VP,OPERS,NORTHERN REG
BURLEY LETT,SR OPERS MGR
KEN BINER,DRLG SUPT
DOUG FOSTER,DRLG SUPT
BOB SADOWAY,DRLG SUPT
IRENE SCHAFFER,CONTROLLER,NORTHERN REG
RHONDA ENGH,HR MGR,NORTHERN REG
BRIAN OSBORN,HSE ADVSR
JAY BROUSSEAU,HSE ADVSR

PRECISION ENERGY SERVICES SEE
WEATHERFORD

PREMIER MINERALS INC
8700 CROWNHILL BLVD STE 700
SAN ANTONIO,TX 78209 PH 800 947-2699
PH 210 804-1500 FAX 210 804-1360
FRANK GABRYSCH,PRES
MARTIN CALK,OPERS SUPT

PREMIER OILFIELD SERVICES SEE
SUPERIOR ENERGY SERVICES COMPANY

PREMIER TANK TRUCK SERVICE
2441 BARTLETT ST
HOUSTON,TX 77098 PH 713 524-8550
WILL BROWN,PRES PH 713 256-2033
WWW.PREMIERTANKTRUCKS.COM

PREMIERE INC
615 N LANDRY DR
NEW IBERIA,LA 70563 PH 800 551-3140

FAX 337 369-1001 WWW.PREMIEREINC.COM
LEE MATHERNE,CEO
KYLE MOWBRAY,PRES

PRENTICE OIL AND GAS CO LLC
PO BOX 1030,HWY 311 8 1/2 MI NW OF HOUMA
HOUMA,LA 70361-1030 PH 504 872-5221
ROBERT B PRENTICE II,MGR

PRESCOTT RICHARD H,PETR GEOL
113 PECANWOOD DR
NATCHEZ,MS 39120 PH 601 442-2896

PRESSURE CONTROL INC,SEE
CUDD PRESSURE CONTROL,INC

PRESTIA MICHAEL G,ATTORNEY AT LAW
P O BOX 1928,1708 23RD AVE
GULFPORT,MS 39502 PH 228 868-6609
FAX 228 868-6695

PRESTON EXPLORATION,LLC
PO BOX 7520
THE WOODLANDS,TX 77387-7520
PH 281 367-8697 FAX 281 364-4919
RONALD G GENTZLER,GEN MGR
TIMOTHY R TIM DEVER,OPERS MGR
JESSE D BO BLUE,LAND MGR

PRESTON INTERESTS OPERATING LP
6101 W COURTYARD DR STE 2-125
AUSTIN,TX 78730 PH 512 428-5425
JONATHAN E PRESTON
PRESTONOFC@YAHOO.COM

PRG ENGINEERING SERVICES,L.L.C.
16 CHATEAU MAGDELAINE DR
KENNER,LA 70065 PH 504 466-7604
FAX 504 835-8751
ROBERT R WOODERSON,ENGR

PRI,LP SEE
PLYMOUTH RESOURCES INC

PRICE ENERGY LLC
474 METAIRIE RD STE 203
METAIRIE,LA 70005-4331 PH 504 834-5559
FAX 504 834-5554 PRICEENERGY@YAHOO.COM
R F PRICE,MGR
S H PRICE,EXEC VP
A P SWANSON,VP
T A FERRARA,ACCT & FIN
C H PRICE,ACQS
S F PRICE,REAL PROPERTY MGR

PRICE GREGORY INTERNATIONAL,INC
920 MEMORIAL CITY WAY STE 600
HOUSTON,TX 77024-2507 PH 713 780-7500
FAX 713 780-9388 WWW.PRICEGREGORY.COM
M R LANGSTON,PRES
R F WISE,COO
T N JONES,SR VP
R E BELL,EXEC VP
J L BURNS,VP WESTERN DIV

PRICE J C,GEOL
1661 SNIDER
WEST,TX 76691-2132 PH 214 729-4691

PRICE RICHARD F,JR
474 METAIRIE RD STE 203
METAIRIE,LA 70005-4331 PH 504 834-5559
FAX 504 834-5554
RICHARD F PRICE JR,OWNER
A P SWANSON,VP
C H PRICE,ACQS MGR
T FERRERA,OFC ACCT MGR
S H PRICE,EXEC VP

S F PRICE,REAL PROPERTY MGR

PRICE SUPPLY INC
109 CASON RD
BROUSSARD,LA 70518-3204 PH 318 837-2466
WWW.PRICESUPPLY.COM SALES@PRICESUPPLY.NET
ROGER PRICE,VP
NORBERT PERRY,OILFIELD SLS
SHANE VIATOR,OILFIELD SLS

PRICE-SAYERS INC/ENGINEERING ASSOCIATES
PO BOX 441
NATCHEZ,MS 39121-0441 PH 318 336-5421
CARL SAYERS,PRES
VIDALIA,LA OFFICE- 237 AUDUBON ACRES RD
71373 PH 318 336-5421

PRIDE EXPLORATION,INC
PO BOX 6856
SHREVEPORT,LA 71136-6856
PH 318 226-1300 FAX 318 226-1504
JOHN C GRUNAU,PRES/GEOL

PRIDE INTERNATIONAL,INC
5847 SAN FELIPE ST STE 3300
HOUSTON,TX 77057-3195 PH 713 789-1400
FAX 713 789-1430
WWW.PRIDEINTERNATIONAL.COM
LOUIS A RASPINO,CEO
RODNEY W EADS,COO
W GREGORY LOOSER,GEN COUNSEL
GARY W CASSWELL,VP,EASTERN HEMISPERE
BRIAN C VOEGELE,SR VP,CFO
KEVIN C ROBERT,SR VP,MKTG & BUS DEV
ROBERT E WARREN,VP,IND & GOV AFFAIRS
DAVID E BRUCE,VP,WESTERN HEMISPHERE
JEFFREY L CHASTAIN,VP,INV RELS & COMM

PRIDE OIL & GAS PROPERTIES,INC
PO BOX 51777
LAFAYETTE,LA 70505-1777 PH 337 233-7761
FAX 337 233-7764
PAUL R ZEHNDER III,PRTNR,LDMN
THOMAS P MOUTON,PRTNR,LDMN

PRIEST & PRIEST LAND SERVICES,INC
2922 ASHFORD TRAIL DR
HOUSTON,TX 77082-2127
PH 281 920-0145
JAMES M PRIEST,PRES
DARLENE PRIEST,VP

PRIGGE,ALAN C & ASSOCIATES INC SEE
ALAN C PRIGGE & ASSOCIATES,INC

PRIMA ENERGY CORPORATION SEE
PETRO-CANADA RESOURCES (USA) INC

PRIME NATURAL RESOURCES,INC
500 DALLAS ST STE 500
HOUSTON,TX 77002-4706 PH 713 784-5634
FAX 713 953-3200
JAN VELDWIJK,CHF EXEC OFCR
ARLEN GROVE,VP,EXPL
JOHN HAGER,CHF FIN OFCR

PRIME OFFSHORE LLC
9821 KATY FWY STE 1050
HOUSTON,TX 77024-1218
PH 713 461-7221 FAX 713 461-9396
WWW.PRIMEENERGY.COM
JIM R BROCK,PRES
JBROCK@PRIMEOFFSHORE.COM

PRIME OPERATING COMPANY
9821 KATY FWY STE 1050
HOUSTON,TX 77024-1218

PH 713 735-0000 FAX 713 735-0090
H G SPEC LIVINGSTON,DIST MGR
MIDLAND,TX (WEST TX DIST) OFFICE - 3300 N
A ST STE 238 BLDG 1 79705 PH 432 682-5600
FAX 432 682-0223
CHAD GARNER,DIST MGR
OKLAHOMA CITY,OK (MID CONT DIST) OFFICE -
5400 NW GRAND BLVD STE 450 73112
PH 405 947-1091 FAX 405 943-9368
SHAWN LEMONS,DIST MGR
CHARLESTON,WV (APPALACHIAN DIST) OFFICE -
714 1/2 LEE ST E STE 17,25301
PH 304 342-0121 FAX 304 343-7019
HALSEY WHITNEY,DIST MGR

PRIMEENERGY CORPORATION
9821 KATY FREEWAY STE 1050
HOUSTON,TX 77024 PH 713 735-0000
FAX 713 735-0090

PRIMERO GAS GATHERING CO SEE
EVERGREEN RESOURCES INC

PRINCE PETROLEUM CORPORATION
26 EAGLE MEAD PL
THE WOODLANDS,TX 77382-6309
PH 318 233-7933
MICHAEL P HARRIS,PRES

PRINCESS THREE CORPORATION
PO BOX 1983
HENDERSON,TX 75653-1983 PH 903 657-4504
FAX 903 657-4506
DONNA LATTANZI,PRES

PRINCETON ENERGY CORP SEE
MYSTIQUE RESOURCES COMPANY

PRITCHARD & ABBOTT INC
VALUATION CONSULTANTS
4900 OVERTON COMMONS CT
FORT WORTH,TX 76132-3687 PH 817 926-7861
FAX 817 927-5314 WWW.PANDAI.COM
VICTOR W HENDERSON,CHRMN OF BOARD
A KENT ALLISON,PRES/CEO
BOB J ATCHESON,SECY/TREAS
FT WORTH,TX DIST OFFICE -
S DALE HEISKELL,DIST MGR
- ENGINEERING SERVICES -
PH 817 926-7861 FAX 817 927-5314
VICTOR W HENDERSON,MGR
- INFORMATION SERVICES -
PH 817 926-3342 FAX 817 370-3261
KEVIN R MCBURNETT,MGR
AMARILLO,TX DIST OFFICE - 5912 AMARILLO
BLVD WEST,79106-4148
PH 806 358-7837 FAX 806 358-7830
E DEAN MCDANIEL,DIST MGR
HENDERSON,TX DIST OFFICE -
1202 HWY 79 NORTH,75652-6012
PH 903 657-2555 FAX 903 657-4700
RODMAN B INSTINE,DIST MGR
HOUSTON,TX DIST OFFICE - 6950 EMPIRE
CENTRAL DR,77040-3204
PH 832 243-9600 FAX 832 243-9606
SHANNON H STARY,DIST MGR

PRITCHARTT W HOWARD,INDEPENDENT LDMN
P O BOX P ,208 MAIN
NATCHEZ,MS 39121-1053 PH 601 446-5766

PRIZE ENERGY CORP SEE
MAGNUM HUNTER RESOURCES,INC

PRO DATA ONLINE
P O BOX 968,600 S 16TH ST 72901
FORT SMITH,AR 72902-0968 PH 479 783-0509
WWW.NEWPROSPECT.COM
SAM GANN SAMG@PRODATAONLINE.COM
TIM SMITH SMITHT@NEWPROSPECT.COM

PROBE RESOURCES,INC
11 GREENWAY PLAZA STE 535
HOUSTON,TX 77046-1141
PH 713 572-8800 FAX 713 572-8807
B R EUBANKS,CHRMN

PROCTER DOUG
209 E 3RD ST
TYLER,TX 75701-3108 PH 903 592-3419
DOUG PROCTER,GEOL,ENGR

PRODUCERS ENERGY MARKETING,LLC SEE
CINERGY MARKETING & TRADING,LLC

PRODUCERS ENGINEERING COMPANY
717 SIXTH ST
DESTIN,FL 32541 PH 850 654-9273
FAX 850 654-9688
PRODUCERSENGINEERING@COX.NET
FREDERICK P DWIGHT,PRES FDWIGHT1@COX.NET
J F DWIGHT,VP

PRODUCING SOLUTIONS
PO BOX 541
LONGVIEW,TX 75606-0541 PH 903 663-3173
W L STEWART JR,PRES
WILLIAM L STEWART,VP,ENGR

PRODUCTION EQUIPMENT COMPANY OF SOUTH
TEXAS,INC
PO BOX 2621,4910 LEOPARD STE 100
CORPUS CHRISTI,TX 78403-2621
PH 361 884-8090 FAX 361 884-8136
WWW.PRODUCTIONEQUIPMENTCO.COM
BILLY THOMAS,OWNER
DEBBIE WARE THOMAS,OFC MGR
GLENN (BUBBA) BROOKS,MGR
KEITH DEATLEY,SLS
DEAN RAVEN,SLS
CHARLIE WALTERS,SLS

PRODUCTION MANAGEMENT COMPANIES
PO BOX 2692
MORGAN CITY,LA 70381-2692 PH 504 366-3594
LAFAYETTE,LA OFFICE - P O BOX 53485,70505
MIKE COFFELT,GEN MGR

PRODUCTION MANAGEMENT INDUSTRIES,INC SEE
SUPERIOR ENERGY SERVICES

PRODUCTION OPERATORS,INC SEE
SCHLUMBERGER

PRODUCTION TECHNOLOGY AND SERVICES
6911 SIGNAT DR
HOUSTON,TX 77041 PH 281 498-7399
FAX 281 498-7286
ROBERT HOFF,PRES
LEONARDO VARGAS,OPERS MGR
TIM KELLY,HSE MGR
ANCHORAGE,AK OFFICE - 440 E 100TH AVE
99515 PH 907 344-2024 FAX 907 344-2022
GREGORY STALZER,DIV MGR

PRODUCTION WIRELINE AND CASED HOLE SVCS
1062 AILLET RD
BROUSSARD,LA 70518 PH 337 839-9516
PH 888 690-8289 FAX 337 839-0315
WWW.PRODUCTIONWL.COM
JASON HORNBACK,SALES

PROEX ENERGY
330 RAYFORD RD #124
SPRING,TX 77386 PH 281 419-9277
FAX 281 419-9270 WWW.PROEXUS.COM
R J ABERCROMBIE,MNGNG DIR
KARA SCHULTZ,OPERS MGR

PROFESSIONAL DIRECTIONAL,LTD
PO BOX 750,750 CONROE PARK NORTH DR
CONROE,TX 77305-0750
PH 936 441-7266 FAX 936 441-7268
WWW.PRODIRECTIONAL.COM
INFO@PRODIRECTIONAL.COM
KAREN O'NEAL,CEO
LEE WRIGHT,PRES
JERRY CALLENS,VP
PAT SPARKS,VP
MARK MILLER,VP
STONEWALL,LA OFFICE - 655 HWY 171
71078-6100 PH 318 925-5395
FAX 318 925-5397
TREY CAMPBELL,DIV MGR
CASPER,WY OFFICE - PO BOX 2845
82602-2845 PH 307 259-0063
DAN MINER,DIV MGR
MORGANTOWN,WV OFFICE - 421 N METRO DR
26501 PH 304 566-7553 FAX 304 566-7503
AL GREEN,DIV MGR
MIDLAND,TX OFFICE - 3001 CR 1260
79706 PH 432 897-4931 FAX 214 452-1310
DAVID CHAPPELL,DIV MGR
OKLAHOMA CITY,OK OFC - 2908 S ANN ARBOR
73127 PH 405 200-1450 FAX 214 452-1311
BJ GOODNIGHT,DIV MGR
CONROE,TX (PROFESSIONAL CORING) OFFICE -
PH 936 441-7266 FAX 936 441-7268
WILLIAM SCOTT,DIV MGR

PROFESSIONAL ENERGY SERVICES,INC
PO BOX 820387,16130 GLEN-MAR DR
HOUSTON,TX 77282-0387 PH 281 496-7022
A BYRON PUGH III,CPL,PRES
K L PUGH,CPL,TREAS

PROFESSIONAL PETROLEUM SERVICES,INC
224 WHETSTONE RIVER RD S
CALEDONIA,OH 43314-9425 PH 740 389-9762
MIKE GRIFFITH,PRES
PPSIGRIFFITH@ROADRUNNER.COM

PROFIT ENERGY COMPANY
36829 TOWNSHIP RD 2067
JERUSALEM,OH 43747 PH 740 472-1018
C F ROUSENBERG,PRES

PROGAS DRILLING AND WELL SERVICES
1775 OAK GLEN
NEW BRAUNFELS,TX 78132 PH 325 370-7868
PROGASTX@GMAIL.COM

PROGAS ENERGY SERVICES
1775 OAK GLEN
NEW BRAUNFELS,TX 78132 PH 325 370-7868
DAN POLK PROGASTX@GMAIL.COM

PROGAS OPERATING,INC
1775 OAK GLEN
NEW BRAUNFELS,TX 78132 PH 325 669-0574
KELSEA POLK KPROGAS@YAHOO.COM

PROGRESS DRILLING INC
PO BOX 547,HWY 183 N
LULING,TX 78648-0547 PH 830 875-3442
JAMES MONTGOMERY,PRES

PROGRESSIVE EPOXY POLYMERS - DISTRIBUTOR
OF OIL FIELD EPOXY COATINGS
48 WILDWOOD DR
PITTSFIELD,NH 03263-3406 PH 603 435-7199
FAX 603 435-7182 WWW.EPOXYPRODUCTS.COM
INFO@EPOXYPRODUCTS.COM
PAUL OMAN

PROLAND LLC
PO BOX 80672
BATON ROUGE,LA 70898 PH 225 925-9658
S PAUL PROVENZA PAULPRO@BELLSOUTH.NET

PROPANE EDUCATION AND RESEARCH COUNCIL
WWW.PROPANECOUNCIL.ORG

PROPERTY DEVELOPMENT GROUP,INC
6805 N CAPITAL OF TX HWY STE 265
AUSTIN,TX 78731 PH 512 687-1111
PDG001@AOL.COM

PROSPECT EVALUATION SERVICES
2218 KINBROOK DR
HOUSTON,TX 77077-6115 PH 281 493-9298
L J LARRY CERNOSEK,SR,CONS

PROSPECT LAND SERVICES
LANDOWNER RESEARCH & RELS/TITLE/MAPPING
5440 SR 96
ROMULUS,NY 14541 PH 607 868-5011
THOMAS A WHITE,OWNER/OPERATOR
TOMLANDMAN@MSN.COM

PROTHRO, JOHN E, SR ESTATE SEE
COMGO, LLC

PROVEN FUEL EXPLORATION,INC
PO BOX 52552,200 TRAVIS ST STE 214
LAFAYETTE,LA 70505-2552 PH 337 232-9371
BILL CLAY,PRES, CHF GEOL

PROVENZA S PAUL,JR,ATTY AT LAW
PO BOX 80672
BATON ROUGE,LA 70898-0672
PH 225 925-9658 PAULPRO@BELLSOUTH.NET

PROVIDENCE EXPLORATION & PRODUCTION,INC
3811 ROGERS AVE STE B
FORT SMITH,AR 72903
PH 479 783-0886 FAX 479 783-5003
HOWARD BAGBY,PRES

PROVIDENCE ROYALTIES,LLC
1837 PEACHTREE ST
JACKSON,MS 39202-1132
PH 601 360-2850 FAX 601 360-1487
BRYANT G MILLER,MGR

PROVIDENT ROYALITIES LLC
1412 MAIN ST STE 2400
DALLAS,TX 75202-4011
PH 214 580-2252 FAX 214 580-2245
WWW.PROVIDENTROYALTIES.COM

PRUET CHESLEY,DRILLING COMPANY SEE
RAPAD DRILLING & WELL SERVICE,INC

PRUET OFFSHORE COMPANY
OFFSHORE GOM OIL & GAS E&P
1515 MISSION SPRINGS DR
KATY,TX 77450-4360 PH 281 579-0956
FAX 281 579-0994
ROBERT J MOSES,PRES
STANLEY L KYNERD,VP,GEN COUNSEL
RICK J CALHOON,DIR
WILLIAM R JAMES,DIR
BARRY GRESHAM,EXPL ADVISOR

PRUET OIL COMPANY,LLC
OIL & GAS EXPLORATION

217 W CAPITOL ST STE 201
JACKSON,MS 39201 PH 601 948-5279
FAX 601 355-5438 FAX 601 944-1281
WILLIAM R JAMES,MGR
RICKY J CALHOON,MGR
DAVE CATE,EXPL MGR

PRUET PRODUCTION CO
OIL & GAS OPERATIONS
217 W CAPITOL ST STE 201
JACKSON,MS 39201-2099
PH 601 948-5279 FAX 601 355-5438
WILLIAM R JAMES,PRES & DRLG OPERS MGR
RICKY J CALHOON,VP
J DAVID HILTON,VP/PROD MGR
DHILTON@PRUET.COM
STAN KYNERD,ATTY
JAMES RIGNEY,CONTROLLER

PSC INDUSTRIAL SERVICES
- CORPORATE HEADQUARTERS -
5151 SAN FELIPE STE 1600
HOUSTON,TX 77056 PH 713 623-8777
BPERRY@PSCNOW.COM WWW.PSCNOW.COM
- PSC INDUSTRIAL OUTSOURCING INC -
LAFAYETTE,LA OILFIELD SVCS GRP OFFICE -
543 RENAUD RD,70507
PH 337 233-4889 FAX 337 233-4106
ROBBIE MONLEZUN,OILFIELD SVCS GEN MGR
RICK WIMBERLEY,FIXED FACILITY GEN MGR
BYRON PERRY,SALES MGR
TERRY VENABLE,BLASTING/PAINTING MGR
DWAIN ST MARTIN,CARPENTRY,INSULATION MGR
JEFF LEMAIRE,HYDRO CLEANING MGR
EDDIE BOUDREAUX,DOCKSIDE CLEANING SVCS
MGR
KIM MERRILL,REMEDIATION TECHNICAL SVCS
HORACE HARGRAVE,SAFETY MGR/OFFSHORE SVCS
BRIAN THOMPSON,SAFETY MGR/FIXED
FACILITIES
BO THIBODEAUX,CREW COORDINATOR/HYDRO
GRP
JAMIE CHAUVIN,SALES-LAFAYETTE
SCOTT ESTAY,SALES-LAFAYETTE,MORGAN CITY
JEANERETTE
RANDY KRAUSE,SALES/HOUSTON
GARY CHANDLER,SALES-NEW ORLEANS,HOUSTON
GIBSON,LA NORM FACILITY OFFICE -
756 GERALDINE RD,70360
PH 985 575-3434 FAX 985 575-8184
GARY DELAFOISSE,FIXED FACILITY GEN MGR
BRAD DANIELS,WASTE COORDINATOR/MGR
GOLDEN MEADOW,LA DOCKSIDE CLEANING SVCS-
FOURCHON BASE OFC - 11 NORMAN DOUCET DR
70357 PH 985 396-5555 FAX 985 396-5556
TOMMY DAVIS,LOCATION MGR
RODERICK YOUNG,CREW COORD
AGNES LEBLANC,SALES
BOOTHVILLE,LA DOCKSIDE & OFFSHORE
CLEANING SVCS OFFICE - PO BOX 397
40360 HWY 23 SOUTH,70038
PH 985 534-2008 FAX 985 534-2876
J P SOLIS,LOCATION MGR
CAMERON,LA DOCKSIDE CLEANING SERVICES
OFFICE - PO BOX 1481,122 SCOTT RD,70631
PH 337 775-5851 FAX 337 775-5795
TONY LUCAS,LOCATION MGR
GARY SONNIER,SALES

(800) 375-1838

WWW.ARMSTRONGOIL.COM

If your company is not listed in our directory, we would like to list it in the next edition of our directory - absolutely FREE. To be listed, we need it in writing. Please fill out the form below or visit our website and fill out the listing form there. If you wish to use the form below, just mail it or fax it to us at (800) 375-1838.

Company Name _____

Physical Address _____

Mailing address if different _____

Phone # _____ Fax # _____

Email address _____

Key personnel and their titles:

_____

_____

_____

_____

If you need to list additional offices, please include on letterhead

To Order Call (800) 375-1838 or
www.armstrongoil.com

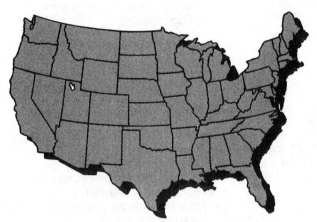

Nationwide Office Directory
Full 8 1/2" x 11" book size
Entire Nation
over 16,000 companies listed

$ 225 (no discount available)

Nationwide Mini Directory (Briefcase)
Small Size 5 1/4" x 8 1/4"
Same complete nationwide information
over 16,000 companies listed

$ 140 w / discount*

Texas Directory
Includes
Texas and S.E. New Mexico

$ 80 w / discount*

Louisana / Gulf Coast Directory
Includes the following states:
Gulf coast of Texas, Louisana
Arkansas, Mississippi,
Alabama, Georgia, Florida
N.E. states

$80 w / discount*

Rocky Mountain / Central U.S. Directory
Includes the following states:
West Texas and Panhandle of Texas
Oklahoma, New Mexico
Colorado, Alaska and all
Western U.S. states

$80 w / discount*

* discount applies when invoice is paid within 30 days after receipt of order.

ABBEVILLE,LA DOCKSIDE CLEANING SERVICES
OFFICE - 12384 OFFSHORE RD
70510 PH 337 898-1565 FAX 337 898-1512
DAYLON DOUCET,LOCATION MGR
GARY SONNIER,SALES
JEANERETTE,LA SALTWATER INJECTION &
SALVAGE OIL FACILITY OFFICE -
PO BOX 132,9523 HWY 87,70544
PH 337 276-5163 FAX 337 276-9834
TERRY SEGURA,LOCATION MGR
SCOTT ESTAY,SALES

PUENTICITAS OIL CO
BOX 466,818 E MAIN ST
ROBSTOWN,TX 78380 PH 361 387-2597
W R TIDWELL,PRES
THOS E PERRY,VP

PUFFER SWEIVEN
621 NAVIGATION BLVD
CORPUS CHRISTI,TX 78408-2641
PH 361 883-6215 FAX 361 889-7453
WWW.PUFFER.COM
ROBERT ILLGEN,BRANCH MGR
JERRY CROSS,SALES
BRUCE BUTERBAUGH,SALES
DAVE HUNTER,INSIDE SALES
ED LONG,INSIDE SALES
FREDDIE MARTINEZ,INSIDE SALES
DAVID HOFFSTADT,SALES
BRYAN THEDIN,INSIDE SALES
TOMMY ZABEL,SALES
BARRY WHELAN,SVCS,MECH

PUGH A BYRON,III,INC
P O BOX 820387
HOUSTON,TX 77282-0387 PH 281 496-7022
A BYRON PUGH,III,CPL,PRES
K L PUGH,CPL,TREAS

PUGH A BYRON,INC
1611 BROOKHAVEN BLVD
NORMAN,OK 73072-3209 PH 405 329-5657,3638
PRESTON L PUGH,PRES
WANDA L PUGH,VP
TAMARA K ELLIS,SECY/TREAS

PULLIN LEASE SERVICE LEASE OPR
9514 CR 1214
TAFT,TX 78390-9704 PH 361 528-3239
J E PULLIN,PRES

PULS OPERATING COMPANY
PO BOX 39
KATY,TX 77492 PH 281 391-0991
FAX 281 391-0963
PULS.OPERATING@SBCGLOBAL.NET
LAYNE L PULS,OWNER/ENGR

PUMPELLY OIL CO
PO BOX 2059,1890 SWISCO RD
SULPHUR,LA 70664-2059
PH 318 474-1361 FAX 318 474-9204
KEITH FARMER,MKTG REPR
CECIL FONTENOT,MKTG REPR
JIM CLOONEY,SALES MGR
RALPH DEROUEN,PROCUREMENT SPEC
VINCE LIGGIO,ASST PROCUREMENT SPEC
RON SHERER,PUR AGT
STEVE BROUSSARD,MKTG REPR
JULES SIMONEAUX,MKTG REPR

PUMPER'S FRIEND RADIATOR SALES,INC
520 W WHITE TAIL ST

DERBY,KS 67037 PH 800 235-2191
ARTHUR GENE MILLER,PRES/OWNER
BEVERLY SMALLEY,OFC MGR

PUPCO INC SEE
ALRAM INC

PURCELL INTERESTS,INC
1415 S VOSS RD 110-513
HOUSTON,TX 77057-1086 PH 713 961-4383
FAX 713 961-0411
TOM E PURCELL,PRES

PURE ENERGY GROUP,INC SEE
CROSS BORDER RESOURCES

PURE RESOURCES,INC SEE
CHEVRON

PURITY OILFIELD SERVICES,LLC
2101 CEDAR SPRINGS RD STE 650
DALLAS,TX 75201 PH 214 880-7190
PH 214 880-8400 FAX 214 880-7101
CONTACTPURITY@PURITYOILFIELDSERVICES.COM
WWW.PURITYOILFIELDSERVICES.COM
MARSHALL T HUNT,PRES
CARTER W HUNT,VP
DAVIN P HUNT,VP
CASEY H HUNT,VP
BAILEY G HUNT,VP
TAYLOR HUNT,VP
AUSTIN HUNT,VP
ED O'CONNOR,OPERS SUPT
STEVE CARLISLE,EXEC SLS
WILLISTON,ND OFFICE - PO BOX 2567,58801
13375 62ND ST NW PH 701 826-7900
DISPATCH 855-221-1600 FAX 701 826-4402
STEVE ATWELL,DIR OPERS ROCKIES/MIDWEST
JESSE ATWELL,SHOP MGR
DOCKERY CATES,TRK SUPVR
STEVE KYATHFIELD,SLS
DOUGLAS,WY OFFICE - 3 LOCKE RD,82633
PH 855 221-1600
SHAUN MOORE,DIST SUPVR
STEVE ATWELL,DIR OPERS ROCKIES/MIDWEST
MIDLAND,TX OFFICE - 11109 W CR 46,79707
PH 844 221-1500
RICHARD MATHIS,OPERS MGR

PURPLE LAND MANAGEMENT
100 E 15TH ST STE 320
FORT WORTH,TX 76102
PH 817 717-3835 WWW.PURPLELANDMGMT.COM
INFO@PURPLELANDMGMT.COM
JESSE HEJNY,PRES
BRYAN CORTNEY,CEO

PURSUE ENERGY CORPORATION
AND GAS PLANT OFFICE
2173 SHELL OIL RD
BRANDON,MS 39043
PH 601 845-2252 FAX 601 845-4218
GENE MCLEOD,DIST MGR
WILLIE JOHNS,PLANT MGR

PURVIN & GERTZ INC
600 TRAVIS ST STE 2150
HOUSTON,TX 77002-2979 PH 713 236-0318
FAX 713 236-8490 WWW.PURVINGERTZ.COM
WILLIAM J SANDERSON,PRES
HOUSTON,TX OFFICE - TEXAS COMMERCE TWR
STE 2150 600 TRAVIS ST,77002-2979
PH 713 236-0318 FAX 713 238-8490
LONG BEACH,CA OFFICE - 111 WEST OCEAN

BLVD STE 1025,90802 PH 562 437-8886
FAX 562 436-8970
MICHAEL E SARNA,SR PRIN
CALGARY,ALTA,CAN OFFICE - 1720 SUNLIFE
PLZ 144-4TH AVE SW,T2P-3N4 CANADA
PH 403 266-7086 FAX 403 264-2556
THOMAS H WISE,VP
LONDON,ENGLAND OFFICE - STRATON HOUSE,1
STRATTON ST,W1J 8LA PH 44-20-7499-0115
FAX 44-20-7499-1985
MICHAEL J CORKE,VP
SINGAPORE,SINGAPORE OFFICE - 69 DUXTON RD
LEVEL 3,089528 PH 65-227-2758
FAX 65-227-2753
JOHN H VAUTRAIN,VP

PVR MIDSTREAM LLC
PENN VIRGINIA RESOURCE PARTNERS
3 RADNOR CORP CTR STE 301
100 MATSONFORD RD
RADNOR,PA 19087 PH 610 975-8200
FAX 610 975-8201 WWW.PVRESOURCE.COM
IRVING,TX (MID-CONT OPERS) OFFICE - 5215
NORTH O'CONNOR BLVD 75039 PH 214 750-9223
FAX 214 750-7120
WILLIAMSPORT,PA (MARCELLUS AREA OPERS)
OFFICE - 101 W THIRD ST STE 100, 17701
PH 570 505-3700 FAX 570 505-3798

PYLE PETROLEUM,INC
7005 CHISWICK DR
CORPUS CHRISTI,TX 78413
PH 361 993-6667 FAX 361 882-7076
TOM PYLE,PRES,OWNER
SHIRLEY PYLE,SECY/TREAS
RUTH B HANS,AGENT

P2 ENERGY SOLUTIONS
1670 BROADWAY STE 2900
DENVER,CO 80202
PH 303 292-0990 FAX 303 292-1812
WWW.P2ENERGYSOLUTIONS.COM
INFO@P2ENERGYSOLUTIONS.COM
CHARLES GOODMAN,CEO
DAVID MUSE,COO
HOUSTON,TX OFFICE - 1221 LAMAR ST
STE 1400,77010 PH 713 481-2000
FAX 713 481-2001
SAN ANTONIO,TX (TOBIN DATA PRODUCTS) -
1355 CENTRAL PKWY S STE 500,78232
PH 210 402-5900 FAX 210 223-3161
FORT WORTH,TX (P2 OUTSOURCING) -
100 THROCKMORTON ST STE 400 76102
PH 817 339-1000 FAX 817 339-1001
LIVINGSTON,NJ OFFICE - 220 S ORANGE AVE
STE 105,07039 PH 973 992-8000
FAX 973 992-8788
TAMPA,FL OFFICE- 405 N REO ST STE 105
33609 PH 813 282-0330
CALGARY,ALBERTA,CANADA OFFICE - 639 5TH
AVE SW STE 2100 T2P 0M9 PH 403 774-1000
FAX 403 774-1010
DUBAI,UAE (MIDDLE EAST) OFFICE -
INTERNET CITY BLDG 3 OFFICE 124
PH 971 4 3910231 FAX 971 4 3910232
TUNIS,TUNISIA OFFICE- RUE DU LAC VICTORIA
APT #6 LES BERGES DU LAC 2048
PH 216 71 862 787

QUAIL CREEK OIL CORPORATION
13831 QUAIL POINTE DR
OKLAHOMA CITY,OK 73134-1021
PH 405 755-7419 FAX 405 755-7994
DON W DAHLGREN,PRES
THOMAS E BIERY,VP
SUSAN BOSTICK,SECY

QUAIL CREEK PETROLEUM MANAGEMENT CORP
13831 QUAIL POINTE DR
OKLAHOMA CITY,OK 73134-1021
PH 405 755-7419 FAX 405 755-7994
DON W DAHLGREN,PRES

QUAIL CREEK PRODUCTION COMPANY
10000 MEMORIAL DR STE 770
HOUSTON,TX 77024-3412
PH 713 956-2070 FAX 713 956-2670
DBUESINGER@QUAILCREEKCOMPANIES.COM
THOMAS E BIERY,PRES
DON W DAHLGREN,VP
DEBRA BUESINGER,REG SPEC/ADMIN

QUAIL TOOLS,LLP
PO BOX 10739
NEW IBERIA,LA 70562-0739
PH 337 365-8154 FAX 337 365-2554

QUALITY SHIPYARDS,LLC
PO BOX 1817,940 HWY 182
HOUMA,LA 70361-1817 PH 504 876-4846
FAX 504 868-7339
JOSEPH R BAOLAUX,GEN MGR
TERREL HEBERT,VP,OPERS
DONALD BOURGEOIS,CONTROLLER

QUALITY TUBING,INC
10303 SHELDON RD
HOUSTON,TX 77049 PH 281 456-0751
PH 800-486-0751 FAX 281 456-7549
DAVID DANIEL,CEO,PRES
JOHN R MARTIN,SR VP,PROD/MKTG DEV
DALE R KLINK,VP,SALES/MKTG
JOHN BOURGEOIS,CFO
NED RADJENOVICH,INTL SALES MGR

QUANAH ENERGY,LLC
221 W EXCHANGE AVE STE 306
FORT WORTH,TX 76164 PH 817 840-7716
FAX 817 339-6722

QUANICO OIL & GAS INC,OIL PROD
PO BOX 1714,478 N WASHINGTON ST
EL DORADO,AR 71731-1714 PH 870 863-7220
FAX 870 863-4670 QUANICO1@YAHOO.COM
JERRY D ALEXANDER,PRES
DOUGLAS K ALEXANDER,VP
SYLVIA A ALEXANDER,SECY/TREAS
WAYNE MCCLISH,OFC MGR

QUANTUM GEOPHYSICAL,INC SEE
GEOKINETICS INC

QUATERNARY RESOURCE INVESTIGATIONS INC
PROMOTING INDUSTRY IN HARMONY WITH ENV
13588 FLORIDA BLVD
BATON ROUGE,LA 70819-3101 PH 225 292-1400
GORDON TRAHAN GTRAHAN@QRI-PULSER.COM

QUAY VALLEY,INC SEE
BIG STAR OIL & GAS,LLC

QUEST ENERGIES GROUP LTD
404 BRAEMAR RD
SHREVEPORT,LA 71106-8534 PH 318 424-3240
DAVID H OGWYN,GEN PRTNR

QUEST EXPLORATION,LLC
PO BOX 51634
LAFAYETTE,LA 70505-1634
PH 337 237-6039 FAX 337 237-7585
E D DAVIS JR,MGR
DANNY DOBBS,EXPL MGR

QUESTAR EXPLORATION AND PRODUCTION CO
PO BOX 45601,180 EAST 100 SOUTH
SALT LAKE CITY,UT 84145-0601
PH 801 324-2600 FAX 801 324-2066
C B STANLEY,PRES,CEO
S E PARKS,VP,CFO,TREAS
M L OWEN,VP,ADMIN SVCS
J B NEESE,EXEC VP
A L JONES,SECY
DENVER,CO DIVISION OFFICE - 1050 17TH ST
STE 500,80265 PH 303 672-6900
FAX 303 294-9632
J P MATHENY,REG MGR
F NIELSEN,REG LAND MGR
OKLAHOMA CITY,OK DIVISION OFFICE -
2601 NW EXPY STE 1200 E,73112
PH 405 840-2761 FAX 405 848-9413
M D PENNER,DIV GEN MGR
J C TAYLOR,DIV LAND MGR
TULSA,OK DIVISION OFFICE - TWO WARREN PL
6120 S YALE AVE,STE 1300,74136-4210
PH 918 488-8962 FAX 918 495-0842
R E NIKKEL,DIV GEN MGR
M K WATANABE,DIV LAND MGR
J R TOMMERUP,PROD & OPERS MGR
HOUSTON,TX DIVISION OFFICE -
510 BERING DR,STE 300,77057
PH 713 974-8813 FAX 713 974-8815
AUSTIN MURR,GEN MGR,BUS DEV
MATT THOMPSON,ACQ ENGR

QUICK & ASSOCIATES,OIL & GAS PROPERTIES
6609 FALCON RIDGE DR
MCKINNEY,TX 75071-7770 PH 972 984-1811
FAX 972 984-1812 QUICKCO@SBCGLOBAL.NET
ALAN D QUICK,MGR
WANDA K QUICK,MGR

QUICK ALAN D
6609 FALCON RIDGE LN
MCKINNEY,TX 75071 PH 972 984-1811
FAX 972 984-1812 QUICKEO@SBCGLOBAL.NET

QUIET SUN INVESTMENTS,INC
4012 LAKEWAY BLVD
BENTON,LA 71006
PH 318 965-4453 FAX 318 965-4453
MATT WHITEHEAD,PRES

QUIGLEY T M,MIKE,OIL OPER
4699 GRAVEL PIT RD
SEGUIN,TX 78155
PH 361 813-9992 FAX 830 639-4107

QUIM EXPORT INC
INTERMEDIATES & FINISHED PRODUCTS
MANUFACTURING/BLENDING
21175 TOMBALL PARKWAY STE 180
HOUSTON,TX 77070 PH 281 251-5280
FAX 281 251-5938 WWW.QUIMEXPORTINC.COM
ANGIE CHAVEZ,OWNER

QUINELLA SEISMIC & EXPL CO SEE
P G S ONSHORE,INC

QUINN B E & SONS,LAND & OIL PROPERTIES
PO BOX 163090

1250 CAPITAL OF TX HWY,SOUTH BLDG 1,#280
AUSTIN,TX 78716-3090 PH 512 327-8988
FAX 512 327-5740
B E QUINN,III

QUINN B E,III,LAND & OIL PROPERTIES
PO BOX 163090
1250 CAPITAL OF TX HWY,SOUTH BLDG 1,#280
AUSTIN,TX 78716-3090 PH 512 327-8988
FAX 512 327-5740

QUINTANA MINERALS CORPORATION
601 JEFFERSON ST STE 3600
HOUSTON,TX 77002-7910 PH 713 751-7500
FAX 713 650-0606 713 751-7580
CORBIN J ROBERTSON JR,PRES
WARREN S HAWKINS,SR VP,EXPL,PROD
CHARLES H KERR,VP,LAND/LEGAL,ADMIN
DWIGHT L DUNLAP,VP,FIN
BO STURDIVANT,VP,INSURANCE/INVESTMENT
PAUL J CORNELL,VP,FIN

QUORUM BUSINESS SOLUTIONS,INC
811 MAIN ST STE 2000
HOUSTON,TX 77002
PH 713 430-8601 FAX 713 430-8697
WWW.QBSOL.COM INFO@QBSOL.COM
CLEVE HOGARTH,VP/CCO
DALLAS OFFICE - 1420 W MOCKINGBIRD LANE
STE 700,75247
PH 214 630-6442 FAX 214 630-6947
CALGARY,AB OFFICE - 101-6TH ST SW STE 210
T2P 5K7 PH 403 806-2568 FAX 403 806-2584

R & A MOORE INC
PO BOX 2258,903 AZLE HWY
WEATHERFORD,TX 76086 PH 817 598-0800
ROBERT L MOORE
RAMOORE@RAMOOREINC.COM

R & R WELL SERVICE INC
PO BOX 1805
WOODWARD,OK 73802-1831 PH 580 254-3068
FAX 580 256-8808
MARK REASNER,PRES
DAVID REASNER,VP
ST CHARLES,MO OFC - 4 PRINZ CIRCLE 63303

R & S GAS MEASUREMENT SERVICES,INC SEE
SOUTHERN FLOW COMPANIES

R & W OIL COMPANY
6166 BIBLE GROVE LN
LOUISVILLE,IL 62858 PH 618 686-3084
AARON KINCAID,PRES

R B O,INC
600 LEOPARD ST STE 1107
CORPUS CHRISTI,TX 78473-0030
PH 361 884-4252
ROBERT B OWEN,GEOL

R C I S CORP
412 W 9TH ST
OTTAWA,KS 66067 PH 903 526-2030
FAX 903 526-2031 MARITA@TYLER.NET
CHARLES W POCOCK,CPL,PRES
MARITA K POCOCK,VP,TREAS

R D T PROPERTIES,INC SEE
MID-CON ENERGY CORPORATION

R G S SEE
STANBERRY OIL COMPANY

R H VENABLE PROPERTIES,LTD
5949 SHERRY LN STE 1400
DALLAS,TX 75225-8010

PH 214 219-1444 FAX 214 219-2227

R LACY SERVICES,LTD
P O BOX 2146,222 E TYLER
LONGVIEW,TX 75606-2146
PH 903 758-8276 FAX 903 758-5098

R N R OIL DRILLING INC SEE
ORTMAN DRILLING INC

R.E. SMITH INTERESTS,INC,OIL OPR
1900 WEST LOOP S STE 1050
HOUSTON,TX 77027-3207 PH 713 622-8611

R.P.C. INC
8 EMERY AVE
RANDOLPH,NJ 07869-1362 PH 973 366-1400
FAX 973 366-5712
LAWRENCE S RAY,PRES
MICHAEL J RAY,VP,TREAS

R.S.E. INC
12000 WESTHEIMER RD STE 320
HOUSTON,TX 77077-6668 PH 281 558-6900
R P SANDERS,JR,PRES
EVA B SANDERS,SECY/TREAS
PATRICIA BING,OFC MGR
JAMES E GUILBEAU,COMPTROLLER

R.W. TYSON PRODUCING CO
675 N LIVINGSTON RD
RIDGELAND,MS 39157 PH 601 856-8300
FAX 601 856-8336
EMMETT A EATON,CEO/PRES
RITA REIBLING,REV SUPVSR

R&B PETROLEUM,INC
A SUBSIDIARY OF CARDINAL RESOURCES,INC
14 HARWOOD CT STE 225
SCARSDALE,NY 10583-4120
PH 914 472-2090 CARDINALRES@AOL.COM
JAMES J BOYLE,CHRMN,PRES

R&R RESOURCES CORPORATION
203 WYNDEN CRESCENT CT
HOUSTON,TX 77056-2521
PH 713 355-5385 FAX 713 355-1344
RICK DOUTEL,PRES RDOUTEL@SWBELL.NET
JANE O'MALLEY,ACCT

R-A-R INTERESTS
PO BOX 6940
SAN ANTONIO,TX 78209-6940 PH 210 824-7640
H L RYMAL,MNGNG PRTNR

RAAM GLOBAL ENERGY COMPANY
1537 BULL LEA RD STE 200
LEXINGTON,KY 40511 PH 859 253-1300
FAX 859 233-7471 WWW.RAAMGLOBAL.COM
HOWARD SETTLE,CEO
JEFF CRAYCRAFT,CFO
ELIZABETH BARR,CHF ADMIN OFCR
THE WOODLANDS,TX OFFICE - 10210 GROGANS
MILL RD STE 300,77380 PH 281 362-3699
FAX 281 362-7124
KEN YOUNG,COO
JERRY SHEETS,SR VP BUS DEV
JOHN SPRINGER,VP CORP PLNG
RICARDO VASQUEZ,VP CORP EXPL
BERNARD COONS,MGR CORP GEOSCIENCE
BLAKE CANTLEY,VP OPERS
METAIRIE,LA OFFICE - 3838 N CAUSEWAY BLVD
STE 2800 70002 PH 504 832-3750
FAX 504 832-3760
MICHAEL WILLIS,SR VP

RADKE OIL COMPANY,INC
P O BOX 915
JENNINGS,LA 70546-0915 PH 318 824-2746
CARROLL E R RADKE,PRES

RADLEY ROBERT M
2503 MEADOW LN
EL CAMPO,TX 77437-2151 PH 409 543-3459

RADZEWICZ EXPLORATION & DRILLING CORP
(REDCO)
PO BOX 2270,655 HWY 61 S
NATCHEZ,MS 39121-2270 PH 601 445-8659
FAX 601 445-8682 REDCO@TELEPAK.NET
MAUREEN E RADZEWICZ,PRES,SECY,GEN MGR
BENNY JEANSONNE,COMPTROLLER
BILLIE ANN SMITH,ACCT/RECORDS
KAY SMITH,ADMIN SECY/ACCT
CINDY HARRIS,RECPT

RADZEWICZ OPERATING CORP (ROC)
PO BOX 1726,655 HWY 61 S
NATCHEZ,MS 39121-1726 PH 601 445-8659
FAX 601 445-8682 REDCO@TELEPAK.NET
MAUREEN E RADZEWICZ,PRES,SECY,OPER MGR
BENNY JEANSONNE,COMPTROLLER
KAY SMITH,ADMIN SECY,PROD & ACCT
CINDY HARRIS,RECPT
BILLIE ANN SMITH,BOOKEEPER

RAFIDI OIL & GAS INC
4913 JAMES DR
METAIRIE,LA 70003-1125 PH 504 722-2942
PH 504 888-1661 FAX 504 888-5539
JASER N RAFIDI,PRES
DAVID J RAFIDI,VP,ADMIN

RAILROAD COMMISSION OF TEXAS
PO BOX 12967,1701 N CONGRESS
AUSTIN,TX 78711-2967 PH 877 228-5740
WWW.RRC.STATE.TX.US
GENERAL INFORMATION - PH 512 463-7158
24 HOUR EMERGENCY - PH 512 463-6788
TELECOMMUNICATIONS DEVICE FOR THE DEAF
PH 800 735-2989
ALTERNATIVE FUELS RESEARCH & EDUCATION
DIVISION - PH 512 463-7110
COMPLAINTS/INQUIRIES - PH 877 228-5746
MEDIA CONTACT - PH 512 463-4817
OIL & GAS - PH 512 463-6838
GAS SERVICES- PH 512 463-7167
GENERAL COUNSEL - PH 512 463-6848
INFORMATION TECH SVCS - PH 512 463-7251
GOVERNMENT & MEDIA AFFAIRS
PH 512 463-6710
HUMAN RESOURCES - PH 512 463-6981
SAFETY DIVISION - PH 512 463-7058
SURFACE MINING & RECLAMATION -
PH 512 463-6900
LICENSE & PERMITS - PH 512 463-7058
PROPANE REBATES,GRANTS,TESTING,
& TRAINING - PH 512 463-7110

- COMMISSIONERS -
BARRY T SMITHERMAN,CHRMN PH 512 463-7144
BARRY.SMITHERMAN@RRC.STATE.TX.US
CHRISTIAN ALVARADO,CHF OF STAFF
PH 512 463-7146
DAVID PORTER,COMMISSIONER PH 512 463-7131
DAVID.PORTER@RRC.STATE.TX.US
AMY MAXWELL,CHF OF STAFF PH 512 463-7134

KATIE CARMICHAEL,DIR OF PUBLIC AFFAIRS
PH 512 463-8870
BUDDY GARCIA,COMMISSIONER PH 512 463-7140
BUDDY.GARCIA@RRC.STATE.TX.US
BECKY WALKER,CHF OF STAFF PH 512 463-7142
KATHY WAY,COMMISSION SECY PH 512 463-7158
FAX 512 463-7161
DAVID POLLARD,CFO PH 512 463-5011
MARY (POLLY) ROSS MCDONALD,EXEC DIR
PH 512 463-7068
EDNA MEDINA,DIR PH 512 463-7268
LINDIL FOWLER,GEN COUNSEL PH 512 463-6715
COLIN LINEBERRY,HEARINGS DIR
PH 512 463-7051
REESE COPELAND,ENFORCEMENT DIR
PH 512 463-8951

- DISTRICT OFFICES -
ABILENE,TX DISTRICT 7B OFFICE -
3444 N 1ST ST,79603 PH 325 677-3545
CORPUS CHRISTI DISTRICT 4 OFFICE -
10320 IH 37 78410 PH 361 242-3113
FORT WORTH,TX OFFICE - 401 W 13TH ST
76102 PH 817 882-8966
HOUSTON,TX DISTRICT 3 OFFICE -
1706 SEAMIST DR 77008 PH 713 869-5001
KILGORE,TX DISTRICTS 5 & 6 OFFICE -
2005 N STATE HWY 42 75662 PH 903 984-3026
MIDLAND,TX DISTRICTS 8 & 8A OFFICE -
10 DESTA DR 79705 PH 432 684-5581
PAMPA,TX DISTRICT 10 OFFICE- 200 W FOSTER
ROOM 300 79065 PH 806 665-1653
SAN ANGELO,TX DISTRICT 7C OFFICE -
622 S OAKES ST 76903 PH 325 657-7450
SAN ANTONIO,TX DISTRICTS 1 & 2 OFFICE -
115 E TRAVIS ST 78205 PH 210 227-1313
TYLER,TX OFFICE - 2202 OLD HENDERSON HWY
75702 PH 903 595-5501
WICHITA FALLS,TX DISTRICT 9 OFFICE -
5800 KELL BLVD 76310 PH 940 723-2153

- ALTERNATIVE ENERGY DIVISION -
GENERAL INFO(AFRED) - PH 512 463-7110
AFRED TOLL FREE - PH 800 642-5327
DAN KELLY,DIR (AFRED) PH 512 463-7291

- LP-GAS OPERATIONS -
GENERAL INFO - PH 512 463-6462
JIM OSTERHAUS,DIR PH 512 463-6692
- DISTRICT OFFICES -
DISTRICT 1 - 10 DESTA DR MIDLAND,TX 79705
PH 432 570-5884 FAX 432 682-1325
LARRY SNELSON
DISTRICT 2 - 10 DESTA DR MIDLAND,TX 79705
PH 432 570-5884 FAX 432 682-1325
KEVIN CLARKE
DISTRICT 3 - 622 S OAKES ST SAN ANGELO,TX
76903 PH 325 657-7469 FAX 325 657-7455
ADAM RODRIQUEZ
DISTRICT 4 - 401 W 13TH ST FORT WORTH,TX
76102 PH 817 882-8966 FAX 817 882-8951
FERNANDO BELMARES PH 817 882-8966 EXT 12
DISTRICT 5 - 619 HENDERSON KILGORE,TX
75662 PH 903 984-8581 FAX 903 983-3413
GREG FULLER PH 903 981-8581 EXT 217
DISTRICT 6 - PO BOX 12967 AUSTIN,TX 78711

PH 512 463-6462 PH 512 463-3213
BRYAN JONES
DISTRICT 7 - 619 HENDERSON KILGORE,TX
75662 PH 903 984-8581 FAX 903 983-3413
DARVIS WILLIS PH 903 984-8581 EXT 218
DISTRICT 8 - 115 E TRAVIS ST SAN ANTONIO,
TX 78205 PH 210 227-1313 FAX 210 227-4822
CHRISTOPHER MANN
DISTRICT 9 - 1706 SEAMIST DR HOUSTON,TX
77008 PH 713 869-8425 FAX 713 869-3219
REX HAVRON PH 713 869-8425 EXT 239
DISTRICT 10 - 1706 SEAMIST DR HOUSTON,TX
77008 PH 713 869-8425 FAX 713 869-3219
ROBERT BRAZEAL PH 713 869-8425 EXT 240
DISTRICT 11 - PO BOX 10307,10320 IH 37
CORPUS CHRISTI,TX 78460 PH 361 242-3117
FAX 361 242-2101
PRUDENCIO LLANOS PH 361 242-3117 EXT 423
DISTRICT 12 - 401 W 13TH ST FORT WORTH,TX
76102 PH 817 882-8966 FAX 817 882-8957
JAMES RILEY

- GAS SERVICES DIVISION -
GENERAL INFO - PH 512 463-7167
BILL GEISE,DIR PH 512 463-8559
- DISTRICT OFFICES-
FORT WORTH,TX OFFICE - 401 W 13TH ST
76102 PH 817 882-8966 FAX 817 882-8951
JOSH SETTLE
HOUSTON,TX OFFICE - 1706 SEAMIST DR
STE 501 77008-3135 PH 713 869-8425
FAX 713 869-3219
MARGIE STONEY

- INFORMATION TECH SERVICES DIVISION -
ITS GENERAL INFO - PH 512 463-7251
DONNA CORDES,INFO RESOURCES MGR
PH 512 463-9162

- OIL & GAS DIVISION -
GIL BUJANO,DEP DIR PH 512 463-4513
LESLIE SAVAGE,CHF GEO PH 512 463-7308
GENERAL INFO - PH 512 463-6838
INFO SVCS/CENTRAL RECORDS-PH 512 463-6882
ROY PHILLIPS,MGR PH 512 475-2482
FIELD OPERS GEN INFO - PH 512 463-6830
FAX 512 463-7328
ADMINISTRATIVE COMPLIANCE-PH 512 463-6838
P-5/FINANCIAL ASSURANCE - PH 512 463-6772
MARIA CASTRO,MGR PH 512 463-6743
TECHNICAL PERMITTING GENERAL INFO -
PH 512 463-6821
INJECTION-STORAGE PERMITS & SUPPORT -
PH 512 463-6792
ENVIRONMENTAL PERMITS & SUPPORT -
PH 512 463-3840
MICHAEL SIMS,PRG MGR PH 512 463-5405
DRILLING PERMITS GENERAL INFO -
PH 512 463-6751 FAX 512 463-7324
LORENZO GARZA,PRG MGR PH 512 463-2184
GROUNDWATER ADVISORY UNIT-PH 512 463-2741
NORMAN GEARHART,MGR PH 512 463-2937
GIS PIPELINE AND WELL MAPPING -
PH 512 463-6851 FAX 512 463-7200
DEBORAH FLADOS,MGR PH 512 463-6844
ENGRG UNIT & SUPPORT - PH 512 463-3840

PRODUCTION AUDIT GEN INFO-PH 512 463-6726
RECOVERED FRAC(P-3) - PH 512 463-6726
FAX 512 463-6955
DEBORAH DAVIS,MGR PH 512 463-6722
SITE REMEDIATION - PH 512 463-6765
PETER POPE,ASST DIR
PH 512 463-8202
OIL & GAS WELL COMPLIANCE -
JOE STASULLI,WELL COMPLIANCE UNIT MGR
PH 512 463-3905 FAX 512 936-6612
- DISTRICT OFFICES -
DISTRICT 01 & 02 - 115 E TRAVIS ST
STE 1610 SAN ANTONIO,TX 78205
PH 210 227-1313 FAX 210 227-4822
TOM MELVILLE,DIR
DISTRICT 03 - 1706 SEAMIST DR STE 501
HOUSTON,TX 77008 PH 713 869-5001
FAX 713 869-9621
CHARLES TEAGUE,DIR
DISTRICT 04 - 10320 IH 37
CORPUS CHRISTI,TX 78410 PH 361 242-3113
FAX 361 242-9613
ARNOLD OTT,DIR
DISTRICT 05 & 06 - 619 HENDERSON BLVD
KILGORE,TX 75662-5998 PH 903 984-3026
FAX 903 983-3413
MICHAEL VANDERWORTH,ASST DIR
DISTRICT 7B - 3444 N 1ST ST STE 600
ABILENE,TX 79603 PH 325 677-3545
FAX 325 677-7122
JOE CRESS,DIR PH 325 677-3545 EXT 409
DISTRICT 7C - 622 S OAKES ST STE J
SAN ANGELO,TX 76903 PH 325 657-7450
FAX 325 657-7455
BARRY WOOD,DIR
DISTRICT 8 & 8A - CONOCO TOWERS
10 DESTA DR STE 500E MIDLAND,TX 79705
PH 432 684-5581 FAX 432 684-6005
SANTOS GONZALEZ,DIR
DISTRICT 09 - 5800 KELL BLVD
WICHITA FALLS,TX 76310 PH 940 723-2153
FAX 940 723-5088
WALTER GWYN,DIR PH 940 723-2153 EXT 211
DISTRICT 10 - 201 W FOSTER ROOM 300
PAMPA,TX 79066-0941 PH 806 665-1653
FAX 806 665-4217
COLE FRALEY,DIR PH 806 665-1653 EXT 14

- PIPELINE SAFETY DIVISION -
GENERAL INFO - PH 512 463-7058
DAMAGE PREVENTION - MAIN PH 512 475-0512
MARY (POLLY) ROSS MCDONALD,DIR
PH 512 463-7008
DAVID FLORES,DEPUTY DIR-PIPELINE
PH 512 936-0959
KENDALL SMITH,DEPUTY DIR-DAMAGE PREV
PH 512 463-7047
- REGIONAL OFFICES -
CORPUS CHRISTI,TX OFFICE - PO BOX 10307
78460 PH 361 242-3117 FAX 361 242-2101
STEVEN ROSS
FORT WORTH,TX OFFICE- 401 W 13TH ST 76102
PH 817 882-8966 FAX 817 882-8951
JODY KERL
HOUSTON,TX OFFICE - 1706 SEAMIST DR
STE 501 77008 PH 713 869-8425

FAX 713 869-3219
RICKY DANIELS
KILGORE,TX OFFICE - 619 HENDERSON BLVD
75662 PH 903 984-8581 FAX 903 983-3413
JAMES ALEXANDER
MIDLAND,TX OFFICE - CONOCO TOWERS
10 DESTA DR STE 500E 79705-4515
PH 432 570-5881 FAX 432 682-1325
GARY PARKER
PAMPA,TX OFFICE - PO BOX 941,201 W FOSTER
79066 PH 806 665-1653 FAX 806 665-4217
ALAN MANN

- SURFACE MINING & RECLAMATION DIVISION -
GENERAL INFO - PH 512 463-6900
FAX 512 463-6709
JOHN CAUDLE,DIR PH 512 463-6901
TYLER,TX OFFICE - 2202 OLD HENDERSON HWY
75702 PH 903 595-5501 FAX 903 595-0437
NANETTE MITCHELL

RAINBOW CHEMICALS INC
12218 JONES RD STE D-193
HOUSTON,TX 77070 PH 281 826-0489
FAX 281 826-0489
BRANDY MORGAN,OWNER
MARK A CAREY JR,PRES
GIDDINGS,TX OFFICE - 2581 HWY 77 S
78942 PH 979 542-9600 FAX 979 542-0484

RAINBOW INVESTMENTS COMPANY
PO BOX 1050
CORPUS CHRISTI,TX 78403-1050
PH 361 882-8407
STEVENS G HERBST,PRES
DUANE S HERBST,VP

RAINE JOHN W,III,IND GEOL
PO BOX 52723,304 LA RUE FRANCE STE 202
LAFAYETTE,LA 70505-2723 PH 318 235-6964
FAX 318 235-6961
JOHN W JACK RAINE,IV,CPL

RAM ASSOCIATES
PO BOX 716,1103 HUNT RD
STERLING CITY,TX 76951
PH 325 378-9365 PH 432 270-4838
RAMASSOC@ATT.NET
RAMANNING_98@YAHOO.COM
ROBERT A MANNING,PRTNR,CONS GEOL
LEWIS A MANNING,PRTNR,ENGR

RAM ENERGY HOLDINGS (LA),INC SEE
HRC ENERGY HOLDINGS (LA),INC
RAM ENERGY LOUISIANA,LLC SEE
HRC ENERGY LOUISIANA,LLC
RAM ENERGY RESOURCES (LAFOURCHE),INC SEE
HRC ENERGY RESOURCES (LAFOURCHE),INC
RAM ENERGY RESOURCES (WV),INC SEE
HRC ENERGY RESOURCES (WV),INC
RAM ENERGY RESOURCES,INC SEE
HALCON RESOURCES CORPORATION
RAM ENERGY,INC SEE
HALCON HOLDINGS,INC
RAM OPERATING COMPANY,INC SEE
HALCON RESOURCES OPERATING,INC
RAMBOLL OIL & GAS US,INC
COMPLETE ENGINEERING & PROJECT SERVICES
3200 WILCREST DR STE 250
HOUSTON,TX 77042 PH 713 952-0828
WWW.RAMBOLL.COM

CRISPIN RICHARDS,PRES
PH 713 579-1707 PH 713 702-1254
CRICHARD@RAMBOLL.COM
KEN BRAUD ROGUS-SALES@RAMBOLL.COM

RAMCO DRILLING,INC
111 W 2ND ST
JAMESTOWN,NY 14701-5207 PH 716 484-0102
STEPHEN J POWNALL,PRES

RAMCO OPERATING CO SEE
RAM ENERGY,INC

RAMPART PETROLEUM INC
2310 BRIARMOOR DR
MONROE,LA 71201-2342 PH 318 325-4303
MAX L RILEY,PRES
MAX L MIKE RILEY,JR,SECY

RAMSAY CORPORATION
PO BOX 52027,OCS
LAFAYETTE,LA 70505-2027
PH 337 237-1750 FAX 337 232-8818
DWIGHT S RAMSAY,PRES
J L HOLDEN,CONTROLLER
LYNN GUIDRY,LAND

RAMSHORN INVESTMENTS,INC
A WHOLLY OWNED SUBSIDIARY OF NABORS IND.
515 W GREENS RD STE 600
HOUSTON,TX 77067-4531
PH 281 874-0035 FAX 281 775-8414
JORDAN R DIGGER SMITH,PRES
BEATRICE PIERSON,OIL/GAS LAND MGR

RANDALL & DEWEY PARTNERS,LP
333 CLAY STE 1000
HOUSTON,TX 77002
PH 281 774-2000 FAX 281 774-2050
WWW.RANDEW.COM
RALPH EADS,III,CHMN
JOE GLADBACH,MNGNG DIR
BILL MARKO,MNGNR DIR
WARREN KEYES,MNRNG DIR
MILTON GILLESPIE,MNGNG DIR
JACK RANDALL,FOUNDER
KEN DEWEY,FOUNDER

RANDALL ENERGY,LLC
16225 PARK TEN PL STE 830
HOUSTON,TX 77084 PH 832 567-0414
RANDALL L COUCH RANDYCOUCH@AOL.COM

RANDELL OIL COMPANY
6630 E LINCOLN WAY
WOOSTER,OH 44691-8643 PH 330 264-7995
FAX 330 264-9846
RANDY DUNCAN,PRES
NANCY DUNCAN,SECY/TREAS

RANGE RESOURCES CORPORATION
100 THROCKMORTON ST STE 1200
FORT WORTH,TX 76102 PH 817 870-2601
FAX 817 869-9100
JOHN A PINKERTON,CEO

RANGE RESOURCES-APPALACHIA,LLC SEE
ENERVEST OPERATING,LLC

RANGE RESOURCES-PINE MOUNTAIN INC
406 W MAIN ST
ABINGDON,VA 24210-8406
PH 276 619-2583 FAX 276 628-7246
PHILIP S HORN

RANSON PROPERTIES
PO BOX 90010
SAN ANTONIO,TX 78209-9010

PH 210 826-8080 FAX 210 820-3324
KRANSON@RANSONPROPERTIES.COM
KELLY M RANSON

RAPAD DRILLING & WELL SERVICE INC
217 W CAPITOL ST STE 201
JACKSON,MS 39201-2099 PH 601 948-5279
FAX 601 355-5438 WWW.RAPADDRILLING.COM
WILLIAM R JAMES,PRES
BRUCE HIGHTOWER,BUS DEV MGR
PH 601 718-9426
ERBIE MASSENGILL,SFTY
LAUREL,MS BRANCH OFFICE - PO BOX 4240,
1309 HILLCREST DR 39440
PH 601 649-0760 FAX 601 649-9431
DONALD WILSON,VP
ROBBIE H HOLBROOK,VP

RAPHAEL PASS FIELD
7317 W ROADWAY ST
NEW ORLEANS,LA 70124-1649 PH 504 524-4918
FAX 504 586-8372
TED ALCUS,MGR

RAPID DRILLING CO INC
8225 ASHLAND RD
WOOSTER,OH 44691-9234 PH 216 264-2293
ROGER BURCKHART,PRES,OWNER
GARY WILHELMY,RIG SUPVSR

RAPP DAVID W,INC,CONS GEOL
10830 SAINT MARYS LN
HOUSTON,TX 77079-3618 PH 713 468-2747

RASHMI RESEARCH INC SEE
CALIFORNIA HYDROCARBONS CORPORATION

RAULSTON RANDALL G,INC,OIL & GAS LEASES
PO BOX 306
WOODWARD,OK 73802-0306 PH 580 698-2641
FAX 580 698-2642
FARGO, OK OFFICE - PO BOX 146,73840
306 W 6TH ST
RANDALL G RAULSTON,LDMN
JEAN L RAULSTON,LDMN
JAMES K RAULSTON,LDMN

RAULT RESOURCES,INC
110 VETERANS MEMORIAL BLVD STE 110
MATAIRIE,LA 70005-3023 PH 504 581-1314
FAX 504 581-1327 JRAULT3356@AOL.COM
JOSEPH M RAULT JR,PRES

RAUSCHER PIERCE REFSNES,INC
1001 FANNIN STE 400
HOUSTON,TX 77002 PH 713 652-3033

RAY ARNOLD C
501 CHOLLA CT
FORT WORTH,TX 76112-1101 PH 817 654-2045

RAYDIP EXPLORATION,LLC
2403 S COLLEGE AVE
BRYAN,TX 77801-2014 PH 979 224-1308
GIL DYLLA,PRES
GILDYLLA@HOTMAIL.COM

RAYES CALVIN M
5033 EIDER DR
CORPUS CHRISTI,TX 78413-2317
PH 361 991-5046

RAYNER RESOURCES,LLC
PO BOX 175
SCIO,NY 14880
PH 585 593-2298
DEAN L PHILLIPS

RAZORBACK BIT SERVICE
PO BOX 115, 262 T J KING RD
LOCKESBURG,AR 71846 PH 870 289-4533
PH 870 584-9430 JANDBBRACKET@GMAIL.COM
JERRY BRACKETT,OWNER

RB OPERATING CO SEE
RAM ENERGY,INC

RDA SERVICE COMPANY,INC
PO BOX 278
CITRONELLE,AL 36522-0278
PH 251 866-2800 FAX 251 866-2804
RDASERVICECO.@AOL
RONALD U DAVIS,PRES
MARY M DAVIS,SECY/TREAS
JEROME WILLIAMS,TRUCKING SUPVSR

READING & BATES PETROLEUM CO,SEE
RB OPERATING CO

READMORE INTERESTS,LP
4605 POST OAK PL DR STE 220
HOUSTON,TX 77027-9728 PH 713 222-0902
FAX 713 751-1761
KEY COLLIE,PRES

REAGAN ENERGY SERVICES,LLC
PO BOX 51194
LAFAYETTE,LA 70505-1194
PH 337 237-1296 FAX 337 237-1299
PREAGAN@REAGANENERGY.COM
PATRICK W REAGAN,MNGNG MEMBER
DAVID DEVILLE,LDMN
KAYLA LEMAIRE,LDMN
STACY HERRINGTON,CAD/MAPPING
LINDA COUVILLION,ACCT

REAGAN EQUIPMENT CO,INC
PO BOX 1850,2550 BELLE CHASSE HWY
GRETNA,LA 70054-1850 PH 504 367-2401
PH 800 487-7173 FAX 504 367-4044
SALES@REAGANPOWER.COM WWW.REAGAN-
POWER.COM
- BRANCH OFFICES -
HARVEY,LA OFFICE - 2230 PETERS ROAD
70058 PH 504 367-1870 PH 800 264-7767
FAX 504 361-4692
MORGAN CITY,LA OFFICE - 9580 HWY 90 E
70380 PH 985 631-0321 PH 877 343-1890
FAX 985 631-0483
VIDALIA,LA OFFICE - 5110 HWY 84 WEST
71373 PH 318 336-7161 PH 877 343-1889
FAX 318 336-8702
HEIDELBERG,MS OFFICE - HWY 528 WEST
39439 PH 601 787-3456 PH 800 530-7112
FAX 601 787-2226
FT LAUDERDALE,FL OFFICE - 2880 SW 42ND ST
33312 PH 954 935-0006 PH 888 545-6725
FAX 954 935 0010
ABITA SPRINGS,LA OFC-70161 HWY 59 STE G
70420 PH 985 801-0620 PH 985 801-0621

REALCO,LTD,INC
PO BOX 97,1212 HWY 12
DEQUINCY,LA 70633-1212
PH 337 786-2656 FAX 337 786-4018
REALCO_FREDDY@HOTMAIL.COM
FREDDY NIXON,PRES
JAMIE LUCHT,VP

REAMCO INC
A DRILLING TOOLS INTL COMPANY
1149 SMEDE HWY

BROUSSARD,LA 70518-8033 PH 337 364-9244
FAX 337 364-9603 WWW.REAMCOINC.COM
  BRENT R MILAM,PRES-MFG
  ASHLEY M LANE,EXEC VP INTL
  DONNA MATTHEWS,OFC MGR
  JOSEPH MALBREAUX,QC/QA MGR
  JEREMY MARCOTTE,DRAFTSMAN
  PHIL HARGRODER,SHOP FRMN
  CRAIG STANFORD,LEAD FRMN

REATA PETROLEUM
  PO BOX 921
  KILGORE,TX 75663-0921 PH 903 984-3443
  CHARLA ROLPH,AGENT

REBB ENERGY LLC
  1106 CASTLE HILL TRAIL
  KINGWOOD,TX 77339-3053 PH 281 359-7777
  STERLING B JONES,CEO
  DICK S JONES,PRES

REBICH ELI
  318 W RUSK ST
  TYLER,TX 75702-1513 PH 903 595-2990

RECILE SAM J,II
  115 ROBERT E LEE BLVD
  NEW ORLEANS,LA 70124 PH 504 488-1960

RECLAMATION RESOURCES
  13893 HIGHWAY 538
  OIL CITY,LA 71061-8785 PH 318 995-6298
  FAX 318 995-6298
  STEVE MCKENNA JR,PLANT FRMN

RED ARROW ENERGY,LLC SEE
  OVERTON ENERGY,LLC

RED CHUTE ENGINEERING,LLC
  4200 RESEARCH FOREST STE 280
  THE WOODLANDS,TX 77381
  PH 281 367-0059
  WMD@REDCHUTEENGINEERING.COM
  WILLIAM M DANIEL,PE/PRES

RED CROWN ROYALTIES,LLC
  PRODUCTION/MINERALS & ROYALTIES
  PO BOX 888
  LITTLETON,CO 80160-0888
  PH 303 794-9260 FAX 303 794-9261
  RONALD HORNIG,PRES
  ALLAN HEINLE,MGR
  BROOK PHIFER,MGR

RED EAGLE RESOURCES CORP SEE
  LOMAK PETROLEUM INC

RED FORK PRODUCTION,LLC
  3030 NACOGDOCHES RD STE 100
  SAN ANTONIO,TX 78217 PH 877 817-9300
  BILL BOLCH REDCLARION@YAHOO.COM

RED MOUNTAIN EXPLORATION,LLC
  EXPLORATION/PRODUCTION/ACQUISITIONS
  1490 W CANAL COURT STE 3000
  LITTLETON,CO 80160-5648
  PH 303 347-2600 FAX 303 347-0196
  RONALD E HORNIG,PRES,MGR

RED RIVER ENERGY,LLC SEE
  PETROHAWK ENERGY CORPORATION

RED WING SERVICE & SUPPLY,INC
  5357 GOODRICH RD
  CROWLEY,LA 70526 PH 337 988-1213
  FAX 337 984-0668 REDWING@REDWINGINTL.COM
  TIM ZAUNBRECHER,PRES
  JUDY ZAUNBRECHER,VP
  GERARD ZAUNBRECHER,MGR

  KAY HABETZ,ADMIN
  GODFREY ZAUNBRECHER,SALES
  GINGER BREAUX,SALES
  JAN ALLEMAN,CFO
  KENDRA RICHARD,ACCT

REDA,A CAMCO COMPANY
  7030 ARDMORE ST
  HOUSTON,TX 77054-2302 PH 281 440-1256
  FAX 281 440-0267
  BEN LUSCOMB,SLS REPR,GULF COAST AREA
  ROBERT NAVO,WESTERN DIV ACCT MGR
  JIM REID,WESTERN DIV PROJ DIR
  PAUL DOCHERTY,PROJ DEV MGR
  NATE THOMPSON,SLS REPR,AFRICA MKTG
  GLENN TONEY,EASTERN DIV ACCT MGR
  LINDA LOFTIS,SLS SPEC EASTERN DIV
  MARSHALL,TX SERVICE CENTER OFFICE -
  3220 W PINECREST DR,75670
  PH 903 938-5500 FAX 903 938-6006
  JIM NEWELL,GULF COAST AREA MGR
  JACK HARLIN,FLD SVC MGR
  DON WISINGER,SLS REPR,GULF COAST AREA
  MIDLAND,TX OFFICE - PO BOX 11046
  4709 SEMINOLE,79705 PH 432 699-2424
  FAX 432 699-2486
  MIKE FAIN,SLS REPR
  CHRIS ROPP,SLS MGR
  MIKE VITELLO,ASST SLS MGR
  PETE SCHROEDER,SLS REPR
  ANDY HOPE,SLS REPR
  THOMAS ANDERSON,SLS REPR
  LAUREL,MS OFFICE - 3048 OLD AMY RD
  39440 PH 601 422-0828
  DALLAS,TX OFFICE - 3100 MCKINNON ST
  STE 330 PH 972 233-9907 FAX 972 233-8943
  PETER SCHRENKEL,DOWNHOLE DEWATERING
  SYSTEMS MGR

REDMAN RESOURCES,LLC
  10375 RICHMOND AVE STE 920
  HOUSTON,TX 77042-4152
  PH 713 782-2870 FAX 713 782-1235
  JVONCANNON@REDMANCOMPANIES.COM

REDSTONE NATURAL RESOURCES,INC
  PO BOX 56383
  HOUSTON,TX 77256-6383 PH 713 623-6650
  FAX 713 623-2306
  STEPHEN S ADAMS,PRES
  JOHN W MOORE,LDMN

REED HYCALOG LP,SEE
  NOV REEDHYCALOG

REED MANUFACTURING CO
  1425 W 8TH ST
  ERIE,PA 16502 PH 800 666-3691
  FAX 800 456-1697 WWW.REEDMFGCO.COM
  REEDSALES@REEDMFGCO.COM
  SCOTT K WRIGHT,PRES-SLS/FIN
  MARK WRIGHT,PRES-MFG/PROD DEV

REED ROBERT R,II,OIL & GAS INTERESTS
  615 LEOPARD ST STE 515
  CORPUS CHRISTI,TX 78476-2201
  PH 361 888-5462

REED STEVE,IND PETR LDMN
  402 WHITEBARK DR
  LAFAYETTE,LA 70508-6360 PH 318 237-1162
  FAX 318 237-1163

REED TOOL COMPANY SEE REED HYCALOG LP
  A DIVISION OF SCHLUMBERGER

REEDER ENERGY
  4925 GREENVILLE AVE STE 1400
  DALLAS,TX 75206 PH 214 373-7793
  FAX 214 373-7832 WWW.REEDERENERGY.COM
  BRYAN T REEDER,PRES
  BREEDER@REEDERENERGY.COM
  GARY WENTE,VP EXPL
  GWENTE@REEDERENERGY.COM
  CURT HUMPHREYS,VP EXPL & DEV
  JEFF HARWELL,OPERS MGR

REEDER OPERATING,LLC
  4925 GREENVILLE AVE STE 1400
  DALLAS,TX 75206
  PH 214 373-7793 FAX 214 373-7832
  BRYAN T REEDER,PRES
  BREEDER@REEDERENERGY.COM
  GARY WENTE,VP EXPL
  GWENTE@REEDERENERGY.COM
  CURT HUMPHREYS,VP EXPL & DEV
  JEFF HARWELL,OPERS MGR

REEF SERVICES LLC
  PO BOX 11347, 7903 W HWY 80 79706
  MIDLAND,TX 79702-8347 PH 432 560-5600
  FAX 432 556-5636 WWW.REEFCORP.COM
  CLAY BALEN,PRES/CEO/COO
  WAYNE CLAYTON,CFO
  DWAYNE JOHNSON,REG DIR SLS-STIMULATION
  PH 432 634-0603
  TOM ROLAND,DIR SAFE & ENVIRO
  PH 432 559-1564
  ERIN ROLAND,DIR HR PH 432 230-6059
  TERRI GAINES,AR/AP MGR
  GARRETT DONNELLY,IT SPEC PH 432 425-2466
  PAUL MASON,CORP BUS DEV MGR
  PH 432 230-1980
  CORRIE GIDEON,EXEC ASST TO PRES
  DENISE STEWART,EXEC ASST TO PRES
  PH 432 557-6209
  - MIDLAND SALES -
  RANDY RODGERS,VP SLS PH 432 967-2987
  LES PREECE,DIR BUS ACQS & DEV
  PH 432 664-4108
  BRANDON MARTIN,AREA SLS MGR
  PH 432 559-3013
  GARY KNORR,SLS REP PH 432 425-8087
  BRYAN WEBB,SLS REP PH 432 631-7887
  JOHNNY HUGHES,SLS REG PH 432 557-7055
  TIFFANI BOHANNON,EXEC ASST TO SLS
  PH 432 560-5648 FAX 800 504-2141
  TIFFANI.BOHANNON@REEFCORP.COM
  ODESSA,TX OFFICE - 2559 W I-20 79766-9703
  PH 432 368-3900 OR 800 299-8105
  FAX 432 368-3936
  WANDA BATEN,DIR FLEET OPERS
  PH 432 894-1566
  GLEN HADLEY,AREA SLS MGR PH 432 631-7870
  MICHAEL MARQUEZ,ENVIRO & SAFE
  SHERRY HOGUE,SVC TECH MGR PH 432 425-4330
  ROBERT KEPPLE,SLS REP PH 432 557-2981
  JOHN MINOR,SLS REP PH 432 266-0617
  FRANK TORRES,SLS REP PH 432 425-4336
  BYWER HUTCHINSON,CHEM PH 432 425-4336
  PEGGY WADLE,CHEM ADMIN PH 432 556-8431
  SNYDER,TX OFFICE - 1600 AVE Q 79549-1781

PH 325 573-1133 OR 800 552-0621

FAX 325 573-4803

 LANE MARTIN,AREA SLS MGR PH 325 207-3148

 KATHY HOLDREN,BILLING MGR

 DAVID B MAYES,SLS REP PH 325 226-9169

 RON MATTHEWS,SLS REP PH 325 201-3641

 GLENN BARTON,SLS REP PH 325 338-7192

 S T DOOLEY,SLS REP PH 325 207-3145

ANDREWS,TX OFFICE - 500 S W MUSTAND DR

79714 PH 432 524-4441 FAX 432 524-4777

 RUDY SAUCEDA,SLS REP PH 432 634-7253

ROBSTOWN,TX OFFICE - 3182 COUNTY RD 48

78380-5945 PH 361 242-9030

FAX 361 242-9967

 DEAN DUKE,SLS REP PH 361 947-0137

GRANBURY,TX OFFICE - 5829 FALL CREEK HWY

76049-5358 PH 817 326-3603

FAX 817 326-3604

 WES SHOOK,AREA SLS MGR PH 817 894-7724

 LANDON HARRIS,SLS MGR PH 817 243-6147

 DENNIS LUKER,SLS REP PH 361 960-5161

 BILLY WEEKS,SLS REP PH 940 634-4412

LEVELLAND,TX OFFICE - 1937 W AVE BLD B

79336 PH 806 897-2744 FAX 806 897-2744

 RANDY ALLISON,AREA SLS MGR

  PH 806 789-3278

 JAYSON JONES,SLS REP PH 806 200-0925

 BRUCE LAIR,SLS TRNG & ACQS

  PH 432 413-0858

LONGVIEW,TX OFFICE - 2328 FM 208-N 75603

PH 903 236-4788 FAX 903 236-4798

 DWAYNE ROGERS,SLS REP PH 817 240-7188

FORT STOCKTON,TX OFFICE - PO BOX 1542

4167 N FM 1053,79735 PH 432 336-3898

FAX 432 336-3076

 BRUCE WINN,REG MGR PH 325 226-5140

 MARCOS VELASQUEZ,SLS REP PH 432 631-7865

POST,TX OFFICE - PO BOX 197A 79356

PH 806 495-3647 FAX 806 495-3647

 BUTCH GIDDENS,AREA SLS MGR

  PH 806 781-6752

 RODNEY ODEN,SLS REP PH 806 781-6750

PERRYTON,TX OFFICE - 2025 HWY 15 W 79070

PH 806 434-0304 FAX 806 434-0085

 MICHAEL HADEN,SLS REP PH 806 202-1816

BRIDGEPORT,TX OFFICE - 5750 US HWY 380

76426 PH 940 683-2134 FAX 940 683-2367

 LESTER NEWKIRK,SLS REP PH 682 224-9916

EDNA,TX OFFICE - 2083 STATE HWY 111 S

77957 PH 361 782-9279 FAX 361 782-9229

 JIMMY JOHNSON,SLS REP PH 361 771-6153

GAINESVILLE,TX OFFICE - 101 E FORELINE ST

76241 PH 940 612-3000 FAX 940 612-3001

 SHAWN HASTINGS,SLS REP PH 940 634-1606

ELECTRA,TX OFFICE - 102 W HWY 287 76360

 RAYMOND BORTON

HOUSTON,TX OFFICE - 3007 HEATHER LANE CT

KINGWOOD,TX 77345

 DON BARBATO,CORP SLS PH 713 471-8741

 CHARLES TOMPKINS,SR ACCT MGR

  PH 713 834-7857

SAN ANGELO,TX OFFICE - PO BOX 60025 76906

13498 HWY 67 S,79604 PH 325 944-2600

FAX 325 944-8811

 LARRY ROUTH,SLS REP PH 325 206-0326

HENNESSEY,OK OFFICE - PO BOX 64,73742

PH 405 853-6755 OR 800 853-6755

FAX 405 853-2599

 RANDY GRAPE,REG DIR SLS-STIMULATION

  PH 405 853-5810

OKLAHOMA CITY,OK OFFICE - 3500 S BLVD

BLDG B STE 5 EDMOND,OK 73118

 DENNIS AUTRY,REG ACCT MGR PH 405 315-2362

 JAYE FLYNN,CORP SLS PH 405 556-1408

 TIM GOOD,CORP SLS PH 405 820-4304

 MARK SOUTHERLAND,DIV MGR PH 405 642-5217

ELK CITY,OK OFFICE - RR4 BOX 7440,73644

PH 580 225-0833 OR 800 364-5366

FAX 580 225-0837

 NATHAN CLEMENTS,SLS REP PH 580 821-4773

LINDSAY,OK OFFICE - PO BOX 518,73052-0518

PH 405 756-4747 FAX 405 756-3213

 BALINE COLDREN,SLS REP PH 405 834-7412

 DON GIROD,SLS REP PH 405 830-8892

 MIKE BEAM,SLS REP PH 405 213-9542

 AMBER KOCH,SLS REP PH 405 818-7666

PAWHUSKA,OK OFFICE - PO BOX 1210,74056

876 OLD HWY 99 PH 918 287-3850

PH 800 300-8437 FAX 918 287-1632

 RICK MIZE,REG ACCT MGR PH 918 630-1454

 CHUCK GLENDENNING,SLS REP PH 918 629-6317

 LARRY KELSEY,SLS REP PH 405 312-7800

TULSA,OK OFFICE - 6400 S LEWIS AVE

STE 1900,74136

 CHARLES TROMPLER,SLS REP PH 918 760-4051

WOODWARD,OK OFFICE - 4119 OKLAHOMA AVE

73801 PH 580 256-5252 OR 800 874-3960

FAX 580 256-0553

 BILLY HOSIER,SLS REP PH 580 334-6393

HOBBS,NM OFFICE - PO BOX 2766 88241-2766

2703 W MARLAND ST 88240-8655

PH 505 391-6730 FAX 505 391-6724

 JIM NELSON,CITY SLS REP PH 432 288-4536

 JUNIOR GARCIA,SLS REP PH 432 894-0409

 BRIAN OVERTON,SLS REP PH 432 631-3545

 STEVE TIGERT,SLS REP PH 575 652-7020

CHANUTE,KS OFFICE - 8072 E HWY 39,66720

MAGNOLIA,AR OFFICE

 BARRY SMITH,AREA ACCT MGR PH 870 949-2066

 DAVID WALLACE,ACCT MGR PH 318 707-3388

 TERRY MCINNIS,ACCT MGR PH 870 949-0854

REESE DALE O INC,OIL & GAS EXPL & PROD

 6816 ROUNDROCK RD

 DALLAS,TX 75248-5027 PH 972 991-9117

  DORGEOL@TX.RR.COM

 DALE O REESE,PRES,IND GEOL,OIL OPER,PROD

REEVES MARY S

 PO BOX 489

 COLLINS,MS 39428 PH 601 765-8279

REEVES WIRELINE SERVICES,INC SEE

 WEATHERFORD INTERNATIONAL

REFINED PRODUCTS,INC

 4120 PIERRE DR

 BEAUMONT,TX 77705 PH 409 833-3936

 FAX 409 842-2395 LJH@SYSMATRIX.NET

REFUGIO ENTERPRISES INC

 P O BOX 825

 REFUGIO,TX 78377-0825 PH 361 526-4582

 W B WALES,PRES

 BILL B WALES,VP

REGAL INTERNATIONAL,INC

 PO BOX 4908

TYLER,TX 75712-4908 PH 903 872-3091

PH 800 442-6316 FAX 903 872-3095

 WWW.REGALRUBBER.COM

 KURT KNAUTH,GEN MGR KURTK3@AIRMAIL.NET

 LANCE REED,MARINE SLS

 BETTY DEMOSS,INTL OILFIELD SLS

 ROCKY HALE,CUSTOM MOLDING SLS

 CHUCK PARKS,INTL SLS MGR

  PH 281 355-7071

 GARY MARSHALL,DOM OILFIELD SLS

  PH 281 351-0912

REGARD RESOURCES CO,INC,GAS PROCESSING

 555 AERO DR

 SHREVEPORT,LA 71107 PH 318 425-2533

 FAX 318 425-1014 REGARDRES@AOL.COM

 RAYMOND REGARD,PRES

REGENCY ENERGY,INC

 2242 S HWY 83

 CRYSTAL CITY,TX 78839 PH 830 374-9000

 PH 830 317-0200 FAX 830 374-0202

 ROYIS WARD,OWNER/CEO

REGIONS BANK

 PO BOX 1628

 MOBILE,AL 36633-1628 PH 251 690-1346

 FAX 251 690-1560 WWW.REGIONS.COM

 MARK WYATT,SR VP,GEOL PH 251 690-1346

 MARK.WYATT@REGIONS.COM

 BIRMINGHAM,AL OFFICE - PO BOX 11426

 35282 PH 205 320-7212 FAX 205 326-5445

 ALLEN MORRIS,VP,GEOL

 ALLEN.MORRIS@REGIONS.COM

 ANTHONY EDWARDS,VP,GEOL

 TONY.EDWARDS@REGIONS.COM

 JACKSON,MS OFFICE - PO BOX 23100

 39225-3100 PH 601 968-4601

 FAX 601 354-8135

 EDWARD WALLER,VP,LDMN

 EDDY.WALLER@REGIONS.COM

 SHREVEPORT,LA OFFICE - 333 TEXAS ST

 SH-2091,71101-3666

 PH 318 429-1866 FAX 318 429-1125

 JOSEPH COLLIER,LDMN

 JOSEPH.COLLIER@REGIONS.COM

 TYLER,TX OFFICE - 100 E FERGSON ST,75702

 PH 903 535-4266

 JOEY HAND,SR VP,LDMN

 JOEY.HAND@REGIONS.COM

 ROSS DURR,LDMN

 ROSS.DURR@REGIONS.COM

REH ENERGY,INC

 500 N WATER ST STE 600

 CORPUS CHRISTI,TX 78401-0243

 PH 361 888-9192 FAX 361 888-9229

 JOYCE HAAS,PRES

 CLIFTON MCMASTERS,SECY/TREAS

REICHMANN PETROLEUM CORP

 711 N CARANCAHUA ST STE 1600

 CORPUS CHRISTI,TX 78401 PH 361 884-9437

 ERIK DOUGHTY

REIDCO ENTERPRISES

 2202 HWY 25 N

 ELECTRA,TX 76360 PH 940 495-2480

 FAX 940 495-2788 REIDCO412@GMAIL.COM

 RANDALL REID PH 940 631-8554

REILLY BENTON CO,INC

 PO BOX 52346,1645 TCHOUPITOULAS ST

NEW ORLEANS,LA 70152-2346
PH 504 525-9550 FAX 504 524-7079
W K WATTERS,PRES

REILLY OPERATING COMPANY INC
3133 PERSIMMON LN
FRISCO,TX 75033 PH 214 618-1723
REILLYOPERATING@GMAIL.COM
ERIC S BRANDENBURG

REINHART OIL AND GAS,INC
PO BOX 6749
SNOWMASS VILLAGE,CO 81615-6749
PH 970 920-0245 FAX 970 920-2610
REINER KLAWITER,PRES

REISIG NORMAN W,JR
28305 CREOLE RD
LACOMBE,LA 70445 PH 504 887-0627

REJISS ASSOCIATES
46 6TH ST
BRADDOCK,PA 15104-1948 PH 412 351-3500
JAMES JOSHOWITZ JIM@JOSHSTEEL@BIZ
STEVE JOSHOWITZ STEVE@JOSHSTEEL.BIZ

RELCO EXPLORATION CO,INC
PO BOX 4630
MONROE,LA 71211-4630 PH 318 387-3351
R W ELLINGTON JR,PRES
PATRICK ELLINGTON,GEN MGR

RELIABLE PRODUCTION SERVICE INC
PO BOX 176,9095 US HWY 190
LIVONIA,LA 70755
PH 225 637-4835 FAX 225 637-4842
WWW.RELIABLEPRODUCTION.COM
JAMES L MOORE,PRES
JOYCELYN NEWTON,EXEC SECY
JAMES (RANDY) MOORE,VP
DONALD AYMOND,CONSLT SLS
HUEY BOUDREAUX,SLS
JOHN HELWEG,CEMENT/P & A
RAY BRILEY,CEMENT/P & A
JAMIE BOUDREAUX,TOOL PUSHER
RICKY HEBERT,TOOL PUSHER
GARY RIVET,TOOL PUSHER
DOUGLAS MARTIN,TOOL PUSHER
ROBERT SOILEAU,TOOL PUSHER
CHARLES HYDLE,TOOL PUSHER
BOBBY LEE,TOOL PUSHER
DWAYNE DAVID,SLS

RELIANCE ENERGY LLC
PO BOX 787
MAGNOLIA,AR 71754-0787
PH 870 234-2700 FAX 870 234-5603
MAX STORY,PRES
MIKE RIPPETOE,GEOL

RELIANCE WELL SERVICE,INC
PO BOX 787
MAGNOLIA,AR 71754-0787 PH 870 234-2700
FAX 870 234-4776
MAX STORY,PRES
DAVID BURGE,WELL SVC MGR
TOM VOSS,SLS
MIKE RIPPETOE,GEOL
CHRIS STORY,DRLG MGR
CSTORY@RELIANCEWELLSERVICE.COM

RELIATERRE-PROFESSIONAL LAND SERVICES
PO BOX 52248
LAFAYETTE,LA 70505 PH 337 280-9989
WWW.RELIATERRE.COM

CHIP CLARK,CPL CHIP@RELIATERRE.COM

REMCO SERVICES,INC
155 MIMOSA DR
RIO GRANDE CITY,TX 78582-6327
PH 956 487-2067 FAX 956 487-0774
D B PINKY MCGUFFIN JR,PRES

REMEDIATION MANAGEMENT SERVICES SEE
BRANDT,A VARCO CO

REMINGTON OIL AND GAS CORPORATION SEE
ENERGY RESOURCE TECHNOLOGY GOM INC

REMMER RICHARD H,ESQ
500 SHORE DR
OAKDALE,NY 11769-2300 PH 631 589-0628

REMORA OIL COMPANY
PO BOX 710914
HOUSTON,TX 77271-0914 PH 281 980-6455
ALAN H MORGAN,VP,LAND
AMORGAN1@FLASH.NET
JOSEPH E FLOWERS,III,EXPL MGR

RENAISSANCE PETROLEUM COMPANY,LLC
17625 EL CAMINO REAL STE 220
HOUSTON,TX 77058 PH 281 480-6909
JOHN BASSETT,PRES
FRANK TURNER,CFO

REPUBLIC CENTRAL REALTY INC
17626 WILD OAK DR
HOUSTON,TX 77090 PH 281 447-5100
FAX 281 447-0069
GARY L SMITH GARY@RCRCORP.COM

REPUBLIC RESOURCES
3303 OAKWELL CT STE 220
SAN ANTONIO,TX 78218-3082
PH 210 805-9488 FAX 210 826-2595
JOHN V YORK,PRES
JVYORK@REPUBLICRESOURCES
STEVEN W PRICE,VP
MARK BARCKLOW,LDMN

RESEARCH OIL WELL SERVICES
PO BOX 211-403
BEDFORD,TX 76095-8403 PH 888 268-2885
ROGER DEAN,OWNER PH 817 627-9267

RESEARCH PLANNING,INC
1121 PARK ST
COLUMBIA,SC 29201-3137 PH 803 256-7322
FAX 803 254-6445 WWW.RESEARCHPLANNING.COM
JACQUELINE MICHEL,PRES
JACK MOORE,CONTROLLER

RESERVE ENERGY EXPLORATION CO
10155 GOTTSCHALK PKWY STE 1
CHAGRIN FALLS,OH 44023-5465
PH 440 543-0770 FAX 440 543-0770
WWW.RESERVE-ENERGY.COM
JAMES HAAS,CPL/DEV DIR
JAMESJHAAS@RESERVE-ENERGY.COM

RESERVOIRS INC - DIVISION OF CORE LABS
6316 WINDFERN RD
HOUSTON,TX 77040-4916 PH 713 328-2673
FAX 713 328-2190 IRS@CORELAB.COM
RESERVOIRS@CORELAB.COM
RANDY S MILLER,PRES
WAYNE D SEALEY,MGR,SALES & MKTG

RESOLVE DRILLING COMPANY SEE
GOLDRUS PRODUCING COMPANY

RESOURCE ACQUISITIONS CORPORATION SEE
PEAK ENERGY,LLC

RESOURCE EVALUATIONS,INC SEE
RESERVE EVALUATIONS,INC

RESOURCE MANAGEMENT,INC
PO BOX 7538
OVERLAND PARK,KS 66207-0538
PH 913 208-9151 HODGESRMI@GMAIL.COM
GREG HODGES,PRES
MARGARET HODGES,SECY/TREAS

RETRORECOVERY RESEARCH,INC
PO BOX 51547
LAFAYETTE,LA 70505-1547 PH 337 235-3578
L LINN SWAN,PRES

RETTIG JOHN W,JR,IND
P O BOX 51594,OCS 820 E ST MARY BLVD
LAFAYETTE,LA 70505-1594 PH 318 984-7091

REVELLE OIL PRODUCING CO
275 HICKORY POINT CT
FORSYTH,IL 62535 PH 217 875-7336
PH 618 676-1850
KAREN S REVELLE,OWNER
DEBI D REVELLE,BOOKKEEPER
MICHAEL YOUNGER,GEOL
PAUL WEIDNER,FLD SUPT

REX ENERGY
PO BOX 318
BRIDGEPORT,IL 62417
PH 618 945-8600 FAX 618 945-9203
JACK S SHAWVER,GEN MGR
JIM FEHRENBACHER,LAND MGR

REX RESOURCES INC
OIL,GAS,MINERAL PROD/GEOL,ENGRG,ENV CONSU
& SVCS/OILFLD,MINING PLUGGING/NEW & USED
OILFLD & MINING EQUIP & SUPPLIES
PO BOX 202,811 EAST 3RD ST
CENTRALIA,IL 62801-0202
PH 618 920-0999

REXCO ENERGY INC
416 TRAVIS ST STE 806
SHREVEPORT,LA 71101-5502 PH 318 424-1320
TERRY PAT REYNOLDS,PRES

REYNOLDS DAN,COMPANY
PO BOX 457
CAMDEN,AR 71711-0457
PH 870 836-2082 FAX 870 836-2085
DRCO@ATT.NET
JOHN R REYNOLDS SR,MNGNG PARTNER

REYNOLDS E & P,INC
7591 FERN AVE STE 2001
SHREVEPORT,LA 71105 PH 318 227-0118
FAX 318 227-0171
TERRY PAT REYNOLDS,PRES
VIRGINIA W REYNOLDS,VP

REYNOLDS J DAVID,COMPANY
P O BOX 659,308 WASHINGTON
CAMDEN,AR 71701-0659 PH 870 836-3500
J DAVID REYNOLDS,III,PRES

REYNOLDS RESOURCES INC
4129 HUNTING CREEK DR
OWENSBORO,KY 42303-7554 PH 270 684-5624
DOUGLAS W REYNOLDS,PRES

RHODES CONSULTING GROUP,LLC
845 LANE ALLEN RD STE B2
LEXINGTON,KY 40504
PH 859 619-4884 FAX 859 317-8685
LARRY R RHODES,PG/CPG-PRES
LARRYRHODESGEO@YAHOO.COM

WWW.RHODESEARTH.COM

RHUMBA OPERATING,LLC
415 TEXAS ST STE 201
SHREVEPORT,LA 71101-3540
PH 318 222-8787 FAX 318 222-7222
ERIC H FLETCHER,MGR

RIAL DRILLING CO INC,SEE
STERLING DRLG CO

RIALTO ENERGY,INC
PO BOX 61206
HOUSTON,TX 77208-1206 PH 713 655-8466
FAX 713 655-8469
F BARON CRAFT,PRES
W EDWARD CIESZKIEWICZ,EXEC VP

RIATA ENERGY,INC SEE
SANDRIDGE ENERGY INC

RICE ENGINEERING CORPORATION SEE
DUOLINE TECHNOLOGIES,L.P.

RICE JOHN H,OIL & GAS PROPERTIES
5210 QUINCY AVE
GULFPORT,MS 39507-4545 PH 228 214-0407

RICE ROGER F,OIL OPERATOR INC
PO BOX 271705
CORPUS CHRISTI,TX 78427
PH 361 765-6399
WWW.SELL4UHOMES.COM
ROGER F RICE,PRES,PETR GEOL
ROGER@SELL4UHOMES.COM

RICE UNIVERSITY LIBRARY
6100 MAIN ST
HOUSTON,TX 77005-1827 PH 713 527-4022
FAX 713 285-5258

RICE WINSTON C,IND OIL OPR
PO BOX 4944
SHREVEPORT,LA 71134-0944 PH 318 221-7456

RICELAND PETROLEUM COMPANY
PO BOX 51368
LAFAYETTE,LA 70505-1368 PH 337 237-5455
FAX 337 237-3622
W G GILLETTE JR,PRES

RICHARDS & WINKLER SEE
RW OPERATING CORP

RICHARDS JAMES V,IND GEOL
353 WESTMINSTER
HOUSTON,TX 77024 PH 713 290-8866
FAX 713 290-8867

RICHARDSON PRODUCTION COMPANY
SEE RICHARDSON OPERATING COMPANY

RICHLAND INVESTMENTS,LLC
305 OHIO ST
DELHI,LA 71232 PH 318 878-2244
FAX 318 878-8777
A J SNIDEN,MNGMG MEMBER
MARY ELLEN LOEWEN,MNGNG MGR

RICOCHET ENERGY INC
16111 VIA SHAVANO
SAN ANTONIO,TX 78249 PH 210 499-5172

RIDDELL EXPLORATION,LTD
2900 WESLAYAN RD STE 500
HOUSTON,TX 77027-5279
PH 713 652-2900 FAX 713 652-2903
BARBARA B RIDDELL,PRES
LOUISE R BLAND,VP
MELISSA R MILLIN,VP
JOAN R MCNAMARA,VP
NICHOLINA P NICHOLS,OFC MGR

RIDER CLARK W AND ASSOCIATES,INC
PO BOX 53751,1003 HUGH WALLIS RD STE D
LAFAYETTE,LA 70505-3751 PH 337 237-8112
FAX 337 237-8176 CWRAINC@COX-INTERNET.COM
CLARK W RIDER III,PRES
CYNTHIA N RIDER,CFO
CLASINA J SEGURA,OFC MGR

RIDGE PETROLEUM INC
3650 OLD BULLARD RD STE 430
TYLER,TX 75701-8668
PH 903 534-1653 FAX 903 534-1654
WWW.RIDGEPETROLEUM.COM

RIDGELINE EXPLORATION II,LLC
2450 FONDREN RD STE 112
HOUSTON,TX 77063-2314 PH 713 266-0322
FAX 713 266-0324
STEPHEN T CARROLL,VP,EXPL
STEPHENTCARROLL@ATT.NET

RIDGEMONT PROPERTIES,INC
5701 BROADWAY ST STE 200
SAN ANTONIO,TX 78209-5722
PH 210 826-1800 FAX 210 826-2754
C TREBES SASSER,PRES
TSASSER@RPITX.COM
NIKKI LAWSON,LDMN
SRO@RPITX.COM

RIDGEWOOD ENERGY CORPORATION
1254 ENCLAVE PKWY STE 600
HOUSTON,TX 77077
PH 281 293-8488 FAX 281 293-7391
W GREG TABOR,EXEC VP
GTABOR@RIDGEWOODENERGY.COM

RIDGWAY & YORK,LLC
PO BOX 195
RIDGELAND,MS 39158
PH 601 427-5388 FAX 601 427-5393
RIDGELAND,MS OFFICE- 701 AVIGNON DR 39157
JULIUS M RIDGWAY,MNGNG PRTNR
ANITA HEMPHILL,OFC MGR

RIDGWAY JULIUS M,OIL
BOX 195,701 AVIGNON DR STE 101 39157
RIDGELAND,MS 39158
PH 601 427-5388 FAX 601 427-5393

RIDGWAY MANAGEMENT INC,OIL PROPERTIES
PO BOX 187
JACKSON,MS 39205-0187 PH 601 353-8349
FAX 601 352-8480
C R RIDGWAY IV,PRES
RICHARD L RIDGWAY,VP
WILLIAM B RIDGWAY JR,SECY/TREAS
JANET TRIMM,CONTROLLER
ELIZABETH FERGUSON,LAND

RIDLEY OIL CORP
100 E FERGUSON ST STE 803
TYLER,TX 75702-5754
PH 903 595-4691 FAX 903 595-1321
WADE C RIDLEY,PRES
THOMAS P RIDLEY,SECY

RIDLEY WADE C
100 E FERGUSON ST STE 803
TYLER,TX 75702-5748
PH 903 595-4691 FAX 903 595-1321

RIG LOCATION & PERMIT REPORT SERVICE SEE
RIGDATA

RIG MANAGERS,INC
1907 DUNBARTON DR STE A

JACKSON,MS 39216-5027 PH 601 362-5121
FAX 601 362-5135 MHARDEE@ACOMPUTER.COM
J MARK HARDEE,PRES

RIGDATA
PO BOX 820547,7001 BOULEVARD 26 STE 600
FORT WORTH,TX 76182-0547
PH 817 285-9600 PH 800 627-9785
FAX 817 285-9404 WWW.RIGDATA.COM
CUSTOMERSERVICE@RIGDATA.COM
HOUSTON,TX SALES OFFICE - 15915 KATY FWY
STE 450,77094-1717
PH 281 646-1960 PH 800 371-0083
FAX 281 646-7158

RIGGS JAMES P,OIL & GAS PROPERTIES
PO BOX 33
FREDERICKSBURG,TX 78624-0033
PH 830 997-4873
JAMES P RIGGS,OWNER
INA VLEESHOUWER,MGR

RIGHT ENERGY LTD
PO BOX 1023
MANDEVILLE,LA 70470-1023
PH 985 502-9104 FAX 985 867-9078
C M JACOBS,GEOL

RILAN LLC
13642 LAKESIDE PLACE DR
WILLIS,TX 77318-5670
PH 713 527-9002 FAX 713 527-8733

RILEY ELECTRIC LOG SEE
A2D TECHNOLOGIES

RILEY MANNON & STURGEON,LTD
PO BOX 517
BARBOURSVILLE,WV 25504-0517
PH 304 736-8850
MICHAEL R MANNON,PRES
CRAIG H ADKINS,VP,GEOPHY DIV

RILEY OIL & GAS
2310 BRIARMOOR DR
MONROE,LA 71201-2342 PH 318 325-4303
MAX L RILEY,OWNER
MAX L MIKE RILEY JR,ASSOC

RINCON PETROLEUM CORPORATION
615 LEOPARD ST STE 722
CORPUS CHRISTI,TX 78476-2214
PH 361 883-9896 FAX 361 883-9876
ROSS C FORD JR,PRES

RINE DRILLING AND EXPLORATION,INC SEE
C. H. TODD,INC

RING EXPLORATION INC
20329 SH 249 STE 375
HOUSTON,TX 77070-2751 PH 281 463-7819
DAVID J DALLY,GEOL
BLAKE P PATTERSON,GEOL
JAMIE L HENRY,ADMIN ASST

RINGWOOD GATHERING COMPANY
810 HOUSTON ST
FORT WORTH,TX 76102-6298
PH 817 870-2800 FAX 817 870-8441
NICK DUNGEY,CHRMN,PRES
SHANE ALEXANDER,DIR OF FACILITIES
SUSAN HOLLEY,MGR CONTRACT ADMIN

RIO BRAVO EXPLORATION & PRODUCTION CO
2000 BERING DR STE 210
HOUSTON,TX 77057-3732
PH 713 781-6055 FAX 713 781-6461
B M GAMBLE,PRES/CEO

BEVERLY GAMBLE,VP EXPL
RUSSELL GIBSON,OFC MGR

RIO BRAZOS ENERGY CO
190 S COLLINS RD STE 102
SUNNYVALE,TX 75182
PH 972 571-2666 PH 972 226-6600
PAUL E.CASH,PRES

RIO EXPLORATION COMPANY
745 E MULBERRY AVE STE 100
SAN ANTONIO,TX 78212   PH 210 820-0404
FAX 210 820-3232 WWW.HUPECOL.COM
JOHN T SAUNDERS JR,PRES
REDGE GREENBERG,GEOL

RIO LAND CLEARING
HYDRO AX WORK FOR SEISMIC & OTHER
OILFIELD RELATED NEEDS
4107 OAK ST
SAN MARCOS,TX 78666 PH 512 393-4399
RIOLANDCLEARING@HOTMAIL.COM
MARK WHEELOCK

RIO-TEX,INC
2015 EVANS RD STE 200
SAN ANTONIO,TX 78258-7428 PH 210 497-1113
FAX 210 497-1116
AL T PERKINS,PRES
NANCI L PERKINS,VP
C GEDRAITIS,OFC MGR

RIPCO
5835 BELLE GROVE AVE
BATON ROUGE,LA 70820-5005 PH 225 769-7088
FAX 225 769-7088
IRION BORDELON,AGT

RIPPY OIL COMPANY
121 S BROADWAY STE 404
TYLER,TX 75702-7275
PH 903 595-0929 FAX 903 592-8701
JAMES REED RIPPY,VP
CHARLIE RIPPY,VP

RISCHE R R & ASSOC
1910 COUNTRY CLUB BLVD
SUGAR LAND,TX 77478-3910 PH 713 759-6991
ROBERT RISCHE,PRTNR
ELI SMITH,PRTNR

RISEDEN SERVICES,INC
PO BOX 56733
HOUSTON,TX 77256-6733 PH 713 781-1537
J E RISEDEN,PRES

RISK MANAGEMENT & PREVENTION SYSTEMS
PRODUCTS/SVCS: WELLSURE,HAZSURE
7908 N SAM HOUSTON PKWY W STE 500
HOUSTON,TX 77064-3513 PH 713 621-7911
FAX 713 621-7988
GARY BO BURRIS,PRES

RIVER BEND ENERGY CORPORATION
PO BOX 5206
SLIDELL,LA 70469-5206 PH 985 201-1139
ROMAN MATRANGA,PRES

RIVER GAS CORPORATION,THE
12031 LAKE NICOL RD
TUSCALOOSA,AL 35406-9315 PH 205 759-3282
FAX 205 759-3188
W C HURTT,CEO
DAVID (MIKE) CHAMBERS,PRES
JEFF RUST,VP,ACCT
JOEY STEPHENSON,VP,LAND
CHARLES WILLIS,VP,SPECIAL PROJ

T BURNS,GEOL
M FARRENS,EXEC VP,UTAH OPERS
W STACY,VP,BLACK WARRIOR OPERS
B SINGLETON,RES ENGR
TUSCALOOSA,AL FIELD OFFICE - 12031
LAKE NICOL RD 35406 PH 205 759-1161
FAX 205 759-1380

RIVER OAKS TRUST COMPANY SEE
COMPASS BANK

RIVER ROUGE MINERALS
OIL & GAS PRODUCER,MINERAL EXPLORATION
PO BOX 865
MANSFIELD,LA 71052-0865 PH 318 872-2728
FAX 318 872-0688 RRM@SHREVE.NET
GARY L MONTCALM,GEOL
RAVEL T MONTCALM,GEOL

RIVERFORD EXPLORATION LLC
35 FREESTONE
THE WOODLANDS,TX 77382
PH 832 928-5303
BILL FAIRHURST
BFAIRHURST@RIVERFORD-RESOURCES.COM

RIVIERA FINANCE
8410 N SAM HOUSTON PKWY W
HOUSTON,TX 77064 PH 800 874-0149
JOSIE RAMIREZ JRAMIREZ@RIVIERAFINANCE.COM

RLP GULF STATES LLC SEE
HLP GULF STATES,LLC

RMN OIL & GAS LLC
5026 REHBURG RD
BURTON,TX 77835-5715 PH 979 289-2198
WWW.RMNOILANDGAS.COM
RUSSELL M NEINAST,PRES
RUSSELL@RMNEINAST.COM
HOUSTON,TX OFFICE - 5740 SAN FELIPE
STE 421,77057 PH 713 898-4327

RMS MONTE CHRISTO,LLC
PO BOX 6749
SNOWMASS VILLAGE,CO 81615-6749
PH 970 920-0245 FAX 970 920-2610
REINER KLAWITER,MNGNG MEMBER
JAMES SPILLANE,LAND/MKTG MGR

ROBBINS PETROLEUM CORPORATION
PO BOX 2347,513 N SECOND ST
LONGVIEW,TX 75606-2347 PH 903 757-4500
FAX 903 757-4034
JOHN CLINTON ROBBINS,PRES
BETTY ROBBINS HURST,VP
DOROTHY ROBBINS SKEANS,ASST SECY/TREAS
NANCY SALMON,EXEC ASST

ROBBINS W H & ASSOCIATES LLC
302 LA RUE FRANCE STE 100
LAFAYETTE,LA 70508-3133 PH 337 232-5004
FAX 337 232-8271 WHR@WHROBBINS.COM
REMY WILLIAMS,OWNER,CONS GEOL
BILL DALE,OWNER,CONS GEOL
ARTHUR CHRISTY,GEOL

ROBERTS & MURPHY INC
PO BOX 7125,1500 N MARKET ST
SHREVEPORT,LA 71137-7125 PH 318 221-8601
FAX 318 226-0965
BRUCE G ROBERTS,PRES
DEBBIE MARTIN,GEN MGR

ROBERTS AND BUNCH OFFSHORE,INC SEE
NCX COMPANY,LLC

ROBERTS BRUCE G
PO BOX 7125,ROBERTS CTR 1500 N MARKET
SHREVEPORT,LA 71137-7125 PH 318 221-8601
FAX 318 226-0965

ROBERTS JAMES C AND ASSOC
PO BOX 53977
LAFAYETTE,LA 70505-3977 PH 337 233-3429
FAX 337 233-4594
JAMES C ROBERTS,PRES

ROBERTS RICK G
200 W 2ND ST
FORTH WORTH,TX 76102-3021 PH 592 592-8326
RICK G ROBERTS,OWNER

ROBERTS W MAC SEE
PETROLEUM LANDS RESOURCES

ROBERTSON & CORBUT SEE
CORBUT & ASSOCIATES LLC

ROBERTSON A E SPECIALTY CO
1265 GRIMMETT DR
SHREVEPORT,LA 71107-6623 PH 318 424-5425
PH 800 234-9449 FAX 318 424-7847
A E ROBERTSON
MIKE ROBERTSON
KILGORE,TX OFFICE - 404 INDUSTRIAL BLVD
75662 PH 903 983-1250 FAX 903 983-5474
ELLISVILLE,MS OFFICE - 5435 HIGHWAY 11 N
35437 PH 601 422-0801 FAX 601 422-0302

ROBERTSON JOHN L OIL & GAS PROPERTIES
PO BOX 1600
JASPER,TX 75951 PH 409 383-0817
FAX 409 383-0820

ROBERTSON ONSHORE DRILLING COMPANY SEE
PATTERSON ONSHORE DRILLING COMPANY

ROBERTSON R B & SON GAS & OIL
PO BOX 190
NEW BETHLEHEM,PA 16242-0190
PH 814 275-1406 PH 814 229-8595
ROCK ROBERTSON,PRTNR

ROBERTSON RESOURCES
600 LEOPARD ST STE 1520
CORPUS CHRISTI,TX 78473-1601
PH 361 882-7404 FAX 361 882-7076

ROBERTSON RICHARD P,CONSULTING GEOL
802 SLATTERY BLVD
SHREVEPORT,LA 71104-4822 PH 318 868-4881

ROBICHAUD ROBERT P
400 TRAVIS ST STE 220
SHREVEPORT,LA 71101-3110 PH 318 424-3235
FAX 318 424-0549 ROBY220@BELLSOUTH.COM

ROBICHEAUX JEAN M,GEOL
7110 UNIVERSITY DR #214
SHREVEPORT,LA 71105-5044 PH 318 425-3919

ROBIN USA,INC
5751 ENGLISH TURN DR
PACE,FL 32571-9545
PH 850 995-0696 FAX 850 994-5716
ROBINUSA2@MCHSI.COM
JOHN C ALBURY,PETROLEUM LDMN

ROBINSON A J,JR,CONS GEOL
PO BOX 53964,OIL CENTER STATION
LAFAYETTE,LA 70505-3964 PH 337 984-4125

ROBINSON GENE R,GEOL
PO BOX 5849
SHREVEPORT,LA 71135-5849 PH 318 429-2424

ROBINSON INTERESTS I,LTD
5005 RIVERWAY DR STE 200

HOUSTON,TX 77056-2123
PH 713 627-9440 FAX 713 627-7398
GEORGE A ROBINSON,PRES
ROBERT S PULITZER,VP
J WARREN DOYLE,LDMN PH 504 865-7900

ROBINSON JOHN M OIL & GAS
AKA RARE TECHNOLOGY
9333 MEMORIAL DR STE 201
HOUSTON,TX 77024-5735
PH 713 956-6274 FAX 713 682-2653
JOHN M ROBINSON,PRES

ROBINSON MINERALS TRUST
2803 GULF TO BAY BLVD STE 424
CLEARWATER,FL 33759
PH 813 287-2643 FAX 813 287-2904
ROBERT ROBINSON,TRUSTEE

ROBINSON RON S,GEOL
1109 BROOKWOOD
EL DORADO,AR 71730-3017 PH 870 863-5896

ROBISON OIL CO
PO BOX 324,5316 E SEVEN HILLS LN
OLNEY,IL 62450-0324 PH 618 395-1866
MARGARET R CARSON,PRES

ROBLYN RESOURCES, INC.
PO BOX 52102,110 SIDNEY ST
LAFAYETTE,LA 70506-2434 PH 337 232-6681
FAX 337 232-6681
ERNEST F CLOONEY JR,PRES

ROBRO ROYALTY PARTNERS,LTD
PO BOX 671099
DALLAS,TX 75367-1099 PH 214 707-7535
FAX 214 572-2600 WWW.TRUNKBAY.NET
BENNY DUNCAN,MGR BDUNCAN@TRUNKBAY.NET

ROCK CHALK ROYALTIES,LTD
6505 E CENTRAL AVE PMB 237
WICHITA,KS 67206-1924
PH 316 613-3401 FAX 316 613-3402
JOHN C CARNES,OWNER/IND PETR GEOL
CHANCE CARNES,ACQS & LAND

ROCK ENERGY CORPORATION
PO BOX 885
SEGUIN,TX 78156-0885 PH 512 754-6868
FAX 512 353-0334
JON NELSON JR,PRES

ROCK ENERGY,INC
100 CREOLE DR
MONTGOMERY,LA 71454 PH 225 266-9631
JAMES L DYSON,C.P.G.,PRES
JAMESDYSON55@GMAIL.COM
JANET FLETCHER DYSON,GEOL

ROCK ISLAND LLC
PO BOX 743
SPENCER,WV 25276
PH 304 927-0940 FAX 304 927-0941
SAM MCCUMBERS,PRES
TOM NUTT,SECY

ROCK RIDGE OIL & GAS,INC
115 TECHE DR
LAFAYETTE,LA 70503-2537
PH 303 283-3280 FAX 303 283-3280
ROLAND DEBRUYN,PRES
SCOTT HESS,VP

ROCK SOLID IMAGES
2600 S GESSNER STE 650
HOUSTON,TX 77063 PH 713 783-5593
WWW.ROCKSOLIDIMAGES.COM

RICHARD COOPER,CEO
GARETH TAYLOR,PRES

ROCKSOLID SYSTEMS LLC
11152 WESTHEIMER #828
HOUSTON,TX 77042 PH 800 880-6440
INFO@ROCKSOLID.SYSTEMS
PAUL YORKI PAUL.YORKI@GMAIL.COM

ROCKY MOUNTAIN STEEL MILLS SEE
EVRAZ INC NA

RODCO PETROLEUM,INC
4600 CASTLEBAR ST NW
CANTON,OH 44708-2139 PH 330 477-9823
BETTY O'NEILL-RODERICK,PRES
BETTYRODERICK@YAHOO.COM

RODEO RESOURCES,LLC
1518 S KIRKWOOD RD
HOUSTON,TX 77077-3122 PH 281 531-6363
FAX 281 531-6365
TOM MCNEILL,MNGNG MEMBER
TMCNEILL@RODEORESOURCES.COM

RODESSA OIL & LAND COMPANY
13828 LAKESIDE DR
CLARKSVILLE,MD 21029-1300
PH 301 854-3767 FAX 301 854-0121
ROLCOINC@AOL.COM
PODGE M REED,JR,PRES
KATHERINE R ROBERTSON,SECY/TREAS

ROEMER INTERESTS LTD
25815 OAK RIDGE ROAD
SPRING,TX 77380 PH 713 623-2183
LAMAR B ROEMER

ROGERS & SON OIL & GAS
12435 S CALHOUN HWY
ARNOLDSBURG,WV 25234-8014 PH 304 655-8975
FAX 304 655-9971
MICHAEL ROGERS,OWNER,OPR

ROGERS JAMES L,OIL LEASE BROKER
PO BOX 147
BLUE SPRINGS,MO 64013-0147
PH 816 650-3565

ROGERS MIKE,DRILLING CO,INC
PO BOX 126
MAGNOLIA,AR 71754-0126
PH 870 234-2356 MRDC1981@GMAIL.COM
MIKE ROGERS,PRES
CRAIG ROGERS,VP

ROGERS OIL & GAS PROPERTIES
PO BOX 889
FRESNO,TX 77545-0889 PH 713 429-5219
WWW.EUROAMERICANMINERALS.TRIPOD.COM
ROYALTY@RRTIERRA.COM
LANDASSETS@AOL.COM
R E THIGPEN III,PRES

ROLLOW THOMAS A,OIL PROPERTIES
307 BRIARGATE WALK
LAFAYETTE,LA 70503-3012 PH 337 269-1362
FAX 337 269-1362

ROLOIL EXPLORATION CO INC
307 BRIARGATE WALK
LAFAYETTE,LA 70503-3012 PH 337 269-1362
THOMAS A ROLLOW,PRES

ROMA ENERGY,INC
PO BOX 45
CORPUS CHRISTI,TX 78403-0022
PH 361 739-4822
MARY ANNE SINCLAIR,PRES

ROMA OIL & GAS,INC
1250 NE LOOP 410 STE 213
SAN ANTONIO,TX 78209-1533 PH 210 828-4522
FAX 210 828-1112 ROMAOIL@SWBELL.NET
GARY W PALMER,PRES
BEVERLY FELTS,CONTROLLER

ROMERO TOMMY J,PETR LDMN
PO BOX 130446
TYLER,TX 75713-0446 PH 903 581-7575
TROMERO1017@GMAIL.COM

RONKARAN OIL COMPANY SEE
ABB OIL CO,INC

ROONEY & ASSOCIATES
1002 CASTLE HILL TRL
KINGWOOD,TX 77339-2902 PH 281 440-6589
DON J ROONEY,PRES

ROOSTH PRODUCTION COMPANY
PO BOX 8300,3310 S BROADWAY STE 200
TYLER,TX 75711-8300
PH 903 593-8333 FAX 903 595-2190
STEVE ROOSTH,PRES
DAVID DECKER,LAND MGR
KATHY HARDY,LAND TECH
KILGORE,TX OFFICE - POWDERHORN RD
75662 PH 903 984-5224

ROSE ENTERPRISES,INC
PO BOX 1455
TYLER,TX 75710-1455
PH 903 245-7673 I.PLM.CPL@GMAIL.COM
CAROLYN TAYLOR,PRES
CSTAYLOR@ROSEOFFICESUPPLYETC.COM

ROSENTHAL STANLEY H
PO BOX 2750
BAY CITY,TX 77404-2750 PH 409 245-9891

ROSS BILL C,IND GEOL
706 FIRST PL
TYLER,TX 75702 PH 903 597-3741
FAX 903 526-7058

ROSS EXPLORATIONS,INC
2917 OLD GREENWOOD RD STE 10
FORT SMITH,AR 72903
PH 479 783-7022 FAX 479 783-7095
TIM ROSS SMITH,PRES

ROSS JACK CPL
202 ANTIGUA DR
LAFAYETTE,LA 70503-5086 PH 318 984-5064

ROSS PETROLEUM,INC
6150 ROMA DR
SHREVEPORT,LA 71105-4636 PH 318 222-4900
FAX 318 222-4910
ALAN N ROSS,PRES

ROSS PRODUCTION COMPANY
6150 ROMA DR
SHREVEPORT,LA 71105-4636 PH 318 222-4900
FAX 318 222-4910
ALAN ROSS
A S ROSS

ROSSON EXPLORATION COMPANY
PO BOX 2065,4021 N STATE ST 39206
JACKSON,MS 39225-2065 PH 601 969-2022
FAX 601 362-0206
BERT J ROSSON

ROTHCHILD ENERGY & MINERALS TRUST
2803 GULF TO BAY BLVD STE 424
CLEARWATER,FL 33759
PH 813 287-9594 FAX 813 287-2904

ROBERT ROBINSON,TRUSTEE

ROTHCHILD OIL AND GAS,INC
2803 GULF TO BAY BLVD STE 424
CLEARWATER,FL 33759
PH 813 287-2643 FAX 813 287-2904
ROBERT ROBINSON,CHRMN

ROTTER ED,ENGINEERING,INC
4455 GOLLIHAR
CORPUS CHRISTI,TX 78411-2907
PH 361 854-2346 FAX 361 854-2347
ED ROTTER,PE,ELECT ENGR

ROUGHNECK RIG SALES
SLS/WELL SVC RIG/MOBILE DRLG RIGS & EQUIP
59 BALD EAGLE LN
SAND SPRINGS,OK 74063 PH 918 496-2342
FAX 918 246-0303
GENE SPELL,PRES

ROUND HILL ROYALTY L.P.
PO BOX 25128,4625 GREENVILLE AVE STE 201
DALLAS,TX 75225-1128 PH 214 691-5977
FAX 214 691-5978
SETH WOODBERRY,MGR

ROUND MOUNTAIN RESOURCES,LLC
3604 CEDAR SPRINGS RD #106
DALLAS,TX 75219-4952 PH 832 515-8690
PH 512 698-6366 512 695-8577
EVAN HUGHES,PRES,CEO
KEVIN MCQUEEN,EXEC VP
ANTONIO LAGERA,CFO,COO

ROUNDTREE & ASSOCIATES INC
210 TRACE COLONY PARK DR
RIDGELAND,MS 39157
PH 601 355-4530 FAX 601 355-1102
RONALD T ROUNDTREE,PRES
BRIAN R ROUNDTREE,VP
DAVID HANCOCK,EXPL MGR

ROUSSEAU JULES A,PETR GEOL
PO BOX 53305
LAFAYETTE,LA 70505-3305 PH 318 981-5406

ROUSSEL & CLEMENT APC
1714 CANNES DR
LA PLACE,LA 70068 PH 504 651-6591
FAX 504 651-6592
GEROLYN P ROUSSEL,ATTY
PERRY J ROUSSEL,ATTY
ROUSSELP@BELLSOUTH.NET
JONATHAN B CLEMENT,ATTY
LAUREN R CLEMENT,ATTY

ROWAN J MIKE
PO BOX 6784
TYLER,TX 75711-6784 PH 903 539-9025
FAX 903 593-2862
MIKEROWAN@SUDDENLINK.COM

ROWAN ROBERT L & ASSOC INC
PO BOX 920760,3816 DACOMA ST
HOUSTON,TX 77292-0760 PH 713 681-5811
PH 800-231-2908 FAX 713 681-5815
WWW.INFO@RLROWAN.COM

ROWE A,III,INC,PROFESSIONAL LAND SERVICES
PO BOX 1815
TEXARKANA,TX 75504-1815 PH 214 794-1010
AUBY ROWE,III

ROWE G M MAC ,III
PO BOX 66802
HOUSTON,TX 77266 PH 713 526-8919
FAX 713 526-9108 GMR3@PEOPLEPC.COM

ROWE G M,JR
PO BOX 66802
HOUSTON,TX 77266 PH 713 526-8919
FAX 713 526-9108 GMR2@PEOPLEPC.COM
DALLAS,TX OFFICE - 4328 BELCLAIRE
75205 PH 214 521-1953

ROWE OIL PROPERTIES,INC
PO BOX 66802
HOUSTON,TX 77266-6802 PH 713 526-8919
FAX 713 526-9108
G M ROWE III,PRES

ROWELL JAMES A,JR,CONS GEOL
509 MARKET ST STE 300
SHREVEPORT,LA 71101-3275 PH 318 221-6156

ROWOIL,INC
PO BOX 447
BROWNSBORO,TX 75756-0447
PH 903 852-3765 FAX 903 852-6698
HORACE E ROWOLD,CPL PRES EMERITUS
SHIRLEY A ROWOLD,RPL,PRES

ROWOLD HORACE E,CPL
PO BOX 447
BROWNSBORO,TX 75756-0447
PH 903 852-3765 FAX 903 852-6698

ROWOLD LEGACY INC
PO BOX 516
TYLER,TX 75710
PH 903 571-9830 FAX 903 852-6698
CHRISTOPHER W WALKER,PRES
CHRISTOPHER.WALKER@SUDDENLINKMAIL.COM

ROYAL INTERNATIONAL PETROLEUM CORP(RIPCO)
5835 BELLE GROVE AVE
BATON ROUGE,LA 70820-5005 PH 225 769-7088
FAX 225 769-7088
NEW ORLEANS,LA OFFICE - 1120 OIL & GAS
BLDG,70112 PH 504 525-6234
IRION J BORDELON,AGT

ROYAL PRODUCTION COMPANY,INC
500 N SHORELINE BLVD STE 807
CORPUS CHRISTI,TX 78471-1008
PH 361 888-4792
J SCOTT SMITH,PRES

ROYAL RESOURCES CORP
PO BOX 98
FARMINGTON,WV 26571-0098
PH 304 363-8131 FAX 304 363-8140
JOHN P STITT,PRES
MARTINSBURG,WV OFFICE - 1604 MEMORIAL PK
AVE 25401

ROYALTY MANAGEMENT & DEVELOPMENT CORP
6516 WILTY ST
METAIRIE,LA 70003 PH 504 887-5688
FAX 504 456-0328
IRA PATTERSON JR,PRES

ROYCE A SCOTT SEE
SCOTT ROYCE A

ROYCE BEN L,INC
LEASE BROKER,PETROLEUM LAND SERVICE
3007 FERNDALE PLACE
HOUSTON,TX 77098 PH 713 542-5295
FAX 713 526-2875 BROYCE5020@AOL.COM
BEN L ROYCE,PRES

ROZEL ENERGY,LLC
PO BOX 52150,100 ASMA BLVD STE 110
LAFAYETTE,LA 70505
PH 337 237-7788 FAX 337 237-4334

C WILLIAM ROGERS,MGR
BUDDY POWELL,SR GEOL
YVONNE B MITCHELL,LAND MGR
JOHN DANSER,SR GEOL

RPS
INTERNATIONAL CONSULTANCY
411 N SAM HOUSTON PKWY STE 400
HOUSTON,TX 77060 PH 281 448-6188
FAX 281 448-6189 WWW.RPSGROUP.COM
PETER FEARN,PRES/DIR FEARNP@RPSGROUP.COM
TOSS STUBBS,EXEC PRES-OPERS
STUBBST@RPSGROUP.COM
SHANON DISORBO,EXEC PRES-ENVIRO
DISORBOS@RPSGROUP.COM
ANDY KIRCHIN,EXEC PRES-CONSLT
KIRCHINA@RPSGROUP.COM
STEVE MUNCEY,EXEC PRES-NAUTILUS
MUNCEYS@RPSGROUP.COM
EOIN HOWLETT,EXEC PRES-METOCEAN/
OCEANOGRAPHY
EOIN.HOWLETT@RPSGROUP.COM
PH 401 789-6224
AUSTIN,TX OFFICE - 1250 S CAPITAL OF TX
HWY BLDG 3 STE 200 78746 PH 512 347-7588
FAX 512 347-8243
BEAUMONT,TX OFFICE - 4180 DELAWARE ST
STE 402 77703 PH 409 838-4400
FAX 409 838-9056
CORPUS CHRISTI,TX OFFICE - 3833 S STAPLES
STE N-229 78411 PH 361 855-7335
FAX 361 855-7410
DALLAS,TX OFFICE - 2777 N STEMMONS FWY
STE 1102 75207 PH 214 951-0807
FAX 214 951-0906
FORT WORTH,TX OFFICE - 100 E 15TH ST
STE 300 76102 PH 817 287-9532
CHARLESTON,SC OFFICE - 3319 MAYBANK HWY
JOHNS ISLAND,SC 29455 PH 843 377-0286
FAX 843 377-0287
SEATTLE,WA OFFICE - 4608 UNION BAY PL NE
98105 PH 206 526-5622 FAX 206 526-5633
SOUTH KINGSTON,RI OFFICE - 55 VILLAGE SQ
DR 02879 PH 401 789-6224 FAX 401 789-1932
RIO DE JANEIRO,BRAZIL OFFICE -
AV PRESIDENTE WILSON 231/5TH FL OFC 525
20030-02 PH 281 448-6188 FAX 281 448-6189

RUBICON RESOURCES & GEOLOGICAL SERVICES
3968 REAGAN LN
ROBSTOWN,TX 78380 PH 361 548-6581
RUBICON@STX.RR.COM
PAT ROBINSON

RUCKS W W,III,IND OPR
PO BOX 51524,110 OIL CENTER DR
LAFAYETTE,LA 70505-1524 PH 337 235-7894
FAX 337 235-8809

RUDMAN PARTNERSHIP THE
1700 PACIFIC AVE STE 4700
DALLAS,TX 75201-4670 PH 214 220-3900
FAX 214 220-3901 TSIBLEY@RUDMANGROUP.COM
TARA RUDMAN,CO-GEN PARTNR
MICHAEL RUDMAN,C0-GEN PRTNR
W R (TREY) SIBLEY III,GEN MGR
TERRY DORRIS,SR MGR
HIRAM LUCIUS,LAND MGR

RUDY,ELLIS
22499 IMPERIAL VALLEY DR

HOUSTON,TX 77073-1173 PH 281 209-1150
FAX 281 209-1154
GEORGE S WEBB,LAND MGR

RUDYARDS
2010 WAUGH DR
HOUSTON,TX 77006-1106 PH 713 521-0521

RUE EDW E,INC
346 OAKLAKE LN
NICEVILLE,FL 32578-4400
PH 618 244-1969

RUFFIN F E,OIL PROPERTIES
1425 ROBERT
JACKSON,MS 39211-6339 PH 601 362-1311

RUNNING W,LTD SEE
KING RANCH MINERALS,INC

RUPERTSLAND RESOURCES INC
1 GREENWAY PLAZA STE 700
HOUSTON,TX 77046 PH 713 629-4490
FAX 713 629-6643

RUSH OIL COMPANY INC
PO BOX 1254,523 MAIN ST
HATTIESBURG,MS 39403-1254 PH 601 544-2000
MARY R LENNON,PRES
STACY LENNON,VP

RUSSELL RESOURCES,INC
4106 SAINT ELIZABETH DR
KENNER,LA 70065-1643 PH 504 888-1705
FAX 504 885-9475
EUGENE W RUSSELL,PRES
PEGGY W MCCARTHY,ACCT

RUSTIC RESOURCES,INC
INTEGRATED EXPL & DEV
1703 HUNTINGTON ST
MIDLAND,TX 79705-8409
PH 330 262-4323
STEVEN P ZODY,PRES,GEOL
ZODYOIL@SSSNET.COM

RUSTY CARLSON & ASSOCIATES
PO BOX 1799
CONROE,TX 77305-1799 PH 936 539-2036
FAX 936 539-2036
RUSTY CARLSON
RUSTYCARLSON2002@YAHOO.COM

RUSTY CLARK SURVEY COMPANY INC
PO BOX 100,625 PARKWAY DR
BREAUX BRIDGE,LA 70517-0100
PH 337 332-5232 337 237-7593
PH 800 256-7593 FAX 337 332-3104
PHILLIP BROUSSARD,CFO/OPERS MGR
DONNIE LAVIOLETTE,PRES-SLS
DALE THERIOT,VP-SLS

RUTHERFORD OIL CORP
8 GREENWAY PLZ STE 1400
HOUSTON,TX 77046-0800 PH 713 622-5555
P R RUTHERFORD,JR
MIKE G RUTHERFORD
DAVID E LEWIS,EXPL MGR
FRANK JAAP,DRLG & PROD MGR
JACK CHENOWETH,LAND MGR
RANDY RUSSELL,CONTROLLER
MIKE G RUTHERFORD,JR

RWG ENERGY,INC SEE
HALCON ENERGY PROPERTIES,INC

RYAN ENERGY TECHNOLOGIES USA & CANADA SEE
NABORS INDUSTRIES LTD

RYAN OIL CO
PO BOX 507
EVANSVILLE,IN 47703-0507 PH 812 422-4168

RYCO EXPLORATION,LLC
401 EDWARDS ST STE 915
SHREVEPORT,LA 71101
PH 318 216-5760
RSMITH@RYCO1.COMCASTBIZ.NET
M ROBIN SMITH,PRES

R2 ENERGY SERVICES,LLC
LAND,RIGHT-OF-WAY AND FIELD SVCS
3160 PARK CENTER DR
TYLER,TX 75701 PH 903 593-9579
MARK A RICH MRICH@R2ENERGYSERVICES.COM

S & C OPERATING
PO BOX 1509
WHITEFISH,MT 59937
PH 406 862-2690 FAX 281 516-1018
STEVE COSBY,PRES
CAROLYN COSBY,SECY/TREAS

S & P CO
330 MARSHALL ST STE 300
SHREVEPORT,LA 71101-3016
PH 318 222-1800 FAX 318 424-1257
FRED L PHILLIPS,PRTNR
COLLIN PHILLIPS,GEN MGR
TERESA DEAN,SEC/TREAS/COMPTROLLER
JILL CRAWFORD,LAND MGR

S & R GAS VENTURES LTD
PO BOX 172
SAND FORK,WV 26430-0172
PH 304 462-7006 304 462-7447
BOB RADABAUGH,PRES
JIM STOUT,VP

S & R RESOURCES,INC
PETROLEUM LAND FIRM
PO BOX 51885
LAFAYETTE,LA 70505-1885
PH 337 988-1110
STEWART C DELCAMBRE

S & S LAND SERVICES LLC SEE
SMITH ENERGY INC

S & S OPERATING CO,INC
P O BOX 1250
WINNIE,TX 77665-1250 PH 409 296-9571

S & T OIL CO
420 WESTERN ST
HOFFMAN EST,IL 60169-3021 PH 309 266-5871
ROBERT THOMAS,CHRMN OF BD
WAYNE STEWART,PRES
RICHARD J THOMAS,VP,SECY/TREAS

S & W OILFIELD SERVICE,INC
PO BOX 548
QUANAH,TX 79252-0548 PH 940 663-6491
FAX 940 663-6329
STEVE WILLIAMS,PRES

S B RESOURCES LLC
PO BOX 8256
TYLER,TX 75711-8256
PH 903 521-5694
BOB BURDICK,PRES
BOBBURDICK@SBCGLOBAL.NET

S D CONSULTING,INC
16 CHESTNUT
CHELSEA,MI 48118 PH 734 475-4686
STEVEN W DAUT,PRES

S G S NORTH AMERICA INC
OIL,GAS & CHEMICALS SERVICES DIVISION
900 GEORGIA AVE #B
DEER PARK,TX 77536-2518 PH 281 479-7170
FAX 281 479-2734 WWW.SGS.COM
WWW.US.SGS.COM
SGSOGC.USA.CUSTOMERCARE@SGS.COM
NEW YORK AREA REGIONAL OFFICE -
2 AVE J,BAYONNE,NJ 07002
PH 201 339-0877 FAX 201 339-8173
SGSOGC.NYHARBOR@SGS.COM
CHICAGO,IL REGIONAL OFFICE - 7315 S 76TH
BRIDGEVIEW,IL 60455
PH 708 458-7982 FAX 708 458-7983
SGSOGC.CHICAGO@SGS.COM
NEW ORLEANS AREA REGIONAL OFFICE -
151 JAMES DRIVE W,ST ROSE,LA 70087
PO BOX 1328,KENNER,LA 70063
PH 504 469-6401 FAX 504 463-3301
SGSOGC.NEWORLEANS@SGS.COM

S I INTERNATIONAL,INC SEE
SERCO NORTH AMERICA

S J R RESOURCES INC
PO BOX 131357
HOUSTON,TX 77219-1357 PH 713 807-9200
FAX 713 513-5671 SMWINDLE@FOCINC.COM
STEPHEN M WINDLE,PRES

S K OPERATING,INC
PO BOX 250
CABOT,PA 16023
PH 724 352-0600 FAX 724 352-0601
SAMUEL L KIMMEL,PRES SAM@SKOPERATING.COM
VALERIE R GRESSANG,VP

S M R NATURAL GAS VENTURES,INC SEE
FOCUS ENERGY INC

S R P PRODUCTION CORP
PO BOX 16805
SUGAR LAND,TX 77496-6805 PH 713 988-4618
FAX 713 988-3712
SCOTT R PULLEN,PRES

S S C GAS PRODUCING CO
3141 CATCAY DR
CORPUS CHRISTI,TX 78418-2910
PH 361 786-3795
DON L CRAWFORD,OWNER

S T Z PETROLEUM,INC
PO BOX 680766
HOUSTON,TX 77268-0766 PH 281 586-7191
FAX 281 586-7195
A M TURMAN,PRES
WANDA MARTIN,VP

S.F.C. INC SEE
STELARON,INC

S.H.A. ENERGY,INC,IND OIL & GAS DEVELOPER
PO BOX 136
REED CITY,MI 49677-0136 PH 231 832-9871
FAX 231 832-9900
S H ANDERSON,PRES

SABCO OIL AND GAS COMPANY,LLC
34 S WYNDEN
HOUSTON,TX 77056 PH 713 840-1980
FAX 713 840-0135
ALI A SABERIOON,PRES

SABINE CONSTRUCTORS
8515 ELLIS RD
WEATHERFORD,TX 76088

PH 817 598-0108 FAX 817 598-0319
JOHNNY BARRETT,AREA MGR-TX DIV
JBARRETT@SABINECON.COM
HUGO ACOSTA,FLD SUPT

SABINE CORPORATION SEE
PACIFIC ENTERPRISES OIL COMPANY (USA)

SABINE OIL & GAS LLC
1415 LOUISIANA ST STE 1600
HOUSTON,TX 77002 PH 832 242-9600
FAX 832 242-9560 WWW.SABINEOIL.COM

SABINE PIPE,INC
PO BOX 100
KILGORE,TX 75663-0100 PH 903 984-3094
BILL ADAMSON

SABINE RIVER LAND CO
PO BOX 10128
FORT SMITH,AR 72917 PH 713 557-4760
PAUL M SHAVER PAULMSHAVER@AOL.COM

SABLE ENERGY CORP
308-B CONGRESS AVE
AUSTIN,TX 78701 PH 713 621-3137
L L TIO NEWTON

SABOUGLA EXPLORATION,INC,GEOPHY CONS
64 EARL DUBUISSON RD
CARRIERE,MS 39426-2648 PH 601 798-3273

SAF-T-CHEM LLC
FRAC,DRILLING & COMPLETION CHEMICALS
PO BOX 1388
MADISONVILLE,TX 77864
PH 936 349-1819 FAX 936 349-0269
SAF-T-CHEM@RODZOO.COM

SAFETY INTERNATIONAL,INC
PO BOX 12060
ODESSA,TX 79768 PH 432 580-3770
FAX 432 332-9223
PHIL GRAVES,CEO
MARK GRAVES,PRES
BOBBY ROACH,AREA MGR
REGGIE PHILLIPS,SLS MGR

SAFETY MANAGEMENT SERVICES,INC
PO BOX 51927
LAFAYETTE,LA 70505-1927
PH 337 235-6524 FAX 337 235-0905
JACK BARNIDGE,PRES

SAFETY TECHNOLOGY & OILFIELD PROTECTORS
SEE TOTAL SAFETY

SAGE ENERGY
PO BOX 367
DUBLIN,OH 43017-0367 PH 614 889-0986
LAWRENCE V ELSTUN,PRES PH 614 937-8340
MANDLE2010@HOTMAIL.COM

SAGE ENERGY COMPANY
100 NE LOOP 410 STE 1300
SAN ANTONIO,TX 78216-4736 PH 210 404-2828
FAX 210 404-1301

SAGE EXPLORATION & PRODUCTION
1822 BRIAR COVE
CARROLLTON,TX 75006 PH 469 952-6622

SAGELY FLOYD E
3017 S 70TH ST #B
FORT SMITH,AR 72903-5000 PH 501 452-5187

SAI GEOCONSULTING,INC
2 FLAGG PLACE STE 1
LAFAYETTE,LA 70508
PH 337 504-3670 FAX 337 456-8948
SAIGEOCONSULTING.COM

BEN SYDBOTEN,PRES/GEOPHY
BSYDBOTEN@GMAIL.COM
VICKI SYDBOTEN,BUS MGR
JIM MILLER,GEOL/GEOPHY
BILL RIPLEY,GEOL
SAM PORTER,GEOL
TRAVIS HELMS,GEOL/GEOPHY
WILLIAM TERRELL,GEOL/GEOPHY
LINDA REIF,GEOL
GARY SQUYRES,GEOPHY
TYLER BETHEA,PETR ENGR
BOB PEATROSS,PETROPHYSICIST

SAKCO LTD
PO BOX 844
HOUSTON,TX 77001-0844 PH 713 881-3400

SAKDRIL INC
PO BOX 844
HOUSTON,TX 77001-0844 PH 713 881-3400

SALAMIS SERVICES,INC
PO BOX 1500
BROUSSARD,LA 70518
PH 337 289-0092
DAVID HEBERT,PRES
GORDON ROMERO,VP OPERS MGR

SALEM INVESTMENT COMPANY
PO BOX 6566
TYLER,TX 75711-6566 PH 903 561-4051
FAX 903 561-7758
J W ARNOLD,MNGNG PRTNR
DREW LANDES,GEOL

SALSMAN,WILLIAM E & ASSOC
233 ORANGEWOOD DR
LAFAYETTE,LA 70503 PH 337 288-6400
WSALSMAN@BELLSOUTH.NET

SAMEDAN OIL CORPORATION SEE
NOBLE ENERGY,INC

SAMSON INVESTMENT COMPANY SEE
SAMSON RESOURCES COMPANY

SAMSON RESOURCES COMPANY
2 W SECOND ST
TULSA,OK 74103-3103 PH 918 583-1791
FAX 918 591-1796 WWW.SAMSON.COM
DAVID ADAMS,CEO
PHIL COOK,CFO
KEITH ST GEMME,SR VP EAST TX/MID-CONT DIV
ROBERT SCHAFFITZEL,SR VP CORP PLNG & DEV
KEN DAVIS,SR VP OPERS
DARRELL MAYFIELD,VP HUMAN RESOURCES
MIKE DANIEL,VP LEGAL
SCOTT ROWLAND,VP BUS DEV
JOEL ALNES,VP NEW VENTURES
MARK ECK,VP OPERS
RON GOBER,VP MKTG
BOB JACKSON,VP IS & T
JOHN SNIVELY,VP OPERATIONAL ACCT
MIDLAND,TX OFFICE - 200 N LORAINE
STE 1010,79701 PH 432 683-7063
FAX 432 683-6847
GARY DUPRIEST,VP PERMIAN DIV
DENVER,CO OFFICE - 370 17TH ST STE 3000
80202 PH 720 904-1391
RICH FROMMER,VP ROCKY MTN DIV
BART BOUDREAUX,VP DRLG

SAN ANDRES CORPORATION
11215 MONTEBELLO CT
HOUSTON,TX 77024-7414

PH 713 973-0426 FAX 713 784-9227
LIN G ESPEY,PRES

SAN ISIDRO DEVELOPMENT COMPANY,LC
400 FM 534
SANDIA,TX 78383-4019
PH 361 547-9111 FAX 361 547-0159
PAUL DIRKS,VP PDIRKS@TOWERSOFTEXAS.COM
CORPUS CHRISTI OFFICE - 600 LEOPARD ST
STE 1812,78473 PH 361 884-5550
FAX 361 884-5559
LARRY ADUDDELL,VP EXPL
LADUDDELL@SANISIDRODEVELOPMENT.COM
JOHN P RICK MCBROOM,VP LAND
RMCBROOM@SANISIDRODEVELOPMENT.COM
BRYAN ALLISON,ENGR & EXPL
BALLISON@SANISIDRODEVELOPMENT.COM

SAN JACINTO OIL COMPANY L C
PO BOX 130865,3701 KIRBY DR STE 820
HOUSTON,TX 77219-0865
PH 713 526-2266 FAX 713 526-6199
JAMES B TENNANT,CHRMN

SAN SABA ENERGY,LP
6101 W COURTYARD DR STE 2-125
AUSTIN,TX 78730-5042
PH 512 428-5425 FAX 512 428-5425
JONATHAN E PRESTON,PRES

SANCHEZ OIL & GAS CORPORATION
PO BOX 2986,1920 SANDMAN
LAREDO,TX 78044-2986 PH 956 722-8092
FAX 956 718-1057
A R SANCHEZ JR,OWNER
FRANK A GUERRA,EXEC VP,CFO
JORGE MENDOZA,VP,TREAS
HOUSTON,TX OFFICE - 1111 BAGBY
STE 1600,77002 PH 713 783-8000
FAX 713 783-9993
A R TONY SANCHEZ,III,OWNER,PRES
PATRICIO PAT SANCHEZ,EXEC VP
MIKE LONG,SR VP,CFO
ED BIRDWELL,VP,MKTG
ROBERT RAMSEY,VP,LAND
MARK COLERICK,LAND MGR
RANDY NICKERSON,VP EXPL
MIKE MATTALIND,CHF GEOL
CHRIS BARRINGER,MGR,EXPL INFO SYS
GLENN ADCOCK,VP DRLG & OPERS

SANCHEZ-O'BRIEN OIL & GAS CORPORATION SEE
SANCHEZ OIL & GAS CORPORATION

SANCHO OIL AND GAS CORPORATION
PO BOX 179,210 SECOND ST
SAINT MARYS,WV 26170-0179 PH 304 684-7686
LOREN E BAGLEY,PRES

SANDALWOOD OIL & GAS,LP
1220 AUGUSTA DR STE 400
HOUSTON,TX 77057-2262 PH 713 759-6095
FAX 713 658-1822 DJLINDBERG@SOGINC.NET
JOHN F LIGON,CEO
DONALD J LINDBERG,CFO
DAN L SMITH,EXEC VP,EXPL
C PHIL FLEMING,VP,LAND
AUDREY W ADAMS,GEOL
TONY H ALMOND,SR GEOL
DELVIN R PHELPS,OPERS MGR

SANDEFER OIL & GAS INC/SANDEFER PETR CO
5300 MEMORIAL DR #870
HOUSTON,TX 77007-8200 PH 713 757-9600

FAX 713 651-3028
J D SANDEFER,III,CHRMN,PRES
STEPHEN F SMITH,EXEC VP,DIR

SANDERS JAMES W
P O BOX 76,THE QUARTER
JACKSON,MS 39205-0076 PH 601 981-2151

SANDIDGE A E,TRUST U/W OF
1250 NE LOOP 410
SAN ANTONIO,TX 78209
PH 210 826-5552 FAX 210 826-1278
JON R SANDIDGE

SANDOZ & ASSOCIATES,INC
PO BOX 53862,120 RUE BEAUREGARD STE 205
LAFAYETTE,LA 70505-3862 PH 337 264-1022
FAX 337 264-1115
PAUL A SANDY SANDOZ,PRES,CPL
DAVID G RAINBOLT,LDMN,CPL

SANDY SUPPLY COMPANY
PO BOX 299,636 KEMROW AVE
WOOSTER,OH 44691-0299 PH 330 262-1730
FAX 330 262-0635
CHARLES R YENNE,PRES
JERRY DANIELSKI,CONTROLLER
RICK YENNE,VP
BOB HESSER,SALES MGR
FRANZ SCHMIDT,SALES
ROB YENNE,PUR AGENT

SANTA FE ENERGY COMPANY SEE
SANTA FE ENERGY RESOURCES,INC

SANTA FE ENERGY RESOURCES,INC SEE
SANTA FE SNYDER CORPORATION

SANTA FE SNYDER CORPORATION SEE
DEVON SFS OPERATING,INC

SANTA MARIA INTERNATIONAL CORP
7506 INWOOD DRIVE
HOUSTON,TX 77063-1802 PH 713 782-2859
ROBERT J S SMITH,PRES
SMITH.RJS2@ATT.NET

SANTA ROSA RESOURCES,INC
1 GREENWAY PLZ STE 700
HOUSTON,TX 77046 PH 713 629-0699
FAX 713 629-6643
SANTAROSARESOURCES.COM
WILLIAM L CHAMBERS,PRES
BILLCHAMBERS@SANROSRES.COM

SANTORO OIL COMPANY INC
101 CORLISS ST
PROVIDENCE,RI 02904-2698 PH 401 421-4541
FAX 401 276-8958 SANTORO4541@AOL.COM

SAPPINGTON ENERGY INTERESTS,LTD
PO BOX 19160
HOUSTON,TX 77224-9160
PH 713 464-0386 FAX 713 464-0783
CHET2309@HOTMAIL.COM
CHESTER SAPPINGTON,GEN PRTNR

SARATOGA OIL CO
PO BOX 157
BATSON,TX 77519-0157 PH 936 262-8455
FAX 936 262-8455
CHARLES F YUST,II,OWNER
TRAVIS YUST,FIELD SUPT

SASSER ROYALTIES
5701 BROADWAY ST STE 200
SAN ANTONIO,TX 78209-6905 PH 210 826-1800
FAX 210 826-2754 SRO@RPITX.COM
C TREBES SASSER,PRES TSASSER@RPITX.COM

NIKKI LAWSON,LDMN

SATER ENTERPRISES
PO BOX 2509
EVANSVILLE,IN 47728-0509 PH 812 477-1529
FAX 812 477-2851
RONALD E SATER,MGR

SATEX ENERGY,INC
PO BOX 171167
SAN ANTONIO,TX 78217-8167 PH 210 366-1380
FAX 210 366-1329
DANNY W MILLS,CEO
WILLIAM P FOSTER,PRES
KYLE C COLE,SECY/TREAS

SAULS V A,INC
PO BOX 299
HEIDELBERG,MS 39439-0299 PH 601 787-4321
PH 800-748-9027
GARY W SAULS,PRES
GLENN STANLEY,SECY & OFC MGR
JOE BOYD,GEN MGR
EDWARD E MCGILL,TOOLPUSHER
LARRY MORGAN,TOOLPUSHER
FARRON B IVY,TOOLPUSHER
CARL BAKER,TOOLPUSHER
JAMIE G ENGLISH,TOOLPUSHER
JOHN PARKER,TOOLPUSHER
KENNY L HOLLAND,TOOLPUSHER
BARRY L BEACH,SLSMN

SAUR MINERALS,LLC
PO BOX 61926
LAFAYETTE,LA 70596-1926
PH 337 236-6693 FAX 337 236-6656
SAURMINERALS@GMAIL.COM
LOUIS EDDIE BERNARD JR,PRES

SAVAGE KEN & ASSOCIATES,INC
PO BOX 2080,300 S ST MARYS
BEEVILLE,TX 78104-2080 PH 361 362-2149
FAX 361 362-1826
KEN SAVAGE,PRES KENSAVAGE25@SBCGLOBAL.NET
KATHY GABBERT,ASST

SAVANNAH OIL AND GAS,LLC
16945 NORTHCHASE DR STE 2100
HOUSTON,TX 77060 PH 281 931-4200
FAX 281 931-4232 WWW.SAVANNAHOIL.COM
JEFFREY S REQUARTH,PRES/GEOL
MICHAEL P MOORE,VP/LDMN
JOHN J MORRIS,VP/GEOL

SAVANNAH OIL COMPANY
1904 STATE HIGHWAY 43
JEFFERSON,TX 75657-6930
PH 903 665-8975 FAX 903 665-9871
GARY L HUGHES,OWNER/OPERATOR

SAVANT INTEREST,LLC SEE SOURCE OIL,LLC

SAWYER DRILLING & SERVICE,INC
PO BOX 5275
BOSSIER CITY,LA 71171-5275
PH 318 746-4356 FAX 318 746-4937
RONALD L SAWYER,PRES
JACK M STERRITT JR,VP

SAWYER HALBERT,GEOPHYS & GEOLOGICAL CONS
412 E DALLAS AVE
MCALLEN,TX 78501-8953 PH 504 524-5313

SAXET EXPLORATION ENT CO,INC
5303 WESTON DR
FULSHEAR,TX 77441-4159 PH 281 346-1644
FAX 281 346-1644

JOHN C HESS,PRES

SAXET PETROLEUM INC
510 BERING DR STE 600
HOUSTON,TX 77057
PH 713 783-4883 FAX 713 783-3039
ROBERT E O'BRIEN,PRES,OWNER
REGGIE HOWARD,FIN
NANCY HASKINS,FIN
AMY PEARMAN,ACCT
SIA MEDRANO,ACCT
DAVID DAVIS,GEOL
CAMERON MCCARTNEY,LAND
JOHN T BRIM,LAND

SAXON ENERGY,INC
PO BOX 52408,1030 E ST MARY BLVD
LAFAYETTE,LA 70505-2408
PH 337 261-0426 FAX 337 233-6784
SAXONRJD@GMAIL.COM
RANDAL DAUTERIVE,PRES

SAXTON DONALD D JR
LAW OFFICES OF DONALD D SAXTON JR
1200 WASHINGTON RD
WASHINGTON,PA 15301-9696
PH 724 222-7205 FAX 724 222-7207
WWW.DONALDSAXTONLAW.COM
DSAXTON@DONALDSAXTONLAW.COM

SAYBOLT INC
190 JAMES DR E STE 110
SAINT ROSE,LA 70087-4008 PH 504 466-1516
FAX 504 466-1923
RONNIE SCHEPPEGRELL,MGR

SAYE OIL COMPANY
PO BOX 137,1015 MID SOUTH TWR
SHREVEPORT,LA 71161-0137 PH 318 221-4504
FAX 318 221-4516
JON E SAYE,PRES,PETR GEOL
JEREMY S SAYE,LAND MGR

SAYE PETROLEUM,INC SEE
SAYE OIL COMPANY

SCANA ENERGY MARKETING,INC
141 MAILCODE
COLUMBIA,SC 29218 PH 800 472-1051

SCANDIA ENERGY CO,INC
124 N DIVISION ST STE A
TRAVERSE CITY,MI 49684-2263
PH 231 946-4499 FAX 231 946-4752
GLEN L SEGERLUND,PRES

SCHAEFER BERNIE, RPL
COMMERCIAL PILOT, CERT FLIGHT INSTRUCTOR
110 REDBUD PKWY
FAIRFIELD,TX 75840
PH 214 236-1588 PH 214 686-1604
CFIGC@AOL.COM

SCHAFER SIDNEY & ASSOCIATES,INC
104 WOODHAVEN CT
RED OAK,TX 75154 PH 713 529-8789
FAX 713 529-3646
STUART SCHAFER,PRES
JACK WEYAND,VP

SCHEH INTERESTS
PO BOX 456
SEALY,TX 77474-0456 PH 979 885-2956
JOHNETTA B SCHEH,CPL
DONALD W SCHEH,CPL

SCHELLSTEDE HERMAN J AND ASSOCIATES,INC
DESIGNERS,ENGRS,MFGRS

109 BRIDGE ST
NEW IBERIA,LA 70563-2411 PH 337 365-7258
FAX 337 365-7259 WWW.SCHELLSTEDE.COM
HJSCHEL@BELLSOUTH.NET

SCHERCK L E
PO BOX 9190
AUSTIN,TX 78766-9190 PH

SCHEXNAYDER A J,PETR GEOL
613 ROSELAND
HARAHAN,LA 70123-3815 PH 504 737-3476

SCHIFF & COMPANY
2828 ROUTH ST STE 600
DALLAS,TX 75201-7607
PH 214 368-8382 FAX 214 572-8008
STEVE S SCHIFF,OWNER
JAN WRIGHT,ASST TO MR SCHIFF
CHRISTOPHER S WRIGHT,GEOL

SCHLUMBERGER
- NORTH AMERICA OFFICE -
300 SCHLUMBERGER DR
SUGAR LAND,TX 77478
PH 281 285-8500
ANCHORAGE,AK OILFIELD SERVICES OFFICE -
2525 GAMBELL ST STE 400,99503
PH 907 273-1700
CALGARY,ALBERTA,CAN OILFIELD SERVICES
OFFICE - EAU CLAIRE PLACE I
525 - 3RD AVE SW,T2P 0G4
PH 403 509-4000
- ARGENTIAN,BOLIVIA,BRAZIL & CHILE -
SCHLUMBERGER SERVICOS DE PETROLEO LTDA
OFFICE - AV PRESIDENTE WILSON 231-20
ANDAR,RIO DE JANEIRO,RJ 20030-021 BRAZIL
PH 55 21 3824 6923
- MEXICO & CENTRAL AMERICA -
MEXICO OILFIELD SERVICES OFFICE -
EJERCITO NACIONAL 425 NIVEL 9
COL GRANADA,MEXICO D.F. 11520
PH 52 55 5263 3000
- GULF COAST -
NEW ORLEANS,LA OILFIELD SERVICES OFFICE -
1515 POYDRAS ST STE 900,70112
PH 504 592-5200
BOGOTA,COLOMBIA,PEUR & ECUADOR OFFICE -
CALLE 100 NO 13-21 PISO 4
EDIFICIO MEGABANCO
PH 57 1 219 5000
- US LAND -
HOUSTON,TX OILFIELD SERVICES OFFICE -
1325 S DAIRY ASHFORD,77077
PH 281 285-1300
- VENEZUELA,TRINIDAD & TOBAGO -
CARACAS,VENEZUELA OILFIELD SERVICES OFC -
AV RIO CAURA,TORRE HUMBOLDT,PISO 23
PRADOS DEL ESTE,URB PARQUE HUMBOLDT
PO BOX 1608,CARACAS 1080,VENEZUELA
PH 58 212 9074700
- EUROPE,C.I.S. & AFRICA AREA (ECA) -
FRANCE AREA OFFICE - LE PALATIN 1
1 COUR DU TRIANGLE
92936 LA DEFENSE CEDEX
PH 33 1 7112 2000
- CASPIAN -
SCHLUMBERGER LOGELCO INC OFFICE -
51,KULMANOV ST
060011,ATYRAU,KAZAKHSTAN

PH 7 3122 586006
- CONTINENTAL EUROPE -
SCHLUMBERGER LOGELCO OFFICE -
4-8 NICOLAE TITULESCU BLVD,5TH FLOOR
011141,BUCHAREST-ROMANIA
PH 40 31 403 6700
- NIGERIA -
LAGOS,NIGERIA OILFIELD SERVICES OFFICE -
17/19 IDOWU TAYLOR ST,VICTORIA ISLAND
PH 234 1 261 9200
- NORTH AFRICA -
VAL D'HYDRA OFFICE -
AVENUE DU 11 DECEMBRE 1960
PH 213 21 922 240
- NORTH SEA -
NORWAY OILFIELD SERVICES OFFICE -
RISABERGVEIEN 3,TANANGER,PO BOX 8013
4068 STAVANGER,NORWAY PH 47 51 94 6000
- RUSSIA -
MOSCOW,RUSSIA OFFICE - 9,TAGANSKAYA
ULITSA,MOSCOW 109004,RUSSIA
PH 7 095 935 8200
- WEST & SOUTH AFRICA -
SCHLUMBERGER TECHNICAL SERVICES,INC OFC -
SONILS OIL SERVICE CENTER,BASE
LUANDA PORT,ANGOLA PH 244 2 310913
- MIDDLE EAST & ASIA AREA (MEA) -
UNITED ARAB EMIRATES AREA OFFICE -
DUBAI WORLD TRADE CENTER,9TH FLOOR
PO BOX 9261,DUBAI,UNITED ARAB EMIRATES
PH 971 4 306 7777
- AUSTRALIA -
SCHLUMBERGER OILFIELD AUSTRALIA OFC -
256 ST GEORGES TERRACE,PERTH,WA 6000
PH 61 8 9420 4800
- SAUDI ARABIA,KUWAIT,BAHRAIN,PAKISTAN -
SAUDI ARABIA SCHLUMBERGER MIDDLE EAST
S.A.,PO BOX 2836,AL-KHOBAR 31952
PH 966 3 331 0300
- BRUNEI,MALAYSIA & PHILLIPINES -
MALAYSIA OFFICE - ROHAS PERKASA,7TH FLOOR
WEST WING,8 JALAN PERAK
50450 KUALA LUMPUR
PH 60 3 2166 7788
- CHINA,JAPAN,KOREA,TAIWAN -
PEOPLES REPUBLIC OF CHINA OFFICE -
BLOCK A-2,6TH FLOOR,LIDO OFFICE TOWER
LIDO PLACE,JICHANG ROAD,BEIJING 100 004
PH 86 10 6479 6699
- EAST AFRICA & EAST MEDITERRANEAN -
CAIRO,EGYPT OFFICE - 25 MISR HELWAN ROAD
ZEINY TOWRE,MAADI,CAIRO,EGYPT
POB 790/11728 MAADI PH 20 2 768 4700
- GULF -
ABU-DHABI,UAE OILFIELD SERVICES OFFICE -
AL MASSOUD TOWER,16TH FLOOR,PO BOX 21
PH 971 2 633 3600
- INDONESIA -
JAKARTA,INDONESIA OILFIELD SERVICES OFC -
16TH FLOOR SENTRA MULIA
JI.H.R. RASUNA SAID KAV X-6 NO 8
JAKARTA 12940,INDONESIA
PH 62 21 522 7050
- INDIA -
NEW DELHI,INDIA OILFIELD SERVICES OFC -
THE CAPITAL COURT,4TH FLOOR

LSC-III,OLOF PALME MARG,MUNIRKA
NEW DELHI,INDIA - 110067
PH 91 11 2610 8354
- IRAN -
TEHRAN,IRAN WELL SERVICES OF IRAN OFC -
SCHLUMBERGER METHODS,NO 3,DAMAN AFSHAR ST
(BEFORE MIRDAMAD INTERSECTION)
VALI ASR AVE,VANAK SQ,TEHRAN,IRAN
PH 98 21 877 8081
- LIBYA -
LIBYA SCHLUMBERGER OILFIELD OFFICE -
THAT EL-IMAD,TOWER 1,7TH FLOOR
PO BOX 91931,LIBYA PH 218 21 335 0060
- THAILAND,MYANMAR,BANGLADESH & VIETNAM-
THAILAND SCHLUMBERGER OVERSEAS S.A. OFC -
RASA TOWER,17TH FLOOR
555 PHAHOLYOTHIN ROAD
CHATUCHAK,CHATUCHAK,BANGKOK 10900
PH 66 2 937 0700
- SCHLUMBERGER SERVICE SEGMENTS -
- DATA & CONSULTING SERVICES -
HOUSTON,TX OFFICE - 5599 SAN FELIPE
STE 1700,77056 PH 713 513-2000
- DRILLING & MEASUREMENTS -
SUGAR LAND,TX OFFICE - 300 SCHLUMBERGER
DR,77478 PH 281 285-8500
- INTEGRATED PROJECT MANAGEMENT -
WEST SUSSEX,IPM HEADQUARTERS OFFICE -
SCHLUMBERGER HOUSE,BUCKINGHAM GATE
GATWICK,WEST SUSSEX,RH6 0NZ. UK
PH 44 1293 556995
- SCHLUMBERGER INFO SOLUTIONS (SIS) -
HOUSTON,TX OFFICE - 5599 SAN FELIPE
STE 1700,77056 PH 713 513-2000
- WELL SERVICES -
SUGAR LAND,TX OFFICE - 300 SCHLUMBERGER
DR,77478 PH 281 285-8500
- WESTERNGECO -
WEST SUSSEX,UK OFFICE - SCHLUMBERGER
HOUSE,BUCKINGHAM GATE,GATWICK AIRPORT
WEST SUSSEX UK RH6 0NZ
PH 44 1293 556655
- WIRELINE -
SUGAR LAND,TX OFFICE - 225 SCHLUMBERGER
DR,MD 2,77478 PH 281 285-8500

SCHLUMBERGER DATA SERVICES SEE
GEOQUEST/SCHLUMBERGER

SCHLUMBERGER OILFIELD SERVICES SEE
SCHLUMBERGER

SCHLUMBERGER RESERVOIR COMPLETIONS CENTER
14910 AIRLINE RD
ROSHARON,TX 77583 PH 281 285-5200
T H TOM ZIMMERMAN,V P,GEN MGR

SCHLUMBERGER TECHNOLOGY CORPORATION
GASLIFT SERVICES
3243 W GENTRY PKWY
TYLER,TX 75702
PH 903 597-9800 FAX 903 597-9803
RUSTY HERRINGTON,FSM

SCHLUMBERGER WELL SERVICES SEE
SCHLUMBERGER WIRELINE & TESTING

SCHLUMBERGER WIRELINE & TESTING SEE
SCHLUMBERGER

SCHMITT JOSEPH M,ATTY,CONS
PO BOX 1936
JAMESTOWN,ND 58402-1936

PH 701 252-0556 307 689-0588

SCHNEIDAU KARL & ASSOC
303 LAKESIDE LN
NASSAU BAY,TX 77058-4314 PH 281 335-9105
KARL SCHNEIDAU,OWNER

SCHNEIDAU KARL,GEOL
303 LAKESIDE LN
NASSAU BAY,TX 77058-4314 PH 281 335-9105

SCHNEIDAU SHEPHERD,LTD
303 LAKESIDE LN
NASSAU BAY,TX 77058-4314 PH 281 335-9105
KARL SCHNEIDAU,MNGNG PRTNR

SCHNEIDER DRILLING CORPORATION
PO BOX 161426
BIG SKY,MT 59716-1426 PH 903 535-9212
FAX 903 535-9214,3 ROTARY RIGS
STEVE SCHNEIDER,PRES

SCHNEIDER JAMES W
6243 BRIAR ROSE DR
HOUSTON,TX 77057-3503 PH 713 667-0413

SCHNEIDER JOHN R
4107 MEDICAL PKWY STE 212
AUSTIN,TX 78756-3735 PH 512 458-4755
FAX 512 458-3827

SCHOEFFLER ENERGY GROUP,INC
224 RUE DE JEAN
LAFAYETTE,LA 70508 PH 337 232-1122
FAX 337 232-1372 WWW.SEGLAND.COM
TODD P SCHOEFFLER,CPL
TSCHOEFFLER@SEGLAND.COM

SCHOFIELD ENERGY/BURAY ENERGY INTL
20 NW FIRST ST STE 200
EVANSVILLE,IN 47788
PH 812 455-5755 FAX 812 303-3770
JOHN O SCHOFIELD,CEO
DONNIE DOUGHILT,PROD SUPT
BARRY MERCER,GEOL ENGR

SCHROCK ROBERT,INC
29333 SEABISCUIT DR
BOERNE,TX 78015-4418 PH 830 755-8333
ROBERT J SCHROCK,PRES

SCHROEDER ROBERT A,CPL
PO BOX 681,151 BROOKSIDE DR 70471-3201
MANDEVILLE,LA 70470-0681 PH 985 626-7843
FAX 800 738-7143 ROB@KEXPLORATION.COM

SCHROEDER WELDING & CONSTRUCTION INC
PO BOX 123,2303 E LONE TREE RD
VICTORIA,TX 77902-0123 PH 361 573-4322
FAX 361 573-1674
ROBERT G SCHROEDER,PRES
ROBERT G SCHROEDER JR,VP
HARVEY PETRU,SUPT
JAMES SMOLIK,SUPT
ROBERT A VALENTA,SUPT

SCHULBERG ARNOLD L,PLLC
ATTORNEY AT LAW
1 STEWART PLAZA
DUNBAR,WV 25064 PH 304 760-2345
ASCHULBERG@SCHULBERGLAW.COM

SCHULTZ COMPANIES
500 N AKARD ST STE 2940
DALLAS,TX 75201-6622 PH 214 954-0030
FAX 214 954-0861
CHARLES H SCHULTZ,CHIEF EXEC

SCHWARTZ JOHN E,JR
219 ARKWOOD LN

PETAL,MS 39465-3609 PH 601 583-8648

SCHWING MANAGEMENT,LLC
9422 COMMON ST STE 2
BATON ROUGE,LA 70809-8414
PH 225 927-4447 FAX 225 927-2181
CHARLES EDWARD SCHWING,PRES

SCIENTIFIC DRILLING INTERNATIONAL
1100 RANKIN RD
HOUSTON,TX 77073-4716 PH 281 443-3300
PH 800 514-8949 FAX 281 443-3311
WWW.SCIENTIFICDRILLING.COM
D H VAN STEENWYK,CEO
G H DUROCHER,PRES, COO
- DOMESTIC FIELD OFFICES -
CASPER,WY DIST OFFICE - PO BOX 1600
7237 W BARTON RD
MILLS,WY 82604 PH 307 472-6621
PH 800 514-8944 FAX 307 472-5439
HOUSTON,TX DIST OFFICE - 1100 RANKIN RD
77073 PH 281 443-4600 800 514-6062
FAX 281 443-4670
MIDLAND,TX DIST OFFICE - PO BOX 9699
2034 TRADE DR,79703 PH 432 563-1339
PH 800 844-0439 FAX 432 697-0324
OKLAHOMA CITY,OK DIST OFFICE - 421 S
EAGLE LANE,73128 PH 405 787-3663
PH 800 514-5414 FAX 405 787-8732
LAFAYETTE,LA DIST OFFICE - PO BOX 1158
SCOTT,LA 70583 PH 337 232-7302
PH 800 676-7302 FAX 337 235-6828
NEW ORLEANS,LA BASE OFFICE - 1515 POYDRAS
ST,#2300,70112 PH 504 522-3598
PH 800 514-6063 FAX 504 522-3603
BAKERSFIELD,CA DIST OFFICE - 4516
DISTRICT BLVD,93313 PH 661 831-0636
PH 800 514-8077 FAX 661 831-4693
DENVER,CO DIST OFFICE - 1600 BROADWAY
STE 2400,80202 PH 303 892-8800
FAX 303 892-1202

SCIENTIFIC INVESTIGATIONS AGENCY
2635 HWY 190 W
DERIDDER,LA 70634-6057 PH 318 463-9612
FAX 318 463-9616
ERNEST RALSTEN ROLL,PRES

SCOPER VINCENT G,JR,CONS GEOL
P O BOX 2366
LAUREL,MS 39442-2366 PH 601 425-2488

SCORPION OIL TOOLS,INC
HYDRAULIC TONGS
13911 FABER ST
HOUSTON,TX 77037-1921 PH 281 999-8664
SALES PH 281 999-2222 FAX 281 999-2502
INFO@SCORPION.CC WWW.SCORPION.CC
KOBI BAR-YAM,PRES
CAROLYNN LAMB,VP,SALES & MKTG

SCOTIA WATEROUS (USA) INC
A MEMBER OF THE SCOTIABANK GROUP
711 LOUISIANA ST STE 1400
HOUSTON,TX 77002-2847 PH 713 222-0546
FAX 713 222-0572 WWW.SCOTIAWATEROUS.COM
HOUSTON@SCOTIAWATEROUS.COM
TIM PISH,DIR
EDGAR LOREDO,HUMAN RES,DATABASE ANALYST
EDGAR_LOREDO@SCOTIAWATEROUS.COM

SCOTT DON DRILLING CO INC
PO BOX 221

HILLSDALE,MI 49242-0221 PH 517 849-9237
FAX 517 849-2051
DON SCOTT,PRES

SCOTT JANACE M SEE
SCOTT ROYCE ARNOLD

SCOTT PETROLEUM
555 HALEY BARBOUR PKWY
YAZOO CITY,MS 39194-9414 PH 662 746-1942

SCOTT ROYALTY COMPANY,SEE
SCOTT ROYCE A

SCOTT ROYCE ARNOLD
PO BOX 69
TUSCOLA,TX 79562-0069
PH 325 721-6808 TIMBERLINE@TAYLORTEL.NET

SCOUT CHECK INC
P O BOX 4095,2621 STRINGTOWN RD
EVANSVILLE,IN 47724-0095 PH 812 425-4321
ROBERT SKEELS,OWNER

SCROGGINS JOE R,OIL OPR & OIL PROD
2120 COUNTY ROAD 199
CLANTON,AL 35046 PH 601 833-6448

SCURLOCK DAN,CONS GEOL
PO BOX 1392
SHREVEPORT,LA 71164-1392 PH 318 222-4550
FAX 318 222-4550

SCURLOCK OIL COMPANY SEE
SCURLOCK PERMIAN LLC

SCURLOCK PERMIAN LLC SEE
PLAINS MARKETING,LP

SCURLOCK RAY,CONS GEOL
PO BOX 1392
SHREVEPORT,LA 71164-1392 PH 318 222-4550

SCURLOCK TED R
330 MARSHALL ST STE 941
SHREVEPORT,LA 71101-3036 PH 318 222-7628

SDG OPERATING COMPANY,INC
3650 OLD BULLARD RD STE 300
TYLER,TX 75701-8667
PH 903 561-0648 FAX 903 561-0680
R D UNGERECHT,PRES,PETR ENGR

SDP FAMILY PARTNERS,LTD
121 S BROADWAY STE 528
TYLER,TX 75702 PH 903 597-0551
FAX 903 597-2893
STEVEN D PINKSTON
SPINK@SWBELL.NET

SEA-LAR MANAGEMENT,INC
535 FREMAUX AVE
SLIDELL,LA 70458 PH 985 847-1274
FAX 985 847-1384 SEA_LAR@BELLSOUTH.NET
JERRY E SEALE,ENGR

SEABOARD INTERNATIONAL,INC
DRILLING & PRODUCTION EQUIPMENT
PO BOX 450989
HOUSTON,TX 77245-0989
PH 713 644-3535 FAX 713 644-3737
J KELLY JOY,PRES,CEO
KENNETH BEAN,VP,OPERS
RUSSELL HARBISON,VP,SLS
HOUSTON,TX OFFICE - 13815 HWY 288 SOUTH
77047-1941 PH 713 644-3535
FAX 713 644-3737
MAX BUSH,DIST MGR
CORPUS CHRISTI,TX OFFICE - 7462 LEOPARD
78409 PH 361 289-6853 FAX 361 289-0216
LACEY HILL,DIST MGR

SCOTT,LA OFFICE - 321 HWY 93,(APOLLO RD)
70583 PH 337 269-7007 FAX 337 269-0046
PAUL HORTON JR,DIST MGR
KILGORE,TX OFFICE - 411 COMMERCE ST
75662 PH 903 983-4481 FAX 903 983-5408
DAVID ALFORD,DIST MGR

SEABOARD-ARVAL CORPORATION SEE
SEABOARD INTERNATIONAL,INC

SEAGULL COMPANIES SEE
SEAGULL OPERATING CO,INC

SEAGULL ENERGY CORPORATION SEE
OCEAN ENERGY INC

SEAGULL MID-SOUTH INC SEE
OCEAN ENERGY INC

SEAGULL OPERATING CO INC
416 TRAVIS ST STE 1215
SHREVEPORT,LA 71101-5504 PH 318 226-9170
FAX 318 425-7957
SCOTT S LOWE,PRES
GLORIA KIRKLAND,SECY
SOMERSET,TX OFFICE - PO BOX 675
78069 PH 512 624-2808
ROBERT ROGERS,TEXAS SUPT
OIL CITY,LA OFFICE - PO BOX 294,71061
PH 318 995-6920
JIMMY TERRY,VP,PROD

SEAL ENERGY COMPANY
2712 ATHANIA PKWY
METAIRIE,LA 70002-5904
PH 504 834-5630 FAX 504 834-5866
WARREN L SEAL,PRES WARRENSEAL@COX.NET
KEVIN T SEAL,VP KEVINSEAL@COX.NET

SEAL WARREN L,CERT PETROLEUM GEOL
2712 ATHANIA PKWY
METAIRIE,LA 70002-5904 PH 504 834-5630
FAX 504 834-5866 WARRENSEAL@COX.NET

SEAL-TITE INTERNATIONAL
500 DEER CROSS DR
MADISONVILLE,LA 70471-2974
PH 985 875-1292 FAX 985 875-0687
INFO@SEAL-TITE.COM WWW.SEAL-TITE.COM
BARRY C ELLIS,MNGNG DIR
D NEIL CARY,OPERS DIR

SEAMSTER BRIAN INC,GEOPHY,EXPL CONSLT
1847 DOCK ST STE 204
NEW ORLEANS,LA 70123-5664 PH 504 733-5865
BRIAN SEAMSTER,PRES

SEARCH DRILLING COMPANY
1221 LAMAR ST STE 1600
HOUSTON,TX 77010-3039 PH 713 650-1246
FAX 713 655-1866
J P BRYAN,CHRMN,CEO
CHARLES C GREEN III,VP

SEBRING LOUIE JR,GEOL
514 RAWLEIGH DR
CORPUS CHRISTI,TX 78412-3168
PH 361 888-6751 FAX 361 882-9071

SECO PETROLEUM CORP OIL PROD
5215 LOOKOUT MOUNTAIN DR
HOUSTON,TX 77069-3339 PH 713 783-9445
CHARLES F MOORE,PRES
J F RUCKER,VP

SECORP INDUSTRIES
PO BOX 3020,779 AVERY BLVD
RIDGELAND,MS 39157 PH 601 607-3151
PH 800 874-7590 FAX 601 607-3255

WWW.SECORP-INC.COM
ROBERT L MAILLY,PRES & CEO
LAFAYETTE,LA (OPERS) OFFICE - PO BOX
53912,70505-3912 2101 JERFFERSON ST 70501
PH 337 237-3471 PH 800 327-5026
FAX 337 235-6278
JOHN (RED) HALL,COO
JOHN (BO) HALL,VP DOMESTIC OPERS
JOHNNY BLISSETT,HSE & QA MGR
TOM WEST,VP OPERS/ENTECH
SCOTT,LA DIST OFFICE - 313 ZACHARY ST
70583, PH 337 237-3471 PH 800 327-5026
FAX 337 237-5919
BRANDON HEBERT,WEST GULF COAST REG MGR
BRANDON BRINSON,DIST SUPVSR
FLOMATON,AL DIST OFFICE - PO BOX 487
1010 PALAFOX ST,36441 PH 251 296-3468
PH 800 745-0194 FAX 251 296-1019
ROB SANDERS,EAST GULF COAST REG MGR
BEN JOHNSON,DIST SUPVSR
VENTURA,CA DIST OFFICE - 2550 EASTMAN AVE
STE 3,93003 PH 805 642-7235 800 642-7235
FAX 805 650-9177
EARL BANDY,BUS ADV
DUSTIN NICEWONGER,DIST SUPVSR
BAKERSFIELD,CA OFFICE - 1732 ART ST,93312
PH 661 589-7284 PH 800 745-0191
FAX 661 589-2734
JERRY TATE,WEST COAST REG MGR
JOHN MCCOY,DIST SUPVSR
DOHA,QATAR DIST OFFICE - PO BOX 2515
INDUSTRIAL AREA, PH 011-974-4460-2944
FAX 011 974-4460-2945
BILL MILLS,INTL DIST MGR
HOUSTON,TX OFFICE - 9850 RICHMOND AVE
STE 6107,77042-4552 PH 800 327-5026
DEVINE,TX OFFICE - 772 HWY 173 S,78016
PH 830 663-1972 FAX 830 663-9574
JAMES STRANGE,DIST SUPVSR
LAUREL,MS DIST OFFICE - PO BOX 3006
294 VICTORY RD,39442 PH 601 422-0203
PH 800 329-9007 FAX 601 422-0162
SECORPLAUREL@SECORP-INC.COM
RANDY ARNOLD,DIST SUPVSR

SECURITY DBS / HALLIBURTON U.S. OPERS
- PERMIAN BASIN NWA -
3000 N SAM HOUSTON PKWY E BLDG Q
HOUSTON,TX 77032 PH 281 871-6174
- SOUTH TEXAS NWA - 3000 N SAM HOUSTON
PKWY E,BLDG Q,HOUSTON,TX 77032
PH 281 871-6168
- GULF OF MEXICO NWA - 110 CAPITAL DR
STE 100,LAFAYETTE,LA 70508
PH 337 572-4736
- SOUTH EAST TX & N LA NWA -
105 JORDAN PLAZA BLVD,STE 406
TYLER,TX 75704 PH 903 533-1555
- MIDCON NWA - 6725 SOUTHWEST 44TH ST
OKLAHOMA CITY,OK 73179 PH 405 552-8543
- ROCKIES NWA - 1125 17TH ST STE 1900
DENVER,CO 80202 PH 305 675-4442

SECURITY EXPLORATION,INC
8509 LINE AVE
SHREVEPORT,LA 71106 PH 318 222-1066
FAX 318 222-4932 JSC@SECURITYEXPL.COM
J S COMEGYS,PRES,GEOL

DONNA M WALKER,GEOL

SEECO INC,SEE
SOUTHWESTERN ENERGY PROD CO

SEEKER OIL CO INC
PO BOX 6557
SAN ANTONIO,TX 78209-0557 PH 210 828-6889

SEELIGSON OIL COMPANY
808 TRAVIS ST STE 2200
HOUSTON,TX 77002-5704 PH 713 224-4676
ARTHUR SEELIGSON,PRES

SEGLUND J A,INC,GEOL
6460 APELEHAMA RD
DIAMONDHEAD,MS 39525-3805 PH 228 255-3451
JASEGLUND@BELLSOUTH.NET

SEHOY ENERGY,LP
333 TEXAS ST STE 619
SHREVEPORT,LA 71101-3679
PH 318 222-9306 FAX 318 221-1520
CHARLENE BARROW,OFC MGR

SEI ENERGY
2826 AMNICOLA HWY
CHATTANOOGA,TN 37406-3605
PH 423 875-6633 FAX 423 875-6040
WWW.SEIENERGY.COM INFO@SEIENERGY.COM

SEIBERT,BIGHAM & TANNER
PO BOX 467,1 NORTH MAIN ST
PINCKNEYVILLE,IL 62274-0467
PH 618 357-2178 FAX 618 357-3314
SBTLAWFIRM@NWCABLE.NET
DONALD BIGHAM,PRTNR
TYSON TANNER,PRTNR
MATT FOSTER,ASSOC

SEIS-TEL INC
19 EAST SHADY LN
HOUSTON,TX 77063 PH 713 780-4434
ASHOKE K NATH,PRES
LOUIS HOOPER,VP

SEISBANKS INC
711 N CARANCAHWA STE 520
CORPUS CHRISTI,TX 78475 PH 361 884-2936
FAX 361 887-7910
RHONDA BROUGHTON,SALES COORD
HOUSTON,TX OFFICE - 9225 KATY FWY STE 426
77024-1511 PH 713 973-7347
FAX 713 973-7377
DAVID WALTON,PRES
DEBBIE CLECKLEY,SALES COORD

SEISCO,INC
5612 BLESSEY ST
NEW ORLEANS,LA 70123 PH 504 731-2995
FAX 504 731-2997 WWW.SEISCOINC.COM
GEORGE H EVANS,PRES
LESLIE J LAMBERT,VP MKTG
LAMBERT@SEISCOINC.COM
WILLIAM G MANSCHOT,OPERS MGR
EARL B ANDERSON,GEOPHY
HUGH E MARQUIS,GEOPHY

SEISMIC CONTRACTS/PERMITTING AND
LANDMAN SERVICES
PO BOX 2473
ARDMORE,OK 73402-2473
PH 580 226-5468 214 649-1572
WILLIAM O (BILL) CARTER,III

SEISMIC EXCHANGE,INC
201 SAINT CHARLES AVE STE 4300
NEW ORLEANS,LA 70170-4300

PH 504 581-7153 FAX 504 581-9591
WWW.SEISMICEXCHANGE.COM
P C HAVENS,CHRMN OF BD
BOBBY PATRICK,EXEC VP
TIM MORAN,VP NEW VENTURES
HOWARD PATTON,VP MKTG
LAYNE WILLIAMS,N O REG MKTG MGR
3D OFFSHORE DIV OFFICE -
PH 504 581-9590 FAX 504 581-6767
HOUSTON,TX OFFICE - 4805 WESTWAY PK BLVD
77041 PH 832 590-5100 FAX 832 590-5290
JOHN HAVENS,PRES
RIVIE CARY,VP ENGR & PLANNING
JUD GRADY,CFO
JULIE K HARDIE,VP LEGAL
JEFF LESTER,VP-3D OFFSHORE MKTG
MELISSA ERWIN,2D MKTG
BEAU PATRICK,2D MKTG
SHONDA MASON,2D MKTG
DAVID WALTON,3D MKTG
JOEY KOENIG,3D MKTG
TONY TRAWEEK,SR MGR-3D SVCS
SHIRLEY ROSS,LICENSE ADMIN
DAVID PRITCHARD,DIR EXTERNAL SVCS
SHERRY BRYANT,DIR INTERNAL SVCS
PAT STONE,HR & OFC MGR
DENVER,CO OFFICE - 1775 SHERMAN ST
STE 2955 80203 PH 303 832-5007
FAX 303 832-5043
STEVE KLOPPEL,VP
LANA LIPINSKI,MKTG
ANNIKA OTNESS,MKTG
TWANA DRYER,MKTG ASST
DALLAS,TX OFFICE - 9400 N CENTRAL EXPY
STE 1211,75231 PH 214 373-1212
FAX 214 373-1208
LARRY TULL,VP
SANDI SMITH,OFC MGR/MKTG
HOLLY DORWARD,MKTG ASST
OKLAHOMA CITY,OK OFFICE - 2601 NW EXPY
STE 500W,73112 PH 405 848-8005
FAX 405 848-8371
CONNIE BRANDT,MKTG ASST
CORPUS CHRISTI,TX OFFICE - 711 N
CARANCAHUA ST STE 520,78475
PH 361 884-2936 FAX 361 887-7910
RHONDA BROUGHTON,SALES COORD
TULSA,OK OFFICE - 2021 S LEWIS STE 610
74104 PH 918 884-2936 FAX 918 712-7188
CLAY WELCH,MKTG
SUSAN WALKER,MKTG ASST

SEISMIC PERMIT SERVICES,INC
346 COUNTY RD 2340
GRAPELAND,TX 75844-5847
PH 409 687-4078

SEISMIC VENTURES,INC
4805 WESTWAY PK BLVD
HOUSTON,TX 77041 PH 281 240-1234
PH 888 456-3306 FAX 281 240-4997
WWW.SEISMICVENTURES.COM
C H HANK SAUNDERS,VP
STEVE KALLINA
RICK PAINE,CHF GEOPHY
LINDA ALBRIGHT,SR GEOPHY,PROC GEOPHY
DALE SWINFORD,SR GEOPHY,PROC GEOPHY
LES VLASIN,SR GEOPHY,PROC GEOPHY

SARA DAVIS,BUS DEV MGR
R D PEREZ,BUS DEV MGR
STEVEN FICK,GEOPHY
MARGARET ERLANDSON,SR GEOPHY
ANDREW MEDINA,JR GEOPHY

SEISTRACE,INC SEE
SEISCO,INC

SELBY AND CLARK ENERGY INC
510 HEARN ST STE 220
AUSTIN,TX 78703 PH 512 322-9781
TAYLOR CLARK,PRES
JON SELBY,GEOL

SELBY MRS LOYIS B,ESTATE
5416 SUFFOLK DR
JACKSON,MS 39211-4506 PH 601 956-6965

SELLERS AND ASSOCIATES INC,ENGRS
148 B EASY ST
LAFAYETTE,LA 70506-3012
PH 337 232-0777 FAX 337 232-0851
TODD A VINCENT,PRES/PE/PLS
ELIZABETH S GIROUARD,CAO
LAWRENCE A CRAMER JR,CHF ENGR/PE/PLS

SELMAN EXPLORATION,INC
PO BOX 12302
JACKSON,MS 39236-2302
PH 601 956-3255 JBSELMAN@AOL.COM
JOHN B SELMAN,PRES

SELMAN JOHN B,CPL
OIL & GAS PROPERTIES
PO BOX 5423
BEAUMONT,TX 77726-5423 PH 409 892-3710
FAX 409 892-3716
JOHN B SELMAN,CPL,PROPRIETOR
SUSAN L SELMAN,TREAS
SANDRA CARRINGTON,GEN COUNSEL

SEMINOLE PRODUCTION CO
PO BOX 1236
SILSBEE,TX 77656-1236 PH 409 385-2937
FAX 409 385-4202
BUFORD CURTIS,OWNER,OPR

SEMPRA ENERGY PRODUCTION COMPANY SEE
PEC MINERALS LP

SENDERO OIL COMPANY,OIL OPR
1595 SPRING MOUNTAIN DR
CANYON LAKE,TX 78133 PH 830 964-2336
FAX 830 964-2624
PEGGY BILLINGS,PRES
L CHARLES BILLINGS,VP

SENDERO RESOURCES,INC
PO BOX 8082
TYLER,TX 75711-8082
PH 903 534-3890 FAX 903 534-3892
TED W WALTERS,PRES TWALTERS.COM

SENECA RESOURCES CORP
1201 LOUISIANA ST STE 2600
HOUSTON,TX 77002 PH 713 654-2600
FAX 713 654-2659 SENECACORPAP@SRCX.COM
MATTHEW D CABELL,PRES
BARRY MCMAHAN,SR VP
JOHN MCGINNIS,SR VP
DON SMITH,MGR BUS DEV & LAND
BAKERSFIELD,CA WEST COAST DIV OFFICE -
2131 MARS CT 93308-6830
PH 661 399-4270 FAX 661 399-7706
BRAD ELLIOTT,VP
PITTSBURGH,PA EAST COAST DIV OFFICE -

5800 CORPORATE DR STE 300 15237
PH 412 548-2500
DALE ROWEKAMP,VP

SENISA ENERGY
5665 FM 775
SEGUIN,TX 78155 PH 830 303-2333
PH 210 269-5263 FAX 830 303-2333
WWW.SENISA.COM
NORWIN H VOGEL,OWNER,BROKER

SENORA RESOURCES,INC
PO BOX 1037
GIDDINGS,TX 78942-1037 PH 979 540-3916
FAX 979 540-3397
JAMES D DANNY DOBOS II,PRES

SENSIDYNE INC
1000 112TH CIRCLE N STE 100
ST PETERSBURG,FL 33716 PH 727 530-3602
PH 800-451-9444 FAX 727 539-0550
WWW.SENSIDYNE.COM INFO@SENSIDYNE.COM
JOE TROY,SLS & MKTG MGR,HEALTH/SAFETY DIV

SEPCO INDUSTRIES,INC
320 TIME SAVER AVE
NEW ORLEANS,LA 70123-3136 PH 504 733-7100
N F LUKE,VP,BRANCH MGR

SEQUA ENGINEERED SERVICES INC SEE
WEATHERFORD INTERNATIONAL INCORPORATED

SEQUOYAH OIL AND GAS COMPANY
PO BOX 742,2315 1/2 SPRADLING AVE
FORT SMITH,AR 72904-0742 PH 501 783-5424
FRANK W BRANT,PRES
ALAN BURD,VP
JONATHAN WILCOX,SECY

SERCEL INC
17200 PARK ROW
HOUSTON,TX 77084-4925 PH 281 492-6688
GEORGE WOOD,PRES
RICHARD MILES,EXEC VP
MARK FARINE,VP SALES
JIMMY LIGON,CUSTOMER SVC
RON HAWKINS,MFG MGR

SERIO ENERGY CORPORATION
PO BOX 17887
NATCHEZ,MS 39122-7887 PH 601 446-7555
S BARNETT SERIO JR,PRES
S BARNETT SERIO III,PROD SUPT

SERVICE OFFSHORE INC
10650 CLEMONS RD
ABBEVILLE,LA 70510
PH 337 893-6843 FAX 337 898-1147
W RAY HINES,PRES
FRANK CORMIER,VP,OPERS MGR
DANE MEAUX,TER MGR
PERRY,LA OFFICE - PO BOX 160,70575
PH 800 725-6496

SEVERSON EXPLORATION COMPANY,INC
EXPLORATION CONSULTING
4049 S INWOOD AVE
NEW ORLEANS,LA 70131-8457 PH 504 394-0939
GEORGE D SEVERSON,PRES

SEWELL LAWSON M (MIKE),LNDMN
P O BOX 6604
TYLER,TX 75711-6604 PH 214 595-0961

SEWELL LAWSON W LUKE ,OIL OPR
PO BOX 6604,808 FIRST PLACE
TYLER,TX 75711-6604 PH 214 595-0961

SG INTERESTS I LTD
100 WAUGH DR STE 400
HOUSTON,TX 77007-5962 PH 713 951-0100
FAX 713 951-0191 SGINE@FLASH.NET
RUSSELL D GORDY,PRTNR
LESTER H SMITH,PRTNR
GARY WEBER,OPERS
ROBBIE GUINN,LAND MGR
RICHARD BROWN,ACQS

SHAKESPEARE OIL CO,INC
202 W MAIN ST
SALEM,IL 62881-1519 PH 618 548-1585
FAX 618 548-1594 WWW.SHAKESPEARE-OIL.COM
BRYAN TEMPLE HOOD,PRES
DONALD R WILLIAMS,PE,VP
REBECCA S WEBER,CPL,LAND MGR
DALE K HELPINGSTINE,RPG

SHALE ROYALTIES SEE
SEE PROVIDENT ROYALTIES LLC

SHALETT MONTE C,OIL OPERATOR
3030 LAUSAT ST
METAIRIE,LA 70001-5924 PH 504 831-7779
FAX 504 831-8315 MSHALETT@MINDSPRING.COM

SHAMROCK DRILLING,INC
118 LOWER WOODVILLE RD STE 2
NATCHEZ,MS 39120 PH 601 442-0785
FAX 601 446-9907
SHAMROCKDRILLING@BELLSOUTH.NET
G STEPHEN GUIDO,PRES

SHAREWELL ENERGY SERVICES,LP
1111 NORTH LOOP W STE 705
HOUSTON,TX 77008-4714 PH 800 637-6461
FAX 713 983-9820 WWW.SHAREWELL.COM
SCOTT MORTON,DENVER SLS
SMORTON@SHAREWELL.COM

SHARON HUNTER RESOURCES,INC DBA
EAGLE FORD HUNTER RESOURCES, INC
777 POST OAK BLVD STE 650
HOUSTON,TX 77056 PH 832 369-6986
FAX 832 369-6992
H C KIP FERGUSON III,PRES
BRIAN BURGHER,LAND VP
JASON WILSON,GEOL

SHARP LAND SERVICES
10 E TWINBERRY PL
THE WOODLANDS,TX 77381 PH 409 321-2500
JIM L SHARP,CPL

SHARPE ENERGY COMPANY
PO BOX 1742
CONROE,TX 77305-1742 PH 713 652-3828
FAX 713 652-3832
ROLAND M LARSEN,CEO
W N VIA,PRES

SHAVER SIDNEY M COMPANY
13825 LEXINGTON BLVD #116
SUGAR LAND,TX 77478-5364 PH 281 980-3987
SIDNEY M SHAVER,OWNER,PETR EXPL GEOL,
GEOPHY

SHAW CHAD R,CPL
LAND ADVISOR-ALTAMONT BA (UTAH)
EP ENERGY E&P COMPANY,LP
PO BOX 4660,1001 LOUISIANA ST
HOUSTON,TX 77210-4660 PH 713 997-3435
FAX 713 997-6370 CHAD.SHAW@EPENERGY.COM
WWW.EPENERGY.COM

SHAW ENERGY INC
PO BOX 192199
DALLAS,TX 75219-2199 PH 214 443-0553
FAX 214 528-8060
EDWARD J HUTLAS,PRES
ROBERT M BRACKBILL,VP

SHAW INTERESTS,INC
PETROLEUM LAND SERVICES
OIL & GAS EXPLORATION
310 W WALL ST STE 305
MIDLAND,TX 79701 PH 432 685-1404
FAX 432 685-1343 WWW.SHAWINTERESTS.COM
MANER B SHAW,PRES
DAVID EVANS,LDMN
BRANDON BEVERSDORF,LDMN
BRADLEY CARTER,LDMN
SHAWN STORRIE,LDMN
JULIE TATE,LDMN
BRAD WATSON,LDMN,HR
DECATUR,TX OFFICE - 1475 FM 2264,76234
PH 940 626-4249
LOUIS CHIPMAN,LDMN

SHAW M R ENERGY CO
35 MIDDAY SUN PL
THE WOODLANDS,TX 77382-2023
PH 281 292-7211 FAX 281 292-7211
MICHAEL R SHAW MSHAW281@SBCGLOBAL.NET

SHEA OIL & GAS CO,INC
6133 POPLAR PIKE
MEMPHIS,TN 38119 PH 901 761-9720
FAX 901 763-4400
MARTIN F SHEA,PRES
CLAY YANGER,CONTROLLER

SHELF ENERGY,LLC
126 HEYMANN BLVD
LAFAYETTE,LA 70503 PH 337 235-1017
FAX 337 235-6355 WWW.SHELFENERGYLLC.COM
THOMAS E POCHE',OPERS & BUS PLAN MGR
DANNY FREDERICKS,EXPL MGR
STACEY S FREDERICK,LAND & BUS DEV MGR

SHELL CHEMICAL CO,DIV OF SHELL OIL CO
PO BOX 2463,ONE SHELL PLZ
HOUSTON,TX 77002 PH 713 241-6161

SHELL DEEPWATER DEVELOPMENT INC SEE
SHELL OFFSHORE INC

SHELL DEEPWATER PRODUCTION INC SEE
SHELL OFFSHORE INC

SHELL DEVELOPMENT CO,DIV OF SHELL OIL CO
PO BOX 2463,ONE SHELL PLZ
HOUSTON,TX 77001 PH 713 241-6161
D G RUSSELL,PRES
L L SMITH,VP,E&P RESEARCH & DEV
N W BOTTING,MGR,EMPLOYEE RELS
C D FACCIPONTE,FIN MGR,SERV MGR

SHELL OFFSHORE INC
PO BOX 61933
NEW ORLEANS,LA 70161-1933 PH 504 728-6161
J H HOLLOWELL,EVP-DEEPWATER

SHELL OIL COMPANY
910 LOUISIANA ST
HOUSTON,TX 77002-4916 PH 713 241-6161
- OFFICERS -
J D HOFMEISTER,PRES
W C LOWREY,SR VP,GEN COUNSEL & CORP SECY
R J BRAUD,VP,FIN & CONTROLLER
T T COLES,VP,GEN TAX COUNSEL

B P MALNAK,VP,GOVERNMENT AFFAIRS
R S MENNITI,TREAS
JOHN M ESQUIVEL,ASST SECY
HECTOR A PINEDA,ASST SECY
STEPHEN J PAUL,ASST SECY
A M NOLTE,ASST CONTROLLER

SHELL PIPELINE COMPANY,LP
PO BOX 2648,TWO SHELL PLZ
HOUSTON,TX 77252-2648 PH 713 241-6161
WWW.SHELLPIPELINE.COM
PAM PEPPER,FIN MGR-DIST US & CANADA
MICHELE F JOY,COMMERCIAL MGR
WILLIE MARQUEZ,MGR INFO TECH
CLORINDA NOTHSTEIN, REG OPERS MGR/WEST
CARSON,CA OFFICE - 29045 WILMINGTON AVE
90745 PH 310 816-2000

SHELL WESTERN E&P INC
PO BOX 576
HOUSTON,TX 77001-0576 PH 713 241-6161
FAX 281 544-2632
R M SPRAGUE,PRES
P A PAYNE,GEN MGR,PROD
D E WHEELER,DIV PROD MGR,WESTERN
P D CHING,DIV PROD MGR,CENTRAL
J N GITTELMAN,GEN MGR,EXPL
W F KIEL,DIV EXPL MGR,CONTINENTAL
G M LARBERG,DIV EXPL MGR,GULF COAST
B D GRIFFIN,MGR,LAND
J C BOYD,DIV LAND MGR,WESTERN
K R SISSELL,DIV LAND MGR,CENTRAL
BAKERSFIELD,CA OFFICE - P O BOX 11164
93389 PH 661 326-5000
B E BERNARD,GEN MGR
T L MARSHALL,MGR,LAND
N G MCKIM,DPM-KERNRIDGE
S B PONTIOUS,DPM-WEST COAST

SHENK JOHN,PETR GEOL
8912 NW 111TH ST
OKLAHOMA CITY,OK 73162-3000
PH 405 787-0352 JCSHENK12@COX.NET

SHICK CABLE TOOLS,INC
PO BOX 37
CASEY,IL 62420-0037 PH 217 932-5721
FAX 217 932-5706
JOE COCHONOUR,PRES
DON COCHONOUR,SECY

SHIDLER MARK L,INC
PETROLEUM EXPLORATION & PRODUCTION
1313 CAMPBELL RD BLDG D
HOUSTON,TX 77055
PH 713 222-9291 FFAX 713 224-5523
MSHIDLER@MARKLSHIDLERINC.COM
MARK L SHIDLER,PRES
GREG GREGSON,GEOL
CLIFFORD CHEADLE,OFC MGR
JEFFREY SHIDLER,ACQS

SHIELD FRED W AND COMPANY
PO BOX 90627
SAN ANTONIO,TX 78209 PH 210 227-7169
H JOSEPH DE COMPIEGNE,MNGNG PRTNR
REBECCA FRANCES GUNTHER,CONTROLLER
MIDLAND,TX OFFICE - 550 W TEXAS AVE
STE 940,PH 432 682-5371

SHIELDS ENERGY,INC
507 S 14TH ST
FORT SMITH,AR 72901-4607

PH 479 785-1222 FAX 479 782-4375
PATRICK E SHIELDS,PRES,OPERS MGR
JOHN F SHIELDS,VP,GEOL
TIM M SHIELDS,SECY/TREAS,EXPL MGR
MICHAEL A SHIELDS,VP,GAS MKTG

SHIELDS JOHN P,INC
507 S 14TH ST
FORT SMITH,AR 72901-4620 PH 501 785-1222
FAX 501 782-4375
JOHN P SHIELDS,CERT PETR GEOL
TIM M SHIELDS,CERT PETR GEOL
PATRICK E SHIELDS,CERT PETR GEOL

SHINEVAR RUSSELL S,CERTIFIED PROF LANDMAN
3610 WEST ST
LANSING,MI 48917-8547
PH 517 331-8126 FAX 517 322-2895
MILANDMAN@COMCAST.NET

SHO-VAN GAS PRODUCING CO,INC
8555 UNITED PLAZA BLVD STE 500
BATON ROUGE,LA 70809-7000 PH 225 248-2070
FAX 225 248-3070
JOHN C BLACKMAN,PRES,DIR
GEORGE W TROUSDALE JR,DIR,TREAS
BENJAMIN M PETERS,DIR,SECY

SHORE PETROLEUM CORP
615 N UPPER BROADWAY STE 1700
CORPUS CHRISTI,TX 78401 PH 361 826-5800
RAJAN AHUJA RAJAN@SHOREPETROLEUM.COM

SHORELINE GAS LLC SEE
MAGNUS-SHORELINE GAS,LLC

SHORELINE OIL PRODUCTION,LLC
PO BOX 6641
SHREVEPORT,LA 71136-6641
PH 318 869-4474 FAX 318 869-4406
JOHN WOODALL,PRES

SHORT J LINDSEY,JR
2 GREENWAY PLZ STE 600
HOUSTON,TX 77046 PH 713 626-0208

SHORTHORN RESOURCES,INC
2636 SOUTH LOOP W STE 550
HOUSTON,TX 77054-2678 PH 713 668-0550
FAX 713 668-0580 WWW.SHORTHORNRES.COM
STEVEN M SCOTT,PRES OF OIL & GAS OPERS
SMSCOTT@SHORTHORNRES.COM
WAYNE L HUFF,PRES OF PIPELINE OPERS
WLHUFF@SHORTHORNRES.COM

SHOUP RESOURCES,INC
GIS MAPPING SPECIALIST
308 BY PASS RD
SUMMERVILLE,PA 15864 PH 814 538-9196
ROBERT SHOUP ROBERT.SHOUP@GMAIL.COM

SHOWS JIM C,LTD
PO BOX 906
NATCHITOCHES,LA 71458-0906
PH 318 352-2426

SHREVE OPERATING CO
PO BOX 4333
SHREVEPORT,LA 71134-0333 PH 318 221-5568
M R MCCOY,JR,OWNER

SHREVEPORT PETROLEUM DATA ASSOCIATION,INC
333 TEXAS ST STE 900
SHREVEPORT,LA 71101-3678 PH 318 429-2237
FAX 318 429-2441 SPDA@SPDALOGS.ORG
DEMETRA MORGAN,MGR

SHULER DRILLING CO,INC
3514 W HILLSBORO ST

EL DORADO,AR 71730-6745 PH 870 863-7234
FAX 870 863-6331
ROBERT REYNOLDS,PRES
VALORA S GRIFFIN,EXEC SECY

SIBONEY ENERGY SERVICES INC
1450 CENTREPARK BLVD STE 100
WEST PALM BEACH,FL 33401-7430
PH 561 832-3110 FAX 561 650-7330
WWW.SIBONEYENERGY.COM
HOBSON,TX OFFICE - 121 PR 6255
78117 PH 830 780-3083
TRAE QUINN,VP

SID RICHARDSON CARBON & GASOLINE CO
201 MAIN ST
FORT WORTH,TX 76102-3105 PH 817 390-8600
PERRY R BASS,CHRMN OF BD
CRAIG F STREHL,PRES
MITCH R ROPER,SR VP,SID RICHARDSON GAS CO
& RICHARDSON PRODUCTS CO
WAYNE J FARLEY,MGR,GAS OPERS

SIDEWAYS,LLC
HORIZONTAL DRILLING SPECIALISTS
2700 W SKYLINE DR
LORAIN,OH 44053-2246 PH 440 244-5309
FAX 440 244-6331
DR HENRY MAZOROW,CEO,CHRMN
SALT LAKE CITY,UT SALES & ENGRG OFFICE -
660 N COLUMBUS ST,84103-2117
PH 801 535-0066 FAX 801 535-0077
DAVID L ALLIN,COO

SIDEWINDER PUMPS,INC
PO BOX 80769,2108 SW EVANGELINE THRUWAY
LAFAYETTE,LA 70508-0769
PH 337 235-9838 FAX 337 235-9852
SALES@SIDEWINDERPUMPS.COM
INFO@SIDEWINDERPUMPS.COM
QUOTES@SIDEWINDERPUMPS.COM
WWW.SIDEWINDERPUMPS.COM
PAUL GEORGE

SIDLEY R W INC / CARR CONCRETE CORP
436 CASEMENT AVE
PAINESVILLE,OH 44077 PH 440 352-9343
WWW.SIDLEYENERGYSUPPLY.COM
ROB SIDLEY,VP AGGREGATES & TRANS (R W
SIDLEY)
JAMES BINEGAR,OPERS MGR (CARR CONCRETE)
JENNIFER GRUNDY,BUS DEV DIR (R W SIDLEY)

SIEGERT RUDOLF B,GEOL
901 SOMERBY DR APT 408
MOBILE,AL 36695 PH 985 641-4265

SIEMENS WATER TECHNOLOGIES
411 COMMERCIAL PKY
BROUSSARD,LA 70518-3629
PH 337 837-3071 FAX 337 837-9908
WWW.SIEMENS.COM/WATER
MICHAEL R ROBICHEAUX,GEN MGR
JEFF GRIST,DIRECTOR/OPERS
TERRI EDWARDS,ACCT
ED GODEAUX,PRODUCED WATER MGR
BENJAMIN POTIER,SVC MGR

SIERRA RESOURCES LLC
333 CLAY ST STE 3600
HOUSTON,TX 77002
PH 713 365-6100 FAX 713 464-9117
WWW.SIERRARESOURCESLLC.COM
JOHN EADS,PRES

ROBERT FABRIS,EXEC VP LAND & BUS DEV
JOHN KELLY,EXEC VP ENGRG
JOHN CARR EADS,CFO
JOHN CAMPBELL,COO/VP OPERS
MARYLYNN GOMEZ,LAND MGR

SIGMA GAS LTD COMPANY
PO BOX 3554
HOUSTON,TX 77253-3554 PH 713 869-1164
CURTIS KING,PRES

SIGMOR PIPELINE COMPANY SEE
ULTRAMAR DIAMOND SHAMROCK CORPORATION

SIGNA ENGINEERING
2 NORTHPOINT DR STE 700
HOUSTON,TX 77060 PH 281 774-1000
SCOTT BOSTON,VP

SIKES R A DICK ,GEOL
88 STEINER RD
LAFAYETTE,LA 70508-6020 PH 337 993-3287

SILVA JULIO
TOPOGRAPHIC LAND SURVEYORS
1400 EVERMAN PKWY STE 197
FT WORTH,TX 76140-5037
PH 817 744-7512 FAX 817 744-7554

SILVER OAK OPERATING,LLC
2393 HG MOSLEY PKWY BLDG 4 STE 100
LONGVIEW,TX 75604-3662
PH 903 753-9665 FAX 903 234-1411
TERRY J COOK,VP TCOOK@SILVEROAKOP.COM

SILVER WAVE INTERESTS LLC
PO BOX 985,6801 CEDAR RUN
MONTROSE,AL 36559-0985 PH 251 990-8732
SILVERWAVE@JELLENC.BIZ

SILVERNAIL JOHN D
4711 GILBERT DR
SHREVEPORT,LA 71106 PH 318 868-9989

SILVERTON RESOURCES CORPORATION
604 W COLLEGE ST
TERRELL,TX 75160-2516 PH 972 551-1333
FAX 972 551-1704
CLIFFORD N TAYLOR,CPA,PRES

SIMMONS RICHARD,DRILLING CO INC
60 DRILL RIG DR
BUCHANAN,VA 24066-9526 PH 540 254-2289
FAX 540 254-1268
RICHARD A SIMMONS,PRES
MURFREESBORO,TN OFFICE - 819 PARK AVE
37129 PH 615 895-2480 FAX 615 890-3162
ALBANY,KY OFFICE - PO BOX 10,42602
PH 606 387-7083 FAX 606 387-8609
MOORESVILLE,NC OFFICE - 415 RINEHARDT RD
28115 PH 704 662-0773 FAX 704 662-0678

SIMS BRIAN J,GEOLOGIST
103 NORTHLAKE DR
MADISON,MS 39110 PH 601 259-8792

SINCLAIR & IMMICH INC SEE
GRAND MESA OPERATING CO

SINCLAIR ENERGY CORPORATION
1017 PATRICIA ST
IRVING,TX 75060 PH 972 986-8840
MAX REESE,PRES

SINCLAIR OIL PROPERTIES SEE
BEARCAT LAND,INC

SINCLAIR ROBERT C & MARY ANNE
PO BOX 45
CORPUS CHRISTI,TX 78403-0045
PH 361 739-4822

SINCLAIRVILLE PETROLEUM CORP
P O BOX 102
WEST FALLS,NY 14170-0102 PH 716 941-5199
ERIC N PEFLEY,PRES
SANDRA L PEFLEV,SECY
CALVIN F JACKSON,GEOL

SIPES WILLIAMSON & ASSOC SEE
WILLIAMSON PETROLEUM CONSULTANTS,INC

SKINNER ENERGY MANAGEMENT,INC
PO BOX 52148
SHREVEPORT,LA 71135-2148 PH 318 861-1150
FAX 318 861-1150
JOHN H SKINNER JR,PRES,GEOL

SKINNER EXPLORATION INC
PO BOX 52148
SHREVEPORT,LA 71135-2148 PH 318 798-0413
JOHN H SKINNER,PRES,GEOL

SKLAR EXPLORATION COMPANY LLC
401 EDWARDS ST STE 1601
SHREVEPORT,LA 71101-5512
PH 318 227-8668 FAX 318 227-9012
HOWARD SKLAR,OWNER
DAVID BARLOW,PRES/COO
CHRIS FARRELL,VP/CFO
CORY EZELLE,VP/EXPL MGR
GREG REMBERT,VP/LAND MGR
VALERIE WALKER,SR GEOL
DON EUSTES,GEOPHY
ROBERT SENCEBAUGH,ENGR
BOULDER,CO OFFICE - 5395 PEARL PKWY
STE 200 80301 PH 303 541-1559
FAX 303 443-1551

SKLAR HOWARD
401 EDWARDS ST STE 1601
SHREVEPORT,LA 71101-5511 PH 318 227-8668
FAX 318 227-9012

SKRIVANOS ENGINEERING,INC
PO BOX 1492
SHREVEPORT,LA 71164-1492 PH 318 424-9200
FAX 318 424-9210
STEPHEN F SKRIVANOS,PRES

SKRIVANOS N C,CERTIFIED PETR GEOL
PO BOX 1492
SHREVEPORT,LA 71164-1492 PH 318 222-0549
FAX 318 424-9210

SKYLINE OIL & GAS,LLC SEE
SUMMIT DISCOVERY RESOURCES LLC

SLATTERY MARINO & ROBERTS
1100 POYDRAS ST STE 1800
NEW ORLEANS,LA 70163-1800
PH 504 585-7800 FAX 504 585-7890
FIRM@SMR-LAWFIRM.COM
WWW.SMR-LAWFIRM.COM
GERALD F SLATTERY,ATTY
ANTHONY C MARINO,ATTY
DAVID S LANDRY,ATTY
HERMAN E GARNER,ATTY
LYNN G WOLF,ATTY
COLLEEN E JARROTT,ATTY
EMILE J DREUIL III,ATTY
NADEGE A ASSALE,ATTY
JEFFERSON B GOLDMAN,ATTY
CHARLES J GOWER,ATTY

SLAUGHTER,J M OIL COMPANY SEE
ZACHARY OIL OPERATING CO

SLAWSON EXPLORATION COMPANY,INC
727 N WACO ST STE 400
WICHITA,KS 67203-3900 PH 316 263-3201
FAX 316 268-0738
R TODD SLAWSON,PRES (DENVER OFC)
KATHY ATKINS,CFO
CINDY HOWELL,JOINT INTEREST ACCT
MARY MCCOOL,REV ACCT,GAS BALANCING,PAYOUT
- MID-CONTINENT DIVISION -
OKLAHOMA CITY,OK EXPL & PROD OFFICE -
204 N ROBINSON STE 2300,73102
PH 405 232-0201 FAX 405 235-5134
STEVE SLAWSON,VP,OPERS MGR
- WESTERN DIVISION -
DENVER,CO EXPLORATION OFFICE -
1675 BROADWAY STE 1600,80202-4714
PH 303 592-8880 FAX 303 592-8881
TODD SLAWSON,VP,OPERS MGR
CARLOS BERNAL,GEOPHY/WILLISTON BASIN
ROBERT BOGLE,GEOL/CA & WILLISTON BASIN
CONI STOKES,LAND ADMIN,DIV ORDER
STEVE SLAWSON,(OKC OFC),OPERS MGR/
WILLISTON/POWDER RIVER BASIN
- GULF COAST DIVISION/EXPLORATION -
HOUSTON,TX EXPLORATION OFFICE -
4801 WOODWAY STE 345W,77056-1884
PH 713 759-1311 FAX 713 759-1309
DAVID KING,REG LAND MGR
JIM GRUBB,GEOL/TX GULF COAST

SLEDGE JAMES R,CPL
PO BOX 10
RUSTON,LA 71273-0010 PH 318 251-2233

SLOAN OIL CORPORATION
PO BOX 4068
HUMBLE,TX 77347-9868 PH 281 876-1297
FAX 281 876-7540
RICHARD SLOAN,PRES

SLR CONSULTING (CANADA) LTD.
ENVIRONMENTAL SVCS/POLLUTION CONTROL
1185,10201 SOUTHPORT ROAD SW
CALGARY,AB,CANADA T2W 4X9
PH 403 266-2030 FAX 403 263-7906
WWW.SLRCONSULTING.COM
ACOUSTICSTEAMNA@SLRCONSULTING.COM

SLR INTERNATIONAL CORPORATION
ENVIRONMENTAL SVCS/POLLUTION CONTROL
6001 SAVOY DR STE 215
HOUSTON,TX 77036-3322 PH 713 789-9400
FAX 713 789-5493 WWW.SLRCONSULTING.COM
ACOUSTICSTEAMNA@SLRCONSULTING.COM

SM ENERGY COMPANY
1775 SHERMAN ST STE 1200
DENVER,CO 80203-1022 PH 303 861-8140
FAX 303 861-0934 WWW.SM-ENERGY.COM
ANTHONY J BEST,CEO
JAVAN D OTTOSON,COO/PRES
A WADE PURSELL,CFO/EXEC VP
DAVID COPELAND,EX VP/GEN COUNSEL
HERB VOGEL,SR VP-PDTS
JOHN MONARK,SR VP HR
DAVID J WHITCOMB,VP MKTG
DENNIS ZUBIETA,VP ENGRG & EVAL
MATTHEW PURCHASE,TREAS
MARK SOLOMON,VP/CONTROLLER
BRENT COLLINS,SR DIR INVESTOR RELS/PLNG
DON RIGGS,DIR ENVIRO HEALTH & SAFETY

MICHAEL ROACH,ASST VP/DIR OF TAXATION
BILLINGS,MT OFFICE - 550 N 31ST ST
STE 500,59101 PH 406 245-6248
FAX 406 245-9106
MARK D MUELLER,SR VP/REG MGR
JAMES ERLANDSON,REG PROD OPERS MGR
TERESA MUHIC,ASSET MGR-WY
ROB DIEDRICH,DIST EXPL MGR
HOUSTON,TX OFFICE - 777 N ELDRIGE PKWY
STE 1100,77079 PH 281 677-2800
FAX 281 677-2810
GREG LEYENDECKER,SR VP/REG MGR
KENNETH KNOTT,VP BUS DEV & LAND
PAUL LARSON,RESERVOIR ENGRG MGR
TOM MATHIS,OPERS MGR
MIDLAND,TX OFFICE - 3300 A ST BLDG 7
STE 200,79705 PH 432 688-1700
FAX 432 688-1701
LEHMAN E NEWTON III,SR VP REG MGR
RITA BURESS,LAND MGR
GEORGE FRIESEN,SR RESERVOIR ENGR
TOM MORROW,RESERVOIR ENGRG MGR
TULSA,OK OFFICE - 6120 S YALE STE 1300
74136-5741 PH 918 488-7600
FAX 918 488-7601
MARY ELLEN LUTEY,VP/REG MGR
HUTCH JOBE,VP GEOSCIENCE & EXPL
JOHN MITCHELL,GEOL/TECH EXPERT
MARLON WELLS,OPERS MGR
RANDY BUCKLEY,RESERVOIR MGR
WILL DOWNS,DIST EXPL MGR
TONY COOK,BUS DEV

SMACKCO OPERATING,LLC SEE ALOG LLC

SMACKOVER DRILLING CO,INC
3825 GILBERT DR STE 125
SHREVEPORT,LA 71104 PH 985 646-1414
MARGIE RECKNAGEL,PRES
THOMAS J ADAIR SR,VP
TERRY STEELMAN,SECY/TREAS
RICKY PEPPER,FLD SUPT

SMAIL OIL & GAS DEVELOPMENT, LLC
3716 LAKE KRISTIN DR
GRETNA,LA 70056
PH 504 393-9264 FAX 504 394-3936
DKSMAIL392@AOL.COM
DON ALBRIGHT,GEN MGR

SMART BURTON II,CONS GEOL
PO BOX 51114
STE 327 TOWNHOUSE TWRS,920 PINHOOK RD
LAFAYETTE,LA 70503 PH 318 235-0916

SMART E HOLMES JR,CONS GEOL
124 DURHAM DR
LAFAYETTE,LA 70508 PH 337 984-4073
FAX 337 984-4073

SMART OILFIELD SERVICES,LLC
PO BOX 3002
LIBERTY,TX 77575-2102
PH 936 336-3768

SMITH ANNA M,INDEPENDENT SEE
SMITH LAND SERVICES INC

SMITH AVERY E IND GEOL
2007 LEXINGTON AVE
OWENSBORO,KY 42301-4688 PH 270 684-4002

SMITH BITS,A SCHLUMBERGER CO
713 MARKET ST
OKLAHOMA CITY,OK 73114-8132

PH 405 840-1621 PH 800 847-4646
FAX 405 752-6964 WWW.SMITHBITS.COM

SMITH CARL E PETROLEUM,INC
PO BOX 27
SANDYVILLE,WV 25275-0027 PH 304 273-9313
FAX 304 273-4261
  EDDIE B SMITH,PRES
  DONALD P SMITH,VP
  E MICHAEL SMITH,SECY/TREAS

SMITH CHESTER B,ATTORNEY AT LAW
1409 NORTHAM HR
COLUMBUS,OH 43221-3408 PH 814 274-7348

SMITH CYNTHIA B & ASSOCIATES
1829 BERING DR STE 12
HOUSTON,TX 77057-3139 PH 713 266-5404
FAX 713 914-0563
  CYNTHIA B SMITH-WINDHAM,PRES

SMITH DISPOSAL
PO BOX 721049
MCALLEN,TX 78504-1049 PH 956 381-0336
FAX 956 381-5590
  KARON SMITH,OWNER
    KARONSMITH24@AOL.COM
  GARY HUGHES,SLS MGR

SMITH DONALD L,CONSULTING GEOPHY
6045 RIDGEWOOD RD STE F
JACKSON,MS 39211-2753 PH 601 957-1440
  DONALD L SMITH,PRES,GEOPHY CONS

SMITH DRILLING AND COMPLETIONS SEE
SMITH SERVICES,BUS UNIT OF SMITH INT'L

SMITH DRILLING COMPANY
PO BOX 1077
BEEVILLE,TX 78104-1077 PH 361 358-3767
  BUDDY SMITH,OWNER

SMITH ELI AND ASSOCIATES,INC
PO BOX 579
KATY,TX 77492
PH 281 391-3949 FAX 281 391-3975
  ELI SMITH,PRES
  CODY SMITH,LDMN
  KORIE SMITH,LAND SECY
  ANGELA POWELL,LAND SECY

SMITH ENERGY INC
458 ASPIN RD
WESTON,WV 26452 PH 304 844-2298
FAX 304 269-4012
  WENDY SKINNER,RL,OWNER
    WENDYSKINNER@FRONTIER.COM
  ROBERT SMITH,PROJ MGR
  SARAH HENLINE,SPEC
  JAMES SKINNER,MNGNG SURV

SMITH ENERGY 1986A PARTNERSHIP
251 W 39TH ST RM 600
NEW YORK,NY 10018-3162 PH 212 376-8537
FAX 212 719-9462
  HOWARD A SMITH,GEN PRTNR

SMITH INTERNATIONAL SEE
SMITH SERVICES,A BUS UNIT OF SMITH INT'L

SMITH J CURTIS,CPL/ESA
    LANDMAN/ENVIRONMENTAL SITE ASSESSOR
400 LAKESIDE DR
MONROE,LA 71201 PH 318 322-5715

SMITH JAMES E & ASSOCIATES,INC
310 S VINE AVE
TYLER,TX 75702 PH 903 593-9660
FAX 903 593-5527 WWW.JES-ENGINEER.COM

JAMES E SMITH,PE,PRES
  SMITHJAMES@JES-ENGINEER.COM
  JOHN GARVEY,FRAC SPEC
  MIKE DONOVAN,GEOL

SMITH LAND SERVICES INC
515 VERNON AVE
WILLIAMSPORT,PA 17701 PH 484 883-4603
  ANNA M SMITH,DIRECTOR
    LANDSKIRT@COMCAST.NET

SMITH M ROBIN,MBA/CPG
401 EDWARD ST STE 915
SHREVEPORT,LA 71101
PH 318 216-5760
    RSMITH@RYCO1.COMCASTBIZ.NET

SMITH OFFSHORE EXPLORATION COMPANY
PO BOX 52890,811 DALLAS STE 800
HOUSTON,TX 77052-2890 PH 713 651-9102
FAX 713 759-0706

SMITH OIL COMPANY
PO BOX 367,832 W NORTH AVE #A-1
FLORA,IL 62839-0367 PH 618 662-6458
    SMITHOII@RSPEEDY.COM
  MILTON SMITH,II,OWNER

SMITH OPERATING AND MANAGEMENT CO
PO BOX 52
SHREVEPORT,LA 71161-0052
PH 318 222-3119 FAX 318 222-0566
  HARRY L AVANT,PRES
  CHERYL MORELAND,ACCT SUPVSR
  AVERY AVANT,ACCNT PAYABLE
  DEBBIE WALTERS,DIV ORDER ANALYST
    & SECY/TREAS
  CYNTHIA TITTLE,PROD CLERK

SMITH PRODUCTION COMPANY
PO BOX 6177,TWO COUNTRY PLACE
JACKSON,MS 39288-6177 PH 601 932-2223
FAX 601 932-1348
  P M MCNAMES,PRES
  J BROOK FURRH III,VP LAND
  DAVID BEARD,SECY/TREAS

SMITH R B,& ASSOCIATES,INC
1 COUNTRY LN
WIMBERLEY,TX 78676-2510 PH 512 840-9770

SMITH ROBERT J S,GEOL
7506 INWOOD DR
HOUSTON,TX 77063-1802 PH 713 782-2859
PH 713 256-5002 SMITH.RJS2@ATT.NET

SMITH SERVICES
- HEADQUARTERS -
PO BOX 60068,16740 HARDY ST
HOUSTON,TX 77205-0068
PH 281 443-3370 FAX 281 233-5336
  BRYAN DUDMAN
ANCHORAGE,AK (TUBULARS & FISHING &
  REMEDIAL) OFFICE - 721 W FIRST AVE,99501
  PH 907 274-5564 FAX 907 279-6729
  RANDY GRAHAM
NIKISKI,AK (TUBULARS & FISHING &
  REMEDIAL) OFFICE - 51490 WICK RD,99635
  PH 907 646-3236 FAX 907 776-7672
  RONNIE BOZE
BAKERSFIELD,CA (REMEDIAL & DRILLING SVCS)
  OFFICE - 3101 STEAM CT,93308
  PH 661 589-8304 FAX 661 589-8306
  MIKE FLORENCE
DENVER,CO SALES OFFICE - 410 17TH ST

STE 800,80202 PH 303 623-7478
  FAX 303 629-0909
  CALEB ZIMMERMAN
RIFLE,CO (FISHING & REMEDIAL SVCS)
  OFFICE - 702B BUCKHORN DR,81650
  PH 970 625-5118 FAX 970 625-2263
  TRENT KITE
BROUSSARD,LA (COMPLETION SYSTEMS/DRILLING
  PRODUCTS & SVCS) OFFICE - 1235 EVANGELINE
  THROUGHWAY,70518 PH 337 365-7327
  FAX 337 364-3827
  DAVID RICHMOND
HOUMA,LA (REMEDIAL SVCS) OFC - 153
  THOMPSON RD,70363,PO BOX 750,70361
  PH 985 876-2852 FAX 985 851-6264
  GENE DEROCHE
HOUMA,LA (FISHING SVCS) OFFICE -
  222 VENTURE BLVD,70360
  PH 985 873-8191 FAX 985 873-9537
  BRYAN RHODES
SHREVEPORT,LA (DRILLING PRODUCTS & SVCS)
  OFC - 805 AERO DR,71107,PO BOX 78273
  71137 PH 318 222-7767 FAX 318 425-0008
  MICHAEL MILLER
HOUMA,LA (DRILLING PRODUCTS & SVCS) OFC -
  4876 HIGHWAY 311,70360
  PH 985 872-6833 FAX 985 868-7620
  CRAIG CLEMENT
BROUSSARD,LA (FISHING & REMEDIAL SVCS)
  OFFICE - 100 S BERNARD RD,70518
  PH 337 837-4540 FAX 337 837-1905
  JIMMY TYRONE
FOURCHON/GOLDEN MEADOW,LA (DRILLING
  PRODUCTS & SVCS) OFC - 121 4TH ST,SLIP 2
  70357 PH 985 396-4100 FAX 985 396-4101
  JOHN GRANDON
MINDEN,LA (COMPLETION SYSTEMS) OFFICE -
  1624 HWY 531,71055,PO BOX 1179,71058
  PH 318 377-8480 FAX 318 377-9114
  KEN COLLINS
NEW IBERIA,LA (DRILLING PRODUCTS & SVCS)
  OFFICE - 3901 HWY 90 E,70560
  PO BOX 9821,70562-9821
  PH 337 364-8141 FAX 337 367-8853
  CARL VIATOR
NEW ORLEANS,LA SALES OFFICE -
  1615 POYDRAS,STE 830,70112
  PH 504 525-2487 FAX 504 561-6391
  MEL ADAMS
LAFAYETTE,LA (DRILLING PRODUCTS & SVCS)
  OFFICE - 105 COMISSION BLVD,70508
  PH 337 837-2226 FAX 337 837-2237
  DOUG BURNS
LAFAYETTE,LA (SALES) OFFICE -
  100 ASMA BLVD,STE 260,70508
  PH 337 235-2219 FAX 337 235-8930
  DANNY HARRELL
LAUREL,MS (DRILLING PRODUCTS & SVCS)
  OFFICE - 1325 HILLCREST DR,39440
  PH 601 649-4211 FAX 601 649-4044
  JASON MORRIS
FARMINGTON,NM (REMEDIAL & DRILLING SVCS)
  OFFICE - 3601 BLOOMFIELD HWY,87401
  PO BOX 2072,87499
  PH 505 327-1212 FAX 505 325-6516
  EPPIE SANCHEZ

HOBBS,NM (REMEDIAL & DRILLING SVCS) OFC -
1000 W COUNTY RD,PO BOX 2008,88241
PH 505 397-1533 FAX 505 397-3675
BRYAN BROWN

OKLAHOMA CITY,OK (COMPLETION SYSTEMS/
REMEDIAL & DRILLING SVCS) OFFICE -
901 N MORGAN RD,73127
PH 405 324-7577 FAX 405 324-8831
ROBERT OWENS

OKLAHOMA CITY,OK SALES OFFICE -
14000 QUAIL SPRINGS PKY,STE 3500,73134
PH 405 752-6900 FAX 405 752-6962
JEFF HUBBARD
KENNY BENNETT

PIEDMONT,OK (COMPLETION SYSTEMS) OFC -
210 PIEDMONT RD,PO BOX 156,73078
PH 405 373-2660 FAX 405 373-2749
JERRY HEIMER

DALLAS,TX SALES OFFICE -
8150 N CENTRAL EXPY,STE 675,75206
PH 214 987-1800 FAX 214 368-2139
GARY ALLEN
MIKE MCCALL

KILGORE,TX (FISHING & REMEDIAL SVCS) OFC-
3310 HIGHWAY 135 N,75662
PH 903 986-9200 FAX 903 983-3502
STEVE MORRIS

SILSBEE,TX (COMPLETION SYSTEMS) OFFICE -
8143 FM 92,PO BOX 405,77656
PH 409 385-4795 FAX 409 385-2765
MICHAEL SCHULZE

HOUSTON,TX (REMEDIAL & DRILLING SVCS)
OFFICE - 16740 HARDY ST,77032
PO BOX 60068,77205
PH 281 443-3370 FAX 281 233-5353
DAN KILLIAN

HOUSTON/PEARLAND,TX (FISHING & REMEDIAL
SVCS) OFFICE - 14713 JERSEY SHORE DR
77047 PH 713 933-0314 FAX 713 933-0321
WILLIE HOFFPAUIR

ODESSA,TX (DRILLING PRODUCTS & SVCS)
OFFICE - 2120 W MAURICE RD,79763
PO BOX 2512,79760
PH 432 337-5541 FAX 432 580-5549
VANCE FORD
DANNY RENFRO

ODESSA,TX (DRILLING PRODUCTS & SVCS)
OFFICE - 4103 BRAZOS AVE,79768
PO BOX 14554,79768
PH 432 550-7473 FAX 432 550-4514
MICKEY PADILLA

TEAGUE,TX (DRILLING PRODUCTS & SVCS)
OFFICE - 465 HWY 489 W,75860
PH 903 389-1947 FAX 903 389-4059
BRYAN JOHNSTON

BRIDGEPORT,TX (TUBULARS & SURFACE
PRODUCTS) OFFICE - 1663 W US HWY 380
PO BOX 1557,76426
PH 940 683-2002 FAX 940 683-5300
BOBBY CANNON

LONGVIEW,TX (COMPLETION SYSTEMS) OFFICE -
5043 WHITEHURST DR,75602
PH 903 236-4584 FAX 903 236-0751
JEFF KIRKPATRICK

MAURICEVILLE,TX (FISHING SERVICES) OFC -
11041 HWY 12,PO BOX 1509,77626

PH 409 745-4300 FAX 409 745-5566
WILLIAM NICHOLS

EL CAMPO,TX (COMPLETION SYSTEMS) OFFICE -
US HWY 59 AT COUNTY RD 307,77437
PH 979 543-3499 FAX 979 543-5567
CHUCK GREEN

EL CAMPO,TX (DRILLING PRODUCTIONS & SVCS)
OFFICE - 148 DUCKETT ST,ST HWY 70 N
77437 PH 979 543-6600 FAX 979 543-6634
STEVE ALDRIDGE

ODESSA,TX (FISHING & REMEDIAL SERVICES)
OFC - 8700 NW LOOP 338,PO BOX 12365
79768 PH 432 550-6909 FAX 432 550-4702
DANNY RENFRO

MIDLAND,TX (SALES) OFFICE -
1004 N BIG SPRINGS,DINERO PLZ,STE 503
PO BOX 50561,79710
PH 432 570-0065 FAX 432 570-0389
GARY PFANNENSTIEL

MIDLAND,TX (THRU-TUBING) OFFICE -
C/O SPS INTERNATIONAL,4401 E BUSINESS
INTERSTATE 20,79701 PH 432 620-8054
FAX 432 687-2156
DWIGHT INMAN

BROWNFIELD,TX (FISHING SVCS) OFFICE -
1215 W MAIN,PO BOX 387,79316
PH 806 637-6444 FAX 806 637-8339
OSCAR MOLINA

MCALLEN,TX (FISHING & REMEDIAL SVCS) OFC-
PO BOX 720364,720364
LOCATED AT:4521 S HWY 281,EDINBURG,TX
78539 PH 956 384-2383 FAX 956 384-2374
RODNEY YOUNGBLOOD

ALICE,TX (DRILLING PRODUCTS & SVCS) OFC -
1601 S HWY 281,78332,PO BOX 770,78333
PH 361 668-9033 FAX 361 668-0502
DAVID RATHKE

SABINE PASS,TX (DRILLING PRODUCTS & SVCS)
OFC - 8010 S FIRST AVE,PO BOX 468,77655
PH 409 971-2534 FAX 409 971-2540
FRED STAFFORD (BROUSSARD)

MADISONVILLE,TX (COMPLETION SYSTEMS) OFC-
610 INTERSTATE 45 S,PO BOX 789,77864
PH 936 348-3140 FAX 936 348-3389
TOM DOWDY

GIDDINGS,TX (COMPLETION SYSTEMS) OFFICE -
1005 LEE CR 217,BLDG B,PO BOX 638,78942
PH 979 542-0604 FAX 979 542-8841
ADAM MOURNING

CORPUS CHRISTI,TX (COMPLETION SYSTEMS)
OFFICE - 353 LANTANA,78408
PH 361 289-2961 FAX 361 289-6727
DAVID NEWMAN

ALICE,TX (REMEDIAL & DRILLING SVCS) OFC -
602 COMMERCE RD,78332
PH 361 668-8866 FAX 361 668-8911
JOE REEVES

VERNAL,UT (DRILLING PRODUCTS & SVCS) OFC-
1175 EAST 135 SOUTH,PO BOX 1499,84078
PH 435 789-3086 FAX 435 789-5663
NED SMUIN

BUCKHANNON,WV (DRILLING PRODUCTS & SVCS)
OFFICE - N MUDLICK RD,RT 33,BOX 392,26201
PH 304 472-2298 FAX 304 472-2332
JEFF BOWYER

CASPER,WY (DRILLING PRODUCTS & SVCS/

COMPLETION SYSTEMS) OFC - 1403 N DERRICK
DR,82604,PO BOX 369,MILLS,WY 82644
PH 307 472-1011 FAX 307 235-9998
JIM CHRISTENSEN

ROCK SPRINGS,WY (COMPLETION SYSTEMS/
FISHING & REMEDIAL SVCS) OFFICE -
31 WILKENS PEAK DR,82901
PH 307 382-4262 FAX 307 382-9334
TIM ERICKSON
RICHARD OLDSON

- SMITH SERVICES CANADA OFFICES -

CALGARY,AB (SALES) OFFICE -
1600,335 - 8TH AVE SW,T2P 1C9
PH 403 264-6077 FAX 403 206-0370
RON BIRNIE-BROWNE
RICK HENDERS
MIKE CULLEN

NISKU,AB SMITH INTL CANADA,LTD
(REMEDIAL & DRILLING SVCS/COMPLETION
SYSTEMS) - 406 - 22ND AVE,T9E 7W8
PH 780 955-4300 FAX 780 955-2756
WAYNE WYMAN

NISKU,AB (FISHING & REMEDIAL SVCS) OFC -
2306 8TH ST,T9E 7Z2
PH 780 955-8998 FAX 780 955-8943
LEE HEARN

RED DEER,AB (COMPLETION SYSTEMS) -
1 & 2 7659 EDGAR INDUSTRIAL DR,T4P 2V5
PH 403 347-1800 FAX 403 346-0414
KEVIN MORIN

WHITECOURT,AB (FISHING & REMEDIAL SVCS)
OFC - 3701 - 37TH ST,T7S 1P4
KEITH WALSH

WHITECOURT,AB (COMPLETION SYSTEMS)
OFFICE - 4233 42ND AVE,T7S 1O6
PH 780 778-6950 FAX 780 778-6950
ROD SPENCE

GRANDE PRAIRIE,AB (COMPLETION SYSTEMS) -
PO BOX 880,11418 89TH AVE,T8V 3Y1
PH 780 539-5554 FAX 780 539-5558
JOE BELLISLE

GRANDE PRAIRIE,AB (FISHING & REMEDIAL
SVCS) OFFICE - 12238 - 101 AVE,T8V 8A9
PH 780 532-7713 FAX 780 513-4161
LARRY BECKER

BROOKS,AB (COMPLETION SYSTEMS) -
290 CANAL ST,T1R 1G5
PH 403 362-5200 FAX 403 362-5538
DAVE BARRY

EDMONTON,AB (COMPLETION SYSTEMS) OFFICE -
SUMMIT BUSINESS CENTER,7023 - 56TH AVE NW
T6B 3L2,PH 780 461-1143 FAX 780 461-2395
KEVIN O'DWYER

LLOYDMINSTER,AB (FISHING & REMEDIAL SVCS)
OFFICE - 5107 - 62ND ST,T9V 2E3
PH 780 875-0800 FAX 780 875-8731
WALLY GULBIS

HINTON,AB (COMPLETION SYSTEMS) OFFICE -
114 WILLIAMS RD,T7V 1X6
PH 780 740-2333 FAX 780 740-2335
SHELDON LADOUCEUR

- SMITH SERVICES INTERNATIONAL OFFICES -
- ARGENTINA -

COMODORO RIVADAVIA-SMITH INTL INC,S.A.
(DRILLING PRODUCTS & SVCS)- LLAMAS MASINI
3276,BARRIO INDUSTRIAL COMODORO RIVADAVIA

CHUBUT C.P. 9000 PH 54 297 4 483018
FAX 54 297 4 480366
JUAN FERNANDEZ
COMODORO RIVADAVIA - JOINT VENTURE SMITH-
REUMANN (COMPLETION SYSTEMS) - MARCIAL
RIADIGOS NO.280 - C.P. 9800 CHUBUT
PH 54-297-4481231 FAX 54-297-4481231
CLAUDIO LARDET
MENDOZA,C.P. SMITH INTL,INC,S.A.
(DRILLING PRODUCTS & SVCS) - RIO DIAMANTE
NORTE 135,GODOY CRUZ,5501
PH 54 261 4 324 460 FAX 54 261 4 324 461
JUAN CARLOS FEDERICI
TARTAGAL,SALTA C.P. SMITH INTL,INC,S.A.
(DRILLING PRODUCTS & SVCS)-WARNES 61,4560
PH 54 3875 4 21505 FAX 54 3875 4 423741
RICARDO GRAU
NEUQUEN,C.P. SMITH INTL,INC,S.A.
(DRILLING PRODUCTS & SERVICES) -
RUTA 22 KM 1221,8300
PH 54 299 4 466108 FAX 54 299 4 466134
CARLOS FRETE
NEUQUEN - JOINT VENTURE-SMITH-REUMANN-
(COMPLETION SYSTEMS) - FELEX SAN MARTIN
NO. 1070 - C.P. 8300
PH 54-299-4489600 FAX 54-299-4482853
EDUARDO MAYA
MARIO DIEZ
BUENOS AIRES,C.P. SMITH INTL,INC,S.A.
(DRILLING PRODUCTS & SVCS) - AVE ROQUE
SAENZ PENA 547 - PISO 3 (C1035AAA)
CIUDAD AUTONOMA DE BUENOS AIRES
PH 5411 4343-4949 FAX 5411 4343-4949
HUGO MARQUEZ
RINCON DE LOS SAUCES - JOINT VENTURE-
SMITH-REUMANN (COMPLETION SYSTEMS) -
RIO NEGRO NO. 735
PH 54-299-4887207 FAX 54-299-4887207
JAVIER MIRANDA
VILLA REGINA - JOINT VENTURE-SMITH-
REUMANN (COMPLETION SYSTEMS) -
COLEGIO NACIONAL NO. 424
PH 54-2941-460310 FAX 54-2941-460325
FRANCISCO LIBERATORE
DANIEL REUMANN
- AUSTRALIA -
CANNING VALE,W AUSTRALIA-SMITH INTL,INC
(REMEDIAL & DRILLING SVCS) - 48 MAGNET RD
6155,PO BOX 1151,6970
PH 61 8 9455 5311 FAX 61 8 9455 5322
ROBERT JOHNSTON
- AZERBAIJAN -
BAKU - SMITH INT'L INC
C/O MURPHY SHIPPING SERVICES
GARADAGH DUSTRUCTM SALYAN HWY 28-30 KM
1008 PH 994-12-445-88-80
FAX 994-12-445-88-81
JOSE MERCADO
- BRAZIL -
SIMOES FILHO-SMITH INTL DO BRASIL,LTDA
(REMEDIAL & DRILLING SVCS) -
VIA DE PENETRACAO MN
NO 1061 (PARTE) CUENTRO INDUSTRIAL DE
ARATU (CIA) SIMOES FILHO,BAHIA CEP:
43 700-000,PH 55 71 3394 8265
FAX 55 71 3594 7163

ARI MEDEIROS (MOSSORO)
MACAE (REMEDIAL & DRILLING SVCS) -
RUA ALUIZIO DA SILVA GOMES
S/NO QUADRA S -LOTE 3
NOVO CAVALEIROS,MACAE,RIO DE
JENEIRO CEP:27 930-560
PH 55 22 2763 3200 FAX 55 22 2773 4946
FERNANDO ZULIANI
MOSSORO-SMITH EQUIPAMENTOS E SERVICOS
S.A. (REMEDIAL & DRILLING SVCS) -
AV. PRESIDENTE DUTRA 2150
RIO GRANDE DO NORTE CEP:59 631 000
PH 55 84 3312 1212 FAX 55 84 3312 1355
ARI MEDEIROS
RIO DE JANEIRO-SMITH INTL DO BRASIL LTDA
(REMEDIAL & DRILLING SVCS) -
RUA SANTA LUZIA,651-21ST FLOOR
20 030-040 PH 55 21 3231 3535
FAX 55 21 2262 9327
NIGEL EVANS
- BRUNEI DARUSSALAM -
BRUNEI-C/O PTAS SENDIRIAN BERHAD (FISHING
& REMEDIAL SVCS) - LOT NO 1,TAPAK
PERINDUSTRIAN PEKAN BELAIT,SIMPANG 114
JALAN SETIA DI-RAJA,KUALA BELAIT KA3131
PH 673 3 331938 FAX 673 3 331418
FRANS ROEMER
- CHINA -
CHANGZHOU,JIANGSU - SMITH DRILLING
EQUIPMENT (CHANGZHOU) LTD -
25 MIDDLE CHANGJIANG RD
PH 86-519-5155-672 FAX 86-519-5155-801
MICHAEL GUO
- COLOMBIA -
YOPAL-SMITH INTERNACIONAL DE COLOMBIA
(REMEDIAL & DRILLING SVCS) - KILOMETRO 2
VIAMORICHAL,BASE HALLIBURTON,YOPAL
CASANARE PH 57 986 355 459
FAX 57 986 355 460
JUAN POLO
BOGOTA-SMITH INTERNACIONAL DE COLOMBIA
(REMEDIAL & DRILLING SVCS) - EDIFICIO
LATINO AMERICANA DE SEGUROS,CRA 9A
NO. 99-02,STE 603,SANTA FE DE BOGOTA
PH 571 651 3888 FAX 571 622 4978
CEES HIDDING
- CONGO -
POINTE NOIRE - SMITH INTERNATIONAL,INC
BP 1771 PH 242-942-245 FAX 242-940-373
NORDINE BENYAHIA
- EGYPT -
CAIRO-C/O SMITH INTERNATIONAL DEVELOPMENT
CORP - VILLA 161,CHOUEFIAT/AKHNATON
INTERSECTION,6TH AREA SECTOR 1
5TH DISTRICT PH 2022-617-5291
FAX 2022-617-5299
BRIAN SUTHERLAND
JIM SUMRALL
- FRANCE -
LONS BILLERE-SMITH INTL FRANCE SARL
(REMEDIAL & DRILLING SVCS)- ZONE INDUSPAL
BP 217,AVENUE JOLIOT CURIE,64142
PH 33 559 923550 FAX 33 559 923596
PIERRE ANDRE
SIMONE GRISMONDI
- GERMANY -

CELLE-SMITH INTL DEUTSCHLAND GMBH
(REMEDIAL & DRILLING SVCS) - GRAFFTRING
5-7,D-29227,POSTFACH 3251,CELLE D-29232
PH 49 5141 8010 FAX 49 5141 81161
DETLEF KUNZE
- INDIA -
MUMBAI,MAHARASHTRA-SMITH INTERNATIONAL
INC (REMEDIAL & DRILLING SVCS) -
PLOT NO. A311/312,M.I.D.C.
T.T.C INDUSTRIAL AREA,MAHAPE
THANE DISTRICT,NEW MUMBAI 400 701
PH 91 22 6510 4203 FAX 91 22 2778 2104
KENNY FORBES
- INDONESIA -
JAKARTA-SMITH INTL,INC (REMEDIAL &
DRILLING SVCS) - PT SMITH TOOL INDONESIA-
COMMERCIAL ESTATE,BLDG 201
PH 62 21 789 2024 FAX 62 21 789 2025
ADRIAN SCHOLTEN
BALIKPAPAN - SMITH INT'L,INC
C/O PT SMITH TOOL,BALIKPAPAN JALAN
MULUWAMAN RT5-NR-105
PH 62 542 743 670 FAX 62 542 743 460
GARY TAN
- ITALY -
BOLOGNA-SMITH INTL ITALIA S.P.A.
(REMEDIAL & DRILLING SVCS)- VIA GRANDI,3A
40013 CASTEL MAGGIORE
PH 390 51 713401 FAX 390 51 713159
VITTORIO LIVERANI
- KUWAIT -
MINA ABDULLAH-SMITH INTERNATIONAL,INC
SHUAIBA WEST BLOCK 5
PLOT B-138-I
PH 965 326-0760 FAX 965 326 0710
JOHNNY RAWLS
- MALAYSIA -
KEMAMAN SUPPLY BASE-SMITH INTL SON BHD
(REMEDIAL & DRILLING SVCS) - WAREHOUSE
NO.12,DOOR 16,KEMAMAN,TERENGGANU
PH 60 9 863 3411 FAX 60 9 863 3410
EDWIN SIRIPALA
KUALA LUMPUR-SMITH INTL SDN BHD
(REMEDIAL & DRILLING SERVICES)
STE 11-C1,11TH FLOOR,SOUTH BLOCK,BOX NO.7
WISMA SELANGER DREDGING,1422A JALAN
AMPANG,50450 PH 60 3.2163.8855
FAX 60 3.2163.8860
TUFFY HOGUE
LABUAN-SMITH INTERNATIONAL SDN BHD
(REMEDIAL & DRILLING SVCS) -
C1 JALAN ARSAT,LIGHT INDUSTRIAL ESTATE
(87000) PO BOX 75,LABUAN F.T. 87008
PH 6087 415664 FAX 6087 415887
DENIS EMPALAH
IAN SCOTT
- NETHERLANDS -
SCHOONEBEEK - SMITH SERVICES
(FISHING & REMEDIAL SERVICES)
INDUSTRIEWEG 17A,7761 PV
PH 31 524 532575 FAX 31 524 532294
GERRY BAKKER
BEVERWIJK - SMITH SERVICES
(DRILLING PRODUCTS & SVCS) - GOOILAND 41
1948RD,PH 31-251-211925 FAX 31-251-272784
THOMAS SCHULZ

- MEXICO -
POZA RICA,VERACRUZ - SMITH INTERNACIONAL
DE MEXICO SA DE CV
KM. 12 CARRETERA POZA RICA-COATZINTLA
LOTE 16,CORREDOR INDUSTRIAL MIGUEL ALEMAN
VELAZCO,CP 93350 PH 52 782 825 7066
FAX 52 782 825 7066
JESUS MALDONADO
CUYDAD DEK CARMEN,CAMPECHE - SMITH
INTERNACIONAL DE MEXICO SA DE CV
CALLE 38 NO 274 ENTRE 69 Y 61
COL MIAMI PH 52 938 1199519
FAX 52 938 1310541
MARCOS ORTIZ DEL LA PENA
- NIGERIA -
PORT HARCOURT,RIVERS STATE-C/O AFRICA
OILFIELD SVCS LTD (JT VENTURE-DRILLING
PRODUCTS & SVCS) - PLOT 272,TRANS AMADI
INDUSTRIAL LAYOUT,P.M.B. 029
PH 234 84 238817 FAX 234 84 238687
LIAM HARVEY
PORT HARCOURT-C/O CISCON NIGERIA,LTD
(COMPLETION SYSTEMS) - KM14 ABA/PORT
HARCOURT EXPY,PO BOX 6082
PH 234 84 610761 FAX 234 84 236773
LIAM HARVEY
- NORWAY -
STAVANGER (REMEDIAL & DRILLING SERVICES)
LAGERVEIEN 24,4033 FORUS,NORWAY
POSTBOKS 151,STAVANGER 4065
PH 47 51 800200 FAX 47 51 800213
TRYGVE BERTHELSEN
STAVANGER,NORWAY - (DRLG PRODUCTS & SVCS)
DUSAVIKVEIEN 17-4007
PH 47-51537900 FAX 47-51537910
EGIL ERIKSEN
- OMAN -
MUSCAT (QURUM-DRILLING SERVICES)-
UNITED ENGINEERING SVCS,LLC (REMEDIAL &
DRILLING SVCS) - DES - PO BOX 2638,P.C.
112 RUWI,QURUM COMMERCIAL AREA,MUSCAT
POST CODE 112
PH 968 24 561850 FAX 968 24 561884
STEVE ARNOTT
- QATAR -
DOHA (REMEDIAL & DRLG SVCS)- PO BOX 12908
PH 974 4600 400 FAX 974 4600 149
DANE HAYNES
- ROMANIA -
BUCHAREST - C/O DOSCO PETROSERVICES
ROMANIA SRL,59,SCARLATESCU STREET,1
PH 421 260 1260 FAX 421 260 1261
FRANCESCO OLIVIERI
- RUSSIA -
MOSCOW,RUSSIA - (REMEDIAL & DRLG SVCS) -
PROSPECKT 60-LETYA OKTYABRYA 9,BLDG 2,
4TH FLR,BUSINESS CENTRE AKADEMICHESKY
117312 PH 70-95-411-8095
FAX 70-95-411-8096
JAN DE VRIES
- SAUDI ARABIA -
AL-KHOBAR-C/O ABDULLAH AL-SUWAIKET FOR
TRAD. & CONT. EST. (FISHING & REMEDIAL
SVCS) - PO BOX 321 AL-KHOBAR 31952
PRINCE MOHAMMED ST,23RD CROSS,31952
PH 966 3 8590525 FAX 966 3 8590533

BOB GALLOWAY
- SINGAPORE -
LOYANG CRESCENT-SMITH INTL,INC
(REMEDIAL & DRILLING SERVICES)
LOYANG OFFSHORE SUPPLY BASE,BOX NO. 5100
JETTY DR,508988
PH 65 6545 1800 FAX 65 6545 1200
JEFF JACKSON
- SOUTH AFRICA -
MOSSELBAY - (REMEDIAL & DRILLING SVCS) -
C/O PETROSA LOGISTICS BASE
DEPOT ROAD,VOORBAAI 6500
PH 27-44-606-6145 FAX 27-44-606-6112
ERIC DYUSHA
- TUNISIA -
SFAX-SMITH INTL TUNISIA (REMEDIAL &
DRILLING SVCS) - ROUTE MENZEL-CHAKER-KM1
3003, PH 216 74 242 414 FAX 216 74 245422
FOUED MEDJOUB
- UNITED ARAB EMIRATES -
DUBAI (MFG JV) OILFIELD SUPPLY CENTER,LTD
SIML DIV,BLDG 57,OILFIELD SUPPLY CENTER
LTD YARD,JEBEL ALI FREE ZONE
PH 971 4 883 6800 FAX 971 4 883 9771
MARVIN MENEZES
DUBAI-JOINT VENTURE-SMITH INTL GULF SVCS
(DRILCO GROUP PRODUCTS) - PO BOX 24983
OILFIELD SUPPLY CENTER LTD
BLDG NO. 2,JEBEL ALI FREE ZONE
PH 971 4 8836268 FAX 971 4 8836502
BARRY PANZER
ABU DHABI-SMITH INTL,INC
(FISHING & REMEDIAL SERVICES) -
PLOT NO. 81,SECTOR NO. M-14
MUSAFFA INDUSTRIAL AREA,PO BOX 47080
PH 971 2 555 3700 FAX 971 2 555 3055
ALISTAIR MALCOLM
DUBAI-SMITH INTL,INC (COMPLETION SYSTEMS/
DRILLING PRODUCTS & SERVICES) -
PO BOX 64900,JEBEL ALI FREE ZONE
PH 971 4 8835072 FAX 971 4 8835082
LIONEL YEOMAN
DUBAI - SMITH INT'L,INC
PO BOX 18699,OILFIELD SUPPLY CENTER B60
JEBEL ALI FREE ZONE
PH 971 4 883 6091 FAX 971 4 883 2175
RON BRUCE
- UNITED KINGDOM -
ABERDEEN-SMITH INTL (NORTH SEA) LIMITED
(DRILLING PRODUCTS & SVCS)- WOODSIDE ROAD
BRIDGE OF DON,AB23 8EF
PH 44 1224 702821 FAX 44 1224 822324
JIM DOWDS
ABERDEEN-SMITH INTL (NORTH SEA) LIMITED
FISHING & REMEDIAL SVCS) - BADENTOY AVE
BADENTOY PARK,PORTLETHEN INDUSTRIAL
ESTATE,PORTLETHEN,AB12 4YB
PH 44 1224 334700 FAX 44 1224 782455
LAWRENCE BARR
ABERDEEN - (DRILLING PRODUCTS & SVCS)
HOWE MOSS AVE
KIRKHILL INDUSTRIAL ESTATE,DYEE AB21 OGP
PH 44-1224-770707 FAX 44-1224-724182
NIALL MACPHERSON
- VENEZUELA -
MATURIN-SMITH INTERNACIONAL DE VENEZUELA

C.A. (COMPLETION SYSTEMS) -
AV.ALIRIO UGARTE PELAYO,EDIF.SMITH
INTERNACIONAL,SECTOR LAS PINAS
MATURIN,EDO.MONAGAS 6202
PH 58 291 6431333 FAX 58 291 6436528
NICANOR ACOSTA
CIUDAD OJEDA-SMITH INTERNACIONAL DE
VENEZUELA,C.A. (COMPLETION SYSTEMS/
REMEDIAL & DRLG SVCS) - AV. INTERCOMUNAL
SECTOR EL PRADO NO. 92
AL LADO DE ASADOS EL TIO
MUN. SIMON BOLIVAR,CIUDAD OJEDA,EDO.ZULIA
PH 58 265 6314897 FAX 58 265 6310412
ATILLO CARRASCO
CARACAS-SMITH INTERNACIONAL DE VENEZUELA
C.A. (SALES OFFICE) -
CALLE LA GUAIRITA,CENTRO PROFESIONAL
EUROBUILDING,PISO 9,OFFICINA 9-A
URBANIZACION CHUGO
PH 58 212 400 1900 FAX 58 212 400 1920
MARIELLYS ZERPA
ANACO - SMITH INTERNACIONAL DE VENEZUELA
C.A. (COMPLETION SYSTEMS) -
CALLE MEXICO,BARRIO LAS CHARAS
NICANOR ACOSTA,NACOSTA@SMITH.COM
FREDDY FIGUEROA,FFIGUEROA@SMITH.COM
- VIETNAM -
VUNG TAU (REMEDIAL & DRLG SVCS) - PETRO
TWR,STE 150M3,8 HOANG DIUE ST,VUNG TAU
S.R.,PH 84 64 848887 FAX 84 64 848509
TRINH CHAU LOAN

SMITH T BAKER INC SEE
T.BAKER SMITH,INC
SMITH TRUCKING CO
PO BOX 691
CONROE,TX 77305-0691 PH 409 756-6960
MIKE SMITH,PRES
SMITH VICTOR P OIL COMPANY
PO BOX 6177,TWO COUNTRY PLACE
JACKSON,MS 39288-6177 PH 601 932-2223
FAX 601 932-1348
VICTOR P SMITH,OWNER,PRES
J BROOKE FURRH,VP,LAND
P M MCNAMES,EXEC VP
SMITH W BRUNER,ESTATE,OIL PROP
PO BOX 2389,300 N GREEN STE 200
LONGVIEW,TX 75606-2389 PH 903 758-2192
SMITH-CLEMENT EXPLORATION INC SEE
STONE-CANYON EXPLORATION,INC
SMITH-RUBIN & ASSOCIATES
PO BOX 639
BELLE CHASSE,LA 70037
PH 888 567-9904 FAX 888 558-3258
GEORGE SMITH,ATTY/DEBT COLLECTION
OILFIELD SPEC
SMYTH OIL CORPORATION
1021 MAIN ST STE 1970
HOUSTON,TX 77002-6504 PH 713 652-4088
FAX 713 652-0448
L D SMYTH,PRES
TRACY D SMYTH,VP
JOAN BREEDEN,SECY
SNELL DWIGHT & ASSOCIATES
PO BOX 407
SIMONTON,TX 77476-0407 PH 281 346-1932
DWIGHT SNELL,OWNER PH 281 344-0569

DWIGHT@YOURLANDMAN.COM

SNOWMASS ENERGY PARTNERS LTD
3300 S 14TH ST STE 322
ABILENE,TX 79605-5052 PH 325 672-5618
TTAYLOR@ABILENE.COM
THOMAS J TAYLOR,PRES
LADDIE GALLOWAY,VP
CAROL DEATHERAGE,SECY
KRISTY MCGEE,RECEIVABLES
MEL BENNETT,CONTROLLER
BRIAN EVERITT,PETR ENGR

SNYDER BROTHERS,INC
PO BOX 1022,ONE GLADE PARK E
KITTANNING,PA 16201 PH 724 548-8101
FAX 724 545-8243 SALES@SNYDERCOS.COM
WWW.SNYDERASSOCIATEDCOS.COM
DAVID E SNYDER,PRES
BRYAN K SNYDER,VP
DAVID C O'HARA,VP

SNYDER ROBERT D,PETR GEOL
PO BOX 51956,110 OIL CENTER DR
LAFAYETTE,LA 70505-1956 PH 318 234-3333
ROBERT SNYDER,PETR GEOL

SOAPE ROGER A,INC
19450 STATE HWY 249 STE 460
HOUSTON,TX 77070-3057
PH 281 440-6347 FAX 281 440-0609
ROGER A SOAPE,PRES
C FRANK ROBINSON,VP
WILL HOLSTEIN,SR PROJ MGR
C ANDREW COOPER,PROJ MGR

SOCIETY OF PETROLEUM EVALUATION ENGINEERS
(SPEE) WWW.SPEE.ORG

SOCIETY OF PROFESSIONAL EARTH SCIENTISTS
(SIPES) WWW.SIPES.ORG

SOCO OFFSHORE SEE SANTA FE SNYDER CORP

SOCOR TECHNOLOGIES,INC
PO BOX 1600
MAGNOLIA,AR 71754
PH 318 226-0100 RCORNET@BELLSOUTH.NET
WWW.SOCORTECH.COM
RYAN CORNET

SOJITZ CORPORATION OF AMERICA
2000 WEST LOOP S STE 1100
HOUSTON,TX 77027-3741 PH 713 966-5750
FAX 713 966-5770

SOLID ROCK ENERGY,INC
PO BOX 556
WORTHINGTON,OH 43085-0556 PH 614 888-2770
JERRY C OLDS,PRES

SOLLENBERGER DAVID,JR
4017 NEYREY DR
METAIRIE,LA 70002-4427 PH 504 887-7576

SOLOCO, SEE
NEWPARK MATS & INTEGRATED SERVICES

SOMERSET DEVELOPMENT INC SEE
PROVIDENT ROYALTIES LLC

SOMERSET LEASE HOLDINGS INC SEE
PROVIDENT ROYALTIES LLC

SOMEX ENERGY COMPANY
4 SLEEPY COVE ST
SAN ANTONIO,TX 78230-5238
PH 210 691-0854 FAX 210 375-8168
L LADDIE LIVEOAK,PRES
DARLA LIVEOAK,VP

SOMOCO,INC
13685 S WEST BAY SHORE DR STE 200
TRAVERSE CITY,MI 49684-6290
PH 231 946-0200 FAX 231 946-8180
ROBERT E TUCKER JR,PRES
PAT GIBSON,VP,LAND/LEGAL
KATIE GIBSON,VP,FIN
MATTHEW A JOHNSTON,GEOPHY
MURRAY M MATSON,CHF GEOL
TIMOTHY L BAKER,VP OPERS
DAVE GREWE,OPERS MGR

SONERRA RESOURCES CORP
PO BOX 631627
NACOGDOCHES,TX 75963-1627
PH 936 569-9662 FAX 936 569-6866
SCOTT HENDERSON,PRES
EARL HERRERA,VP/TREAS

SONOR RESOURCES,INC
PO BOX 11403
FORT SMITH,AR 72917-1403
PH 479 783-6699 FAX 479 783-6696
JIM SLADE,PRES
JIMSLADE@SONORRESOURCES.COM

SONORA ACQUISITION CORP SEE
AMERICAN EXPLORATION CO

SOONER PIPE,L.L.C.
1331 LAMAR ST STE 970
HOUSTON,TX 77010 PH 713 759-1200
PH 800 888-9161 FAX 713 759-0442
WWW.SOONERPIPE.COM
JOHN SHOAFF,PRES
RICHIE RICHARDSON,VP SLS & BUS DEV
MIKE CULLATHER,VP SLS ADMIN
NEW ORLEANS,LA SALES OFFICE -
650 POYDRAS ST STE 1917,70130
PH 504 581-4201 OR 800-727-4201
FAX 504 524-3216
DOUG NETHERLAND,ACCT MGR
COVINGTON,LA SALES OFFICE - 2000 PRESERVE
LAKE DR STE A,70433 PH 504 361-9002
FAX 504 361-0102
JOHN HOFFMAN,ACCT MGR
MIKE BULOT,ACCT MGR
DARLA DUFRENE,ACCT MGR
TULSA,OK OFFICE - PO BOX 1530
MID-CONTINENT TWR 74101-1530
PH 918 587-3391 OR 800 888-3391
FAX 918 587-0863
DORINDA BARKER,VP/CONTROLLER
RICHARD TOWNLEY,ACCT MGR
MIDLAND,TX OFFICE - 6810 EAST I-20
PO BOX 790,79702
PH 432 684-4342 FAX 432 682-3345
JOE PHILLIPS,VP
JUSTIN HAM,INSIDE SLS MGR
GODLEY,TX OFFICE - 8000 COUNTY ROAD 1001
76044-5201 PH 817 309-2629
FAX 817 389-2638
LEX LEWIS,ACCT MGR
WEXFORD,PA OFFICE- STONEWOOD COMMONS 1
101 BRADFORD RD STE 200,15090
PH 724 934-6801 FAX 724 934-3376
JIM SHEETS,ACCT MGR

SOTEC,LLC
9517 MAURICE AVE
MAURICE,LA 70555 PH 337 893-8881

LOVELESE MARCEAUX

SOUR ARTHUR W,JR,OIL OPR
444 ALBERT AVE
SHREVEPORT,LA 71105-2908 PH 318 226-9332

SOURCE ENVIRONMENTAL SERVICES INC
PO BOX 1409
BREAUX BRIDGE,LA 70517-1409
PH 337 845-5468 FAX 337 845-5474
JIM BURTON,PRES JMBURTON@COX.NET
RONNIE COCKERHAM,SLS
LOU THERIOT,OFC MGR
DAVID WOOD,RADIATION SAFETY OFCR
BRAD ROMERO,RADIATION SAFETY OFCR
LESTER BOUDREAUX,OPERS

SOURCE OIL,LLC
1102 GREENBRIAR RD
LAFAYETTE,LA 70503-3654 PH 337 984-8207
FAX 337 984-4341
JOSEPH FRANKLIN,GEOL FRANKLINGEO@COX.NET

SOURCE ROCK MINERALS II,LLC
PO BOX 670713
DALLAS,TX 75367 PH 214 306-8142
FAX 214 593-4031
BILL@SOURCEROCKMINERALS.COM

SOURCE ROCK MINERALS,LP
PO BOX 670713
DALLAS,TX 75367 PH 214 306-8142
BILL@SOURCEROCKMINERALS.COM

SOURGASCO,INC SEE AMERICAN EXPLORATION CO

SOUTH CARLTON OPERATING COMPANY,LLC
PO BOX 822
NATCHEZ,MS 39121 PH 601 446-5992
FAX 601 446-5964

SOUTH LOUISIANA CONTRACTORS,INC SEE
SOLOCO,L L C

SOUTH POINTE ENERGY,LLC
PO BOX 4215,5048 LAKE SHORE DR
JACKSON,MI 49204 PH 517 787-8621
FAX 517 787-8080 LANDPRO515@COMCAST.NET
JEFFREY G WRAY,MGR

SOUTH STATES OIL & GAS CO SEE
AMERICAN EXPLORATION CO

SOUTH TEXAS LAND LIMITED PARTNERSHIP
PO BOX 430,HEFNER BLDG
EL CAMPO,TX 77437-0430 PH 979 543-4251
FAX 979 543-5326

SOUTH TEXAS WELL SERVICE CO
PO BOX 750
CORPUS CHRISTI,TX 78403-0750
PH 361 882-8882 FAX 361 882-1808
MIKE W HARVEY,PRES
KENNETH S HARVEY JR,VP

SOUTHCENTRAL PRODUCTION CORPORATION
PO BOX 2845
MOBILE,AL 36652-2845 PH 251 621-9699
FAX 251 621-6778

SOUTHCOAST RESOURCES
24900 PITKIN RD STE 305
SPRING,TX 77386 PH 832 616-3040
PVERMA@SCOASTRESOURCES.COM

SOUTHEASTERN OIL REVIEW,OIL REPORTS
PO BOX 9621
JACKSON,MS 39286-9621 PH 601 353-6213
PH 353-0511 FAX 601 353-0512
J ISHEE,EDITOR
BOBBIE HARRIS,CIRCULATION MGR

SOUTHEASTERN PIPE LINE COMPANY SEE
FAULCONER VERNON E,INC

SOUTHEASTERN PRODUCING COMPANY
PO BOX 71
WAYNESBORO,MS 39367-0071
PH 601 735-4891 FAX 601 735-5346
BEN C DAWS,PRES
JUDY H DAWS,RECORDS MGR

SOUTHERN AVIONICS COMPANY
NON-DIR RADIO BEACONS & ASSOC PRODUCTS
PO BOX 5345
BEAUMONT,TX 77726-5345 PH 409 842-1717
FAX 409 842-2987 WWW.SOUTHERNAVIONICS.COM
SALES@SOUTHERNAVIONICS.COM

SOUTHERN FLOW COMPANIES,INC SEE
ZEDI US INC

SOUTHERN GAS MARKETING CO
500 N SHORELINE BLVD STE 910
CORPUS CHRISTI,TX 78401 PH 361 882-2761
FAX 361 882-8946
FRED E LONG,CEO
MARTIN MADRO,VP MKTG

SOUTHERN GULF OPERATORS,INC
406 ROSELAWN BLVD
LAFAYETTE,LA 70503-3912
PH 337 233-7925 FAX 337 988-9294
JERRY BLANKENSHIP,PRES

SOUTHERN LAND & EXPLORATION,LLC
729 WICHITA ST
SHREVEPORT,LA 71101
PH 318 222-0916 FAX 318 222-6120
KEVIN SEVERSON,MNGNG MEMBER
KSEVERSON@SOLAEX.COM

SOUTHERN LANDMEN INC
416 TRAVIS ST STE 1106
SHREVEPORT,LA 71101-5504 PH 318 221-6400

SOUTHERN MINERAL CORPORATION SEE
PETROCORP INCORPORATED

SOUTHERN MUD LOGGING INC
PO BOX 725,104 OZONE ST
WEST MONROE,LA 71294-0725 PH 318 325-3393

SOUTHERN NATURAL GAS COMPANY
PO BOX 2563
BIRMINGHAM,AL 35202-2563
PH 205 325-3800 FAX 205 326-2071
- OFFICERS -
NORMAN G HOLMES,SR VP,CHF COMMERCIAL
OFCR
JOE P DICKENSON,VP,COMMERCIAL OPERS
PATRICK B POPE,VP,GEN COUNSEL/SOUTHERN
MICHAEL J VARAGONA,VP,BUS DEV
E E THOMAS,DIR,ENGRG

SOUTHERN OIL EXPLORATION,INC
1513 RIDGELAND RD W
MOBILE,AL 36695-2719 PH 251 635-1139
FAX 251 635-1151
JOHN C SIPPLE,PRES
MIKE A DAMOFF,VP

SOUTHERN PACIFIC EXPLORATION COMPANY LLC
14781 MEMORIAL DR STE 2212
HOUSTON,TX 77079 PH 281 785-1872
ADMIN@SPXCO.COM
J FOSTER,GEOL ADV
J S MOSBY,OPERS
L S ROSS,ENGR
W JAMES,LAND

J F DOBEY,LEGAL

SOUTHERN PETROLEUM LABORATORIES,INC
OIL & GAS TESTING
8880 INTERCHANGE DR
HOUSTON,TX 77054 PH 800 696-6775
PH 713 660-0901
DR. DOSS,ENVIRO LAB MGR
DRDOSS@SPL-INC.COM
CHRIS STALEY,HYDROCARBON LAB MGR
CSTALEY@SPL-INC.COM
-LABORATORY LOCATIONS-
SCOTT,LA LAB - 500 AMBASSADOR CAFFERY
PKWY 70583 PH 800 304-5227
FAX 337 237-4775
RON BENJAMIN,ENVIRO LAB DIR
RBENJAMIN@SPL-INC.COM
PATTI PETRO,HYDROCARBON LAB MGR
PPETRO@SPL-INC.COM
TRAVERSE CITY,MI LAB - 459 HUGHES DR
49686 PH 888 775-6424 231 947-5777
STEVE GRENDA,LAB MGR SGRENDA@SPL-INC.COM
BELLE CHASSE,LA LAB - 9221 HIGHWAY 23
70037, PH 504 391-1333 FAX 504 391-0013
MATT WYCHE,HYDROCARBON LAB MGR
MWYCHE@SPL-INC.COM
LARRY LINCECUM,HYDROCARBON FLD SUPR
LLINCECUM@SPL-INC.COM
CARTHAGE,TX LAB- 1595 US 79 S, 75633
PH 903 693-6242 FAX 903 693-8606
JOE WOOLEY,HYDROCARBON LAB MGR
JWOOLEY@SPL-INC.COM
MIKE MORRIS,HYDROCARBON MEASUREMT SUPR
MMORRIS@SPL-INC.COM
VENUS,TX LAB - 2440 CHAMBERS ST STE A
76084 PH 817 539-2168 FAX 817 539-2170
DEE ORR,LAB/FLD MGR   DORR@SPL-INC.COM
-FIELD OFFICE LOCATIONS-
HOUSTON,TX OFFICE- 110 S PETRO LN 77045
PH 713 668-4448 FAX 713 668-4969
JIM REED,MGR JREED@SPL-INC.COM
CARENCRO,LA OFFICE-
4790 NE EVANGELINE THRUWAY 70520
PH 337 896-3055 FAX 337 896-3077
LOWELL CHAPMAN,DIR CENTRAL REGION
LCHAPMAN@SPL-INC.COM
LAUREL,MS OFFICE - 1961 BUSH DAIRY RD
39440 PH 601 428-0842 FAX 601 428-0654
RANDY MCCALLUM,DIR RMCCALLUM@SPL-INC.COM
PEARLAND,TX OFFICE - 2640 E BROADWAY
STE 109 77581 PH 281 485-8705
FAX 281 485-6417
JEFF WILD,COO JWILD@SPL-INC.COM
BILL THERIOT,TECH DIR
BTHERIOT@SPL-INC.COM
OWASSO,OK OFFICE- 17423 E 88TH ST N
74055, PH 918 527-3287 FAX 918 274-7181
FRED VAN ORSDOL,VP AUDITING & LOSS CONTRL
FVANORSDOL@SPL-INC.COM
DALLAS,TX OFFICE - 2861 S BELT LINE RD
75253, PH 972 224-5111
ROYCE MILLER,MGR RMILLER@SPL-INC.COM
SHREVEPORT,LA OFFICE - 231 MOUNT ZION RD
71106 PH 318 686-1811
MARK CHASE,LAB MGR MCHASE@SPL-INC.COM
- SALES REPRESENTATIVES -

- HYDROCARBON -
CRAIG FALGOUT,CFALGOUT@SPL-INC.COM
ROBERT BIENVENU,RBIENVENU@SPL-INC.COM
SHANA HART,SHART@SPL-INC.COM
ZACK GARZA,ZGARZA@SPL-INC.COM
-ENVIRONMENTAL -
WAYNE BOLING,WBOLING@SPL-INC.COM
DWAYNE COCO,DCOCO@SPL-INC.COM
TODD BEASLEY,TBEASLEY@SPL-INC.COM
LINDA BUTLER,LBUTLER@SPL-INC.COM
ADINA WALKER,AWALKER@SPL-INC.COM

SOUTHERN PRODUCER SERVICES,LLC
19 BRIAR HOLLOW LN STE 130
HOUSTON,TX 77027 PH 713 728-7913
CARL M CARTER
CARL.CARTER@SOUTHERNPRODUCERSERVICES.C
OM

SOUTHERN RESOURCE CO,A TEXAS CORP
PO BOX 6483,1400 MERCANTILE BANK TWR
CORPUS CHRISTI,TX 78466-6483
PH 361 882-9999
JAMES E THAXTON,PRES
BORDEN JENKINS,VP,GEOL,EXPL
BILL COOK,CONS GEOL
GERRY HEINZELMAN,CONS GEOL

SOUTHERN STRUCTURES LLC
METAL COMPONENTS - BLDG DIV
100 GEOLOGY CIR
BROUSSARD,LA 70518-5739 PH 337 856-5981
PH 800 264-5981 FAX 337 856-5980
LARRY BLANCHET,OWNER
YOUNGSVILLE,LA PLANT - HWY 92
COMMERICAL INDUSTRIAL FABRICATION

SOUTHERN TITLE & ABSTRACT CO,INC
2200 PAKENHAM DR
CHALMETTE,LA 70043 PH 504 276-5858
FAX 504 277-0502
HAROLD J ANDERSON,PRES

SOUTHERN TRADING & PRODUCTION CO INC
3825 BEE CAVE RD
AUSTIN,TX 78746-6401 PH 512 328-6000
FAX 512 328-6070
STEVE MASSEY,MNGNG PRTNR

SOUTHERN TRIANGLE OIL CO
PO BOX 427,600 CHESTNUT ST
MOUNT CARMEL,IL 62863-0427
PH 618 262-4131
LESTER D MOORE,PRES
ROGER KEEN,TOOLPUSHER
LYNETTE K WILES,BOOKKEEPER

SOUTHFORK INVESTMENTS,INC
6513 PERKINS RD
BATON ROUGE,LA 70808-4259 PH 225 769-9555
FAX 225 769-0023 THEBEAV@INTERSURF.COM
JOSEPH P BRANTLEY,PRES,CEO
JPBRANTLEY@GMAIL.COM
SUSAN BRANTLEY,OFC MGR

SOUTHLAND ROYALTY COMPANY SEE
MERIDIAN OIL INC

SOUTHWEST BANK OF TEXAS SEE
AMEGY BANK

SOUTHWEST ELECTRONIC ENERGY GROUP
823 BUFFALO RUN
MISSOURI CITY,TX 77480 PH 281 240-4000
WWW.SWE.COM INFO@SWE.COM

SOUTHWEST GAS SYSTEMS,INC
17010 SEVEN PINES DR STE 101
SPRING,TX 77379-4976
PH 281 251-5121 FAX 281 251-5141
JEFF J PAWELEK,PRES

SOUTHWEST GUARANTY TRUST COMPANY SEE
NATIONAL FIDUCIARY SERVICES,NA

SOUTHWEST LAND & MINERALS,INC
PO BOX 331654
CORPUS CHRISTI,TX 78463
PH 361 882-6951 FAX 361 882-6966
R S LUKER,VP STEVE.LUKER1@GMAIL.COM

SOUTHWEST OPERATING,INC-TYLER
727 S CHILTON
TYLER,TX 75701-1554
PH 903 597-4279 FAX 903 597-4282
JOHN MUSSELMAN,PRES
ELLEN MUSSELMAN,VP
ELLEN@SOUTHWESTOPERATING.COM

SOUTHWEST ROYALTIES,INC
SUBSIDIARY OF WILLIAMS CLAYTON ENERGY,INC
6 DESTA DR STE 3000
MIDLAND,TX 79705
PH 432 688-3238 FAX 432 688-3246
MEL G RIGGS,PRES
GREG WELBORN,VP LAND PH 432 682-6324

SOUTHWESTERN ENERGY COMPANY (SWN)
SOUTHWESTERN ENERGY PRODUCTION CO
10000 ENERGY DR
SPRING,TX 77389-4954 PH 832 796-1000
FAX 832 796-8891 WWW.SWN.COM
STEVE L MUELLER,CHRMN OF BOARD & CEO
WILLIAM J WAY,PRES & COO
MARK K BOLING,EXEC VP & PRES V+ DEV SOLU
JEFFREY B SHERRICK,EXEC VP-CORP DEV
R CRAIG OWEN,SR VP & CFO
JOHN C ALE,SR VP/GEN COUNSEL/SECY
JENNIFER N MCCAULEY,SR VP-HUMAN RESOURCES
JAMES W VICK,SR VP-BUS INF SYSTEMS
JAMES L BOLANDER JR,SR VP - V+ RES DEV
JOANNE C HRESKO,SR VP-CORP DEV
JOSH C ANDERS,VP & CONTROLLER
JENNIFER E STEWART,VP-TAX
DANNY W FERGUSON,VP-GOV & COMMUNITY RELS
JAMES A TRAMUTO,VP-GOV & REGULATORY STRAT
ROY D HARTSTEIN,VP-STRATEGIC SOLUTIONS
THOMAS M ALEXANDER,VP-HEALTH SFTY & ENVIR
JOHN C GARGANI,VP & GEN MGR-STRATEGY,
PERFORMANCE & INNOVATION
J ALAN STUBBLEFIELD,SR VP-OPERS
RANDALL D PONDER,SR VP-EXPL
JIM R DEWBRE,SR VP-LAND
JOHN E JACK BERGERON JR,SR VP-
NE APPALACHIA DIV
PAUL W GEIGER,SR VP-SW APPALACHIA DIV
DOUGLAS H VAN SLAMBROUCK,SR VP-
FAYETTEVILLE SHALE DIV
C GREG STOUTE,GEN MGR-ARKLATEX DIV
HARRY H SONNY BRYAN,VP-NEW VENTURES
GEORGE A SHEFFER,VP-OPERS - FAYETTEVILLE
STEPHEN M GUIDRY,VP-LAND - FAYETTEVILLE
JAMES N PERKINS,VP-LAND - NEW VENTURES
DAVID A DELL'OSSO,GEN MGR-SAND WASH BASIN
CONWAY,AR OFFICE - 1000 SOUTHWESTERN
ENERGY DR 72032 PH 501 548-6500
FAX 501 548-6550

SOUTHWESTERN OIL COMPANY
PO BOX 460,225 N LAFAYETTE ST
GREENVILLE,MI 48838-0460 PH 616 754-7149
PH 616 754-7140 FAX 616 754-5947
JEFFREY D COOK,PRES,SECY
WILLIAM F COOK,VP
BYRON J COOK,VP

SOUTHWESTERN PUBLIC SERVICE CO SEE
XCEL ENERGY

SOVEREIGN ENERGY CORPORATION
PROFESSIONAL LAND SERVICE
545 N UPPER BROADWAY STE 1101
CORPUS CHRISTI,TX 78401-0678
PH 361 774-3040 FAX 361 884-4622
SAN FOX,PRES STANFOXLANDMAN@YAHOO.COM

SPARTAN OPERATING COMPANY,LLC
25901 PLUMA RD
CALABASAS,CA 91302
PH 517 372-5566
KENNETH N ALCINI,PRIN
KEN@SPARTANOPERATING.COM
SANDRA HENSLEY,VP MKTG

SPARTAN PETROLEUM CORPORATION
14027 MEMORIAL DR #266
HOUSTON,TX 77079-6826 PH 281 493-1022
FAX 281 493-1022
LARRY L JONES,PRES
LJONES1239@COMCAST.NET
W K JONES,VP,ASST SECY
NORMA J JONES,VP,SECY

SPEC-MONT ENERGY CORP SEE
COMPASS EXPLORATION INC

SPECIALTIES COMPANY
14141 S WAYSIDE DR
HOUSTON,TX 77048-5707 PH 713 644-1491
LARRY BAXTER,GEN MGR

SPECTER EXPLORATION,INC
5800 ONE PERKINS PL STE 9A
BATON ROUGE,LA 70808
PH 225 769-6292 FAX 225 769-6294
STEPHEN M JENKINS,PRES

SPECTRA ENERGY CORPORATION
5400 WESTHEIMER CT
HOUSTON,TX 77056-5310 PH 713 627-5400
FAX 713 627-5314 WWW.SPECTRAENERGY.COM
JOHN BREMNER,VP,MARKETER SVCS & BUS DEV
PH 713 627-4933
BILL PENNEY,VP,NE MARKETING & BUS DEV
PH 617 560-1383
PAT GIBSON,VP,EAST TENNESSEE NATURAL GAS
PH 713 627-5880
RICHARD TERRAZAS,VP,MKTNG,BUS DEV & REG
AFFAIRS,MARITIMES & NE PIPELINE LLC
PH 713 627-4604
PAT WHITTY,VP,CORPORATE BUS DEV
PH 713 627-5432
FULKRA MASON,VP,SE TRANSMISSION & STORAGE
PH 713 627-5712
PAUL RIETDYK,VP,DIST OPERS,UNION GAS
PH 519 436-4691
TOM WOODEN,VP,NE TRANSMISSION
PH 617 560-1345
ALLEN CAPPS,VP,BUS DEV STRGE TRANSMISSION
UNION GAS PH 519 436-5216
MARION BURNYEAT,VP,MIDSTREAM,CANADA WEST
PH 403 699-1955

TIM GRACEL,VP,NGL,MRKTNG,CANADA WEST
PH 403 699-1706
GARY WEILINGER,VP,STRATEGIC DEV &
EXTERNAL AFFAIRS,CANADA WEST
PH 403 699-1523
AL RITCHIE,VP,FIELD OPERS,CANADA WEST
PH 250 262-3420
DUANE RAE,VP,FLD SVCS,CANADA WEST
PH 403 699-1551
ROB WHITWHAM,VP,PIPELINE,CANADA WEST
PH 403 699-1884
MIKE WHALEN,GEN MGR,MRKTNG,BUS DEV & REG
AFFAIRS,MARITIMES & NE PIPELINE L.P.
PH 902 425-0628
GARY METZ,MGR,LANDS MGMNT,CANADA WEST
PH 604 691-5792
KENT DENNY,DIRECTOR,TRANSMISSION SVCS
PH 713 627-5572
WENDY OLSON,DIRECTOR,MEDIA RELATIONS
PH 713 627-4072
TONI BECK,GROUP VP,INT & EXT AFFAIRS
PH 713 627-5720
LISE-ANN JACKSON,DIR,PUBLIC AFFAIRS,
COMMUNITY & ABORIGINAL RELATIONS,CANADA
W
PH 403 699-1506
STEVE RANKIN,DIR,EXT RELATIONS,MARITIMES
& NE PIPELINE LP PH 902 425-4293
ANDREA STASS,MGR,MEDIA RELATION,UNION GAS
PH 519 436-5490
ROSEMARY SILVA,TEAM LEADER,EXT COMM
CANADA WEST PH 604 488-8147
BOSTON,MA OFFICE- 890 WINTER ST STE 300
WALTHAM,MA 02451 PH 617 254-4050
CALGARY,ALBERTA,CANADA OFFICE-
425 1ST ST SW STE 2600, T2P 3L8
PH 403 699-1999
HALIFAX,NOVA SCOTIA,CAN OFC-1801 HOLLIS
B3J 3N4 PH 902 425-4474 OR 800 223-1716
- UNION GAS -
CHATHAM,ONTARIO,CAN OFC-PO BOX 2001
50 KEIL DR N,N7M 5M1 PH 519 352-3100
OR 800 265-5230
VANCOUVER,BRITISH COLUMBIA,CAN OFFICE-
PO BOX 11162,1055 W GEORGIA ST STE 1100
V6E 3R5,PH 604 691-5500

SPECTRUM FIELD SERVICES,INC SEE
ATLAS PIPELINE MID-CONTINENT LLC

SPEEDMAN OIL COMPANY,OIL PROD
P O BOX 8709
CORPUS CHRISTI,TX 78468-8709
PH 361 854-8091

SPEEREX LIMITED PARTNERSHIP
PRODUCTION,GEOLOGIST
PO BOX 1363
MT PLEASANT,SC 29465-1363 PH 843 884-0011
FAX 843 884-0011 SPEEREX@COMCAST.NET
STEPHEN W SPEER,GEN PRTNR

SPENCE RALPH OIL COMPANY,INC
813 FIRST PL
TYLER,TX 75702-5745 PH 903 593-3202
RALPH SPENCE JR,PRES
OLIVER R HOLLENSHEAD,EXEC VP/COO
SHERRY BRAGG,ADMIN ASST
DAWN LOGAN,OIL & GAS ADMIN

SPENCER COMPANIES INC,THE
PO BOX 18128,120 WOODSON ST NW
HUNTSVILLE,AL 35804-8128 PH 205 533-1150
WWW.SPENCERCOS.COM
GUY SPENCER JR,CHRMN
JAMES M SEGREST,PRES,CEO
SARAH S CHAPPELL,SR VP
GUY J SPENCER III,EXEC VP
W GARY TUCKER JR,CFO

SPERLING GEOPHYSICS CORPORATION
600 BLUEBELL DR
LANSING,MI 48911-3729 PH 517 393-1339
WWW.GEOPHYSICS.COM TEDD@GEOPHYSICS.COM
TEDD F SPERLING,PRES,GEOL & GEOPHY CONS
CAROL L SPERLING,VP,CEO
SAM PARKER,ACCT
CINDY STORIE,ADMIN ASST

SPERRY SUN DRILLING SERVICES SEE
HALLIBURTON ENERGY SERVICES

SPIDLE TURBECO
- FLOTEK INDUSTRIES -
10603 W SAM HOUSTON PKWY N STE 300
HOUSTON,TX 77064-4660 PH 713 849-9911
WWW.FLOTEKIND.COM
BOSSIER CITY,LA OFFICE - PO BOX 5724
3514 E TEXAS ST,71111 PH 318 549-1551
FAX 318 549-1553
CHICKASHA,OK OFFICE - PO BOX 848
7040 S HWY 81,73023-0848 PH 405 222-2494
FAX 405 222-2495
EVANSTON,WY OFFICE - PO BOX 371
105 PASTURE RD,82930 PH 307 789-9341
FAX 307 789-1410
FARMINGTON,NM OFFICE - 537 E ANIMAS,87401
PH 505 486-3691
GRANBURY,TX OFFICE - PO BOX 7113,76049
5281 OLD GRANBURY RD PH 817 579-6027
FAX 817 579-6109
LAFAYETTE,LA OFFICE - PO BOX 82009,70598
1553 VEROT SCHOOL RD PH 337 264-7113
FAX 337 837-5789
MIDLAND/ODESSA,TX OFFICE -
4306 S COUNTY RD #1290,ODESSA 79765
PH 432 561-9495 FAX 432 561-8238
PITTSBURGH,PA OFFICE - PO BOX 9356,15225
3407 GRAND AVE PH 412 778-0166
FAX 412 778-0448
ROBSTOWN,TX OFFICE - 1435 DERRICK ST
78380 PH 361 767-7100 FAX 361 837-4332
ROSS,ND OFFICE - PO BOX 23,58776
PH 701 629-1219
TOWANDA,PA OFFICE - RR 6 BOX 6019-3,18848
PH 570 265-8762 FAX 570 265-8767
VERNAL,UT OFFICE - PO BOX 46,84078
PH 435 789-1833

SPIDLE TURBECO TRIUMPH SEE
SPIDLE TURBECO

SPILLER GUY
PO BOX 791514
SAN ANTONIO,TX 78279-1514 PH 210 822-0322

SPINDLETOP TUBULAR SERVICE SEE
ALLIS-CHALMERS ENERGY INC

SPINGAS ENERGY INC
PO BOX 53745
LAFAYETTE,LA 70505 PH 337 264-1470
SPRINGAS@ATT.NET

OWEN SCOTT,PRES

SPIRIT GLOBAL ENERGY SOLUTIONS
PO BOX 8529,3406 S STATE HWY 349
MIDLAND,TX 79708 PH 432 522-2288
WWW.SPIRITENERGYSOLUTIONS.COM
DARRELL TROTTER,PERMIAN AUTOMATION DIV
DTROTTER@SPIRITENERGYSOLUTIONS.COM
JUSTIN RAMIREZ,PERMIAN DOWNHOLE DIV
JRAMIREZ@SPIRITENERGYSOLUTIONS.COM
RUSSELL MESSER,EAGLEFORD DIV
MESSER@SPIRITENERGYSOLUTIONS.COM
GEORGE CENICEROS,PERIMAN SLS DIV
GC@SPIRITENERGYSOLUTIONS.COM
BRANDON VANHUSS,BAKKEN DIV
BVANHUSS@SPIRITENERGYSOLUTIONS.COM
NISKU,ALBERTA,CANADA OFFICE - BAY 3
1206 - 10TH ST,T9E 8K2 PH 780 979-9934
STEVE TRELFORD,CANADIAN DIV
STRELFORD@SPIRITENERGYSOLUTIONS.COM

SPIVEY LLOYD G,JR,IND
PO BOX 8
CANTON,MS 39046-0008
PH 601 859-5251 FAX 601 859-5258
RJOHNSON@NETDOOR.COM

SPN RESOURCES,LLC
1301 MCKINNEY STE 900
HOUSTON,TX 77010 PH 713 728-7840
FAX 713 728-7860 WWW.DYNAMICOSR.COM
G MATT MCCARROLL,PRES/CEO
HOWARD TATE,CFO
JAMES BROKMEYER,VP PROD OPERS
GARY JANIK,VP EXPLOITATION & DEV
CAREY NAQUIN,VP WELL OPERS
JOHN H SMITH,VP LAND & BUS DEV
BILL SWINGLE,ACCT

SPOONER ENERGY INC
625 HIGHLAND COLONY PKWY STE 101
RIDGELAND,MS 39157-8809
PH 601 969-1831 FAX 601 353-4117
HSPOONER@SPOONERCOMPANIES.COM
HARRY SPOONER,PRES
MICHAL SPOONER,VP
JOE JOHNSON,GEOL
BOB MCELROY,LAND MGR

SPOONER PETROLEUM COMPANY
625 HIGHLAND COLONY PRWY STE 101
RIDGELAND,MS 39157
PH 601 969-1831 FAX 601 353-4117
WWW.SPOONERCOMPANIES.COM
MICHAL SPOONER,PRES
MSPOONER@SPOONERCOMPANIES.COM
HARRY SPOONER,VP
KEN MAGEE,OPERS MGR
BOB MCELROY,LAND MGR
MARY ANN VANLANDINGHAM,ACCT
CINDY KELLER,PROD ACCT
RONNIE TURNER,FLD SUPVSR
TONI MOORE,LAND ASST
JOE JOHNSON,EXPLOR GEOL

SPOT MARKET CORPORATION
2003 CANDLELIGHT PLACE DR
HOUSTON,TX 77018-1118 PH 713 526-5016
STAN PYNDUS,PRES

SPRADLEY ENERGY,INC
4901 CHERRY HILLS DR
CORPUS CHRISTI,TX 78413-2734

PH 361 992-4114
JOAN B SPRADLEY,PRES

SPRADLEY GUS,PETR GEOL
216 NORTH BOEKE ROAD
EVANSVILLE,IN 47711-6018 PH 812 476-3347

SPUR ENERGY,INC
110 KENNEDY AVE #3
SAN ANTONIO,TX 78209 PH 503 888-1085
E C WELSH,PRES

SPUR LAND COMPANY
819 THORNWICK DR
HOUSTON,TX 77079-4512 PH 281 242-6363
RANDY B LEE,PRES

SRW,INC
PO BOX 100,175 THOMPSON RD
BAD AXE,MI 48413-0100
PH 989 269-8528 FAX 989 269-8622
LYNETTE DRAKE,PRES
LINDA JANKS,OFC MGR
GAYLORD,MI FIELD OFFICE - 1847 CALKINS DR
49735 PH 989 732-8884 FAX 989 732-8068
JOHN STEGMAN,FLD SUPVSR

ST MARTIN LAND COMPANY
1908 HENDERSON LEVEE RD
BREAUX BRIDGE,LA 70517-7877
PH 337 228-7501 FAX 337 228-2729
SUSAN J CORRIGAN,PRES
SANDRA MARTIN,OFC MGR
SHANE J VERRET,SURFACE OPERS MGR
KEVIN BONIN,ASST SURFACE OPERS MGR
DEBBIE SPRINGER,OIL & GAS OPERS
LAFAYETTE,LA OFFICE - 130 S AUDUBON BLVD
STE 101,70503 PH 337 205-6301
FAX 337 205-6302

ST MARY LAND & EXPLORATION COMPANY
SEE SM ENERGY COMPANY

ST MARY PARISH LAND COMPANY SEE
ST MARY LAND & EXPLORATION COMPANY

ST PIERRE OIL CO
PO BOX 380,102 N VAN BUREN ST
NEWTON,IL 62448-0380 PH 618 783-4441
J E ST PIERRE JR,PRES,SECY/TREAS
SHIRLEY HOFFEDITZ,OFC MGR

STABIL DRILL SEE
SUPERIOR ENERGY SERVICES COMPANY

STACY ROBERT A,LLC
OIL & GAS EXPLORATION
6219 TIME PLACE
SHREVEPORT,LA 71106 PH 318 221-7184
R A STACY JR,MNGNG PRTNR

STAGECOACH PETROLEUM,INC
PO BOX 7801
DALLAS,TX 75209 PH 214 336-5969
MARK BRISTOL,PRES MARKABRISTOL@YAHOO.COM

STAGG RESOURCE CONSULTANTS,INC
PO BOX 7028,5457 BIG TYLER RD
CROSS LANES,WV 25356-0028 PH 304 776-6660
FAX 304 776-7867 WWW.STAGGCONSULTANTS.COM
STAGG@STAGGCONSULTANTS.COM
ALAN K STAGG,PG,CMA,CEO
E GAYE HAGER,EXEC VP/COO
CRAIG R WOOD,VP/CFO

STALKER ENERGY LP SEE
KALER ENERGY CORPORATION

STALL ALBERT M,OIL PROPERTIES
1715 VALENCE ST

NEW ORLEANS,LA 70115-4839 PH 504 891-5746

STALLION CONSTRUCTION
402 SERVICE RD
RAYNE,LA 70578 PH 337 873-8698
WILLIAM STEVENSON III,OPERS MGR
RENEE DUHON,OPERS SUPPORT/DISPATCHER
DAVID STUTES,PURCH
ROBERT LEBLANC,REG CONTROLLER

STALLION ENERGY,LLC
411 W RICHEY RD
HOUSTON,TX 77090-5713
PH 281 872-1982 FAX 281 873-8597
GEORGE SANFILIPPO,PRES
PAUL KING,VP,OPERS
JEFF TRAMBAUGH,VP,FIN
MIKE POTTER,OPERS MGR

STANBERRY OIL COMPANY
625 MARKET ST STE 200
SHREVEPORT,LA 71101-5392 PH 318 221-3957
FAX 318 221-8835
WALLACE A STANBERRY,PRES
WALLACE LYNN STANBERRY,VP
PAT JONES,SECY/TREAS

STANBERRY WALLACE A,PETR ENGR
625 MARKET ST STE 200
SHREVEPORT,LA 71101-5392 PH 318 221-3957
FAX 318 221-8835
WALLACE LYNN STANBERRY

STANCO PETROLEUM,INC
OIL & GAS EXPLORATION & PRODUCTION
PO BOX 6
VIDALIA,LA 71373-0006
PH 318 757-2900 FAX 318 757-2905
STAN COOPER,PRES

STANDARD ENERGY COMPANY
1105 SCHROCK RD STE 602
COLUMBUS,OH 43229-1174 PH 614 885-1901
FAX 614 885-3006
GERALD S JACOBS,PRES

STANDARD GAS CORP
5900 FAIRDALE
HOUSTON,TX 77057-6307 PH 713 789-1930

STANDARD OIL COMPANY (INDIANA) SEE
AMOCO PRODUCTION CO

STANDARD OIL COMPANY INC
PO BOX 620
NEW HAVEN,WV 25265-0630 PH 304 489-2777
FAX 304 489-2778 WWW.STANDARDOIL.BIZ
RICHARD ZELNAR,PRES/CEO
RZELNAR@STANDARDOIL.BIZ
ANDREW ZELNAR,VP PROD
KATHY ZINGACE,TREAS
ROBERT GERMAN,SECY

STANDARD SOUTHERN CORPORATION
PO BOX 270415
HOUSTON,TX 77277-0415 PH 713 627-1700
LARRY RAUCH,PRES
GARY GLESBY,VP
LINDA SPRUNG,SECY/TREAS

STANDCO INDUSTRIES INC
PO BOX 820969
HOUSTON,TX 77282-0969 PH 713 224-6311
PH 800 231-6018 FAX 713 229-9312
WWW.STANDCO.NET SALES@STANDCO.NET
L D MCCANN,PRES,CEO
DONALD GIVENS,EXEC VP

STANFORD OIL COMPANY,LLC
716 SILVER OAK GRV
COLORADO SPRINGS,CO 80906-8627
PH 719 576-2783 FAX 719 527-0026
JAMES PRICE,PRES JIMHPRICE@COMCAST.NET

STARCO EXPLORATION,INC
4699 GRAVEL PIT ROAD
SEGUIN,TX 78155
PH 361 813-9992 FAX 830 639-4107
T M (MIKE) QUIGLEY,PRES

STATE OF LOUISIANA,OFFICE OF CONSERVATION
DEPT OF NATURAL RESOURCES
PO BOX 94275,617 N 3RD ST
BATON ROUGE,LA 70804-9275
PH 225 342-5540 FAX 225 342-2584
DNR.LOUISIANA.GOV/CONSERVATION
JAMES H WELSH,COMMISSIONER
GARY ROSS,ASST COMMISSIONER
TODD KEATING,DIR,ENGRG DIV (ADMIN)
BRENT CAMPBELL,DIR,ENGRG DIV (REG)
DAVE ELFERT,DIR,GEOL OIL/GAS DIV
STEPHEN LEE,DIR,INJECTION & MINING DIV
STEVEN GIAMBRONE,DIR,PIPELINE DIV
GARY SNELLGROVE,DIR/ENVIRO DIV

STATE REVIEW OF OIL AND NATURAL GAS
ENVIRONMENTAL REG WWW.STRONGERINC.ORG

STATEX OPERATING,LLC
PO BOX 797545
DALLAS,TX 75379-7545 PH 972 869-2800
DHAR CARMAN,MGR
DONALD WIESE,JR,MGR
THOMAS R FULLER,MGR
B TRAVIS BASHAM,MGR

STATION 12 ACQUISITIONS INC
2301 SPRINGTIME RD
GREENWOOD,IN 46143 PH 317 496-0923
NICK WELCH NICK.WELCH@HOTMAIL.COM

STEAD F L,CONS GEOL
4001 WINTER PARK RD
ADDISON,TX 75001-4904 PH 972 239-8742
FLSTEAD@ATT.NET

STEAUA ROMANA (US) INC SEE
AMBRIT ENERGY CORP

STEDMAN ENERGY INC
PO BOX 1006
CHAUTAUQUA,NY 14722-0041
PH 716 789-3018 FAX 716 789-3017
KEVIN E MCCHESNEY,PRES/OWNER

STEDMAN WEST INTERESTS INC
PO BOX 7
HOUSTON,TX 77001-0007 PH 713 520-0400
WWW.STEDMANWEST.COM LAND@STEDMAN-
WEST.COM
STUART W STEDMAN,PRES
RANDOLPH L PULLIN,CFO
SHELLIE HAYES,LAND MGR
STELLA SUMBERA,LDMN

STEDMAN WEST LAND & CATTLE CO LLC
PO BOX 7
HOUSTON,TX 77001-0007 PH 713 520-0400

STEEL TRADING CORP OF AMERICA
5800 5TH ST
KATY,TX 77493 PH 281 578-5383
FAX 281 578-2404 SALES@STCOU.COM
WWW.STEELTRADINGCORP.COM
STEVEN J HAUCK,PRES/CEO

DIANE COX,VP ADMIN
GREGG HAWKINS,VP PRODUCTS & OPERS
CHRIS HAUCK,VP QLTY-QMR
PEDRO MORALES,FLD SVCS
STACY HAWK,CUSTOMER SVC REPR
JASON RUIZ,FLD SVCS/OPERS MGR
HOLLAND CURTIS III,PUR & SLS
DOUG MARMARO,SLS
MARK VANDERVOORDT,SLS
CASEY LOWE,SLS
JAKE BLANKENSHIP,SLS
JAMES CARRANZA,PRODUCT/OPERS REPR
SANDRA G. PALMA,QLTY ADMIN/FLD SVC COORD
LAUREN SOMMERFIELD,SLS/SVC CORRESP
JENNIFER DUNCKEL,IT ASST

STEELE POSEY MINERALS LLC
7409 STALLION CIR
FLOWER MOUND,TX 75022
PH 817 430-1412 214 529-7592
B J POSEY

STEELMAN INVESTMENTS,INC
4420 VALLEY RANCH RD
LONGVIEW,TX 75602-6671 PH 903 984-3443
KENDALL STEELMAN,OWNER
CHARLA ROLPH,AGENT

STEEN PRODUCTION SERVICE INC SEE
BAKER ENERGY

STEINHOFF RAYMOND O, IND CONS PETR GEOL
104 TEA OLIVE CT
PRATTVILLE,AL 36067 PH 850 433-7918
ROS1925@GMAIL.COM

STELLY C L JACK & ASSOCIATES,INC
REGISTERED LAND SURVEYORS
PO BOX 53353
LAFAYETTE,LA 70505-3353 PH 318 237-0746
FAX 318 237-6779
C L JACK STELLY,PRES
C L JACK STELLY JR,REG LAND SURV
JOHN MILLER,SURV TECH
PAUL HEBERT,PERMIT COORD
BARBARA STELLY,OFC MGR
BRAD GIBSON,REG LAND SURV
RONALD DECOU,SURV TECH

STENBERG R B,SR,SEE
PAWNEE CORP,THE

STEPHENS PRODUCTION COMPANY
PO BOX 2407,623 GARRISON AVE STEPHENS BL
FORT SMITH,AR 72902-2407
PH 479 783-4191 FAX 479 783-4195
WILLIAM S WALKER,PRES/CEO
GARY BOLAND,VP EXPL
WILLIAM L DAWKINS JR,GEN COUNSEL
KEN JACKSON,MGR NEW VENTURES
STEVEN MESSER,VP ENGRG
ROBERT LINER,SR GEOL ADVSR
LUKE MARTIN,GEOL DEV MGR
ROB CALAWAY,GEOL
ALAN MARTINKEWIZ,VP LAND
DENVER,CO OFFICE - ROCKIES DIVISION
1825 LAWRENCE ST STE 300,80202
PH 303 296-2012 FAX 303 298-1181
DAVE SEUK,VP
DSUEK@STEPHENSPRO.COM
DOUG WEIN,LAND MGR
DWEIN@STEPHENSPRO.COM
CHRIS OSHEA,LEASE & DO ANALYST

COSHEA@STEPHENSPRO.COM

STERLING ENERGY USA
333 CLAY ST STE 700
HOUSTON,TX 77002-4115
PH 713 850-1880 FAX 713 850-1879
NBROWN@STERLINGENERGYUSA.COM
WWW.STERLINGENERGYUSA.COM
DAN SILVERMAN,PRES
GEOFFREY STONE,CFO
JOHN D BROUILLETTE,LAND MGR,SR LAND ATTY
JBROUILLETTE@STERLINGENERGYUSA.COM

STEVENSON KEN,AND ASSOCIATES
864 S JEFFERSON
LA GRANGE,TX 78945-3231 PH 409 968-3250
KEN STEVENSON,OWNER

STEVER REX H
44 CAMDEN PL
CORPUS CHRISTI,TX 78412-2613
PH 361 991-6085 FAX 361 991-4688
RHSTEVER@HOTMAIL.COM
REX H STEVER

STEWARD DAVID W,IND LDMN,CPL
PO BOX 653
FAIRFIELD,TX 75840-3132 PH 903 389-2320
FAX 903 389-4542 DSTEWARD3@GMAIL.COM

STEWARD ENERGY RESOURCES/OIL & GAS
PO BOX 653
FAIRFIELD,TX 75840
PH 903 389-2320 FAX 903 389-4542
STEWARD9@WINDSTREAM.NET
DAVID STEWARD,PTNR
CORPUS CHRISTI,TX OFFICE - PO BOX 3093
78463 PH 361 854-0410 FAX 361 854-0444
RANDY C STEWARD,PTNR
AUSTIN,TX OFFICE - 1524 S I-H 35 STE 330
78704,PH 512 448-0755
R W STEWARD,PTNR

STEWART PRODUCERS,INC
PO BOX 546,305 US BANK BLDG
MOUNT VERNON,IL 62864-0012
PH 618 244-3754 FAX 618 244-3756
ROBERT G STEWART,PRES,PETR ENGR

STEWART THOMAS C,CONSULTING ENGR,ATTY
PO BOX 82373
LAFAYETTE,LA 70598-2373
PH 318 231-0032 FAX 318 235-8385

STIM-LAB,INC
PETROLOGY & RESERVOIR ANALYSIS
PO BOX 1644
DUNCAN,OK 73534-1644
PH 580 252-4309 FAX 580 252-6979
STIMLAB@STIMLAB.COM
CHRIS PRICE,MGR

STINCHCOMB BLUFORD
PO BOX 342
AUSTIN,TX 78767-0342 PH 512 472-4732
FAX 512 474-2383

STINGER SERVICES,LLC
PO BOX 81083
LAFAYETTE,LA 70598-1083
PH 337 254-6986 FAX 337 943-1978
STINGERSERVICESLLC@GMAIL.COM
DEAN DAYE

STINGRAY WELLS,LLC
1201 S MAIN STE 204
BOERNE,TX 78006 PH 830 331-8531

FAX 830 331-8520
BLAKE STEWARD,OPERS DIR
BO WINSTON,MGR
TOMMY PUTNAM,MGR
WAYLAN OWENS,MGR

STOCKARD WALTER A
2001 KIRBY DR STE 510
HOUSTON,TX 77019 PH 713 522-1693
WALTER JENSEN,GEN MGR

STOCKSTILL DALE & ASSOCIATES
PO BOX 292
PICAYUNE,MS 39466-0292 PH 601 798-2326
DALE STOCKSTILL

STOKES & SPIEHLER REGULATORY SERVICES,LLC
PO BOX 52006,110 RUE JEAN LAFITTE STE 100
LAFAYETTE,LA 70505 PH 337 233-6871
FAX 337 233-7198
WWW.STOKESANDSPIEHLER.COM
MAIL.STOKESANDSPIERHLER.COM
BLAIR LEBLANC,MGR MEMB
BLEBLANC@STOKESANDSPIEHLER.COM
RUSS BELLARD,MGR MEMB
RBELLARD@STOKESANDSPIEHLER.COM
JOHN LONG,MGR MEMB
LONGJ@STOKESANDSPIEHLER.COM
PAULA DAIGLE,SR ENVIRO SPEC
PDAIGLE@STOKESANDSPIEHLER.COM
BRADY DUGAS,REG SPEC
BDUGAS@STOKESANDSPIEHLER.COM
TINA JUMONVILLE,REG SPEC
TJUMONVILLE@STOKESANDSPIEHLER.COM
JESSICA LEGER,REG SPEC
JLEGER@STOKESANDSPIEHLER.COM
LARRY FONTENOT,SR REG SPEC
LFONTENOT@STOKESANDSPIEHLER.COM
CINDY ROGERS,REG SPEC
CROGERS@STOKESANDSPIEHLER.COM
MELANIE SHEPARD,REG SPEC
MSHEPARD@STOKESANDSPIEHLER.COM
NATALIE MARTIN,REG SPEC
NMARTIN@STOKESANDSPIEHLER.COM
LAUREN MILLER,CHEM & ENVIR ENGR
LMILLER@STOKESANDSPIEHLER.COM
HEATHER ROMERO,ADMIN ASST
HROMERO@STOKESANDSPIEHLER.COM

STOKES & SPIEHLER USA,INC
PO BOX 52006,110 RUE JEAN LAFITTE STE 100
LAFAYETTE,LA 70505-2006
PH 337 233-6871 FAX 337 233-7198
WWW.STOKESANDSPIEHLER.COM
MAIL.STOKESANDSPIEHLER.COM
BRUCE M JORDAN,PRES
BJORDAN@STOKESANDSPIEHLER.COM
GEORGE W STOKES,EXEC VP
GSTOKES@STOKESANDSPIEHLER.COM
JOHN LONG,SR VP & GEN MGR
JLONG@STOKESANDSPIEHLER.COM
JACQUELINE BROUSSARD,TREAS & CFO
JBROUSSARD@STOKESANDSPIEHLER.COM
MARK STRINGER,CONTRACTS MGR
MSTRINGER@STOKESANDSPIEHLER.COM
SID COX,COMP ENGR MGR
SIDCOX@STOKESANDSPIEHLER.COM
RUSSELL BELLARD,PETR ENGR
RBELLARD@STOKESANDSPIEHLER.COM
BUTCH SCELFO,PETR ENGR

BSCELFO@STOKESANDSPIEHLER.COM
DONNIE BUSSCHER,PETR ENGR
DBUSSCHER@STOKESANDSPIEHLER.COM
RICHARD ANDRUS,PETR ENGR
RANDRUS@STOKESANDSPIEHLER.COM
CARLOS RIERA,PETR ENGR
CRIERA@STOKESANDSPIEHLER.COM
DEREK JORDAN,PETR ENGR
DJORDAN@STOKESANDSPIEHLER.COM
GENE GUIDRY,DRLG ENGR
GGUIDRY@STOKESANDSPIEHLER.COM
BLAIR LEBLANC,PETR ENGR
BLAIRLEBLANC@STOKESANDSPIEHLER.COM
BRYAN STRINGER,PETR ENGR
BSTRINGER@STOKESANDSPIEHLER.COM
JOHN SHERIDAN,PETR ENGR
JSHERIDAN@STOKESANDSPIEHLER.COM
HEIDI MEAUX,OPERS SPEC
HMEAUX@STOKESANDSPIEHLER.COM
LEXI GUIDRY,OPERS & COMPL SPEC
LGUIDRY@STOKESANDSPIEHLER.COM
ROBERT BARRIENTES,PETR ENGR
RBARRIENTES@STOKESANDSPIEHLER.COM
KEITH STOKES,COORD CONSLT OPERS
KSTOKES@STOKESANDSPIEHLER.COM
BRIAN FOTI,COORD CONSLT OPERS
BFOTI@STOKESANDSPIEHLER.COM
BOB MACDONALD,SR FAC ENGR
BMACDONALD@STOKESANDSPIEHLER.COM
REED LORMAND,CORP ACCT MGR
RLORMAND@STOKESANDSPIEHLER.COM
DARYL DUBOIS,REG ACCT MGR
DDUBOIS@STOKESANDSPIEHLER.COM
LARRY FOWLER,CORP ACCT MGR
LFOWLER@STOKESANDSPIEHLER.COM
MARGERY PATIN,SUPVSR CONSLT OPERS
MPATIN@STOKESANDSPIEHLER.COM
JOY PROVOST,OPERS SPEC
JPROVOST@STOKESANDSPIEHLER.COM
TAMMY LEON,OPERS & COMPL SPEC
TAMMY@STOKESANDSPIEHLER.COM
JENNIFER DUGAS,ACCT PAY/REC SUPVSR
JDUGAS@STOKESANDSPIEHLER.COM
KATHY GUILLOT,ADMIN ASST
KGUILLOT@STOKESANDSPIEHLER.COM
AMY FOREMAN,ADMIN ASST
AFOREMAN@STOKESANDSPIEHLER.COM
CHERYL TALBOT,RECPT
ADAQUIN@STOKESANDSPIEHLER.COM
HOUSTON,TX OFFICE - ONE PARK CENTRE
14450 T C JESTER BLVD STE 208,77014
PH 281 444-8395 FAX 281 444 8681
HOLLI CRAMM,VP OPERS
HCRAMM@STOKESANDSPIEHLER.COM
DON LONG,OFF DRLG MGR
DONLONG@STOKESANDSPIEHLER.COM
TONY SHELL,SR ACCT MGR
AGSHELL@STOKESANDSPIEHLER.COM
CHRIS ALLEN,REG ACCT MGR
CHRISALLEN@STOKESANDSPIEHLER.COM
DREW STOKES,PETR ENGR
DSTOKES@STOKESANDSPIEHLER.COM
JEANNE SYMMANK,RECPT
JSYMMANK@STOKESANDSPIEHLER.COM
DALLAS,TX OFFICE - 14579 BERKLEE DR
ADDISON,TX 75001 PH 241 561-8751

DAVID GAUTREAUX,VP CORP ACCT
SSOFFSHORE@AOL.COM

STOKES & WATSON INC,OIL LEASES
222 RAMBLEWOOD DR
LAFAYETTE,LA 70508-7404 PH 318 984-1707
THOMAS L STOKES
BERNARD WATSON,JR

STOLLENWERCK CAROL ELLISON
PO BOX 25124
DALLAS,TX 75225-1124 PH 214 526-2878

STONE BOND TECHNOLOGIES
INTL MGMNT/BUS CONSULTING FIRM
1021 MAIN ST #1550
HOUSTON,TX 77002-6502 PH 713 622-8798
FAX 713 623-0503 WWW.STONEBOND.COM
ANTONIO M SZABO,PRES

STONE ENERGY CORPORATION
PO BOX 52807,625 E KALISTE SALOOM RD
LAFAYETTE,LA 70505
PH 337 237-0410 WWW.STONEENERGY.COM
DAVID H WELCH,CHMN BD,PRES & CEO
KENNETH H BEER,EXEC VP,CFO
LISA JAUBERT,SR VP,GEN COUNSEL & SECY
ELDON J LOUVIERE,SR VP LAND & ASST SECY
RICHARD TOOTHMAN,SR VP,APPALACHIA
FLORENCE M ZIEGLER,SR VP,HR,COMM & ADMIN
KEVIN HURST,VP GOM SHELF/DEEP GAS
JOHN LEONARD,VP EXPLOR
KEITH SEILHAN,VP DEEPWATER
CHRIS WHITNEY,DEEPWATER PROJ MGR
MICHELLE HEBERT,OPERS MGR
STEVEN BODDEN,DEEPWATER OPERS MGR
CRAIG BRAZAN,SHELF/GULF CST RIG PROJ MGR
GENE CELLA,DIR CORPORATE HSE & REG
STEVE P GARY,MRKTING MGR
TOM L MESSONNIER,DIR STRATEGIC PLANNING
JAMES GAMBLE,ASSET MGR,DEEPWATER
MIKE COX,DIR DEEPWATER EXPLOR ASSETS
BRETT HEATH,DIR DEEP GAS EXPLOR
MIKE SCHNEIDER,DEEPWATER NEW VENTURES MGR
HOUSTON,TX DIST OFFICE -
16800 GREENSPOINT PARK DR STE 225 S
7700υ PH 2δ1 872-1999 FAX 281 423-0501
MORGANTOWN, WV OFFICE - 6000 HAMPTON DR
STE E 26505 PH 304 599-1457

STONE ENERGY OFFSHORE, LLC SEE
STONE ENERGY CORPORATION

STONE PETROLEUM CORPORATION,THE SEE
STONE ENERGY CORPORATION

STONE RESOURCE AND ENERGY CORPORATION SEE
NGO DEVELOPMENT CORPORATION

STONETEX OIL CORP
12377 MERIT DR STE 777
DALLAS,TX 75251 PH 972 788-0708
DAVID S CROCKETT JR,VP

STONEWALL PETROLEUM INC SEE
SCOTT ROYCE ARNOLD

STORK E H,JR,GEOL & PALEONTOLOGIST
207 PECORE ST STE 2
HOUSTON,TX 77009-5415
PH 713 802-9731 FAX 713 802-9732
SLATER MCEACHERN,PALEONTOLOGIST
STORKANDASSOC@SBCGLOBAL.NET
SLATER@STORKANDASSOC.COM

STORM JAMES C
101 N SHORELINE BLVD STE 510

CORPUS CHRISTI,TX 78401-2826
PH 361 888-7070 FAX 361 888-6870

STOUT GABE LANDMAN SERVICES
4958 FARM RD 1567 W
SULPHUR SPRINGS,TX 75482 PH 903 243-2814
GABESTOUT@YAHOO.COM

STOVALL GUY F,JR
PO BOX 906
EL CAMPO,TX 77437-0906 PH 979 543-6713

STOVALL GUY F,TRUSTS
PO BOX 906
EL CAMPO,TX 77437-0906 PH 979 543-3812

STOVER HOWARD E,OIL & GAS EXPL
PO BOX 16545
JACKSON,MS 39236-6545 PH 601 984-3702
FAX 601 984-3706
OILMAN1244@AOL.COM

STRAGO PETROLEUM CORPORATION
3900 MAGNOLIA ST
PEARLAND,TX 77584-1610 PH 281 485-7100
FAX 281 485-7131 STRAGO@STRAGO.NET
L F GOZA,PRES
LFGOZA@STRAGO.NET
R K STRAHAN,VP RKSTRAHAN@STRAGO.NET
PH 281 358-1608

STRAIN WILLIAM S & ASSOCIATES
A PROFESSIONAL LAW CORPORATION
7470 HIGHLAND RD
BATON ROUGE,LA 70808 PH 225 769-5492
WILLIAM S STRAIN
WWW.STRAINLAWLOUISIANA.COM
STRAINANDASSOCIATES@COX.NET

STRAKE ENERGY,INC
712 MAIN ST STE 3300
HOUSTON,TX 77002-3215 PH 713 216-2400
FAX 713 216-2401 GSTRAKE@STRAKE.ORG
GEORGE W STRAKE JR,OWNER
P L ROBISON,CONTROLLER
ALICIA GIST,LAND DEPT

STRAND ENERGY LC
919 MILAM ST STE 1820
HOUSTON,TX 77002-5885 PH 713 658-8096
WWW.STRANDENERGY.COM
H KENT BROCK,PRES
SCOTT M AIREY,VP LAND
RICK HEMMEN,OPERS MGR
CHRISTOPHER E BETZ,EXPL MGR
ROB PENNINGTON,ENGRG MGR

STRAT LAND EXPLORATION COMPANY
15 E 5TH ST STE 2020
TULSA,OK 74103-4318
PH 918 584-3844 FAX 918 584-3205
LARRY B DARDEN,PRES
RICK HALL,COO
RICK SPELLMAN,VP,LAND
RUSTY MCGHEE,CFO
PERRYTON,TX FLD OFFICE - 800 N MAIN STE B
79070 PH 806 435-7292 FAX 806 435-3494
MIKE SCOTT,DRLG/COMPLETION FRMN
STAN KARBER,PROD FRMN

STRATA INTERNATIONAL
4336 MILLSTEAD ST
SAN ANTONIO,TX 78230 PH 888 594-5329
WWW.STRATAINTL.COM STRATA@SPRYNET.COM

STRATA RESOURCES
2725 GRUBBS RD

SEALY,TX 77474 PH 409 885-3489
CHARLES BRANDES,PRTNR
STEVE EPPS,PRTNR

STRATAGRAPH INC
PO BOX 53848
LAFAYETTE,LA 70505-3848 PH 337 232-5510
FAX 337 237-8120 WWW.STRATAGRAPH.COM
RANDY P HALE,PRES/CEO
WILLIAM A HAGAN,VP SLS
DAVID VIZINA,SFTY/OPERS MGR
LEON BORDELON,TECH SUPPORT MGR
JOHN BOGGS,MAINT/PUR MGR
DAVID BEGNEAUD,R&D MGR
DENNIS KROGER,APPL DEV MGR
RICH RICHARDS,SLS
JAMES SMALL,SLS
LEE PREJEAN,SLS
AL ESCOBAR,SLS
NEW ORLEANS,LA OFFICE - PH 504 561-0649
HOUSTON,TX OFFICE - PH 713 784-2144
DALLAS,TX OFFICE - PH 214 739-1965

STRATCO INC
6363 COLLAGE BLV STE 300
OVERLAND PARK,KS 66211 PH 913 338-2559
FAX 913 338-0003 WWW.STRATCO.COM
S DIANE GRAHAM,PRES
GLENN LIOLIOS,VP,ENGRG
PAM PRYOR,MGR,MKTG

STREAMLINE PRODUCTION SYSTEMS,INC
1447 HWY 69
KOUNTZE,TX 77625 PH 800 780-4011
STREAMLINETEXAS.COM

STREETMAN COMPANY INC
PO BOX 129
NATCHEZ,MS 39121-0129 PH 601 442-1216
PH 601 442-7551 FAX 601 442-0240
CHRIS STREETMAN,PRES

STRESS ENGINEERING SERVICES INC
13800 WESTFAIR EAST DR
HOUSTON,TX 77041-1101 PH 281 955-2900
FAX 281 955-2638 WWW.STRESS.COM
TERRY LECHINGER,VP TML@STRESS.COM
WALLER,TX OFFICE - 42403A OLD HOUSTON HWY
77484 PH 281 671-2550 FAX 936 732-1052
TERRY LECHINGER
NEW ORLEANS,LA OFFICE - 3314 RICHLAND AVE
METAIRE,LA 70002 PH 504 889-8440
FAX 504 889-8441
GREG GARIC GREG.GARIC@STRESS.COM
BATON ROUGE,LA OFFICE - 9191 SIEGEN LN
STE 3A 70810 PH 225 769-9772
FAX 225 769-9068
GREG GARIC
CINCINNATI,OH OFFICE - 7030 STRESS
ENGINEERING WAY, MASON OH 45040
PH 513 336-6701 FAX 513 336-6817
GARY VISSING,MEDICAL & PRODUCT DEV
GARY.VISSING@STRESS.COM
DERRICK ROGERS,GAS,OIL & POWER
DERRICK.ROGERS@STRESS.COM
CALGARY,ALBERTA,CAN OFFICE - 12111 - 40TH
ST SE,#125 T2Z 4E6 PH 403 256-2527
FAX 403 256-2578
ROBERT THOM ROBERT.THOM@STRESS.COM

STRIC-LAN COMPANIES CORPORATION
PO BOX 62288

LAFAYETTE,LA 70596-2288 PH 337 984-7850
PH 800 749-4586 FAX 337 989-8924
WWW.STRIC-LAN.COM
GARY LANDRY,PRES
KAREN L OERTLING,CEO KARENO@STRICLAN.COM
BILL NICE,CORP VP
LAKETA GLENN,CONTROLLER
VICTOR DANIELS,OPERS MGR,WELL TESTING/
FLOWBACK
BRIAN ISAAC,QA/QC
 - DATA ACQ/ENGINEERING/AUTOMATION
TOSH TAYLOR,OPERS MGR/SCADA/AUTOMATION
DICK SIMPER,RESERVOIR ENGRG MGR
 - SALES -
WES SIMS,SLS/MKTG
CHRISTIAN FALCON,SR CORP SLS
LUIS MARCADO,CORP SLS
ARMANDO SAUCEDA,PIPELINE OPS MGR
NICK DECECCO,FLOWBACK OPS MGR-APPALACHI-
AN
JASON LANDRY,W/T FLOWBACK-SOUTH TEXAS
KEVIN SUMMERS,SCADA/AUTOMATION - ALABAMA

STRICKLER JOHN C CHRIS ,JR CPL
2112 JUSTICE ST
MONROE,LA 71201 PH 318 325-7788
FAX 318 398-0069
CSTRICKLER@JCPETROLEUM.COM

STRINGER OIL & GAS CO,INC
PO BOX 3037
SAN ANGELO,TX 76902-3037 PH 325 949-8506
FAX 325 223-8253
J FRANK STRINGER JR,PRES

STRIPLING RESOURCES SEE
KIAMICHI OIL COMPANY,LLC

STRONG ROCK ENERGY,LLC
PO BOX 2840
RIDGELAND,MS 39158 PH 601 927-9499
JACKSON,MS OFFICE - 1501 LAKELAND DR
STE 301 39216
MAC MCGEHEE
MAC.MCGEHEE@STRONGROCKENERGY.COM
NEIL BARNES
NEIL.BARNES@IEPMGROUP.COM

STROOPE JAMES L & ASSOCIATES
5773 WOODWAY DR STE 444
HOUSTON,TX 77057 PH 713 783-9160

STROUBE OIL COMPANY OIL PROD
PO BOX 730
CORSICANA,TX 75151 PH 903 872-5663
STEVE STROUBE,OWNER

STROUD EXPLORATION CO,LLC
PO BOX 565,416 TRAVIS ST STE 600
SHREVEPORT,LA 71162-0565
PH 318 425-0101 FAX 318 425-2211
SCOTT D STROUD,PRES,GEOL

STROUD OIL COMPANY
P O BOX 68
JOINERVILLE,TX 75658-0068 PH 214 847-3322
J C STROUD,OWNER

STROUD PETROLEUM,INC
PO BOX 565,416 TRAVIS ST STE 600
SHREVEPORT,LA 71162-0565
PH 318 425-0101 FAX 318 425-2211
SCOTT D STROUD,PRES
JOHN STROUD,VP
THANE HUGGS,GEN COUNSEL

NATHAN HARVEY,CONTROLLER
BUTCH HICKEY,OPERS MGR
MORRIS P NICHOLS,EXPL MGR
TED SCURLOCK,LAND MGR

STROUD PRODUCTION LLC
333 TEXAS ST STE 860
SHREVEPORT,LA 71101-5302
PH 318 429-2260 FAX 318 429-2255
ROBERT STROUD,MGR
TERRI MOORE,ACCT MGR
TMOORE@SPLLC.COM
SHANNON JOHNSTON,CPA,BUS MGR
SJOHNSTON@SPLLC.COM
RHONDA DRACH,ADMINS ASST
RDRACH@SPLLC.COM

STROUD PRODUCTION SERVICE INC
PO BOX 786
BASILE,LA 70515-0786 PH 318 432-5090
JOEY R MARSH,PRES

STRYKER ENERGY DIRECTIONAL SERVICES,LLC
PO BOX 1250
MONTGOMERY,TX 77356 PH 936 582-7296
FAX 936 582-7297
WWW.STRYKERDIRECTIONAL.COM

STUDDARD MIKE & ASSOCIATES INC
1219 AN CO RD 397
PALESTINE,TX 75801-1826
PH 903 729-2914 MSASSOCCO@EARTHLINK.NET
MIKE STUDDARD,OWNER,LDMN
PAT STUDDARD,CO/OWNER

STUDLEY RESOURCES CORPORATION
PO BOX 4068
HUMBLE,TX 77347-9868 PH 281 876-1297
FAX 281 876-7540
RICHARD M SLOAN,PRES

STURLESE DAVID B,GEOL
PO BOX 51405,OCS
124 HEYMANN BLVD STE 106
LAFAYETTE,LA 70505 PH 337 232-1700
FAX 337 234-0403

STXRA (CONSULTING SERVICES)
1416 CAMPBELL RD STE B208
HOUSTON,TX 77055 PH 281 716-5730
WWW.STXRA.COM
SEAN FITZGERALD SEAN.FITZGERALD@STXRA.COM

SUAREZ OIL CO INC
301 W ST BERNARD HWY
CHALMETTE,LA 70043-4961 PH 504 279-4364

SUB SURFACE TOOLS,INC SEE
SUPERIOR ENERGY SERVICES

SUBMERSIBLE OIL SERVICES, INC, SEE
CENTRILIFT-A BAKER HUGHES CO

SUBSEA OIL & GAS,INC
PO BOX 102,2330 BOWEN RD
ELMA,NY 14059-0102 PH 716 655-4800
FAX 716 655-4801
WALTER P HAKER,PRES

SUBSURFACE CONSULTANTS & ASSOCIATES LLC
GEOLOGISTS,GEOPHYSICISTS,ENGINEERS
10700 RICHMOND AVE STE 325
HOUSTON,TX 77042-4133 PH 713 789-2444
FAX 713 789-4449 WWW.SCACOMPANIES.COM
INFO@SCACOMPANIES.COM
HAL MILLER,PRES

SUE ANN OPERATING,LC
PO BOX 3910,120 S MAIN STE 600

VICTORIA,TX 77903-3910
PH 361 576-6090 FAX 361 576-6099
JOHN R GAYLE,PRES,CEO JRGAYLE@SAOLC.COM
DICK POWELL,CFO DPOWELL@SAOLC.COM
STUART B GAYLE,VP,OPERS
BARBARA J KOLODZIE,VP,FIN & CONTROLLER
ALLYSON COLE,OFC ASST

SUEMAUR EXPLORATION & PRODUCTION LLC
802 N CARANCAHUA ST STE 1000
CORPUS CHRISTI,TX 78401 PH 361 884-8824
FAX 361 884-9623 WWW.SUEMAUR.COM
DANIEL PEDROTTI,FOUNDING PRTNR
ROBERT W MAXWELL JR,CHRMN OF BOARD
BRENT HOPKINS,PRES & CEO
JAMES T DEVIN,VP LAND
DAVID J WEBSTER,VP ENGRG
LUCIE M HARRIS,CONTROLLER
RICHARD E PAIGE,SR GEOL
CHARLES A JAMES,SR LDMN
GEORGE CLARK,OPERS MGR
LEIGHTON DEVINE,EXPL GEOL
ANDREW GRUBB,DRLG MGR

SUEMAUR EXPLORATION PARTNERS
802 N CARANCAHUA ST STE 1000
CORPUS CHRISTI,TX 78401-0015
PH 361 884-8824 FAX 361 884-9623
ROBERT W MAXWELL JR,CHRMN
BRENT HOPKINS,PRES,CEO
JAMES T DEVLIN,VP

SUEMAUR NOUVEAU ENERGY LLC
802 N CARANCAHUA STE 1000
CORPUS CHRISTI,TX 78401-0015
PH 361 884-2443
DANIEL A PEDROTTI

SUGAR CREEK PRODUCING CO
PO BOX 1756
SHREVEPORT,LA 71166-1756
PH 318 221-2899 FAX 318 221-2931
ROBERT E SMITHERMAN,PRES
MATTHEW R SMITHERMAN,VP
MARK E DUNHAM,GEOL

SULIK JOHN F,GEOL CONS
3102 TOPEKA ST
CORPUS CHRISTI,TX 78404
PH 361 882-1220 FAX 361 882-9071

SULLIVAN FAMILY PARTNERSHIP
PO BOX 1001,1121 S E 9TH ST
FORT LAUDERDALE,FL 33302-1001
PH 954 522-4294 FAX 954 525-1347
ELZALENE SULLIVAN,TRUSTEE,GEN PRTNR

SUMBERA ASSOCIATES
1115 DRAVA LN
HOUSTON,TX 77090-1264 PH 281 444-0037
FAX 281 580-8687 SUMTXNA@EARTHLINK.NET
PATRICK SUMBERA,OWNER

SUMMERS PAUL H
3906 BROOKWOODS DR
HOUSTON,TX 77092-8322 PH 830 257-7530

SUMMIT DISCOVERY RESOURCES LLC
820 GESSNER STE 600
HOUSTON,TX 77024
PH 713 463-2000 FAX 713 468-3303
KAZUYUKI ONOSE,PRES,CEO
ROBERT E ORTH,COO/GEN MGR
MARC W JARVIS,SR VP ENGRG

SUMMIT DRILLING,LTD
5220 HOLLYWOOD AVE
SHREVEPORT,LA 71109-7717 PH 318 636-6811
WILCOX@WILCOXOPERATINGCORP.COM
MARK F PREDDY,PRES TO GEN PRTNR

SUMMIT PETROLEUM INC
243 E STREETSBORO ST
HUDSON,OH 44236-3404 PH 216 232-7868
WILLIAM G KINNEY,PRES
JAMES D DARROW,SECY-TREAS
LINDA S MAHNE,OFC MGR

SUMMITT G G,GEOL
401 N 14TH ST
CORSICANA,TX 75110 PH 903 874-8181
FAX 903 874-8181 JACKTEX@AIRMAIL.NET

SUN DRILLING PRODUCTS CORPORATION
4400 POST OAK PKWY STE 2100
HOUSTON,TX 77027 PH 713 690-3939
DOUGLAS P HELLER,PRES
BELLE CHASSE,LA MFG & OPERATIONS OFFICE -
PO BOX 129,503 MAIN ST,70037-0129
PH 504 393-2778 FAX 504 391-1383

SUN EXPLORATION AND PRODUCTION CO SEE
ORYX ENERGY COMPANY

SUNBELT ENERGY LTD
PO BOX 54048,OCS
309 LA RUE FRANCE STE 104,70508
LAFAYETTE,LA 70505-4048 PH 337 233-8670
FAX 337 235-8066 WWW.SUNBELTENERGY.COM
SUNBELT@SUNBELTENERGY.COM
J MICHAEL POOLE SR,PRES
TONY WEBER,EXPL MGR
CLYDE COURTRIGHT,GEOL
SHANE POOLE,GEOL
LINDA LANDRY,BOOKKEEPER

SUNCOAST LAND SERVICES,INC
4906 AMB CAFFERY PKWY
BLDG B STE 201
LAFAYETTE,LA 70508 PH 337 265-2900
FAX 337 265-2901 WWW.SUNCOASTLAND.COM
RUSSELL E THOMAS,PRES
RUSSELLT@SUNCOASTLAND.COM
HOUSTON,TX OFFICE - MILLENNIUM TOWER
10375 RICHMOND AVE STE 252,77042
PH 713 375-3300 FAX 713 375-3301
ERIC M THOMAS,VP
ERICT@SUNCOASTLAND.COM

SUNCOAST TECHNICAL SERVICES,INC
PO BOX 860037
PLANO,TX 75086-0037 PH 972 424-6553
FAX 972 424-5641
JOHN KIMBRELL,PRES

SUNCOR ENERGY INC
- HEAD OFFICE -
PO BOX 38,112 - 4 AVENUE SW
CALGARY,AB CAN T2P 2V5
PH 403 269-8100 FAX 403 269-6200
BRAD BELLOWS,MEDIA RELS
PH 403 269-8717 FAX 403 269-6217
GAIL CLAYTON,INVESTOR RELS
PH 403 269-8742 FAX 403 269-6218
CHRIS MCINTOSH,ADVERTISING INQUIRIES
PH 403 205-6725 FAX 403 269-6217
CALGARY,AB ACCOUNTS PAYABLE OFFICE -
PO BOX 1720,STN M,T2P 0A2
PH 403 693-2042

CALGARY,AB COMMUNITY INVESTMENT & SUNCOR
ENERGY FOUNDATION OFFICE - PO BOX 38
112 - 4 AVENUE SW,T2P 2V5
LORI GAMMELL,PH 403 269-8775
DANIELLE SHAW,PH 403 269-8779
CALGARY,AB (NATURAL GAS & RENEWABLE
ENERGY) OFFICE - PO BOX 38
112 - 4 AVENUE SW,T2P 2V5
PH 403 269-8100 FAX 403 269-6200
SHERWOOD PARK,AB (SUNCOR ENERGY PIPELINE
OPERS) OFFICE - 241 KASKA RD,T8A 4E8
PH 780 449-2100 FAX 780 467-6886
FORT MCMURRAY,AB (OIL SANDS) OFFICE -
PO BOX 4001,T9H 3E3
PH 780 743-6411 FAX 790 791-8300
NORTH YORK,ONTARIO (SUNCOR ENERGY
PRODUCTS INC)(SUNOCO) OFFICE -
36 YORK MILLS RD,M2P 2C5
PH 416 733-7000 FAX 416 733-7201
SUNOCO CUSTOMER SVC PH 888 858-7242
SARNIA,ONTARIO (SUNCOR ENERGY PRODUCTS
INC-SARNIA REFINERY) - PO BOX 307
1900 RIVER RD,N7T 7J3
PH 519 337-2301 FAX 519 332-3309
GREENWOOD VILLAGE,CO (SUNCOR ENERGY USA
INC-CORPORATE HEAD OFFICE -
7800 E ORCHARD RD,STE 300,80111
PH 303 793-8000 FAX 303 793-8003
COMMERCE CITY,CO (SUNCOR ENREGY USA INC-
COMMERCE CITY REFINERY -
5801 BRIGHTON BLVD,80022
PH 303 286-5701 FAX 303 286-5702
CHEYENNE,WY (SUNCOR ENERGY USA PIPELINE
COMPANY) DIST REG PIPELINE OFFICE -
2234 W LINCOLN WAY,82001
PH 307 634-1853

SUNDANCE ENERGY CORPORATION
PO BOX 16
BENTON,LA 71006 PH 318 326-5101
FAX 318 326-4453
BO ROSEBERRY,PRES

SUNDOWN ENERGY LP
KNOLL TRAIL PLAZA
16400 DALLAS PKWY STE 100
DALLAS,TX 75248-2609 PH 214 368-6100
FAX 214 365-9695

SUNDOWN PRODUCTION LLC SEE
PGP HOLDINGS 1,LLC

SUNLAND PRODUCTION CO,INC
416 TRAVIS ST STE 1404
SHREVEPORT,LA 71101-5506
PH 318 222-3538 FAX 318 222-3526
DON G EASTERWOOD JR,PRES

SUNOCO PARTNERS MARKETING & TERMINALS,LP
PO BOX 5095
SUGAR LAND,TX 77487-5095 PH 281 637-6423
WWW.SUNOCOLOGISTICS.COM
DAVID A JUSTIN,VP OPER
DAJUSTIN@SUNOCOLOGISTICS.COM

SUNRAY OPERATING COMPANY LLC
16444 OLD RICHMOND RD
SUGAR LAND,TX 77498 PH 281 879-9973
DAVE TOPP W5BXX@AOL.COM

SUNRISE EXPLORATION,INC
PO BOX 65
MCLEANSBORO,IL 62859-0065 PH 618 643-4092

FAX 618 643-5600
KEN LANKFORD,PRES
LEX ANDERSON,SECY

SUNSET PRODUCTION CORPORATION
PO BOX 2239
GEORGETOWN,TX 78627-2239
PH 713 869-0077 FAX 713 869-0078
JONATHAN S LINKER,VP

SUPERIOR CRUDE GATHERING INC
PO BOX 260784
CORPUS CHRISTI,TX 78420-0784
PH 361 882-5117 FAX 361 882-4881
JEFF KIRBY,PRES
CINDY KIRBY,SECY/TREAS

SUPERIOR ENERGY CO,THE
PETROLEUM LAND SERVICES
PO BOX 23278
CHAGRIN FALLS,OH 44023 PH 330 487-0700
JOSEPH W HAAS,PRES

SUPERIOR ENERGY SERVICES,INC
OILFIELD SERVICES & EQUIPMENT PROVIDER
11000 EQUITY DR STE 300
HOUSTON,TX 77041
PH 281 999-0047 FAX 281 820-2064
WWW.SUPERIORENERGY.COM
INFO@SUPERIORENERGY.COM
TERRY HALL,CHRMN OF THE BOARD
DAVID DUNLAP,PRES & CEO
ROBERT TAYLOR,EXEC VP/CFO & TREAS
PAT BERNARD,SR EXEC VP GLOBAL TECH/SUBSEA
BRIAN MOORE,SR EXEC VP NORTH AMERICA SVCS
DANNY YOUNG,EXEC VP CORP SVCS
WESTY BALLARD,EXEC VP INT'L SVCS
GUY COOK,EXEC VP GLOBAL RENTAL TOOLS
BILL MASTERS,EXEC VP & GEN COUNSEL
GREG ROSENSTEIN,EXEC VP CORP DEV

- ADMINISTRATION -
NEW ORLEANS,LA OFFICE - 601 POYDRAS ST
STE 2400 70130 PH 504 587-7374
FAX 504 362-1818
BROUSSARD,LA OFFICE - 5801 HWY 90 EAST
70518 PH 337 714-4545 PH 877 733-2473
FAX 337 714-2102
- ARTIFICAL LIFT -
BELLE CHASSE,LA OFFICE - 136 KEATING DR
70037 PH 800 256-5709 PH 504 393-1111
FAX 504 393-1121
LUMBERTON,TX OFFICE - 565 N LHS DR STE F
77657 PH 409 751-0900 FAX 409 751-0901
- COMPLETION SERVICES -
COVINGTON,LA OFFICE - 631 B RIVER
HIGHLANDS BLVD 70433 PH 985 809-3576
LAFAYETTE,LA OFFICE - 203 COMMISSION BLVD
70508 PH 337 837-6047 FAX 337 839-7522
HOUSTON,TX OFFICE - 16610 ALDINE
WESTFIELD 77032 PH 281 784-5700
FAX 281 784-5746
- HUMAN RESOURCES SERVICE CENTER -
LAFAYETTE,LA OFFICE - 203 COMMISSION BLVD
STE 200,70508 PH 866 306-3899
FAX 337 839-7210
- MARINE TECHNICAL SERVICES -
HOUSTON,TX OFFICE - 13333 NORTHWEST FWY
STE 100 77040 PH 832 590-6500
FAX 832 590-6501

ANCHORAGE,AK OFFICE - 1001 NORTHWAY DR
STE 201 99508 PH 907 792-2600
FAX 907 272-5379
- PRESSURE PUMPING SERVICES -
CROWLEY,LA OFFICE - 6132 EGAN HWY,70526
PH 337 785-8400
BROOKSHIRE,TX OFFICE - 3943 FM 362,77423
PH 281 934-2181 FAX 281 934-2183
LONGVIEW,TX OFFICE - 907 LINCO RD,75604
PH 903 295-8500 FAX 903 295-8503
YANCEY,TX OFFICE - 10065 FM 462 SOUTH
78886 PH 830 426-8282
- SALES OFFICE -
HOUSTON,TX OFFICE - 11000 EQUITY DR
STE 300,77041 PH 281 999-0047
FAX 281 999-6505
- TUBING CONVEYED PERFORATING -
HARVEY,LA OFFICE - 1209 PETERS RD,70058
PH 800 741-9009 PH 504 367-0857
FAX 504 263-8637
- WELL PERFORMANCE TESTING & EVALUATION -
BROUSSARD,LA OFFICE - 110 BERCEGEAY RD
70518 PH 800 235-8604 PH 337 837-8604
FAX 337 837-9041
- WELL SERVICES -
BROUSSARD,LA OFFICE - 1117 MAURICE RD
70518 PH 866 805-8378 PH 337 769-7110
FAX 331 769-7114
HARVEY,LA OFFICE - 1105 PETERS RD,77058
PH 800 259-7774 PH 504 362-5558
FAX 504 263-4270
- CEMENTING AND ACIDIZING -
BROOKSHIRE,TX OFFICE - 3943 FM 362 77423
PH 281 934-2181 FAX 281 934-2183
- WIRELINE -
BROUSSARD,LA OFFICE - 110 BERCEGEAY RD
70518 PH 337 837-2956 FAX 337 837-4658
HARVEY,LA OFFICE - 1209 PETERS RD,70058
PH 504 367-0857 PH 800 741-9009
SIBLEY,LA OFFICE - 141 CORPORATE DR,71073
PH 318 371-0330 FAX 318 371-0330
ALVIN,TX OFFICE - 1111 EAST FM 517,77511
PH 800 248-7710 PH 281 388-0992
FAX 281 388-0673
CLEBURNE,TX OFFICE - 209 KIMBERLY,76033
PH 817 556-5815 FAX 817 556-5815
BELLE VERNON,PA OFFICE - 203 FINLEY RD
BLDG 2,15012 PH 724 929-5982
FAX 724 929-3194
- WIRELINE - LAND -
LONGVIEW,TX OFFICE - 1919 E LOOP 281
75605 PH 800 638-0261 PH 903 758-2691
FAX 903 758-7950
- WIRELINE - OFFSHORE -
BROUSSARD,LA OFFICE - 110 BERCEGEAY RD
70518 PH 800 741-9008 PH 337 714-2120
FAX 337 714-2110
- WIRELINE/WPT&E/ARTIFICIAL LIFT -
GRAND JUNCTION,CO OFFICE - 703 23 2/10 RD
81505 PH 970 263-0400 FAX 970 263-0411
- NORTH AMERICAN SERVICES -
HOUSTON,TX OFC - 11700 KATY FRWY STE 300
77079 PH 281 372-2300
- UK CORPORATE OFFICE -
ABERDEEN,SCOTLAND OFFICE - KIRKTON AVE
AB21 OBF PH 44 1224 724-900

FAX 44 1224 770-191
- COLUMBIA,SOUTH AMERICA -
BOGATA,CUNDINAMARCIA OFFICE -
CRA 10 NO 97A-13 TORRE A OF.509
PH 57 1 742-7642 FAX 57 1 742-7654
VILLAVICENCIO,META OFFICE - CRA.22#5B-114
BODEGA 3 PARQUE PH 57 8 660-4821
NEIVA HUILA OFFICE -
KM 1 VIA PALERMO CONJUNTO COLINAS DEL
LAGO PH 57 8 874-8140
BARRANCABERMEJA SANTANDER OFFICE -
KM 11 VIA AL CENTRO,PARQUE INDUSTRIAL
LAS ALPUIARRAS PH 313 871-5925
BRICENO,CUNDINAMARCA OFFICE - KM 1 VIA
BRICENO ZIPAQUIRA PH 57 313 294-4023
FRANCISO DE ORELLANE,ECUADOR OFFICE -
KM 8 1/2 VIA LAGO AGRIO,DESVIO NUEVO
PARARSO PH 593 8 462-6192
QUITO PINCHINCHA,ECUADOR OFFICE - AV ELOY
ALFARO N35-09 Y PORTUGAL
PH 593 2 333-2228
YOPAL,CASANARE OFFICE - KM 7 VIA MORICHAL
PH 57 8 632-0039
CILLAVICENCIO,META OFFICE - CRA.22#5B-114
BODEGA 3 PARQUE PH 57 8 660-4821
- VENEZUELA,SOUTH AMERICA -
CIUDAD OJEDA,ZULIA OFC - AV INTERCOMUNAL
SECTOR LIBERTAD EDIF SES
PH 58 265 400-7900 FAX 58 265 631-1508
ANACO,ANZOATEGUI,VENEZUELA OFFICE -
AUTOPISTA ANACO-BARCELONA A 200 MTS DEL
DISTRBUIDOR MIRANDA EDIFICIO SUP ANACO
ESTADO 876 VE PH 58 282 425-5875
FAX 58 282 425-2911
- BRAZIL,SOUTH AMERICA -
CARMOPOLIS,SERGIPE OFFICE - AV ANTONIO
CARLOS FRANCO 1750 CENTO 49740-00
PH 55 79 32771811
MACAE,RIO DE JANEIRO OFFICE - ESTRADA
PROJETADA 3,S/N IMBOASSICA-MACAE
PH 55 22 3717-1296 FAX 55 22 3717-1295
BARRA DA TIJUCA,RIO DE JANEIRO OFFICE -
AVDA AMERICAS 4200, 22640-102
PH 55 21 3385-4010
MACAE,RIO DE JANEIRO OFFICE - AV N.S.
GLORIA 1861,CAVALEIROS,27920-320
PH 55 22 3723-0100
ARACAJU,SERGIPE OFFICE - AV PEDRO
VALADARES 600,TERRERO,SALA 4,JARDINS
LAROMAIN,TRINIDAD OFC- 8A BAMBOO JUNCTION
PH 868 657-7039 FAX 868 657-7040
MACAE,RIO DE JANEIRO OFFICE - RODOVIA
AMARAL PEIXOTO,KM 164.5,27923-420
PH 55 22 2773-6284 FAX 55 22 2773-6284
- AUSTRALIA -
SALE,VICTORIA OFFICE - 6-10 HUNT PL 3850
PH 6 3 5143-2225 FAX 61 3 5143-2226
PERTH,WESTERN AUSTRALIA OFFICE - LEVEL 2
165 ADELAIDE TERRACE 6004
PH 61 8 9325-8279 FAX 61 8 9325-1193
PERTH,WESTERN AUSTRALIA OFC - 32 COCOS DR
BIBRA LAKE 6163 PH 61 8 9418-1935
FAX 61 8 9418-1936
- DUBAI,UNITED ARAB EMIRATES,MIDDLE EAST-
DUBAI OFFICE - OFFICE NO 70, LEVEL 3
OASIS CENTRE,SHEIKH ZAVED RD

PH 971 4 339-7017 FAX 971 4 339-7851

- BALANCE POINT CONTROL -
ABERDEEN,SCOTLAND,UNITED KINGDOM OFFICE -
ABERDEEN BUSINESS PARK UNIT 2
DYCE AB21 OLQ PH 44 0 1224-215392
CELLE,NIEDERSACHSEN GERMANY OFFICE -
BRUCHKAMPWEG 28
PH 49 5141-82033 FAX 49 5141-86069
EMMEN,HOLLAND OFFICE - KAREL
DOORMANSTRAAT 4,7825 VT
PH 31 581 667 687 FAX 31 591 667 680

- BTI SERVICES -
ELK CITY,OK OFFICE - 3404 S HWY 8,73644
PH 877 285-6996 PH 580 225-6996
FAX 580 225-3563
OKLAHOMA CITY,OK OFFICE - 6701 S EASTERN
73129 PH 877 670-4415 PH 405 670-4415
FAX 405 672-2924
LAFAYETTE,LA OFFICE - 214 S PARK,70508
PH 337 839-3180 FAX 337 839-3195
SEARCY,AR OFFICE - 2903 SHILOH RD,72143
PH 501 305-3872 FAX 501 305-3532
YANCEY,TX OFFICE - 10065 HWY 462 S BLDG A
78886 PH 831 741-6550 FAX 831 741-6565
HOUSTON,TX OFFICE - 19450 E HARDY 77073
PH 281 784-4700 FAX 281 443-8873
HOUSTON,TX OFFICE - 2202 OIL CENTER CT
77073 PH 281 784-4780 FAX 281 784-4785
ODESSA,TX OFFICE - 7522 W I-20,79763
PH 432 385-3000 FAX 432 385-3050
CARLSBAD,NM OFFICE - 5010 NATIONAL PARK
88220 PH 432 385-3000 FAX 432 385-3050
TROY,PA OFFICE - 37 STATE RT 14 NORTH
16947 PH 570 297-3400 FAX 570 297-3415
CARROLLTON,OH OFFICE - 1100 STEUBENVILLE
RD 44615 PH 330 627-2692 FAX 330 627-2930

- CAREER TRAINING CENTER -
HARVEY,LA OFFICE - 1209 PETERS RD,70058
PH 504 227-0476 FAX 504 227-2053
NEW IBERIA,LA OFFICE - 3703 S LEWIS ST
PH 337 492-8002 FAX 337 492-8010

- CONCENTRIC PIPE & TOOL RENTALS -
HOUSTON,TX (SALES) OFFICE - 11000 EQUITY
77041 PH 281 999-0047 FAX 281 999-6505
HOUMA,LA OFFICE - 3529 TAXI RD,70363
PH 985 851-0306 FAX 985 873-7369
HARVEY,LA OFFICE - 2540 BREAUX AVE,70058
PH 504 367-6844 FAX 504 367-6858
NEW IBERIA,LA OFFICE - 6203 HWY 90 W
70560 PH 337 837-2345 FAX 337 365-4333
MACAE,RIO DE JANEIRO BRAZIL OFFICE - ESTR
PROJETADA 3 27.901-00 PH 55 22 3723-0100
FAX 55 22 27773-6284

- CONNECTION TECHNOLOGY -
HARVEY,LA OFFICE - 1105 PETERS RD,70058
PH 800 256-8324 PH 504 392-2579
FAX 504 362-7884

- CSI TECHNOLOGIES -
HOUSTON,TX OFFICE - 2202 OIL CENTER CT
77073 PH 281 784-7990 FAX 281 784-7995

- FASTORQ -
HARVEY,LA OFFICE - 1215 PETERS RD,70058
    PH 800 837-7117 PH 504 392-2579
    FAX 504 392-1688
BROUSSARD,LA OFFICE - 1037 FREEMAN RD
    70518 PH 888 651-0707 PH 337 839-0441
    FAX 337 839-0446
SHREVEPORT,LA OFFICE - 8810 ST VINCENT ST
    71106 PH 318 861-7633 FAX 318 861-7642

- HB RENTALS -
BROUSSARD,LA OFFICE - 5813 HWY 90 EAST
    70518 PH 800 262-6790 PH 337 839-1641
    FAX 337 839-1628
SHREVEPORT,LA OFFICE - 8279 W ANTOINE
    LOOP,71129 PH 318 603-0740
    FAX 318 603-0742
MENIFEE,AR OFFICE - 31 BELL MOUNTAIN RD
    72017 PH 877 931-1900 PH 501 977-1900
    FAX 501 977-1904
ALICE,TX OFFICE - 4976 HWY 281 SOUTH
    78332 PH 888 464-8591 PH 361 664-8591
    FAX 361 664-8762
ALVORD,TX OFFICE - 149 W BYPASS 287,76225
    PH 866 710-9673 PH 940 427-9673
    FAX 940 427-9676
FAIRFIELD,TX OFFICE - 130 HWY 75 SOUTH
    75840 PH 866 552-9230 PH 903 389-9230
    FAX 903 389-7961
LIVERPOOL,TX OFFICE - 8525 HWY 35 SOUTH
    77577 PH 800 237-6062 PH 281 393-1210
    FAX 281 581-9034
MIDLAND,TX OFFICE - 3319 E HWY 158,79706
    PH 866 874-3362 PH 432 570-0975
    FAX 432 570-0973
HOUSTON,TX OFFICE - 11000 EQUITY DR
    STE 300,77041 PH 800 999-0040
    PH 281 999-0047 FAX 281 999-6505
CANADIAN,TX OFFICE - 10951 US 83 HWY
    79014 PH 806 323-9311 FAX 806 323-9372
LAREDO,TX OFFICE - 120 RANCH RD 6086-C
    78043 PH 956 718-2322 FAX 956 718-2808
YANCEY,TX OFFICE - 10065 FM 462 S 78886
    PH 832 590-1451
EL RENO,OK OFFICE - 3701 S CHOCTAW 73036
    PH 800 262-6790 PH 405 422-1062
    FAX 405 422-1064
GRAND JUNCTION,CO OFFICE - 598 23-1/2 RD
    81505 PH 877 288-4555 PH 970 242-4555
    FAX 970 242-4556
CARLSBAD,NM OFFICE - 903H AIRPORT RD
    88220 PH 575 628-8389
CANONSBURG,PA OFFICE - 257 JOHNSON RD
    15317 PH 877 320-8875 PH 724 916-4215
    FAX 724 916-4592
MILL HALL,PA OFFICE - 7484 NITTANY VALLEY
    DR,17751 PH 570 726-8034 FAX 570 726-8247
RIVERTON,WY OFFICE - 12674 US HWY 26
    82501 PH 800 850-9761 PH 307 856-9761
    FAX 307 856-7916
WILLSTON,ND OFFICE - 14071 49TH ST NW
    58001 PH 701 572-5029 FAX 701 572-1310
ABERDEEN,SCOTLAND OFFICE - HOWE MOSSE DR
    DYCE,AB21 OGL PH 44 1224 772 304
    FAX 44 1224 772 641

SINGAPORE OFFICE - 25 LOYANG CRESCENT
    BLK 106,TOPS AVE 1,ST 12 PH 65 6546-6670
    FAX 65 6546-0342
SAN FERNANDO,TRINIDAD OFFICE - 8 EDOO
    ESTATES PH 868 657-7039 FAX 868 697-7719
KUALA LUMPUR,MALAYSIA OFFICE - 9-2,JALAN
    SOLARIS 2 50480 PH 603 6204-9759
    FAX 603 6204-9758

- INTERNATIONAL SNUBBING SERVICES (ISS) -
ARNAUDVILLE,LA OFFICE - 190 INDUSTRIES LN
    70512 PH 337 754-7233 FAX 337 754-5765
WURRUK,VICTORIA,AUSTRALIA (SES AUSTRALIA)
    OFFICE - 6-10 HUNT PL,3850
    PH 61 351 432 225 FAX 61 351 432 226
WURRUK,VICTORIA,AUSTRALIA(LEIGHTON ENGRG)
    OFFICE - 6-10 HUNT PL,3850
    PH 61 351-432312
CIUDAD OJEDA,ZULIA,VENEZULA OFFICE -
    AV INTERCUMUNAL,SECTOR LIBERTAD EDIF
    PH 58 265 662-3097 FAX 58 265 631-1508
SAN FERNANDO,TRINIDAD OFFICE - EDOOS
    INDUSTRIAL ESTATE,8A BAMBOO JUNCTION
    PH 868 657-7039 FAX 868 697-7719

- PRODUCTION MANAGEMENT INDUSTRIES (PMI)-
MORGAN CITY,LA OFFICE - 9761 HWY 90 EAST
    70380 PH 888 229-3837 PH 985 631-3837
    FAX 985 631-9938
MORGAN CITY,LA OFFICE - PO BOX 2692 70381
    9743 HWY 123 E 70380 PH 888 229-3837
    PH 985 631-3837 FAX 985 631-0729
FOURCHON,LA OFFICE - 181 ANSELMI DR 70357
    PH 877 396-3084 PH 985 396-3084
    FAX 985 396-3086
VENICE,LA OFFICE - 290 MCDERMOTT RD 70091
    PH 504 534-5406 FAX 504 534-1021
HOUSTON,TX OFFICE - 11000 EQUITY DR 77041
    PH 866 999-0040 PH 281 999-0047
    FAX 281 999-6505
MIDLAND,TX OFFICE - PO BOX 50457,79710
    2704 E I-20 PH 432 686-2927
    FAX 432 686-0828

- SPC RENTALS -
ALICE,TX OFFICE - 908 CECILLA ST 78332
    PH 361 668-0661 FAX 361 668-4703
ROSHARON,TX OFFICE - 3735 A CR 56 77583
    PH 281 431-2393 FAX 281 431-0767
ODESSA,TX OFFICE - 10901 W CR 125 79765
    PH 432 561-5887 FAX 432 561-5171
ELK CITY,OK OFFICE - PO BOX 1456
    1602 ENTERPRISE RD 76344 PH 580 243-5500
    FAX 580 225-3092
MINDEN,LA OFFICE - 1397 ALLEN DR 70155
    PH 318 377-2500 FAX 318 377-2510
YOUNGSVILLE,LA OFFICE - 114 E ANGUS DR
    70592 PH 337 856-1379 FAX 337 856-2453
SANDERSVILLE,MS OFFICE-1383 SANDERSVILLE/
    SHARON RD 39477 PH 601 335-0037
    FAX 601 335-0038
- SPC MOTORS -
BROUSSARD,LA OFFICE - 309 MINERAL RD
    70518 PH 337 839-0181

- STABIL DRILL -

LAFAYETTE,LA OFFICE - 110 CONSOLIDATED DR
    70508 PH 337 837-3001 FAX 337 837-3043
HOUMA,LA OFFICE - 119 VENTURE BLVD 70360
    PH 985 851-6161 FAX 985 851-6170
SHREVEPORT,LA OFFICE - 1915 BARTON DR
    71107 PH 318 670-2103 FAX 318 670-2012
YUKON,OK OFFICE - 101 N SARA RD 73099
    PH 405 789-5111 FAX 405 789-5101
CORPUS CHRISTI,TX OFFICE -
    426 S NAVIGATION BLVD 78405
    PH 361 883-7966 FAX 361 883-7575
HOUSTON,TX OFFICE - 608 W RICHEY RD 77090
    PH 281 583-9945 FAX 281 587-2927
MIDLAND,TX OFFICE - 2805 COUNTRY RD
    1207 S,79701 PH 432 522-7872
    FAX 432 689-0535
MILLS,WY OFFICE - 1118 FALCON AVE 82644
    PH 307 234-4203 FAX 307 234-9057
MT PEARL,NEWFOUNDLAND/LABRADOR CANADA
    OFFICE - 106 CLYDE AVE,A1N 4S2
    PH 709 364-4342 FAX 709 964-4579
ABERDEEN,SCOTLAND OFC - ABERDEEN BUSINESS
    PARK UNIT 2 DYCE,AB21 OLQ
    PH 44 0 1224-215932

- SUB SURFACE TOOLS -
LUBBOCK,TX OFFICE - 2424 SLATON RD 79404
    PH 806 745-2498 FAX 806 745-1503
MORGAN CITY,LA OFFICE - 1550 YOUNGS RD
    70380 PH 985 384-4425 FAX 985 384-5736
BRIDGEPORT,TX OFFICE - 1767 W HWY 380
    76426 PH 940 683-8283 FAX 940 683-1883
CORPUS CHRISTI,TX OFFICE - 1202 SOUTHERN
    MINERALS RD 78409 PH 361 299-6058
    FAX 361 299-6258
ROCK SPRINGS,WY OFFICE - 57 MESA DR 82901
    PH 307 362-2852 FAX 307 382-3541
ALTOONA,PA OFFICE - 3753 E PLEASANT
    VALLEY BLVD 16602 PH 814 742-7826
    FAX 814 742-7820
CONWAY,AR OFFICE- 955 PLANE RD 72034
    PH 504 328-5300 FAX 504 328-5304

- SUPERIOR INSPECTION SERVICES -
BROUSSARD,LA OFFICE - 1110 SMEDE HWY
    70518 PH 337 367-6200 FAX 337 367-6216
WILLISTON,ND OFFICE - 14071 49TH ST NW
    58001 PH 701 572-1370 FAX 701 572-1379

- WARRIOR ENERGY SERVICES -
COLUMBUS,MS OFFICE - PO BOX 9188,39705
    100 ROSECREST LN 39701 PH 888 552-4495
    FAX 662 329-1089
- SNUBBING -
LAKE WORTH,TX OFFICE- 4200 WHITE ST 76136
    PH 817 237-9223 FAX 817 237-9202
DECATUR,TX OFFICE - PO BOX 1192,76234
    3271 US HWY 287 S PH 940 626-1504
    FAX 940 626-4147
CORPUS CHRISTI,TX OFFICE - 2001 LEXINGTON
    78408 PH 956 383-0793
RICHARDTON,ND OFFICE - 120 SOUTH AVENUE W
    58652 PH 701 974-4200 FAX 701 974-4203
ROCK SPRINGS,WY OFFICE - 510 SIGNAL DR
    82901 PH 956 383-0793
BELLE VERNON,PA OFFICE - 203 FINLEY RD

15012 PH 724 775-0109 FAX 724 775-6019
DUSHORE,PA OFFICE - 11107 RT 220 18614
PH 940 210-9437
WILLIAMSPORT,PA OFFICE - 2462 LYCOMING
CREEK RD 17701 PH 570 651-9002
FAX 570 601-4845
- FLOWBACK -
PENFIELD,PA OFC-10865 BENNETTS VALLEY HWY
15849 PH 814 637-5191 FAX 814 637-5194
PLEASANTON,TX OFFICE - 4541 CR 430 78064
PH 830 569-2096
RIVERTON,WY OFFICE - 11019 HWY 789 82501
PH 307 857-0077
EVANSTON,WY OFFICE - 2539 WASATCH DR
82390 PH 307 789-9213 FAX 307 789-0150
MARBLETON,WY OFFICE - 12 FIRST NORTH RD
83113 PH 307 276-5265
-CEMENTING & ACIDIZING/SLICKLINE -
SANDERSVILLE,MS OFFICE - 1383 SHARON-
SANDERSVILLE RD 39477 PH 601 335-0034
FAX 601 335-0038
HOBBS,NM OFFICE - 1727 SW COUNTY RD 88240
PH 575 391-0092
ODESSA,TX OFFICE - 6106 CARGO RD 79762
PH 432 617-0114
- MANUFACTURING -
LAUREL,MS OFFICE - 339 AVE A,39440
PH 601 425-5127 FAX 601 425-5080
- PIPE RECOVERY -
MINDEN,LA OFFICE - 1391 ALLEN DR 71055
PH 318 382-1990
- SAFETY -
BROUSSARD,LA OFFICE - 5801 US 90 EAST
70518 PH 337 714-2400 FAX 337 714-0010
- SALES -
LAFAYETTE,LA OFFICE - 413 TRAVIS ST
STE 100,70503 PH 337 234-7487
FAX 337 234-7459
NEW ORLEANS,LA OFFICE - 1100 POYDRAS ST
STE 2929,70163 PH 504 585-7377
FAX 504 585-7387
DALLAS,TX OFFICE - 4242 N CAPISTRANO DR
STE 175,75287 PH 504 220-8080
FAX 972 447-4924
HOUSTON,TX OFFICE - 11000 EQUITY DR
STE 300,77041 PH 832 775-0016
FAX 832 775-0021
DENVER,CO OFFICE - 621 7TH ST STE 2210
80293 PH 303 825-0282 FAX 303 573-5365
- SLICKLINE -
KINGSVILLE,TX OFFICE - 326 N CR 1050
78363 PH 361 668-0811
TRANSFER,PA OFC - 102 CRESTVIEW EXTENSION
16154 PH 724 985-4093 FAX 724 985-4106
- WIRELINE -
BROUSSARD,LA OFFICE - 102 BERCEGEAY RD
70518 PH 337 714-2550 FAX 337 714-2119
GRAY,LA OFFICE - 325 SERVICE RD SW,70359
PH 888 822-7668 FAX 985 223-2995
MINDEN,LA OFFICE - 1391 ALLEN DR 71055
PH 318 382-1991 FAX 318 382-1992
DENTON,TX OFFICE - 2269 N MASCH BRANCH RD
STE 1 76207 PH 940 484-4481
FAX 940 387-5711
IOWA PARK,TX OFFICE - 334 RIFLE RANGE RD
76367 PH 940 592-4906 FAX 940 592-5568

TYLER,TX OFFICE - 11783 FM 3270,75703
PH 903 877-2610 FAX 903 877-2640
LAUREL,MS OFFICE - PO BOX 4244,39441
3611 INDUSTRIAL BLVD PH 601 425-9684
FAX 601 649-5574
FARMINGTON,NM OFFICE - 700 S DESTIN RD
87401 PH 505 326-6669 FAX 505 326-4167
HOBBS,NM OFFICE - PO BOX 66 88240
527 N WEST COUNTY RD PH 505 397-0567
FAX 505 397-0571
OKLAHOMA CITY,OK OFFICE - 4100 S COUNCIL
RD 73179
GREELY,CO OFFICE - 1314 FIRST NORTH RD
80631 PH 970 353-5118 FAX 970 475-0180
ROCK SPRINGS,WY OFFICE - 480 N ENERGY RD
82901 PH 307 382-7575
ROCK SPRINGS,WY OFFICE - PO BOX 566 82902
359 BLAIRTOWN RD 82901
PH 307 362-9445 FAX 307 382-9946
CASPER,WY OFFICE - 1330 N DERRICK DR
82604 PH 800 524-4562 FAX 307 265-5772
MINOT,ND OFFICE - 520 64TH ST SE STE B
58701 PH 701 838-2286
WATFORD CITY,ND OFFICE - 401 12TH ST SE
58854 PH 701 570-4915
BELLE VERNON,PA OFFICE-203 FINLEY RD BD 1
15012 PH 724 775-0109 FAX 727 775-6019
TUNKHANNOCK,PA OFFICE - 785 RT 29 N 18657
MINDEN,LA OFFICE - 1391 ALLEN DR 71055
PH 318 382-1991 FAX 318 382-1992
- WIRELINE / PIPE RECOVERY -
ODESSA,TX OFFICE - 853 NW LOOP 338,79763
PH 432 530-1322 FAX 432 530-3302
- WIRELINE / RENTALS -
ALICE,TX OFFICE - 5690 E HWY 44,78332
PH 281 431-6600
ROSHARON,TX OFFICE - 3735 COUNTY RD 56
77583 PH 866 944-6600 FAX 281 431-6607

- WILD WELL CONTROL -
HOUSTON,TX OFFICE - 2202 OIL CENTER CT
77073 PH 281 784-4700 FAX 281 784-4785
- WELL CONTROL SERVICES -
HOUSTON,TX OFFICE - 2202 OIL CENTER CT
77073 PH 281 784-4780 FAX 281 443-8873
- WELL CONTROL TRAINING -
ODESSA,TX OFFICE - 4901 E UNIVERSITY WCT/
PETEX 79762 PH 281 784-4700
CORPUS CHRISTI,TX OFFICE - 2209 N PADRE
ISLAND DR STE C,78408 PH 832 851-5509
OKLAHOMA CITY,OK OFFICE - 6701 S EASTERN
73149 PH 405 686-0330 FAX 281 784-4750
CASPER,WY OFC- 907 N POPLAR STE 190 82601
PH 307 235-3030 FAX 307 472-3765
CANNONSBURG,PA OFFICE - 380 SOUTHPOINTE
BLVD 15317 PH 281 784-4700
- WILD WELL CONTROL - INTERNATIONAL -
ABERDEEN,SCOTLAND OFFICE - ABERDEEN
BUSINESS PARK UNIT 2,DYCE DR,AB21 OLQ
PH 44 1224-215380
AL-KHOBAR,SAUDI ARABIA OFFICE -
PO BOX 31800 31952
DUBAI OFFICE - THE OASIS CENTRE LEVEL 3
OFFICE 86 283128 PH 97 14339-7017
QATTAMIYA HEIGHTS,NEW CAIRO OFFICE -
BLDG 160 5TH NEIGHBOURHOOD 11771

- WORKSTRINGS INTERNATIONAL -
HOUSTON,TX OFC-11000 EQUITY BLVD STE 300
77041 PH 866 999-0040 PH 281 999-0047
FAX 832 590-7394
BROUSSARD,LA OFFICE - 1150 SMEDE HWY
70518 PH 888 978-7464 PH 337 989-9675
FAX 337 492-0012
WILLISTON,ND OFFICE - 14071 49TH ST NW
58801 PH 701 572-1335 FAX 701 572-1345
DENVER,CO OFFICE - 600 17TH ST S STE 2800
80202 PH 303 634-2250 FAX 303 260-6401
MT PEARL,NEWFOUNDLAND/LABRADOR CANADA
OFFICE - 106 CLYDE AVE,A1N 4S2
PH 709 364-4342 FAX 709 964-4579
PERTH,WESTERN AUSTRALIA OFFICE-LEVEL 2
165 ADELAIDE TERRACE COCOS DR 6000
PH 61 0 8 9325-6953 FAX 61 0 8 9325-1193
ABERDEEN,SCOTLAND OFFICE - KIRKTON AVE
DYCE,AB21 0BF PH 44 0 1224 724 724900
FAX 44 0 1224 770191
EMMEN,DRENTHE,NETHERLANDS OFFICE - KAREN
DOORMANSTRATT 4,7825 VT PH 31 591 676 959
FAX 31 591 634 691
GREAT YARMOUTH,NORFOLK OFFICE - UNITS 1
1&2 ENTERPRISE CT NR31 ONL
PH 44 1493 443 276 FAX 44 1493 665 632
NAERBO,ROGALAND,NORWAY OFFICE -
BJORHAUGSLETTA 5,4365 PH 47 51 31 5585
FAX 47 51 31 5556
QUITO,AYACUCHO,ECUADOR OFFICE - AV ELOY
ALFARO N35-09 Y PORTUGAL,EDIF MILENIUM
PLAZA,OFC 302 PH 593 2 333 2570
DUBAI OFFICE - OF SPACE 3RD FL NO 85
SHEIK ZAYAD RD PH 971 4 339-7017
FAX 971 4 339-7851
ABU DHABI,UNITED ARAB EMIRATES OFFICE -
PO BOX 29408,PLOT NO 2,SEC M15,MUSSAFAH
PH 971 2 554-4407 FAX 971 2 554-0734
ACCRA,GHANA OFFICE - 5 ALEMA AVE APT 3
PH 233 245 35 09 28
BOGOTA DC,CUNDINAMARCA,COLUMBIA OFFICE -
COLOMBIA CRA 10 NO 97 A 13 TORRE A OF 509
PH 571 742-7642 FAX 571 742-7654
MACAE,RIO DE JANEIRO,BRAZIL OFFICE -
RODOVIA AMARAL PEIXOTO,KM 164.5 27923-420
PH 55 22 2773 6284 FAX 55 22 2773 6284

- HALLIN MARINE SUBSEA INTERNATIONAL -
- HALLIN MARINE SYSTEMS / PROSPECT -
SINGAPORE OFFICE - 25 LOYANG CRESCENT BLK
106 TOPS ST 12,BOX 5083,508988
PH 65 6546 0341 FAX 65 6546 6270
- HALLIN MARINE AUSTRALIA PTY LTD -
EAST PERTH,WESTERN AUSTRALIA OFFICE -
2ND FLOOR 165 ADELAIDE TERRACE
PH 61 8 9325-6953 FAX 61 8 9325-1193
- HALLIN MARINE UK LTD -
ABERDEEN,SCOTLAND OFFICE-CUMBERLAND HOUSE
ENDEAVOR DR AB32 6UF PH 44 1224 729-944
FAX 44 1224 729-071
- PROSPECT -
ABERDEEN,SCOTLAND OFFICE-CUMBERLAND HOUSE
ENDEAVOR DR AB32 6UF PH 44 1224 651 831
FAX 44 1224 633 633
DERBY OFFICE - 42 FRIAR GATE,DE1 1DA

PH 44 1332 223 999 FAX 44 1332 344 740
- PROSPECT FLOW SOLUTION INC -
HOUSTON,TX OFFICE - 11000 RICHMOND AVE
STE 190,77042 PH 713 974-1929
FAX 866 574-7705
- PT HALLIN MARINE INDONESIA -
JAKARTA OFFICE - GARDEN CENTRE BLDG STE
5-11,12560 PH 62 21 782 7052
FAX 62 21 782 7052

- APPALACHIAN WELL SERVICES -
PITTSBURGH,PA OFFICE - 2 PENN CENTER WEST
STE 227 15276 PH 412 490-9200

- COMPLETE ENERGY SERVICES -
HOUSTON,TX OFFICE- 11700 KATY FWY STE 300
77079 PH 281 372-2300
- FLUID MANAGEMENT -
OKLAHOMA CITY,OK OFFICE - 4727 GAILLARDIA
PKWY 73142 PH 800 366-6024
- WELL SERVICES -
GAINESVILLE,TX OFFICE- 3333 1-35 N BLDG F
76240 PH 940 668-8344

- IPS -
HOUSTON,TX OFFICE- 16800 GREENSPOINT PARK

- PUMPCO ENERGY SERVICES -
VALLEY VIEW,TX OFFICE - 117 ELM GROVE RD
76272 PH 940 726-1800

- SINGAPORE PTE LTD -
SINGAPORE OFFICE - BLOCK 201 TOOL DR
508988 PH 65 6777-713465 FAX 65 6777-8256
SUPERIOR GAUGING SERVICES,INC
1030 JULIE ST
BREAUX BRIDGE,LA 70517
PH 337 332-2093 FAX 337 332-2093
RODNEY QUIBODEAUX,PRES
SUPERIOR MARINE,INC
PO BOX 2443
MORGAN CITY,LA 70381-2443 PH 985 631-2187
FAX 985 631-4564 DIAMONDSERVICESCORP.COM
GENE H DARNELL,III,PRES
JULIE MARCOTTE,SECY JULIE@DSCGOM.COM
SUPERIOR PLANT SERVICES SEE
SUPERIOR ENERGY SERVICES COMPANY
SUPPLE TIMOTHY H,OIL & GAS PROPERTIES
315 S COLLEGE RD STE 163
LAFAYETTE,LA 70503-3213 PH 318 234-1125
FAX 318 237-2607
SUPREME SOURCE ENERGY SERVICES,INC
410 W GRAND PKWY S STE 240
KATY,TX 77494-8361 PH 281 395-5202
FAX 281 395-5204 WWW.SSES.US
DANNY WILLIAMS,PRES
CHAD WILLIAMS,SECY/TREAS
SUPREME VACUUM SERVICES INC
P O BOX 834
PLEASANTON,TX 78064 PH 830 780-4777
FAX 830 780-4999 WWW.SUPREMEVSINC.COM
BARCLEY HOUSTON,COO
FRANK GUZMAN,OPERS MGR
IGNACIO FARIAS,SLS
REED BAKER,SLS

SURFACE TRANSPORTATION BOARD
WWW.STB.DOT.GOV
SURFSIDE ABSTRACTING,INC
11106 STATE HWY 18
CONNEAUT LAKE,PA 16316 PH 814 382-2500
PH 814 382-3460 FAX 814 382-2550
JIM BOURBEAU JBOURBEAU@JIMBOURBEAU.COM
SURVCON INC,SURVEYORS SEE
MCKIM & CREED,INC
SURVIVAL SYSTEMS INTERNATIONAL,INC
34140 VALLEY CENTER RD
VALLEY CENTER,CA 92082-6017
PH 760 749-6800 FAX 760 749-6804
GEORGE L BEATTY,PRES
BARBIE PARKER,VP,FIN
KENNER,LA OFFICE - PO BOX 1567
70063,931 INDUSTRY RD PH 504 469-4545
FAX 504 466-1884
CLAUDIO ZAVALA,GEN MGR OPERS
SUTHERLAND RESOURCES INC
675 BERING DR STE 100
HOUSTON,TX 77057-2269 PH 713 914-9610
FAX 713 914-9665
GEORGA FINLEY HARRISON,CHRMN
A JUDD HARRISON,PRES
GEORGE W SUTPHEN,EXEC VP
LAURA LIN,CONTROLLER
LORRAINE ZOGG,LDMN
SUTTER ROBERT,GEOL
P O BOX 51211
LAFAYETTE,LA 70505-1211 PH 337 984-7128
SUTTON BEN E,OIL OPR
PRODUCING PROP & MIN RIGHTS
PO BOX 521
102 N COLLEGE AVE STE 513
TYLER,TX 75710-0521 PH 903 597-9061
SUTTON H E,OIL PROD
P O BOX 639
OIL CITY,LA 71061-0639 PH 318 995-7184
H E SUTTON,OWNER
SUTTON PRODUCING CORP
PO BOX 701130,106 TOMAHAWK TRAIL
SAN ANTONIO,TX 78270 PH 210 402-3355
FAX 210 402-3262
SUTTON VIRGINIA E,ESTATE
PRODUCING OIL PROP & MINERAL RIGHTS
PO BOX 521,102 N COLLEGE AVE STE 513
TYLER,TX 75710-0521 PH 903 597-9061
SWACO,A DIVISION OF M-I L.L.C. SEE
M-I L.L.C.
SWEARINGEN W P
11715 WENDOVER
HOUSTON,TX 77024-5114 PH 713 465-4835
W P SWEARINGEN,OWNER
SWECO SEE
BRANDT,A VARCO CO
SWICK N EUGENE,PETR GEOL
809 DAFNEY DR
LAFAYETTE,LA 70503-4749 PH 337 235-9613
FAX 337 237-4334 GENESWICK@ROZEL.COM
SWIFT ENERGY COMPANY
16825 NORTHCHASE DR STE 400
HOUSTON,TX 77060-6098 PH 281 874-2700
FAX 281 874-2701 WWW.SWIFTENERGY.COM
TERRY E SWIFT,CEO,DIR
BRUCE H VINCENT,PRES,SECY,DIR

ROBERT J BANKS,EXEC VP,COO
ALTON HECKAMAN,EXEC VP,CFO
JAMES M KITTERMAN,SR VP,OPERS
RICHARD KIMBERLIN,DIR,LAND
SWN SEE SOUTHWESTERN ENERGY COMPANY
SWOPE CORP
1200 BARTON CREEK BLVD APT 49
AUSTIN,TX 78735-1621
PH 512 327-9807 FAX 512 327-0360
SYDBOTEN & ASSOCIATES,INC SEE
SAI GEOCONSULTING,INC
SYDSON ENERGY,INC
4550 POST OAK PLACE STE 300
HOUSTON,TX 77027 PH 713 820-6300
MICHAEL MAYELL,PRES MMAYELL@SYDSON.COM
JAMES L GUNDERSON,LAND MGR
JGUNDERSON@SYDSON.COM
ROBERT GOLDSTEIN,CONSLT GEOL
SYLVAN ENERGY
1305 GRANDVIEW AVE STE 450
PITTSBURGH,PA 15211
PH 412 222-9600 FAX 866 249-7162
SYMBOL OIL CORP
PO BOX 400,2330 BOWEN RD
ELMA,NY 14059-0400 PH 716 655-4800
FAX 716 655-4801
WALTER P HAKER,PRES
SYNERGETICS INTERNATIONAL,INC (OILFIELD
SUPVSR CONTROL & DATA ACQUISITION)
600 OAK AVE
EATON,CO 80615-3404 PH 970 353-0800
FAX 970 353-0884
TOM PIERSON,PRES
FRED KING,MGR
MARTY HAASE,DIR,ENGRG
SYNERGY LAND & MINERALS,LLC
5700 MARILYN DR
AUSTIN,TX 78757 PH 512 772-1226
WWW.SYNLM.COM
SYNTROLEUM CORPORATION
10026A S MINGO RD STE 297
TULSA,OK 74133 PH 918 592-7900
FAX 918 592-7979 INVESTOR@SYNTROLEUM.COM
WWW.SYNTROLEUM.COM
JOHN B HOLMES JR,PRES,COO
HOUSTON,TX BRANCH OFFICE - 16800 S
GREENSPOINT PARK DR STE 150S,77060
T & N MARINE,INC
PO BOX 129,103 EAST 57TH ST
CUT OFF,LA 70345-0129 PH 504 632-3733
FAX 504 632-2751
TIMMY P ADAMS,PRES
DON M ADAMS,SECY
T & P WELL TESTERS OF LAFAYETTE,INC
PO BOX 80456
LAFAYETTE,LA 70598-0456
PH 337 364-6176 PH 800 349-1139
FAX 337 364-5936 WWW.TPWELLTESTERS.COM
CARL HAMMOND,PRES
CHAMMOND@TPWELLTESTERS.COM
MATT CECIL,VP OPERS
MCECIL@TPWELLTESTERS.COM
SHELLEY HAMMOND,SECY/TREAS/OWNER
SHAMMOND@TPWELLTESTERS.COM
C.J. HAMMOND,EXEC ACCT MGR
RICKY DUHON,GEN MGR

RDUHON@TPWELLTESTERS.COM
TARA WILLIAMSON,OFC MGR
TWILLIAMSON@TPWELLTESTERS.COM

T C OIL COMPANY
427 FM 774
REFUGIO,TX 78377-4432 PH 361 526-4693

T N T ENERGY,INC
250 FM 1849
BROWNWOOD,TX 76801 PH 325 752-7416

T P PETROLEUM INC
120 S BROADWAY AVE STE 108
TYLER,TX 75702-7232 PH 903 597-9432

T W C OIL COMPANY
PO BOX 2000
JENA,LA 71342-2000 PH 318 992-5728
FAX 318 992-6911
T W COON,OWNER
CHRISTY WILSON,GEOL

T.BAKER SMITH LLC
LAND & OFFSHORE SURVEYORS & ENV SVCS
PO BOX 2266,412 S VAN AVE
HOUMA,LA 70361-2266 PH 985 868-1050
TOLL FREE 866 357-1050 FAX 985 868-5843
WWW.TBSMITH.COM
INFORMATION@TBSMITH.COM
KENNETH WM SMITH,PRES,CEO
DAVID MARTINEZ,VP,SURV BUS UNIT
KENNY KING,VP,ENVIRO BUS UNIT
MARSHALL J FAULK,VP,OPER
JIMMY LEDET,VP,ENGRG BUS UNIT
JOSH GILLIS,OFFSHORE BUS UNIT
LAFAYETTE,LA OFFICE -
107 GLOBAL CIR STE 100,70503
PH 337 735-2800 FAX 337 735-2850
JUDE M COMEAUX,GEN MGR
BATON ROUGE,LA OFFICE -
17534 OLD JEFFERSON HWY STE D-1
PRAIRIEVILLE,LA 70769
PH 225 744-2100 FAX 225 673-6550
KEVIN O'GORMAN,GEN MGR,PRIN IN CHARGE
THIBODAUX,LA OFFICE - 1100 S ARCADIA
70301 PH 985 446-7970 FAX 985 446-9535
ANDREE CORTEZ,GEN MGR,PRIN IN CHARGE
HOUSTON,TX OFFICE - 12825 TRINITY DR
STAFFORD,TX 77477
PH 281 240-0113 FAX 281 240-0245
ANDREW MCLAUGHLIN,GEN MGR,PRIN IN CHARGE
SAN ANTONIO,TX OFFICE - 14100 SAN PEDRO
STE 300 78232 PH 210 892-4700
KEITH KEPPLER,GEN MGR,PRIN IN CHARGE

T.L.C. MARINE SERVICE,INC
PO DRAWER 586
LOCKPORT,LA 70374-0586 PH 985 532-5342
FAX 985 532-5361
RAY DUFRENE,OWNER,PRES

T.S. DUDLEY LAND COMPANY,INC
5925 N ROBINSON AVE
OKLAHOMA CITY,OK 73118
PH 405 848-4649 PH 800 611-3600
FAX 405 507-0120 WWW.TSDUDLEY.COM
TOM HAVENSTRITE,PRES
RUSSELL SHAW,VP
JOSH PARSONS,MGR
HOUSTON,TX OFFICE - 3100 S GESSNER RD
STE 425,77063 PH 713 952-7944
PH 800 536-7200 FAX 713 952-7980

ED MCLAIN,SR PROSPECT MGR
CHRIS GIDEON,SR PROSPECT MGR
BRENT BROUSSARD,AREA MGR
DENVER,CO OFFICE - 1888 SHERMAN STE 403
80203 PH 303 813-0901 FAX 303 813-0583
BRYCE WINTERS,PROSPECT MGR
RUSSELLVILLE,AR OFFICE - 1112 WEST B ST
72801-5133 PH 479 967-2970
FAX 479 967-2982
BRENT BROUSSARD,AREA MGR
DUFF STURGEON,PROSPECT MGR
CANONSBURG,PA OFFICE - 375 SOUTHPOINTE
BLVD STE 210,15317 PH 724 745-4717
FAX 724 745-4715
STEPHEN CARR,AREA MGR
TIM JACKSON,PROSPECT MGR
MICHAEL ENGLISH,PROSPECT MGR
RICK LEE,PROSPECT MGR
CHRISTINA COLEMAN,MGR
NACOGDOCHES,TX OFFICE - 1128 NW STALLINGS
75964 PH 936 462-1400 FAX 936 462-1401
BRENT BROUSSARD,AREA MGR
CHRIS GIDEON,SR PROSPECT MGR

T-M WELL SERVICE
449 M CR 3630
JEFFERSON,TX 75657 PH 903 407-1622
CHARLIE MCDONALD,OWNER

T-PLAN TECHNIQUES
4125 MEADOWLARK PT
EAGAN,MN 55122-1759 PH 651 681-9622
TOM J PEDERSON,OWNER,LDMN,CONSLT
TOMJPEDERSON@GMAIL.COM

T-REX ENGINEERING + CONSTRUCTION
ENGRG & FABRICATION SVCS-ONSHORE/OFF-
SHORE
8100 WASHINGTON AVE STE 200
HOUSTON,TX 77007 PH 281 833-9200

TABCO EXPLORATION,INC
5401 WIMBLEDON CT
NEW ORLEANS,LA 70131-5323 PH 504 394-5571
CALL BEFORE SENDING FAX 504 394-5571
TOM BLANKENSHIP,PRES
SAMMIE BLANKENSHIP,SECY/TREAS
VINTON,LA OFFICE - 2570 TOOMEY RD
70668 PH/FAX 318 589-3028

TACKABERRY CO THE
1515 W 13TH ST
DEER PARK,TX 77536-2535 PH 281 479-9700
ROBERT R TACKABERRY,PRES
JERRY SCHRAMME,VP,MKTG

TAG OPERATING CO,INC
7447 HARWIN DR STE 145
HOUSTON,TX 77036-2020 PH 713 789-5538
FAX 713 789-2387
THEODORE N SNYDER,PRES

TAGGART OIL CO,INC
PO BOX 8759
HOT SPRINGS VILLAGE,AR 71909-8759
PH 501 922-0182
R O TAGGART,PRES
M R TAGGART,SECY/TREAS

TAGGART R O,OIL & GAS EXPL & DEV
PO BOX 8759
HOT SPRINGS VILLAGE,AR 71910-8759
PH 501 922-0182

TALBERT & HAYS
PO BOX 315
TRINIDAD,TX 75163-0315 PH 972 592-4374
EUGENE TALBERT,CO-OWNER
MACK L HAYS,JR,CO-OWNER

TALBERT EUGENE
PO BOX 315
TRINIDAD,TX 75163-0315 PH 972 592-4374

TALBOT PROPERTIES,INC
PO BOX 53908
LAFAYETTE,LA 70505-3908 PH 318 984-8522
TOMMY@TALBOTPROPERTIESINC.COM
THOMAS L TALBOT,CPL

TALENT OIL COMPANY,INC
RR 8 BOX 336-AA
FAIRMONT,WV 26554-8733
PH 304 366-9572 FAX 304 366-9572
ROBERT J YEDLOSKY,PRES,GEOL
BYEDLOSKY@COMCAST.NET
FRANKLIN SCOTT YEDLOSKY,VP
JOYCE COOK,SECY
WALTER JOE YEDLOSKY,TREAS
PAMELA R DEBARR,RECORD KEEPER

TALISMAN ENERGY INC
888 - 3RD ST SW STE 2000
CALGARY,AB,CAN T2P 5C5
PH 403 237-1234 FAX 403 237-1902
TLM@TALISMAN-ENERGY.COM
- CANADIAN FIELD OFFICES -
CALGARY,AB TALISMAN ENERGY MIDSTREAM
OPERATIONS OFFICE - 888 - 3RD ST SW
STE 2000,BANKER'S HALL,T2P 5C5
PH 403 231-2816
CHAUVIN,AB OFFICE - PO BOX 99,T0B 0V0
CHETWYND,BRITISH COLUMBIA OFFICE -
PO BOX 1270,V0C 1J0
QUEBEC,CANADA OFFICE -
475 BOUL DE L'ATRIUM BUREAU 401,G1H 7H9
SHAUNAVON,SASKATCHEWAN OFFICE -
PO BOX 1177,122 - 3RD AVE E,S0N 2M0
- INTERNATIONAL OFFICES -
TALISMAN VIETNAM LIMITED OFFICE -
29 LE DUAN,FLR 18
5A1 GON TOWER DIST 1,HCMC
PH 848 3823-8232 FAX 848 823-8237
TALISMAN (ASIA) LTD. OFFICE -
TOWER 1,11 FLR, SUDIRMAN CENTRAL BUSINESS
DIST,J1 JEND SUDIRHMAN,KAVLING 52-53
JAKARTA,INDONESIA 12190 PH 62 21 515-1601
FAX 62 21 515-1602
TALISMAN (MALAYSIA) LTD. OFFICE -
LEVEL 33,165 JALAN AMPANG,MENARA CITIBANK
KUALA LUMPUR,50450
PH 603-2055-2888 FAX 603-2162-6972
TALISMAN ENERGY (QATAR) INC OFFICE -
BOX 22630,2-1,MUSEUM ST,AL JABER TWR,DOHA
PH 974-435-1815 FAX 974-435-0980
TALISMAN ENERGY (UK) LTD. OFFICE -
163 HOLBURN ST,TALISMAN HOUSE
ABERDEEN,SCOTLAND AB10 6BZ
PH 1224-352-500 FAX 1224-353-400
TALISMAN ENERGY NORGE AS OFFICE -
VERVEN 4,POSTBOKS 649,
SENTRUM 4003 STAVENGER,NORWAY
PH 47-5200-2000 FAX 47-5200-1500
TALISMAN (PERU) LTD SUCURSAL PERUANA

OFFICE - AV VICTOR A BELARINDE 147,VIA
PRINCIPAL 155,EDIFICIO REEL TRES OF 602
CENTRO EMPRESARIAL REAL LIMA 27 PERU
TALISMAN AUSTRALASIA OFFICE - LEVEL 21
AMP PLACE,10 EAGLE ST BRISBANE,QLD
AUSTRALIA 4000
- U.S. OFFICES -
FORTUNA ENERGY INC OFFICE - STE 101
337 DANIEL ZENKER DR,HORSEHEADS,NY 14845
PH 607 562-4000 FAX 607 562-4001
WWW.FORTUNAENERGY.COM
FEX - ALASKA OFFICE - STE 370
3900 C ST STE 101,ANCHORAGE 99503-5966
PH 907 644 4429 FAX 907 644-4892

TALLEY C B,L.C.,LDMN & APPRAISERS
PO BOX 51649
LAFAYETTE,LA 70505-1649 PH 337 234-2427
FAX 337 237-9714 WWW.CBTALLEY.COM
C B TALLEY,OWNER
PAULA VIZINAT, APPRAISER
CHRIS DECLOUET,APPRAISER/LDMN
KATHY HEBERT,APPRAISER/LDMN
LESLIE DESLATTE,APPRAISER
EVAN HIMEL,APPRAISER
JAMES DECLOUET,APPRAISER
ANISSA TALLEY,OFC MGR,APPRAISER
ANISSA@CBTALLEY.COM

TALON DEVELOPMENT COMPANY
206 S SAUNDERS ST
BOERNE,TX 78006-2324 PH 830 249-1442
FAX 830 249-7852
BRIAN WELCH,PRES
TONY GIARDINELLI,VP

TALON SOLUTIONS & SERVICES,LLC
415 MUNSON AVE STE 102
TRAVERSE CITY,MI 49686
PH 231 933-6167 FAX 231 933-6232
DAVID LARSEN,LAND MGR
MARVIN JENSEN,TITLE MGR
ROLAND B CILKE,CPL-SR/WA-BUS DEV
PH 231 218-9018

TALUS RESOURCES LLC
770 S POST OAK LN STE 330
HOUSTON,TX 77056 PH 832 767-6787
INFO@TALUSRESOURCES.COM

TAM INTERNATIONAL,INC
INFLATABLE & SWELLABLE PACKERS
4620 SOUTHERLAND RD
HOUSTON,TX 77092-3020 PH 713 462-7617
PH 800 462-7617 FAX 713 462-1536
WWW.TAMINTL.COM INFO@TAMINTL.COM
L BENTLEY SANFORD,PRES
MICHAEL MACHOWSKI,COO
RAY FRISBY,VP TECH

TAMARACK PETROLEUM COMPANY,INC
777 E WISCONSIN AVE STE 3020
MILWAUKEE,WI 53202-5341 PH 414 276-0304
FAX 414 276-0803
D F MCKEITHAN,JR,CEO
DEBORAH MCKEITHAN-GEBHARDT,PRES
THOMAS A MIRSBERGER,CFO
MIDLAND,TX OFFICE - 303 W WALL ST
STE 1901,79701
PH 432 683-5474 FAX 432 683-7306
ROBERT LIEM,SR VP

TANA EXPLORATION CO LLC
25025 IH 45 N STE 600
THE WOODLANDS,TX 77380-3063
PH 832 325-6000 WWW.TANAEXP.COM
KEVIN TALLEY,PRES
MIKE SIMON,VP ENGRG & OPERS
CARL COMSTOCK,VP LAND
CELESTE FONTENOT,CONTROLLER

TANMAR COMPANIES
711 S CHESTNUT ST
TOMBALL,TX 77375 PH 281 591-6480
BRENT JASPER
BJASPER@TANMARCOMPANIES.COM

TANNER & ASSOCIATES LAND & TITLE,LLC
PO BOX 1109
LIVINGSTON,TX 77351
PH 936 327-3800

TANOS EXPLORATION II,LLC
821 E SOUTHEAST LOOP 323 STE 400
TYLER,TX 75701 PH 903 597-7667
FAX 903 597-7884 WWW.TANOSEXP.COM
MARK A BRANDON,PRES/CEO
NICK POLLARD,VP GEOL
JOE FREEMAN,VP ACQS & BUS DEV
GEOFF DOKE,CFO
BRIAN DURMAN,VP LAND

TAOS RESOURCES OPERATING COMPANY LLC
1455 W LOOP S STE 600
HOUSTON,TX 77027 PH 713 993-0774
FAX 713 993-0906
LOGAN MAGRUDER,PRES
KEITH L FITE,EXEC VP
KFITE@TAOSRESOURCES.COM

TARGA RESOURCES
1000 LOUISIANA STE 4300
HOUSTON,TX 77002 PH 713 584-1000
FAX 713 584-1100 WWW.TARGARESOURCES.COM
JAMES WHALEN,EXEC CHRMN
JOE BOB PERKINS,CEO
MICHAEL A HELM,PRES & COO
PAUL W CHUNG,GEN COUNSEL & SECY
JEFFREY J MCPARLAND,PRES-FIN & ADMIN
MATTHEW J MELOY,SR VP,CFO & TREAS
JOHN R SPARGER,SR VP & CAO

TARGET ENERGY,INC
OIL & GAS OPERATORS
PO BOX 1135
INDIANA,PA 15701-1135 PH 724 349-7339
MARK A YANOSKI,CPG,PRES

TARGET EXPLORATION SERVICES
4811 MANOR LN
ELLICOTT CITY,MD 21042-6119
PH 410 730-4364
NED TILLMAN,PRES

TARLTON JOHN S,LDMN
3105 BELMONT AVE
BATON ROUGE,LA 70808 PH 225 389-9193

TARPLEY ENGINEERING,PETR ENGRG
308 S HARDING ST
BRECKENRIDGE,TX 76424-4118
PH 254 559-5323
JAMES M TARPLEY,PETR ENGRG CONSLT
JIMTARPLEY@AOL.COM

TARPON OPERATING & DEVELOPMENT,LLC
333 CLAY ST STE 4200
HOUSTON,TX 77002

PH 281 493-6262 FAX 281 493-6821
RALPH MCBEE,PRIN/ENGR
STEPHEN LOCKE,PRIN/ENGR

TARTAN OIL COMPANY
P O BOX 338
CARMI,IL 62821-0338 PH 618 382-4109
CONRAD SHAW,GEOL

TARTAN RESOURCES CORPORATION
PO BOX 1227
HOUSTON,TX 77251 PH 281 665-1469
E FORBES GORDON,OWNER

TAS ENVIRONMENTAL SERVICES,LP
3929 CALIFORNIA PKWY E
FORT WORTH,TX 76119 PH 817 535-7222
FAX 817 535-8187 WWW.TASLP.COM
LMCENTIRE@TASLP.COM
DALLAS,TX - RESPONSE OFFICE
17714 BANNISTER ST STE 104,75252
PH 972 638-9700
SAN ANTONIO,TX - RESPONSE OFFICE
14350 LOOKOUT RD,78233 PH 210 496-5310
AUSTIN,TX - RESPONSE OFFICE
13720 IMMANUEL RD,78660 PH 512 990-9903
LONGVIEW,TX - RESPONSE OFFICE
8988 FM 2011 EAST,75603 PH 903 643-7901
TEXARKANA,TX - RESPONSE OFFICE
6409 W 7TH ST,75501 PH 903 838-2182
BOSSIER CITY,LA - RESPONSE OFFICE
3869 INDUSTRIAL CIR,71112 PH 318 747-2662
LITTLE ROCK,AR - RESPONSE OFFICE
180 CORNERSTONE RD,72022 PH 501 847-7200

TATHAM OIL & GAS INC SEE
ACADIANA ENERGY INC

TAUBER EXPLORATION & PRODUCTION CO
55 WAUGH DR STE 601
HOUSTON,TX 77007 PH 713 869-5656
FAX 713 869-1997
RICHARD E TAUBER,PRES
TIM G TADE,PE,OPERS MGR
JACK KRAMBERGER,CHF GEOL
DAVID VOIGHT,GEOL/GEOPHY
JOHN F ROBINSON,LAND MGR

TAURUS EXPLORATION,INC SEE
ENERGEN RESOURCES CORPORATION

TAYLAND RESOURCES
12827 ROLLING VALLEY DR
CYPRESS,TX 77429-2224 PH 281 373-4770
FAX 281 304-1965 TAYLAND1@GMAIL.COM
ROBERT H TAYLOR,OWNER

TAYLOR & ASSOCIATES
6207 GLENHILL DR # 200
SPRING,TX 77389-5224 PH 281 257-8585
FAX 281 257-8939
RUSSELL M TAYLOR,OWNER
RMTRISK@EARTHLINK.NET

TAYLOR B P & ASSOC,INC
P O BOX 175
MONTGOMERY,TX 77356-0175 PH 281 870-0505
BILLY P TAYLOR,PRES

TAYLOR CHARLES W,INC
P O BOX 445
SHREVEPORT,LA 71162-0445 PH 318 746-7729
CHARLES W TAYLOR,PRES

TAYLOR ENERGY COMPANY LLC
OIL & GAS/GULF OF MEXICO
1 LEE CIR

NEW ORLEANS,LA 70130-3931
PH 504 581-5491 FAX 504 589-0504
  PHYLLIS M TAYLOR,CHRMN,CEO
  WILLIAM W PECUE,PRES
  FRANK PERTUIT,CONTROLLER
  DINA B RIVIERE,CFO

TAYLOR ENERGY SERVICES,LLC
  11111 KATY FWY STE 910,ONE KATY PLAZA
  HOUSTON,TX 77079 PH 903 705-3875
    JETAYLOR@TAYLORENERGY.US

TAYLOR J WADE COMPANY,THE
  6126 MEADOW LAKE LN
  HOUSTON,TX 77057-3522 PH 713 975-1790
  J WADE TAYLOR,PRES

TAYLOR JAMES L,ASSOCIATES
  PO BOX 56418
  METAIRIE,LA 70055-6418 PH 504 451-1418
  FAX 504 837-6144
    JAMES LYLE TAYLOR,OWNER

TAYLOR STEVEN P,CPL,IND PETR LDMN
  19503 HURST WOOD DR
  HUMBLE,TX 77346-2148
  PH 318 988-0351 FAX 318 264-1928

TCW ASSET MANAGEMENT CO
  333 CLAY ST STE 4150
  HOUSTON,TX 77002-4178 PH 713 615-7400
  FAX 713 615-7460
    PATRICK HICKEY,SR VP
    KURT TALBOT,MNGNG DIR

TDT DIVERSE LP
  SEE FNRC TDT LP

TEAGUE GENE E,RLP,PETR LDMN
  505 CENTER PARK DR
  SPRINGHILL,LA 71075-3427 PH 908 230-4040

TEAL ENERGY USA INC
  1616 S VOSS RD STE 875
  HOUSTON,TX 77057-2631
  PH 713 781-4350 FAX 713 781-0271
    JOHN M GLENN,PRES
      JOHNGLENN@TEALENERGY.COM
    ANTHONY E KRANCER
    DEBORAH G SHANKS

TEAM SPIRIT PETROLEUM
  1121 LOUISIANA AVE
  SHREVEPORT,LA 71101-5502 PH 318 221-4959
  FAX 318 703-2804 GASMAN4959@AOL.COM
    HAROLD H HOLLENSHEAD,OWNER/PRES
    DON USRY,BUS MGR

TEC ENGINEERING GROUP,INC
  3650 OLD BULLARD RD STE 300
  TYLER,TX 75701-8667
  PH 903 561-0648 FAX 903 561-0680
    ROBERT D UNGERECHT,PE

TECH TOOL INC
  2901 COUNTY RD 150
  MILLERSBURG,OH 44654-8510
  PH 330 674-1176 FAX 330 674-1176
    KIM KAUFFMAN,PRESIDENT

TECHNIP OFFSHORE MOORINGS,INC SEE
  INTERMOOR INC

TECHNOLOGY DEVELOPMENT INC
  401 HIGHVIEW PLACE
  MORGANTOWN,WV 26505-4715 PH 304 292-7590
    DR L ZANE SHUCK,PRES

TECO INDUSTRIAL GAS COMPANY SEE
  EL PASO PIPELINE GROUP

TECO OPERATING COMPANY
  2721 COLOSSEUM WAY
  GRAND PRAIRIE,TX 75052-7000
  PH 903 675-5035 FAX 903 675-5080
  T E COVINGTON,PRES

TEETER ROBERT G,ATTORNEY
  524 N STATE ST STE B
  BIG RAPIDS,MI 49307 PH 231 335-3111
    WWW.TEETERLAW.COM
    RTEETER@TEETERLAW.COM

TELEDYNE MERLA SEE
  OTIS ENGINEERING CORP

TELLUS OPERATING GROUP,LLC
  602 CRESCENT PL STE 100
  RIDGELAND,MS 39157-8676
  PH 601 898-7444 FAX 601 898-7445
    TELLUSOPERATING.COM
    RICHARD H MILLS JR,MGR
    MIKE PUMPHREY,GEN COUNSEL
    TOM WOFFORD,CFO
    GEORGE RHODES,ADMINS MGR
    CHRIS JONES,RESERVOIR ENGRG MGR
    BRIAN SIMS,GEOL MGR
    JAMES F BOBO CLARKE,MGR OF LAND
    KEVIN MACUMBER,DRLG MGR
    SAM RHODES,MGR OF PROD
    MILT MAY,COMPRESSOR & ENGINE
      AFFILIATE MGR
    NEIL BARNES,EXPL MGR

TEMA OIL AND GAS COMPANY
  16200 PARK ROW STE 300
  HOUSTON,TX 77084-5056
  PH 281 829-3206 FAX 281 829-2676
    INFO@TEMAOG.COM WWW.TEMAOG.COM
    ALAN TOWNSEND,PRES
    BRIAN AYERS,VP GEOL
    COLBY WILLIFORD,VP LAND
    R F FILEY,CONTROLLER
  MIDLAND,TX WEST TX/NM DIST OFFICE -
  2605 GARDEN CITY HWY,79701
  PH 432 684-4463 FAX 432 684-4246
    ROBERT VANHUSEN,MIDLAND AREA MGR

TEMPEST ENERGY RESOURCES LP
  5151 BELTLINE RD STE 360
  DALLAS,TX 75254-1457
  PH 972 934-0081 FAX 972 934-2055
    TIM S CASHON,EXEC VP,LAND
    MARK L STANGER,COO,ENGRG
  HOUSTON,TX BRANCH OFFICE - PO BOX 79429
  77279-9429 PH 713 353-5058
    DON R ROLLINS JR,MNGNG DIR
    DROLLINS@CARSONROLLINS.COM

TEMPLE OIL COMPANY LLC SEE
  BEAR CREEK PETROCHEMICALS,LLC

TEMPLE-INLAND SEE
  FORESTAR MINERALS LLC

TENARIS GLOBAL SERVICES
  2200 W LOOP S STE 800
  HOUSTON,TX 77027 PH 713 767-4400
  FAX 713 767-4444
  CALGARY,ALBERTA,CANADA OFFICE -
  400, 530-8TH AVE SW T2P 3S8
  PH 403 767-0100 FAX 403 767-0299

TENEXCO INCORPORATED
  414 N CLINTON STE 106
  RIVER FOREST,IL 60305-2248

PH 312 771-7870 FAX 708 771-6616
  RICHARD S INCANDELA,PRES
  RICK INCANDELA,VP
  MICHAEL REED,VP,GEOL,GEOPHY
  SHARON SUE INCANDELA,SECY
  ROBERT ANDERSON,ASST SECY

TENKAY RESOURCES,INC
  24 WATERWAY AVE STE 700
  THE WOODLANDS,TX 77380
  PH 281 363-2406 FAX 281 292-7758
    D K CREWS,MNGNG DIR
    J T COOK,CONSLT GEOL

TENNECO GAS MARKETING COMPANY SEE
  EL PASO CORPORATION

TENNECO GAS SEE
  EL PASO CORPORATION

TENNECO VENTURES CORPORATION SEE
  EL PASO CORPORATION

TENNESSEE GAS PIPELINE
  1001 LOUISIANA ST
  HOUSTON,TX 77002 PH 713 420-2600
    BRYAN NESKORA,COO
    DANIEL B MARTIN,SR VP,OPERS
    WILLIAM G COPE,VP OPERS (TGP & SNG)
    SUSANNA B BARRY,VP,COMMERCIAL OPERS
    STANLEY CHAPMAN,VP,MKTG & BUS DEV
    JESUS SOTO JR,VP,OPERS SVCS
    JOHN GILLESPIE,VP,SUPPLY CHAIN MGMNT
    CECILIA A BODEY,DIR,AVIATION
    TERESA L HARRIS,DIR,MATERIALS/
      CONTRACT MGMT
    THOMAS D HUTCHINS,DIR,ENV,HEALTH &
      SAFETY

TENNYSON OIL CO LTD
  P O BOX 125,704 N BROADWAY
  SMACKOVER,AR 71762-0125 PH 870 725-3401
    TIMOTHY A TENNYSON,PRTNR,GEN MGR

TENSAS DELTA EXPLORATION COMPANY
  401 EDWARDS ST STE 1900
  SHREVEPORT,LA 71101-5536
  PH 318 222-0026

TEPEE PETROLEUM COMPANY,INC
  500 DALLAS ST STE 2920
  HOUSTON,TX 77002-4701 PH 713 659-8300
  FAX 713 659-6909
    TOWNES G PRESSLER,PRES

TEPPCO CRUDE OIL,LP
  210 PARK AVE STE 1600
  OKLAHOMA CITY,OK 73102-8805
  PH 405 239-7900 FAX 405 232-1815
    J MICHAEL COCKRELL,PRES

TEPPCO/TE PRODUCTS PIPELINE CO,LTD
  PARTNERSHIP
  PO BOX 2521
  HOUSTON,TX 77252-2521 PH 713 759-3636
    - BOARD OF DIRECTORS -
    JIM W MOGG,CHRMN
    MARK A BORER
    MICHAEL J BRADLEY
    MILTON CARROLL
    DERRILL CODY
    JOHN P DESBARRES
    WILLIAM H EASTER,III
    BARRY R PEARL
    R A WALKER
    - OFFICERS -

(800) 375-1838
WWW.ARMSTRONGOIL.COM

If your company is not listed in our directory, we would like to list it in the next edition of our directory - absolutely FREE. To be listed, we need it in writing. Please fill out the form below or visit our website and fill out the listing form there. If you wish to use the form below, just mail it or fax it to us at (800) 375-1838.

Company Name _____

Physical Address _____

Mailing address if different _____

Phone # _____ Fax # _____

Email address _____

Key personnel and their titles:

_____

_____

_____

_____

If you need to list additional offices, please include on letterhead

To Order Call (800) 375-1838 or
www.armstrongoil.com

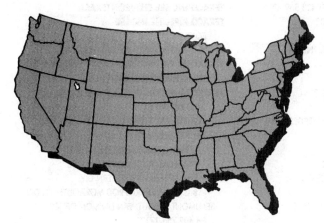

Nationwide Office Directory
Full 8 1/2" x 11" book size
Entire Nation
over 16,000 companies listed
$ 225 (no discount available)

Nationwide Mini Directory (Briefcase)
Small Size 5 1/4" x 8 1/4"
Same complete nationwide information
over 16,000 companies listed
$ 140 w / discount*

Texas Directory
Includes
Texas and S.E. New Mexico

$ 80 w / discount*

Louisana / Gulf Coast Directory
Includes the following states:
Gulf coast of Texas, Louisana
Arkansas, Mississippi,
Alabama, Georgia, Florida
N.E. states
$80 w / discount*

Rocky Mountain / Central U.S. Directory
Includes the following states:
West Texas and Panhandle of Texas
Oklahoma, New Mexico
Colorado, Alaska and all
Western U.S. states
$80 w / discount*

* discount applies when invoice is paid within 30 days after receipt of order.

BARRY R PEARL,PRES,CEO
BARBARA A CARROLL,VP ENVIRO HEALTH &
SAFETY
J MICHAEL COCKRELL,SR VP COMMERCIAL
UPSTREAM
JOHN N GOODPASTURE,VP,CORP DEV
THOMAS R HARPER,SR VP COMMERCIAL
DOWNSTREAM
CHARLES H LEONARD,SR VP,CFO
LEONARD W MALLETT,VP OPERS
STEPHEN W RUSSELL,VP SUPPORT SVCS
JAMES C RUTH,SR VP,GEN COUNSEL,SECY

TERCERO EXPLORATION COMPANY
OIL & GAS EXPLORATION/PRODUCTION
1524 S IH-35 STE 330
AUSTIN,TX 78704   PH 512 264-0222
FAX 512 448-0780 TOMMILES@AUSTIN.RR.COM
THOMAS F MILES,PRES,PETR GEOL

TERM ENERGY CORPORATION
713 E MAIN ST
HARRISVILLE,WV 26362-1301 PH 304 643-4500
FAX 304 643-4656

TERRA ENGINEERS,INC
1526 SKYLINE RD
CHARLESTON,WV 25314-2366 PH 304 346-7035
GEORGE A HALL,PHD,PRES,PROF ENGR
IRA S LATIMER JR,VP,GEOL

TERRA RESEARCH PARTNERS
LAND SVCS - APPALACHIAN BASIN
2 BOSLEY AVE
PARKERSBURG,WV 26101 PH 855 902-4877
MICHAEL S WILSON INFO@TERRARP.COM

TERRA RESOURCES,INC SEE
PACIFIC ENTERPRISES OIL COMPANY (USA)

TERRAFINA ENERGY LLC
212 LOSOYA STE 7
SAN ANTONIO,TX 78205
PH 210 305-5100 WWW.TERRAFINAENERGY.COM
MARSHA HENDLER
MARSHA@TERRAFINAENERGY.COM

TERRAFLUIDS,LLC
1221 LAMAR STE 1600
HOUSTON,TX 77010-3039
PH 713 753-1394 FAX 713 210-7394
WWW.TERRAFLUIDS.COM
JOHN C HUNTER,PRES
JOHN E HOSTETTLER,VP,OPERS
HOSTETJ@TEAI.COM
J DAVID LAPRADE,VP,MKTG

TERRASYS GEOPHYSICS
800 GESSNER RD STE 150
HOUSTON,TX 77024 PH 713 893-3630
FAX 713 893-3631 WWW.TERRASYSGEO.COM
INFO@TERRASYSGEO.COM

TERRI-JON MANAGEMENT CO
5563 RIDGE RD
WADSWORTH,OH 44281-9763 PH 330 239-1141
PH 330 848-0080 FAX 330 848-0881
JOHN KING,PRES

TERRIER OIL COMPANY
405 CHATEAU PLACE
LAFAYETTE,LA 70503 PH 337 991-0333
FAX 337 991-0338 ARDEN@CAJUNOIL.COM
ARDEN A ANDERSON,PRES

TERRONNE PETROLEUM CORPORATION
PO BOX 15018

MONROE,LA 71207-5018 PH 318 322-4910
KENNETH D PILGREEN,PRES

TERRY CRAIG B & ASSOCIATES
20 S DOE RUN DR
THE WOODLANDS,TX 77380 PH 713 962-6050
CRAIG B TERRY CTERRY003@COMCAST.NET

TERRY SHIRLENE
PO BOX 45
HUNTSVILLE,TN 37756-0045 PH 423 569-4775
FAX 423 663-4095 OR 569-2533
SPERRY@HIGHLAND.NET

TERTIARY TRENDS EXPLORATION,INC
6532 MERCER ST
HOUSTON,TX 77005-3736
PH 713 661-7112 FAX 713 661-2354
ANN AYERS MARTIN,PRES
ANNM@ROGERMARTINPROPERTIES.COM

TES ACQUISITION CORP SEE
AMERICAN EXPLORATION CO

TESCO OFFSHORE SERVICES INC
OILFIELD RENTAL & SERVICE CO
3209 MOSS ST
LAFAYETTE,LA 70507 PH 337 354-0900
FAX 337 354-0959
FRANK RICHARD,OPERS SUPVSR
BUDDY SCRANTZ,MGR
BRITT WIRTZ,MGR
JUDE BUTCH ABSHIRE,SR SLS REPR
KEN COMEAUX,SLS

TESNUS ENERGY
7622 HOLLY COURT EST
HOUSTON,TX 77095-3576 PH 281 550-7010
FAX 281 855-7401 MSLOONEY@ATT.NET
R MICHAEL LOONEY

TESORO COASTWIDE SERVICES COMPANY SEE
TESORO MARINE SERVICES,LLC

TESORO MARINE SERVICES,LLC SEE
MIDSTREAM FUEL SERVICE,LLC

TESORO WEST COAST COMPANY
3450 S 344TH WAY STE 100
AUBURN,WA 98001-5931 PH 253 896-8700
FAX 253 896-8887

TETON EXPLORATION INC
124 HEYMANN BLVD STE 210
LAFAYETTE,LA 70503-2363 PH 337 232-3293
FAX 337 234-8992 TETONRR@BELLSOUTH.NET
RANDOLPH BLACKBURN,PRES
STEWART STOVER,EXPL MGR

TETRA ENERGY,LLC
PO BOX 10476
FORT SMITH,AR 72917 PH 479 434-5441
FAX 479 434-5671
FORT SMITH,AR OFFICE - 5704 EUPER LN
STE 100,72903
KEVIN S VAUGHT,GEN MGR
KSVAUGHT@TETRA-ENERGY.COM
DARRELL D STOVAL,ENGRG MGR
DSTOVALL@TETRA-ENERGY.COM
C R (DICK) SAMPSON,EXPLOITATION MGR
DSAMPSON@TETRA-ENERGY.COM
STAN STEVENS,EXPL MGR
SSTEVENS@TETRA-ENERGY.COM

TEX TUBE COMPANY
PO BOX 55710,1503 N POST OAK RD
HOUSTON,TX 77255-5710 PH 713 686-4351
FAX 713 681-5256

MR ISIDRO CANTU,GEN MGR
J RAYMOND DAVILA,SLS MGR

TEX-KEN OIL AND GAS LLC
2530 SCOTTSVILLE RD STE 12
BOWLING GREEN,KY 42104 PH 270 843-0660
TOM SPROUSE

TEXACO EXPLORATION AND PRODUCTION,INC SEE
CHEVRONTEXACO

TEXACO INC SEE CHEVRONTEXACO

TEXACO PIPELINE INC SEE
EQUILON PIPELINE COMPANY

TEXACO PRODUCING INC,SEE TEXACO,INC

TEXAKOMA OIL AND GAS CORPORATION SEE
TEXAKOMA OPERATING,LP

TEXAKOTA INC,OIL CO,OIL PROD & OPR
2707 KIPLING ST
HOUSTON,TX 77098-1214 PH 713 520-7600
FAX 713 520-7632
STEVEN J BORICK,PRES,TREAS
BRADFORD R SCHMALFUSS,VP,EXPL
PHIL BECKER,VP,NORTHERN DIV
BILLY BLANCHARD,PROD MGR,SOUTHERN DIV
BEAUMONT,TX SOUTHERN DIVISION OFFICE -
PH 409 755-1717
TIOGA,N D NORTHERN DIVISION OFFICE -
PH 701 664-2595

TEXAN OILFIELD SERVICES,INC
2210 SHELBY PARK DR
KATY,TX 77450-6600 PH 281 578-6400
PH 800 749-6173 FAX 281 578-9295
CARL DORE',PRES
GLORIA DORE',VP
JESUS BLANCO JR,OPERS MGR

TEXAN PETROLEUM CORPORATION SEE
CHEYENNE PETROLEUM CORPORATION

TEXANA EXPLORATION CO,INC
4 DUCHESS CT
HOUSTON,TX 77024-5057
PH 713 973-1820 FAX 713 650-6421
G B BILL HOWARD IV,PRES

TEXANA OPERATING COMPANY
1115 DRAVA LN
HOUSTON,TX 77090-1264 PH 281 444-0037
FAX 281 580-8687 SUMTXNA@EARTHLINK.NET
PATRICK SUMBERA,PRES
DENNIS SUMBERA,VP,ENGR

TEXANA RESOURCES PARTNERS,INC
815 WALKER STE 1650
HOUSTON,TX 77002
PH 713 622-7707 FAX 713 626-7977
MAX L MAZY,PRES
M S STUDE,CHRMN

TEXAS A & M UNIV
CAREER CENTER
COLLEGE STATION,TX 77843-1233
PH 979-845-5139 CAREERCENTER.TAMU.EDU

TEXAS ACQUISITION & TITLE SERVICES,INC
SEE CONTRACT LAND STAFF,INC

TEXAS ALLIANCE OF ENERGY PRODUCERS
900 8TH ST STE 400
WICHITA FALLS,TX 76301
PH 940 723-4131 FAX 940 723-4132
PH 940 322-9371 (CRUDE OIL INFO)
WWW.TEXASALLIANCE.ORG
TEXASALLIANCE@TEXASALLIANCE.ORG
ALEX MILLS,PRES

GEORGE ROGERS,CHRMN
HOUSTON,TX OFFICE - 3701 KIRBY STE 962
77098 PH 713 529-6707 FAX 713 529-6855
AUSTIN,TX OFFICE - 823 CONGRESS AVE
STE 1010,78701 PH 512 322-0047

TEXAS AMERICAN RESOURCES COMPANY
401 CONGRESS STE 1600
AUSTIN,TX 78701-4039
PH 512 480-8700 FAX 512 480-8732
DAVID HONEYCUTT,PRES
JULIAN BOTT,CFO
TROY GIESELMAN,VP LAND
BIG WELLS,TX OFFICE - PO BOX 187,78830
PH 830 457-2202   FAX 830 457-2674
PERRYTON,TX OFFICE -
PH 806 434-2306   FAX 806 434-0466

TEXAS CRUDE ENERGY LLC
PO BOX 56586,2803 BUFFALO SPEEDWAY
HOUSTON,TX 77256-6586
PH 713 599-9900 FAX 713 599-9910
CHARLES WEINER,CHRMN EMERITUS
PETER J FLUOR,CHRMN,CEO
KANE C WEINER,PRES
DOUGLAS O'BRIEN,VP EXPL
MICHAEL HUHNKE,VP OPERS
CHARLES H KANA,VP LAND
FORT WORTH,TX ACCOUNTING OFFICE -
PO BOX 122389,76121-2389
6640 CAMP BOWIE BLVD,PH 817 738-1917
MRS HELEN CROWDER,VP FIN
MIDLAND,TX DIVISION OFFICE - PO BOX
2359,415 W WALL STE 706,79702
PH 432 684-7806

TEXAS EASTERN TRANSMISSION,LP SEE
DUKE ENERGY GAS TRANSMISSION

TEXAS ENERGY & ENVIRONMENTAL,INC
PO BOX 691187
HOUSTON,TX 77269-1187 PH 281 812-8359
FAX 281 812-5320
CHARLIE W PLUMB,CEO

TEXAS ENERGY EFFICIENCY
WWW.TEXASEFFICIENCY.COM

TEXAS GAS ASSOCIATION (TGA)
WWW.TEXASGAS.COM

TEXAS GAS GATHERING SEE
TGG PIPELINE,LTD

TEXAS GENERAL LAND OFFICE
PO BOX 12873
AUSTIN,TX 78711-2873
PH 512 305-9104 FAX 512 475-1543
WWW.GLO@STATE.TX.US
C LOUIS RENAUD,DEPUTY COMM
LOUIS.RENAUD@GLO.TEXAS.GOV
ROBERT HATTER,MINERAL LEASING DIR
DREW REID,RELINQUISHMENT ACT LEASING
GEORGE MARTIN,SEISMIC PERMITTING
MATTHEW SCOTT,RESERVOIR ENG

TEXAS GULF COMPANY
PO BOX 490,15008 MAIN ST
LYTLE,TX 78052-0490 PH 830 772-3262
FAX 830 772-3629
TOM CHANEY,PRES
NATALIA,TX OFFICE - PO BOX 710,78059
PH 830 772-3262

TEXAS INDEPENDENT EXPLORATION,LTD
6760 PORTWEST DR

HOUSTON,TX 77024 PH 713 751-0419
FAX 713 650-8023 WWW.TEXASINDEPENDENT.COM
RICK ZIMMERMAN,PRES,GEOL
JOHN JACOBSON,EXPL MGR

TEXAS IRON WORKS,INC SEE
TIW CORPORATION

TEXAS LAND & ENERGY,LLC
2820 SUMMIT RIDGE
SAN MARCOS,TX 78666
PH 512 392-6956 FAX 713 392-6958
C M WILBANKS,PRES PH 713 253-2324

TEXAS LAND AND MINERAL ASSOCIATION
WWW.TLMA.ORG

TEXAS LAND TITLES
1801 21ST ST
GALVESTON,TX 77550 PH 409 765-8883

TEXAS MERIDIAN RESOURCES CORPORATION SEE
MERIDIAN RESOURCE CORPORATION,THE

TEXAS MINING & RECLAMATION ASSOCIATION
(TMRA) WWW.TMRA.COM

TEXAS OIL & GAS ASSOCIATION SEE
TXOGA INC

TEXAS OIL & GAS CORP SEE
MARATHON OIL COMPANY

TEXAS OIL AND GAS PLC
2021 PONDEROSA PL
MANDEVILLE,LA 70448-7525 PH 504 727-1225
FAX 504 727-1225
DAVID PARLONS,PRES
THOMAS H PHILPOTT,AGENT

TEXAS PETROLEUM INVESTMENT CO
5850 SAN FELIPE ST STE 250
HOUSTON,TX 77057-8007
PH 713 789-9225 FAX 713 782-2086
H B SALLEE,PRES
WILLIAM H CRAWFORD,CO-OWNER
TERRY B COLLIER,GEN COUNSEL
TCOLLIER@TXPETINV.COM

TEXAS PRECISION LAND SERVICES
13927 PLACID WOOD
SUGAR LAND,TX 77498 PH 218 433-4190
DOUGLAS W HABRYL
DWH@TEXASPRECISIONLAND.COM

TEXAS PUBLIC UTILITY COMMISSION
WWW.PUC.STATE.TX.US

TEXAS RAILROAD COMMISSION OF TEXAS SEE
RAILROAD COMMISSION OF TEXAS

TEXAS REEXPLORATION,LC
PO BOX 1159,1150 N US 87 STE 1159
FREDERICKSBURG,TX 78624
PH 713 725-8177
ROBERT K HILLIN,PRES
B.HILLINSR@TREXEC.COM

TEXAS SECONDARY OIL CORPORATION
7210 FALCON DR
BROOKSHIRE,TX 77423-9155
PH 281 375-8757   TEXASSECONDARY.COM

TEXAS SHALE GAS RESOURCES,LLC
309 W 7TH ST STE 400
FORT WORTH,TX 76102
PH 817 332-3891 FAX 817 332-3894
GLENN ADAMS,CO-0WNER/CEO
JOHN THURSBY,CO-OWNER/CFO
JENNIFER GLASCO,EXEC ASST
JENNIFER@TXSGR.COM
WILL ADAMS,LAND

TEXAS SOUTHERN PETROLEUM CORP
13709 N HILLWOOD TRL
CORPUS CHRISTI,TX 78410-1079
PH 361 241-6965 FAX 361 241-0179
ROBERT P AFFLERBACH,PRES

TEXAS STANDARD OIL & GAS LP
6575 WEST LOOP S STE 455
BELLAIRE,TX 77401 PH 713 655-1195
FAX 713 655-1197 WWW.TXSOIL.COM
TIMOTHY M ROBERSON,PRES & CEO
CHARLES A SHARMAN,GEN COUNSEL
PATRICIA JOHNSON,ACCT MGR

TEXAS TANK TRUCKS,INC
PO BOX 1723
BRECKENRIDGE,TX 76424 PH 254 559-5404
FAX 254 559-9802
RUSTY@TEXASTANKTRUCKS.COM

TEXAS TREND RESOURCES LLC
14101 W HIGHWAY 290 STE 202 BLDG 100
AUSTIN,TX 78737 PH 512 858-0412
DON F TOBIN JR,OWNER TOBINLAND@MSN.COM

TEXAS UNITED ENERGY CO
414 KICKERILLO CT
HOUSTON,TX 77079-7420 PH 281 497-6503
GILBERT H BOYD

TEXAS 5020 PROPERTIES,LTD
3405 DEL MONTE
HOUSTON,TX 77019-3115 PH 713 874-0033
FAX 713 874-0037
F R LAUSEN

TEXCEL EXPLORATION,INC
108 E SAM RAYBURN DR
BONHAM,TX 75418-3609
PH 903 583-3072 FAX 903 583-3072
WWW.TEXCELEXP.COM
DAVID P STAPP,PRES
DAVID@TEXCELEXP.COM
TERESA STAPP,VP
LISA KOPF,ADMIN
VICKI HOPPER,ADMIN ASST

TEXICAN ENERGY CORPORATION
500 DALLAS ST STE 1150,ONE ALLEN CTR
HOUSTON,TX 77002 PH 713 650-6579
FAX 713 750-0982
ROBERT L BLEVINS,PRES
A ALAN GRIFFIN,VP

TEXICAN NATURAL GAS COMPANY
500 DALLAS ST ONE ALLEN CTR STE 1150
HOUSTON,TX 77002 PH 713 650-6579
FAX 713 750-0982
ROBERT L BLEVINS,CHRMN,CEO,PRES
A ALAN GRIFFIN,VP,CFO
STEVE MCADORY,VP
DARREN J LIPPE,VP,GAS OPERS

TEXKAN RESOURCES INC
14875 LANDMARK BLVD STE 111
DALLAS,TX 75254-6205
PH 214 484-2322 FAX 214 484-2170
TEXOKANINFO@AOL.COM
GEORGE C BURRELL,PRES
ROBERT WELDON,PE

TEXMA PETROLEUM MACHINERY LLC
15320 PARK ROW
HOUSTON,TX 77084-2887 PH 281 579-2121
FAX 281 579-6663 WWW.TEXMAUS.COM
TEXMASALES@TEXMAUS.COM

TEXOIL INC
12007 FLUSHING MEADOWS DR
HOUSTON,TX 77089 PH 281 481-5863
FAX 713 652-9601
  RUBEN MEDRANO,PRES,CEO
  DENNIS DRAKE,GEOL

TEXOKAN OPERATING INC
14875 LANDMARK BLVD STE 111
DALLAS,TX 75254-6205
PH 214 484-2322 FAX 214 484-2170
  TEXOKANINFO@AOL.COM
  GEORGE C BURRELL,PRES
  ROBERT WELDON,PE
  RUSS MONTGOMERY,FLD OPERS MGR

TEXON ENERGY,LP
  777 TAYLOR ST STE P II-A
FORT WORTH,TX 76102 PH 817 335-2592
  TIM BLAKELY TIM444442004@YAHOO.COM
  JON STICKLAND

TEXON LP
11757 KATY FWY STE 1400
HOUSTON,TX 77079-1725 PH 281 531-8400
FAX 281 531-5954 WWW.TEXONLP.COM
  SUZIE BOYD,VP SUPPLY
  BRANDON BELLO,VP BUS DEVLP
  KYM GRIFFITH,VP MARKET

TEXOZ E & P I,INC
6700 WOODLANDS PKWY STE 230
SPRING,TX 77382 PH 281 419-4976
   FAX 281 419-4930 TALONPETROLEUM.COM.AU
  CLIFFORD S FOSS,PRES/CEO
  CATHERINE THOMPSON,FIN CONTROLLER
  BRUCE S HAMILTON,LAND & LEGAL DIR

TEXSEIS INC
10810 OLD KATY RD #201
HOUSTON,TX 77043-5013 PH 713 465-3181
FAX 713 465-8416
  CHERI D WILLIAMS
  J MICHAEL GRAUL

TEXXOL OPERATING COMPANY INC
780 N JIM WRIGHT FWY
WHITE SETTLEMENT,TX 76108-1222
PH 817 546-3921 FAX 817 886-3495
  KEVIN GRUBBS,PRES/CEO
   KEVIN.GRUBBS@TEXXOLENERGY.COM

TGC ACQUISITION FUND INC
  EXPLORATION & LANDMAN SERVICES
36 N CREEKSIDE CT
HOUSTON,TX 77055
PH 713 252-8116 WWW.TGCACQUISITION.COM
  JOHN D HUMBLE,PRES

TGGT MIDSTREAM
12377 MERIT DR STE 300A
DALLAS,TX 75251 PH 972 201-0700
  ERNST DEN HARTIGH,PRES/GEN MGR
  CRISS DOSS,COO
  MICHAEL SHORT,VP/GEN COUNSEL/SECY
  BO MALMQVIST,VP ASSET INTEGRITY
  AARON COLEY,VP FIN & BUS SVCS
  WAYNE JOHNSON,VP HLTH SFTY SCRTY & ENVIRO
  VICTOR DAVIS,VP OPERS
  BRIAN ESSNER,VP BUS DEV & COMMER OPRS
  CHARLES ROSS,REG AFFAIRS DIR
  AUDREY O'NEIL,ENGRG DIR
  XAVIER DAVILA,IT DIR
  DAVID COOK,CONTRACTS & PROCURE MGR

JACK CHANEY,LAND MGR
GRAND CANE,LA (HOLLY) REGIONAL OFFICE -
  8451 HWY 175,71032 PH 318 603-4800
KILGORE,TX REGIONAL OFFICE - 5625 FM 349
  75662 PH 903 643-9533
MARSHALL,TX REGIONAL OFFICE - 201 W GRAND
  AVE PH 903 702-6000
CENTER,TX (SHELBY) REGIONAL OFFICE -
  7011 STATE HWY 7W PH 936 598-3905
JONESVILLE,LA REGIONAL OFFICE -
  4389 FM 134 PH 903 687-3101

TGS NOPEC GEOPHYSICAL COMPANY ASA
2500 CITYWEST BLVD STE 2000
HOUSTON,TX 77042-3099
PH 713 860-2100 FAX 713 334-3308
   WWW.TGS.COM INFO@TGS.COM
  ROBERT HOBBS,CEO
  KRISTIAN JOHANSEN,CFO
  JOHN ADAMICK,SP VP/GPS
  ROD STARR,SR VP/WESTERN HEMISPHERE
  ZHIMING LI,SR VP/IMAGING SVCS
  MARTIN BETT,SR VP/RESERVOIR SOLUTIONS
  BRYAN DEMPSEY,VP/GEN COUNSEL
  KAREN EL-TAWIL,VP/BUS DEV
  STEIN OVE ISAKSEN,SR VP/EAST HEMISPHERE

TGS OFFSHORE GEOPHYSICAL COMPANY SEE
  TGS NOPEC GEOPHYSICAL CO

TGS ONSHORE GEOPHYSICAL COMPANY SEE
  TGS NOPEC GEOPHYSICAL CO

TGS WELL DATA DIVISION
785 GREENS PKWY STE 100
HOUSTON,TX 77067-4451 PH 281 319-4944
PH 888 LOG-LINE FAX 281 319-4945
  WWW.TGSNOPEC.COM/WELLDATA
  WELLDATA@TGSNOPEC.COM

TGX OIL & GAS,INC
1330 POST OAK BLVD STE 2540
HOUSTON,TX 77056 PH 713 965-9400
FAX 713 626-3858
  DAWSON O GEORGE III,PRES

THARP C T & CO
952 ECHO LN STE 390
HOUSTON,TX 77024 PH 713 881-9036
FAX 713 881-9078
  CARLA THARP

THE DEAS COMPANY,LLC
PO BOX 52093,124 HEYMANN BLVD STE 107
LAFAYETTE,LA 70505-2093 PH 337 232-5063
FAX 337 232-5059 RDSOAK1030@ATT.NET
  RUTLEDGE H DEAS III,GEOL
  PAT KLINE,ADMIN

THEVENET D DALE & ASSOCIATES,INC
PO BOX 52197
LAFAYETTE,LA 70505-2197 PH 337 289-5999
FAX 337 289-5993 PH 337 739-2605
  DDALE5999@BELLSOUTH.NET

THIGPEN DALTON & ASSOCIATES,INC SEE
  MISSION LAND SERVICES,INC

THIGPEN JAMES S,GEOL
21214 ATASCOCITA PLACE DR
HUMBLE,TX 77346 PH 281 217-3192

THIONVILLE LABORATORIES INC,ANALYTICAL
CHEMISTS & INSPECTORS
P O BOX 23687,5440 PEPSI ST
NEW ORLEANS,LA 70183-0687 PH 504 733-9603
  PAUL C THIONVILLE,PRES

THIRD COAST ENTERPRISES,INC
  EXPERT SEISMIC CONSULTANTS
PO BOX 1416
HEMPSTEAD,TX 77445
PH 979 826-7019 PH 713 705-2576
  SAMUEL T SLOAN III,PRES
  WWW.THIRDCOASTENTERPRISESINC.COM

THOMAS CO,THE
PO BOX 130
STEELES TAVERN,VA 24476 PH 540 377-5015
PH 540 447-6226 WMTHOMAS4@JUNO.COM
  BILL THOMAS,PRES

THOMAS DEVELOPMENT CORPORATION
  FULL SERVICE OIL & GAS LAND SVCS
PO BOX 53412,420 OIL CENTER DRIVE
LAFAYETTE,LA 70505-3412
PH 337 988-4898 FAX 337 988-0998
  WWW.THOMASDEVELOPMENTCORP.COM
  EDWARD D BARRY,PRES
  EBARRY@TDOIL.COM

THOMAS MRS JOHN,ET AL
BOX 61,1102 YATES DR
LONGVIEW,TX 75601 PH 972 758-7715
  NASEEP THOMAS,PROD SUPT

THOMAS PHILLIP W,CPL
  PETRO-LAND RESOURCES,INC
PO BOX 53712
LAFAYETTE,LA 70505-3712
PH 337 265-3948 FAX 337 265-3905
  PHIL.THOMAS@PETRO-LAND.COM

THOMAS RONNY G,GEOL
4305 BRAGGS
CORPUS CHRISTI,TX 78413-3026
PH 361 853-0740

THOMAS TOMMY F IND LDMN
312 KEENEY AVE
LAFAYETTE,LA 70501-6508 PH 318 234-2190
FAX 318 234-2197

THOMASON GARY,LANDMAN LLC
PO BOX 3142
MCKINNEY,TX 75070 PH 214 862-1976
  AMERICANLANDMAN@GMAIL.COM

THOMPSON ACQUISITIONS,LLC
PO BOX 758
FAIRHOPE,AL 36533-0758 PH 251 605-2458
FAX 251 217-9381
  WWW.THOMPSONACQUISITIONS.COM
  JIM THOMPSON JR,CPL,PRES
  JIMTHOMJR@AOL.COM

THOMPSON E G,OIL & GAS PROPERTIES
2335 ADDISON RD
HOUSTON,TX 77030-1127 PH 713 523-1711

THOMPSON JOHN D JACK ,RPL,IND LDMN
2116 RICHVIEW RD
MOUNT VERNON,IL 62864-6314
PH 618 244-0562

THOMPSON R N,GEOL
PO BOX 216
SHREVEPORT,LA 71162-0216 PH 318 425-2407

THOMPSON STEVE P
1133 MILAM BLDG
SAN ANTONIO,TX 78205-1606 PH 210 224-8880

THOMPSON THOMAS G,CPL
  OIL & GAS LEASES
PO BOX 131116
TYLER,TX 75713-1116 PH 903 530-0959

LAND.LEASES@YAHOO.COM

THOMPSON W L,JR,GEOL
PO BOX 1317
CORSICANA,TX 75151-1317 PH 903 874-4211
PH 903 874-3803

THOMSEN ROBERT L,OIL PROD & OIL PROPERTIE
PO BOX 1847
JACKSON,MS 39215-1847 PH 601 982-5705
FAX 601 981-2371

THORNELL G WARREN
A PROFESSIONAL LAW CORP
PO BOX 362
SHREVEPORT,LA 71162 PH 318 869-2900
FAX 318 869-2999 WWW.THORNELL-LAWFIRM.COM
THORNELL@BELLSOUTH.NET

THORNHILL CRAVER SEE
CAMERON,A DIV OF COOPER CAMERON CORP

THORNTON LLOYD D,OIL & GAS
11134 HUNTERS LNDG
MONTGOMERY,TX 77356 PH 361 884-9010

THORNTON PRODUCING CO.,LLC
7928 VISTA RIDGE DR N
FORT WORTH,TX 76132 PH 817 361-1909
ROBERT L THRONTON TOPCO@ATT.NET

THREADGILL BURNEY F,OIL & GAS PROPERTIES
PO BOX 16909
JACKSON,MS 39236 PH 601 982-5533

THREE M CO
P O BOX 212
GLADEWATER,TX 75647 PH 903 984-3443
CHARLA R WISDOM,AGENT

THREE RIVERS OPERATING COMPANY II LLC
5301 SOUTHWEST PKWY STE 400
AUSTIN,TX 78735-8949 PH 512 600-3190
FAX 512 600-3199 WWW.3ROC.COM

THREE STAR DRILLING & PRODUCING,INC
201 S CHRISTY AVE
SUMNER,IL 62466-1141
PH 618 936-2301 FAX 618 936-2929
WWW.HOME.EARTH.NET OIL@EARTHLINK.NET
MIKE PATTON,PRES
GAYLE PATTON,VP
DARRELL HUNDLEY,TREAS
MITZI TATE,SECY

THREE-D EXPLORATION PARTNERS SEE
3-D EXPLORATION PARTNERS (END OF ALPHA)

THRESHOLD LAND SERVICES INC
PO BOX 9396
COLLEGE STATION,TX 77842-9396
PH 979 694-2954 WWW.THRESHOLDLS.COM
KIMBROUGH JETER,CPL,PRES
KJETER@THRESHOLDLS.COM
ANDREW GRONBERG,VP LAND

THUNDER EXPLORATION INC
PO BOX 541674
HOUSTON,TX 77254 PH 713 823-8288
WALTER S LIGHT JR,PRES/GEOL
WTHUNDERX@AOL.COM

THURMON OIL COMPANY
P O BOX 519
RUSTON,LA 71273-0519 PH 318 255-3845

TI ENERGY SERVICES,INC
5773 WOODWAY DR
HOUSTON,TX 77057-1501 PH 713 757-1721
FAX 713 651-9994 713 757-1081
I MEADE HUFFORD,CPL,VP LAND & EXPL

TICKONO ENERGY CORPORATION
631 N MARKET ST
MT CARMEL,IL 62863
PH 618 262-8611 FAX 618 262-7145
JOHN E RHINE,PRES
STANTON D ERNEST,VP OPERS

TIDE AIR & GAS SEE
UNIVERSAL COMPRESSION,INC

TIDELAND SIGNAL CANADA,LTD
2170-21331 GORDON WAY
RICHMOND,BC,CAN V6W 1J9 PH 604 247-0988
FAX 604 247-0987 WWW.TIDELANDSIGNAL.COM
SUSAN WINSTANLEY,OFC MGR
SUSANW@TIDELANDSIGNAL.COM

TIDELAND SIGNAL CORP
PO BOX 924507,4310 DIRECTORS ROW
HOUSTON,TX 77092 PH 713 681-6101
FAX 713 681-6233 HQ@TIDELANDSIGNAL.COM
WWW.TIDELANDSIGNAL.COM
ALLEN W MITCHENER,PRES
LAFAYETTE,LA OFFICE - PO BOX 52370,OCS
708 BEAU PRE RD,70505-2370
PH 337 269-9113 FAX 337 269-9052

TIDELAND SIGNAL LIMITED SEE
TIDELAND SIGNAL CORP

TIDELAND SIGNAL PETROLEUM,LTD SEE
TIDELAND SIGNAL CORP

TIDELANDS DRILLING COMPANY
PO BOX 1598,103-A S MECHANIC
EL CAMPO,TX 77437-1598
PH 979 541-5454 FAX 979 541-5500
C J WOFFORD,PRES/OPER

TIDELANDS GEOPHYSICAL COMPANY
101 E PARK BLVD STE 955
PLANO,TX 75074 PH 972 881-1099
FAX 972 424-3943 WWW.TGCSEISMIC.COM
INFO@TGCSEISMIC.COM
WAYNE A WHITENER,PRES,CEO
DAN WINN,VP
TOM PIERCE,MKTG MGR
HOUSTON,TX OFFICE - 11281 RICHMOND AVE
STE J100B,77082 PH 281 589-8089
FAX 281 589-8099
POWELL YTSMA,SLS REP
OKLAHOMA CITY,OK OFFICE - 4411 HIGHLINE
BLVD STE 104,73108-1865 PH 405 942-9930
FAX 405 942-9929
JIM CRAFT,MKTG REP
DENVER,CO OFFICE - 1660 LINCOLN ST STE 29
80202 PH 303 860-7133 FAX 303 860-7137
TYLER MINTZ,SLS REP

TIDELANDS RESOURCES,INC
PO BOX 660566
BIRMINGHAM,AL 35266 PH 205 706-8021
TOM FOUTS,PRES

TIDEMARK CORPORATION
PO BOX 12272
DALLAS,TX 75225-1272 PH 214 484-5976
FAX 214 484-5977
RICHARD B HAMM,PRES

TIDEWATER INC
601 POYDRAS ST STE 1900
NEW ORLEANS,LA 70130-6040 PH 504 568-1010
FAX 504 566-4582 WWW.TDW.COM
DEAN E TAYLOR,PRES,CEO,CHRMN
STEPHEN W DICK,EXEC VP

JEFF PLATT,EXEC VP,COO

TIERRA OIL COMPANY,LLC
PO BOX 1948
SANTA FE,NM 87504
PH 505 986-0540 FAX 830 438-7198
W CHRIS BARNHILL,PRES WCBARNHILL@AOL.COM

TIGER STRIPE RESOURCES,LLC
21364 PROVINCIAL BLVD
KATY,TX 77450-7580
PH 281 578-6969 FAX 281 578-6802
WWW.TIGERSTRIPERESOURCES.COM
RAYMOND R MITCHELL,PRES
RMITCHELL@TIGERSTRIPERESOURCES.COM
BRITNI L KEY,MARKETING MGR

TIMBERLAND GATHERING & PROCESSING CO,INC
810 HOUSTON ST
FORT WORTH,TX 76102-6223
PH 817 870-2800 FAX 817 870-8441
NICK DUNGEY,CHRMN,PRES
SHANE ALEXANDER,MGR FACILITIES
SUSAN HOLLEY,CONTRACT ADM

TIMBERLINE PETROLEUM INC SEE
SCOTT ROYCE ARNOLD

TIMES PICAYUNE,THE
3800 HOWARD AVE
NEW ORLEANS,LA 70140-1002 PH 504 826-3351
FAX 504 826-3369
PAM RADTKE RUSSELL,ENERGY EDITOR

TIMKO DONALD J,CONSULTANT
5555 DE MONTE UNIT 505
HOUSTON,TX 77056
PH 713 621-8458 FAX 713 629-1108

TIMMINS JAMES R,OIL & GAS PROPERTIES
1221 LAMAR STE 1600
HOUSTON,TX 77010 PH 713 753-1543

TIPPENS OIL COMPANY
2303 NORTH STAR DR
CELINA,TX 75009 PH 914 391-8868
G R BUD TIPPENS,PRES TIPPENS@AOL.COM

TIPTON BILL R,OPR
BOX 907,501 LAUREL LANE
MARSHALL,TX 75670 PH 972 938-1048

TIROS OIL & GAS CO
PO BOX 2985
FORT SMITH,AR 72913-2985 PH 501 782-2686
BUDDY SMITH,PRES

TITAN ENERGY CORP
33621 HWY 43 STE 102
THOMASVILLE,AL 36784 PH 334 636-5836
FAX 334 636-8125 BEDCO@BELLSOUTH.NET
R R BUDDY BEDWELL JR,PRES

TITAN PETROLEUM,INC
301 MOORE ST
TOMBALL,TX 77375 PH 281 250-7217
FAX 719 487-9429
JEFFREY R LINDOW,PRES

TITLEX.COM
AN ONLINE SELF-SEARCH SITE WITH COUNTY
CLERK RECORDS FOR TEXAS COUNTIES
PO BOX 4010,502 E KOLSTAD
PALESTINE,TX 75801-4010
PH 903 723-2072 INFORMATION@TITLEX.NET
WWW.TITLEX.COM
STACEY CARR

TIW CORPORATION
PO BOX 35729

HOUSTON,TX 77235-5729
PH 713 729-2110 FAX 713 728-4767
WWW.TIWTOOLS.COM MKT@TIWTOOLS.COM
HOUSTON,TX OFFICE - 5151 GASMER,77035
PH 713 728-9250 FAX 713 728-4309
CORPUS CHRISTI,TX OFFICE - PO BOX
4147,WEST END STA,207 WESTCHESTER,78408
PH 361 882-3802 FAX 361 882-2825
ODESSA,TX OFFICE - 4903 SCR 1305,79765
PH 432 563-3913 FAX 432 563-5025
LAFAYETTE,LA OFFICE - PO BOX 407
HWY 89N,YOUNGSVILLE,LA 70592
PH 337 856-7271 FAX 337 856-7827
OKLAHOMA CITY,OK OFFICE - 1634 SE 23RD
73143 PH 405 672-0145 FAX 405 672-0164

TMBR/SHARP DRILLING,INC SEE
PATTERSON-UTI DRILLING COMPANY,LLC

TMR EXPLORATION,INC
PO BOX 5625
BOSSIER CITY,LA 71171-5625
PH 318 746-3616 FAX 318 746-6218
RAYMOND J LASSEIGNE,PRES
MACK M THOMAS,OPERS MGR
LARRY G FRIZZELL,EXPL MGR
RAJ KUMAR,RESERVOIR ENGRG

TOBIN DATA PRODUCTS SEE
P2 ENERGY SOLUTIONS

TOBIN INTERNATIONAL,LTD SEE
P2 ENERGY SOLUTIONS

TOBIN SURVEYS INC SEE
TOBIN INTERNATIONAL,LTD

TOC ACQUISITION CORP SEE
AMERICAN EXPLORATION CO

TOCE ENERGY LLC
PO BOX 52401,969 COOLIDGE BLVD
LAFAYETTE,LA 70505
PH 337 232-6637 FAX 337 235-5907
WWW.TOCEENERGY.COM
VICTOR A TOCE,PRES
VTOCE@TOCEENERGY.COM
PAUL M TOCE
RICK DUPUIS,VP
STEPHEN SERE',PROD & DRLG ENGR
VIRGINIA PECK,LAND ASST
CAROLE CREDEUR,ACCT
JENNIFER ROBERT,PROD ANALYST
JROBERT@TOCEENERGY.COM
KENDAL ROLLINS,RECEPTIONIST

TOCE PAUL M,GEOL
PO BOX 52401,969 COOLIDGE
LAFAYETTE,LA 70505-2401 PH 337 232-6637
FAX 337 235-5907

TOLAS OIL & GAS EXPLORATION CO,INC
PO BOX 308,306 E BROADWAY ST STE 1
MOUNT PLEASANT,MI 48804-0308
PH 989 773-9467 FAX 989 772-4733
PETRO JAMES TOLAS,PRES

TOM BROWN INC SEE
ENCANA OIL & GAS (USA)

TOMLINSON J CLYDE,OIL PROPERTIES
PO BOX 6260
LONGVIEW,TX 75608 PH 903 295-2561

TOMLINSON,RALPH G,CPL
125 SILVERLEAF CT
KINGSPORT,TN 37664 PH 423 765-0433
RGTOMLINSON@CHARTER.NET

TONG SPECIALTY,LLC SEE
TESCO SERVICES,INC

TOOLS INTERNATIONAL CORP
PO BOX 52323,HWY 90 EAST
LAFAYETTE,LA 70505-2323 PH 318 837-9261
FAX 318 837-4623
LARRY J PEARSON,PRES
JOHN BOULANGER,VP,MFG
DODD FOREMAN,VP,OPERS

TOPAZ INC
1221 LUMPKIN RD
HOUSTON,TX 77043-4196 PH 713 461-1000
PH 800-223-8277 FAX 713 465-9324
WWW.TOPAZINC.COM SALES@TOPAZINC.COM
PERRY R HESTER,PRES

TOPOGRAPHIC LAND SURVEYORS
6709 N CLASSEN BLVD
OKLAHOMA CITY,OK 73116-7311
PH 405 843-4847 PH 800 654-3219
FAX 405 843-0975 WWW.TOPOGRAPHIC.COM
INBOX@TOPOGRAPHIC.COM
SUSAN BLUEHER,PRES
MIDLAND,TX OFFICE - 2903 N BIG SPRING
79705 PH 432 682-1653 PH 800 767-1653
FAX 432 682-1743
BILL KEATING,AREA MGR
PAMPA,TX OFFICE - 2225 PERRYTON
PARKWAY,79065 PH 806 665-7218
PH 800 658-6382 FAX 806 665-7210
BILL ALLEN,GEN MGR
FT WORTH,TX OFFICE - 1400 EVERMAN STE 197
76140 PH 817 744-7512 PH 866 706-8542
FAX 817 744-7548
JULIO SILVA JULIO.SILVA@TOPOGRAPHIC.COM

TORCH DRILLING SERVICES,LLC
1221 LAMAR STE 1600
HOUSTON,TX 77010-3039
PH 713 753-1477 FAX 713 210-7168
HUNTERJ@TEAI.COM,
WWW.TORCHDRILLING.COM
JOHN C HUNTER,PRES
J DAVID LAPRADE,EXEC VP

TORCH ENERGY ADVISORS,INC
1221 LAMAR ST STE 1600
HOUSTON,TX 77010-3039 PH 713 650-1246
FAX 713 655-1866 TEAI.COM
J P BRYAN SR,MNGNG DIR
MICHAEL B SMITH,CFO

TORCH ENERGY SERVICES,INC
1331 LAMAR ST STE 1450
HOUSTON,TX 77010-3039 PH 713 650-1246
FAX 713 655-1866 WWW.TEAI.COM
RANDY ZIEBARTH,VP

TORCHLIGHT ENERGY,INC
5700 W PLANO PKWY STE 3600
PLANO,TX 75093 PH 214 432-8002
FAX 214 432-8005 WWW.TORCHLIGHTENERGY.COM
WILL MCANDREW III
NICK DEVITO
ROGER WURTELE

TORCUP OF TEXAS
4201-B1 CENTER ST
DEERPARK,TX 77536 PH 713 249-7657
FAX 281 476-5583 WWW.TORCUPTEXAS.COM
SCOTT BAUER SBAUER@TORCUP.COM

TORNADO PRODUCTION SERVICES
PO BOX 1707,1587 WEST FM 624
ORANGE GROVE,TX 78372-1707
PH 361 384-9020
WWW.TORNADOPRODUCTIONSERVICES.COM
SCOTT KIRCHOFF,PRES
ROGER FLOYD,CHF FLUIDS ENGR
MIDLAND,TX OFFICE - 3001 CR 1260 79706
PH 432 892-4931 FAX 214 452-1310
CLAYTON STEWARD,DIV MGR

TORTUGA INVESTMENTS,LTD
P O BOX 191
OBLONG,IL 62449-0191 PH 618 592-4136
R L WHEELER,PRES

TORTUGA OPERATING COMPANY
7412 SHADY VILLA LN
HOUSTON,TX 77055-5116 PH 713 680-3600
P L TURBETT,PRES
J E HINE,VP
B K PUGH,REGULATORY

TOTAL BIOSTRATIGRAPHIC SERVICES,INC
117 EVANGELINE DR
SLIDELL,LA 70460 PH 504 643-8684
TERRY CHRISTIAN,PRES
JOE BOUDREAUX,VP
RICHARD GEORGE,SECY/TREAS

TOTAL COMPRESSION INCORPORATED SEE
GLOBAL COMPRESSION SERVICES,INC

TOTAL E&P NEW VENTURES INC
1201 LOUISIANA STE 1800 FL 18
HOUSTON,TX 77002
PH 713 647-3300 FAX 713 647-3345
VICTOR OBADIAH,PRES,CEO

TOTAL E&P USA INC
PO BOX 4397,1201 LOUISIANA STE 1800 77002
HOUSTON,TX 77210-4397
PH 713 647-3000 FAX 713 647-3345
RICARDO DARRE,PRES/CEO
DIDIER POULET,VP PROJECTS & DEVELOPMENT
TOM RYAN,VP & GEN COUNSEL
JEAN FOURNIER,VP FIN,MKTG & CORP SUPPORT
PIERRE GERMAIN,VP BUS DEV & STRATEGY
PHILIPPE RENAUD,VP EXPL
KEITH BOEDECKER,DIR HEALTH,SAFETY,
ENVIRO & REGULATORY AFFAIRS
HERVE COUTRIX,RESEARCH & TECH PRES
STAN COTTRELL,CONTROLLER
DAVID HOUCK,ASST GEN COUNSEL
NIKITA TALDYKIN,COMMERCIAL MGR,BUS DEV
DAVID FOULON,DIR OF SUBSURFACE DEV

TOTAL OILFIELD PRODUCTION SERVICES,INC
214 DENNING DR
HOUMA,LA 70360 PH 504 868-1533
FRANCIS J LEBOEUF,PRES
TRUDY LEBOEUF,SECY/TREAS

TOTAL SAFETY
11111 WILCREST GREEN DR STE 300
HOUSTON,TX 77042-4740 PH 713 353-7100
PH 888 328-6825 FAX 713 785-1475
WWW.TOTALSAFETY.COM
MAIL@TOTALSAFETY.COM
LARRY SOLIS,REG MGR - REGION 3
LAFAYETTE,LA REGIONAL SERVICE CTR
5749 HWY 90 E,BROUSSARD,LA 70518
PH 337 837-1888 800 824-4250
FAX 337 837-1064

JUDE TAYLOR,DIST MGR
SHREVEPORT,LA OFFICE - 500 FLOURNOY
LUCAS RD,BLDG 5,71106 PH 318 671-8965
PH 888 869-6952 FAX 318 671-8961
LARRY SOLIS,REG MGR
JEREMY DEAN,BRANCH MGR
LAROSE,LA OFFICE - 9045 E AVE A,70345
PH 985 325-4064 866 272-6805
FAX 985 325-3588
JAIMY ADAMS,BRANCH MGR
SCOTT,LA TRAINING CENTER - 103 N PAT ST
70583 PH 337 237-6388 888 493-5939
FAX 337 237-9368
GEORGE LANG,BRANCH MGR
SCOTT,LA PROFESSIONAL DEV CNTR (PDC) -
103 N PAT ST 70583 PH 337 237-5882
PH 888 493-5939 FAX 337 237-8587
VICKI BOUDREAUX,PDC ADMIN
SCOTT,LA TRAINING CENTER - 103 N PAT ST
70583 PH 337 237-5882 FAX 337 237-8587
ELLIS PELLERIN,DIR OF HSE
DAVE MYSLENSKI,VP - REGION 1
HOUSTON,TX REGIONAL SVC CTR - 11111 HWY
225, LA PORTE,TX 77571 PH 281 867-2300
PH 800 231-6578 FAX 281 867-2400
DONNIE HOLMES,DIST MGR
DENVER,CO OFFICE - 5590 HAVANA ST UNIT A
80239-2100 PH 303 766-1501 866 336-8374
FAX 303 766-1503
DAVE MYSLENSKI,MGR
TULSA, OK OFFICE - 1327 N 105TH EAST AVE
74116 PH 918 835-8242 866 380-4299
FAX 918 835-5332
LOREN HUFFMAN,DIST MGR
CORPUS CHRISTI,TX OFFICE - 6810 LEOPARD
ST,78409 PH 361 289-5995 800 495-5595
FAX 361 289-5568
C J MORENO,DIST MGR
FREEPORT,TX OFFICE - 903 INDUSTRIAL ST
CLUTE,TX 77531 PH 979 265-4338
FAX 979 265-4230
TERRY RIMATO,DIST MGR
PASADENA,TX OFFICE - 3130 PASADENA FRWY
77503 PH 281 867-2300 FAX 713 475-8504
GLENN LINDSEY,TRNG/RESCUE/HEALTH MGR
JEFF SEWELL,REG MGR - REGION 2
BEAUMONT,TX OFFICE - 2722 HWY 69 N
NEDERLAND,TX 77627 PH 409 729-3229
PH 800 833-4974 FAX 409 729-3235
FLOYD SPEARMAN,DIST MGR
SULPHUR,LA OFFICE - 3205 METRIC DR,70665
PH 337 708-2100 800 833-0474
FAX 337 708-2190
DAN ARDOIN,DIST MGR
ST CROIX,VIRGIN ISLANDS DIST OFFICE
HOVENSA,1 ESTATE HOPE-BOX 37
CHRISTIANSTED,VI 00820-5652
PH 340 692-7223 FAX 340 692-7373
MARK JOHANSEN,IPSC MGR
GARY ROWLAND,REG MGR - REGION 4
BATON ROUGE,LA OFFICE -
2636 HODGESON AVE GONZALES,LA 70737
PH 225 644-8577 800 833-6974
FAX 225 644-5994
MICKEY BERCEGEAY,DIST MGR
DECATUR,AL OFFICE - 1313 COMMERCE DR

35601 PH 256 355-1995 888 833-4974
FAX 256 355-1495
BILLY EDDY,DIST MGR
MOBILE,AL DIST OFFICE - 5237 HALLS MILL
RD,BLDG J,36619 PH 251 666-4103
PH 800 833-2974 FAX 251 666-4350
JERRY LOCKIER,DIST MGR
PAUL GREGG,REG MGR - REGION 5
CHICAGO,IL OFFICE - 320 INDUSTRIAL DR
GRIFFITH,IN 46319
PH 219 922-9415 FAX 219 922-9425
STEPHEN CURTIS,DIST MGR
PHILADELPHIA,PA OFFICE - 10 INDUSTRIAL
HWY,BLDG X,MS-17 ESSINGTON,PA 19029
PH 610 521-3323 866 375-0200
FAX 610 521-3299
JILL KOZUR,DIST MGR
MIKE LEWIS,REG MGR - REGION 6
ANCHORAGE,AK OFFICE - 209 E 51ST AVE
99503 PH 907 743-9871 866 743-9871
FAX 907 743-9872
TYLER ZOLLINGER,DIST MGR
DICKINSON,ND OFFICE - 4054 1ST ST SW
58601 PH 701 483-1527 FAX 701 483-1531
JACK EISENHART,DIST MGR
EVANSTON,WY OFFICE - PO BOX 2135,82931
106 MEADOW DR STE A,82930 PH 307 789-3882
FAX 307 789-2783
MIKE PARK,DIST MGR
MIDLAND/ODESSA, TX OFFICE - 11020 W HWY
80 EAST ODESSA,TX 79765 PH 432 561-5049
FAX 432 561-5439
GREG CRISWELL,OPERS MGR
FARMINGTON,NM OFFICE - 3601 N 1ST ST
BLOOMFIELD,NM 87413 PH 575 634-0216
FAX 575 634-0232
DANNY OWNES,AREA MGR
ARTESIA, NM OFFICE - 1101 S FIRST ST
88211 PH 575 746-2847 FAX 575 746-3431
RANDY SANCHEZ,OPERS MGR
HOBBS, NM OFFICE - 3229 INDUSTRIAL DR
PH 800 833-4974 FAX 409 729-3235
88240 PH 575 392-2973 877 422-6345
FAX 575 392-4990
DANNY OWENS,AREA MGR
JOHN VAN KOOY,REG MGR - REGION 9
BENICIA,CA NORTHERN CA SVC CTR OFFICE -
518 STONE RD 94510 PH 707 747-5879
PH 877 747-5879 FAX 707 747-5924
ESPERANZA MOTA,DIST MGR
SIGNAL HILL,CA SOUTHERN CA SVC CTR -
2701 JUNIPERO AVE 90755 PH 866 380-4298
PH 562 490-6800 FAX 562 490-6890
JOHN VAN KOOY,DIST MGR

- TECHNICAL SERVICES -
GONZALES,LA OFFICE - SPECIALIZED SAFETY
PERSONNEL (SSP) - 2636 S HODGESON AVE
70737 PH 225 644-4354 FAX 225 644-4366
ROBBIE PAYNE,GEN MGR
EDMONTON,ALBERTA,CANADA OFFICE -
4030 78TH AVE NW,T6B 3M8 PH 780 461-0738
FAX 780 461-6392
KIM HOLMAN,AREA MGR

- HZWR (COMMUNICATIONS) -

HOUSTON,TX OFFICE - 5805 CENTRALCREST
77092 PH 713 681-2525 FAX 713 681-5940
ALAN VAN VELKINBURGH,MGR

- ICU SAFETY,HEALTH & ENVIRONMENTAL -
THE WOODLANDS,TX OFFICE - 26022 OAK RIDGE
DR,77380 PH 281 363-9939 FAX 281 363-4744
KATHY HARKEY,MGR
NEDERLAND,TX OFFICE - 2300 HWY 365
STE 370 PH 409 727-8227 866 727-8227
FAX 409 729-5075
BRAD JONES,MGR
WASHINGTON,DC (THE PENTAGON) OFFICE -
ETSD,SEMB ROOM 5E320,20301
PH 703 614-3049 FAX 703 614-9671
CHELSEA FORD,INDUSTRIAL HYGIENIST
WASHINGTON,DC (DEPT OF STATE) OFFICE -
2201 C ST NW,A/OPR/FMS/DESD,ROOM B2A51
20520 PH 202 736-4890 FAX 202 647-1873
CHRIS WILLIAMS,SR INDUSTRIAL HYGIENIST

- INTERNATIONAL OFFICES -
DUBAI REGIONAL SERVICE CENTER
PLOT #246-376
AL QUSAIS INDUSTRIAL AREA #3,DUBAI,UAE
PH 971 4267 8829 FAX 971 4267 8839
GIOVANNI ALVAREZ,DIST MGR
EQYPT DISTRICT OFFICE - C/O DREXEL
OILFIELD EQUIPMENT,PO BOX 459 ATABA
6 STR,301 FIFTH SECTOR,NEW MAADI,CAIRO
PH 202 703-6444 FAX 202 702-7649
ALI BEN SLIMAN,DIST MGR
QATAR DISTRICT WAREHOUSE -
C/O GULF MARKETS,SPECIALIZED OIL SVCS
DOHA, QATAR OFFICE - 298A D-RING RD
PH 974 455-3174 FAX 974 455-3190
JAMIE SHAW,REG MGR
PETER HEMINGWAY,DIST MGR
AL KHOBAR, SAUDI ARABI OFFICE -
PO BOX 31684,AL BAROUDI ST,AL KHALDIYA
DIST,DANNAN PH 966 3 859 3530
FAX 966 3 857 2298
CARL BRADSHAW,DIST MGR
TUNISIA DISTRICT OFFICE - ROUTE DE GABES
KM 9.5,BP 71-3083, THYNA,SFAX,TUNISIA
PH 216 74 289 622 FAX 216 74 289 621
ALI BEN SLIMAN,REG MGR
UNITED KINGDOM REGIONAL SERVICE CENTER -
LEEDS OFFICE - MALVERN RD KNOTTINGLEY,
ENGLAND WF 11 8EQ PH 01977 677931
FAX 01977 672798
MARTY TESSELAAR,DIST MGR
WEST AFRICA REGIONAL SVC CENTER -
UNIT 4,CREATION PARK,COMPUTER RD
MARCONI BEAM,MILNERTON 7441,CAPETOWN
SOUTH AFRICA,PO BOX 37225,CHEMPET 7442
CAPE TOWN,SOUTH AFRICA
PH 27 21 555 4609 FAX 27 21 555 4614
ASHLEY SMITH,GEN MGR
MEXICO/LATIN AMERICA REG OFFICE -
CALLE 38 NO 31 ENTRE 61Y61A, COL.
REVOLUCION C.P. 24120 CIUDAD DEL CARMEN
CAMPECHE
PH 52 938 38 73481 FAX 52 938 11 20008
KARLA CARAVEO,BRANCH MGR

TOTALFINAELF E&P USA,INC SEE
TOTAL E&P USA,INC
TOUPS LEON G,GEOL
3904 CLIFFORD DR
METAIRIE,LA 70002-1809 PH 504 250-7658
FAX 504 250-7658
TOURMALINE EXPLORATION COMPANY
3609 TANGLEY ST
HOUSTON,TX 77005-2251 PH 713 665-8807
JERRY R GIPS,PRES
TR ENERGY,INC
PO BOX 479
TYLER,TX 75710
PH 903 595-4139 FAX 903 595-0344
MICHAEL H NEUFELD,PRES
W L SUDDERTH,VP
BILLY DENMAN,LAND MGR
TRACE ENERGY SERVICES LTD/ SEE
GEOKINETICS INC
TRACE OIL & GAS COMPANY
675 BERING DR STE 650
HOUSTON,TX 77057-2276 PH 713 757-7883
FAX 713 650-0911 TOG2@SBCGLOBAL.NET
JIM BOB JACKSON,PRES
STEVE FERGUSON,VP
TRADE EXPLORATION CORP
500 COMMERCE ST #600
FT WORTH,TX 76102-5460 PH 817 335-2222
DUER WAGNER III,VP
CHRIS HERNDON,CFO
TRADEQUIP INTERNATIONAL
174 FOURTH ST
CROSSVILLE,TN 38555-4303
PH 931 484-5137 FAX 800 423-9030
WWW.TRADEQUIP.COM
DISPLAY@TRADEQUIP.COM
DAVID HOLLINGSWORTH,PUBLISHER
DHOLLINGSWORTH@TRADEQUIP.COM
BRENDA JOSEPH,ADVERTISING CONSLT
DONNA ENGLAND,ADVERTISING CONSLT
SHERI PHILLIPS,ADVERTISING CONSLT
JOHN SHANKS,ADVERTISING CONSLT
ANDY PETERSON,ADVERTISING CONSLT
TRADEWINDS OIL AND GAS,INC
8955 KATY FRWY STE 220
HOUSTON,TX 77024-2924
PH 713 465-7590 FAX 713 465-8154
JAMES E SCOTT III,PRES
WADE S MCALISTER,MGR INTL NEGOTIATIONS
C GENE SCOTT,MGR BUS DEV
LARRY HOOGENDOORN,TECH ADVSR
TRADITION ROYALTIES,LLC
1860 FM 359 RD
RICHMOND,TX 77406-1296
PH 281 794-9938 FAX 281 346-2319
WWW.TRADITIONROYALTIES.COM
GUY L FULLER
GFULLER@TRADITIONROYALTIES.COM
TRAFALGAR HOUSE OIL AND GAS INC,SEE
HARDY OIL & GAS USA INC
TRAILBLAZER ENERGY LLC
3000 CUSTER RD STE 270-118
PLANO,TX 75075 PH 972 964-2356
G W AUBREY
GWAUBREY@TRAILBLAZERENERGY.COM

TRAINOR ROBERT C,OIL LEASES & TITLEWORK
1385 CHRISTMAS LN NE
ATLANTA,GA 30329-3507 PH 601 981-0808
TRANS SABINE PIPELINE
2826 AMNICOLA HWY
CHATTANOOGA,TN 37406 PH 423 875-6633
FAX 423 875-6040 TRANSABINE@SEIENERGY.COM
TRANS-PAC DRILLING SEE
TRANS PACIFIC OIL CORP
TRANS-TEXAS RESOURCES,INC
120 S BROADWAY AVE STE 206
TYLER,TX 75702-7265 PH 903 596-7200
FAX 903 596-7203
R K WILSON III,PRES
TRANSATLANTIC EXPLORATION,LTD
670 HWY 41-A
HENDERSON,KY 42420-4634 PH 270 826-7400
JERRY HOWARD,PROD SUPT
TRANSCO ENERGY COMPANY TEC SEE
WILLIAMS COMPANIES,THE
TRANSCONTINENTAL OIL AND GAS INC
1509 PAGE RD
AURORA,OH 44202-6644 PH 330 995-0777
FAX 330 562-2742
CALVIN R MARKS,PRES
BARBARA J OROSZ,TITLE EXAMINER,COURTHOUSE
RESEARCH
TRANSMONTAIGNE INC
A DELAWARE CORPORATION/LOGISTICALLY
INTEG
TRANS,TERMINALING,SUPPLY,DISTB,MKTG SVCS
PO BOX 5660,1670 BROADWAY STE 3100
DENVER,CO 80217-5660
PH 303 626-8200 FAX 303 626-8228
WWW.TRANSMONTAIGNE.COM
CHARLES DUNLAP,PRES/CFO
GREGORY J POUND,EXEC VP-ASSET OPS
FREDERICK W BOUTIN,EXEC VP/CFO
ERIK B CARLSON,EXEC VP,GEN COUNSEL & SECY
RANDY MAJORS,SR VP BUS DEV
ATLANTA,GA OFFICE - 200 MANSELL COURT E
STE 600,PO BOX 103076 ROSWELL,GA
30076-9076 PH 770 518-3500
FAX 770 518-3567
TRANSMONTAIGNE PARTNERS L.P.
1670 BROADWAY STE 3100
DENVER,CO 80202
PH 303 626-8200 FAX 303 626-8228
JACKSON,LA TERMINAL OFFICE - 1478 HWY 61
70748 PH 225 658-2563 FAX 225 658-2565
ROB ENFINGER,TERMINAL MGR
BROWNSVILLE,TX SW TERMINAL OFFICE -
10150 STATE HWY 48,78521
PH 956 831-3531 FAX 956 831-3870
KEVIN GARCIA,TERMINAL MGR
BROWNSVILLE,TX BORDER TERMINAL OFFICE -
8700 SH 48,78520(SEND ALL MAIL TO SW OFC)
PH 956 831-3531 FAX 956 831-3870
KEVIN GARCIA,TERMINAL MGR
BROWNSVILLE,TX TERMINAL OFFICE - 14701
R L OSTOS RD,78520(SEND ALL MAIL TO SW
OFC) PH 956 831-3531 FAX 956 831-3870
KEVIN GARCIA,TERMINAL MGR
- GREENVILLE,MS COMPLEX -
GREENVILLE,MS NORTH TERMINAL OFFICE -
PO BOX 499,208 SHORE CLAY ST,38701

PH 662 335-1264 FAX 662 335-7743
FRANK JOHNSON,TERMINAL MGR
GREENVILLE,MS SOUTH TERMINAL OFFICE -
310 WALTHALL ST,38701
PH 662 332-2692 FAX 662 378-3594
FRANK JOHNSON,TERMINAL MGR
GREENVILLE,MS MISSISSIPPI TERMINAL OFFICE
PO BOX 499,2081 HARBOR FRONT RD,38701
PH 662 332-4849 FAX 662 335-8249
FRANK JOHNSON,TERMINAL MGR
HENDERSON,KY TERMINAL OFFICE - 2633
SUNSET LN,42420 PH 270 830-6187
FAX 270 826-3430
JEFF WALKER,TERMINAL MGR
NEW ALBANY,IN KENTUCKIANA TERMINAL OFC -
20 JACKSON ST,47150
PH 812 948-2458 FAX 812 945-5692
OWEN CHUCK M HARRIS,AREA MGR
LOUISVILLE,KY TERMINAL OFFICE - 4510
BELLS LN,40211 PH 502 772-7575
FAX 502 772-2110
CHUCK HARRIS,TERMINAL MGR
ARKANSAS CITY,AR MIDSOUTH TERMINAL OFC -
HWY 4 E,PO BOX 457,71630
PH 870 877-2404 FAX 870 877-2457
CHRIS LEE,TERMINAL MGR
CAPE GIRARDEAU,MO TERMINAL OFFICE -
1400 S GIBONEY,PO BOX 704,63701
PH 573 335-6688 FAX 573 339-1475
BILLY PIERCEY,TERMINAL MGR
EAST LIVERPOOL,OH TERMINAL OFFICE -
425 RIVER RD,PO BOX 1084,43920
PH 330 385-5424 FAX 330 385-0321
CHRIS SEAY,TERMINAL MGR
OWENSBORO,KY TERMINAL OFFICE - 900
PLEASANT VALLEY RD,42303 PH 270 691-0096
OR 270 691-0079 FAX 270 691-0054
CHRIS WEEKS,TERMINAL MGR
- PADUCAH,KY COMPLEX -
PADUCAH,KY TERMINAL OFFICE - PO BOX 390
42001,233 ELIZABETH ST,42003
PH 270 442-1606 FAX 270 443-8571
BOB FISH,TERMINAL MGR
PADUCAH,KY RIVERWAY TERMINAL OFFICE -
PO BOX 390,42001,1350 S 3RD ST,42003
PH 270 443-3424 FAX 504 444-9132
ROBERT BOB A FISH,TERMINAL MGR
CAPE CANAVERAL,FL TERMINAL OFFICE -
8952 N ATLANTIC AVE,32920
PH 321 783-3393 FAX 321 783-3496
REX THOMPSON,TERMINAL MGR
MIAMI BEACH,FL TERMINAL OFFICE - ONE B ST
FISHER ISLAND,FL 33109
PH 305 672-1065 FAX 305 672-0323
PEDRO REDONDO,TERMINAL MGR
JACKSONVILLE,FL TERMINAL OFFICE -
3425 TALLEYRAND AVE,32206
PH 904 358-6725 FAX 904 633-9233
MARK OLENSKI,TERMINAL MGR
PALMETTO,FL TERMINAL OFFICE - 804 N DOCK
ST,34221 PH 941 722-7727 FAX 921 723-6610
CASEY BROUWER,TERMINAL MGR
FORT LAUDERDALE,FL PORT EVERGLADES
TERMINAL OFFICE - PO BOX 13132,33316-0100
2701 SE 14TH AVE,33316
PH 954 523-8828 FAX 954 462-5921

KEVIN BROOKS,TERMINAL MGR

FORT LAUDERDALE,FL OFFICE - PO BOX 13124
33316,PHYSICAL LOCATION: 2401 EISENHOWER
BLVD,PORT EVERGLADES,FL
PH 954 525-4261 FAX 954 355-4244
KARL BERNARD

ROGERS,AR TERMINAL OFFICE - 2801 W HUDSON
72756 PH 479 631-8098 FAX 479 631-0266
KEVIN R SEARS,MGR/RAZORBACK SYSTEM

TAMPA,FL TERMINAL OFFICE - 1523 PORT AVE
33605 PH 813 248-5041 FAX 813 248-1961
RON BRERETON,TERMINAL MGR

TRANSMONTAIGNE PIPELINE INC SEE
TRANSMONTAIGNE PRODUCT SERVICES,INC

TRANSMONTAIGNE PRODUCT SERVICES INC
WHOLLY OWNED SUB OF TRANSMONTAIGNE INC
1670 BROADWAY STE 3100
DENVER,CO 80202
PH 303 626-8200 FAX 303 626-8228
CHARLES DUNLAP,PRES & CEO
RICHARD C EATON,SR VP MKTG
CHEE S OOI,EXEC VP SUPPLY & TRADING
ERIK B CARLSON,EXEC VP/GEN COUNSEL/SECY
GREG POUND,EXEC VP ASSET OPERS
FREDERICK W BOUTIN,EXEC VP/TREAS & FIN

ALBANY,GA TERMINAL OFFICE - PO BOX 487
31702-0487,1162 GILLIONVILLE RD 31707
PH 229 435-4014 FAX 229 435-4641
PHILLIP G SHEARER,TERMINAL MGR

AMERICUS,GA TERMINAL OFFICE - PO BOX 256
31709-0256,HWY 280 W,PLAINS RD 31709
PH 229 924-3464 FAX 229 928-5080
JEFF GORDON,TERMINAL MGR

ATHENS,GA TERMINAL OFFICE - 3450
JEFFERSON RD,30607-1477
PH 706 543-2254 FAX 706 549-3775
GREGORY K HOLLAND,TERMINAL MGR

BAINBRIDGE,GA TERMINAL OFFICE -
PO BOX 427,39818-0427,1909 E SHOTWELL ST
39817 PH 229 246-0955 FAX 229 246-6926
WAYNE W GRIMES,TERMINAL MGR

BELTON,SC #1 TERMINAL OFFICE - PO BOX 647
29627-0647,14300 HWY 20 N,29627
PH 864 338-7122 FAX 864 338-8094
GEORGE D CAMPBELL III,TERMINAL MGR

BELTON,SC #2 TERMINAL OFFICE - PO BOX 250
13410 HWY 20 N,29627 PH 864 338-5812
FAX 864 338-7531
GEORGE D CAMPBELL,TERMINAL MGR

BIRMINGHAM,AL TERMINAL OFFICE - 1600 MIMS
AVE SW,35211-3738 PH 205 925-1824
FAX 205 925-6311
HENRY J JACK SMALL,SR,TERMINAL MGR

CHARLOTTE,NC #1 TERMINAL OFFICE - 7401
OLD MT HOLLY RD 28214-1788
PO BOX 86,PAW CREEK,NC 28130-0086
PH 704 399-3371 FAX 704 399-1755
ROBERT KEITH LEWIS,JR,TERMINAL MGR

CHARLOTTE,NC #2 TERMINAL OFFICE - 7615
OLD MT HOLLY RD,PO BOX 61,PAW CREEK,NC
28130 PH 704 399-8378 FAX 704 399-6256
GEORGE LAMBERT,TERMINAL MGR

CHATTAHOOCHEE TERMINAL OFFICE - 3132
PARROTT AVE NW,ATLANTA,GA 30318-3306
PH 404 794-3371 FAX 404 794-3976
JAMES F LASNESKI,TERMINAL MGR

COLLINS,MS TERMINAL OFFICE - PO BOX 1596
39428-1596,OLD HWY 49 S,39428
PH 601 765-6878 FAX 601 765-0446
GEORGE R LAYTON,TERMINAL MGR

COLLINS,MS STORAGE FACILITY - 135 HWY 588
39428 PH 601 795-6631 FAX 601 765-1127
ROBERT DAVIS,TERMINAL MGR

DORAVILLE,GA TERMINAL OFFICE -
2836 WOODWIN RD 30360
PH 770 458-5588 FAX 770 451-4298
JAY BAILEY,TERMINAL MGR

GREENSBORO,NC #1 TERMINAL OFFICE -
6801 W MARKET ST 27409
PH 336 299-2611 FAX 336 632-1732
TREY RHODES,TERMINAL MGR

GREENSBORO,NC #2 TERMINAL OFFICE -
6907B W MARKET ST 27409
PH 336 299-1805 FAX 336 854-0116
TREY RHODES,TERMINAL MGR

GRIFFIN,GA TERMINAL OFFICE - 643-B E
MCINTOSH RD 30223-1248
PH 770 227-2033 FAX 770 228-4478
ALAN PANGLE,TERMINAL MGR

KNOXVILLE,TN TERMINAL OFFICE - PO BOX 336
37901-0336,1720 ISLAND HOME AVE 37920
PH 423 577-6634 FAX 423 577-3678
LEE STREET,TERMINAL MGR

CHATTANOOGA,TN LOOKOUT MTN TERMINAL
OFFICE - 5800 ST ELMO AVE 37409-2317
PH 706 820-0826 FAX 706 820-1877
JOHN C FORD,TERMINAL MGR

MACON,GA TERMINAL OFFICE -
5041 FORSYTH RD 31210-2106
PH 478 477-1711 FAX 478 471-9454
ED WATTS,TERMINAL MGR

MERIDIAN,MS TERMINAL OFFICE - 1401 65TH
AVE S 39307-7023 PH 601 482-0832
FAX 601 482-8918
DALE POLK,TERMINAL MGR

MONTVALE,VA TERMINAL OFFICE - PO BOX 339
11685 LYNCHBURG SALEM TURNPIKE W 24122
PH 540 947-5004 FAX 540 947-2643
JOE WILLIAMS,TERMINAL MGR

FAIRFAX,VA TERMINAL OFFICE - 3790 PICKETT
RD 22031 PH 703 323-1500 FAX 703 323-3966
MIKE MIDDLETON,TERMINAL MGR

MT VERNON,MO TERMINAL OFFICE - 15376 HWY
96,65712 PH 417 452-3238 FAX 417 452-2372
JASON DELAY,RAZORBACK SYSTEM

CHESAPEAKE,VA NORFOLK TERMINAL OFFICE -
PO BOX 5708,23324-0708,7600 HALIFAX LN
23324 PH 757 545-8455 FAX 757 545-2375
MICHAEL J STEELE,TERMINAL MGR

COVINGTON,KY TERMINAL OFFICE -
700 RIVER RD,HWY 8,41017
PH 859 331-0900 FAX 859 331-8874
CHRIS SEAY,TERMINAL MGR

PENSACOLA,FL TERMINAL OFFICE - 511 S
CLUBBS ST 32502-5573
PH 850 432-5133 FAX 850 434-8564
DONNIE J ELLISON,TERMINAL MGR

PURVIS,MS TERMINAL OFFICE - PO BOX 689
5151 US HWY 11,39475
PH 601 794-6031 FAX 601 794-6707
ROBERT DAVIS,TERMINAL MGR

RICHMOND,VA TERMINAL OFFICE - PO BOX

24567,23224-0567,1314 COMMERCE RD 23224
PH 804 233-9231 FAX 804 233-9508
VIC PATTERSON,TERMINAL MGR

ROME,GA TERMINAL OFFICE -
2671 CALHOUN RD,30161-9603
PH 706 295-2521 FAX 706 290-0912
STACY ELLIOTT,TERMINAL MGR

SELMA,NC NORTH TERMINAL OFFICE -
2600 W OAK ST,27576
PH 919 965-9442 FAX 919 965-9473
TERRY MURRAY,TERMINAL MGR

SELMA,NC SOUTH TERMINAL OFFICE - 24-27 W
OAK ST 27576 PH 919 965-9442
FAX 919 965-9473

SPARTANBURG,SC TERMINAL OFFICE -
680 DELMAR RD 29302-4352
PH 864 583-4168 FAX 864 583-1520
DAVID E MILLARD,TERMINAL MGR

SPARTANBURG,SC TERMINAL OFFICE -
2300 SOUTHPORT RD 29302
PH 864 585-5447 FAX 864 585-0556
DAVID MILLARD,TERMINAL MGR

CHIPPEWA FALLS,WI TERMINAL OFFICE -
3689 STATE HWY 124,54729-8305
PH 715 723-2955 FAX 715 723-4961
DON PRAUSE,TERMINAL MGR

TRANSNATIONAL EXPLORATION,INC
PO BOX 19642
HOUSTON,TX 77224
PH 713 467-8709 FAX 713 467-8709
NORMAN J PAGE,PRES

TRANSOCEAN
PO BOX 2765
HOUSTON,TX 77252-2765
PH 713 232-7500 WWW.DEEPWATER.COM
- EXECUTIVE OFFICERS & SR MANAGEMENT -
STEVEN L NEWMAN,PRES/CEO
IHAB TOMA,EXEC VP/OPERS
DAVID A TONNEL,SR VP/FIN & CONTROLLER
NICK DEEMING,SR VP/GEN COUNSEL & ASST
CORP SECY
GREGORY L CAUTHEN,EXEC VP/INTERIM CFO
DEEPAK C MUNGANAHALLI,SR VP/CORP PLANNING
& BUS DEV
KEELAN I ADAMSON,VP/MJR CAPITAL PROJECTS
TERRY B BONNO,SR VP/MKTG
IAN M CLARK,VP/JACKUP SEGMENT
STEPHEN L HAYES,SR VP/TAX
ROBERT L HERRIN JR,VP/INTERNAL AUDIT
MICHAEL F MUNRO,VP/CCO & DEP GEN COUNSEL
ALAN QUINTERO,SR VP/OPERS
PAUL H TRANTER,VP/ASSET MGMNT
JOHN L TRUSCHINGER,SR VP/SUPPORT SVCS &
CIO
MARK K MONROE,VP/ACCT MGMNT
DAVID WALLS,VP/QLTY HEALTH SFTY & ENVIRO
KATHLEEN S MCALLISTER,VP/TREAS
LARRY MCMAHAN,VP/PERFORMANCE
GUILHERME COELHO,VP AFRICA/MEDITERRANEAN
R THADDEUS VAYDA,VP/INVESTOR RELS & COMM
JONATHAN HOUSE,VP/GLOBAL SUPPLY CHAIN
HOUSTON,TX OFFICE - PARK TEN CENTRE
1311 BROADFIELD BLVD STE 400,77084
PH 832 587-8500
VENIER,SWITZERLAND (TRANSOCEAN MANAGEMENT
LTD) OFFICE - CHEMIN DE BLANDONNET 10

CH-1214 PH +41 22 930-9000
ZUG,SWITZERLAND (TRANSOCEAN LTD) OFFICE -
TURMSTRASSE 30 CH-6300 PH 41 41 749-0500
BUNGO,LUANDA,ANGOLA (TRANSOCEAN) OFFICE -
RUA MAE ISABEL NO 6
PH 244 226 42 4000 FAX 244 226 42 4110
DOUALA,CAMEROON OFFICE -
FORMERLY GLOBAL SANTA FE
C/O SAGA LOGISTICS BASE,B P 5893
PH 237 3343 8713 FAX 237 3343 6712
PARIS,FRANCE (SERVICES PETROLIERS
TRANSOCEAN) OFFICE - TOUR EGEE
FAUBOURG DE L'ARCHE 9-11 ALLEE DE L'ARCHE
92400 COURBEVOIE PH 33 1 46 67 21 50
PORT GENTIL,GABON OFFICE -
FORMERLY GLOBAL SANTA FE
BOITE POSTALE 556
PH 241 552040 OR 555634 FAX 241 560458
ABIDJAN,IVORY COAST (TRANSOCEAN OFFSHORE
VENTURES) OFFICE - ZONE 4C BIETRI,
ZONE 4C BIETRI,RUE DU CANAL
RUE DU CANAL PH 225 21 235060
TRIPOLI,LIBYA (GLOBAL SANTA FE DRILLING
OPERATION) OFFICE - PO BOX 81206
C/O ADM EXPRESS CARGO SERV
GURGI NEAR EL-ANDLUS MKT
VICTORIA ISLAND,LAGOS,NIGERIA OFFICE -
MAERSK HOUSE,121 LOUIS SOLOMON CLOSE
PH +234 1 271 9770
PORT HARCOURT,RIVERS STATE,NIGERIA OFFICE
PO BOX 5125 PH 234 84 610633
PORT HARCOURT,NIGERIA OFFICE -
FORMERLY GLOBAL SANTA FE
PO BOX 7086,KILOMETER 14,ABA EXPY
PH 234 24 231356 FAX 234 84 231353
STAVANGER,NORWAY OFFICE - PO BOX 8200
4069 STAVANGER NORWAY PH 47 51 50 43 00
DOHA,QATAR OFFICE -
FORMERLY GLOBAL SANTA FE
PO BOX 4396,AL BARASHOUT BLDG #274,3RD FL
MAIN AIRPORT RD,OLD AIRPORT AREA
PH 974 455 0797 FAX 974 455 1298
ABERDEEN,SCOTLAND OFFICE-TRANSOCEAN HOUSE
CRAWPEEL RD,ALTENS INDUSTRIAL ESTATE
AB12 3LG PH 44 1224 427700
ABERDEEN,SCOTLAND,UK (TRAINING CTR) OFC -
HARENESS CIRCLE,ALTENS INDUSTRIAL ESTATE
AB12 3LG PH 44 1224 427942
ABERDEEN,SCOTLAND,UK OFFICE -
FORMERLY GLOBAL SANTA FE
LANGLANDS HOUSE,HUNTLY ST AB10 ISH
PH 44 1224 654400 FAX 44 1224 654401
PERTH WA,6000 AUSTRALIA OFFICE -
LEVEL 6,THE CAPITAL CENTRE
220 ST GEORGE'S TERRACE
PH 61 8 9213 3700 FAX 61 8 9213 3777
CAIRO,EGYPT OFFICE -
FORMERLY GLOBAL SANTA FE
PO BOX 341,KILOMETER 11,KATTAMEYA-
EINSOUKHNA DESERT RD PH 202-275 95 000
FAX 202-275 95 116
POWAI,MUMBAI,400 076 INDIA OFFICE -
TRANSOCEAN HOUSE,LAKE BLVD RD
HIRANANDANI BUSINESS PARK
PH 91 22 4000 0000 FAX 91 22 4000 0300
BALIKPAPAN,INDONESIA OFFICE -

76116,JALAN MULAWARMAN RT 01 NO. 06
PH 62 542 520 200 FAX 62 542 202 203
JAKARTA,INDONESIA OFFICE -
12310,PLAZA AMINTA,5TH FL,STE 501
JI TB SIMATUPANG KAV 10
PH 62 21 7591 4550 FAX 62 21 7591 4551
KUALA LUMPUR,MALAYSIA OFFICE -
50400,G TOWER,LEVEL 24,199
JALAN TUN RAZAK,KUALA
PH +6 03 2332 4888 FAX +6 03 2381 7005
MAKATI CITY,MANILA,PHILIPPINES OFFICE -
FORMERLY SANTA FE CONSTRUCTION COMPANY
139 CORPORATE CENTER,10TH FL,UNIT 1001
139 VALERO ST,SALCEDO VILLAGE
PH 63 2 830 2210 FAX 63 2 818 8237
AL KHOBAR,SAUDI ARABIA OFFICE -
FORMERLY GLOBAL SANTA FE SAUDI ARABIA LTD
PO BOX 901 17TH FL,AL SUBEAEI
TOWERS,KING ABDUL AZIZ RD 31952
KINGDOM OF SAUDIA ARABIA
PH +966 3 887 1364 FAX +966 3 887 1365
SINGAPORE OFFICE - 150 BEACH RD
07-01 GATEWAY WEST 189720
PH +65 6512 4700 FAX +65 6292 7855
SINGAPORE (TRAINING CENTRE) OFFICE -
NO 3 TUAS AVE 8,639217
PH +65 6494 2000 FAX +65 6861 5953
FAX +65 6861 5607
CHATUCHAK,BANGKOK 10900 THAILAND OFFICE -
SEDCO FOREX INTERNATIONAL,INC
RASA TOWER II,25TH FL,555 PHAHOLYOTHIN RD
PH +66 2 797 8888
FAX +66 2 797 8889
VUNG TAU CITY,S R VIETNAM OFFICE -
PETRO VIETNAM TOWERS STE 210,2ND FL
8 HOANG DIEU ST,WARD 1 PH 84 64 580990
FAX 84 64 3 580993
HO CHI MINH CITY,S R VIETNAM OFFICE -
UNIT 1501,15TH FL,GEMADEPT TOWER
6 LE THANH TON ST,DIST 1
PH 84 8 3520 2366 FAX 84 8 3520 2365
MACAE RIO DE JANEIRO,BRAZIL OFFICE &
TRAINING CENTER
AV PREFEITO ARISTEU FERREIRA DA SILVA
2500 NOVO CAVALAEIROS 27930-070
PH 55 22 2791 4444
BOTOFOGO,RIO DE JANEIRO,RJ BRAZIL OFFICE-
PRAIA DE BOTAFOGO,228/SALA 1801,22250-906
PH 55 21 3035 9900
ST JOHN'S,NEWFOUNDLAND,CANADA OFFICE -
KENMOUNT BUSINESS CENTER STE 302
66 KENMOUNT RD A1B 3V7 PH 709 724-6600
FAX 709 724-6610
GEORGE TOWN,GRAND CAYMAN,CAYMAN ISLANDS
OFFICE -
PO BOX 10342,70 HARBOUR DR,FL 4,KY-1003
PH 345 745 4500
ST MICHAELS,BARBADOS OFFICE - GROUND FL
CHELSEA HOUSE,BB14022 PH +1 246 227 990
RAVENNA,ITALY OFFICE - VIA MAGAZZINI
ANTERIORI,TRAVERSA NORD 51,48100
PH 39 0544 422626 FAX 39 0544 422640
TRANSOCEAN OFFSHORE INC
PO BOX 2765
HOUSTON,TX 77252-2765 PH 713 871-7500
FAX 713 871-7880

J MICHAEL TALBERT,CHRMN,CEO
DENNIS HEAGNEY,PRES,COO
ROBERT L LONG,SR VP,CFO
JON C COLE,SR VP,EUROPEAN OPERS
DONALD R RAY,SR VP,TECH SVCS
ERIC B BROWN,VP,GEN COUNSEL & CORP SECY
ALAN B BROUSSARD,VP,MKTG
DENNIS R LONG,VP,HUM RES
METAIRIE,LA GULF COAST OFFICE -
LAKEWAY TWO,3850 N CAUSEWAY BLVD STE 500
70002 PH 504 849-3100 FAX 504 849-3179
MIKE HALL,DIV MGR
TRANSOIL MARKETING LLC
PO BOX 6697,4401 MAPLE ST
ABILENE,TX 79608 PH 325 698-0200
WWW.TRANSOILTX.COM
SCOT MARTIN,VP
ROBERT CRABTREE,VP
TRANSPETCO ENGINEERING OF THE SOUTHWEST
110 N MARIENFELD ST STE 150
MIDLAND,TX 79701-4412 PH 432 686-7209
FAX 432 684-7009 TRANSPETCO.COM
W A FLANDERS,PRES
ALAN SHATTO,MGR
TRANSPETCO TRANSPORT CO
625 MARKET ST STE 200
SHREVEPORT,LA 71101-5392 PH 318 221-3957
FAX 318 221-8835
WALLACE A STANBERRY,PRES
WALLACE L STANBERRY,VP
CHARLES GERARD,SECY/TREAS
TRANSPORT GAS CORPORATION,(MARKETERS GAS)
PO BOX 27888
FRESNO,CA 93729-7888 PH 559 326-7491
FAX 559 326-7721 WWW.TRANSPORTGAS.COM
PAUL W LERRO,PRES/CEO
CLOVIS,CA OFFICE - 3391 E VIA MONTIANO
93619-8391
TRANSQUEST INC
13718 HAWKSNEST BAY
CORPUS CHRISTI,TX 78418 PH 361 884-4141
DAVID ROWLING,PRES
TRAVAINI PUMPS USA
200 NEWSOME DR
YORKTOWN,VA 23692
PH 757 988-3930 FAX 757 243-0000
WWW.TRAVAINI.COM
CUSTOMERSERVICE@TRAVAINI.COM
TREASURE BAY CORPORATION,LTD
PO BOX 53844
LAFAYETTE,LA 70505-3844 PH 337 233-2111
PH 337 233-2123 FAX 337 234-0586
HARVEY R GUTHREY,CPL,LDMN,CONTROLLER
TREND DRILLING CO SEE
NABORS DRILLING USA,INC
TRENDWELL ENERGY CORPORATION
PO BOX 560
ROCKFORD,MI 49341 PH 616 866-5024
FAX 616 866-3750 WWW.TRENDWELLENERGY.COM
THOMAS H MALL,CEO,TREAS
THOMAS@TRENDWELLENERGY.COM
TODD MALL,PRES
TODD@TRENDWELLENERGY.COM
ANGELA ADAMS,VP
ANGELA@TRENDWELLENERGY.COM
RICHARD SANDTVEIT,VP,ENGRG

RICK@TRENDWELLENERGY.COM
THERESA THOMSEN,CORP TREAS
DANITA GREENE,RECORDS DEPT
JULIE DEJOHN,ACCT DEPT
ANGELA RIGGS,LEASE ANALYST

TREPAGNIER A J,GEOL
PO BOX 53607
LAFAYETTE,LA 70505-3607 PH 337 848-6537
TREPAGNIERALBERT@YAHOO.COM

TRERICE H O,CO
12950 W 8 MILE RD
OAK PARK,MI 48237-3214 PH 248 399-8000
FAX 248 399-7246 WWW.TRERICE.COM
SALES@TRERICE.COM
JIM MACKIE,GEN MGR
B J JARVIE,ENGRG COORD

TREY EXPLORATION INC
PO BOX 906
NEWBURGH,IN 47629 PH 812 858-3146
FAX 812 490-5098 WWW.TREYEXPLORATION.COM
HOWARD A NEVINS,PRES
HOWARDN@TREYEXPLORATION.COM
ANDY SCHWEISS,ENGR
ROSS BASNETT,GEOL

TRI ENERGY ASSET MANAGEMENT,INC
13910 CHAMPION FOREST DR STE 105
HOUSTON,TX 77069 PH 281 880-8984
FAX 281 880-8234 WWW.TEAMINCONLINE.COM
RANDY HELMS,PRES/CEO
GARY GOLDSMITH,CIO/TREAS
RHELMS@TEAMINCONLINE.COM
CAROLYN GIBBS,COO

TRI K ENTERPRISES INC,OIL OPR
P O BOX 6414
TYLER,TX 75711-6414 PH 972 561-0146

TRI STATE ENVIROMENTAL SERVICES
4028 SOUTHWESTERN ST
HOUSTON,TX 77005-4341 PH 713 660-8634
JENE C GILMORE,PRES
LINDA A GILMORE,VP

TRI STATE OIL TOOL,INC SEE
BAKER OIL TOOLS (FISHING DIVISION)

TRI-C RESOURCES,LLC
909 WIRT RD
HOUSTON,TX 77024-3405 PH 713 685-3600
GEOL/LAND FAX 713 685-3620
ACCT/ENGRG FAX 713 685-3630
WWW.TRICRESOURCES.COM
INFO@TRICRESOURCES.COM
P M HOLMES,CFO
M S CONE,PRES
R T HERRIN III,EXEC VP
J CHRIS CONE,VP OPERS
ALBERT G NANCE,VP LAND

TRI-ENERGY LAND,INC
PO BOX 359
ROUND TOP,TX 78954 PH 724 263-5007
WWW.TRIENERGYLAND.COM
SARA WORSHAM
SWORSHAM@TRIENERGYLAND.COM

TRI-PAR EXPLORATION,INC
PO BOX 5686
SHREVEPORT,LA 71135-5686 PH 318 798-3100
FAX 318 798-0200
JARED Y EVANS,PRES

TRI-STATE OIL & GAS TRADER
TRADE,SELL,SWAP OIL & GAS RELATED ITEMS
PO BOX 367,832 WEST NORTH AVE STE A-1
FLORA,IL 62839-0367 PH 618 662-6457
TRISTATEOILGASTRADER.COM
MILTON SMITH

TRI-STATE PRODUCING AND DEVELOPING,INC
PO BOX 99
OLNEY,IL 62450-0099 PH 618 393-2176
STEVEN A ZANETIS,PRES

TRIAD ENERGY CORPORATION
1616 S VOSS RD STE 650
HOUSTON,TX 77057 PH 713 337-1440
FAX 713 337-1490 WWW.TRIAD-ENERGY.COM
S K BRADSHAW,PRES
K S BRADSHAW,VP
M A FOSTER,CONTROLLER

TRIAD LAND SERVICES,LLC
PO BOX 7668
TYLER,TX 75711-7668
PH 903 592-6011 FAX 903 596-9019
BILL JAMISON,PRTNR BILL@TRIADLAND.NET
DAVID W KRAFVE,PRTNR DAVID@TRIADLAND.NET

TRIAD OIL & GAS CO,INC
PO BOX 16340,1855 LAKELAND DR STE B20
JACKSON,MS 39236-6340 PH 601 981-4422
FAX 601 981-7047
MARCIAL FORESTER,PRES
CHALMAS B STINSON,SECY/TREAS
W KENT FORD,SR STAFF ENGR

TRIANGLE OIL PRODUCERS,INC,OIL PROD
6 MALLARD PT
NATCHEZ,MS 39120-9354 PH 601 442-2941
HARVEY W JONES,PRES

TRIBO PRODUCTION COMPANY,LTD
PO BOX 130347
HOUSTON,TX 77219-0347 PH 713 659-7551
RICHARD BOWMAN,PRES

TRICH PRODUCTION,INC
300 N GREEN ST STE 417
LONGVIEW,TX 75601 PH 903 758-0646
FAX 903 758-0650
JAMES NATHAN TRICH,PRES
WENERT TRICH,VP,GEOL

TRIDENT OFFSHORE PETROLEUM
PO BOX 1594
COVINGTON,LA 70434-1594 PH 985 807-7921
TRIDENTOFFSHORE@AOL.COM
DOUGLAS BRADFORD

TRIDENT STEEL CORPORATION
12825 FLUSHING MEADOWS DR STE 110
SAINT LOUIS,MO 63131-1837 PH 800 777-9687
FAX 314 821-3151 WWW.TRIDENTSTEEL.COM
KEVIN BECKMANN,PRES
HOPE SNOW,VP LINE PIPE
MATTHEW BECKMANN,VP

TRIENERGY
PO BOX 89,412 BEAVER ST 2ND FLOOR
SEWICKLEY,PA 15143-0089
PH 412 741-4188 FAX 412 741-0118
JBTRIENERGY@COMCAST.NET
JOSEPH E BOJALAD III,PRES

TRIJON EXPLORATION,INC
615 N UPPER BROADWAY ST STE 2040
CORPUS CHRISTI,TX 78401-0783
PH 361 888-7794

TRINACA INVESTMENT CORPORATION
PO BOX 14858
SCOTTSDALE,AZ 85267-4858 PH 480 860-5413
JEFF K RAMSEY,PRES JEFF@TRINACA.COM
TONI RAMSEY,SECY/TREAS

TRINIDAD OIL & GAS CORPORATION
PO BOX 8207
BACLIFF,TX 77518 PH 281 339-2451
FAX 281 339-1157 TRINIDADOILANDGAS.COM
WILLIAM A LITTLE III,PRES
WLITTLE@TRINIDADOILANDGAS.COM
RON REDD,ADMIN VP
M C LITTLE,ENGRG VP

TRINITY ENERGY AND MINERALS CO
LAND CONSULTANT,LEASE BROKER,EXPL
1250 S WILLIAMS ST
DENVER,CO 80210-1824 PH 502 893-1831
JACK F GANZER,PRES
B J GANZER,LAND MGR
N G STEARMAN,CPA,CONTROLLER

TRINITY GAS CORPORATION
PO BOX 3488
ENID,OK 73702-3488 PH 580 233-1155
FAX 580 233-1647
J A CHAMPLIN,PRES
CLARK L YOUNG,VP

TRINITY MINERAL TRUST,THE
PO BOX 131116
TYLER,TX 75713-1116 PH 903 530-0959
LAND.LEASES@YAHOO.COM
THOMAS G THOMPSON,TRUSTEE

TRINITY PETROLEUM CONSULTANTS
2500 TANGLEWILDE ST STE 400
HOUSTON,TX 77063-2126 PH 713 783-7769
FAX 713 783-5739
SAM BRAVENEC,PRES
S.BRAVENEC@TPCLTD.COM
ROOSEVELT WASHINGTON,VP
R.WASHINGTON@TPCLTD.COM
PAUL THERRIEN,VP
PAUL.THERRIEN@TPCLTD.COM

TRINITY RESOURCES INC SEE
EQUION CORP,THE

TRINITY RIVER ENERGY,LLC
OIL & GAS EXPL/PROD
777 MAIN ST STE 3600
FORT WORTH,TX 76102 PH 817 872-7800
FAX 817 872-7898
WWW.TRINITYRIVERENERGY.COM
CHRISTOPHER L HAMMACK,PRES & CEO
MARK HOLCOMB,SR VP/COO
JOHN E STEVENSON,SR VP/CFO
AARON THESMAN,SR VP/LAND & GEN COUNSEL
PAUL BENACQUISTA,VP/CAO
GREGORY J BRADDOCK,VP/CIO
MARK CRANER,VP/PLNG & SPEC PROJ
DAVID DUNN,VP DRLG
DANIEL EMMER,VP GEOSCIENCE
MATT ENGLEMAN,VP CORP DEV
TONY GARDNER,VP OPERS
KEVIN HAGGARD,VP FIN & TREAS
ANDY R LOWE,VP MKTG
HOUSTON,TX OFFICE - 15021 KATY FWY
STE 200, 77094 PH 281 644-5900
FAX 281 644-5901

TRINITY ROYALTY CO INC
P O BOX 1756
SHREVEPORT,LA 71166-1756
PH 318 221-2899 FAX 318 221-2931
ROBERT E SMITHERMAN,PRES
MATTHEW R SMITHERMAN,VP
MARK E DUNHAM,GEOL

TRIPLE 'A' ENERGY INC
703-B S MAIN ST
BOERNE,TX 78006-2641 PH 830 249-8256
TIM F MCCLOSKEY,PRES TFM@GVTC.COM

TRIPLE A LLC
249 WALL ST LN
RUSSELLVILLE,AR 72802 PH 479 970-8590
KYLE HOOD TRIPLEALLC@GMAIL.COM

TRIPLE C OIL PRODUCERS INC
PO BOX 37
CASEY,IL 62420-0037 PH 217 932-5721
FAX 217 932-5706
JOE COCHONOUR,PRES
J M COLLINS,SECY

TRIPLE F OILFIELD SERVICE
3393 FM 417 EAST
SHELBYVILLE,TX 75973
PH 936 590-9961
TRIPLEFOILFIELD.MANDYTYRE@YAHOO.COM
CHRIS TYRE,OWNER,PRES

TRIPLE J & ASSOCIATES,LLC
PO BOX 6164
TYLER,TX 75711
PH 504 234-5202 TRIPLEJASSOC@AOL.COM
PAMELA J PHOENIX,CEO

TRIPLE J HIGH PRESSURE,INC
WINCH,POLE,VACUUM AND PUMP TRUCKS
PO BOX 879,3306 LAS CRUCES RD
ZAPATA,TX 78076-0879
PH 956 765-3232 FAX 956 765-9686

TRIPLE L COMPANY INC
484 N WASHINGTON
EL DORADO,AR 71730-5650 PH 501 862-4959
R R LANDES,MGR

TRIPLE S DRILLING COMPANY
6471 KY 49
LIBERTY,KY 42539-9724 PH 606 787-5869
FAX 606 787-8018
LARRY SCOTT,PRES
BENNY SCOTT,VP
MARY SHOOPMAN,SECY

TRITTIPO J L,INC
20150 GOLDEN PANTHER DR APT 1
ESTERO,FL 33928-2036 PH 239 992-1691
JACK L TRITTIPO,PRES

TRIUMPH DRILLING TOOLS SEE
SPIDLE TURBECO TRIUMPH

TRIUMPH ENERGY,INC
309 LA RUE FRANCE STE 202
LAFAYETTE,LA 70508-3137
PH 337 984-1397

TRIUMPH PETROLEUM COMPANY,LLC SEE
ARCADIA EXPLORATION & PRODUCTION COMPANY

TRIUMPH RESOURCES CORPORATION
555 5TH AVE 15TH FLR
NEW YORK,NY 10017-2416
PH 212 850-2530 FAX 212 490-7446
A T STAUTBERG JR,PRES

TROPHY PETROLEUM CORPORATION
PO BOX 426
CARTHAGE,MS 39051-0426 PH 601 298-0200
E WAYNE UPCHURCH,PRES

TROTTER LAND SERVICES LLC
3666 KINGSMAN DR
HOUSTON,TX 77082 PH 713 444-9154
JACKIE TROTTER JCK_TROTTER@YAHOO.COM

TROY JACO,INC
PO BOX 1476
SHERMAN,TX 75091 PH 903 868-2703
FAX 903 893-0697

TRR INC - ENERTECH RESOURCE
9720 CYPRESSWOOD DR STE 228
HOUSTON,TX 77070 PH 281 970-4800
FAX 281 970-4801 WWW.ENERTECHRESOURCE.COM
JACQUE CHAPMAN - CHICAGO,IL
DANIELLE WESTOVER - IRVINE,CA
DIANE WESTOVER - HOUSTON,TX
NANCY EUDY - HOUSTON,TX
DAN WESTOVER - HOUSTON,TX

TRYALL,INC
507 N SAM HOUSTON PKWY E STE 415
HOUSTON,TX 77060-4081 PH 281 741-1589
FAX 832 369-1734
WWW.TRYALLINCORPORATION.COM

TSESMELIS JOHN G,INC,OIL & GAS CO
OIL OPR & OIL PROPERTIES
BOX 1316,312 WEST 6TH
ALICE,TX 78332 PH 361 664-6471
J G TSESMELIS,VP
W A LEMOND,LDMN

TUBE DEVELOPMENTS LIMITED
KILSYTH,QUEENZIEBURN INDUSTRIAL ESTATE
GLASGOW,UNITED KINGDOM G65 9BN
PH +44 1236 823551 FAX +44 1236 825660
WWW.TUBEDEV.COM
GREGOR FRASER GREGOR@TUBEDEV.COM

TUBULAR SYNERGY GROUP
5055 KELLER SPRINGS RD STE 350
ADDISON,TX 75001
PH 214 623-5071 FAX 214 623-5076
BYRON DUNN,CEO
ZANE CARLSON,VP COMM DEV
BRYON DUNN JR,VP BUS DEV
BOWMAN URECH,VP TUBULAR TECHNOLOGY
ROGER NAFZIGER,VP SLS
JONATHAN ARNOLD,MGR LINE PIPE
COURT ALLEY,BUS DEV
HOUSTON,TX OFFICE - PO BOX 925306
77292 PH 713 853-5865
RYAN TOWNSEND,VP SLS

TUCKER OPERATING COMPANY,INC
CONTRACT OPERS,CONSULTING PETR ENGRS
PO BOX 4966,2607 E RIO GRANDE
VICTORIA,TX 77903-4966 PH 361 578-6297
FAX 361 578-6376
TOMMY W TUCKER,PRES,REG PROF ENGR
TROY W TUCKER,VP,PETR ENGR

TUFTS ENERGY LLC
EXPLORATION & DEVELOPMENT
601 POYDRAS ST STE 2365
NEW ORLEANS,LA 70130
PH 504 525-4848 FAX 504 525-4850
J DAVID TUFTS III

TULSA ROYALTIES COMPANY
C/O BAPTIST FOUNDATION OF TEXAS
1601 ELM ST STE 1700
DALLAS,TX 75201
PH 214 978-3338 WWW.BFTX.ORG
WILLIAM T FRANCIS PH 214 978-3333
WILL.FRANCIS@BFTX.ORG

TURBINE SPECIALTIES INC SEE
ELLIOTT TURBOCHARGER GROUP INC

TURNER J C,INC
719 W FRONT ST STE 186
TYLER,TX 75702-7967
PH 903 592-3500 FAX 903 592-3504
JTURNER54@SBCGLOBAL.NET
JOHN C JAY TURNER III,PRES

TURNER JAY
719 W FRONT ST STE 186
TYLER,TX 75702 PH 903 592-3500
FAX 903 592-3504 JTURNER54@SBCGLOBAL.NET

TURNER JOHN C,GEOL
635 ALONDA DR
LAFAYETTE,LA 70503-4415 PH 318 981-2618

TURNHAM INTERESTS,INC
20 SUNSET BLVD
HOUSTON,TX 77005 PH 713 528-4007
ROBERT C TURNHAM
ELISSA TURNHAM

TURNHAM ROBERT C,PETR ENGR
2030 LOVERS LANE
SHREVEPORT,LA 71105-3814 PH 318 865-8167

TURRIS COAL COMPANY
P O BOX 21
ELKHART,IL 62634-0021 PH 217 947-2604
F K BLACKARD,PRES
J W HUGHES,VP,OPERS
L M MISINAY,MGR,ENGRG
R S JONES,CONTROLLER
P J HUNT,MGR EMPLOYEE RELS

TWIN OAKS CONSTRUCTION CO LLC
5005 W ROYAL LN STE 136
IRVING,TX 75063 PH 940 564-8871
INFO@TWINOAKS-OIL.COM
OLNEY,TX OFFICE - 408 S HWY 79,76374
PH 940 564-8871

TWINER J W BUDDY ,PETR GEOL
PO BOX 970
BRANDON,MS 39043-0970 PH 601 825-0156

TWISTER GAS SERVICES LP SEE
WINDSOR ENERGY GROUP LLC

TWO BAYOUS,INC
3306 RIVERSIDE RD
JENNINGS,LA 70546-0281 PH 318 824-6672
EDWIN L SIMAR,PRES
SHANNON M SIMAR,VP,SECY

TWO-J ENTERPRISES,INC
PO BOX 468
WEST COLUMBIA,TX 77486 PH 979 345-6556
J H JACKSON,PRES

TWOJO,LLC
2393 H G MOSLEY PKWY #4 STE 100
LONGVIEW,TX 75604-3565
PH 903 753-9665 FAX 903 234-1411
TERRY J COOK,PRES TCOOK@SILVEROAKOP.COM

TXCO RESOURCES INC
PO BOX 160727
SAN ANTONIO,TX 78280-2927

PH 210 496-5300 FAX 210 496-3232
JAMES SIGMON,CEO,PRES
JAMES BOOKOUT,VP,COO
GARY GRINSFELDER,VP,EXPL
GGRINSFELDER@TXCO.COM

TXOGA
TEXAS OIL & GAS ASSOCIATION
304 W 13TH ST
AUSTIN,TX 78701-1823 PH 512 478-6631
FAX 512 472-3859 WWW.TXOGA.ORG
JONNY JONES,CHRMN
D TODD STAPLES,PRES
SHANNON W RUSING,VP OPERS & CHF STAFF
WILLIAM L ENNIS,VP MEM & COMMUNICATION
CORY A POMEROY,VP & GEN COUNSEL
MARI V RUCKEL,VP GOVT & REG AFFAIRS
JIM SIERRA,VP FIN

TXU ENERGY SERVICES
680 ANDERSEN DR STE 200
PITTSBURGH,PA 15220-2700 PH 412 920-0800
FAX 412 920-0669
MICHAEL C GIBBS,VP
AMY HUNT,MGR,OPERS

TYCOON OPERATING CO INC
555 REPUBLIC DR STE 100
PLANO,TX 75074 PH 972 422-7555
MATT NERBONNE
MATT@TYCOONOPERATING.COM

TYLER OIL & GAS,LTD
102 N COLLEGE AVE STE 1200
TYLER,TX 75702-7260 PH 903 593-3071
FAX 903 595-6579
RUSSELL W JACKSON,GEOL
DAVID E NELSON,PETR ENGR

TYLER ROCKIES EXPLORATION LTD
PO BOX 119
TYLER,TX 75710-0119 PH 903 595-4886
FAX 903 533-8525 TEXCOMO@SBCGLOBAL.NET
J MARK STRAWN,GEN PRTNR
BARRY ROBINSON,CFO
BREE SCHOCK,OFC MGR

TYSON R.W. PRODUCING CO SEE
R.W. TYSON PRODUCING CO

U M C PETROLEUM CORPORATION SEE
OCEAN ENERGY,INC

U S ARMY ENGINEER DISTRICT,NEW ORLEANS
7400 LEAKE AVE
NEW ORLEANS,LA 70118 PH 504 862-1121

U S ENERGY DEVELOPMENT CORP
2350 N FOREST RD STE 31
GETZVILLE,NY 14068-1296
PH 716 636-0401 FAX 716 636-0418
JOSEPH M JAYSON,CEO
DOUGLAS K WALCH,PRES

U S ROYALTIES,C/O IMPERIAL OIL CO
22499 IMPERIAL VALLEY DR
HOUSTON,TX 77073-1173
PH 281 209-1150 FAX 281 209-1154
ELLIS RUDY,PRES
SUZANNE WHITE,SECY
GEORGE S WEBB,LAND
GSWEBB@IMPERIAL-OIL-COMPANY.COM

U.S. CORPS OF ENGINEERS
WWW.USACE.ARMY.MIL/

U.S. DEPARTMENT OF ENERGY
WWW.ENERGY.GOV

U.S. DEPARTMENT OF LABOR,OSHA
WWW.OSHA.GOV

U.S. DEPARTMENT OF TRANSPORTATION
(U.S.DOT) WWW.DOT.GOV

U.S. DEPARTMENT OF TRANSPORTATION'S OFC
OF PIPELINE SAFETY WWW.PHMSA.DOT.GOV

U.S. DIRECTIONAL DRILLING (USDD)
PO BOX 1206
ROCKDALE,TX 76567 PH 512 543-5006
WWW.USDDRILLING.COM
SALES@USDDRILLING.COM
DANIEL REYNOSA SR

U.S. EMERALD ENERGY
616 FM 1960 RD W STE 600
HOUSTON,TX 77090-3027
PH 281 872-9900 FAX 281 872-1768
MICHAEL SLAVIN,PRES
PATRICK CANNEY,GEOL

U.S. ENERCORP,LTD SEE AGERON ENERGY,LLC

U.S. ENERGY EXPLORATION CORP
237 S WATER ST
RURAL VALLEY,PA 16249-0237
PH 724 783-7624 FAX 724 783-7624
MICHAEL J BOYER,VP
DENNIS C BOYER,PRES
PENNIE J BOYER,SECY/TREAS
JOANN BLOSE,OFC MGR
DEBORAH PARKS,RECPT,SECY

U.S. ENVIRONMENTAL PROTECTION AGENCY
ON-SCENE COORDINATOR WWW.EPAOSC.ORG

U.S. OIL & GAS CORP
PO BOX 576
SALEM,IL 62881 PH 618 548-9900
FAX 618 548-5051 WWW.USOILANDGAS.NET
INFO@USAOILANDGAS.NET
ANITHALEE ALEX,JR,PRES
ALEX@USOILANDGAS.NET
JUDITH ALEX,VP,SECY

U.S. OIL & GAS INC
P O BOX 9158
HOUMA,LA 70361-9158 PH 504 876-4651
FAX 504 868-7759

UGA
714 PALM BLVD
LAGUNA VISTA,TX 78578 PH 956 299-0688
LOUIS GARCIA
OSOOBOY@YAHOO.COM

UHC PETROLEUM SERVICES CORPORATION
PO BOX 1956
CLEBURNE,TX 76033-1956
PH 817 477-5324 817 641-3681
FAX 817 641-3683
WALTER G MIZE
MIKE FRIZZELL

ULTRA PETROLEUM CORP
ULTRA RESOURCES INC
400 N SAM HOUSTON PKWY E STE 1200
HOUSTON,TX 77060-3539
PH 281 876-0120 FAX 281 876-2831
MICHAEL D WATFORD,CEO/PRES/CHRMN OF BD
MARSHALL MARK SMITH,CFO/SR VP
CLIFTON BRAD JOHNSON,SR VP/OPERS

ULTRAMAR DIAMOND SHAMROCK CORPORATION
SEE VALERO COMPANIES

UNDERWOOD & ASSOCIATES,OIL & GAS
EXPLORATIONISTS & CONSULTANTS

205 LONG PLANTATION BLVD APT G
LAFAYETTE,LA 70508-6152 PH 318 235-0750
JAMES ORLAND UNDERWOOD,OWNER,GEOL

UNDERWOOD OIL WELL SERVICE,INC
731 LAKESHORE DR
MONROE,LA 71203-4139 PH 318 345-1033
QUILLIE N UNDERWOOD,PRES
BOBBY N UNDERWOOD,VP

UNICHEM SEE
BJ UNICHEM CHEMICAL SERVICES

UNIFLUX INC SEE EXOTHERM CORPORATION

UNION CARBIDE INDUSTRIAL GASES
OIL FIELD SERVICES
THE DOW CTR
MIDLAND,MI 48674-0001 PH 281 872-2100
C B POLLOCK
L W KUBIN
R J SCHULTZ
P N MASSING

UNION CENTRAL LIFE INSURANCE COMPANY SEE
AMERITAS LIFE INSURANCE CORP

UNION CRUDE OPERATING CO
1810 S HWY 146
BAYTOWN,TX 77520-7611
PH 281 837-0671 FAX 281 427-3027
THOMAS E FEREDAY,PRES

UNION DRILLING INC
952 ECHO LN STE 460
HOUSTON,TX 77024-2816
PH 817 735-8793 FAX 817 546-4368
UNIOND.COM
CHRISTOPHER STRONG,PRES,CEO
POCOLA,OK BRANCH OFFICE - PO BOX 811
74902-0811 PH 918 626-4100
FAX 918 626-4105
DARWIN HALE,OPER MGR

UNION GAS CORPORATION
14505 TORREY CHASE BLVD STE 205
HOUSTON,TX 77014 PH 281 397-0077
FAX 281 397-0093
RANDALL K LOWRY JR,PRES

UNION GAS LIMITED SEE
DUKE ENERGY GAS TRANSMISSION

UNION GAS OPERATING CO
14505 TORREY CHASE BLVD STE 205
HOUSTON,TX 77014-1024
PH 281 397-0091 FAX 281 397-0093

UNION OIL COMPANY OF CALIFORNIA SEE
UNOCAL CORPORATION

UNION PACIFIC RESOURCES COMPANY SEE
ANADARKO PETROLEUM CORPORATION

UNION RESOURCES SEE
DAVIS BROS,LLC

UNION SEABOARD CORPORATION
11215 MONTEBELLO CT
HOUSTON,TX 77024-7414 PH 713 973-0426
FAX 713 784-9227
LIN G ESPEY,PRES

UNIT DRILLING COMPANY
PO BOX 702500
TULSA,OK 74170-2500 PH 918 493-7700
FAX 918 481-7151 WWW.UNITCORP.COM
LARRY D PINKSTON,PRES,CEO
OKLAHOMA CITY,OK YARD OFFICE - 7101 SW
29TH,73179 PH 405 745-4948
FAX 405 745-2136

JOHN CROMLING,EXEC VP,DRLG
KEITH ROWEKAMP,VP DIV MGR/MID-CONT
JIM GREER,VP MKTG/MID-CONT
HUMBLE,TX OFFICE - 1029 ATASCOCITA RD
77396 PH 281 446-6889 FAX 281 446-6335
RANDY MILES,VP/GULF COAST DIV MGR
CASPER,WY OFFICE - 5710 W YELLOWSTONE
82604 PH 307 472-7020 FAX 307 235-4745
ROBERT SANDS,SUPVSR
BORGER,TX OFFICE - PO BOX 5320,79008-5320
PH 806 273-7573 FAX 806 274-4811

UNIT MANAGER,CITRONELLE UNIT
PO BOX 408
CITRONELLE,AL 36522-0408 PH 334 866-5572
FAX 334 866-2946
R H STECHMANN,UNIT MGR
STAN CLAYTON,GEOL
ED BLAIR,ENGR
BILL NEWBERRY,PUR AGT
JERRY W FRETWELL,PROD SUPT
L V ROUNSAVILLE,PROD FRMN
ROBERT L WALKER,GANG FRMN
LELAND JAMES,FLD MECH FRMN
JACK HARTLEY,WAREHOUSEMAN

UNIT PETROLEUM COMPANY
PO BOX 702500
TULSA,OK 74170-2500 PH 918 493-7700
FAX 918 493-7711 WWW.UNITCORP.COM
LARRY PINKSTON,PRES,CEO
BRAD GUIDRY,EXEC VP/EXPL
MARK W COLCLASURE,SR VP/OPERS
CARL HANSEN,VP/EAST DIV
FRANK YOUNG,VP CENTRAL DIV
HOUSTON,TX OFFICE - 24 E GREENWAY PLZ
STE 501,77046-2406 PH 713 960-8870
FAX 713 960-8801
K M BLONDEAU,VP GEOL/GULF COAST
J K KAHLDEN,VP LAND/GULF COAST
JIM GUINN,VP ENGR/GULF COAST

UNIT TEXAS DRILLING LLC
PO BOX 5320,1414 S CEDAR
BORGER,TX 79008-5320 PH 806 273-7573
FAX 806 274-4811 WWW.UNITCORP.COM
GENE GALLEGOS,GEN MGR
J D HAND,DRLG MGR
OSCAR CHAPARRO,DRLG SUPT
JOE HERMOSILLO,SAFETY DIR

UNITED DIAMOND
SEE WEATHERFORD INTER

UNITED ENERGEX INC
PO BOX 6027,4940 BROADWAY STE 200
SAN ANTONIO,TX 78209-0027 PH 210 826-0681
FAX 210 826-1855
CALVIN MICHELSON,PRES
MITCH MICHELSON,VP
ROBERT FANNIN,VP,FIN

UNITED NORTH AMERICAN RESOURCES,INC SEE
ALLIANCE RESOURCES

UNITED PETRO LTD
2538 CHARLESTON ROAD
SPENCER,WV 25276 PH 304 927-4126
EILEEN HINES-ADKINS,PRES

UNITED RESOURCES INC
P O BOX 5127
EVANSVILLE,IN 47716-5127
PH 812 476-7556 FAX 812 476-5737

L PEARSON,PRES

UNITED RESOURCES,LP
1001 WESTBANK DR
AUSTIN,TX 78746-6669
PH 512 328-8184 FAX 512 328-8189
WWW.UNRES.COM
BRAD WATSON,PRES/CEO

UNITED SECURITY ASSOCIATES
12100 E SPINNAKER LN
SUTTONS BAY,MI 49682-9594
PH 231 271-2111
DAVID J HALL,PRES,OIL,GAS EXPL SPEC

UNITED WORLD ENERGY CORP
2006 AMBASSADOR CAFFERY PKWY
LAFAYETTE,LA 70506-2810
PH 337 981-1657 FAX 337 981-1653
WAYNE LANDRY,PRES
DEBBIE LEMOINE,SECY
DONNA MARQUETTE,SECY

UNIVERSAL COMPRESSION,INC SEE
EXTERRAN

UNIVERSAL EQUIPMENT INC
PO BOX 51206,BOWERS RD
LAFAYETTE,LA 70505-1206 PH 318 233-5292
FAX 318 233-6833
O M CARMICHAEL,PRES
DAVID ADAMS,VP

UNIVERSAL HYDROTESTING COMPANY
PIPE TEST,HYDROSTATIC & PNEUMATIC TEST
PO BOX 2329
AMARILLO,TX 79105-2329 PH 806 371-8851
FAX 806 371-8856 HYDROTEST@AOL.COM
MIKE R BRISTER,CEO
G H RIFFE,VP
MUNITH,MI REG OFFICE - PO BOX 218
49259 PH 517 596-2629 FAX 517 596-3172
PAUL T MOONEY,PRES
ORIN CORNISH,SUPT
HOUSTON,TX REG OFFICE - 15937 RIDLON
CHANNELVIEW,TX 77530 PH 281 457-6600
FAX 281 457-6641
LEE MCINTIRE,REG MGR

UNIVERSAL OPERATING,INC
1521 S GREEN RIVER RD
EVANSVILLE,IN 47715-5659 PH 812 477-1584
FAX 812 477-2597
WILLIAM W SMITH,PRES
NANCY L MONTGOMERY,OFC MGR

UNIVERSAL RESOURCES CORPORATION SEE
QUESTAR EXPLORATION AND PRODUCTION CO

UNIVERSAL RESOURCES HOLDINGS,INC
3152 E MAIN RD
DUNKIRK,NY 14048 PH 716 673-9116
JOHN J NALBONE JR,PRES
LOUIS J NALBONE,VP

UNIVERSITY OF LOUISIANA
PO BOX 43570
LAFAYETTE,LA 70504-0001 PH 337 482-6087
FAX 337 482-5898
OLIVER J LEBLANC III,PLRM COORD
OJL1383@LOUISIANA.EDU

UNIVERSITY OF OKLAHOMA
MEWBOURNE SCHOOL OF PETR & GEOL ENGRG
100 E BOYD ST RM T301
NORMAN,OK 73019-1003 PH 405 325-2921
FAX 405 325-7477 MPGE@OU.EDU

DR CHANDRA S RAI,DIR

UNOCAL CORPORATION SEE
CHEVRON

UOP GAS PROCESS GROUP/SEPAREX
MEMBRANES SYSTEMS
1250 W SAM HOUSTON PKWY S STE 450
HOUSTON,TX 77042 PH 713 744-2861
FAX 713 744-2880
HANK TRAYLOR,ACCT REPR

UPG FALCO,A DIV OF UPG INC SEE
ENRON OIL TRADING & TRANSPORTATION CO

UPSHUR AGENCY,INC (COMPLETE LAND SERV CO)
PO BOX 326
BUCKHANNON,WV 26201-0326 PH 304 472-6992
PH 800 833-6922 FAX 304 472-6997
STEPHEN A HOLMES,CPL,PRES

UPSON RESOURCES MANAGEMENT,INC
1701 N GREENVILLE AVE STE 820
RICHARDSON,TX 75081-1851 PH 972 744-0455
FAX 972 744-0458
TODD UPSON TUPSON@BLUERIVEROIL.COM

UPSTART EXPLORATION,INC
339 N STERLING ST
LAFAYETTE,LA 70501 PH 337 298-1154
UPSTART1@COX.NET
FRANK S VINCENT,SR IND CONS GEOL

UPSTREAM ENERGY SERVICES
2277 PLAZA DR STE 440
SUGAR LAND,TX 77479-6602
Ph 281 277-4200 FAX 281 277-4203
WWW.UPSTREAMENERGY.COM
ROBERT HAWORTH JR,PRES
WAYNE BRINTON,VP
RUSSELL ALLEN,CFO
SAM RHOADES,PRODUCER SERVICES
GABINA WILM,VOLUME ANALYST
JEANNIE ALONZO,MGR OF TRANS
MARK HAYS,VP
CHARLES CAMPBELL,PRODUCER SVCS

UPSTREAM MARKETING
800 BERING DR STE 180
HOUSTON,TX 77450
PH 832 594-5390 WWW.UPSTREAMMARKETING.NET
BRIAN BEARDEN BRIAN@UPSTREAMMARKETING.NET

URS CORPORATION
PROCESS & ENERGY GROUP
1515 POYDRAS ST STE 2700
NEW ORLEANS,LA 70112-4516
PH 504 586-8111 FAX 504 522-0554
WWW.URSCORP.COM
K W MARTINEZ,P&E GROUP MGR
G J BUCKERT,NEW ORLEANS MGR
W T CHANDLER,OIL & GAS MGR
E N FROST,BUS DEV
EDWARDS_FROST@URSCORP.COM
BATON ROUGE,LA OFFICE - 10550 AIRLINE
HWY,70816-4191
MOBILE,AL OFFICE - 917 WESTERN AMERICA
CIR,STE 400,36609 PH 334 344-4744
LAKE CHARLES,LA OFFICE - 3519 PATRICK ST
70605 PH 318 479-0005
HOUSTON,TX OFFICE - 7600 E TIDWELL
STE 600,77040 FAX 713 744-9099
DENVER,CO OFFICE - 8181 E TUFTS AVE
80237 PH 303 740-2600 FAX 303 740-2650

URSA RESOURCES GROUP II LLC
602 SAWYER ST STE 710
HOUSTON,TX 77094 PH 713 456-3009
DON SIMPSON
DSIMPSON@URSARESOURCES.COM

US INFRASTRUCTURE
20329 STATE HWY 249 STE 450
HOUSTON,TX 77070 PH 281 655-3239
GARY BRYAN,SVP
GBRYAN@USINFRASTRUCTURE.COM

US OIL & GAS ASSOCIATION
MISSISSIPPI/ALABAMA DIVISION
513 N STATE ST STE 202
JACKSON,MS 39201
PH 601 948-8903 FAX 601 948-8919
WWW.USOGA.COM USOIL@USOGA.COM
BEN THOMPSON,PRES
ALICIA VINCENT,OFC ASST

USENCO SEE ARCH PETROLEUM INC

USI SOUTHWEST
3850 N CAUSEWAY BLVD STE 1050
METAIRIE,LA 70002-7277 PH 504 355-5000
FAX 504 210-4490 WWW.USI.BIZ
CHRIS CASBARIAN,VP-MARINE & ENERGY
CHRISTOPHER.CASBARIAN@USI.BIZ

V F NEUHAUS PROPERTIES INC
3503 N TAYLOR RD
MISSION,TX 78573 PH 956 686-2491
FAX 956 686-7065
BRUCE G WELCH,VP

VAALCO ENERGY (USA) INC
4600 POST OAK PL DR STE 309
HOUSTON,TX 77027-9727 PH 713 623-0801
FAX 713 623-0982 WWW.VAALCO.COM
VAALCO@VAALCO.COM
ROBERT L GERRY,III,CHRMN & CEO
W RUSSELL SCHEIRMAN,II,PRES & CFO
GAYLA CUTRER,VP,ADMIN

VALE PETROLEUM CORPORATION
535 CONNECTICUT AVE STE 108
NORWALK,CT 09854-1713 PH 212 599-1707
FAX 212 949-0639
GAY LAND,PRES

VALENCE OPERATING CO
600 ROCKMEAD STE 200
KINGWOOD,TX 77339 PH 281 359-3659

VALERO ENERGY CORPORATION
ONE VALERO WAY
SAN ANTONIO,TX 78249 PH 210 345-2000

- REFINERIES -

ARDMORE,OK - HWY 142 BYPASS AND
EAST CAMERON RD 73401 PH 580 223-0534
WILMINGTON,CA - 2402 E ANAHEIM 90744
PH 562 491-6877
BENICIA,CA - 3400 E 2ND ST
94510-1097 PH 707 745-7011
CORPUS CHRISTI,TX (BILL GREEHEY) -
1147 CANTWELL LN 78407 PH 361 289-6000
HOUSTON,TX - 9701 MANCHESTER 77012
PH 713 923-3300
SUNRAY,TX (MCKEE REFINERY) - 6701 FM 119,
HRC BOX 36,79086 PH 806 935-2141
MEMPHIS,TN - 543 W MALLORY AVE
38109 PH 901 774-3100

PORT ARTHUR,TX - 1801 S GULFWAY DR
77640 PH 409 985-1000
MERAUX,LA - 2500 E ST BERNARD HWY 70075
PH 504 271-4141
NORCO,LA (ST CHARLES) - 14902 RIVER RD
70079 PH 985 764-8611
TEXAS CITY,TX - 1301 LOOP 197 S
77590 PH 409 945-4451
THREE RIVERS,TX - 301 LEROY 78071
PH 361 786-4610
SAN NICOLAS,ARUBA - 5 LAGO WEG
PH 800 877-3906
PEMBROKE,WALES,UNITED KINGDOM SA71 5SJ -
PH +44 (0) 1646 641 331
SAINT-ROMUALD,QUEBEC,CANADA (JEAN
GAULIN) 165 CHEMIN DES ILES G6W 5M4
PH 418 837-3641

- ETHANOL PLANTS -

ALBERT CITY,IA - 2356 510TH ST 50510
PH 712 843-5100
ALBION,NE - 2615 260TH ST 68620
PH 402 395-3500
AURORA,SD - ONE VALERO PLACE 57002
PH 605 693-6800 OR 888 693-2676
CHARLES CITY,IA - 1787 QUARRY RD
50616 PH 641 715-3000
FORT DODGE,IA - 1930 HAYES AVE
50501 PH 515 955-5000 PH 877 694-2676
HARTLEY,IA - 3260 VAN BUREN AVE
51346 PH 712 928-5800 PH 866 931-2676
WELCOME,MN - 1444 120TH ST 56181
PH 507 728-4000
BLOOMINGBURG,OH - 3979 STATE RT 238 NE
43106 PH 740 437-6200
LINDEN,IN - 203 WEST COUNTY RD 1100N
47955 PH 765 522-3100
JEFFERSON,WI - N 5355 JUNCTION RD
53549 PH 920 674-8500

- (ULTRAMAR IN CANADA) -

MONTREAL,QUEBEC,CANADA HEAD OFFICE-
2200,MCGILL COLLEGE,H3A 3L3
PH 514 499-6111 PH 800 363-6949
FOR GENERAL INFORMATION
PH 888 871-4404 (CUSTOMER SVC-COMMERCIAL
PIPELINE)

- WESTERN EUROPE -

LONDON,ENGLAND,UNITED KINGDOM -
1 WESTFERRY CIRCUS,CANAR WHARF
E14 4HA PH +44 (0) 20 7513 3000

VALERO GAS STORAGE COMPANY SEE
PG&E TEXAS GAS STORAGE COMPANY

VALERO HYDROCARBONS COMPANY SEE
PG&E HYDROCARBONS COMPANY

VALERO MANAGEMENT COMPANY SEE
PG&E TEXAS MANAGEMENT COMPANY

VALERO NATURAL GAS COMPANY SEE
PG&E TEXAS NATURAL GAS COMPANY

VALERO TRANSMISSION COMPANY SEE
PG&E TEXAS PIPELINE COMPANY

VALIOSO PETROLEUM CO,INC
504 KEYWOOD CIR #A
FLOWOOD,MS 39232-3018 PH 601 936-3601
FAX 601 936-3646
KARL J KAUFMANN,PRES,GEOPHY

VALLET PEGGY,CPL
PO BOX 53406
SHREVEPORT,LA 71135-3406 PH 318 226-8935

VALTEP INC
535 CONNECTICUT AVE STE 108
NORWALK,CT 06854-1713 PH 212 599-1707
FAX 212 949-0639
GAY V LAND,CHRMN
JOHN C AUBREY,PRES,CEO

VALUATION AND ASSETS SERVICES
MULTI-DISCIPLINE APPRAISALS & VALUATIONS
2108 CARROLL CREEK VIEW
FREDERICK,MD 21702 PH 301 646-4119
WWW.VALUATIONANDASSETS.COM
PROJECTS@VALUATIONANDASSETS.COM
K BOISON

VALVCON SEE
HYDRIL COMPANY LP

VAN DER WEIDE, SAM W
138 CANYON CREEK DR
SAN ANTONIO,TX 78232-1304
PH 210 494-2901
SAMVANDERWEIDE@SBCGLOBAL.NET

VAN DYKE ENERGY COMPANY
11 GREENWAY PLAZA STE 2010
HOUSTON,TX 77046
PH 713 457-8100 FAX 713 457-8099
WWW.VANDYKE-ENERGY.COM
GENE VAN DYKE,PRES/CEO

VAN OPERATING,LTD
PO BOX 2530
ALBANY,TX 76430
PH 325 762-3353 FAX 325 762-3359
A V JONES JR,CHRMN
K C JONES,LAND MGR
JEFF JONES,EXPL MGR
WILL TUCKER,OPERS MGR
RANDY WALKER,ACCT MGR

VAN PELT DESIGN
OIL & GAS WEBSITE DESIGN SERVICES
PO BOX 12512
AUSTIN,TX 78711-2512 PH 512 270-9076
WWW.VANPELTDESIGN.COM
INFO@VANPELTDESIGN.COM
JEREMY VAN PELT

VAN PETROLEUM,INC
PO BOX 5327
188 E CAPITOL ST STE 1375 ONE JACKSON PL
JACKSON,MS 39296-5327 PH 601 354-2522
FAX 601 354-4896
WILLIAM J VAN DEVENDER,PRES
HENRY M BROWN,VP

VAN REENAN INTERNATIONAL
PO BOX 1302
MONTGOMERY,TX 77356-1302 PH 936 448-6165
EARL VAN REENAN,PRES EARLVANR@AOL.COM

VAN TYNE CONSULTING (GEOLOGICAL)
PO BOX 326
WELLSVILLE,NY 14895-0326 PH 585 593-6650
FAX 585 593-6650
ARTHUR M VANTYNE,OWNER

AVANTYNE@YAHOO.COM

VANADO,LLC
12606 RIFLEMAN TRL
CYPRESS,TX 77429-2630 PH 281 469-2272
GERALD B MURRELL,PRES

VANCO ENERGY COMPANY SEE
VAN DYKE ENERGY COMPANY

VANE LLC
333 TEXAS ST STE 840
SHREVEPORT,LA 71101-3678
PH 318 221-4499 FAX 318 222-3216
GERALD E HUGGS JR,PRES

VANGUARD GEOSCIENCE LLC
5800 BANCROFT DR
NEW ORLEANS,LA 70122 PH 504 583-9521

VARI-JAK WELL PUMPING UNITS
358 WILSON SHARPESVILLE RD
WARREN,OH 44481-9323 PH 216 847-8545
RAY RATELL SR,OWNER
RAY RATELL JR,OWNER

VARIABLE BORE RAMS INC
1086 AILLET ROAD
BROUSSARD,LA 70518
PH 800 233-3603 WWW.VBRI.COM
HINES M MARSHALL JR,CEO/PRES/PE
KENNY LEE,VP SALES
ERNIE BENNETT,SR SLS MGR
JARED PRIMEAUX,BOP RAM SPEC
BRANDON LEGER,QHSE ENGR
SHAY BELLARD,CONTROLLER
HEATHER LEBLANC,ACCT
ASHLEY CARRIERE,ACCT
JACELYNN LAFLEUR,ACCT
CAMERON MCCREARY,REG SLS SPEC
JAKE PEMBERTON,REG SLS SPEC
BRIAN KAPLAN,BOP RAM SPEC
ROLAND DITCH,BOP RAM SPEC
WESLEY CRAFTON,BOP RAM SPEC

VASTAR RESOURCES,INC SEE
BP AMERICA,INC

VAUGHEY AND VAUGHEY,LLC
1515 WAZEE ST #350
DENVER,CO 80202
PH 303 318-0717 FAX 303 318-0720
DAVID C MILHOLM,VP/GEN MGR
DCMILHOLM@GMAIL.COM

VAUGHN ENERGY SERVICES
P O BOX 261021
CORPUS CHRISTI,TX 78426 PH 800 606-4976
SALES@VAUGHNENERGY.COM

VAUGHN PETROLEUM INC
PO BOX 671099
DALLAS,TX 75367-1099
PH 214 707-7535 FAX 214 572-2600
BENNY DUNCAN,MGR BDUNCAN@TRUNKBAY.NET
BDUNCAN@TRUNKBAY.NET

VAUGHN PETROLEUM ROYALTY PARTNERS,LTD
PO BOX 671099
DALLAS,TX 75367-1099
PH 214 707-7535 FAX 214 572-2600
BENNY DUNCAN,MGR BDUNCAN@TRUNKBAY.NET

VAUGHT OIL CO
PO BOX 26286
AKRON,OH 44319-6286 PH 330 644-7600
FAX 330 644-0148
BILL D VAUGHT

LORI STOCKERT

VECTOR INVESTMENTS
PO BOX 376,416 TRAVIS STE 806
SHREVEPORT,LA 71101-0376 PH 318 425-7712
FAX 318 425-7729
F LANE MITCHELL,MNGNG PRTNR
JILL SIMONS,ACCT
BOBBIE TRUST,SECY

VENABLE EXPLORATION,LTD
5949 SHERRY LN STE 1400
DALLAS,TX 75225-8010
PH 214 219-1444 FAX 214 219-2227
JOE H TYDLASKA

VENADO OIL & GAS LLC
12600 HILL COUNTRY BLVD BLDG R STE 250
AUSTIN,TX 78738
PH 512 735-9000 FAX 512 735-9010
WWW.VOGLLC.COM
SCOTT GARRICK,CEO
PAUL C LEE JR,CFO
JOE D SULLIVAN JR,EVP LAND
JASON CHURCHILL,OPERS ENGRG MGR
STACY SHIVERS,DRILLING ENGRG MGR
PAUL JANACEK,DIR ADMIN
KENNY NADLER,CONTROLLER

VENEX CORPORATION
PO BOX 670505
HOUSTON,TX 77267-0505 PH 281 587-2531
FAX 281 587-2531 VENEX@SBCGLOBAL.NET
KAMAL C JAIN,PRES
RICHARD O WEBSTER,VP

VENQUEST RESOURCES INC
OIL AND GAS PRODUCER (OPERATOR)
1010 LAMAR STE 800
HOUSTON,TX 77002
PH 713 654-9200 FAX 713 652-9090
DOUGLAS STILLWAGON,PRES DOUG-
S@SWBELL.NET

VENTURE CHEMICALS INC
PO BOX 53631,106 BOARD RD
LAFAYETTE,LA 70505-3631
PH 337 232-1977 FAX 337 237-5340
MIKE KILCHRIST,PRES
WWW.VENTURECHEMICALS.COM
SALES@VENTURECHEMICALS.COM

VENTURE OIL & GAS CORP
28305 CREOLE RD
LACOMBE,LA 70445 PH 504 887-0627
NORMAN W REISIG JR,PRES

VENTURE OIL & GAS INC
207 S 13TH AVE
LAUREL,MS 39440-4357 PH 601 428-7725
FAX 601 428-7738
JAY FENTON,PRES
NEIL SCRIMPSHIRE,VP

VENTURE PRODUCTION INC SEE
VENTURE ROYALTIES

VENTURETECH CORP INT'L
POWER SWIVELS - MFG,SALES,PARTS & SERVICE
6901 ALABONSON RD
HOUSTON,TX 77088 PH 713 895-8700
FAX 713 895-8720, WWW.VENTURETECHNET.COM
LARRY G KEAST,PRES

VENUS OIL COMPANY
19240 REDLAND RD STE 200
SAN ANTONIO,TX 78259-3332 PH 210 824-8253

FAX 210 824-6423 GAMESJR33@GMAIL.COM
EUGENE L AMES JR,PRES/CEO

VEOLIA ES INDUSTRIAL SERVICES
106 FORD CT
NEW LENOX,IL 60451 PH 815 836-8813
TARA POTE,OPERS
MIKE DONNELLY,DIV MGR

VERADO ENERGY,INC
8150 N CENTRAL EXPY STE 850
DALLAS,TX 75206-1815
PH 214 368-5322 FAX 214 363-2074
CHRISTOPHER S GRAHAM,PRES
PAULA L YOKE,CFO/VP FIN
JACK CORDARD,VP OPERS
VALLIE S CAMPBELL,VP LAND/SECY

VERITAS DGC INC
10300 TOWN PARK DR
HOUSTON,TX 77072-5236 PH 832 351-8300
FAX 832 351-8701
DAVID B ROBSON,CHRMN,CEO
STEPHEN J LUDLOW,V CHRMN
TIMOTHY L WELLS,PRES,COO
MATTHEW FITZGERALD,EXEC VP,CFO,TREAS
ROBERT HOBBS,PRES,VES
VICKI MESSER,PRES,LAND SURV
CRAIG ROTHWELL,PRES,LAND
ANDY PHIPPS,PRES,MARINE SURV
RICHARD PRICE,PRES,MARINE ACQS

VERMILION ABSTRACT CO
126 HACKER ST
NEW IBERIA,LA 70560-4524
PH 337 369-7377
KEITH E LAPEROUSE

VERMILION PARISH ASSESSORS' OFFICE
100 N STATE ST STE 110
ABBEVILLE,LA 70510-5167
PH 337 893-2837
WWW.VERMILIONPARISHASSESSOR.COM
VPAO@CONNECTIONS-LCT.COM
GABE G MARCEAUX,ASSESSOR

VERMILLION PROPERTIES LLC
5930 ROYAL LANE STE E-233
DALLAS,TX 75230
PH 972 896-4114 FAX 866 223-4471
KATHRYN A VERMILLION,PRES
KATIE@VERMILLIONPROPERTIESLLC.COM

VERUS ENERGY,LP
800 BERING DR ST 130
HOUSTON,TX 77057 PH 713 524-5800
JOSEPH R FRAZIER,PRES
JFRAZIER@VERUSENERGY.COM

VESCAL CORP
PO BOX 459
ELIZABETH,WV 26143-0459 PH 304 275-3972
FAX 304 275-3972
RUSSELL L CLINE,PRES

VESEY BRIAN K & ASSOCIATES
PO BOX 51344
LAFAYETTE,LA 70505-1344 PH 337 237-2609
PH 337 230-0235 FAX 337 237-6727
MEXICO PH 0115213141224994
BRIAN K VESEY,GEOL

VF-RUSSIA INC SEE
HILLWOOD INTERNATIONAL ENERGY

VIBRA-TECH ENGINEERS,INC
4818 E BEN WHITE BLVD STE 202

AUSTIN,TX 78741 PH 512 442-6464
FAX 512 442-6552 WWW.VIBRA-TECH-INC.COM
JOE CROWNOVER,VP & AREA MGR
JOECR@VIBRA-TECH-INC.COM

VICTAULIC COMPANY
PO BOX 31
EASTON,PA 18044-0031 PH 610 559-3300
FAX 610 250-8817 WWW.VICTAULIC.COM
J MALLOY,PRES,CEO
G MOORE,EXEC VP,SALES
SCOTT FREY,MKTG COMMUNICATIONS MGR

VICTORIA BEARING & INDUSTRIAL SUPPLY,INC
1703 N NAVARRO ST
VICTORIA,TX 77901-5219
PH 361 575-7478 FAX 361 576-5842
VBIS@SBCGLOBAL.NET

VICTORIA EQUIP & SUPPLY CO,INC
PO BOX 3791
VICTORIA,TX 77903-3791
PH 361 573-2416 FAX 361 573-3902
MELVIN KLOTZMAN,PRES
MARK KLOTZMAN,VP
THOMAS SANTOS,OPERS MGR

VICTORIA GAS CORPORATION
8080 N CENTRAL EXPY STE 1000
DALLAS,TX 75206-1804 PH 214 891-8400
FAX 214 891-8414
KENNETH C ENGLISH,PRES & CEO
PAUL LECOCKE,VP & TREAS

VICTORY ENERGY CORPORATION
220 AIRPORT RD
INDIANA,PA 15701-8944
PH 724 349-6366 FAX 724 349-6649
VICTORY@VICTORYENERGYCORP.COM
LYNN A DOVERSPIKE,PRES

VICTORY FINANCIAL GROUP,INC
PO BOX 5902
METAIRIE,LA 70009-5902 PH 504 837-2230
FAX 504 831-8269

VIEWPOINT ENERGY,LLC
932 14TH ST N
TEXAS CITY,TX 77590 PH 409 945-4897
FAX 409 945-4892 WWW.VIEWPOINTENERGY.COM
ROBERT WATKINS,PRES,CEO
RWAT@VIEWPOINTENERGY.COM

VIKING EXPLORATION,INC
PO BOX 2647
FORT WORTH,TX 76113-2647
PH 817 439-9850 FAX 817 439-9858
LARRY LYDICK,PRES
LARRY@LYDICKOIL.COM
DREW LYDICK,VP
DREW@LYDICKOIL.COM

VIKING OIL COMPANY
PO BOX 70
MOUNT CARMEL,IL 62863-0070
PH 618 262-4197
JAMES E CAPIN,PRES
RICHARD F CAPIN,VP

VINCENT GEORGE A,JR,OIL OPERATOR
758 4TH AVE
LAUREL,MS 39440 PH 601 319-6050
FAX 601 649-3313

VINCENT JAMES K,GEOL & PETR ENGR
3520 NEW HARTFORD RD STE 204
OWENSBORO,KY 42303-1781 PH 270 684-8223

FAX 270 684-8223
JAMES K VINCENT,PG,PE,OWNER

VINTAGE EXPLORATION INC
25311 SINGLETON BEND RD EAST
MARBLE FALLS,TX 78654-3682
PH 512 267-0904 FAX 512 267-2008
VINTAGERESOURCES@SBCGLOBAL.NET
JERRY M ROBERTSON,PRES

VINTAGE PETROLEUM,INC SEE
OCCIDENTAL OIL & GAS CORP

VINTAGE RESOURCES CORPORATION
25311 SINGLETON BEND RD EAST
MARBLE FALLS,TX 78654
PH 512 267-0904 FAX 512 267-2008
VINTAGERESOURCES@SBCGLOBAL.NET
JERRY M ROBERTSON,PRES

VIPER WELL SERVICES,LLC
402 DAM RD
EL CAMPO,TX 77437-2541 PH 979 541-5262
FAX 979 543-6696
DAVID PRATKA,OWNER ECMR@SBCGLOBAL.NET

VIRGINIA GAS COMPANY SEE
SPECTRA ENERGY CORP

VIRTEX OPERATING COMPANY,INC
615 N UPPER BROADWAY STE 525 WF-168
CORPUS CHRISTI,TX 78401
PH 361 882-3046 PH 361 882-3440
FAX 361 882-2374
DALE PHIPPS,PRES
BASIL PHIPPS,VP
JEFF UECKER,GEN MGR
TERSH BAKER,LAND MGR
BOB CRITCHLOW,GEOL MGR
STEPHEN BROLL,DRLG ENGR
KIMBERLEY GUERRA,OFC MGR

VISION ENERGY,LLC
PO BOX 51881
LAFAYETTE,LA 70505-1881 PH 337 262-0460
JOE PHILLIPS,MEMBER

VISTA ENERGY CORPORATION
PO BOX 694
MADISON,TN 37115-0694 PH 615 227-8011
AUBREY GREGORY,VP
STEVE GREGORY,ENGR

VITRUVIAN EXPLORATION LLC
4 WATERWAY SQUARE PLACE STE 400
THE WOODLANDS,TX 77380
PH 832 458-3100 FAX 832 458-3101

VOORHIES OIL PROPERTIES,LLC
PO BOX 52917
LAFAYETTE,LA 70505-2917
PH 337 233-2085 FAX 337 233-2766
P J VOORHIES III,PRES
PJ@VOORHIESOILPROPERTIES.COM
REBECCA B VOORHIES,SECY/TREAS

VOORHIES-RAYMOND KAY,CPL
PO BOX 51747
LAFAYETTE,LA 70505-1747 PH 337 278-8016
KAYRAYMOND@COX.NET

VOYAGER PETROLEUM INC
406 WARTH AVE
LAFAYETTE,LA 70508 PH 337 288-4037
C BARRY GREER,PRES

VREELAND JOHN B
PO BOX 2603,600 LEOPARD ST STE 1616
CORPUS CHRISTI,TX 78403-2603

PH 361 882-6251 FAX 361 882-9071

VWM PROPERTIES
PO BOX 5745
SHREVEPORT,LA 71135-5745 PH 318 798-3070
ROBERT M MILLS
VASSAR WHEMITT MILLS

W & T OFFSHORE,INC
9 GREENWAY PLZ STE 300
HOUSTON,TX 77046 PH 713 626-8525
FAX 713 626-8527 WWW.WTOFFSHORE.COM
NEW ORLEANS,LA OFFICE - 1100 POYDRAS
STE 1100 70163 PH 504 831-4171
TRACY W KROHN,FOUNDER,CHRMN & CEO
JAMIE L VAZQUEZ,PRES
J DANIEL GIBBONS,SR VP/CFO
THOMAS MURPHY,SR VP/COO
STEPHEN L SCHROEDER,SR VP/CTO
THOMAS F GETTEN,VP/GEN COUNSEL/SECY
KAREN S ACREE,VP/CONTROLLER
PAUL R BAKER,VP/GEN MGR ONSHORE
STEVEN M FREEMAN,VP LAND & BUS DEV
TOD E GRABOIS,VP/TREAS
GREGORY E PERCIVAL,VP INF TECH
JOSEPH P SLATTERY,VP DRLG & HR&E
W ALLEN TATE,VP MKTG & MIDSTREAM
CLIFFORD J WILLIAMS,VP/GEN MGR OFFSHORE

W B I PRODUCTION,INC SEE
FIDELITY EXPLORATION & PRODUCTION CO

W H C INC
PO BOX 2340
LAFAYETTE,LA 70502-2340 PH 337 837-8765
FAX 337 837-4500 WWW.WHC-INC.COM
VINCE@WHC-INC.COM
GEORGE L CRAIN JR,PRES
VINCE COREIL,VP
SCOTT KREBSBACH,ESTIMATOR,PROJ MGR
DANIEL J FRUGE',CHF FIN OFCR
DOLORES LANIER,PAINT SLS MGR
RICKY WYATT,SAFETY DIR
RICHARD DICKERSON,PIPELINE SUPT
BURT GOULD,ESTIMATOR,PROJ MGR
BUDDY CLARK,SUPT

W K M COOPER INDUSTRIES SEE CAMERON
A DIV OF COOPER CAMERON CORPORATION

W W PETROLEUM SERVICE INC
PO BOX 74
DIXON,KY 42409-0074 PH 270 639-5374
PH 270 639-9353
WAYNE WILLSON,PRES
LUTHER WILLSON,SECY/TREAS

W.S. RED HANCOCK,INC
OIL FIELD CONSTRUCTION & HAULING
PO BOX 207
BENTONIA,MS 39040-0207 PH 662 755-2931
PH 800 545-2222 FAX 662 755-8767
EDDIE JONES
ROY HANCOCK
FRANKIE BURTON
GLENN CLARK

W.T. DRILLING COMPANY,INC
PO BOX 1345
NATCHEZ,MS 39121 PH 601 442-1607
FAX 601 442-2192 WWW.WTDRILLING.COM
LEO JOSEPH,PRES
WAYNE JOHNSON,VP
NANETTE NEW,SECY/TREAS

W.T.W. OIL CO,INC
1804 ROLLINGWOOD CT
BEDFORD,TX 76021 PH 682 503-4046
PH 214 770-8677 WWW.WTWOIL.COM
BILL WAGGONER,PRES,GEOLCPG 4602
BILL.WTWOIL@GMAIL.COM
BETTY WAGGONER,SECY/TREAS

W-B SUPPLY COMPANY
PO BOX 2479,111 N NAIDA ST
PAMPA,TX 79066 PH 806 669-1103
FAX 806 669-0369 PIPE FAX 806 665-0453
WWW.SHOPOILSUPPLIES.COM
ODESSA,TX OFFICE - 13500 W HWY 80 E STE D
PO BOX 12468,79768 PH 432 561-5852
FAX 432 561-8216
TOMMY DWORSKY,VP-OPERS
HENNESSEY,OK OFFICE/STORE - 106 E JACK
CHOATE AVE,PO BOX 205,73742
PH 405 853-2731 FAX 405 853-6637
DON WEBB,VP/COO
DEAN GIBSON,OPERS MGR (NORTHERN AREA)
JOHNNY MATHEWS,OPERS MGR (SOUTHERN AREA)
MIKE CLAYTON,CORP SLS MGR
JAMIE GOFF,OFC MGR
ROCKY BENTZ,STORE MGR
- TEXAS STORES/LOCATIONS -
PAMPA,TX STORE - 200 N PRICE RD
PO DRAWER 2479 79066-2479 PH 806 665-0901
FAX 806 669-3172 WBPAMPA@WSUPPLY.COM
JOSH SIRMANS,MGR
CARROLL LANGLEY,PUMP SHOP MGR
DOUG SHOFFNER,WAREHOUSE MGR
PERRYTON,TX STORE - 315 SE 9TH ST
PO BOX 726 79070 PH 806 435-9654
FAX 806 435-9650 WBPERRYTON@WBSUPPLY.COM
AL SHARPTON,AREA MGR
JEFF SMITH,ASST MGR
GERRY STEPHENS,PUMP SHOP MGR
WHEELER,TX - 305 E OKLAHOMA AVE
PO BOX 391 79096 PH 806 826-0775
FAX 806 826-0774 WBWHEELER@WBSUPPLY.COM
DENNY ESLIN,MGR
ALVARDO,TX STORE - 5016 E HWY 67 76009
PH 817 783-7761 FAX 817 783-3271
WBALVARDO@WBSUPPLY.COM
SOUP ALVARDO,MGR
TISH MOORE,ASST MGR
HOUSTON,TX SALES OFFICE - 4912 APPLE
SPRINGS DR PEARLAND,TX 77584
PH 281 412-0514 FAX 866 527-6335
JACLYN WENZELL JWENZELL@WBSUPPLY.COM
JOURDANTON,TX STORE - 1900 HWY 97 E 78026
PH 830 569-8777 FAX 830 569-2452
WBJOURDANTON@WBSUPPLY.COM
IRMA ROCHA,MGR
ODESSA,TX (TUMBLEWOOD WAREHOUSE) - 13500
W HWY 80 E STE D,PO BOX 12468 79768-2468
PH 432 275-0554 FAX 432 275-0555
WBODESSA@WBSUPPLY.COM
TOM DWORSKY,PUR/INVENTORY MGR
JERMEY INGMIRE,WAREHOUSE MGR
GOLDSMITH,TX STORE - 115 W GULF AVE
PO BOX 739 79741 PH 432 827-3334
PH 432 827-3356 FAX 432 827-3334
KEITH BITNER,MGR
STERLING CITY,TX STORE - 919 4TH ST

PO BOX 1129 76951 PH 325 378-3301
FAX 325 378-3311
DEAN JONES,MGR
BIG LAKE,TX STORE - 610 HWY 137
PO BOX 573 76932 PH 325 884-1228
FAX 325 884-9458
MITCH DAVIS,MGR
FORSAN,TX STORE - 309 S REX AVE
PO BOX 243 79733 PH 432 457-0014
FAX 432 457-0016
TERRY WHETSEL,MGR
MIDLAND,TX STORE - 3401 GAREN CITY HWY
PO BOX 7662,79708 PH 432 682-7337
FAX 432 682-8788
NATE STEADMON,MGR
WESTBROOK,TX STORE - 502 W THORNE
PO BOX 181 79565 PH 325 644-3711
FAX 325 644-3521
REGI ROBERTS,MGR
SUNDOWN,TX STORE - 3700 S STATE RD 303
PO BOX 944 79372 PH 806 229-6894
FAX 806 229-2229
CLYDE BOYTE,MGR
LAMESA,TX STORE - 509 S 2ND ST 79331
PH 806 870-1200 FAX 806 870-1202
DAVID ALAMAN,MGR
ANDREWS,TX STORE - 1703 W BROADWAY
PO BOX 207 79714 PH 432 524-1111
FAX 432 524-1108
JEFF BEAL,MGR
- OKLAHOMA STORES/LOCATIONS -
CHICKASHA,OK STORE/WAREHOUSE - 2803 S 4TH
73018 STORE PH 405 224-8080
FAX 405 224-8087
MARK RANKIN,STORE MGR
WHSE PH 405 224-0199 FAX 405 224-0195
MEDFORD,OK STORE - 515 N HWY 81 73759
PH 580 395-3001 FAX 580 395-3003
TIM RIDGWAY,STORE MGR
LINDSAY,OK STORE - 1112 SE 4TH 73052
PH 405 756-1614 FAX 405 756-1627
BLAKE WILSON,STORE MGR
BEAVER,OK STORE - 1302 S DOUGLAS ST 73932
H 580 625-3475 FAX 580 625-3802
WBBEAVER@WBSUPPLY.COM
BOB LINDSEY,MGR
- COLORADO/KANSAS/NEW MEXICO STORES -
EVANS,CO STORE - 3817 CARSON 80620
PH 970 352-0101 FAX 970 352-3357
WBGREELEY@WBSUPPLY.COM
KENT WOLF,MGR
JONI EVANS,ASST MGR
PARACHUTE,CO STORE - 143 1/2 UNIT B
RUSSEY AVE,PO BOX 488 81635
PH 970 285-0311 FAX 970 285-0313
WBPARACHUTE@WBSUPPLY.COM
BONNIE HANCOCK,MGR
NICOLE WELLER,ASST MGR
DENVER,CO SALES OFFICE - 5619 DTC PKWY
STE 850 GREENWOOD VILLAGE,CO 80111
PH 720 200-0535 FAX 720 529-3546
PH 303 220-0830 (TUBULAR SLS)
RENAE HOTZ RENAE@WBSUPPLY.COM
WRAY,CO STORE - 155 S ASH ST 80758
PH 970 332-3464 FAX 970 332-3467
WBWRAY@WBSUPPLY.COM

LIBERAL,KS STORE - 211 S COUNTRY ESTATE
RD,PO BOX 2557 67905 PH 620 624-4820
FAX 620 624-2482 WBLIBERAL@WBSUPPLY.COM
ANTHONY HALL,MGR
EUNICE,NM STORE - 1119 TEXAS AVE
PO BOX 96 88231 PH 575 394-2161
FAX 575 394-2858
DONNY CUETO,MGR
CARLSBAD,NM STORE - 106 S MAIN 88221
PH 575 887-0584 FAX 575 887-0586
ANDREW PARRAZ,MGR
- NORTH DAKOTA/PENNSYLVANIA STORES -
WATFORD CITY,ND STORE - 2491 HWY 85 N
PO BOX 2040 58854 PH 701 842-6991
FAX 701 842-6992 WATFORD@WBSUPPLY.COM
CHUCK HARRIS,MGR
KARRYN HARRIS,ASST MGR
WYSOX,PA STORE - 30188 ROUTE 6,18854
PH 570 268-1016 FAX 570 268-1019
KEITH THOMSON,STORE MGR

WABASH RESOURCES & CONSULTING,INC
6350 GLEN COE DR
INDIANAPOLIS,IN 46260-4750
PH 317 257-3323
KEVIN LEE STRUNK,PRES,GEOL
KSTRUNK@INDY.NET

WABON MANAGEMENT,INC
2900 WESLAYAN STE 430
HOUSTON,TX 77027 PH 713 871-1106
FAX 713 871-1616
JOHN DORN JOHNDORN@MSN.COM

WADI PETROLEUM INC
4355 SYLVANFIELD DR STE 200
HOUSTON,TX 77014 PH 281 583-2888
FAX 281 583-0504 WADI@WADIPETROLEUM.COM
BRUCE B DICE,PRES
KEVIN B DICE,VP
KIRK B DICE,VP

WADSWORTH A H,JR,GEOL
PETROLEUM & MINERAL EXPLORATION
10114 SUGAR HILL DR
HOUSTON,TX 77042-1505 PH 713 789-2354
FAX 713 789-2354

WAGGONER OSBORNE LAND SERVICES
3973 W VICKERY STE 101
FT WORTH,TX 76107 PH 817 763-8112
TODD WAGGONER,CPL/PRTNR
JOHN OSBORNE,PRTNR

WAGNER DUER III,INC
301 COMMERCE ST STE 1830,CITY CTR TWR II
FORT WORTH,TX 76102 PH 817 335-3338
FAX 817 335-3351
DUER WAGNER,III,OWNER,PRES
ROY GUINNUP,VP,FIN
DALLAS,TX BRANCH OFFICE - 2305 CEDAR
SPRINGS RD STE 400,75201 PH 214 247-4076
FAX 214 247-4069
DAVID TALBOT,ACQS MGR

WAGNER ENERGY,INC
PO BOX 79562
HOUSTON,TX 77279-9562 PH 713 827-0403
RUBY WAGNER,PRES
LINDA W WARD,SECY
JAMES G WAGNER,VP OPERS
ROSS E WAGNER,VP FIN

WAGNER OIL & GAS REPORTING INC SEE
COMBINED SYSTEMS,INC
WAGNER OIL COMPANY
500 COMMERCE ST STE 600
FORT WORTH,TX 76102-4134 PH 817 335-2222
FAX 817 338-0139
PROD FAX 817 332-3876
BRYAN WAGNER,OWNER/PRES
H ED PATTERSON,SR EXEC VP
WILLIAM W LESIKAR,CFO
MARK BELCHER,VP-RESERVOIR ENGRG
DAN EMMER,VP-GEOSCIENCE
MARK BELCHER,VP,RESERVOIR ENGR
WAGNER RESOURCES,LTD
PO BOX 79562
HOUSTON,TX 77279-9562 PH 713 827-0403
LINDA W WARD,PRTNR
JAMES G WAGNER,PRTNR
ROSS E WAGNER,PRTNR
WAGNER RICHARD,PETR GEOL
2943 CEDAR GROVE LOOP
THE VILLAGES,FL 32163 PH 315 447-8137
RAWAGNER47@GMAIL.COM
WAGUESPACK LESLIE J,SR
OIL & GAS SEVERANCE TAX ENGR
91 BURNHAM RD
BOLTON,MA 01740-1121 PH 318 234-3575
WAINWRIGHT MARK S,CPL
3017 KANSAS AVE
KENNER,LA 70065-4622 PH 504 443-5721
FAX 504 443-2410 MARKWAINWRIGHT@COX.NET
WAKEFIELD PARTEN
PO BOX 2910
BRYAN,TX 77805-2910 PH 979 589-3774
WALDRON ROBERT P,INC,GEOL CONS
9400 SHARLA DR
RIVER RIDGE,LA 70123 PH 504 738-7592
RICHARD L WALDRON,PRES
WALKER J G,JR,LTD,LLP,OIL OPR
PO BOX 6928,1121 ESE LOOP 323 STE 120
TYLER,TX 75711-6928 PH 903 561-6650
WALKER JOHN W JR SEE
CORBAN EXPLORER,INC
WALKER KELLY W OIL PROD
PO BOX 6496,1121 ESE LOOP 323 STE 120
TYLER,TX 75711-6496 PH 903 561-6650
WALKER ROBERT E & ASSOCIATES
ENVIRONMENTAL SITE ASSESSMENTS,LANDWORK
PO BOX 467
SUMRALL,MS 39482 PH 601 818-6300
ROBERT E WALKER,J.D.,CPL,ESA,GEN MGR
BOBTHELANDMAN@GMAIL.COM
WALL,VICTORIA GARDNER,ATTY
6019 WAKEFOREST AVE
HOUSTON,TX 77005-2003 PH 713 661-1580
FAX 713 661-1580
VICTORIA.G.WALL@HOTMAIL.COM
WALLACE AND WALLACE,ATTORNEYS
421 BROAD ST STE 8
UTICA,NY 13501-1210 PH 315 735-4599
FAX 315 735-4562
CWALLACE@WALLACEANDWALLACE-LAW.COM
WALLER BROTHERS,INC,OIL & GAS PROPERTIES
PO BOX 1
JACKSON,MS 39205 PH 601 352-6556
FAX 601 354-2681

EDWARD C WALLER,PRES
DONALD E WALLER,SECY/TREAS,OPERS MGR
ELLEN J WILLIAMS,SECY/BOOKKEEPER
WALSH & TRANT PETR CORP SEE
WATCO ENERGY INC
WALSH PAUL J,OIL OPR
PO BOX 131918
TYLER,TX 75713-1918 PH 214 595-2127
WALTER JIM RESOURCES,INC
PO BOX 133, 16243 HIGHWAY 216
BROOKWOOD,AL 35444-0133 PH 205 554-6131
DANN KING,LAND MGR
DANN.KING@WALTERENERGY.COM
WALTER OIL & GAS CORPORATION
1100 LOUISIANA ST STE 200
HOUSTON,TX 77002-5299 PH 713 659-1221
FAX 713 756-1177
J C WALTER,III,PRES
C J LOOKE,VP,OPERS
BRENDA ROLIARD,TREAS
JACK HORTON,CONSTR MGR
RON WILSON,VP LAND
RICHARD LUCAS,LDMN
WALTERS MANNON L,INC
6015B HECKEL RD
EVANSVILLE,IN 47725
PH 812 867-5946 FAX 812 867-5956
MANNONOIL.COM
MANNONLWALTERSINC.COM
MANNON L WALTERS,PRES
MANNON@MANNONOIL.COM
GRAPEVINE,TX OFFICE- 611 SOUTH MAIN ST
76051 PH 817 410-4777
DALE MAHAFFEY,HEAD ENGRG
WALTERS TED W,OIL PROP
P O BOX 6216
TYLER,TX 75711-6216 PH 972 561-1958
WAPITI ENERGY,LLC
800 GESSNER RD STE 700
HOUSTON,TX 77024-4257 PH 713 468-6866
FAX 713 468-0066
RICHARD E AGEE,CHRMN
BART AGEE,PRES & CEO
WARBONNET EXPLORATION COMPANY
5702 SPANISH OAK DR
HOUSTON,TX 77066-2338 PH 281 580-7546
KENNETH R LYLE,PRES
MARY LOUISE HABLINSKI,SECY,TREAS
WARD BERNIE,GEOL
315 S BROADWAY AVE STE 100
TYLER,TX 75702-7348 PH 903 592-6770
WARD GAS MARKETING,INC SEE
ONEOK GAS MARKETING COMPANY
WARD J E,JR,PETR GEOL
122 OTTO LN
SHREVEPORT,LA 71105-3356 PH 318 219-1989
FAX 318 219-1569
WARD LAKE ENERGY
685 EAST M-32
GAYLORD,MI 49735 PH 989 732-8499
DAVID BECKER,PRES
GRANT S ELLIOTT,CPL
GRANT.ELLIOTT@BELDENBLAKE.COM
NANCY M JOHNSON,CONTROLLER
JEFF RILING,PROD MGR

WARD ROYIS
2242 S HWY 83
CRYSTAL CITY,TX 78839
PH 830 374-0202 830 374-9000
FAX 830 374-0202
WARING & ASSOCIATES CORPORATION
1101 DEALERS AVE STE 200
NEW ORLEANS,LA 70123-2203 PH 504 733-3117
FAX 504 733-6040 WWW.OCSBBS.COM
WARING@OCSBBS.COM
BENJAMIN J WARING,PRES,CEO
BWARING@OCSBBS.COM
CHARLES MILLER,III,DIR OF INFO SVCS
CMILLER@OCSBBS.COM
DEE CASKEY,LEASE ANALYST/ABSTRACTER
JANEL BREAUX,ACCT PAYABLE DEPT
F WILLIAM VOLLENWEIDER,GEOL
CHUCK HOPSON,DIR OF MKTG/LDMN
NICOLE MILLER,OFC MGR
WARREN PETROLEUM CO,DIV OF GULF OIL CORP
PO BOX 10,10319 HWY 146
MONT BELVIEU,TX 77580-0010
PH 713 754-7360 FAX 713 754-7387
WARREN PETROLEUM COMPANY SEE
DYNEGY MIDSTREAM SERVICES,LP
WARTSILA NORTH AMERICA INC
819 CENTRAL AVE
JEFFERSON,LA 70121 PH 504 733-2500
FAX 504 734-7730 WWW.WARTSILA.COM
RANDALL NUNMAKER,SLS MGR
JERRY ZERINGUE,PARTS MGR
MIKE BAILEY,MKTG
KEVIN SCHULTZ,SALES
KEVIN.SCHULTZ@WARTSILA.COM
DAN WALLEY,SERVICE MGR
WASHINGTON ROTATING CONTROL HEADS,INC
63 SPRINGFIELD AVE
WASHINGTON,PA 15301 PH 724 228-8889
FAX 724 228-8912
WWW.WASHINGTONROTATING.COM
JOYCE MAYERNIK,OWNER
RICK MCKINNEY,TECH DIR
JEFF YOSKOSKY,OPERS MGR
CAMERON BROADWATER,SLS SUPPORT
WASHINGTON ROYALTIES,C/O IMPERIAL OIL CO
22499 IMPERIAL VALLEY DR
HOUSTON,TX 77073-1173 PH 281 209-1150
FAX 281 209-1154
GSWEBB@IMPERIAL-OIL-COMPANY.COM
ELLIS RUDY,PRES
GEORGE S WEBB,LAND
WASTE AUDITORS INC
PO BOX 53391,440 INDUSTRIAL PKWY STE 10
LAFAYETTE,LA 70505-3391
PH 337 269-0522 800 317-2206
FAX 337 269-0274 ADMIN@WASTEAUDITORS.COM
WWW.WASTEAUDITORS.COM
IRVING PRATT,PRES/CEO
CHAD EDEN,VP/SAFETY/HR
WASTEWATER DISPOSAL SERVICES,INC
PO BOX 649
BREWTON,AL 36427-0649
PH 251 867-5413 FAX 251 867-5427
RAY ROBERTSON,JR
SRROBERTSON@LEIGHPLACE.COM

WASTEWATER SPECIALTIES INC
2205 INDUSTRIAL DR
SULPHUR,LA 70665-8330
PH 888 436-6805 FAX 318 436-6758
SAM J DIGIGLIA,PRES
BRETT J FELDES,OPERS MGR

WASTEX CO INC
PO BOX 1737,109 TEXAS AVE
WASKOM,TX 75692 PH 903 687-2733
SAM F COOKE,PRES

WATERBURY ENTERPRISES,INC
PO BOX 126
MOUNT CARMEL,IL 62863-0126
PH 618 262-7012 FAX 618 262-7442
WEIOIL91@FRONTIER.COM
RIAN P WATERBURY,PRES

WATERLINK C'TREAT OFFSHORE
309 BRIAR ROCK RD
THE WOODLANDS,TX 77380-3529
PH 281 367-2800 FAX 281 367-1761
TERRY DUPUIS,PRES
DOUGLAS DELLMORE,EXEC VP
CHARLES BOLIN,VP,MFG

WATKINS H VAUGHAN,JR
7570 OLD CANTON RD STE 201
MADISON,MS 39110 PH 601 898-9347
VAUGHAN WATKINS

WATSON DAVE P
PO BOX 51722
LAFAYETTE,LA 70505-1722 PH 337 277-0752
DWATSON305@AOL.COM

WATSON DEVELOPMENT CO
PO BOX 2253
MIDLAND,TX 79702-2253
PH 432 683-3131 FAX 432 683-3131
WILLIAM G WATSON,PRES

WATSON LAND & TITLE,INC
PO BOX 1216
LAKE CHARLES,LA 70602-1216
PH 318 436-6044 FAX 318 439-6358
WADE E WATSON,PRES

WATSON REPORT SERVICE
PO BOX 921,3106 STONE RD
KILGORE,TX 75663-0921 PH 903 984-3443
FAX 903 983-2526
CHARLA ROLPH,OWNER/AGENT

WATSON WILLIAM T,LLC
1651 MCFARLAND BLVD N
TUSCALOOSA,AL 35406-2212
PH 205 345-1577 FAX 205 345-1583
TOM WATSON,ATTY TWATSON@WDHLLP.COM
DEBRA WALKER,PARALEGAL

WATT BECKWORTH THOMPSON HENNEMAN
& SULLIVAN LLP
711 LOUISIANA ST STE 1800 S TOWER
HOUSTON,TX 77008 PH 713 333-9125
JAMES T THOMPSON
JATHOMPSON@WATTBECKWORTH.COM

WATTS BOBBY EXCAVATING INC
1703 S COLLEGE ST
DECATUR,TX 76234-2822
PH 940 627-5315 FAX 940 627-5317
WWW.BOBBYWATTSEXCAVATIONINC.COM
BOBBYWATTS@EMBARQMAIL.COM

WCT LEASING CO
PO BOX 341809

AUSTIN,TX 78734 PH 512 261-7700
GENE VILLANUEVA,FIN VP
GENEVILLANUEVA@AUSTIN.RR.COM

WEATHERFORD
2000 ST JAMES PL
HOUSTON,TX 77056 PH 713 693-4000
FAX 800 257-3826 WWW.WEATHERFORD.COM

- WEATHERFORD US LP -

ADDISON,TX OFFICE - 14135 MIDWAY RD
STE G-100,75001 PH 972 702-9222
FAX 972 243-1104
ALICE,TX OFFICE - 250 S FLOURNEY RD
78332 PH 361 668-8362 FAX 361 668-8621
ANCHORAGE,AK OFFICE - 12860 OLD SEWARD
HWY,99515 PH 907 561-1632
FAX 907 345-7513
ARCADIA,LA OFFICE - 6161 HWY 80,71001
PH 800 736-8560 FAX 318 263-9072
ARDMORE,OK OFFICE - 911 W BROADWAY
STE 208,73401 PH 580 490-9888
FAX 580 490-9889
ARTESIA,NM OFFICE - 11357 LOVINGTON HWY
88210 PH 575 746-8882 FAX 575 746-4577
BAKERSFIELD,CA OFFICE - 21139 BURGESS CT
93312-9714 PH 661 587-9773
FAX 661 587-4175
BOSSIER CITY,LA OFFICE - 3813 NO.2 SHED
RD 71111 PH 318 747-6860 FAX 318 747-6861
BRAWLEY,CA OFFICE - 1509 RIVER DR 92227
PH 760 344-7550 FAX 760 344-6323
BRIDGEPORT,TX OFFICE - 1650 CUBA RD
76426-6716 PH 940 683-8389
FAX 940 683-8398
BRYAN,TX OFFICE - 820 INDUSTRIAL BLVD
77803 PH 979 822-4594
CANONSBURG,PA OFFICE - 121 HILLPOINTE DR
STE 300,15317 PH 724 745-7050
FAX 724 745-7342
CASPER,WY OFFICE - 2122 MELODI LN 82601
PH 307 266-1873 FAX 307 266-3939
COMPTON-RANCHO DOMINQUEZ,CA OFFICE -
19722 S ALAMEDA ST 90221 PH 310 635-7125
FAX 310 763-4067
CONWAY,AR OFFICE - 235 TILK,72032
PH 501 764-1950 FAX 501 336-6590
CORPUS CHRISTI,TX OFFICE - 442 NAVIGATION
78408-2748 PH 361 904 0300
FAX 361 904-0304
COVINGTON,LA OFFICE - 60 LOUIS PRIMA
UNIT B,70433 PH 985 893-6628
FAX 985 893-9749
DEADHORSE,AK OFFICE - AIRPORT WAY,POUCH
#340120,LAKE COLLEEN RD,POUCH #340120
99734 PH 907 659-2356 FAX 907 659-2156
DENVER,CO OFFICE - 410 17TH ST STE 400
80202 FAX 303 825-2927
DENVER CITY,TX OFFICE - 1251 STATE HWY 83
79323 PH 806 592-3407 FAX 806 592-7012
EDINBURG,TX OFFICE - 3 1/2 MI N HWY 281
78539 PH 956 687-8536 FAX 956 381-6893
EDLERTON,PA OFFICE - 124 WINDY RIDGE LN
15736 PH 724 354-3090 FAX 724 354-4188
ELK CITY,OK OFFICE - 1800 S MERRIT RD
PH 580 225-4400 FAX 580 225-1281

EVANS,CO OFFICE - 4329 BRANTNER RD 80620
PH 970 339-9747 FAX 970 339-9741
73644 PH 580 225-4400 FAX 580 225-1281
FARMINGTON,NM OFFICE - 5432 HWY 64,87401
PH 575 327-5180 FAX 575 325-8893
FORT SMITH,AR OFFICE - 8820 HWY 271 S
72908-7962 PH 479 646-8866
FAX 479 646-3502
GRAND JUNCTION,CO OFFICE - 1101 WINTERS
AVE,UNIT B 81501 PH 970 245-5610
FAX 970 245-5616
HASLET,TX OFFICE - 1150 BLUE MOUND RD W
STE 201 PH 817 439-2123 FAX 817 439-2142
HOBBS,NM OFFICE - 8600 LOVINGTON HWY
88240-8838 PH 575 392-7770
FAX 575 392-1574
HOUMA,LA OFFICE - 9868 E MAIN 70363
PH 985 851-0600 FAX 985 868-6836
HOUSTON,TX OFFICE - 15710 JOHN F KENNEDY
BLVD,WORLD HOUSTON PLAZA,77032
PH 281 260-1300 FAX 281 260-5672
HUNTSVILLE,TX OFFICE - 7587 HWY 75 SOUTH
77340 PH 936 295-0080 FAX 936 291-6802
KILGORE,TX OFFICE - 2013 HWY 135 N,75662
PH 903 984-5541 FAX 903 984-2335
LAFAYETTE,LA OFFICE - 202 RUE IBERVILLE
STE 310,ENERGY PLAZA OFFICE BLDG 70508
PH 337 291-2485 FAX 337 291-9893
LAKE CHARLES,LA OFFICE - 120 FREDS RD
70601 PH 800 492-3351 FAX 337 433-6532
LAREDO,TX OFFICE - HWY 359 E 78043
PH 956 723-2056 FAX 956 723-9370
LAUREL,MS OFFICE - 1315 HILLCREST
39440 PH 601 428-1551 FAX 601 428-8624
LIBERAL,KS OFFICE - 121 S COUNTRY ESTATES
RD 67901 PH 620 624-9324 FAX 620 624-9329
LINDSAY,OK OFFICE - 1/2 MILE N ON HWY 76
WEST SIDE 73052 PH 405 756-4331
FAX 405 756-8268
LONGVIEW,TX OFFICE - 21 FRJ DR 75602
PH 903 236-7879 FAX 903 236-0846
MAYFLOWER,AR OFFICE - 30 WHEELER RD 72106
PH 501 470-1549 FAX 501 470-0459
MCALLEN,TX OFFICE - 1117 E TAMARACK 78501
PH 956 994-8729 FAX 956 994-8962
MIDLAND,TX OFFICE - #10 DESTA DR STE 350
E 79705 PH 432 687-3048 FAX 432 683-2205
MINOT,ND OFFICE - 5000 7TH AVE SW 58701
PH 701 420-9740 FAX 704 420-9743
NEW IBERIA,LA OFFICE - 1416 W ADMIRAL
DOYLE WAY 70560 PH 337 560-1220
FAX 337 560-5559
NEW ORLEANS,LA OFFICE - 1201 DEALERS AVE
70123 PH 504 733-5555 FAX 504 733-0651
NIKISKI,AK OFFICE - MILE 26 1/2 KENAI
SPURR HWY 99635 PH 907 776-8148
FAX 907 776-5531
NORTON,VA OFFICE - 545 HAWTHORNE DR
PH 276 679-0050 FAX 276 679-0067
ODESSA,TX OFFICE - 3935 S CR 1292
79711 PH 432 563-2255 FAX 432 563-2346
OKLAHOMA CITY,OK OFFICE - 6525 N MERIDIAN
AVE, STE 201 73116
PH 405 773-1100 FAX 405 773-1200
OZONA,TX OFFICE - 211 CROCKETT LN 76943
PH 325 392-3715 FAX 325 392-2994

PALESTINE,TX OFFICE - 3100 W OAK 75801
PH 903 729-2106
PEARLAND,TX OFFICE - 3632 S MAIN 77581
PH 281 485-1899 FAX 281 485-4784
PERRYTON,TX OFFICE - 301 E 9TH ST 79070
PH 806 434 2671 FAX 806 434-2673
POCOLA,OK OFFICE - 301 HWY 112 N
74902-3396 PH 918 436-1922
FAX 918 436-8122
POWELL,WY OFFICE - 415 ALAN RD, 82435
PH 307 754-9554 FAX 307 754-1583
RIO VISTA,CA OFFICE - 1000 CHURCH RD
94571 PH 707 374-6493 FAX 707 374-6192
RIVERTON,WY OFFICE - 2510 AIRPORT RD
82501 PH 307 857-6848 FAX 307 857-2460
ROCK SPRINGS,WY OFFICE - 512 N ENERGY RD
82901 PH 307 362-4224 FAX 307 362-4225
SAN ANTONIO,TX OFFICE - 1250 NE LOOP 410
STE 215 78209 PH 210 930-7588
FAX 210 930-7610
SANTA PAULA,CA OFFICE - 201 S HALLOCK DR
93060 PH 805 933-0200 FAX 805 525-1079
SCHRIEVER,LA OFFICE - 249 WEATHERFORD DR
PH 985 493-6400 FAX 985 493-6490
SCOTT,LA OFFICE - 100 N PAT ST 70583
PH 337 269-5976 FAX 337 269-1641
SEARCY,AR OFFICE - 111 W BOOTH RD
PH 501 268-0900 FAX 501 268-2645
SHREVEPORT,LA OFFICE - 1005 MARS BLVD
71107 318 429-4997 FAX 318 424-5227
SNYDER,TX OFFICE - 3505 23RD ST 79549
PH 325 573-3563 FAX 325 573-7263
SONORA,TX OFFICE - 3269 S SERVICE RD
76950 PH 325 387-3280 FAX 325 387-9316
SOUTH WILLIAMSPORT,PA OFFICE - 359 OLD
MONTGOMERY PIKE PH 570 326-2754
FAX 570-326-2501
TITUSVILLE,PA OFFICE - 11046 SKYLINE DR
16354 PH 814 827-4034 FAX 814 827-3115
TRINIDAD,CO OFFICE - 3801 FREEDOM RD
81082 PH 719 846-0015 FAX 719 846-0016
TULSA,OK OFFICE - WILLIAMS CENTER TOWER I
ONE WEST THIRD ST,STE 1210 74103
PH 918 529-1776 FAX 91 582-3458
VENTURA,CA OFFICE - 250 W STANLEY AVE
93001 PH 805 643-1200 FX 805 652-1480
VERNAL,UT OFFICE - 2620 S 1500 EAST 84078
PH 432 789-0445 FAX 435 789-3612
WEATHERFORD,OK OFFICE - 1201 LOOMIS RD
73096 PH 580 772-8133 FAX 580 772-8141
WESTON,WV OFFICE - 132E 6TH ST 26542
PH 304 269-3290 FAX 304 269-6784
WHITE OAK,TX OFFICE - 1316 HWY 42, 75693
PH 903 295-0473 FAX 903 295-5867
WILBURTON,OK OFFICE - 1704 E ROCK ISLAND
BLVD,HWY 270 E,74578 PH 918 465-3500
FAX 918 465-3507
WILLISTON,ND OFFICE - AKA 3520 2ND AVE W
58801 PH 701 572-6714 FAX 701 572-0220
WOODWARD,OK OFFICE - 607 MARTIN RD,73801
PH 580 256-3888 FAX 580 256-3883

- WEATHERFORD ARTIFICIAL LIFT SYSTEMS -

ANCHORAGE,AK OFFICE - 12860 OLD SEWARD
HWY 99515 PH 907 248-1005

FAX 907 243-4350
ANDREWS,TX OFFICE - 203 ALBRIGHT RD,79714
PH 432 524-5003 FAX 432 523-6360
ARTESIA,NM OFFICE - 2404 PARKLAND,88210
FAX 575 746-8902
ASPERMONT,TX OFFICE - 8401 US HWY 83 N
79502 PH 940 989-3545 FAX 940 989-2216
BAKERSFIELD,CA OFFICE - 21728 ROSEDALE
HWY 93314 PH 661 589-3883
FAX 661 589-4744
BENBROOK,TX OFFICE - 113 SPROLES
PH 817 249-7325 FAX 817 249-4248
BIG LAKE,TX OFFICE - HWY 137 & 12TH ST
76932 PH 325 884-2354 FAX 325 884-3516
BIG SPRING,TX OFFICE - 1409 E HWY 350
79720-0477 PH 432 267-6525
FAX 432 267-6599
BROUSSARD,LA OFFICE - 3724 PINHOOK RD
70518 PH 337 232-4250 FAX 337 837-6568
CASPER,WY OFFICE - 2690 OIL DR 82604
PH 307 266-4227 FAX 307 266-4240
CHARLESTON,WV OFFICE - 300 SUMMERS
STE 820,25301 PH 304 344-8290
FAX 304 344-8296
CLEBURNE,TX OFFICE - 1975 PIPELINE RD
PH 817 641-4700 FAX 817 641-4705
CLINTON,OK OFFICE - 1717 SOUTH 28TH 73601
PH 580 334-3520 FAX 580 323-3855
COAHOMA,TX OFFICE - 311 NE BROADWAY 79511
PH 432 394-4289 FAX 432 394-4989
COLORADO SPRINGS,CO - 3445 N MARKSHEFFEL
RD 80922 PH 713 574-1090 FAX 719 637-9545
CORPUS CHRISTI,TX OFFICE - 6720 LEOPARD
78409 PH 361 289-1858 FAX 361 289-1892
DECATUR,TX OFFICE - 3000/3261 BUSINESS
HWY 287 S,76234 PH 940 627-2817
FAX 940 627-6724
DENVER CITY,TX OFFICE - 2541 STATE HWY
214,79323 PH 806 592-3827
FAX 806 592-7961
DICKINSON,ND OFFICE - 2780 5TH AVE W
58601 PH 701 227-8768 FAX 701 227-8769
EL DORADO,KS OFFICE - 622 OIL HILL RD
67042 PH 316 321-1604 FAX 316 321-4425
ELK CITY,OK OFFICE - 200 HUGHES ACCESS RD
73644-9146 PH 580 225-5926
FAX 580 225-5947
ELKVIEW,WV OFFICE - 4996 S ELK RIVER RD
25071 PH 304 965-1562 FAX 304 965-3606
FARMINGTON,NM OFFICE - 514 E ANIMAS ST
87401 PH 575 326-5141 FAX 575 326-4141
FORT WORTH,TX OFFICE - 500 W 7TH ST
STE 702 PH 817 882-9955 FAX 817 882-9966
FT SMITH,AR OFFICE - 6513 STATE LINE RD
72903 PH 479 646-2439
GIDDINGS,TX OFFICE - 1596 S LEON ST 78942
PH 979 542-5154 FAX 979 542-6202
GILLETTE,WY OFFICE - 3307 E 2ND ST 82716
PH 307 682-8056 FAX 307 682-1513
GRAYVILLE,IL OFFICE - 125 INDUSTRIAL PARK
PH 618 375 6611 FAX 618 375-7212
GREENVILLE,TX OFFICE - 6501 LEE ST 75401
PH 903 455-4441 FAX 903 455-4952
HENNESSEY,OK OFFICE - HWY 81 S 73742
PH 405 853-7181 FAX 405 853-2645
HOBBS,NM OFFICE - 1213 W COUNTY RD 88240

PH 575 397-1165 FAX 575 397-3750
HOUSTON,TX OFFICE - 918 HODGKINS 77032
PH 281 449-1383 FAX 281 449-6235
KEENE,ND OFFICE - RR5 BOX 276,58701
PH 701 774-1030 FAX 701 774-1169
KERMIT,TX OFFICE - 159 W HWY 302
PH 432 586-3883 FAX 432 208-1070
KILGORE,TX OFFICE - 2706 HWY 135 N,75662
PH 903 984-1543 FAX 903 984-5291
LAFAYETTE,LA OFFICE - 104 SIGNAL CIRCLE
70508 PH 337 839-8871 FAX 337 837-0013
LAUREL,MS OFFICE - 2932 INDUSTRIAL BLVD
39440 PH 601 649-4467 FAX 601 428-5522
LEETSDALE,PA OFFICE - 100 LEETSDALE
INDUSTRIAL DR 15056 PH 724 318-1050
FAX 724 318-1049
LEVELLAND,TX OFFICE - 1909 W HWY 114
79336 PH 806 894-6653 FAX 806 894-8754
LONGVIEW,TX OFFICE - 21 FRJ DR 75602
PH 903 553-1433 FAX 903 553-1715
LULING,TX OFFICE - 202 E FANNIN 78648
PH 830 875-2435 FAX 830 875-9436
MARSHALL,TX OFFICE - 5605 MEDCO DR 75672
PH 903 935-2416 FAX 903 935-3803
MIDLAND,TX OFFICE - 10000 CR 116 W
79711 PH 432 561-5505 FAX 432 561-5604
MONTEREY,LA OFFICE - 113 BEARD RD 71354
PH 318 386-7532 FAX 318 386-8023
NEW ORLEANS,LA OFFICE - 1010 COMMON ST
STE 1600,70112 PH 800 394-2614
FAX 504 671-8955
NORPHELT,AR OFFICE - 211 E CROTTY RD
71759 FAX 870 546-3514
ODESSA,TX OFFICE - 8866 W LOOP 338 N
79764 PH 432 363-0462 FAX 432 363-0013
OKLAHOMA CITY,OK OFFICE - 717 N MORGAN RD
73127 PH 405 577-5590 FAX 405 577-5593
PERRYTON,TX OFFICE - NW LOOP 143,79070
PH 806 435-6801 FAX 805 435-6803
POWELL,WY OFFICE - 415 ALAN RD, 82435
PH 307 754-7234 FAX 307 754-5875
PRICE,UT OFFICE - 3288 S 225 WEST,84501
PH 435 637-2497 FAX 435 637-2541
PUNXSUTAWNEY,PA OFFICE - 106 BLOSE RD
15767 PH 814 938-9662 FAX 814 938-3351
RATLIFF CITY,OK OFFICE - 220 HWY 7 WEST
73481 PH 580 856-3095 FAX 580 856-3981
RIVERTON,WY OFFICE - 2510 AIRPORT RD
82501 PH 307 857-0090
ROCK SPRINGS,WY OFFICE 416 & 565C MOHAWK
82901 PH 307 362-1883 FAX 307 362-7677
ROOSEVELT,UT OFFICE - 1555 S 2000 W 84066
PH 435 722-0990 FAX 435 722-2087
SCOTT,LA OFFICE - 200 APOLLO RD 70583
PH 337 232-8198 FAX 337 234-1008
SIDNEY,MT OFFICE - HWY 16 59270
PH 701 774-1030 FAX 701 774-1169
SIGNAL HILL,CA OFFICE - 3356 LIME AVE
90755 PH 562-0931 FAX 562-988-1035
TULSA,OK OFFICE - 6217 S MINGO RD 74133
PH 918 459-0476 FAX 918 459-0590
VENTURA,CA OFFICE - 400 ROCKLITE RD 93001
PH 805 643-1279 FAX 805 643-8298
VERNAL,UT OFFICE - 5203 S 4630 E 74078
PH 435 789-5808 FAX 435 789-4922
VICTORIA,TX OFFICE - 90 CRAWFORD DR 77904

PH 361 575-2328 FAX 361 575-2155
WICHITA FALLS,TX OFFICE - 6013 JACKSBORO
HWY, 76302 PH 940 767-2081
FAX 940 761-3274
WILLISTON,ND OFFICE - 2304 4TH AVE WEST
58801 PH 701 774-1030 FAX 701 774-1169
WOODWARD,OK OFFICE - 600 AIRPARK RD,73801
PH 580 254-3997 FAX 580 256-0411
YUKON,OK OFFICE - 11133 NW 10TH ST, 73099
PH 405 350-3357 FAX 405 350-1002

- COMPUTALOG USA -

ALICE,TX OFFICE - 2280 HARKINS AVE,78332
PH 361 661-1726 FAX 361 661-1514
FARMINGTON,NM 87401 - 1121 MADISON LN
87401 PH 575 564-9131 FAX 575 325-0627
KREBS,OK OFFICE - 1200 W WASHINGTON
PH 918 426-3000 FAX 918 426-3300
ODESSA,TX OFFICE - 2800 E I-20,79766
PH 432 580-8443 FAX 432 580-4967
ROCK SPRINGS,WY OFFICE - 46 WILKINS PEAK
PH 307 362-7131 FAX 307 362-7133

- PRECISION ENERGY SERVICES -

BENBROOK,TX OFFICE - 7500 BENBROOK PKWY
76126 PH 817 443-3080 FAX 817 249-7090
CASPER,WY OFFICE - 1929 SKYVIEW DR,82601
PH 307 472-9078 FAX 307 472-9081
DUNBAR,WV OFFICE - 402 28TH ST
PH 304 768-4933 FAX 304 768-4972
GRAND JUNCTION,CO OFFICE - 719 ARROWEST
CT 81505 PH 970 262-8501 FAX 970 242-2687
LONDON,KY OFFICE - 40 WESTINGHOUSE DR
40741 PH 606 864-9165 FAX 606 878-9130
OKLAHOMA CITY,OK OFFICE - 2800 S MERIDIAN
73179 PH 405 681-1095 FAX 405 685-7501
TYLER,TX OFFICE - 9464 FM 2767 75708
PH 903 535-8265 FAX 903 535-8268

- INTERNATIONAL LOGGING INC -

MIDLAND,TX OFFICE - 1000 S GOODE ST,79701
PH 432 687-1823 FAX 432 687-1689

- WEATHERFORD INTERNATIONAL INC -

BENBROOK,TX OFFICE - 7504 BENBROOK PKWY
PH 817 443-3004 FAX 972 409-6016
SHREVEPORT,LA OFFICE - 1005 MARS BLVD
71107 PH 318 429-4997 FAX 318 424-5227
VERNAL,UT OFFICE 2644 S 1500 EAST 84078
PH 435 781-0324 FAX 435 781-0326

- WEATHERFORD DRILLING INTERNATIONAL -

HOUSTON,TX OFFICE - 10920 WEST SAM
HOUSTON PKWY STE 100 PH 281 807-2100
FAX 281 807 2150

- WEATHERFORD CANADA PARTNERSHIP -

BLACKFALDS,ALBERTA,CAN OFFICE- 4300 SOUTH
ST T0M0J0 PH 403 885-4412
FAX 403 885-5454

BONNYVILLE,ALBERTA,CAN OFFICE-6401 49 AVE
T9N2N7 PH 780 826-6339 FAX 780 826-5882
BROOKS,ALBERTA,CAN OFC- 250 INDUSTRIAL RD
T1R1B9 PH 403 362-8880 FAX 403 362-4424
CALGARY,ALBERTA,CAN OFFICE-333 5TH AVE SW
STE 1100 T2P3B6 PH 403 693-7500
FAX 403 693-7724
CLAIRMONT,ALBERTA,CAN OFC- 8001 102ND ST
T0H0W0 PH 780 539-6400 FAX 780 539-7027
CROSSFIELD,ALBERTA,CAN OFFICE- 42 MCCOOL
CRESCENT T0M0S0 PH 403 946-2399
FAX 403 946-4675
DARTMOUTH,NOVA SCOTIA CANADA OFFICE-
121 THORNHILL B3B1S2 PH 902 468-4606
FAX 902 468-2606
DRESDEN,ONTARIO,CAN OFC-25351 KENT BRIDGE
RD PH 519 683-2010 FAX 519 683-2577
EDMONTON,ALBERTA,CAN OFFICE-2204 64TH AVE
T6P1Z3 PH 780 395-8900 FAX 780 469-0744
EDSON,ALBERTA,CAN OFFICE- BENCH CREEK
INDUSTRIAL PARK T7E1T1 PH 780 723-2336
FAX 780 723-6424
ESTEVAN,SASKATCHEWAN,CAN OFFICE-
422 MISSISSIPPIAN DR S4A2H8
PH 306 634-2924 FAX 306 634-3404
FORT NELSON,B.C.,CAN OFFICE-4751 44TH AVE
BAY #1,2,&3 PH 250 774-7772
FAX 250 774-7773
FORT ST JOHN,B.C.,CAN OFFICE- ALASKA HWY
MILE 49 V1J4M7 PH 250 785-7038
FAX 250 785-0447
GRANDE PRAIRIE,ALBERTA,CAN OFFICE-
11489 95 AVE T8V5P7 PH 780 539-3163
FAX 780 539-1033
HARDISTY,ALBERTA,CAN OFFICE- 4612 47TH ST
T0B1V0 PH 780 888-3933 FAX 780 888-3812
HIGH LEVEL,ALBERTA,CAN OFFICE-11908 95 ST
T0H1Z0 PH 780 926-4046 FAX 780 926-4048
HINTON,ALBERTA,CAN OFC- 116 HAMPSHIRE RD
#5 T7V1G8 PH 780 865-4552
FAX 780 865-4530
KERROBERT,SASKATCHEWAN,CAN OFFICE-
5 ALBERTA AVE S S0L1R0 PH 780 834-5577
FAX 306 834-5999
LLOYDMINSTER,ALBERTA,CAN OFFICE-
4604 62ND AVE T9V2V4 PH 780 871-2333
FAX 780 871-2339
NISKU,ALBERTA,CAN OFFICE- 507 13TH AVE
T9E7P4 PH 780 955-7933 FAX 780 955-2973
PARADISE,NEWFOUNDLAND,CAN OFFICE-
8 ST ANNE'S CRESCENT A1L1A0
PH 709 782-8683 FAX 709 782-8688
RED DEER,ALBERTA,CAN OFFICE- 6767 GOLDEN
WEST AVE T4P1A7 PH 403 340-2505
FAX 403 340-2514
WEYBURN,SASKATCHEWAN,CAN OFC- 24 12TH ST
NE S4H1K2 PH 306 842-2699
FAX 306 842-0676
WHITECOURT,ALBERTA,CAN OFFICE- 3903 35 ST
T7S1N7 PH 780 778-8080 FAX 780 778-8581
DR 62844 PH 618 375-6611 FAX 618 375-7212

WEATHERFORD ARTIFICAL LIFT SYSTEMS SEE
WEATHERFORD
WEATHERFORD DRILLING INTERNATIONAL SEE
WEATHERFORD

WEATHERFORD INTERNATIONAL INC SEE
WEATHERFORD
WEATHERFORD US LP SEE
WEATHERFORD
WEATHERS DON,OIL ROYALTIES
3401 HEINES DR
TYLER,TX 75701-9034 PH 903 597-3464
WEBB OIL & GAS EXPLORATION
PO BOX 98
HEFLIN,LA 71039-0098 PH 318 226-1676
D W WEBB,OWNER
WEBB SHANNON & HAAS,INC SEE
WSH LAND (LANDMEN)
WEDEBERG JIM
333 TEXAS ST STE 1106
SHREVEPORT,LA 71101-3679
PH 318 424-4314
WEDGE DIA-LOG,INC SEE
BAKER ATLAS
WEDGE WIRELINE,INC SEE
BAKER ATLAS
WEEKS ENVIRONMENTAL LLC
PO BOX 1169
PREMONT,TX 78375-1169 PH 361 348-4700
FAX 361 348-4500
WEIBYE CAROLYN S
3272 WESTHEIMER RD STE 11
HOUSTON,TX 77098-1008 PH 713 526-1089
FAX 713 526-1345
CWEIBYE@YAHOO.COM
WEIL RESOURCES INC
PO BOX 163,74 N AURORA ST
LANCASTER,NY 14086-0163 PH 716 684-3800
FAX 716 684-3802
KATHLEEN A WEIL,PRES
WEIMER,LTD
PO BOX 2020
TYLER,TX 75710
PH 903 535-4266 FAX 903 535-4247
JOSEPH E HAND JR,SR VP (REGIONS BK)
JOEY.HAND@REGIONS.COM
PATRICIA NARRAMORE TRUST
REGIONS BANK,TRUSTEE
WEINMAN GEOSCIENCE SEE
GLOBAL GEOPHYSICAL SERVICES INC
WEISER-BROWN OPERATING COMPANY
PO BOX 500,117 E CALHOUN
MAGNOLIA,AR 71754-0500 PH 870 234-3050
FAX 870 234-3839
CHRIS WEISER,PRES
RALPH WEISER
NATE CALDWELL,OPERS
WELCH ROBERT A,FOUNDATION,THE
5555 SAN FELIPE ST STE 1900
HOUSTON,TX 77056-2730 PH 713 961-9884
WWW.WELCH1.ORG
NORBERT DITTRICH,PRES
WELCH VAN S,II
2901 WILDWOOD PL
DUNCAN,OK 73533-1183 PH 580 255-7153
WELDER EXPLORATION & PRODUCTION INC
100 W OLMOS DR
SAN ANTONIO,TX 78212
PH 210 354-1515 FAX 210 472-1756
WWW.WELDERGROUP.COM INFO@WELDER-
GROUP.COM

WELEX,A HALLIBURTON CO SEE
   HALLIBURTON LOGGING SERVICES,INC

WELKER INC.
   13839 W BELLFORT ST
   SUGAR LAND,TX 77498 PH 800 776-7267
   FAX 281 491-8344 WWW.WELKERENG.COM
      SALES@WELKERENG.COM

WELL COMPLETION TECHNOLOGY
   7903 ALAMAR DR
   HOUSTON,TX 77095-2840
   PH 281 859-6464 FAX 281 855-3004
      WWW.WCTHOU.COM
      WILLIAM K OTT,PRES
      BILLOTT@WCTHOU.COM

WELL CONTROL SCHOOL
   16770 IMPERIAL VALLEY DR STE 290
   HOUSTON,TX 77060 PH 713 849-7400
   FAX 713 849-7474 STAFF@WELLCONTROL.COM
      WWW.WELLCONTROL.COM

WELL STIMULATION INC
   5606 PENINSULA PARK DR
   HOUSTON,TX 77041-6417 PH 281 217-6690
      A RICHARD SINCLAIR,PE,PRES

WELL-FLOW INTERNATIONAL,LLC
   312 PEARL PKWY UNIT 2403
   SAN ANTONIO,TX 78215-1295 PH 337 232-3466
   PH 800 245-4620 FAX 337 232-2810
      WWW.WELL-FLOW.COM INQUIRY@WELL-
      FLOW.COM
      PAUL BELL,PRES
      PHIL MCINTYRE,MNGNG DIR
      ROGER MALLETT,SALES

WELLBORN GEORGE G JR OIL ACCT,LLC
   196 TRACY DR PRIVATE
   EL DORADO,AR 71730-9163 PH 870 866-3495
      GEORGE G WELLBORN JR,OWNER/OPER

WELLCO SERVICES
   ENVIRONMENTAL SVCS
   5423 LOTUS
   HOUSTON,TX 77085-1903 PH 713 729-1440
   FAX 713 729-1496
      JIMMY DAVIS,OWNER

WELLS ALBERT G JR,GEOL
   25 CREEKWOOD CIR
   RICHARDSON,TX 75080-2677 PH 361 664-1591

WELLS CONSULTING
   4276 SOUTHMOOR PARK
   LEXINGTON,KY 40514-1816 PH 606 269-3517
      DAN WELLS,P.G.

WELLS FARGO OIL,GAS & MINERAL MGT GROUP
   201 MAIN ST STE 400
   FT WORTH,TX 76102 PH 817 334-7460
      PAUL MIDKIFF,CPL,MGR
      BRYAN FRAZIER PH 817 334-7031
   DENVER,COLORADO OFC - 1700 LINCOLN ST
      48TH FLOOR,80203-4500
      TIM DAVIES PH 303 863-5705
      EVAN BEKKEDAHL PH 303 863-5022
      DUSTY MADISON PH 303 863-5719
   JACKSONVILLE,FL OFC - 3563 PHILLIPS HWY
      BLDG F 1ST FLOOR,32207-5663
      LINN WILLERS PH 904 360-1653
      JON JOHNSON PH 904 360-1652
   MIDLAND,TX OFC - 500 W TEXAS AVE
      STE 760,79701-4200
      ROBERT SYKES PH 432 685-5131

      BRENDA ROGERS PH 432 685-5228
      JACKIE SELF PH 432 685-5294
      CHUCK WALLACE PH 432 685-5148
      MAYRA WIGGINS PH 432 685-5132
   SAN ANTONIO,TX OFC - 750 E MULBERRY AVE
      STE 402,78212-3159
      JERRY DITTMAR PH 210 856-5144
      SHANNON ECKOLS PH 210 856-5117
      PETE KEEDY PH 210 856-5063

WELLS H D OIL & GAS EXPLOR & DEV,INC
   PO BOX 1785
   CHARLESTON,WV 25326-1785
   PH 304 346-2829 FAX 304 346-2829
      H D WELLS,III,PRES

WELLS RESOURCES,INC
   PO BOX 513
   CLIFTON,TX 76634-0513
   PH 254 675-4600 FAX 254 675-4601
      STEPHEN A WELLS,PRES SWELLS01@VVM.COM
      JUDY B WELLS,SECY/TREAS
   ROGERS,TX ACCOUNTING & RANCH OFFICE -
      PO BOX 39,76569 PH 254 642-3510
      FAX 254 642-3766
      RAN K WELLS,VP
      JOANNA F KING,ACCT

WELSH OIL CO,INC
   PO BOX 5003
   SHREVEPORT,LA 71135-5003 PH 318 429-1400
   FAX 318 429-2114
      JOHN J WELSH,PRES

WENTWORTH OIL CO
   10 WAVERLY LN
   NATCHEZ,MS 39120-8669 PH 601 442-1696
      JAMES C WENTWORTH
      DAVID N HEARD

WEPCO ENERGY,LLC
   PO BOX 849
   TRAVERSE CITY,MI 49685-0849
   PH 231 932-8615 FAX 231 932-8635
      EDWARD C WALKER,CHRMN
   CASTLE ROCK,CO OFFICE - 12943 HORIZON TR
      80108 PH 303 771-8551 FAX 303 771-9514
      RICHARD K ELLIS,PRES

WESLEY WEST CATTLE LP
   PO BOX 7
   HOUSTON,TX 77001-0007 PH 713 520-0400

WESLEY WEST MINERALS LTD
   PO BOX 7
   HOUSTON,TX 77001-0007 PH 713 520-0400

WEST BAY EXPLORATION CO
   13685 S WEST BAY SHORE DR STE 200
   TRAVERSE CITY,MI 49684-1399
   PH 231 946-0200 FAX 231 946-8180
      WWW.WESTBAYEXPLORATION.COM
      ROBERT E TUCKER JR,PRES
      PAT GIBSON,VP,LAND/LEGAL
      KATIE GIBSON,VP,FIN
      MATTHEW A JOHNSTON,GEOPHY
      MURRAY M MATSON,SR GEOL
      TIMOTHY L BAKER,VP OPERS
   MIDLAND,TX EXPL OFFICE - 500 W TEXAS AVE
      STE 1235,79701 PH 432 687-3330
      FAX 432 682-4959
      HARRY L GRAHAM,VP,EXPL

WEST BELLEVUE, INC
   129 FONTANELLE BLVD

   MADISON,MS 39110 PH 601 856-6676
   PH 601 260-0118
      THOMASKRAFFT@BELLSOUTH.NET

WEST EMERALD PIPE LINE CORPORATON SEE
   ULTRAMAR DIAMOND SHAMROCK CORPORATION

WEST ENGINEERS
   2914 VIRGINIA ST
   HOUSTON,TX 77098 PH 713 522-9675
   FAX 281 482-1197 WESTENG@HAL-PC.ORG
      DONALD F WEST,OWNER

WEST H D,ESTATE OF
   810 RUE BOURBON
   METAIRIE,LA 70005-3421 PH 504 523-7994
   FAX 504 832-7975

WEST MOUNTAIN OPERATING CO,INC
   OPERS & CONS SVCS
   107 WAIN DR
   LONGVIEW,TX 75604 PH 903 297-8496
   FAX 903 297-4477
      ARTHUR E DAVIS,PRES
      GLORIA B CROSSLAND,SECY/TREAS

WEST TEXAS GAS INC
   P O BOX 1621,WEST HWY 290
   FORT STOCKTON,TX 79735-1621
   PH 432 336-8589
   SEMINOLE,TX OFFICE - P O BOX 96,79360
      1103 NE F ST PH 432 758-5824
      WAYNE STOWE
   CLARENDON,TX OFFICE - P O BOX 296,79226
      715 E 2ND PH 806 874-2151
      LYNDEL MOFFETT
   MORTON,TX OFFICE - P O BOX 836,79346
      501 N MAIN PH 806 266-5571
      RICK TANNER
   ANDREWS,TX OFFICE - PO BOX 1307,79714
      SW 13TH & AVE D PH 432 523-2666
      KENNY SMITH
   PLAINS,TX OFFICE - P O BOX 747,79355
      102 ROSWELL RD PH 806 456-2566
   DIMMITT,TX OFFICE - PO DRAWER 879,79027
      E HWY 86 PH 806 647-5166
      CLYDE SCHULTE
   PLAINVIEW,TX OFFICE - PO BOX 239,79072
      810 N DATE PH 806 296-0866
      JACK MORRIS
   KERMIT,TX OFFICE - PO BOX 843,79745
      201 N PINE PH 432 586-5821
      TYE REICH
   BALLINGER,TX OFFICE - PO BOX 679,76821
      1702 HUTCHINGS PH 325 365-2625
      CHARLEY LOPEZ
   COLEMAN,TX OFFICE - PO BOX 956,76834
      HWY 206 NORTH PH 325 625-2925
   OLTON,TX OFFICE - P O BOX 810,79064
      6TH & MAIN PH 806 285-2165
      ROY HARMON
   ALPINE,TX OFFICE - P O BOX 1398,79830
      E HWY 90 PH 432 837-5200
      TRAVIS DEHART
   MONAHANS,TX OFFICE - PO BOX 1569,79756
      3100 S STOCKTON PH 432 943-3841
   CRANE,TX OFFICE - PO BOX 395
      1.5 M EAST OF CRAINE PH 432 558-7436
   PECOS,TX OFFICE - P O BOX 129,79772
      E HWY 80 PH 432 445-9811
      JERRY PATTERSON

DENVER CITY,TX OFFICE - PO BOX 313Y,79323
PLAINS HWY 214 PH 806 592-2224
MIDLAND,TX OFFICE - 211 N COLORADO
79703 PH 432 682-4349
ODESSA,TX OFFICE - 11501 W CR 125,79765
PH 432 563-0848
CHRIS GUYETT
SAN ANGELO,TX OFFICE - PO BOX 1709,76902
4006 S CHADBOURNE PH 325 651-4931
TOMMY DAVIS

WEST TEXAS GEOLOGICAL SOCIETY
WWW.WTGS.ORG

WEST TEXAS PETROLEUM SEE
P M B ENERGY INC

WEST TULETA OPERATING CORP
PO BOX 200
TULETA,TX 78162-0200
PH 361 375-2194 FAX 361 375-2100
R W DIRKS,PRES/CEO
SUSAN DIRKS,VP ACCT
JON R FISCHER,VP OPERS
JFISHER@RWDIRKSPETROLEUM.COM

WESTAR OIL & MINERALS
PO BOX 1990
LEE'S SUMMIT,MO 64063-1990
PH 816 246-0606
GREG CARNES,OWNER GCARNES@KC.RR.COM

WESTARK PRODUCTION COMPANY,INC
PO BOX 5316
FORT SMITH,AR 72913 PH 479 414-9994
LARRY D PORTER,PRES

WESTERN ATLAS INTERNATIONAL,INC SEE
BAKER HUGHES INCORPORATED

WESTERN ATLAS LOGGING SERVICES SEE
BAKER ATLAS

WESTERN BLDG & MINING CORP
448 W FOOTHILL RD
DRUM,PA 18222 PH 570 579-3113
FAX 570 454-8477
A J ROMAN,PRES
AL ROMAN

WESTERN COMPANY OF NORTH AMERICA,THE SEE
BJ SERVICES COMPANY,USA

WESTERN COMPANY,THE,SEE
BJ SERVICES CO

WESTERN EXPLORATION INC
DEVELOPS DRLG PROSPECT FOR 3RD PARTIES IN
IL BASIN,RKY MTN,GREAT BASIN & ALASKA
PO BOX 5446
BLOOMINGTON,IN 47407
PH 812 327-5180 WESTX@INSIGHTBB.COM
JOHN C MACKEY,EXPL GEOL

WESTERN GAS PARTNERS, LP
1201 LAKE ROBBINS DR
THE WOODLANDS,TX 77380
PH 832 636-1000 WWW.WESTERNGAS.COM
DONALD SINCLAIR,PRES,CEO
MILTON CARROLL,DIR
ANTHONY R CHASE,DIR
JAMES R CRANE,DIR
ROBERT K REEVES,DIR
DAVID J TUDOR,DIR

WESTERN GAS RESOURCES INC SEE
ANADARKO PETROLEUM CORPORATION

WESTERN GEOPHYSICAL EXPLORATION PRODUCTS
SEE WESTERN GEOPHYSICAL

WESTERN GEOPHYSICAL SEE
WESTERNGECO,LLC

WESTERN LAND SERVICES,INC
1100 CONRAD INDUSTRIAL DR
LUDINGTON,MI 49431-2679 PH 231 843-8878
FAX 231 843-3183 WLS@WESTERNLS.COM
WWW.WESTERNLS.COM
JOHN K WILSON,PRES

WESTERN OIL & GAS DEVELOPMENT CO
8544 E 1050TH AVE
ROBINSON,IL 62454
PH 618 544-8646 FAX 618 544-2496
GREG LEAVELL,PRES

WESTERN PETROLEUM RESERVES,INC
728 CHARTER OAKS DR
CONROE,TX 77302-3104 PH 713 628-1850
FAX 936 273-9872
JIMMY R GRAY,PRES

WESTERN PETROLEUM SERVICES SEE
WESTERN COMPANY OF NORTH AMERICA,THE

WESTERN PIPE LINE SEE
SOUTHEASTERN PIPE LINE COMPANY

WESTERN PRODUCTION CO SEE
BLACK HILLS EXPLORATION & PRODUCTION INC

WESTERN RESERVES OIL CO,INC
PO BOX 993,310 W WALL STE 301
MIDLAND,TX 79702-0993
PH 432 683-5533 FAX 432 683-4537
GERAL BEVERIDGE,PRES
CHRIS RENAUD,ENGR
BOB ELLIOTT,LAND LEGAL
SHERI COLLINS,REVENUE ACCT,SECY
LISA HERBIG,TREAS
BILLIE PERKINS,JIB
SHERRY WALLER,PROD

WESTERN UNICHEM SEE
UNICHEM,A DIV OF BJ SERVICES CO

WESTERNGECO LLC
PO BOX 2469
HOUSTON,TX 77252-2469 PH 713 689-9600
FAX 713 789-0172 WWW.WESTERNGECO.COM
HOUSTON,TX OFFICE - 10001 RICHMOND AVE
77042 PH 713 689-9600 FAX 713 789-0172
CALGARY,ALBERTA CANADA - 125 9TH AVE SE
STE 200,T2G0P6
PH 1 403 509 4000 FAX 1 403 509 4217
DALLAS,TX OFFICE - 3011 INTERNET BLVD
STE 200,FRISCO,TX 75034 PH 469 213-5040
FAX 469 213-5001
DENVER,CO OFFICE - 1625 BROADWAY STE 1300
80202 PH 303 629-9250 FAX 303 595-0497
MIDLAND,TX OFFICE - PO BOX 152,79702-0152
3117 S CR 1250 79706 PH 432 742-5400
FAX 432 742-5601
NEW ORLEANS,LA OFFICE - 1515 POYDRAS ST
STE 900,70112 PH 504 523-6781
FAX 504 522-6270

WESTPORT TECHNOLOGY CENTER INTERNATIONAL
6700 PORTWEST DR
HOUSTON,TX 77024-8005 PH 713 479-8400
FAX 713 864-9357 WWW.WESTPORT1.COM
PAT JACOBS,DIR

WESTSTAR EXPLORATION CO
1001 WEST LOOP S STE 525
HOUSTON,TX 77027
PH 713 223-5837 FAX 713 933-0261

BILL GILMORE,OWNER

WEVAB INC,TITLE ABSTRACTING
PO BOX 326
BUCKHANNON,WV 26201-0326 PH 304 472-6997
FAX 304 472-6997
STEPHEN A HOLMES,CPL,PRES
RICHARD A EVE,VP,OPERS

WEYERHAEUSER COMPANY
MINERAL RESOURCES
PO BOX 9777 CH1L34
FEDERAL WAY,WA 98063
PH 253 924-2754 FAX 253 924-3862
DAVID L GODWIN,VP MINERALS & ENERGY PROD
PAMELA J REED,LAND MGR

WG ENERGY HOLDINGS,INC SEE
HALCON RESOURCES CORPORATION

WG OPERATING,INC SEE
HALCON OPERATING CO.,INC

WGR,INC & RESOURCES SEE
WESTERN GAS RESOURCES,INC

WHALEY THOMAS,TRUSTEE
PO DRAWER P
MARSHALL,TX 75671-0320 PH 903 938-1777

WHEAT BUCK RESOURCES,SEE
BUCK WHEAT RESOURCES INC

WHEELER OIL CO,INC
6320 SOUTHWEST BLVD STE 100
FORT WORTH,TX 76109-3961 PH 817 332-6145
GEORGE JACKSON,PRES

WHICO LTD
PO BOX 924
PORTLAND,TX 78374 PH 713 523-6673

WHIPP CHARLEY B,GEOLOGIST
PO BOX 51689
LAFAYETTE,LA 70505-1689 PH 337 278-5362
FAX 337 232-1707 OILXPLORER@AOL.COM

WHISTLE WELL SERVICE
P O BOX 644
BARBOURVILLE,KY 40906-0644
PH 606 546-5991
L M MESSER,SECY
D MANGUS,CONSLT

WHITAKER FRED
301 N SAINT MARY ST
CARTHAGE,TX 75633 PH 903 693-3851
FAX 903 693-3852

WHITAKER PETROLEUM LLC
333 TEXAS ST STE 521
SHREVEPORT,LA 71101 PH 318 221-7197

WHITE BEAR ACQUISITIONS,INC
PO BOX 2408,716 CHEROKEE
TRAVERSE CITY,MI 49685-2408
PH 231 941-5654 FAX 231 941-8495
DANIEL J KOSTRZEWA,PRES DJKOST@AOL.COM

WHITE BRUCE E,OIL & GAS PRODUCER
PO BOX 600488
DALLAS,TX 75360-0488 PH 214 696-0808
FAX 214 692-1802
BEWHITEATTY@SBCGLOBAL.NET

WHITE BRUCE,IND OIL OPER
312 MARGUERITE RD
METAIRIE,LA 70003-2444 PH 504 456-2632
FAX 504 885-8339

WHITE CASTLE LUMBER/MINERALS,LLC
228 ST CHARLES AVE STE 1424
NEW ORLEANS,LA 70130 PH 504 568-1922

FAX 504 568-9438
DOWNMANS@DOWNMANSASSOC.COM
LANE M KINCANNON,PRES/CEO
MICHELLE KITTO,EXEC ADMIN ASST
DEBRA ORR-MOONEY,ACCT MGR
SUE SHELLEY,LAND TECH
TIMMY AUCOIN,LAND MGR

WHITE GEORGE R,GEOL
PO BOX 52370
LAFAYETTE,LA 70505 PH 337 237-2797
GEORGE R WHITE,OWNER
TANYA SMITH,OFC MGR

WHITE KENNETH S SEE
WHITE EXPLORATION,INC

WHITE LAND & MINERALS,INC
PO BOX 308
MOUNT CARMEL,IL 62863-0308
PH 618 262-5102 FAX 618 262-8235

WHITE MARLIN OIL AND GAS COMPANY,LLC
15990 N BARKERS LANDING STE 350
HOUSTON,TX 77079 PH 713 595-3600
TERRELL J CLARK,PRES & CEO
CLARKT@WHITEMARLINOG.COM
PAUL DUNNING,SR VP/GEN MGR
DUNNINGP@WHITEMARLINOG.COM
RANA K HASSEN,CFO
HASSENR@WHITEMARLINOG.COM
DOUGLAS W FEHR,COO
FEHRD@WHITEMARLINOG.COM

WHITE ROCK EXPLORATION INC
313 E CHARNWOOD ST
TYLER,TX 75701 PH 903 597-0279
RICHARD CLAY,PRES RCLAY@WREXPLORATION.COM

WHITE TIGER PRODUCTION EQUIPMENT
NEW & RECONDITIONED OIL/GAS PROCESS
EQUIP
TANKS & PRESSURE VESSELS,PUMPING UNITS
23 IRIS CIR
LONGVIEW,TX 75601
PH 281 455-2524 FAX 903 753-9677
WHITETIGERPRODEQUIP@YAHOO.COM
MARK R GILBERT,OWNER PH 281 455-2524

WHITE WALTER H,III,OIL LEASES
424 ADAIR ST
MANDEVILLE,LA 70448-5704 PH 985 626-7647

WHITEHORSE OIL & GAS CORPORATION SEE
LAS COLINAS ENERGY CORP

WHITESANDS OPERATING LLC
PO BOX 60208
CORPUS CHRISTI,TX 78466-0208
PH 361 884-4935 FAX 361 884-5964
COLEMAN E HATHERLY,JR,MGR/MEMBER AGENT

WHITEWING & WHITEWING OIL CO,LLC SEE
BLACK DIAMOND ENERGY,LLC

WHITEWING OIL PROPERTIES,INC
PO BOX 127,119 AMERICAN LEGION DR
RAYNE,LA 70578-0127 PH 337 334-0611
FAX 337 334-2309 WWHITEWING@AOL.COM
W K WHITEWING,PRES
ANDRE WHITEWING,VP
KELLIE MOREAU,OFC MGR
DEMERRIS WHITEWING,LEASE RECORDS,TITLES
& LAND DEPT
ANDRUS C WHITEWING,PROJ COORD

WHITING OILFIELD RENTAL SEE
WEATHERFORD ENTERRA

WHITING PETROLEUM CORP
1700 BROADWAY STE 2300
DENVER,CO 80290-2300 PH 303 837-1661
FAX 303 861-4023
JAMES J VOLKER,PRES,CEO
JAMES BROWN,SR VP
DAVID SEERY,VP,LAND
MICHAEL STEVENS,VP,FIN
MARK WILLIAMS,VP,EXPL & DEV
HEATHER DUNCAN,VP,HR
DOUG LANG,VP,ACQS,RESERVOIR ENGRG
RICK ROSS,VP,OPERS
DOUG WALTON,VP,DRLG
CHUCK LACOUTURE,VP,MKTG

WHITMAR EXPLORATION COMPANY
555 17TH ST STE 880
DENVER,CO 80202-3908 PH 303 991-9400
WWW.WHITMAR.COM
WHITNEY H MARVIN,PRES
KEVIN BROWN,GEOL
MARK WEIGT,OPERS

WHITNEY CARROLL ENTERPRISES
PO BOX 1162,926 BRADLEY DR
ATHENS,TX 75751-1162 PH 903 675-8464

WHITNEY OIL & GAS CO LLC
177 E 18TH BOX 155
OWENSBORO,KY 42303
PH 270 852-0533 FAX 270 926-1420
WHITNEYOILANDGAS@YAHOO.COM
GENE BOWLDS,OPERS MGR
CAROLYN A BOWLDS,MEMBER

WHITSON,JAMES A.JR,OIL OPER
7660 WOODWAY DR STE 312
HOUSTON,TX 77063-1532 PH 713 975-8963
FAX 713 975-7139 JAWFD@WHITSONJR.COM

WHITTENBURG TOM ED
6142 S FOSTER RD
SAN ANTONIO,TX 78222-4406
PH 210 648-9478 FAX 210 648-7298
TOMWHITTENBURG@CS.COM
TOM ED WHITTENBURG,VP SALES

WHITTINGTON OIL & GAS,LLC
3127 RIVER FOREST DR
RICHMOND,TX 77469 PH 713 303-5009
WFWHITTINGTON@AOL.COM
WILLIAM F WHITTINGTON

WHITTON CO INC
PO BOX 276
HOMER,LA 71040-0276 PH 318 927-4189
FAX 318 927-4189
JERRY L WHITTON,PRES
GERALD D WHITTON,VP

WHP OPERATING
P O BOX P ,208 MAIN
NATCHEZ,MS 39120-1053 PH 601 446-5766
FAX 601 445-4681
W HOWARD PRITCHARTT JR,PRTNR
W HOWARD PRITCHARTT III,PRTNR

WICHITA RIVER OIL CORPORATION
2602 MCKINNEY AVE STE 400
DALLAS,TX 75204 PH 214 871-2889
FAX 214 871-5040
R D RINEHART,PRES
DOUGLAS R EVANS,EXEC VP
JOHN R SEARS,VP,FIN
PHILIP KREICK,VP,PROD

WICKLUND PETROLEUM CORPORATION
4521 EXECUTIVE DR STE 101
NAPLES,FL 34119
PH 239 431-7066 FAX 239 431-7067
WWW.WICKPET.COM
DOUGLAS F WICKLUND,PRES

WICKSTROM ALDEN,IND GEOL
535 CAMELLIA BLVD
LAFAYETTE,LA 70503-4701 PH 337 984-0961
WICKSTROM535@COX.NET

WIGGINS NOLAN
PO BOX 921
KILGORE,TX 75663-0921 PH 903 984-3443
CHARLA ROLPH,AGENT

WIKA INSTRUMENT CORPORATION
1000 WIEGAND BLVD
LAWRENCEVILLE,GA 30043-5868
PH 770 513-8200 888 945-2872
FAX 770 338-5118 WWW.WIKA.COM
INFO@WIKA.COM

WILAND INC
PO BOX 6446
BOSSIER CITY,LA 71171-6446
PH 318 465-7885 FAX 318 752-8437
J BRAD CUMMINGS,PRES
BRADC_PJ8@MSN.COM

WILBANKS ENERGY CORPORATION
2820 SUMMIT RIDGE
SAN MARCOS,TX 78666 PH 512 392-6956
PH 713 253-2324 FAX 512 392-6958
C M WILBANKS,PRES
CMWILBANKS@GMAIL.COM
ELAINE G WILBANKS,VP

WILBANKS EXPLORATION INC SEE
WILBANKS RESERVE CORPORATION

WILBANKS RESOURCES CORP SEE
CRANE ORIN C

WILCO ENERGY CORPORATION
PO BOX 146
CAMPBELLSVILLE,KY 42719-0146
PH 270 932-3120 FAX 270 932-3730
WILLIAM K COLLINS,PRES
CONNIE S COLLINS,SECY/TREAS
W SCOTT COLLINS,GEOL
SHEA M COLLINS,COUNCIL

WILCOX ENERGY COMPANY
PO BOX V,304 FRANKLIN ST
NATCHEZ,MS 39121-1257 PH 601 442-5191
FRED L CALLON,PRES
MIKE A HOPKINS,VP

WILCOX OIL AND GAS,INC
1001 MCKINNEY STE 1445
HOUSTON,TX 77002 PH 713 650-3060
FAX 713 650-3069
WILLIAM M SMITH,GEOL
WMSMITH@FLASH.NET
MITCH P ANDERSON,GEOL

WILCOX OPERATING CORPORATION
5220 HOLLYWOOD AVE
SHREVEPORT,LA 71109-7717 PH 318 636-6811
FAX 318 636-6844
WILCOX@WILCOXOPERATINGCORP.COM
MARK F PREDDY,PRES
BETTY C WILLIAMS,VP

WILD WELL CONTROL,INC SEE
SUPERIOR ENERGY SERVICES COMPANY

WILDCO RESOURCES INC
PO BOX 130909
TYLER,TX 75713-0909
PH 903 597-5102 FAX 903 597-5110
BRUCE WILDER,PRES
STEVE WILDER,VP

WILDER C BRUCE,GEOL
PO BOX 130909
TYLER,TX 75713
PH 903 597-5102 FAX 903 597-5110

WILDER STEVE B,LDMN
PO BOX 130909
TYLER,TX 75713
PH 903 597-5102 FAX 903 597-5110

WILDER V JOHN,LANDMAN
1925 CANTERBURY ST
HOUSTON,TX 77030-4103 PH 713 790-0821

WILDWING INVESTMENTS,INC
PO BOX 51423
LAFAYETTE,LA 70505-1423 PH 337 232-3191
STEPHEN E WILSON,OWNER,PRES

WILKENS WEATHER TECHNOLOGIES,LP
2925 BRIARPARK DR STE 710
HOUSTON,TX 77042-3720 PH 713 430-7100
FAX 713 430-7490 WWW.WILKENSWEATHER.COM
WWT@WILKENSWEATHER.COM
MARK WALQUIST,GEN MGR
RUDY RAMIREZ,OPERS MGR

WILKES ENERGY,INC
17 S MAIN ST STE 101A
AKRON,OH 44308-1803 PH 330 252-4560
SCOTT J WILKES,PRES

WILKINS PETROLEUM
400 WILSON AVE
DEVINE,TX 78016-3333 PH 512 663-2881
JAMES N WILKINS,OWNER
RUTH WILKINS,OWNER

WILL-DRILL OPERATING,LLC SEE
WILL-DRILL RESOURCES,INC.

WILL-DRILL PRODUCTION,INC SEE
WILL-DRILL RESOURCES,INC

WILL-DRILL RESOURCES,INC
416 TRAVIS ST STE 1200
SHREVEPORT,LA 71101-5515 PH 318 222-7464
FAX 318 222-7466
LACY H WILLIAMS,PRES
C ALLEN WILLIAMS,VP
DARYL R FULTZ,EXPL MGR
KEMERTON D HARGROVE,LDMN
CURRIE SMITH,LDMN
DAVE GIDDINGS,DIV-ORDER ANALYST

WILLBROS ENERGY SERVICES CO SEE
WILLBROS GROUP,INC

WILLEY EDWARDS & WRIGHT
2121 SAGE RD STE 250
HOUSTON,TX 77056
PH 713 650-1550 FAX 713 650-3753

WILLIAM HERBERT HUNT TRUST ESTATE
C/O PETRO-HUNT,LLC
2101 CEDAR SPRINGS RD STE 600
DALLAS,TX 75201 PH 214 880-8400
FAX 214 880-7101 WWW.PETRO-HUNT.COM
GAGE A PRICHARD SR,TRUSTEE

WILLIAM J DAIGLE,LLC SEE
MAGNOLIA ENERGY SERVICES,LLC

WILLIAMS (TRANSCO & GULF COAST MIDSTREAM)
PO BOX 1396,2800 POST OAK BLVD
HOUSTON,TX 77251-1396
PH 713 215-2000 WWW.WILLIAMS.COM
RORY MILLER,SR VP
FRANK J FERAZZI,VP/GM-TRANSCO
SCOTT HUNKIN,DIR FIN PLANNING
JIM MOORE,VP COMMERCIAL OPERS (TRANSCO)
AL TAYLOR,VP/GM-GULF EAST
PAT CARROLL,VP/GM-GULF WEST
KEVIN REHM,VP/GM-DISCOVERY

WILLIAMS & CHAO
PO BOX 291366,819 WATER ST STE 105
KERRVILLE,TX 78029-1366
PH 830 792-4250 FAX 830 896-6695
L BRYANT WILLIAMS JR,PRTNR
LBWJR2@WINDSTREAM.NET
TSU K CHAO,PRTNR

WILLIAMS & COMPANY
3104 EDLOE ST STE 210
HOUSTON,TX 77027-6513
PH 713 552-0344 FAX 713 552-0346
WYATT WILLIAMS,OWNER
MAC THOMPSON,CONSLT

WILLIAMS CLARENCE T
PO BOX 1808
SPRING,TX 77383-1808 PH 281 350-1900

WILLIAMS CLAYTON ENERGY,INC
6 DESTA DR STE 3000
MIDLAND,TX 79705-5520 PH 432 682-6324
FAX 432 688-3225 WWW.CLAYTONWILLIAMS.COM
MEL RIGGS,COO
MICHAEL POLLARD,CFO
CLAYTON WILLILAMS,CEO
GREG WELBORN,VP LAND
RON GASSER,VP ENGNG
JOHN KENNEDY,VP DRLG
SAM LYSSY,VP EXPL
ED UZZELL,LAND MGR
KINGWOOD,TX OFFICE - 700 ROCKMEAD STE 159
77339 PH 281 359-5511 FAX 281 359-8603
PAT REESBY,VP,ACQS/NEW VENTURES
KELLY BECKHAM,LDMN
DEANVILLE,TX FIELD OFFICE - PO BOX 400
77852 PH 979 535-3032 FAX 979 535-7750
CLARENCE WOLFSHOHL,DIV PROD SUPT

WILLIAMS FAMILY INTERESTS
3104 EDLOE ST STE 210
HOUSTON,TX 77027-6513
PH 713 552-0344 FAX 713 552-0346

WILLIAMS FIELD SERVICES COMPANY
GULF COAST DIV-MIDSTREAM
2800 POST OAK BLVD STE 900
HOUSTON,TX 77056 PH 713 215-2000
FAX 713 215-3050 WWW.WILLIAMS.COM
ALAN ARMSTRONG,VP (TULSA)

WILLIAMS FINANCIAL CORP
1785 CAVERLY RD
MEADOWBROOK,PA 19046-1001 PH 215 947-9390
FAX 215 947-9392
HOWARD W BLEIMAN,PRES
SUSAN BLEIMAN SOLL,VP

WILLIAMS GAS PIPELINE (TRANSCO) SEE
WILLIAMS (TRANSCO)

WILLIAMS GEOLOGICAL CONSULTING INC
4008 VISTA RD STE A204

PASADENA,TX 77504 PH 832 382-7675
LYNN WILLIAMS,PRES
GEOLYNN2000@YAHOO.COM

WILLIAMS HERBERT E,ESTATE OF,OIL PROD SEE
WILLIAMS FAMILY INTERESTS

WILLIAMS INC
228 ST CHARLES AVE STE 1323
NEW ORLEANS,LA 70130-2646 PH 504 581-2355
FAX 504 525-9841
CHARLES S WILLIAMS,PRES
DAVID O'FLYNN,CFO
RUDY C SPARKS,VP LAND
PATTERSON,LA LAND OFFICE - PO BOX 460
107 MCGEE DR,70392 PH 985 395-9576
FAX 985 395-9578

WILLIAMS JACK J,CERTIFIED PETR GEOL
PO BOX 448
JEFFERSON,TX 75657-0448 PH 903 665-6004
PH 903 256-0582 WJACKNAN@YAHOO.COM

WILLIAMS JOSEPH G
11111 KATY FWY STE 600
HOUSTON,TX 77079-2116 PH 713 463-6700
FAX 713 463-6722

WILLIAMS KENNETH O,JR,OIL PROPERTIES
PO BOX 1832,118 N COMMERCE
NATCHEZ,MS 39121-1832 PH 601 445-9594

WILLIAMS LAND COMPANY,LLC
228 ST CHARLES AVE STE 1323
NEW ORLEANS,LA 70130-2646
PH 504 581-2355 FAX 504 525-9841
CHARLES S WILLIAMS,PRES
DAVID O'FLYNN,CFO
RUDY C SPARKS,VP LAND
PATTERSON,LA LAND OFFICE - PO BOX 460
107 MCGEE DR,70392 PH 985 395-9576
FAX 985 395-9578

WILLIAMS PRODUCTION COMPANY SEE
WPX ENERGY

WILLIAMS PRODUCTION RMT COMPANY SEE
WPX ENERGY ROCKY MOUNTAIN,LLC

WILLIAMS PUMP DISTRIBUTOR
ALLEN PERRY CO
PO BOX 652,212 MARKET ST
WINNSBORO,TX 75494-0652 PH 903 342-3074
PH 800 256-6868 FAX 903 342-5774
ANN BRADSHAW,PRES
CLARENCE BRADSHAW,MGR

WILLIAMS R E,DRLG CO,INC,OPR & DRLG CONTR
619 ANDERSON ST
MEMPHIS,TN 38104-5104 PH 901 454-1182
R E WILLIAMS,OWNER
ROBERT E WILLIAMS,JR,CHRMN OF BD
MOLLIE A BEASLEY,LDMN
NATCHEZ,MS OFFICE - P O BOX 698
HWY 61 NORTH,39120
PH 601 445-9651
P E COCHRAN,JR
AMORY,MS OFFICE - P O BOX 434
HWY 6,38821 PH 662 256-3110
JERRY SPEARS

WILLIAMS ROBERT L,CONSULTING GEOL
PO BOX 27
GRANVILLE,OH 43023-0027 PH 740 587-1409

WILLIAMSON & SMITHERMAN,INC,SEE
WILLIAMSON OIL & GAS,INC

WILLIAMSON DON B
410 FAIRWAY
ATHENS,TX 75751-1054 PH 903 675-7546
WILLIAMSON OIL & GAS,INC
PO BOX 1772,400 TRAVIS ST STE 1410
SHREVEPORT,LA 71166-1772 PH 318 221-2923
ROBERT L WILLIAMSON,PRES
GLORIA HOOPES,VP
WILLIAMSON T D,INC
6120 S YALE STE 1700
TULSA,OK 74136-4235 PH 918 447-5084
FAX 918 447-5050 WWW.TDWILLIAMSON.COM
INFO@TDWILLIAMSON.COM
NORTH & SOUTH AMERICA PH +1 918 447-5000
EUROPE/AFRICA/MID EAST PH +32 67 28 3611
ASIA PACIFIC PH +65 6364 8520
OFFSHORE SERVICES PH +1 832 448-7200
WILLIFORD ENERGY COMPANY
6100 S YALE AVE STE 2000
TULSA,OK 74136-1919
PH 918 495-2700 FAX 918 495-2701
DAVID L FOSTER,PRES
P DOUGLAS STORTS,SR VP
- ACCOUNTING -
LARRY GROWNS,VP/SYSTEMS & ACCT
BOOKER,TX FIELD OFFICE - PO BOX 478
79005 PH 806 658-9758
CORKY HUBBARD,SUPT
KIT CARSON,CO FIELD OFFICE - PO BOX 302
80825 PH 719 962-3451
WILLISCO INC SEE
SEISMIC EXCHANGE,INC
WILLISTON PROJECTS,INC
515 N SAM HOUSTON PKWY E STE 485
HOUSTON,TX 77060 PH 281 590-3313
FAX 281 590-3381
DKESSEL@MUREXPETROLEUM.COM
DON A KESSEL,PRES
WILLMUT GAS & OIL CO
PO BOX 6195
PEARL,MS 39288 PH 601 939-3275
WILMAR PIPELINES,INC
PO BOX 19130
HOUSTON,TX 77224 PH 713 464-8800
FAX 713 464-8868
R M ZEID,PRES
WILPRO
PO BOX 331
CARMI,IL 62821-0331
PH 618 382-4666 FAX 618 382-5313
LES WILSON,PRES
PAT WILSON,SECY
WILSHUSEN R C,PETR ENGR
PO BOX 1699,626 WILSON PLAZA NORTH
CORPUS CHRISTI,TX 78403-1699
PH 361 883-0172 FAX 361 882-5546
WILSON & JOHNSON,ATTYS
2603 AUGUSTA DR STE 1150
HOUSTON,TX 77057-5681 PH 713 781-7550
FAX 713 781-7550
KENTON L WILSON,PRTNR
JOHNNY B JOHNSON,PRTNR
ERIKA J HARMS,ASSOC
WILSON EDWARD C,JR,OIL & GAS OPER
11114 WICKWOOD DR
HOUSTON,TX 77024-7523 PH 713 621-7862

WILSON ENERGY
EXPLORATION,PRODUCTION EOR
1300 N 45TH ST STE 822
CORSICANA,TX 75110 PH 903 875-2398
VERN WILSON
WILSON EXPLORATION COMPANY
1212 W EL PASO ST
FORT WORTH,TX 76102-5997 PH 817 332-6324
JOHN H WILSON II,PRES
WILSON LAND SERVICES
305 S BROADWAY STE 901
TYLER,TX 75702 PH 903 531-0201
RYAN A WILSON, PRES
WILSON LES,INC
205 INDUSTRIAL DR
CARMI,IL 62821 PH 618 382-4666
FAX 618 382-5313
ROBERT L WILSON,PRES
STEPHANIE WILSON,VP
WILSON PATRICIA N
PO BOX 93898
SOUTHLAKE,TX 76092-0118
PH 817 706-7277
WILSON R K,III,LEASES & OIL PROP
120 E BROADWAY AVE STE 206
TYLER,TX 75702-7206 PH 903 596-7200
FAX 903 596-7203 RKWILSONIII@YAHOO.COM
WILSON RESOURCES INCORPORATED
PO BOX 375
GRANVILLE,OH 43023-0375 PH 614 890-4401
FAX 614 890-5617
D S WILSON,PRES
WILSON STEPHEN E,LANDMAN
PO BOX 51423
LAFAYETTE,LA 70505-1423 PH 337 232-3191
WILSON VERN ENERGY INC
4606 BOGEY CT
COLLEGE STATION,TX 77845 PH 979 224-2233
VERN WILSON VERNO@WILSONENERGY.COM
WINCHESTER PRODUCTION COMPANY
8451 HWY 175
GRAND CANE,LA 71032-6125 PH 318 687-3232
FAX 318 687-3236
BILL CHANEY,PRES
MATT ELLARD,OPERS MGR
NICK MAYFIELD,EH&S MGR
STEVE GREBER,SR GEOL
CHRIS MIDDLETON,LAND MGR
CARLA ELLIOTT,MKTG/REGULATORY MGR
WINDRUSH OPERATING CO LLC
12836 HIGHWAY 171
LONGVILLE,LA 70652-5005
PH 337 725-3704 FAX 337 725-4168
DICKEY DARDEAU,OWNER
DD_WINDRUSH@CENTURYTEL.NET
TOM GAYLORD,OWNER
TOMGAYLORD@COMCAST.NET
THERESA CRAFT,OFC ACCT MGR
TCRAFT@CENTURYTEL.NET
WINDSOR INTERESTS LTD,OIL PROPERTIES
PO BOX 236,121 S BROADWAY STE 602
TYLER,TX 75710-0236 PH 903 597-7561
WINN EXPLORATION CO,INC
800 N SHORELINE BLVD 19 N
CORPUS CHRISTI,TX 78401-3700
PH 361 844-6900 FAX 361 844-6901

CHARLES A WINN,CHRMN OF BOARD
MICHAEL W CALLEY,EXEC VP
RODNEY MURR,OPERS MGR
SOUTHERN WINN,GEOL
TOM WINN,GEOL
MIKE LAYMAN,GEOPHY
ARLEN WALKER,PROD SUPT
WINNE LAND & MINERALS,INC
10330 LAKE ROAD BLDG 26
HOUSTON,TX 77070 PH 281 290-4990
FAX 281 290-4992 GWINNE@WINNELAND.COM
GILBERT L WINNE JR,PRES
WINROCK ENGINEERING INC
PO BOX 797366
DALLAS,TX 75379-7366
PH 405 822-6761 BINGWINES@COX.NET
WWW.WINROCKENGINEERINGINC.COM
G BING WINES,PRES
WINSHIP GEOLOGICAL CONSULTANTS
419 HOLLOW DR
HOUSTON,TX 77024 PH 713 248-3634
STEVE H HILL,OWNER,CONS GEOL
WINSTEAD PC
300 CONVENT ST STE 2700
SAN ANTONIO,TX 78205 PH 210 277-6800
JON R RAY JRAY@WINSTEAD.COM
WINTER GARDEN ENGINEERING,INC
PO BOX 60716
CORPUS CHRISTI,TX 78466 PH 830 374-7315
WINTERGREEN ENERGY CORPORATION
500 TURTLE COVE BLVD STE 120
ROCKWALL,TX 75087 PH 469 698-0500
FAX 469 698-0510
ALICE J GARNER,VP,SECY/TREAS
SANDRA JARECKI,ASST SECY/TREAS
WINTON COMPANY THE
CHARLES,JOEL,JUDSON AND DAVID WINTON
OIL LIMITED PARTNERSHIPS
730 2ND AVE S STE 1300
MINNEAPOLIS,MN 55402-2416 PH 612 338-5781
FAX 612 238-2499
TENA HALL,CONTACT
PH 612 238-2496
WINWELL,LLC
416 TRAVIS ST STE 910
SHREVEPORT,LA 71101
PH 318 424-4986 FAX 318 227-0736
WIRELINE CONSULTANTS INC
223 RAMBLEWOOD DR
LAFAYETTE,LA 70508-7403 PH 337 233-9451
FAX 337 233-9471 ARROW/BRUCE@AOL.COM
BRUCE HAMPTON,PRES
WIRELINE TECHNOLOGIES,INC
MFG WIRELINE & SLICKLINE SHEAVES/PRODUCTS
2140 N REDWOOD RD STE 60
SALT LAKE CITY,UT 84116
PH 800 743-2831 PH 801 323-5533
FAX 801 323-7033
RUSS VANCE,CEO,SLS
KENN DAYTON,COO,OPERS
DEREK CARLSON,VP,ENGRG
GEORGE VENT,VP,QUALITY
BRIAN MACE,MATERIALS MGR
WISCONSIN GROUP,THE
960 S MONROE ST
NEW LISBON,WI 53950-1352

PH 608 562-5558 FAX 608 562-5913
BECKY PALAMARUK,CONTROLLER

WISE OIL CORPORATION
3601 13TH ST E
TUSCALOOSA,AL 35404 PH 205 556-8691
GARY M WISE,PRES
HARTWISE@COMCAST.NET

WISE SUPPLY CO
PO BOX 801,1609 HWY 59 NORTH
BOWIE,TX 76230-0801
PH 940 872-2461 FAX 940 872-1302
CHARLES E WALLACE,PRES
CHUCK WALLACE,VP,SECY/TREAS

WISEMAN WILLIAM M,IND GEOPHY
1627 NOCTURNE
HOUSTON,TX 77043-3319 PH 713 465-2854

WISENBAKER PRODUCTION COMPANY
218 N BROADWAY AVE
TYLER,TX 75702 PH 903 593-2588
FAX 903 593-1997
CLORINDA WISENBAKER,OWNER
MIKE FARRELL,PROD SUPT
TYLER,FIELD OFFICE - OLD BASCOM RD
75707 PH 903 566-3511
MIKE FARRELL,PROD SUPT

WISNER ENERGY,LLC
19173 NORTH SHORE DR
SPRING LAKE,MI 49456 PH 616 298-0017
FAX 616 842-7958 WISNERENERGY@GMAIL.COM
BRIAN WISNER,OWNER

WITT OIL PRODUCTION INC
470 ASHLEY RIDGE BLVD
SHREVEPORT,LA 71106-7228 PH 318 219-3388
FAX 318 869-4736
ZOE WITT MOORER,PRES
STEPHENS,AR OFFICE - RR 3 BOX 34,71764
PH 870 786-5131

WJH ENERGY,INC
102 N COLLEGE AVE STE 1015
TYLER,TX 75702 PH 903 526-0722
WILLIAM J HARDY,PRES

WLE,INC
PO BOX 13840
NEW IBERIA,LA 70562-3840 PH 337 369-3853
FAX 337 364-6429
JOHNNY ESTIS,PRES
JAMELL ESTIS,SECY/TREAS

WM HUGHES INVESTMENTS
16050 TROY CT
FLINT,TX 75762 PH 903 939-9888
WILLIAM M HUGHES,OWNR/CEO PH 903 521-7822
BADBILLHUGHES@GMAIL.COM

WM OIL AND GAS,INC
6969 STONECREEK AVE NE
CANTON,OH 44721-2924 PH 330 492-1687
RICHARD J WINGERTER,OWNER

WOFFORD C J
PO BOX 1598,103-A S MECHANIC
EL CAMPO,TX 77437-1598 PH 979 541-5454
FAX 979 541-5500 CJ-WOFFORD@SBCGLOBAL.NET
C J WOFFORD,PRES/OPER
GWEN WILLIS,VP/COMPTROLLER

WOHNER COLLINS
PO BOX 56
CANTON,MS 39046-0056 PH 601 859-4373

WOLDA D AND ASSOCIATES
10819 W HIDDEN LAKES
RICHMOND,TX 77406 PH 281 341-7323
FAX 281 341-7323 DWOLDASR@SBCGLOBAL.NET
DAVID E WOLDA

WOLFF & ASSOCIATES,INC,REALTORS
1775 ST JAMES PLACE,STE 100
HOUSTON,TX 77056-3403 PH 713 622-9339
FAX 713 622-0225 BETHWOLFFREALTORS.COM
BETHWOLFF@BETHWOLFFREALTORS.COM
BETH WOLFF,PRES,RELOCATION DIR

WOMACK ENERGY,INC
WOMACK OPERATING,LLC
1811 BERING STE 230
HOUSTON,TX 77057 PH 713 623-2201
KEN WOMACK,PRES

WOMACK RICHARD H
4001 MOORHEAD DR
CORPUS CHRISTI,TX 78410-5521
PH 361 387-2654 FAX 361 387-2654

WOOD COUNTY GAS PARTNERS
PO BOX 689
TYLER,TX 75710
PH 903 592-3811 FAX 903 597-3587
JOHN R GARRETT,PRES
RODNEY K THOMSON,PROD MGR

WOOD DONALD E,ATTY
4437 WRIGHT AVE
WHITEHALL,OH 43213-3011 PH 614 235-8078
FAX 614 235-0040

WOOD EDMUND R,WOOD LEASE BROKERAGE
LEASES & OIL & GAS PRODUCER
PO BOX 2047,315 E HOUSTON STE 200
MARSHALL,TX 75671 PH 903 935-1008
EDMUND R WOOD,OWNER
MELISA LEWIS,LAND OFC MGR
HALEY LINDLEY,LDMN
SANDY EVANS,LAND ACCT

WOOD GREGORY L
3203 ETHAN ALLEN RD
BARBERTON,OH 44203 PH 330 858-0202
GREG@UTICASHALEINVESTING.COM
WWWOOODDD@SBCGLOBAL.NET

WOOD GROUP PRESSURE CONTROL
3245 STAGE COACH RD
KEITHVILLE,LA 71047-8095
PH 318 221-0714 FAX 318 425-7530
RICHARD W HAILEY,CORP SLS

WOOD LEASE BROKERAGE
PO BOX 2047
MARSHALL,TX 75671 PH 903 935-1008
EDMUND R WOOD AINGRFOOT@YAHOO.COM

WOODALL OIL COMPANY
PO BOX 6641
SHREVEPORT,LA 71136-6641
PH 318 869-4474 FAX 318 869-4406
JOHN O WOODALL,OWNER
JDWOODALL@COMCAST.NET
NEAL WOODALL,EXEC VP

WOODARD ENERGY CO
2600 S GESSNER RD STE 320
HOUSTON,TX 77063
PH 713 975-9755 FAX 713 975-9765
A.E.(GENE) WOODARD,PRES
WOODARDENERGY@YAHOO.COM

WOODBERRY ROYALTY,INC
PO BOX 25128,4625 GREENVILLE AVE STE 201
DALLAS,TX 75225-1128 PH 214 691-5977
FAX 214 691-5978
SETH WOODBERRY,PRES

WOODCO USA
PO BOX 1261
HOUSTON,TX 77251-1261 PH 713 672-9491
FAX 713 672-8768 WWW.WOODCOUSA.COM
SALES@WOODCOUSA.COM
ASHLEY GEORGE,PRES

WOODS GIB OIL CO
4 JEFFREY LN
NEWTON,IL 62448-2019 PH 618 783-2137
GIB WOODS,PRES

WOODS HERBERT S
PO BOX 1367,1215 HILLSBORO
EL DORADO,AR 71731-1367 PH 870 863-3637

WOODSIDE ENERGY (USA) INC
5151 SAN FELIPE STE 980
HOUSTON,TX 77056 PH 714 401-0000
FAX 713 401-0091 WWW.WOODSIDE.COM.AU
DAVID MOON,WELL DELVRY MGR
HOUSTONADMIN@WOODSIDEENERGY.COM

WOODSTONE RESOURCES LLC
7500 SAN FELIPE STE 475
HOUSTON,TX 77063 PH 713 706-3090
WARREN MCFATTER,PRES
WMCFATTER@WOODSTONERESOURCES.COM
KEN TRAHAN,VP LAND & LEGAL
VINCE MANARA,VP EXPLOR

WOODWARD HOLDINGS,INC
PO BOX 310542,144 LANDA ST STE 157
NEW BRAUNFELS,TX 78131 PH 830 626-3479
MARK S WOODWARD,PRES
MARK@WOODWARDHOLDINGS.COM

WOODWARD MARK S,INDEPENDENT PRODUCER
PO BOX 310542,144 LANDA ST STE 157
NEW BRAUNFELS,TX 78131 PH 830 626-3479
MARK@WOODWARDHOLDINGS.COM

WOOLPERT,INC
4454 IDEA CENTER BLVD
DAYTON,OH 45430-1500 PH 937 461-5660
SCOTTSDALE,AZ OFFICE - 16427 N SCOTTSDALE
RD STE 410 85254 PH 480 696-2435
REEDLEY,CA OFFICE - 1120 I ST 93654
PH 559 326-2589
ENGLEWOOD,CO OFFICE - 116 INVERNESS DR E
STE 105 80112 PH 303 925-1400
FAX 303 925-1401
MIAMI,FL OFFICE - 10900 NW 25TH STE 100
PH 305 418-9370 FAX 305 418-9377
WINTER PARK,FL OFFICE - 1 PURLIEU PL
STE 122 32792 PH 407 381-2192
FAX 407 384-1185
ATLANTA,GA OFFICE - 375 NORTHRIDGE RD
STE 300 30350 PH 770 391-4095
FAX 770 391-4104
OAKBROOK TERRACE,IL OFFICE - 1815 S
MEYERS RD STE 120 60181-5226
PH 630 424-9080 FAX 630 495-3731
FAIRVIEW HEIGHTS,IL OFFICE - 343 FOUNTAIN
PKWY STE 100 62208 PH 618 632-7004
FAX 618 632-0100
INDIANAPOLIS,IN OFFICE - 7635 INTERACTIVE
WAY STE 100 46278 PH 317 299-7500

FAX 317 291-5805
FLORENCE,KY OFFICE - 7310 TURFWAY RD
STE 550 41042 PH 859 372-6787
ST LOUIS,MO OFFICE - 3636 S GEYER RD
STE 100 63127 PH 314 436-0865
CHARLOTTE,NC OFFICE - 11301 CARMEL
COMMONS BLVD STE 300,28226
PH 704 525-6284 FAX 704 525-8529
CANTON,OH OFFICE - 3801 WHIPPLE AVE NW
44718 PH 330 456-9355 FAX 330 456-9356
CINCINNATI,OH OFFICE - 312 WALNUT ST
STE 1600 45242 PH 513 272-8300
FAX 937 461-0743
CLEVELAND,OH OFFICE - 600 SUPERIOR AVE
STE 1300 44114 PH 216 416-1501
COLUMBUS,OH OFFICE - ONE EASTON OVAL
STE 310 43219 PH 614 476-6000
FAX 614 476-6225
MT PLEASANT,SC OFFICE - 1671 BELLE ISLE
STE 125 29464 PH 843 216-0401
FAX 843 216-0405
COLUMBIA,SC OFFICE - 2000 CENTER POINT RD
STE 2200 29210 PH 803 731-0261
FAX 803 731-0132
GREENVILLE,SC OFFICE - 148 RIVER STE 220
29601 PH 864 252-3705 FAX 864 421-9909
DALLAS,TX OFFICE - 3500 OAK LAWN AVE
STE 460 75219 PH 972 226-8181
FAX 972 226-8184
CRANBERRY TOWNSHIP,PA OFFICE - 2009
MACKENZIE WAY STE 100 16066
PH 724 584-5185
ARLINGTON,VA OFFICE - 2800 SHIRLINGTON RD
STE 405 22206 PH 703 820-3840
FAX 703 820-3894
CHESAPEAKE,VA OFFICE - 676 INDEPENDENCE
PKWY STE 100 23320 PH 757 549-3549
FAX 757 549-3540
RICHMOND,VA OFFICE - 6802 PARAGON PLACE
STE 410 23230 PH 804 774-2000
FAX 804 441-6001
WORDEN/GRAVITY METER COMPANY
2116 THOMPSON RD STE H1
RICHMOND,TX 77469-5428
PH 281 342-2884 WWW.GRAVITYSERVICES.COM
B.NEESE@GRAVITYSERVICES.COM
BOB NEESE,PRES
DENNIS ROHAN,LAB MGR
CHARLES PUSTEJOVSKY,QUARTZ PRODUCT MGR
WORKSTRINGS SEE
SUPERIOR ENERGY SERVICES
WORLD PRODUCERS INC
1450 PRESTON FORREST SQUARE STE 216
DALLAS,TX 75230 PH 214 954-3040
FAX 214 954-3041
JOHN J COYLE,CHRMN OF BD,CEO
CYNTHIA BOWMAN,CONTROLLER
WORLDWIDE DRILLING RESOURCE,INC
PO BOX 660,3089 NORTHRIDE LN
BONIFAY,FL 32425 PH 850 547-0102
WWW.WORLDWIDEDRILLINGRESOURCE.COM
RONNIE@WORLDWIDEDRILLINGRESOURCE.COM
WORLDWIDE GEOSCIENCES INC
6100 CORPORATE DR STE 320
HOUSTON,TX 77036-3425 PH 713 988-9401
NEIL F PETERSEN,PRES

PATRICK J HICKEY,VP
WORLEY JOHN C,GEOL
7015 RED BUG LAKE RD #237
OVIEDO,FL 32765-5058 PH 406 388-0561
JWNCW27@BRESNON.NET
ROCKPORT,TX OFFICE - 120 SUGAR CREEK
78382 PH/FAX 361 790-7900
WORMSER PRODUCING PROPERTIES,INC
1624 WINDING VIEW
SAN ANTONIO,TX 78260 PH 210 364-4361
WPPI@SATX.RR.COM
DAVID WORMSER,PRES
LAURA WORMSER,VP
WORREL EXPLORATION,INC SEE
WORREL CHARLES J, CONS GEOL
WORSHAM TOM,OIL & GAS LEASES
PO BOX 812
JACKSONVILLE,TX 75766-0812
PH 903 586-1797
STEVE WORSHAM,OWNER
WORTHAM INSURANCE
PO BOX 1388
HOUSTON,TX 77251-1388
PH 713 526-3366 FAX 713 526-5872
WWW.WORTHAMINSURANCE.COM
RICHARD BLADES
RYAN SMITH
MICHAEL RUEHMAN
WOTTRING W PAUL & ASSOCIATES INC
2914 VIRGINIA
HOUSTON,TX 77098
PH 713 522-2040 FAX 713 524-2719
W PAUL WOTTRING,OWNER & ENGR
CHUCK FLEMING,DRAFTSMAN
WPM EXPLORATION,INC
PO BOX 52592
LAFAYETTE,LA 70505-2592 PH 337 232-1438
FAX 337 269-1783
WILLIAM P MILLS,III,PRES
WRAY JEFFREY GIBBS,LANDMAN,BROKER
AAPL,MOGA,MAPL
5048 LAKESHORE DR
JACKSON,MI 49203-5633 PH 517 787-8621
FAX 517 787-8080 LANDPRO515@COMCAST.NET
WRESSELL & COMPANY
505 SCOFIELDTOWN RD
STAMFORD,CT 06903-3307 PH 814 838-8168
FAX 814 838-7743
JOHN W WRESSELL,PRES
WRIGHT BROTHERS ENERGY,INC
13423 BLANCO RD
SAN ANTONIO,TX 78216-2187 PH 830 249-6305
CRAIG H WRIGHT,PRES
GARY S WRIGHT,VP,SECY/TREAS
BEA HUBER,EXEC SECY
DAVID BUSTOS,LDMN
WRIGHT LAND SERVICES INC
301 ST PATRICK ST
LAFAYETTE,LA 70506-4550
PH 337 235-0903 FAX 337 593-9025
ROBERT F WRIGHT,RLP
CAROLYN D WRIGHT,CPL
WRIGHT R WM G,CONS PETR ENGR
PO BOX 33
CARTERSVILLE,VA 23027-0057
PH 804 512-6689 BILL94571@GMAIL.COM

WSH LAND,INC (LANDMEN)
2727 ALLEN PKWY STE 1815
HOUSTON,TX 77019
PH 713 622-4823 FAX 713 622-4879
WWW.WSHLAND.COM
BENJAMIN K WEBB,PRTNR
DAVID C SHANNON,JR,PRTNR
FORT WORTH,TX OFFICE - 3221 COLLINSWORTH
ST STE 240,76104
PH 817 338-1222 FAX 817 338-1224
DENVER,CO OFFICE - 12303 AIRPORT WAY
STE 200, BROOMFIELD,CO 80021
PH 303 748-9101
WWW.OILGASMINERALS.COM
333 BLACKLATCH LANE
CAMP HILL,PA 17011 PH 717 439-2897
JIM LINDHOME JLINDHOME@GMAIL.COM
WYATT STANLEY D,CONSULTING GEOL
2860 PENNSYLVANIA AVE
CHARLESTON,WV 25302-4913 PH 304 346-8135
FAX 304 342-7622 ROCKSMELLER@HOTMAIL.COM
STANLEY D WYATT OWNER
GARY W INGRAM,PHYSICIST
WYNN-CROSBY
14241 DALLAS PKWY STE 800
DALLAS,TX 75254 PH 972 380-5500
FAX 972 380-9570
RONALD W CROSBY,PRES
DICK SUNDSTROM,VP/CFO
DAN KOONTZ,VP LAND & BUS DEV
JERRY ELGIN,VP OPERS
WYNNE J C,JR
2024 REBULIC DR
TYLER,TX 75701 PH 903 509-9795
WYO BEN INC
PO BOX 1979,1345 DISCOVERY DR
BILLINGS,MT 59102 PH 406 652-6351
WWW.WYOBEN.COM EMAIL@WYOBEN.COM
DAVID S BROWN,PRES,CEO
JOHN WORNOM,VP SALES & MKTG
GREYBULL,WY OFFICE - PO BOX 1072
PH 307 765-4446
MINING & PROD
WYOMING REFINING COMPANY
1600 BROADWAY STE 2300
DENVER,CO 80202-4927 PH 303 894-9966
FAX 303 837-9089
K SPENCER ZINN
GLENDA J BRANCH
DENVER,CO OFFICE - 1600 BROADWAY STE 2300
80202 PH 303 894-9966 FAX 303 837-9089
T PERARDI
RAPID CITY,SD OFFICE - PO BOX 8245,57709
PH 605 342-1614 FAX 605 342-4523
R L GLANZER
NEWCASTLE,WY OFFICE - PO BOX 820,82701
PH 307 746-4445 FAX 307 746-9710
C P HAVENER
WYTEX PRODUCTION CORPORATION
4520 PHOENIX AVE
FORT SMITH,AK 72903-6006 PH 501 646-9660
FAX 501 646-9664
CHARLES W JENKINS,PRES
X C O PRODUCTION COMPANY
520 POST OAK BLVD STE 200
HOUSTON,TX 77027-9416 PH 713 861-2918

FAX 713 861-0026

ROBERT A GRAY,PRES

X RAY INSPECTION,INC

1145 N UNIVERSITY AVE

LAFAYETTE,LA 70506-1005 PH 337 233-7676

PH 800 737-7695 FAX 337 233-1470

WWW.TEAMINDUSTRIALSERVICES.COM

ARLENE DUPUIS,ACCT MGR

KEITH CHATAGNIER,TECH SVC MGR

REBECCA MIXON,SECY

GABE HOLLIER,CORP SAFETY MGR/ASST RSO

LARRY CARRIERE,OPER MGR

ED MANUEL,ACNT MGR

HERB SIMPSON,TEXAS REG MGR

LISA SIMON,ACCT RECEIVABLE

LACEY OLIVIER,ADMIN ASST

RONNY ZUMO,ACCT MGR

SULPHUR,LA OFFICE -

3124 METRIC DR 70663

PH 337 882-0582 FAX 337 882-1364

KEVIN SCHULZE,BRANCH MGR

DENNIS GORDON,OPER MGR

SCOTT THERIOT,ACCT MGR

TIFFANY CARLIN,SECY

GONZALES,LA OFFICE - 9356 ASHLAND RD

70737 PH 225 647-7477 FAX 225 647-0407

MIKE LALONDE,OPER MGR

BRANDON STELLY,BRANCH MGR

STEVE JOHNSTON,OPER MGR

KIM DUBROC,SECY

BEAUMONT,TX OFFICE - 4832 WASHINGTON BLVD

77707 PH 409 840-9955 FAX 409 842-4190

MARK CLARK,BRANCH MGR

REX TOUSHA,OPER MGR

JAMES AMY,TECH SVC MGR

CHRISTY DUPUY,SECY

PEARLAND,TX OFFICE - 16823 HWY 35,77581

PH 281 992-0333 FAX 281 992-1820

CHRIS POWELL,BRANCH MGR

TONY MEDINA,OPER MGR

PAUL SNYDER,ACCT MGR

BONNIE BLANCHARD,ACCT MGR

AMY TRAVIS,SECY

CORPUS CHRISTI,TX OFFICE - 1599 N

LEXINGTON BLVD,78409

PH 361 289-6291 FAX 361 289-0705

BILL ERWIN,BRANCH MGR

JAMES SIMPSON,OPER MGR

ROSE GATES,SECY

XCALIBUR LAND & XPLORATION,LLC

1113 N AL DAVIS RD

NEW ORLEANS,LA 70123-2189 PH 504 302-2020

XCALIBURXPLORATION@GMAIL.COM

BRENT ABADIE

XCEL SEISMIC,INC

2218 WINDMILL RD

RICHMOND,TX 77406 PH 281 599-7226

JOE P WINSTON,PRES

XH LLC, SEE

XTO ENERGY

XPLORER PETROLEUM,LLC

PO BOX 51689

LAFAYETTE,LA 70505 PH 337 278-5362

FAX 337 232-1707 OILXPLORER@AOL.COM

XTO ENERGY INC

NATURAL GAS PRODUCER

810 HOUSTON ST

FORT WORTH,TX 76102-6298

PH 817 870-2800 FAX 817 870-1671

BOB SIMPSON,CHRMN,CEO

KEITH HUTTON,PRES

LOUIS BALDWIN,EXEC VP,CFO

TIM PETRUS,EXEC V P,ACQUISITIONS

VAUGHN VENNERBERG,SR EXEC VP &

CHIEF OF STAFF

BENNIE KNIFFEN,SR VP,CONTROLLER

JOY WEBSTER,VP,FACILITIES

KEN STAAB,SENIOR VP,ENGRG

NICK DUNGEY,SR VP,NATURAL GAS OPERS

MARK POSPISIL,SR VP,GEOL & GEOPHY

FRANK MCDONALD,SR VP,GEN COUNSEL &

ASST SECY

KAREN WILSON,VP,HUMAN RESOURCES

BRENT CLUM,SR VP,TREAS

WIN RYAN,SR VP,LAND

TERRY SCHULTZ,SR VP,GAS MKTG

GARY D SIMPSON,SR VP,INVESTOR RELS & FIN

MARK STEVENS,SR VP,TAX

FRANK THOMAS,VP,INFO TECHNOLOGY

JAMES DEATH,SR VP,LAND

NINA HUTTON,VP,ENVIRO HEALTH SAFETY

VIRGINIA ANDERSON,VP,CORP SECY

OKLAHOMA CITY,OK MID-CONTINENT DIV OFC -

210 W PARK AVE STE 2350,73102

PH 405 232-4011 FAX 405 232-5538

DOUG SCHULTZE,SR VP/MID-CONTINENT

MIDLAND,TX OFFICE - 200 N LORAINE STE 800

79705 PH 432 682-8873 FAX 432 687-0862

KYLE HAMMOND,VP OPERS/PERMIAN BASIN &

ALASKA

TYLER,TX OFFICE - 6141 PALUXY DR,75701

PH 903 939-1200 FAX 903 939-1300

KEN KIRBY,SR VP/EAST TX OPER

FARMINGTON,NM OFFICE - 2700 FARMINGTON

AVE,BLDG K,STE 1,87401

PH 505 324-1090 FAX 505 564-6700

DELBERT CRADDOCK,VP,OPERS/SAN JUAN

FARMINGTON,NM FIELD OFFICE - 6001 US HWY

64,87401 PH 505 632-5200

FAX 505 632-5906

XTO OFFSHORE INC, SEE

XTO ENERGY

YAHN & YAHN INC

PO BOX 588,23 LIBERTY ST

HAMMONDSPORT,NY 14840

PH 607 569-2878

WILLIAM K YAHN,PRES,VP

WYAHN@INFOBLVD.NET

YANDELL WILLIAM M,III,OIL PROPERTIES

5350 POPLAR AVE STE 730

MEMPHIS,TN 38119-0608 PH 901 763-3333

YARBROUGH LARRY

PO BOX 22883,121 N STATE ST

JACKSON,MS 39225-2883 PH 601 948-3080

FAX 601 948-3095 LYLAW@BELLSOUTH.NET

YATES DON DRILLING CO

2560 RUSSELL SPRINGS ROAD

COLUMBIA,KY 42728 PH 270 384-3656

DON YATES,OWNER

YATES ENERGY CO

P O BOX 3050,3119 MEADOW

LAREDO,TX 78041 PH 512 722-7658

THOMAS H YATES JR,PRTNR

SAM YATES,PRTNR

HOUSTON,TX OFFICE - 4900 WOODWAY,STE

600,77056 PH 713 621-5060

YATES EXPLORATION CO

P O BOX 3050,3119 MEADOW

LAREDO,TX 78041 PH 512 722-7658

THOMAS H YATES JR,PRTNR

SAM YATES,PRTNR

HOUSTON,TX OFFICE - 4900 WOODWAY,

STE 600,77056 PH 713 621-5060

YATES HARVEY E CO SEE

HARVEY E YATES COMPANY (HEYCO)

YEGUA ENERGY ASSOCIATES,LLC

19240 REDLAND RD STE 200

SAN ANTONIO,TX 78259

PH 210 489-7320 FAX 210 824-6423

JOHN Y AMES,OWNER

BONNIE R WEISE,OWNER

TOM EWING,OWNER

YEMEN HUNT LNG COMPANY LLC SEE

HUNT OIL COMPANY

YEMEN HUNT OIL COMPANY SEE

HUNT OIL COMPANY

YENTZEN INVESTMENTS,INC

OIL & GAS PRODUCER

12926 DAIRY ASHFORD STE 130

SUGAR LAND,TX 77478 PH 713 249-3960

W M YENTZEN,PRES

BONNIE C YENTZEN,SECY/TREAS

YOCKEY OIL,INC

PO BOX 70,1043 W MAIN

OLNEY,IL 62450-0070 PH 618 393-6236

CAROLYN LEADTKA CROW,OWNER

DONALD QUILLEN,CO-MGR

CONNIE S SHAFER,CO-MGR

YOHN TOM PETROLEUM LANDMAN,INC

PO BOX 770

WASKOM,TX 75692-0770

PH 318 286-5580 YOHNINC@AOL.COM

TOM YOHN

PENNY JO YOHN

YOUNG L PERRY,ATTY AT LAW

PO BOX 788

WHARTON,TX 77488-0788 PH 979 532-8590

FAX 979 532-8711 LPYOUNG10@HOTMAIL.COM

YOUNG LEIGHTON F,JR,GEOL

PO BOX 42429

HOUSTON,TX 77242-2429 PH 713 782-3831

FAX 713 782-6439 LFY@OILGASCONSULT.COM

YOUNG MICHAEL S

11823 PRIMWOOD DR

HOUSTON,TX 77070-2355 PH 281 376-6124

MICHAEL S YOUNG,OWNER

YOUNG WAYNE ENTERPRISE

P O BOX 158

PANOLA,TX 75685-0158 PH 972 766-3792

WAYNE YOUNG,PRES

BOB FONVILLE,GEN MGR

JIM OSWALT,CONTROLLER

YOUNGBLOOD FRANK M OIL OPR

111 OFFICE PARK DR # D

BRANDON,MS 39042-2403 PH 601 591-2240

FAX 601 591-2242

ANGELA REEDER,OFC MGR

YTURRIA FAUSTO PROPERTIES
ONE NORTH PARK PLAZA
BROWNSVILLE,TX 78521-1496 PH 956 542-7444
FAX 956 548-2057
FAUSTO YTURRIA JR,CEO,OWNER

YUMA EXPLORATION AND PRODUCTION CO INC
1177 W LOOP S STE 1825
HOUSTON,TX 77027-9006 PH 713 968-7068
FAX 713 968-7017 WWW.YUMACOMPANIES.COM
SAM L BANKS,CHRMN & CEO
SAMBANKS@YUMACOMPANIES.COM
KIRK SPRUNGER,CFO
SPRUNGER@YUMACOMPANIES.COM
MICHAEL F CONLON,PRES & COO
MCONLON@YUMACOMPANIES.COM
RICK TALBOT,CONTROLLER
STAN MORRIS,SR GEOL
STANM@YUMACOMPANIES.COM
MARK HARTMAN,VP EXPL
MARKH@YUMACOMPANIES.COM
T J LAFOSSE,VP,PIPELINES/FACILITIES
LAFOSSE@YUMACOMPANIES.COM
RICH ARMIN,SR GEOPHY
RICHA@YUMACOMPANIES.COM
MOMIN SYED,VP PLANNING & EVALS
MIKE STAMATEDES,CHF GEOPHY
MSTAMATEDES@YUMACOMPANIES.COM
KRISTINA STACEY,LAND MGR
KRISTINAS@YUMACOMPANIES.COM

YUMA PETROLEUM COMPANY SEE
YUMA EXPLORATION AND PRODUCTION CO,INC

ZACHRY EXPLORATION, LLC
300 CONVENT ST STE 2800
SAN ANTONIO,TX 78205-3709
PH 210 258-2200 FAX 210 258-2299
TIMOTHY L HILDENBRAND,PRES
CHARLES B REIS,CHF EXPLORATIONIST
SUSAN GOADE,DIR LAND

ZAP MINERALS LP
PO BOX 570174,1616 S VOSS RD STE 875
HOUSTON,TX 77257-0174 PH 713 952-0705
ROBERT E ZIMMERMAN JR,MNGNG MEMBER
MICHAEL H ASHER,MNGNG MEMBER

ZAPATA GULF MARINE CORPORATION SEE
TIDEWATER INC

ZAPATA-FENDER,L.L.C. SEE
FENDER EXPLORATION & PRODUCTION CO,LLC

ZARSKY DRILLING FLUIDS
PO BOX 4205
CORPUS CHRISTI,TX 78469-4205
PH 361 883-6366 FAX 361 288-0533
JOHN CLENDENNEN,MGR
JCLENDENNEN@ZARSKY.COM

ZARUBA FRANK,IND LDMN
PO BOX A
HALLETTSVILLE,TX 77964-1001
PH 361 798-3953 FRANK7188@ATT.NET

ZBYTE DATA SERVICES
10111 RICHMOND AVE STE 230
HOUSTON,TX 77042 PH 713 899-3054
KYLE HILL KYLE.HILL@ZBYTEDATA.COM

ZEDI US INC
ZEDI SOUTHERN FLOW
132 DEMANADE BLVD
LAFAYETTE,LA 70503 PH 337 233-2066
FAX 337 237-3790 WWW.ZEDI.US

GARY GRAY,PRES GARY.GRAY@ZEDI.US
DAVID HAMNER,CONTROLLER
OLIVER CUMMINGS,VP GULF COAST REG
GARY EDWARDS,VP WESTERN REG
PH 361 575-4528 FAX 361 575-9512
TIM VEILLEUX,VP NORTHERN REG
PH 903 472-4900 FAX 903 472-4903
LAFAYETTE,LA SUPPLY/TRAINING/LIQUID
PROVING FACILITY - 109 ROW 3,70508-4319
PH 337 234-7017 FAX 337 233-0314
MICKEY MIRE,CORP MGR
CHAD HORNSBY,SUPVSR (LAKE CHARLES,LA)
BELLE CHASSE,LA OFFICE - 8656 HWY 23
70037 PH 504 394-9440 FAX 504 392-6075
LOCKPORT,LA OFFICE - 1201 CRESCENT AVE
70374 PH 985 532-9977 FAX 985 532-9978
KRIS CHABERT,SUPVSR
HOUSTON,TX OFFICE - 2075 E GOVERNORS CIR
77092 PH 713 527-9591 FAX 713 527-8530
SCOTT SCHAP,SUPVSR
JOHN UTTER,FLD SUPVSR
DALLAS,TX OFFICE - 4011 SHILLING WAY
75237 PH 214 339-8301 FAX 214 339-8304
GABE SAUSEDA,DIV MGR
VICTORIA,TX OFFICE - 3001 N CAMERON ST
77901 PH 361 575-4528 FAX 361 575-9512
BRIAN HATCH/JOYCE BITTERLY,SUPVSR
CARRIZO SPRINGS,TX OFFICE - 3415 HWY 277
78834 PH 830 876-2777 FAX 830 865-2779
NORMAN BRISCOE,MGR
SCOTT SCHAP,DIV MGR
SAN ANTONIO,TX OFFICE - 15600 SAN PEDRO
AVE STE 309,78232 PH 210 490-4527
FAX 210 490-8869
SHARON PEBBLES,CHART SUPVSR
MARSHALL,TX OFFICE - 2308 E END BLVD S
75672 PH 903 472-4900 FAX 903 472-4903
KENNY PHILLIPS,SUPVSR
AMARILLO,TX OFFICE - 3131 BELL ST STE 108
79106 PH 806 678-3001
LEON BROWN,DIV MGR
BRANDON,MS OFFICE - 307-B GOVERNMENT ST
39042 PH 601 591-1526 FAX 601 591-1528
BOB SPINELLO,MGR
SAPULPA,OK OFFICE - 1409 S MAIN,74066
PH 918 227-2283 FAX 918 227-2386
DUKE STINNETT,MGR
WILLIAMSPORT,PA OFFICE - 1009 W FRONT ST
17702 PH 570 326-5014 FAX 318 686-0268
GEOFF WALTZ,FIELD TECH
SIDNEY,MT OFFICE - 1055 S CENTRAL AVE
59270 PH 701 609-0098
DAMON VOSBURY,FLD SUPVSR
CALGARY,ALBERTA,CANADA OFFICE (ZEDI INC)-
902 11TH AVE SW,T2R 0E7 PH 403 444-1100
FAX 403 444-1101

ZELLWEGER ANALYTICS INC
405 BARCLAY BLVD
LINCOLNSHIRE,IL 60069-3609
PH 847 955-8421 FAX 847 955-8208
NOEL HETZEL,SLS MGR

ZENTECH INC
14800 ST MARY'S LN STE 270
HOUSTON,TX 77079 PH 281 558-0290
FAX 281 558-0295 WWW.ZENTECH-USA.COM
ZENTECH@ZENTECH-USA.COM

RAMESH K MAINI,PRES
S RAO GUNTUR,SR VP
EDWARD BRUNING,SALES MGR
S NEJAD,MGR OF COMP ENGRG

ZEPHYR GAS SERVICES LP
20405 TOMBALL PKWY STE 700
HOUSTON,TX 77070 PH 713 467-3600
GLEN WIND GWIND@ZEPHYRGAS.COM

ZERUST - OIL & GAS SOLUTIONS
2601 TAOS TRAIL
DEER PARK,TX 77536 PH 281 853-5404
JOE DYSON

ZIEGENFUSS DRILLING,INC
PO BOX 308
RINGOES,NJ 08551-0308
PH 800 673-0328 FAX 908 788-0604
WWW.ZIEGENFUSSDRILLING.COM
MARK R ZIEGENFUSS,PRES
ALBERT E PICKETT,VP,SALES

ZIMMERMAN R EUGENE
5934 SHADY RIVER DR
HOUSTON,TX 77057-1321 PH 713 621-6523

ZIMMERMAN RESOURCES COMPANY
PO BOX 570174,1616 S VOSS STE 875
HOUSTON,TX 77257-0174 PH 713 952-0705
FAX 713 781-0271
ROBERT E ZIMMERMAN,JR,OWNER

ZIMMERMAN ROBERT E,JR,IND OIL PROP
PO BOX 570174,1616 S VOSS STE 875
HOUSTON,TX 77257-0174 PH 713 952-0705

ZINK, JOHN CO SEE JOHN ZINK HAMWORTHY
COMBUSTION

ZINKE & TRUMBO,INC SEE
ZENERGY INC

ZINN PETROLEUM COMPANY
3400 BISSONNET ST STE 250
HOUSTON,TX 77005-2153
PH 713 838-2900 FAX 713 838-2800
ROBERT L ZINN,OWNER

ZO ENERGY CORPORATION
800 NAVARRO ST STE 240
SAN ANTONIO,TX 78205-1725 PH 210 299-1450
ZOLITE@SWBELL.NET
STEVE J HARPER

ZOANDRA PETROLEUM,INC SEE
GREAT EASTERN ENERGY & DEVELOPMENT CORP

ZOE OIL & ENERGY LP
PO BOX 48307
FORT WORTH,TX 76148
PH 972 322-8134
ZOEDMEADOWS@AOL.COM
DONNY MEADOWS,PRES
JEANIE MEADOWS,SECY

ZORRO PETROLEUM CORPORATION
PO BOX 6186
CORPUS CHRISTI,TX 78466-6186
PH 361 888-8880 FAX 361 888-8880
RAUL M MIKE SAENZ,PRES

ZUHONE WILLIAM,INDEPENDENT OIL PROD
1317 WABASH AVE
MATTOON,IL 61938-4019 PH 217 235-9191

ZWAHLEN EXPLORATION
4461 SENTINEL ROCK TER
LARKSPUR,CO 80118-8909 PH 303 681-3142
FAX 303 681-3799
JACK J ZWAHLEN,OWNER

ZWIENER WILLIAM F
34011 DOBBIN HUFSMITH RD
MAGNOLIA,TX 77354 PH 832 934-2002
FAX 832 934-2005
BZWIENER@JONESANDZWIENER.COM

ZYSK STANLEY W
303 PRINCETON CT
BRYN MAWR,PA 19010-2118 PH 914 968 6798

1400 CORPORATION SEE
AMERICAN EXPLORATION COMPANY

1987 NYL LIMITED PARTNERSHIP SEE
AMERICAN EXPLORATION COMPANY

3-D GEOPHYSICAL,INC SEE
WESTERN GEOPHYSICAL

3D GEOPHYSICAL,INC DBA KEMP GEOPHYSICAL
SEE WESTERN GEOPHYSICAL

3D SEISMIC SURVEYS
10718 OLYMPIA DR
HOUSTON,TX 77042-2819 PH 713 952-2252
FAX 713 952-2252
JIM WINZELER,OWNER,LDMN,CPL

3300 CORPORATION SEE
AMERICAN EXPLORATION COMPANY

4 WINDS MARKETING COMPANY
PO BOX 51352
LAFAYETTE,LA 70505-1352
PH 337 781-7776
MATT ANGERS,PRES
MATTANGERS@LUSFIBER.NET

4-SIGHT OPERATING COMPANY
PO BOX 639
KILGORE,TX 75663-0639 PH 903 984-0013
FAX 903 984-4956
KEITH W CHERRY,PRES

4700 CORP SEE
AMERICAN EXPLORATION COMPANY

500 CORPORATION SEE
AMERICAN EXPLORATION COMPANY

6 D OIL CO,SEE
SIX D OIL COMPANY

7711 OIL COMPANY
PO BOX 69
COLLEYVILLE,TX 76034-0069 PH 817 369-4171
PRESTON BRYANT,OWNER

- CROSS REFERENCE SECTION -

A N R PIPELINE SEE
TENNESSEE GAS PIPELINE

A.E. ACQUISITION CORP SEE
AMERICAN EXPLORATION COMPANY

ACE RENTAL TOOLS SEE
SUPERIOR ENERGY SERVICES

ACID ENGINEERING,INC SEE
NOWSCO WELL SERVICE INC

ACME TOOL SEE
HOMCO INTERNATIONAL,INC

ADA OIL EXPLORATION CORPORATION SEE
ADAMS RESOURCES EXPLORATION CORP

ADAIR & ASSOC
SEE ADAIR LAND AND LEASING

ADAIR DUANE & ASSOC SEE
ADAIR OIL AND GAS PROPERTIES

ADAIR DUANE OIL & GAS PROP SEE
ADAIR OIL AND GAS PROPERTIES

ADAIR LAND AND LEASING SEE
ENERGY LAND CONSULTANTS

ADCOR DRILLING INC SEE
NABORS DRILLING USA,LP

ADIT PETROLEUM,INC SEE
SCOTT ROYCE ARNOLD

AGATE PETROLEUM,INC SEE
ST MARY LAND & EXPLORATION COMPANY

AGHORN OIL & GAS,INC, SEE
AGHORN ENERGY,INC

AIKMAN BROTHERS LLC SEE
AIKMAN COMPANIES

AIKMAN OIL AND GAS COMPANY SEE
AIKMAN COMPANIES

AIR DRILLING SERVICES,INC SEE WEATHERFORD

AIR LOGISTICS,LLC SEE BRISTOW U.S.,LLC

ALEXANDER ENERGY CORPORATION SEE
NATIONAL ENERGY GROUP,INC

ALGONQUIN GAS TRANSMISSION SEE
DUKE ENERGY GAS TRANSMISSION

ALI-BRON LTD SEE
BOYD THOMAS & ASSOC

ALL STATE PIPE TESTERS INC SEE
ALLSTAR PIPE SERVICES,INC

ALLIANCE BUSINESS INVESTMENT CO SEE
ENERGY MINERALS,LLC

ALRAM INC,MFG OF OILFIELD PUMPING UNITS
SEE WEATHERFORD

ALTEX ENERGY CORPORATION SEE
EQUAL ENERGY US INC.

AMBAR LONE STAR TECHNOLOGY CENTER SEE
NATIONAL OILWELL VARCO TECHNOLOGY CENTER

AMCOG ACQUISITION CORP SEE
AMERICAN EXPLORATION CO

AMERAC ENERGY CORP SEE
PETROCORP INCORPORATED

AMERADA HESS CORPORATION SEE
HESS CORPORATION

AMERICAN ENERGY SERVICES SEE
KEY ENERGY PRESSURE PUMPING SERVICES

AMERICAN EXPLORATION ACQUISITION CO SEE
AMERICAN EXPLORATION CO

AMERICAN EXPLORATION ACQUISITION-VI CORP
SEE AMERICAN EXPLORATION CO

AMERICAN EXPLORATION COMPANY SEE
LOUIS DREYFUS NATURAL GAS CORP

AMERICAN EXPLORATION GAS SYSTEMS CORP SEE
AMERICAN EXPLORATION CO

AMERICAN EXPLORER,INC SEE
PETROQUEST ENERGY,LLC

AMERICAN GAS ASSOCIATION
WWW.AGA.ORG

AMERICAN PRODUCING PROPERTIES CO SEE
AMERICAN EXPLORATION CO

AMERICAN PRODUCTION PARTNERSHIPS SEE
AMERICAN EXPLORATION CO

AMERICAN RESERVE CORP SEE
AMERICAN EXPLORATION CO

AMERICAN TRADING & PRODUCTION CORP
SEE TEMA OIL AND GAS COMPANY

AMERIPLOR CORP SEE
AMERICAN EXPLORATION CO

AMERITEX MINERALS & EXPLORATION,LTD SEE
AMERITEX MINERALS,INC

AMEROX ACQUISITION CORP SEE
AMERICAN EXPLORATION CO

AMEX OIL CO SEE
AMERICAN EXPLORATION CO

AMKAM ACQUISITION CORP SEE
AMERICAN EXPLORATION CO

AMOCO CORPORATION SEE
BP AMOCO CORPORATION

AMOCO PRODUCTION CO SEE
AMOCO CORPORATION

ANADARKO GATHERING COMPANY SEE
ANADARKO PETROLEUM CORPORATION

ANADRILL/SCHLUMBERGER LOGGING SVC SEE
SCHLUMBERGER

ANCON PARTNERSHIP,LTD SEE
AMERICAN EXPLORATION CO

ANDERSON OIL & GAS INC SEE
ANDERSON FEAZEL MANAGEMENT,INC

ANDERSON OIL CO INC SEE
ANDERSON OPERATING,LLC

ANDERSON WELL REPORTS
WWW.WELLREPORTS.COM

ANDRESS OIL & GAS CO SEE
BREITBURN ENERGY COMPANY LLC

ANDRIKOPOULOS OIL AND GAS SEE
A.G. ANDRIKOPOULOS RESOURCES INC

ANM SERVICES CORP SEE
AMERICAN EXPLORATION CO

ANR PIPELINE COMPANY SEE
EL PASO PIPELINE GROUP

ANSARCO LLC
SEE YOAKAM COLER A JR,PETR GEOL

APEX LAND CORP SEE
ANCHOR OGM,LLC

APPLIED RADON TECHNOLOGY SEE
COMPUTER PLACE

ARCH PETROLEUM INC SEE POGO PRODUCING CO

ARDO PRODUCTION CO,SEE
ARLEDGE TERRY & CO

ARKANSAS LA GAS CO,SEE ARKLA INC

ARRINGTON BROTHERS SEE
ARRINGTON PRODUCTION CO

ARTHUR PATRICK W PRODUCTION COMPANY SEE
PENDRAGON PRODUCTION COMPANY

ASSOCIATED ENERGY CONSULTANTS,LLC SEE
BAUGH RONALD

ASSOCIATED NATURAL GAS CORPORATION SEE
PANENERGY NATURAL GAS CORPORATION

ASSOCIATED NATURAL GAS,INC SEE
PANENERGY FIELD SERVICES,INC

ASSOCIATION OF AMERICAN RAILROADS
WWW.AAR.ORG

ATASCA RESOURCES,INC SEE
TRIBO PRODUCTION COMPANY,LTD

ATHANOR TEXAS INC SEE
APPROACH RESOURCES INC

ATLANTIC ENERGY HOLDINGS,LLC SEE
CENTENNIAL RESOURCE PRODUCTION LLC

ATLANTIC EXPLORATION,LLC SEE
CENTENNIAL RESOURCE PRODUCTION LLC

ATLANTIC RICHFIELD COMPANY,SEE
BP AMERICA,INC

ATLAS WIRELINE SERVICES SEE
WESTERN ATLAS LOGGING SERVICES

ATWOOD H KIRBY SEE GULF CAPITAL RESOURCES

AUSTRAL OIL COMPANY INC SEE
AMERICAN EXPLORATION CO

AWS-TECHNOLOGY SEE
WESTERN ATLAS LOGGING SERVICES

AX ACQUISITION CORP SEE
AMERICAN EXPLORATION CO

AXCON CORP SEE
AMERICAN EXPLORATION CO

AXELSON INC SEE
DRESSER OIL TOOLS

A2D TECHNOLOGIES SEE
TGS WELL DATA DIVISION

B B L LTD,SEE
BRECK OPERATING CORP

B T OPERATING CO SEE B & B PRODUCTION CO

B.W.R INVESTMENT,INC SEE
BUCK WHEAT RESOURCES INC

BAIRD GEOPHYSICAL COMPANY SEE
BAIRD PETROPHYSICAL INTERNATIONAL,INC

BAKER ATLAS NORTH AMERICA SEE
BAKER HUGHES

BAKER ATLAS SEE BAKER HUGHES
BAKER HUGHES

BAKER HUGHES INCORPORATED SEE
BAKER HUGHES

BAKER HUGHES INTEQ SEE
BAKER HUGHES

BAKER OIL TOOLS (FISHING DIVISION) SEE
BAKER HUGHES

BALCONES PRODUCTION CO SEE
TEXAS AMERICAN RESOURCES COMPANY

BALLANTYNE J ROYALTY CORP SEE
BLAKE BRUCE W CPL/ESA MGMNT SERVICES

BANK ONE,N.A.
SEE J P MORGAN CHASE BANK

BARBOUR CORPORATION SEE
BARBOUR WELL INC

BARFIELD WILLIAM G SEE
AQS RECRUITERS

BARNES EXPLORATION COMPANY SEE
B E X,INC

BAROID DRILLING FLUIDS SEE
HALLIBURTON ENERGY SERVICES

BAROID INDUSTRIAL DRILLING PRODUCTS SEE
HALLIBURTON ENERGY SERVICES

BASS ENTERPRISES PRODUCTION CO SEE
BOPCO,LP

BAWDEN DRILLING INC SEE
NOBLE DRILLING CORP

BAYARD DRILLING TECHNOLOGIES,INC SEE
NABORS DRILLING USA,LP

BAYOU PIPE BENDING COMPANY SEE
BAYOU COMPANIES

BAYOU PIPE COATING COMPANY SEE
BAYOU COMPANIES

BC PIPELINE AND FIELD SERVICES SEE
DUKE ENERGY GAS TRANSMISSION

BEACON GROUP,THE SEE
BEACON ROYALTY

BEAR PAW ENERGY LLC SEE
TRANSMONTAIGNE INC

BELNORTH PETROLEUM CORPORATION SEE
ENRON OIL & GAS CO

BIG PINEY OIL & GAS CO SEE
NATIONAL ENERGY GROUP INC

BIGHEART PIPE LINE CORP SEE
KOCH OIL CO

BJ CHEMICAL SERVICES SEE
BAKER HUGHES

BJ SERVICES COMPANY,USA SEE
BAKER HUGHES

BJ UNICHEM CHEMICAL SERVICES SEE
BJ CHEMICAL SERVICES

BLACK STONE OIL COMPANY SEE
COMSTOCK RESOURCES

BLACK STONE OIL COMPANY SEE
BLACK STONE MINERALS COMPANY,L.P.

BLACKWELL BAXTER & MOORE INS SPEC SEE
DON MOORE INSURANCE SERVICES,LLC

BLOWOUT TOOLS,INC SEE
SUPERIOR ENERGY SERVICES COMPANY

BLUE RIDGE ENERGY INC SEE
BAYOU CITY EXPLORATION,INC

BOCO OF LOUISIANA,INC SEE
SALAMIS SERVICES,INC

BOGERT OIL COMPANY SEE
LOUIS DREYFUS NATURAL GAS CORP

BOIS D'ARC ENERGY,INC SEE
STONE ENERGY CORPORATION

BOIS D'ARC OFFSHORE LTD SEE
STONE ENERGY CORPORATION

BOIS D'ARC PROPERTIES LP SEE
STONE ENERGY CORPORATION

BOISE CASCADE CORPORATION SEE
FOREST CAPITAL PARTNERS

BOISE SEE
FOREST CAPITAL PARTNERS

BOLD ENERGY LP,SEE
OXY USA INC

BONRAY DRILLING CORPORATION SEE
NABORS DRILLING USA,INC

BOUNDARY OIL CO SEE
AMERICAN EXPLORATION CO

BOX ENERGY CORPORATION SEE
REMINGTON OIL AND GAS CORPORATION

BP AMERICA INC SEE
BP

BP AMERICA PRODUCTION COMPANY SEE
BP AMERICA INC

BP AMOCO CORPORATION SEE
BP CORPORATION

BP CORPORATION SEE
BP AMERICA INC

BP EXPLORATION (ALASKA) INC SEE
BP ALASKA,INC

BP EXPLORATION & OIL INC SEE
BP AMERICA,INC

BP EXPLORATION,INC SEE
BP AMERICA,INC

BRACKEN ENERGY COMPANY SEE
BRACKEN OPERATING LLC

BRANDT CO,THE SEE
BRANDT,A VARCO CO

BRANDT PETROLEUM INC,SEE
KARBUHN OIL CO

BRANDT/EPI SEE
BRANDT,A VARCO COMPANY

BRANDT,A VARCO COMPANY SEE
NOV BRANDT

BRAVO NATURAL RESOURCES,INC SEE
CHESAPEAKE ENERGY CORPORATION

BRAVO OIL COMPANY SEE
SANTA FE ENERGY RESOURCES,INC

BRG LONE STAR LTD SEE
BRG ENERGY INC

BRG PETROLEUM LLC SEE
BRG ENERGY INC

BRG PRODUCTION COMPANY SEE
SEE BRG ENERGY INC

BRIDAS ENERGY USA,INC SEE
BEUSA ENERGY,INC

BRIGHT STAR MANAGEMENT,LLC SEE
CRAFT EXPLORATION COMPANY,LLC

BRISTOL MUNGER PROP LLC
SEE HUNT OIL COMPANY

BRITOIL U.S. HOLDINGS INC SEE
AMERICAN EXPLORATION CO

BRITOIL VENTURES INC SEE
AMERICAN EXPLORATION CO

BROCK EXPLORATION CORPORATION SEE
KEY PRODUCTION COMPANY,INC

BROOKLYN UNION EXPLORATION COMPANY SEE
HOUSTON EXPLORATION COMPANY,THE

BROWN & ROOT ENERGY SERVICES SEE
KELLOGG BROWN & ROOT,INC

BROWN G A,OIL PROP SEE
GILA GROUP,LP

BRUNSON & MCKNIGHT INC,SEE
NEW TEX OIL CO

BRYANT-CHASE ENERGY CORPORATION SEE
RIDGE PETROLEUM INC

BULLOCK VAN K,EXPLOR,PROD SEE
BULLOCK CORPORATION

BUREAU OF ECONOMIC GEOLOGY
WWW.BEG.UTEXAS.EDU

BUREAU OF OCEAN ENERGY MANAGEMENT
WWW.BOEMRE.GOV

BURLINGTON RESOURCES OIL AND GAS CO SEE
CONOCOPHILLIPS COMPANY

BURNS & PERKINS OIL,LLC SEE
BURNS ENERGY CO,LLC

BUTLER ASSOCIATES INC,SEE
WILLBROS ENGINEERS,INC

BWB OPERATING INC SEE
BLAKE BRUCE W CPL/ESA MGMNT SERVICES

C OIL INC SEE
CANADAY OIL CORPORATION

C X Y ENERGY INC SEE
NEXEN PETROLEUM U.S.A.,INC

C.W. MOORE,INC SEE
INTERNATIONAL DEVELOPMENT CORP

CABLE PETROLEUM COMPANY SEE
CABLE & ASSOCIATES,LP

CABOT ENERGY CORPORATION SEE
CABOT OIL & GAS CORPROATION

CAIRN ENERGY USA,INC SEE
MATRIX PETROLEUM,LLC

CAL-T MANAGEMENT CORP SEE
CAL-T OIL CO

CAMCO COILED TUBING SERVICES SEE
SCHLUMBERGER

CAMCO INTERNATIONAL INC SEE
SCHLUMBERGER

CAMCO PRODUCTS & SERVICES CO SEE
SCHLUMBERGER

CAMCO WIRELINE SEE
CAMCO PRODUCTS & SERVICES COMPANY

CAMWEST EXPLORATION LLC SEE
STEPHENS ENERGY COMPANY,LLC

CANRIG DRILLING TECHNOLOGIES
SEE NABORS INDUSTRIES LTD

CANYON REEF MINERALS LTD SEE
BRECK OPERATING CORP

CARBON ENERGY CORPORATION SEE
EVERGREEN RESOURCES,INC

CARDINAL SERVICES,INC SEE
SUPERIOR ENERGY SERVICES

CARNES JOHN C SEE
ROCK CHALK ROYALTIES,LTD

CARPENTER OIL & GAS COMPANY SEE
ENERGY PRODUCTION CORPORATION

CARTER BARNEY ESTATE SEE
MATTYE CARTER FAMILY TRUST

CASHCO ENERGY CORP SEE
CASHCO OIL CO

CAY PRODUCTION LLC SEE
YOAKAM COLER A JR,PETR GEOL

CAZA DRILLING (CA) INC SEE
ENSIGN U.S. DRILLING INC

CAZA DRILLING INC SEE
SEE ENSIGN U.S. DRILLING INC

CEMENTATION (OEMOCO) SEE WEATHERFORD

CENERGY CORP SEE
AMERICAN EXPLORATION CO

CENERGY EXPLORATION CO SEE
AMERICAN EXPLORATION CO

CENTENNIAL NATURAL GAS CORPORATION SEE
ASSOCIATED NATURAL GAS,INC

CENTRAL INDUSTRIES INC SEE
STALLION CONSTRUCTION

CENTRAL STALLION SEE
SEE STALLION CONSTRUCTION

CENTURY EXPLORATION COMPANY SEE
CENTURY EXPLORATION NEW ORLEANS,LLC

CENTURY OFFSHORE MANAGEMENT CORP SEE
CENTURY EXPLORATION COMPANY

CENTURY ONSHORE EXPLORATION COMPANY SEE
CENTURY EXPLORATION HOUSTON,INC

CHAMA PETROLEUM COMPANY SEE
NEARBURG PRODUCING COMPANY

CHAMPION CHEMICALS INC/ARKLATEX DIST SEE
CHAMPION TECHNOLOGIES INC

CHAMPLIN PETROLEUM COMPANY SEE
UNION PACIFIC RESOURCES CO (UPRC)

CHASE MANHATTAN BANK SEE
J P MORGAN CHASE BANK

CHEROKEE RESOURCES INCORPORATED SEE
WYNN-CROSBY ENERGY INC

CHESAPEAKE OPERATING,INC SEE
CHESAPEAKE ENERGY CORPORATION

CHESAPEAKE PANHANDLE,INC SEE
CHESAPEAKE ENERGY CORPORATION

CHEVRON U S A INC SEE
CHEVRONTEXACO EXPLORATION & PRODUCTION CO

CHEVRONTEXACO EXPLORATION & PRODUCTION
SEE CHEVRON

CHIEFTAIN INTERNATIONAL (U.S.) INC
SEE HUNT OIL COMPANY

CIMA EXPLORATION CO SEE
BARNEBURG,INC

CIMARRON OPERATING COMPANY SEE
LOMAK PETROLEUM INC

CINERGY MARKETING & TRADING,LP SEE
BNP PARIBAS

CITY EXPLORATION CO SEE
CENTRAL UNIVERSAL CO

CLARUS ENERGY PARTNER LP SEE
HUNT OIL COMPANY

CMS OIL AND GAS COMPANY SEE
PERENCO LLC

CNG PRODUCING COMPANY SEE
DOMINION EXPLORATION & PRODUCTION,INC

COASTAL COORDINATION COUNCIL
WWW.GLO.STATE.TX.US/COASTAL/CCC.HTML

COASTAL CORPORATION AND SUBSIDIARIES SEE
EL PASO PIPELINE GROUP

COASTAL MANAGEMENT CORPORATION SEE
SCHLUMBERGER-IPM

COASTAL OIL & GAS CORPORATION SEE
EL PASO PIPELINE GROUP

CODA ENERGY INC SEE
BELCO OIL & GAS CORP

COILED TUBING CORP SEE
CUDD PRESSURE CONTROL,INC

COLLIER & ELY,L.P. SEE
EBR ENERGY,LP

COLONY ENERGY CORPORATION SEE
ASSOCIATED NATURAL GAS,INC

COLORADO CRUDE CO SEE
GULF ENERGY EXPLORATION CORP

COLORADO INTERSTATE GAS COMPANY SEE
EL PASO PIPELINE GROUP

COLUMBIA GAS DEVELOPMENT CORPORATION SEE
AVIARA ENERGY CORPORATION

COLUMBUS ENERGY CORP SEE
CIMAREX ENERGY CO

COMDISCO EXPLORATION,INC SEE
DUNCAN ENERGY COMPANY

COMPLETION TOOL COMPANY SEE
CTC INTERNATIONAL

COMPUTALOG USA SEE
SEE WEATHERFORD

CONCENTRIC PIPE & TOOL RENTALS SEE
SUPERIOR ENERGY SERVICES COMPANY

CONCHO EQUITY HOLDING CORP SEE
COG OPERATING LLC

CONCHO OIL & GAS CORP SEE
COG OPERATING LLC

CONNECTION TECHNOLOGY SEE
SUPERIOR ENERGY SERVICES

CONQUEST EXPLORATION COMPANY SEE
AMERICAN EXPLORATION COMPANY

CONTOUR ENERGY CO SEE
SAMSON COMPANIES

COOPER OIL TOOL SEE
CAMERON

COOPERATIVE REFINING,LLC SEE
NATIONAL COOPERATIVE REFINERY ASSOC(NCRA)

COPAS INTERPRETATIONS SEE
AUDITORS - OIL & GAS

CORONADO ENERGY E&P COMPANY LLC SEE
EL PASO PRODUCTION & EXPLORATION

COSDEN OIL & CHEMICAL CO SEE
FINA OIL AND CHEMICAL CO

COTTON PETROLEUM CORPORATION SEE
APACHE CORPORATION

CPAC SEE
COMPACT PUMPING & COIL SPECIALISTS,INC

CRATON ENERGY CORP SEE
ARCHON RESOURCES LLC

CREEDE,LTD SEE
CREEDE MINERALS LTD

CRESCENDO RESOURCES,L.P. SEE
BP AMOCO CORPORATION

CRIMSON EXPLORATION OPERATING INC SEE
CONTANGO OIL & GAS COMPANY

CROSS TIMBERS OIL COMPANY SEE
XTO ENERGY INC

CROSS TIMBERS OPERATING COMPANY SEE
XTO ENERGY INC

CROSSTEX ENERGY SERVICES,LP SEE
ENLINK MIDSTREAM OPERATING LP

CROSSTEX LIG LIQUIDS,LLC SEE
ENLINK LIG,LLP

CROSSTEX LIG,LLC SEE ENLINK LLG,LLC

CRS SEE
COMPRESSOR RENEWAL SERVICES LTD

CTC MINERALS,INC SEE
BANK OF AMERICA

D L MUD INC SEE
AMBAR LONE STAR TECHNOLOGY

D R DRILLING RECORDS SEE
DIVESTCO USA INC

DAILEY DAMCO SEE WEATHERFORD

DAILEY DWS SEE WEATHERFORD

DAILEY INTERNATIONAL INC SEE WEATHERFORD

DAILEY PETROLEUM SERVICES CORP SEE
DAILEY INTERNATIONAL,INC

DALE-ANN ENTERPRISES SEE
DALE-ANN CO,INC

DALE-ANN GAS SPECIALISTS
SEE DALE-ANN CO,INC

DALE-ANN INDUSTRIAL SEE
DALE-ANN CO,INC

DALE-ANN UTILITIES SEE
DALE-ANN CO,INC

DALEN RESOURCES OIL & GAS CO SEE
ENSERCH EXPLORATION,INC

DAMAC DRILLING INC SEE
MCKOWN OIL INC

DAMSON OIL CORPORATION SEE
PARKER & PARSLEY PETROLEUM CO

DATAGAS,INC SEE
ATHENA ENERGY,INC

DAUGHERTY PETROLEUM INC SEE
NGAS RESOURCES,INC.

DAVIS BROTHERS SEE
BENSON & SCHOEN OIL CO,INC

DAVIS INC (DAVIS INTERESTS) SEE
DAVIS BROS,LLC

DAVIS OIL COMPANY SEE
DAVIS PETROLEUM CORPORATION

DAVIS RESOURCES SEE
DAVIS BROS,LLC

DEEPKO LEASE & ROYALTY CO SEE
REVARD OIL AND GAS PROPERTIES,INC

DELHI GAS PIPELINE CORPORATION SEE
KOCH MIDSTREAM SERVICES COMPANY

DEMCO DIVISION COOPER INDUSTRIES,INC SEE
CAMERON,A DIV OF COOPER CAMERON CORP

DEMINEX U S OIL COMPANY SEE
SOUTHWEST ROYALTIES,INC

DEVON SFS OPERATING,INC SEE
DEVON ENERGY CORPORATION

DI INDUSTRIES,INC SEE
DRILLERS INC

DIA LOG COMPANY SEE
WEDGE DIA-LOG,INC

DIAMOND M - ODECO DRILLING INC SEE
DIAMOND OFFSHORE DRILLING INC

DIAMOND SHAMROCK EXPLORATION COMPANY SEE
MAXUS EXPLORATION COMPANY

DIAMOND SHAMROCK INC SEE
ULTRAMAR DIAMOND SHAMROCK CORPORATION

DIAMOND SHAMROCK PIPELINE COMPANY SEE
ULTRAMAR DIAMOND SHAMROCK CORPORATION

DIAMONDBACK OPERATING,LP SEE
PATRICK ENERGY GROUP

DIGICON GEOPHYSICAL CORPORATION SEE
VERITAS DGC INC

DINERO OIL CORP SEE
ANDERSON OIL LTD

DIRECTIONAL TECHNOLOGIES,INC SEE
RYAN ENERGY TECHNOLOGIES USA,INC

DIXON EXPLORATION INC SEE
DXN INTERESTS,LLC & DXN ASSOCIATES

DIXON-DEARMORE OIL COMPANY,INC SEE
DIXON ENERGY,INC

DLB OIL & GAS,INC SEE
CHESAPEAKE OPERATING,INC

DOMINION OKLAHOMA TEXAS EXPL & PROD,INC
(DOTEPI) SEE HIGH MOUNT E&P

DOUGLAS DALE OIL & GAS PROPERTIES SEE
DZ RESOURCES,LLC

DOW CHEMICAL USA OIL & GAS DIV SEE
APACHE CORPORATION

DOWDCO/DIAMOND OIL WELL DRILLING CO,INC
SEE CORPRO

DOWNHOLE SEISMIC SERVICES SEE
ATLAS WIRELINE SERVICES

DRESSER ATLAS,DRESSER INDUSTRIES SEE
ATLAS WIRELINE SERVICES

DRESSER OIL TOOLS SEE
HALLIBURTON ENERGY SERVICES

DRILLERS,INC SEE
GREY WOLF DRILLING CO

DRILLING RECORDS,DIV OF CANAMERA CORP SEE
DIVESTCO USA INC

DRILLING-PROSPECTS.COM SEE
BLAKE BRUCE W CPL/ESA MGMNT SERVICES

DUKE ENERGY FIELD SERVICES,INC SEE
DCP MIDSTREAM

DUNCAN ENERGY COMPANY SEE
BABCOCK & BROWN ENERGY,INC

DUNCAN WALTER,OIL PROPERTIES SEE
DUNCAN OIL PROPERTIES INC

DUNDEE PETROLEUM,INC SEE
SCOTT ROYCE ARNOLD

DUNDEE RESOURCES INC SEE
SCOTT ROYCE ARNOLD

DWIGHTS ENERGY DATA SEE
PETROLEUM INFORMATION/DWIGHTS LLC

DYCO PETROLEUM CORPORATION SEE
SAMSON RESOURCES CO

DYN MCDERMOTT PETROLEUM OPERATIONS CO SEE
DM PETROLEUM OPERATIONS CO

EAGLE ROCK ACQS PARTNERSHIP II SEE
EAGLE ROCK OPERATING COMPANY LLC

EAST TENNESSEE NATURAL GAS SEE
DUKE ENERGY GAS TRANSMISSION

EASTERN GEOPHYSICAL INC SEE
SEISMIC EXCHANGE,INC

EASTMAN TELECO SEE
BAKER HUGHES INTEQ

EBY AND PETRUS SURVEY SEE EBY SURVEY INC

EDMUNDSON & ASSOCIATES,INC SEE
UNITSOURCE INCORPORATED

EEX CORPORATION SEE
NEWFIELD EXPLORATION COMPANY

EIGHTY EIGHT PETROLEUM CO INC SEE
88 PETROLEUM CO,INC (END OF ALPHA)

EISEMAN CHEMICAL SEE
BAKER HUGHES INTEQ

EL PASO CORPORATION SEE
KINDER MORGAN

EL PASO ENERGY CORPORATION SEE
KINDER MORGAN

EL PASO NATURAL GAS COMPANY SEE
KINDER MORGAN

EL PASO PIPELINE GROUP SEE
KINDER MORGAN

EL PASO PRODUCTION & EXPLORATION SEE
EP ENERGY

ELF AQUITAINE PETROLEUM SEE
ELF EXPLORATION INC

ELF EXPLORATION,INC SEE
TOTALFINAELF E&P USA,INC

ENCORE ACQUISITION COMPANY SEE
DENBURY RESOURCES INC

ENERGY CONNECTION
WWW.ENERGYCONNECT.COM

ENERGY DEVELOPMENT CORPORATION SEE
SAMEDAN OIL CORPORATION

ENERGY ENTERPRISES INC SEE
REH ENERGY

ENERGY INDUSTRIES SEE
WEATHERFORD ENTERRA COMPRESSION CO

ENERGY INFORMATION ADMINISTRATION
WWW.EIA.DOE.GOV

ENERGY INVESTMENTS COMPANY SEE
LOUISIANA ONSHORE EXPLORATION,LLC

ENERGY MANAGEMENT CORP SEE
TELLUS OPERATING GROUP,LLC

ENERGY MARKETING EXCHANGE INC SEE
KCS ENERGY,INC

ENERGY MINERALS,INC SEE
DAVIS BROS,LLC

ENERGY MINERALS,LLC SEE
DAVIS BROS,LLC

ENERGY PARTNERS,LTD SEE EPL OIL & GAS,INC

ENERGY RESERVES GROUP INC SEE
BHP PETROLEUM (AMERICAS) INC

ENERGY RESOURCES MANAGEMENT LLC SEE
KBL E&P LIMITED COMPANY

ENRON OIL & GAS CO SEE
EOG RESOURCES,INC

ENRON OIL TRADING & TRANSPORTATION CO SEE
EOTT ENERGY OPERATING LTD PRTNR

ENSERCH EXPLORATION,INC SEE
EEX CORPORATION

ENSIGN OPERATING CO SEE
EL PASO EXPLORATION & PRODUCTION

ENSOURCE INC SEE
U M C PETROLEUM CORP

ENTERRA OIL FIELD RENTAL SEE
WEATHERFORD COMPRESSION

ENTRADE CORPORATION SEE
TENNECO GAS MARKETING COMPANY

ENVIRONMENTAL PROTECTION AGENCY
WWW.EPA.GOV

ENVIRONMENTAL TREATMENT TEAM (ETT) SEE
SUPERIOR ENERGY SERVICES COMPANY

ENVISION ENERGY RESOURCES,INC SEE
SIGNATURE OIL & GAS LLC

EOG OKLAHOMA INC SEE
ENSIGN OPERATING CO

EOTT ENERGY OPERATING LIMITED PRTNR SEE
LINK ENERGY LIMITED PARTNERSHIP

EPL OIL & GAS,INC SEE ENERGY XXI

EPOCH WELL SERVICES,INC SEE
CANRIG DRILLING TECHNOLOGIES

EQUILON PIPELINE COMPANY SEE
SHELL PIPELINE COMPANY,LP

EQUITY COMPRESSORS,INC SEE
OUACHITA ENERGY CORPORATION

ETHYL PETROLEUM ADDITIVES,INC SEE
AFTON CHEMICAL CORPORATION

EVANS A R SEE
A.R. EVANS & ASOCIATES

EXCEL ENGINEERING,INC SEE
RAMBOLL OIL & GAS US,INC

EXCO MIDCONTINENT DIVISION SEE
SHERIDAN PRODUCTION COMPANY,LLC

EXETER DRILLING COMPANY SEE
NABORS DRILLING USA,INC

EXPLORATION FUNDS INC SEE
MCCOY OIL & GAS CO

EXPLORATION INVESTMENTS,INC SEE
WYNNE PETROLEUM CO

EZ HULL,LLC SEE
LCM SOLUTIONS,LLC

F & F WIRELINE SERVICES,INC SEE
SUPERIOR ENERGY SERVICES

FAGADAU ENERGY CORPORATION SEE
PRIMEXX OPERATING CORPORATION

FAIRFIELD INDUSTRIES INC SEE
FAIRFIELDNODAL

FALCON BAY ENERGY,LLC SEE
CAZA OPERATING LLC

FALCON BAY OPERATIONS,LLC SEE
CAZA OPERATING,LLC

FASTORG,INC SEE
SUPERIOR ENERGY SERVICES

FEDERAL ENERGY REGULATORY COMMISSION
WWW.FERC.GOV

FEDERAL RAILROAD ADMINISTRATION
WWW.FRA.DOT.GOV

FELMONT OIL CORPORATION SEE
TORCH ENERGY ADVISORS,INC

FIN OIL INC SEE
TOTALFINAELF E&P USA,INC

FINA LA TERRE SEE
TOTALFINAELF E&P USA,INC

FINA OIL AND CHEMICAL COMPANY SEE
TOTALFINAELF E&P USA INC

FLAG REDFERN OIL COMPANY SEE
KERR-MCGEE CORPORATION

FLANAGAN AND WILEY,CONSULTING ENGRS SEE
WINTER GARDEN ENGINEERING

FLARE RESOURCES,INC SEE DISCOVER E&P LLC

FLECK MATHER & STRUTZ,PLLP SEE
CROWLEY FLECK,PLLP

FLORES & RUCKS,INC SEE
OCEAN ENERGY,INC

FMC INVALCO SEE
INVALCO PRODUCTS

FONTENOT PETROLEUM LAND SERVICES,INC SEE
ACADIAN LAND SERVICES,LLC

FORAN OIL COMPANY SEE
MATADOR RESOURCES COMPANY

FORCENERGY INC SEE
FOREST OIL CORPORATION

FOREST OIL CORPORATION SEE
SABINE OIL AND GAS LLC

FORNEY & MCCOMBS SEE
MCCOMBS ENERGY

FORNEY OIL CORP SEE
FORNEY & MCCOMBS

FOUR CORNERS DRILLING CO SEE
BIG A WELL SERVICE

FP INC SEE
LOMAK PETROLEUM INC.

FREEMAN JOHN C,ESTATE SEE
FREEMAN LIVING TRUST,JEAN L

FRENCH ENERGY,INC SEE
BISON INVESTMENTS,LLC

FRISCO OIL CORPORATION SEE
KEW DRILLING

GARY A MONROE & ASSOCIATES PETROLEUM
LAND SERVICES SEE MONROE GARY A & ASSOC

GAS PROCESSORS ASSOCIATION
WWW.GASPROCESSORS.COM

GAS RESEARCH INSTITUTE
WWW.GASTECHNOLOGY.ORG

GAUTHIER BROTHERS INC SEE
BRANDT,A VARCO CO

GAUTHIER BROTHERS RECOVERY SYSTEMS SEE
BRANDT,A VARCO CO

GCO MINERALS COMPANY SEE
IP PETROLEUM COMPANY,INC

GE OIL & GAS SEE
HYDRIL PRESSURE CONTROL

GEAR PETROLEUM CO INC SEE
PETROLEUM PROPERTY SERVICES,INC

GEARHART INDUSTRIES,INC SEE
HALLIBURTON LOGGING SERVICES,INC

GECO-PRAKLA SEE
WESTERNGECO LLC

GEMOCO SEE
WEATHERFORD ENTERRA

GENERAL ATLANTIC RESOURCES,INC SEE
U M C PETROLEUM CORPORATION

GENERAL PRODUCING COMPANY SEE
U M C PETROLEUM CORPORATION

GENOVA POWER COMPANY LP SEE
HUNT OIL COMPANY

GEOLOGICAL CONSULTING SERVICES,INC SEE
IHS INTERPRETED FORMATION TOPS

GEOLOGICAL DATA SERVICES SEE
IHS INTERPRETED FORMATION TOPS

GEOLOGRAPH PIONEER SEE
SWACO,A DIV OF M-I

GEOPHYNQUE INTERNATIONAL SEE
HYDROGEOPHYSICS,INC

GEOPHYSICAL DEVELOPMENT CORPORATION SEE
GEOKINETICS INC

GEOPHYSICAL SERVICE INC SEE
HALLIBURTON GEOPHYSICAL SERVICES,INC

GEOQUEST/SCHLUMBERGER SEE
SCHLUMBERGER

GEORGE ASSOCIATES DRILLING SEE
GEORGE ENTERPRISES

GLOBAL GEOPHYSICAL SERVICES LTD
SEE GLOBAL GEOPHYSICAL SERVICES INC

GLOBAL MILLENNIUM ENERGY INC SEE
GMX RESOURCES INC

GLOBAL NATURAL RESOURCES INC SEE
SEAGULL ENERGY CORPORATION

GLOBAL/WEINMAN GEOSCIENCE
SEE GLOBAL GEOPHYSICAL SERVICES INC

GPM GAS CORPORATION SEE
PHILLIPS PETROLEUM COMPANY

GRACE PETROLEUM CORPORATION SEE
SAMSON INVESTMENT COMPANY

GRAHAM BILL J OIL AND GAS CORP SEE
INCLINE ENERGY,INC

GRANT GEOPHYSICAL SEE
GEOKINETICS INC

GRAYHAWK ENERGY/GRAYHAWK OPERATING SEE
CHESAPEAKE ENERGY CORPORATION

GREAT SOUTHERN DRILLING SERVICE SEE
DAILEY PETROLEUM SERVICES,INC

GREAT WESTERN RESOURCES INC SEE
FORCENERGY,INC

GREENBRIER OPERATING CO SEE
CAMDEN RESOURCES INC

GREGORY & COOK CONSTRUCTION INC SEE
PRICE GREGORY CONSTRUCTION INC

GREY WOLF DRILLING COMPANY,LP SEE
PRECISION DRILLING OILFIELD SERVICES CORP

GRUY PETROLEUM MANAGEMENT CO,LLC SEE
CIMAREX ENERGY CO

GUERRA ENGINEERING INC SEE
HANOVER COMPRESSOR COMPANY

GUIBERSON AVA SEE
DRESSER OIL TOOLS

GULF CANADA RESOURCES LIMITED SEE
CONOCOPHILLIPS CANADA RESOURCES CORP

GULF OIL EXPLORATION & PRODUCTION CO SEE
CHEVRON U S A,INC

GULFSTREAM NATURAL GAS SYSTEM SEE
DUKE ENERGY GAS TRANSMISSION

H & N OPERATING COMPANY,INC SEE
NEW DAVID OPERATING CO,INC

H G B LAND SERVICES COMPANY,INC SEE
H G B OIL CORPORATION

HALCON ENERGY PROPERTIES,INC SEE
HALCON RESOURCES CORPORATION

HALCON HOLDINGS,INC SEE
HALCON RESOURCES CORPORATION

HALCON OPERATING CO.,INC SEE
HALCON RESOURCES CORPORATION

HALCON RESOURCES OPERATING,INC SEE
HALCON RESOURCES CORPORATION

HALLIBURTON GEODATA SEE
HALLIBURTON ENERGY SERVICES

HALLIBURTON GEOPHYSICAL SERVICES,INC SEE
HALLIBURTON ENERGY SERVICES

HALLIBURTON LOGGING SERVICES,INC SEE
HALLIBURTON ENERGY SERVICES

HALLIBURTON RESERVOIR SERVICES SEE
HALLIBURTON ENERGY SERVICES

HALLIBURTON RESOURCE MANAGEMENT SEE
HALLIBURTON ENERGY SERVICES

HALLIBURTON SERVICES SEE
HALLIBURTON ENERGY SERVICES

HAMON OIL & GAS RESOURCE CENTER
WWW.DALLASLIBRARY2.ORG

HANLAD OIL CORP SEE
MCBRIDE OIL & GAS CORP

HANOVER COMPRESSOR COMPANY SEE
HANOVER COMPANY,THE

HARDY OIL & GAS USA,INC SEE
MARINER ENERGY,INC

HARRIS, WILLIAM P OIL & GAS PROP SEE
TASCOSA LAND RESOURCES,LLC

HARRISBURG/WOOLEY SEE
NATIONAL OILWELL VARCO

HART RESOURCE TECHNOLOGIES,INC SEE
FLUID RECOVERY SERVICES,LLC

HARVEY ENERGY SEE
HARVEY MINERAL PARTNERS,LP

HARVEY MINERAL PARTNERS,LP SEE
HARVEY VENTURES GROUP,LLC

HARVEY ROYALTY PARTNERS,LP SEE
HARVEY VENTURES GROUP,LLC

HAYNES PRODUCTION CO,INC SEE
CREEK ENERGY,INC

HB RENTALS SEE
SUPERIOR ENERGY SERVICES

HCI COASTAL CHEMICAL COMPANY,LLC SEE
COASTAL CHEMICAL CO,LLC

HDC ENERGY COMPANY SEE
HDBC INVESTMENTS,LIMITED

HECI EXPLORATION COMPANY SEE
BROWNING OIL COMPANY,INC

HEI-VENTURES ENGLAND LP SEE
HUNT OIL COMPANY

HELIX ENERGY SOLUTION GROUP SEE
SEE ENERGY RESOURCE TECHNOLOGY GOM INC

HEMERA LAND,INC SEE
JACKFORK LAND,INC

HENRY & SANDOZ,INC SEE
SANDOZ & ASSOC,INC

HERINGER ENERGY RESOURCES CO SEE
HERCO

HEROLD JOHN S INC SEE
IHS HEROLD

HERSHEY OIL CORP (U.S. PROPERTIES) SEE
AMERICAN EXPLORATION CO

HFP ACOUSTICAL CONSULTANTS INC SEE
SLR CONSULTING (CANADA) LTD

HHE COMPANY SEE
SEE XTO ENERGY

HIGHLAND ENERGY COMPANY SEE
CALPINE PRODUCER SERVICES,LP

HINES E R,JR,GEOL SEE MOON & HINES,LLC

HNG OIL COMPANY SEE
ENRON OIL & GAS CO

HNG/INTERNORTH INC SEE
ENRON OIL & GAS CO

HOC FAR EAST VENTURES INC SEE
HUNT OIL COMPANY

HOLDEN ENERGY CORP SEE
UNO,INC

HOLDITCH-RESERVOIR TECHNOLOGIES SEE
SCHLUMBERGER

HOMCO CORING SERVICES SEE
WEATHERFORD INTERNATIONAL INCORPORATED

HOMCO INTERNATIONAL,INC SEE
WEATHERFORD ENTERRA

HOODOO LAND AND CATTLE COMPANY SEE
 HUNT OIL COMPANY
HORNING GROVE HULETT & THOMPSON SEE
 GROVE & HULETT,P.C.
HOUSTON PIPE LINE COMPANY LP SEE
 ENERGY TRANSFER PARTNERS,LP
HOWELL & SANDLIN INC SEE
 HOWELL OIL & GAS,INC
HRC ENERGY HOLDINGS (LA),INC SEE
 HALCON RESOURCES CORPORATION
HRC ENERGY LOUISIANA,LLC SEE
 HALCON RESOURCES CORPORATION
HRC ENERGY RESOURCES (LAFOURCHE),INC SEE
 HALCON RESOURCES CORPORATION
HRC ENERGY RESOURCES (WV),INC SEE
 HALCON RESOURCES CORPORATION
HS RESOURCES,INC SEE
 QUESTAR EXPLORATION AND PRODUCTION CO
HSSG LP SEE
 HUNT OIL COMPANY
HUBBARD DEV CO,SEE
 BRECK OPERATING CORP
HUFFORD ENERGY LAND SERVICES SEE
 ENERGY LAND SERVICES
HUNT ARENA CORPORATION SEE
 HUNT OIL COMPANY
HUNT CHIEFTAIN DEVELOPMENT LP
 SEE HUNT OIL COMPANY
HUNT CONSOLIDATED INC SEE
 HUNT OIL COMPANY
HUNT EQUITIES INC
 SEE HUNT OIL COMPANY
HUNT GROWTH CAPITAL LP
 SEE HUNT OIL COMPANY
HUNT HASSIE EXPLORATION CO SEE
 HHE COMPANY
HUNT INTERNATIONAL RESOURCES SEE
 HUNT OIL COMPANY
HUNT INVESTMENT COMPANY LP
 SEE HUNT OIL COMPANY
HUNT MEXICO INC SEE
 HUNT OIL COMPANY
HUNT OIL COMPANY OF LOUISIANA INC SEE
 HUNT OIL COMPANY
HUNT OIL COMPANY OF NEVADA SEE
 HUNT OIL COMPANY
HUNT OIL COMPANY OF PERU LLC SEE
 HUNT OIL COMPANY
HUNT OIL USA INC SEE
 HUNT OIL COMPANY
HUNT OVERSEAS OIL COMPANY SEE
 HUNT OIL COMPANY SEE
HUNT PETROLEUM AEC INC SEE
 XTO OFFSHORE INC
HUNT PETROLEUM CORPORATION SEE
 XH LLC
HUNT POWER CANADA SEE
 HUNT OIL COMPANY
HUNT PRIVATE EQUITY GROUP SEE
 SEE HUNT OIL COMPANY
HUNT SECURITIES CORP
 SEE HUNT OIL COMPANY
HUNT VENTURES SEE
 HUNT OIL COMPANY
HUSKY OIL CO SEE
 MARATHON OIL CO

HYCALOG SEE
 NOV REEDHYCALOG
HYDRAULIC WELL CONTROL SEE
 BOOTS & COOTS SERVICES
HYDRIL COMPANY LP SEE
 TENARIS GLOBAL SERVICES
HYDRO-SEARCH,INC SEE
 H S I GEOTRANS,INC
HYDROCARBON CAPITAL PARTNERS LLC SEE
 LEOR EXPLORATION,LLC
IBEX PARTNERSHIP,SEE
 BRECK OPERATING CORP
IHS ENERGY SEE
 IHS
IMPERIAL SNUBBING SERVICES SEE
 SUPERIOR ENERGY SERVICES COMPANY
INGRAM CACTUS COMPANY SEE
 CAMERON
INNOVATIVE BUSINESS SOLUTIONS,INC SEE
 TOBIN INTERNATIONAL,LTD
INTERNATIONAL LOGGING,INC SEE
 WEATHERFORD
INTERNATIONAL PETROLEUM & EXPLORATION
 OPERATING CORPORATION - SEE INTERNATIONAL
 PETROLEUM & EXPLORATION
INTERNATIONAL PETROLEUM & EXPLORATION
 ROYALTY CORPORATION SEE INTERNATIONAL
 PETROLEUM & EXPLORATION
INTERNATIONAL SNUBBING SERVICES,LLC SEE
 SUPERIOR ENERGY SERVICES
INTERSTATE ROYALTIES SEE
 DAVIS BROS,LLC
IRI INTERNATIONAL CORPORATION SEE
 NATIONAL OILWELL VARCO
IRONWOOD OIL & GAS LLC SEE CL&F RESOURCES
J & B ENTERPRISES SEE
 HUCKABAY JOHN
J L H CORPORATION SEE
 HENSON EXPLORATION LP
J-W GATHERING COMPANY SEE
 J-W MIDSTREAM COMPANY
J-W POWER COMPANY SEE
 J-W OPERATING COMPANY
JACOBI-JOHNSON ENERGY INC SEE
 EXCO RESOURCES,INC
JANNAH HUNT OIL COMPANY SEE
 HUNT OIL COMPANY
JATH OIL COMPANY SEE
 MACK OIL CO
JAY PETROLEUM INC SEE
 CHESAPEAKE ENERGY CORPRATION
JN EXPL & PROD LTD PRTNR SEE
 SEE ENERGY CONSULTANTS,LLC
JN OIL & GAS,INC SEE
 ENERGY CONSULTANTS,LLC
JONES OBRIEN INC SEE
 J-O'B OPERATING CO
JUNCTION CITY OPERATING,LLC SEE
 FIELD MANAGEMENT,LLC
JUSTISS MEARS OIL CO INC SEE
 JUSTISS OIL CO,INC
JW ENERGY RESOURCES SEE
 CHOCTAW NATURAL GAS,LLC
K-N OPERATING CORP SEE
 KACHINA OIL & GAS,INC

KAISER HERMAN,GEOL,OIL PRODUCER SEE
 KAISER-FRANCIS OIL CO
KATTY INDUSTRIES OF ODESSA LTD SEE
 COMPRESSOR RENEWAL SERVICES LTD
KCS ENERGY INC
 SEE PETROHAWK ENERGY CORP
KEARY JON A SEE
 BENCHMARK LAND SERVICE,LLC
KEC ACQUISITION CORP SEE
 AMERICAN EXPLORATION CO
KELLEY OIL & GAS CORPORATION SEE
 CONTOUR ENERGY CO
KELLOGG BROWN & ROOT,INC SEE
 KBR
KEMP GEOPHYSICAL CORPORATION SEE
 3D GEOPHYSICAL,INC (END OF ALPHA)
KERR ED SEE
 ARMSTRONG OIL & GAS,INC
KERR JAIN & ASSOC,SEE
 VENEX CORP
KERR-MCGEE CORPORATION SEE
 ANADARKO PETROLEUM CORPORATION
KERR-MCGEE OIL & GAS CORPORATION SEE
 ANADARKO PETROLEUM CORPORATION
KERR-MCGEE OIL & GAS ONSHORE LLC SEE
 ANADARKO PETROLEUM CORPORATION
KESTREL ENERGY INC SEE
 SAMSON RESOURCES COMPANY
KEY PRODUCTION COMPANY,INC SEE
 CIMAREX ENERGY CO
KNOX INSURANCE GROUP,LLC SEE
 BANCORPSOUTH INSURANCE SERVICE
KOCH OIL CO,DIV OF KOCH INDUSTRIES SEE
 KOCH PETROLEUM GROUP,LP
KOCH PETROLEUM GROUP,LP SEE
 FLINT HILLS RESOURCES,LP
KRONFELD LYDIA B TRUST SEE
 PLYMOUTH RESOURCES INC
L & M OIL CO SEE
 CHOLLA PETROLEUM INC
LACY & BYRD INC SEE
 BYRD OPERATING CO
LAGCOE SEE
 LOUISIANA GULF COAST OIL EXPOSITION
LANDER OPERATING AND PRODUCTION CO SEE
 J&J PETROLEUM LAND SERVICES LLC
LARIAT PETROLEUM INC SEE
 NEWFIELD EXPLORATION MID-CONTINENT INC
LAUREL OPERATING COMPANY,INC SEE
 UNION PACIFIC RESOURCES COMPANY
LAWSON ENGINEERING,INC SEE
 OAKLAND AGENCY ACCOUNT
LEBEN OIL CORPORATION SEE
 KAISER-FRANCIS OIL COMPANY
LG&E NATURAL GATHERING & PROCESSING SEE
 CONOCO,INC
LINCOLN PETROLEUM RESOURCES CORP SEE
 PREMIER ENERGY LLC
LINK ENERGY LIMITED PARTNERSHIP SEE
 PLAINS MARKETING,LP
LINN OPERATING INC SEE
 LINN ENERGY,LLC
LLECO HOLDINGS,INC SEE
 LOUISIANA LAND & EXPLORATION COMPANY,THE
LOGAN SHEETS EXPLORATION CO,INC SEE
 SHEETS EXPLORATION CO,INC

LOGTECH WIRELINE SERVICES,INC SEE
WEDGE DIA-LOG,INC

LOMAK PETROLEUM INC SEE
RANGE RESOURCES CORPORATION

LONQUIST & COMPANY,LLC SEE
LONQUIST FIELD SERVICE

LOUIS DREYFUS NATURAL GAS CORP SEE
DOMINION OKLAHOMA TEXAS EXPLORATION &
PRODUCTION,INC (DOTEPI)

LOUISIANA LAND OFFSHORE EXPLORATION CO
SEE LOUISIANA LAND & EXPLORATION COMPANY

LYNX ENERGY COMPANY,INC SEE
LYNX OPERATING CO,INC

M G N OIL & GAS CORP SEE
KACHINA OIL & GAS,INC

M.S.D. OIL & GAS,MINERAL & LEASE ACQ SEE
DEASON MARK S

M-I L.L.C. SEE
M-I SWACO

MADISON ENERGY ADVISORS,INC SEE
OIL & GAS JOURNAL EXCHANGE

MAGNUM HUNTER RESOURCES,INC SEE
CIMAREX ENERGY CO

MAPCO OIL & GAS CO,SEE
CNG PRODUCING CO

MARITIMES & NORTHEAST PIPELINE SEE
DUKE ENERGY GAS TRANSMISSION

MARK PRODUCTS SEE
SERCEL INC

MARKET HUB PARTNERS SEE
DUKE ENERGY GAS TRANSMISSION

MASON A GEORGE JR,PSC SEE
MASON GEORGE LAW FIRM,PSC

MASSEY & MASSEY OIL & GAS SEE
MASSEY,W T

MATAGORDA PIPELINE PARTNERSHIP SEE
AMERICAN EXPLORATION CO

MAXUS EXPLORATION COMPANY SEE
MIDGARD ENERGY COMPANY

MAZE EXPLORATION INC SEE
AMERICAN EXPLORATION CO

MCBRIDE L R,ENGINEERING,INC SEE
L.R. MCBRIDE,INC

MCCLYMOND,LTD SEE
PETROLEUM EXPLORATION CO,LTD

MCCORD EXPLORATION CO SEE
MCCORD PRODUCTION LTD

MCCULLOUGH/WESTERN ATLAS INTERNATIONAL
SEE ATLAS WIRELINE SERVICES DIV OF
WESTERN ATLAS INTERNATIONAL,INC

MCEVOY WILLIS SEE
CAMERON

MCMORAN OIL & GAS LLC SEE
MCMORAN EXPLORATION CO

MCMURRY-MACCO LIFT SYSTEMS SEE
WEATHERFORD

MERIDIAN OIL INC SEE
BURLINGTON RESOURCES OIL AND GAS COMPANY

MERIT ENERGY SERVICES LLC SEE
PENTERRA SERVICES,LLC

MERLIN EXPLORATION INC SEE
ZORTH INC

MERRICO ACQUISITION SEE
AMERICAN EXPLORATION CO

MESA OPERATING CO SEE
PIONEER NATURAL RESOURCES COMPANY

MESA PRODUCTS,INC SEE
MESA

METERSMART,LP SEE
HUNT OIL COMPANY

METRON GAS MEASUREMENT COMPANY SEE
J-W MEASUREMENT COMPANY

MICHAEL PETROLEUM CORPORATION SEE
LAREDO ENERGY

MID AMERICAN INVESTMENT CORP SEE
AMERICAN EXPLORATION CO

MID-CONTINENT OIL & GAS ASSOCIATION
(MISSISSIPPI-ALABAMA DIV) SEE US OIL &
GAS ASSOCIATION (ALABAMA/MISSISSIPPI DIV)

MIDAMERICA RESOURCES,INC SEE
SEABOARD OIL COMPANY

MIDCOAST ENERGY RESOURCES,INC SEE
ENBRIDGE ENERGY COMPANY,INC

MIDGARD ENERGY COMPANY SEE
CRESCENDO RESOURCES,LP

MIDLAND RESOURCES OPERATING COMPANY,INC
SEE VISTA RESOURCES,INC

MILLICO ENERGY INC SEE
TRIDENT OFFSHORE PETROLEUM

MILPARK DRILLING FLUIDS SEE
BAKER HUGHES INTEQ

MINERAL RESEARCH & CONSULTING,INC SEE
KME TITLES & RESEARCH INC

MISSISSIPPI BUREAU OF GEOLOGY SEE
MISSISSIPPI OFFICE OF GEOLOGY

MITCHELL ENERGY & DEVELOPMENT CORP SEE
DEVON ENERGY CORPORATION

MITCHELL ENERGY COMPANY,LP SEE
DEVON ENERGY CORPORATION

MOBIL EXPLORATION & PRODUCING U S INC SEE
EXXON MOBIL CORPORATION

MOHR ENGINEERING SEE
STRESS ENGINEERING SERVICES INC

MONSANTO OIL COMPANY SEE
BHP PETROLEUM (AMERICAS) INC

MOORE MCCORMACK ENERGY INC,SEE
C X Y ENERGY INC

MULTI-SHOT DIRECTIONAL SERVICES SEE
MS ENERGY SERVICES

MUSSELMAN JAMIE B,OIL OPR SEE
MUSSELMAN OILFIELD SERVICES LLC

MUSTANG RESOURCES CORP SEE
BLUE DOLPHIN ENERGY COMPANY

N & M RESOURCES, LLC
SEE PHILLIPS WM N, CPL

NAA,LP SEE
PLYMOUTH RESOURCES INC

NABORS ABANDONRITE SEE
NABORS INDUSTRIES LTD

NABORS ALASKA DRILLING INC SEE
NABORS INDUSTRIES LTD
2525 C STREET # 200

NABORS CANADA DRILLING SEE
NABORS INDUSTRIES LTD

NABORS INTERNATIONAL,INC SEE
NABORS INDUSTRIES LTD

NABORS OFFSHORE CORPORATION SEE
NABORS INDUSTRIES LTD

NABORS PRODUCTION SERVICES SEE
NABORS INDUSTRIES LTD

NABORS SWABTECH SEE
NABORS INDUSTRIES LTD

NALCO/EXXON ENERGY CHEMICALS,LP SEE
ONDEO NALCO ENERGY SERVICES,LP

NAMIBIA HUNT OIL COMPANY SEE
HUNT OIL COMPANY

NATCO (NATIONAL TANK CO) SEE CAMERON

NATIONAL ENERGY GROUP,INC SEE
NEG OPERATING LLC

NATIONAL PIPELINE MAPPING SYSTEM
WWW.NPMS.RSPA.DOT.GOV

NATIONAL PROPANE GAS ASSOCIATION
WWW.PROPANEGAS.COM

NATIONAL REGULATORY RESEARCH INSTITUTE
WWW.NRRI.OHIO-STATE.EDU

NATIONAL RENEWABLE ENERGY LABORATORY
WWW.NREL.GOV

NATURAL GAS SUPPLY ASSOCIATION
WWW.NGSA.ORG

NCA ENERGY SERVICES,LLC SEE
CRESCENT ENERGY SERVICES,LLC

NEINAST RUSSELL & ASSOCIATES SEE
RMN OIL & GAS LLC

NEUHAUS V F PROPERTIES INC
SEE V F NEUHAUS PROPERTIES INC

NEVIS ENERGY SERVICES,INC SEE
PHOENIX TECHNOLOGY SERVICES USA INC

NEW & HUGHES DRILLING CO INC SEE
NEW,DAVID DRILLING CO INC

NEW YORK LIFE OIL & GAS PRODUCTION
PARTNERSHIPS SEE AMERICAN EXPLORATION CO

NFR ENERGY LLC SEE SABINE OIL & GAS LLC

NICOR DRILLING COMPANY SEE
ADCOR DRILLING INC

NIELSON ENTERPRISES INC SEE
TEX-OK ENERGY,LIMITED PARTNERSHIP

NINIAN OIL CO SEE
AMERICAN EXPLORATION CO

NINIAN OIL FINANCE CORP SEE
AMERICAN EXPLORATION CO

NL HYCALOG SEE
HYCALOG

NOMECO OIL & GAS CO SEE
CMS OIL AND GAS COMPANY

NORCEN EXPLORER,INC SEE
UNION PACIFIC RESOURCES

NORTH CENTRAL OIL CORPORATION SEE
POGO PRODUCING COMPANY

NORTH COAST ENERGY EASTERN,INC SEE
EXCO RESOURCES

NORTH COAST ENERGY,INC SEE
EXCO RESOURCES,INC

NORTHERN GEOPHYSICAL OF AMERICA SEE
3-D GEOPHYSICAL,INC (END OF ALPHA)

NORTHLAND-NORWARD ENERGY SERVICES SEE
WEATHERFORD INTERNATIONAL LTD

NORTHWEST CRUDE CORPORATION SEE
EIGHTY EIGHT OIL LLC

NORTHWEST HYDRAULICS INC SEE
VARI-JAK WELL PUMPING UNITS

NOV BRANDT SEE
NOV FLUIDCONTROL

NOWCAM SERVICES SEE
CAMCO COILED TUBING SERVICES

NOWSCO WELL SERVICE INC SEE
BJ SERVICES COMPANY,USA

NUEVO ENERGY COMPANY SEE
PLAINS EXPLORATION & PRODUCTION CO

NYLIFE RESOURCES,INC SEE
AMERICAN EXPLORATION CO

O C S,INC SEE
OPERATORS & CONSULTING SERVICES,INC

OAKLAND CORP,SEE
J-O'B OPERATING CO

OCEAN ENERGY INC SEE
DEVON ENERGY CORPORATION

OCEAN ENERGY RESOURCES,INC SEE
DEVON ENERGY CORPORATION

OFFICE OF SURFACE MINING RECLAMATION &
ENFORCEMENT (OSM) WWW.OSMRE.GOV

OFFSHORE LOGISTICS INC SEE
BRISTOW U.S.,LLC

OFFSHORE SANITATION & EQUIP RENTAL,SEE
OSERS,INC

OGS LABORATORY,INC SEE NEWPARK RESOURCES

OIL AIR HYDRAULICS,INC SEE
PARKER HANNIFIN CORP

OIL FIELD RENTAL SERVICE CO SEE
ENTERRA OIL FIELD RENTAL

OIL INDUSTRIES LIBRARY,INC SEE
COASTAL BEND GEOLOGICAL LIBRARY,INC

OIL STOP,INC SEE
SUPERIOR ENERGY SERVICES

OKLAHOMA BASIC ECONOMY CORP,DRLG CONTR
SEE PONTOTOC PRODUCTION COMPANY INC

OMAN HUNT OIL COMPANY SEE
HUNT OIL COMPANY

OMNI PETROLEUM SERVICES INC SEE
OMNI LABORATORIES INC

ONE HUNDRED ONE ENERGY CORP SEE
101 ENERGY CORP (END OF ALPHA)

ONSITE SERVICES SEE
SUPERIOR ENERGY SERVICES

ORION ENERGY CORPORATION SEE
AMBRIT ENERGY CORP

ORYX ENERGY COMPANY SEE
KERR-MCGEE CORP

OSO ROYALTY COMPANY SEE
SASSER ROYALTIES

OTIS ENGINEERING CORP SEE
HALLIBURTON ENERGY SERVICES

OXLEY PETROLEUM CO SEE
CHESAPEAKE ENERGY CORPORATION

OXY PETROLEUM INC
SEE OCCIDENTAL PETROLEUM CORPORATION

OXY RESOURCES CALIFORNIA LLC SEE
VINTAGE PRODUCTION CALIFORNIA LLC

OXY USA INC SEE
OCCIDENTAL OIL & GAS CORP

PACIFIC ENTERPRISES ABC CORPORATION SEE
SEMPRA ENERGY PRODUCTION CO

PACIFIC ENTERPRISES OIL COMPANY (USA) SEE
HUNT OIL COMPANY

PALMETTO RESOURCES INC SEE
PALM PRODUCTION CO

PAN MUTUAL ROYALTIES INC SEE
HERITAGE ROYALTIES,INC

PANENERGY FIELD SERVICES,INC SEE
DUKE ENERGY FIELD SERVICES,INC

PANENERGY NATURAL GAS CORPORATION SEE
DUKE ENERGY NATURAL GAS CORPORATION

PANHANDLE EASTERN CORPORATION SEE
PANENERGY FIELD SERVICES,INC

PARKER & PARSLEY PETROLEUM CO SEE
PIONEER NATURAL RESOURCES COMPANY

PATRICK PETROLEUM LLC SEE
PATRICK ENERGY GROUP

PATTCO INC,SEE
GREAT EASTERN ENERGY & DEVELOPMENT CORP

PATTON OIL CO SEE
GREAT EASTERN ENERGY & DEVELOPMENT CORP

PC LTD SEE
BRECK OPERATING CORP

PEAK ENERGY SERVICES
SEE NABORS INDUSTRIES LTD

PEAK OILFIELD SERVICES COMPANY SEE
NABORS INDUSTRIES LTD

PELTO OIL COMPANY SEE
ENERGY DEVELOPMENT CORPORATION

PENKOTA WIRELINE SEE
PIONEER ENERGY SERVICES

PENNTEX RESOURCES LP SEE
SNOWMASS ENERGY PARTNERS LTD

PEPPARD & ASSOCIATES SEE
GEOMAP COMPANY

PERMIAN OPERATING LIMITED PARTNERSHIP SEE
SCURLOCK PERMIAN LLC

PERRET P C AND ASSOCIATES SEE
VANGUARD GEOSCIENCE LLC

PERRY & PERRY INC SEE
LANDSMITH PETROLEUM RESOURCES,INC

PERU HUNT OIL DEVELOPMENT COMPANY SEE
HUNT OIL COMPANY

PETCO LIMITED SEE
BRECK OPERATING CORP

PETCOM SEE
PETROLEUM CORP OF MISSISSIPPI

PETROCORP INCORPORATED SEE
UNIT PETROLEUM COMPANY

PETROFINA DELAWARE,INCORPORATED SEE
TOTALFINAELF E&P USA,INC

PETROL ENERGY CORPORATION SEE
SCOTT ROYCE ARNOLD

PETROLEUM CORPORATION OF TEXAS,SEE
BRECK OPERATING CORP

PETROLEUM INFORMATION/DWIGHTS LLC SEE
IHS

PETROLEUM PRODUCTION MANAGEMENT,INC SEE
GMX RESOURCES INC

PETTY RAY GEOPHYSICAL,DIV GEOSOURCE INC
SEE HALLIBURTON GEOPHYSICAL SERVICES,INC

PG&E GAS TRANSMISSION TECO,INC SEE
EL PASO PIPELINE GROUP

PG&E GAS TRANSMISSION,TEXAS CORP SEE
EL PASO PIPELINE GROUP

PG&E HYDROCARBONS COMPANY SEE
EL PASO PIPELINE GROUP

PG&E TEXAS ENERGY COMPANY SEE
EL PASO PIPELINE GROUP

PG&E TEXAS GAS STORAGE COMPANY SEE
EL PASO PIPELINE GROUP

PG&E TEXAS MANAGEMENT COMPANY SEE
EL PASO PIPELINE GROUP

PG&E TEXAS NATURAL GAS COMPANY SEE
EL PASO PIPELINE GROUP

PG&E TEXAS PIPELINE COMPANY SEE
EL PASO PIPELINE GROUP

PHAROS CORPORATION SEE
HDR/PHAROS ONE COMPANY

PHIBRO ENERGY USA,INC SEE
BASIS PETROLEUM,INC

PHILCO (SUB OF WORKSTRINGS) SEE
SUPERIOR ENERGY SERVICES

PHILLIPS CHEMICAL COMPANY SEE
PHILLIPS PETROLEUM COMPANY

PHILLIPS LEE,JR,ESTATE,D/B/A SEE
PHILLIPS,LEE OIL COMPANY

PHILLIPS PETROLEUM COMPANY SEE
CONOCOPHILLIPS COMPANY

PHILLIPS PETROLEUM RESOURCES,LTD SEE
PHILLIPS PETROLEUM COMPANY

PHILLIPS PIPE LINE CO SEE
PHILLIPS PETROLEUM COMPANY

PHILLIPS 66 COMPANY SEE
PHILLIPS PETROLEUM COMPANY

PHOENIX RESOURCE COMPANIES,INC,THE,SEE
APACHE CORPORATION

PIONEER DE COLUMBIA SEE
PIONEER ENERGY SERVICES

PIONEER DRILLING COMPANY SEE
PIONEER ENERGY SERVICES

PIONEER DRILLING SERVICES LTD SEE
PIONEER ENERGY SERVICES

PIONEER FISHING AND RENTAL SERVICES SEE
PIONEER ENERGY SERVICES

PIONEER PRODUCTION SERVICES SEE
PIONEER ENERGY SERVICES

PIONEER WELL SERVICES SEE
PIONEER ENERGY SERVICES

PIONEER WIRELINE SERVICES SEE
PIONEER ENERGY SERVICES

PIRTLE BOBBIE SHERWOOD,OIL PROP SEE
BGSPE ENERGY,LTD

PLAINS EXPLORATION & PRODUCTION CO SEE
FREEPORT-MCMORAN OIL & GAS COMPANY

PLYMOUTH GAS MARKETING SEE
PLYMOUTH RESOURCES INC

POGO PRODUCING COMPANY SEE
PLAINS EXPLORATION AND PRODUCTION CO

POLAR COMPLETIONS ENGINEERING SEE
WEATHERFORD INTERNATIONAL LTD

POOL CALIFORNIA ENERGY SERVICES,INC SEE
POOL WELL SERVICES CO

POOL COMPANY SALT WATER DISPOSALS SEE
NABORS WELL SERVICES

POOL COMPANY SEE
POOL WELL SERVICES CO

POOL COMPANY TEXAS LTD SEE
NABORS WELL SERVICES

POOL WELL SERVICES CO SEE
NABORS WELL SERVICES

PRECISION ENERGY SERVICES SEE
WEATHERFORD

PREMIER OILFIELD SERVICES SEE
SUPERIOR ENERGY SERVICES COMPANY

PRESSURE CONTROL INC,SEE
CUDD PRESSURE CONTROL,INC

PRI,LP SEE
PLYMOUTH RESOURCES INC

PRIGGE,ALAN C & ASSOCIATES INC SEE
ALAN C PRIGGE & ASSOCIATES,INC

PRIMA ENERGY CORPORATION SEE
PETRO-CANADA RESOURCES (USA) INC

PRIMERO GAS GATHERING CO SEE
EVERGREEN RESOURCES INC

PRINCETON ENERGY CORP SEE
  MYSTIQUE RESOURCES COMPANY
PRIZE ENERGY CORP SEE
  MAGNUM HUNTER RESOURCES,INC
PRODUCERS ENERGY MARKETING,LLC SEE
  CINERGY MARKETING & TRADING,LLC
PRODUCTION MANAGEMENT INDUSTRIES,INC SEE
  SUPERIOR ENERGY SERVICES
PRODUCTION OPERATORS,INC SEE
  SCHLUMBERGER
PROPANE EDUCATION AND RESEARCH COUNCIL
  WWW.PROPANECOUNCIL.ORG
PROTHRO, JOHN E, SR ESTATE SEE
  COMGO, LLC
PRUET CHESLEY,DRILLING COMPANY SEE
  RAPAD DRILLING & WELL SERVICE,INC
PUPCO INC SEE
  ALRAM INC
PURE ENERGY GROUP,INC SEE
  CROSS BORDER RESOURCES
PURE RESOURCES,INC SEE
  CHEVRON
QUANTUM GEOPHYSICAL,INC SEE
  GEOKINETICS INC
QUAY VALLEY,INC SEE
  BIG STAR OIL & GAS,LLC
QUINELLA SEISMIC & EXPL CO SEE
  P G S ONSHORE,INC
R & S GAS MEASUREMENT SERVICES,INC SEE
  SOUTHERN FLOW COMPANIES
R D T PROPERTIES,INC SEE
  MID-CON ENERGY CORPORATION
R G S SEE
  STANBERRY OIL COMPANY
R N R OIL DRILLING INC SEE
  ORTMAN DRILLING INC
RAM ENERGY HOLDINGS (LA),INC SEE
  HRC ENERGY HOLDINGS (LA),INC
RAM ENERGY LOUISIANA,LLC SEE
  HRC ENERGY LOUISIANA,LLC
RAM ENERGY RESOURCES (LAFOURCHE),INC SEE
  HRC ENERGY RESOURCES (LAFOURCHE),INC
RAM ENERGY RESOURCES (WV),INC SEE
  HRC ENERGY RESOURCES (WV),INC
RAM ENERGY RESOURCES,INC SEE
  HALCON RESOURCES CORPORATION
RAM ENERGY,INC SEE
  HALCON HOLDINGS,INC
RAM OPERATING COMPANY,INC SEE
  HALCON RESOURCES OPERATING,INC
RAMCO OPERATING CO SEE
  RAM ENERGY,INC
RANGE RESOURCES-APPALACHIA,LLC SEE
  ENERVEST OPERATING,LLC
RASHMI RESEARCH INC SEE
  CALIFORNIA HYDROCARBONS CORPORATION
RB OPERATING CO SEE
  RAM ENERGY,INC
READING & BATES PETROLEUM CO,SEE
  RB OPERATING CO
RED ARROW ENERGY,LLC SEE
  OVERTON ENERGY,LLC
RED EAGLE RESOURCES CORP SEE
  LOMAK PETROLEUM INC
RED RIVER ENERGY,LLC SEE
  PETROHAWK ENERGY CORPORATION

REED HYCALOG LP,SEE
  NOV REEDHYCALOG
REED TOOL COMPANY SEE REED HYCALOG LP
  A DIVISION OF SCHLUMBERGER
REEVES WIRELINE SERVICES,INC SEE
  WEATHERFORD INTERNATIONAL
REMEDIATION MANAGEMENT SERVICES SEE
  BRANDT,A VARCO CO
REMINGTON OIL AND GAS CORPORATION SEE
  ENERGY RESOURCE TECHNOLOGY GOM INC
RESOLVE DRILLING COMPANY SEE
  GOLDRUS PRODUCING COMPANY
RESOURCE ACQUISITIONS CORPORATION SEE
  PEAK ENERGY,LLC
RESOURCE EVALUATIONS,INC SEE
  RESERVE EVALUATIONS,INC
RIAL DRILLING CO INC,SEE
  STERLING DRLG CO
RIATA ENERGY,INC SEE
  SANDRIDGE ENERGY INC
RICE ENGINEERING CORPORATION SEE
  DUOLINE TECHNOLOGIES,L.P.
RICHARDS & WINKLER SEE
  RW OPERATING CORP
RICHARDSON PRODUCTION COMPANY
  SEE RICHARDSON OPERATING COMPANY
RIG LOCATION & PERMIT REPORT SERVICE SEE
  RIGDATA
RILEY ELECTRIC LOG SEE
  A2D TECHNOLOGIES
RINE DRILLING AND EXPLORATION,INC SEE
  C. H. TODD,INC
RIVER OAKS TRUST COMPANY SEE
  COMPASS BANK
RLP GULF STATES LLC SEE
  HLP GULF STATES,LLC
ROBERTS AND BUNCH OFFSHORE,INC SEE
  NCX COMPANY,LLC
ROBERTS W MAC SEE
  PETROLEUM LANDS RESOURCES
ROBERTSON & CORBUT SEE
  CORBUT & ASSOCIATES LLC
ROBERTSON ONSHORE DRILLING COMPANY SEE
  PATTERSON ONSHORE DRILLING COMPANY
ROCKY MOUNTAIN STEEL MILLS SEE
  EVRAZ INC NA
RONKARAN OIL COMPANY SEE
  ABB OIL CO,INC
ROYCE A SCOTT SEE
  SCOTT ROYCE A
RUNNING W,LTD SEE
  KING RANCH MINERALS,INC
RWG ENERGY,INC SEE
  HALCON ENERGY PROPERTIES,INC
RYAN ENERGY TECHNOLOGIES USA & CANADA SEE
  NABORS INDUSTRIES LTD
S & S LAND SERVICES LLC SEE
  SMITH ENERGY INC
S I INTERNATIONAL,INC SEE
  SERCO NORTH AMERICA
S M R NATURAL GAS VENTURES,INC SEE
  FOCUS ENERGY INC
S.F.C. INC SEE
  STELARON,INC
SABINE CORPORATION SEE
  PACIFIC ENTERPRISES OIL COMPANY (USA)

SAFETY TECHNOLOGY & OILFIELD PROTECTORS
  SEE TOTAL SAFETY
SAMEDAN OIL CORPORATION SEE
  NOBLE ENERGY,INC
SAMSON INVESTMENT COMPANY SEE
  SAMSON RESOURCES COMPANY
SANCHEZ-O'BRIEN OIL & GAS CORPORATION SEE
  SANCHEZ OIL & GAS CORPORATION
SANTA FE ENERGY COMPANY SEE
  SANTA FE ENERGY RESOURCES,INC
SANTA FE ENERGY RESOURCES,INC SEE
  SANTA FE SNYDER CORPORATION
SANTA FE SNYDER CORPORATION SEE
  DEVON SFS OPERATING,INC
SAVANT INTEREST,LLC SEE SOURCE OIL,LLC
SAYE PETROLEUM,INC SEE
  SAYE OIL COMPANY
SCHLUMBERGER DATA SERVICES SEE
  GEOQUEST/SCHLUMBERGER
SCHLUMBERGER OILFIELD SERVICES SEE
  SCHLUMBERGER
SCHLUMBERGER WELL SERVICES SEE
  SCHLUMBERGER WIRELINE & TESTING
SCHLUMBERGER WIRELINE & TESTING SEE
  SCHLUMBERGER
SCOTT JANACE M SEE
  SCOTT ROYCE ARNOLD
SCOTT ROYALTY COMPANY,SEE
  SCOTT ROYCE A
SCURLOCK OIL COMPANY SEE
  SCURLOCK PERMIAN LLC
SCURLOCK PERMIAN LLC SEE
  PLAINS MARKETING,LP
SEABOARD-ARVAL CORPORATION SEE
  SEABOARD INTERNATIONAL,INC
SEAGULL COMPANIES SEE
  SEAGULL OPERATING CO,INC
SEAGULL ENERGY CORPORATION SEE
  OCEAN ENERGY INC
SEAGULL MID-SOUTH INC SEE
  OCEAN ENERGY INC
SEECO INC,SEE
  SOUTHWESTERN ENERGY PROD CO
SEISTRACE,INC SEE
  SEISCO,INC
SEMPRA ENERGY PRODUCTION COMPANY SEE
  PEC MINERALS LP
SEQUA ENGINEERED SERVICES INC SEE
  WEATHERFORD INTERNATIONAL INCORPORATED
SHALE ROYALTIES SEE
  SEE PROVIDENT ROYALTIES LLC
SHELL DEEPWATER DEVELOPMENT INC SEE
  SHELL OFFSHORE INC
SHELL DEEPWATER PRODUCTION INC SEE
  SHELL OFFSHORE INC
SHORELINE GAS LLC SEE
  MAGNUS-SHORELINE GAS,LLC
SIGMOR PIPELINE COMPANY SEE
  ULTRAMAR DIAMOND SHAMROCK CORPORATION
SINCLAIR & IMMICH INC SEE
  GRAND MESA OPERATING CO
SINCLAIR OIL PROPERTIES SEE
  BEARCAT LAND,INC
SIPES WILLIAMSON & ASSOC SEE
  WILLIAMSON PETROLEUM CONSULTANTS,INC

SKYLINE OIL & GAS,LLC SEE
SUMMIT DISCOVERY RESOURCES LLC

SLAUGHTER,J M OIL COMPANY SEE
ZACHARY OIL OPERATING CO

SMACKCO OPERATING,LLC SEE ALOG LLC

SMITH ANNA M,INDEPENDENT SEE
SMITH LAND SERVICES INC

SMITH DRILLING AND COMPLETIONS SEE
SMITH SERVICES,BUS UNIT OF SMITH INT'L

SMITH INTERNATIONAL SEE
SMITH SERVICES,A BUS UNIT OF SMITH INT'L

SMITH T BAKER INC SEE
T.BAKER SMITH,INC

SMITH-CLEMENT EXPLORATION INC SEE
STONE-CANYON EXPLORATION,INC

SOCIETY OF PETROLEUM EVALUATION ENGINEERS
(SPEE) WWW.SPEE.ORG

SOCIETY OF PROFESSIONAL EARTH SCIENTISTS
(SIPES) WWW.SIPES.ORG

SOCO OFFSHORE SEE SANTA FE SNYDER CORP

SOLOCO, SEE
NEWPARK MATS & INTEGRATED SERVICES

SOMERSET DEVELOPMENT INC SEE
PROVIDENT ROYALTIES LLC

SOMERSET LEASE HOLDINGS INC SEE
PROVIDENT ROYALTIES LLC

SONORA ACQUISITION CORP SEE
AMERICAN EXPLORATION CO

SOURGASCO,INC SEE AMERICAN EXPLORATION CO

SOUTH LOUISIANA CONTRACTORS,INC SEE
SOLOCO,L L C

SOUTH STATES OIL & GAS CO SEE
AMERICAN EXPLORATION CO

SOUTHEASTERN PIPE LINE COMPANY SEE
FAULCONER VERNON E,INC

SOUTHERN FLOW COMPANIES,INC SEE
ZEDI US INC

SOUTHERN MINERAL CORPORATION SEE
PETROCORP INCORPORATED

SOUTHLAND ROYALTY COMPANY SEE
MERIDIAN OIL INC

SOUTHWEST BANK OF TEXAS SEE
AMEGY BANK

SOUTHWEST GUARANTY TRUST COMPANY SEE
NATIONAL FIDUCIARY SERVICES,NA

SOUTHWESTERN PUBLIC SERVICE CO SEE
XCEL ENERGY

SPEC-MONT ENERGY CORP SEE
COMPASS EXPLORATION INC

SPECTRUM FIELD SERVICES,INC SEE
ATLAS PIPELINE MID-CONTINENT LLC

SPERRY SUN DRILLING SERVICES SEE
HALLIBURTON ENERGY SERVICES

SPIDLE TURBECO TRIUMPH SEE
SPIDLE TURBECO

SPINDLETOP TUBULAR SERVICE SEE
ALLIS-CHALMERS ENERGY INC

ST MARY LAND & EXPLORATION COMPANY
SEE SM ENERGY COMPANY

ST MARY PARISH LAND COMPANY SEE
ST MARY LAND & EXPLORATION COMPANY

STABIL DRILL SEE
SUPERIOR ENERGY SERVICES COMPANY

STALKER ENERGY LP SEE
KALER ENERGY CORPORATION

STANDARD OIL COMPANY (INDIANA) SEE
AMOCO PRODUCTION CO

STATE REVIEW OF OIL AND NATURAL GAS
ENVIRONMENTAL REG WWW.STRONGERINC.ORG

STEAUA ROMANA (US) INC SEE
AMBRIT ENERGY CORP

STEEN PRODUCTION SERVICE INC SEE
BAKER ENERGY

STENBERG R B,SR,SEE
PAWNEE CORP,THE

STONE ENERGY OFFSHORE, LLC SEE
STONE ENERGY CORPORATION

STONE PETROLEUM CORPORATION,THE SEE
STONE ENERGY CORPORATION

STONE RESOURCE AND ENERGY CORPORATION SEE
NGO DEVELOPMENT CORPORATION

STONEWALL PETROLEUM INC SEE
SCOTT ROYCE ARNOLD

STRIPLING RESOURCES SEE
KIAMICHI OIL COMPANY,LLC

SUB SURFACE TOOLS,INC SEE
SUPERIOR ENERGY SERVICES

SUBMERSIBLE OIL SERVICES, INC, SEE
CENTRILIFT-A BAKER HUGHES CO

SUN EXPLORATION AND PRODUCTION CO SEE
ORYX ENERGY COMPANY

SUNDOWN PRODUCTION LLC SEE
PGP HOLDINGS 1,LLC

SUPERIOR PLANT SERVICES SEE
SUPERIOR ENERGY SERVICES COMPANY

SURFACE TRANSPORTATION BOARD
WWW.STB.DOT.GOV

SURVCON INC,SURVEYORS SEE
MCKIM & CREED,INC

SWACO,A DIVISION OF M-I L.L.C. SEE
M-I L.L.C.

SWECO SEE
BRANDT,A VARCO CO

SWN SEE SOUTHWESTERN ENERGY COMPANY

SYDBOTEN & ASSOCIATES,INC SEE
SAI GEOCONSULTING,INC

TATHAM OIL & GAS INC SEE
ACADIANA ENERGY INC

TAURUS EXPLORATION,INC SEE
ENERGEN RESOURCES CORPORATION

TDT DIVERSE LP
SEE FNRC TDT LP

TECHNIP OFFSHORE MOORINGS,INC SEE
INTERMOOR INC

TECO INDUSTRIAL GAS COMPANY SEE
EL PASO PIPELINE GROUP

TELEDYNE MERLA SEE
OTIS ENGINEERING CORP

TEMPLE OIL COMPANY LLC SEE
BEAR CREEK PETROCHEMICALS,LLC

TEMPLE-INLAND SEE
FORESTAR MINERALS LLC

TENNECO GAS MARKETING COMPANY SEE
EL PASO CORPORATION

TENNECO GAS SEE
EL PASO CORPORATION

TENNECO VENTURES CORPORATION SEE
EL PASO CORPORATION

TERRA RESOURCES,INC SEE
PACIFIC ENTERPRISES OIL COMPANY (USA)

TES ACQUISITION CORP SEE
AMERICAN EXPLORATION CO

TESORO COASTWIDE SERVICES COMPANY SEE
TESORO MARINE SERVICES,LLC

TESORO MARINE SERVICES,LLC SEE
MIDSTREAM FUEL SERVICE,LLC

TEXACO EXPLORATION AND PRODUCTION,INC SEE
CHEVRONTEXACO

TEXACO INC SEE CHEVRONTEXACO

TEXACO PIPELINE INC SEE
EQUILON PIPELINE COMPANY

TEXACO PRODUCING INC,SEE TEXACO,INC

TEXAKOMA OIL AND GAS CORPORATION SEE
TEXAKOMA OPERATING,LP

TEXAN PETROLEUM CORPORATION SEE
CHEYENNE PETROLEUM CORPORATION

TEXAS ACQUISITION & TITLE SERVICES,INC
SEE CONTRACT LAND STAFF,INC

TEXAS EASTERN TRANSMISSION,LP SEE
DUKE ENERGY GAS TRANSMISSION

TEXAS ENERGY EFFICIENCY
WWW.TEXASEFFICIENCY.COM

TEXAS GAS ASSOCIATION (TGA)
WWW.TEXASGAS.COM

TEXAS GAS GATHERING SEE
TGG PIPELINE,LTD

TEXAS IRON WORKS,INC SEE
TIW CORPORATION

TEXAS LAND AND MINERAL ASSOCIATION
WWW.TLMA.ORG

TEXAS MERIDIAN RESOURCES CORPORATION SEE
MERIDIAN RESOURCE CORPORATION,THE

TEXAS MINING & RECLAMATION ASSOCIATION
(TMRA) WWW.TMRA.COM

TEXAS OIL & GAS ASSOCIATION SEE
TXOGA INC

TEXAS OIL & GAS CORP SEE
MARATHON OIL COMPANY

TEXAS PUBLIC UTILITY COMMISSION
WWW.PUC.STATE.TX.US

TEXAS RAILROAD COMMISSION OF TEXAS SEE
RAILROAD COMMISSION OF TEXAS

TGS OFFSHORE GEOPHYSICAL COMPANY SEE
TGS NOPEC GEOPHYSICAL CO

TGS ONSHORE GEOPHYSICAL COMPANY SEE
TGS NOPEC GEOPHYSICAL CO

THIGPEN DALTON & ASSOCIATES,INC SEE
MISSION LAND SERVICES,INC

THORNHILL CRAVER SEE
CAMERON,A DIV OF COOPER CAMERON CORP

THREE-D EXPLORATION PARTNERS SEE
3-D EXPLORATION PARTNERS (END OF ALPHA)

TIDE AIR & GAS SEE
UNIVERSAL COMPRESSION,INC

TIDELAND SIGNAL LIMITED SEE
TIDELAND SIGNAL CORP

TIDELAND SIGNAL PETROLEUM,LTD SEE
TIDELAND SIGNAL CORP

TIMBERLINE PETROLEUM INC SEE
SCOTT ROYCE ARNOLD

TMBR/SHARP DRILLING,INC SEE
PATTERSON-UTI DRILLING COMPANY,LLC

TOBIN DATA PRODUCTS SEE
P2 ENERGY SOLUTIONS

TOBIN INTERNATIONAL,LTD SEE
P2 ENERGY SOLUTIONS

TOBIN SURVEYS INC SEE
TOBIN INTERNATIONAL,LTD
TOC ACQUISITION CORP SEE
AMERICAN EXPLORATION CO
TOM BROWN INC SEE
ENCANA OIL & GAS (USA)
TONG SPECIALTY,LLC SEE
TESCO SERVICES,INC
TOTAL COMPRESSION INCORPORATED SEE
GLOBAL COMPRESSION SERVICES,INC
TOTALFINAELF E&P USA,INC SEE
TOTAL E&P USA,INC
TRACE ENERGY SERVICES LTD/ SEE
GEOKINETICS INC
TRAFALGAR HOUSE OIL AND GAS INC,SEE
HARDY OIL & GAS USA INC
TRANS-PAC DRILLING SEE
TRANS PACIFIC OIL CORP
TRANSCO ENERGY COMPANY TEC SEE
WILLIAMS COMPANIES,THE
TRANSMONTAIGNE PIPELINE INC SEE
TRANSMONTAIGNE PRODUCT SERVICES,INC
TREND DRILLING CO SEE
NABORS DRILLING USA,INC
TRI STATE OIL TOOL,INC SEE
BAKER OIL TOOLS (FISHING DIVISION)
TRINITY RESOURCES INC SEE
EQUION CORP,THE
TRIUMPH DRILLING TOOLS SEE
SPIDLE TURBECO TRIUMPH
TRIUMPH PETROLEUM COMPANY,LLC SEE
ARCADIA EXPLORATION & PRODUCTION COMPANY
TURBINE SPECIALTIES INC SEE
ELLIOTT TURBOCHARGER GROUP INC
TWISTER GAS SERVICES LP SEE
WINDSOR ENERGY GROUP LLC
TYSON R.W. PRODUCING CO SEE
R.W. TYSON PRODUCING CO
U M C PETROLEUM CORPORATION SEE
OCEAN ENERGY,INC
U.S. CORPS OF ENGINEERS
WWW.USACE.ARMY.MIL/
U.S. DEPARTMENT OF ENERGY
WWW.ENERGY.GOV
U.S. DEPARTMENT OF LABOR,OSHA
WWW.OSHA.GOV
U.S. DEPARTMENT OF TRANSPORTATION
(U.S.DOT) WWW.DOT.GOV
U.S. DEPARTMENT OF TRANSPORTATION'S OFC
OF PIPELINE SAFETY WWW.PHMSA.DOT.GOV
U.S. ENERCORP,LTD SEE AGERON ENERGY,LLC
U.S. ENVIRONMENTAL PROTECTION AGENCY
ON-SCENE COORDINATOR WWW.EPAOSC.ORG
ULTRAMAR DIAMOND SHAMROCK CORPORATION
SEE VALERO COMPANIES
UNICHEM SEE
BJ UNICHEM CHEMICAL SERVICES
UNIFLUX INC SEE EXOTHERM CORPORATION
UNION CENTRAL LIFE INSURANCE COMPANY SEE
AMERITAS LIFE INSURANCE CORP
UNION GAS LIMITED SEE
DUKE ENERGY GAS TRANSMISSION
UNION OIL COMPANY OF CALIFORNIA SEE
UNOCAL CORPORATION
UNION PACIFIC RESOURCES COMPANY SEE
ANADARKO PETROLEUM CORPORATION

UNION RESOURCES SEE
DAVIS BROS,LLC
UNITED DIAMOND
SEE WEATHERFORD INTER
UNITED NORTH AMERICAN RESOURCES,INC SEE
ALLIANCE RESOURCES
UNIVERSAL COMPRESSION,INC SEE
EXTERRAN
UNIVERSAL RESOURCES CORPORATION SEE
QUESTAR EXPLORATION AND PRODUCTION CO
UNOCAL CORPORATION SEE
CHEVRON
UPG FALCO,A DIV OF UPG INC SEE
ENRON OIL TRADING & TRANSPORTATION CO
USENCO SEE ARCH PETROLEUM INC
VALERO GAS STORAGE COMPANY SEE
PG&E TEXAS GAS STORAGE COMPANY
VALERO HYDROCARBONS COMPANY SEE
PG&E HYDROCARBONS COMPANY
VALERO MANAGEMENT COMPANY SEE
PG&E TEXAS MANAGEMENT COMPANY
VALERO NATURAL GAS COMPANY SEE
PG&E TEXAS NATURAL GAS COMPANY
VALERO TRANSMISSION COMPANY SEE
PG&E TEXAS PIPELINE COMPANY
VALVCON SEE
HYDRIL COMPANY LP
VANCO ENERGY COMPANY SEE
VAN DYKE ENERGY COMPANY
VASTAR RESOURCES,INC SEE
BP AMERICA,INC
VENTURE PRODUCTION INC SEE
VENTURE ROYALTIES
VF-RUSSIA INC SEE
HILLWOOD INTERNATIONAL ENERGY
VINTAGE PETROLEUM,INC SEE
OCCIDENTAL OIL & GAS CORP
VIRGINIA GAS COMPANY SEE
SPECTRA ENERGY CORP
W B I PRODUCTION,INC SEE
FIDELITY EXPLORATION & PRODUCTION CO
W K M COOPER INDUSTRIES SEE CAMERON
A DIV OF COOPER CAMERON CORPORATION
WAGNER OIL & GAS REPORTING INC SEE
COMBINED SYSTEMS,INC
WALKER JOHN W JR SEE
CORBAN EXPLORER,INC
WALSH & TRANT PETR CORP SEE
WATCO ENERGY INC
WARD GAS MARKETING,INC SEE
ONEOK GAS MARKETING COMPANY
WARREN PETROLEUM COMPANY SEE
DYNEGY MIDSTREAM SERVICES,LP
WEATHERFORD ARTIFICAL LIFT SYSTEMS SEE
WEATHERFORD
WEATHERFORD DRILLING INTERNATIONAL SEE
WEATHERFORD
WEATHERFORD INTERNATIONAL INC SEE
WEATHERFORD
WEATHERFORD US LP SEE
WEATHERFORD
WEBB SHANNON & HAAS,INC SEE
WSH LAND (LANDMEN)
WEDGE DIA-LOG,INC SEE
BAKER ATLAS

WEDGE WIRELINE,INC SEE
BAKER ATLAS
WEINMAN GEOSCIENCE SEE
GLOBAL GEOPHYSICAL SERVICES INC
WELEX,A HALLIBURTON CO SEE
HALLIBURTON LOGGING SERVICES,INC
WEST EMERALD PIPE LINE CORPORATON SEE
ULTRAMAR DIAMOND SHAMROCK CORPORATION
WEST TEXAS GEOLOGICAL SOCIETY
WWW.WTGS.ORG
WEST TEXAS PETROLEUM SEE
P M B ENERGY INC
WESTERN ATLAS INTERNATIONAL,INC SEE
BAKER HUGHES INCORPORATED
WESTERN ATLAS LOGGING SERVICES SEE
BAKER ATLAS
WESTERN COMPANY OF NORTH AMERICA,THE SEE
BJ SERVICES COMPANY,USA
WESTERN COMPANY,THE,SEE
BJ SERVICES CO
WESTERN GAS RESOURCES INC SEE
ANADARKO PETROLEUM CORPORATION
WESTERN GEOPHYSICAL EXPLORATION PRODUCTS
SEE WESTERN GEOPHYSICAL
WESTERN GEOPHYSICAL SEE
WESTERNGECO,LLC
WESTERN PETROLEUM SERVICES SEE
WESTERN COMPANY OF NORTH AMERICA,THE
WESTERN PIPE LINE SEE
SOUTHEASTERN PIPE LINE COMPANY
WESTERN PRODUCTION CO SEE
BLACK HILLS EXPLORATION & PRODUCTION INC
WESTERN UNICHEM SEE
UNICHEM,A DIV OF BJ SERVICES CO
WG ENERGY HOLDINGS,INC SEE
HALCON RESOURCES CORPORATION
WG OPERATING,INC SEE
HALCON OPERATING CO.,INC
WGR,INC & RESOURCES SEE
WESTERN GAS RESOURCES,INC
WHEAT BUCK RESOURCES,SEE
BUCK WHEAT RESOURCES INC
WHITE KENNETH S SEE
WHITE EXPLORATION,INC
WHITEHORSE OIL & GAS CORPORATION SEE
LAS COLINAS ENERGY CORP
WHITEWING & WHITEWING OIL CO,LLC SEE
BLACK DIAMOND ENERGY,LLC
WHITING OILFIELD RENTAL SEE
WEATHERFORD ENTERRA
WILBANKS EXPLORATION INC SEE
WILBANKS RESERVE CORPORATION
WILBANKS RESOURCES CORP SEE
CRANE ORIN C
WILD WELL CONTROL,INC SEE
SUPERIOR ENERGY SERVICES COMPANY
WILL-DRILL OPERATING,LLC SEE
WILL-DRILL RESOURCES,INC.
WILL-DRILL PRODUCTION,INC SEE
WILL-DRILL RESOURCES,INC
WILLBROS ENERGY SERVICES CO SEE
WILLBROS GROUP,INC
WILLIAM J DAIGLE,LLC SEE
MAGNOLIA ENERGY SERVICES,LLC
WILLIAMS GAS PIPELINE (TRANSCO) SEE
WILLIAMS (TRANSCO)

WILLIAMS HERBERT E,ESTATE OF,OIL PROD SEE
WILLIAMS FAMILY INTERESTS

WILLIAMS PRODUCTION COMPANY SEE
WPX ENERGY

WILLIAMS PRODUCTION RMT COMPANY SEE
WPX ENERGY ROCKY MOUNTAIN,LLC

WILLIAMSON & SMITHERMAN,INC,SEE
WILLIAMSON OIL & GAS,INC

WILLISCO INC SEE
SEISMIC EXCHANGE,INC

WORKSTRINGS SEE
SUPERIOR ENERGY SERVICES

WORREL EXPLORATION,INC SEE
WORREL CHARLES J, CONS GEOL

XH LLC, SEE
XTO ENERGY

XTO OFFSHORE INC, SEE
XTO ENERGY

YATES HARVEY E CO SEE
HARVEY E YATES COMPANY (HEYCO)

YEMEN HUNT LNG COMPANY LLC SEE
HUNT OIL COMPANY

YEMEN HUNT OIL COMPANY SEE
HUNT OIL COMPANY

YUMA PETROLEUM COMPANY SEE
YUMA EXPLORATION AND PRODUCTION CO,INC

ZAPATA GULF MARINE CORPORATION SEE
TIDEWATER INC

ZAPATA-FENDER,L.L.C. SEE
FENDER EXPLORATION & PRODUCTION CO,LLC

ZINK, JOHN CO SEE JOHN ZINK HAMWORTHY
COMBUSTION

ZINKE & TRUMBO,INC SEE
ZENERGY INC

ZOANDRA PETROLEUM,INC SEE
GREAT EASTERN ENERGY & DEVELOPMENT CORP

1400 CORPORATION SEE
AMERICAN EXPLORATION COMPANY

1987 NYL LIMITED PARTNERSHIP SEE
AMERICAN EXPLORATION COMPANY

3-D GEOPHYSICAL,INC SEE
WESTERN GEOPHYSICAL

3D GEOPHYSICAL,INC DBA KEMP GEOPHYSICAL
SEE WESTERN GEOPHYSICAL

3300 CORPORATION SEE
AMERICAN EXPLORATION COMPANY

4700 CORP SEE
AMERICAN EXPLORATION COMPANY

500 CORPORATION SEE
AMERICAN EXPLORATION COMPANY

6 D OIL CO,SEE
SIX D OIL COMPANY

To Order Call (800) 375-1838 or
www.armstrongoil.com

Nationwide Office Directory
Full 8 1/2" x 11" book size
Entire Nation
over 16,000 companies listed

$ 225 (no discount available)

Nationwide Mini Directory (Briefcase)
Small Size 5 1/4" x 8 1/4"
Same complete nationwide information
over 16,000 companies listed

$ 140 w / discount*

Texas Directory
Includes
Texas and S.E. New Mexico

$ 80 w / discount*

Louisana / Gulf Coast Directory
Includes the following states:
Gulf coast of Texas, Louisana
Arkansas, Mississippi,
Alabama, Georgia, Florida
N.E. states

$80 w / discount*

Rocky Mountain / Central U.S. Directory
Includes the following states:
West Texas and Panhandle of Texas
Oklahoma, New Mexico
Colorado, Alaska and all
Western U.S. states

$80 w / discount*

* discount applies when invoice is paid within 30 days after receipt of order.

NOTES